Woodwind Music Guide
Volume 1
1982 Edition

Ensemble Music in Print

compiled by
Himie Voxman & Lyle Merriman

The Instrumentalist Company
1418 Lake Street, Evanston, Illinois

PREFACE

The present work is an updated version of the *Woodwind Solo and Study Material Music Guide* published by The Instrumentalist Co. in 1973. Several hundred additions and deletions have occurred since that date. The changes in the ownership of publishing firms and their locations have continued at a rapid pace. This listing is based on catalogs provided by more than 300 publishers and agencies who responded to our requests.

We can make no claim for completeness or accuracy. Lack of response by some publishers, a certain degree of confusion and ambiguity in some catalogs as to authorship and instrumentation, and our own oversights preclude this. Nonetheless, we are hopeful that students, teachers, and the publishing industry will welcome this centralized source of information.

The compilers wish to express their deep appreciation to Professor Paul Anderson of The University of Iowa, who devised the computer program used in the present format. Thanks are due to James Rohner for his encouragement and helpful suggestions.

Lyle Merriman
Himie Voxman
Iowa City, Iowa U.S.A.
December 1981

ABBREVIATIONS

A	alto voice
ACC	accordion
ACL	alto clarinet
AFL	alto flute
AREC	alto recorder
ARR	arranger
ASAX	alto saxophone
B	bass voice
BAR	baritone voice
BAR SAX	baritone saxophone
BC	basso continuo
BCL	bass clarinet
BFL	bass flute
BK	book
BR	brass
BSN	bassoon
CBSN	contrabassoon
CEL	celeste
CEMB	cembalo
CL	clarinet
COMP	compiler
CT	cornet
DB	double bass
DR	drum
ED	editor
E FL CL	E♭ clarinet
EHN	English horn
ELEC	electric
EU	euphonium
FL	flat, when used to designate a tonality, as in E FL (E♭)
FL	flute, when not used as above
GO	gong
GUIT	guitar
HN	French horn
HP	harp
HPCD	harpsichord

INCL	including
INSTR	instrument(s)
MA	major
MAR	marimba
MI	minor
MS	mezzo soprano voice
NAR	narrator
NO(S)	number(s)
OB	oboe
OPT	optional
ORG	organ
PERC	percussion
PF	pianoforte
PIC	piccolo
PUB	published
REC	recorder
REV	revised
S	soprano voice
SAX	saxophone
SDR	snare drum
SH	sharp
SOP SAX	soprano saxophone
STR	string(s)
T	tenor voice
TAMB	tambourine
TIMP	timpani
TPT	trumpet
TRB	trombone
TRI	triangle
TSAX	tenor saxophone
TU	tuba
V	voice
VA	viola
VC	violoncello
VIB	vibraphone
VN	violin
VOL	volume(s)
WW	woodwind
XYL	xylophone

SYMBOLS

Instrumentation inside parentheses indicates an alternate part:
   FL(OB) - flute or oboe

Slash between two instruments indicates doubling by one player:
   OB/EHN - oboe and English horn

GENERAL INFORMATION

Basso continuo

Because catalogs do not usually indicate whether a basso continuo part includes separate bass and keyboard parts, we have arbitrarily considered it to be a single keyboard part. Thus, a trio sonata for flute, violin, and basso continuo will be listed in the *Three Instruments* section under the "Woodwind-String-Keyboard" category. When looking for trio sonatas, however, the reader should also check the *Four Instruments* section of the "Woodwind-String-Keyboard" category.

Ad libitum

Instruments designated as *ad libitum* are not counted in classifying a category. For example, a work for three clarinets and piano *ad lib* is classified as a clarinet trio.

Collections

The "Collections" category includes those publications containing a group of pieces by more than one composer.

French horn

In the *Two, Three*, and *Four Instruments* sections, the French horn is classified as a brass instrument. Beginning with *Five Instruments*, the French horn is regarded as a woodwind instrument to minimize the number of categories.

Percussion

The number of required percussionists is based on the number of percussion instruments indicated in the catalog. Vibraphone, xylophone, and cow bell would be counted as three players, although it is possible that one performer could cover the three parts.

Guitar, Harp, Percussion, Recorder, Tape

We have made separate categories for devotees of the guitar, harp, etc. Any composition using one of these instruments is cross-referenced. For example, a work that includes guitar and percussion will be found in the "Instruments Including Guitar" category as well as under "Instruments Including Percussion."

CONTENTS

ALESSANDRO, R.D,. SONATINE, OP 77	EUL
AMBROSIUS, H. SONATA	S&C
ARMA, P. 3 RESONANCES	BIL
ARNELL, R. 5 INVENTIONS	HI
ARNOLD, J. VERY FIRST FLUTE DUETS	HN
ARRIEU, C. DUO IN 4 MOVEMENTS	APH
AUBERT, J.-HARF. PETITS CONCERTS, LES, 2 VOLS	HEI
AVIDOM, M. REFLECTIONS	IMP
BACH, C.P.E.-WALTHER. 10 EASY DUETS(WQ.81,82,193)	WZ
BACH, J.C. 3 SONATAS	SCH
BACH, J.S.-DISHINGER. EXCERPTS (SONATA IN C MA)	SP
BACH, J.S. 15 2-PART INVENTIONS	CF
BACH, J.S.-SCHONICKE. 2-PART INVENTIONS	WZ
BACH, J.S.-WUMMER. 15 TWO-PART INVENTIONS	INT
BACH, W.F.-MAGANINI. CANON (SONATA IN E MI)	CF
BACH, W.F. 6 DUETS, 2 VOLS.	EDK
BACH, W.F.-WUMMER. 6 DUETS,2VOL	INT
BACH, W.F. DUO SONATA	EDM
BACH, W.F.-SCHITTLER. SONATA # 4IN E MI	T&J
BACH, W.F.-SCHITTLER. SONATA #1 IN G MA	T&J
BACH, W.F.-GLOEDER. SONATA IN E-FLAT MA	INT
BACH, W.F. 3 SONATAS	CF
BACH, W.F.-RODEMANN. 2 SONATAS IN E MI, F MI	B&N
BACH, W.F. 2 SONATAS	EDK
BACKOFEN, J.(DELIUS). GRAND DUO	EUL
BACKOFEN, J. GRAND DUO, OP 37	EUL
BARBOTEU, G. RAMPALUNE (4 PIECES)	ECH
BARRE, M. DE LA-ZOLLER. SUITE IN E MI,OP 4	HSM
BARRE, M. DE LA-SCHECK/RUF. SUITE, G	RC
BECK, C. SONATINE	SCH
BECK, F. CONVERSATION FOR 2 SOLO FL, A	AMC
BECKWITH, J. 5 PIECES (1951)	BER
BEETHOVEN, L. VAN-WALTHER. ALLEGRO & MINUET	WZ
BEETHOVEN, L. VAN. ALLEGRO & MINUET	EDM
BEETHOVEN, L. VAN-HILTON. ALLEGRO AND MINUET	RD
BEETHOVEN, L. VAN. ALLEGRO AND MINUET, WOO 26	EDK
BEETHOVEN, L. VAN-BRODSZKY. SONATA	EMB
BEETHOVEN,L. VAN-WUMMER. ALLEGRO & MINUET	INT
BENNETT, RICHARD. CONVERSATIONS	UE
BERBIGUIER, T. 7 DUETS,OP 28	INT
BERBIGUIER, T. 6 DUETS,OP 59	INT
BERBIGUIER, T. 3 DUOS CONCERTANTES	EDM
BERBIGUIER, T. 3 DUOS,OP 4	EDH
BERBIGUIER, T. 3 DUOS,OP 22	SIM
BERBIGUIER, T. 3 DUOS,OP 46/1	EDH
BERBIGUIER, T. 6 EASY DUETS	EDM
BERBIGUIER, T.-ALTES. 18 EXERCICES OU ETUDES	BIL
BERBIGUIER, T. 3 GRANDS DUOS BRILLANS,OP 38/1	EDH
BERBIGUIER, T. 3 GRANDS DUOS BRILLANS,OP 38/2	EDH
BERBIGUIER, T. 3 GRANDS DUOS BRILLANS,OP 38/3	EDH
BERTONI, F.-HAAS. CANZONA	RU
BIALAS, G. KANONISCHE ETUDEN	B&N
BIENENMANN, F. 14 DUETS	HU
BINET, J. 3 DIALOGUES (1958)	HEN
BLANK, A. 2 SIMPLE CANONS	BH

2 FLUTES - 200

BLAVET, M-PATERO. 6 SONATAS, 2 VOLS.	ALE
BLAVET, M-KOLNEDER. 6 SONATAS	WMS
BLAVET, M.-RUF. 2 DUETS,CP 1/5,6	SCH
BLAVET, M.-NAGEL. 15 DUETTE	HEI
BLAVET, M.-MANN. FRENCH DUETS	M&M
BLAVET, M.-RUF/ZOLLER. SONATA IN G MA,OP 1/4	HSM
BLAVET, M. 6 SONATEN,OP 1/1-3	RC
BODINUS, S.-BIRKNER. SONATA IN E MA	HMO
BODINUS, S.-HAVELAAR. SONATA IN E MI	B&V
BOISMORTIER, J.-HARF. 6 EASY DUETS, OP 11,2 VOLS.	OHN
BOISMORTIER, J.-RUF. 6 EASY DUETS,OP 17,2VOLS	SCH
BOISMORTIER, J.-DOFLEIN. 55 LEICHTE STUCKE,OP 22	SCH
BOISMORTIER, J.-RAUGEL. SONATA,B MI,OP 6/6	B&N
BOISMORTIER, J. 2 SONATAS IN C MA AND G MI	EDK
BOISMORTIER, J.-SCHLENGER. 2 SONATAS IN C MA, G MI	WZ
BOISMORTIER, J.-BEECHEY. 2 SONATAS, OP 2/3, 4	OX
BOISMORTIER, J.-NAGEL. 6 SONATAS, OP 2	MV
BOISMORTIER, J. 6 SONATAS, OP 6	PET
BOISMORTIER, J.-NAGEL. 6 SONATAS, OP 47	EUL
BOISMORTIER, J.-FROTSCHER. 6 SONATAS,OP 1	B&N
BOISMORTIER, J. 6 SONATAS,OP 1	PET
BOISMORTIER, J.-FROTSCHER. 6 SONATAS,OP 6	B&N
BOISMORTIER, J. 2 SONATAS	INT
BOISMORTIER, J. SUITE, OP 17/1	BIL
BOOM, J.V.D. 6 PIECES	T-M
BORRIS, S. DUETTINO,OP116/2	GBV
BOSSLER, K. SONATINE	HG
BOTTJE, W. MUSIC FOR A JOYOUS OCCASION	ACA
BOUSQUET, N. FAVORITE FLUTE DUETS(TWO SONATAS)	CF
BRICCIALDI, G. DUO CONCERTANT #2, OP100	INT
BRICCIALDI, G. DUO CONCERTANT, OP100/2	EDK
BRICCIALDI, G. 16 FLUTE DUETS "DIALOGUES",OP132	BE
BRITAIN, R. DANCE GROTESQUE	SS
BROWN, R. MUSIC	WI
BUCQUET, P. SUITE #1	EDM
BUCQUET, P.-BOUVET. SUITE #2	EES
BUCQUET, P. SUITE #2	EDM
BUTTERWORTH, N. 3 DIALOGUES	PET
CAGE, J. 3 PIECES(1935)	PET
CAMBINI, G.-LEBERMANN. DUO, OP 11/4 (E MI)	SCH
CAMBINI, G.-LEBERMANN. DUO, OP 11/5 (A MA)	SCH
CAMBINI, G.-LEBERMANN. DUO, OP 11/6 (G MA)	SCH
CARDON, J. 3 DUO CONCERTANS	EDH
CARLES, M. 5 ETUDES CONCERTANTES	ALE
CASTELNUOVO-TEDESCO, M. DIVERTIMENTO	TP
CECCONI, M. JEUX	COM
CHAGRIN, F. 6 DUETS	NO
CHANDLER(ARR.). 7 SCOTT JOPLIN RAGS	SH
CHARLTON, F. HARLEQUIN	CF
CHEDEVILLE, E.-ARX. 6 GALANTE DUOS	B&N
CHEDEVILLE, N.-TAYLOR. PASTORAL SONATA"L'ALLEMANDE"	RC
CHEDEVILLE, N.-UPMEYER. 2 PASTORALSONATEN,OP 8	B&N
CHEDEVILLE, N.-UPMEYER/WUMMER. 2 SONATAS	INT
CHERUBINI, L.-GODFREY. 2 FUGUES	PO
CHILDS, B. MUSIC	TP
COLF, D. 3 PIECES	M&M
CONTEMPORANEI, A. COMPOSITION	EBE
CORRETTE, M.-NAGEL. 6 DUETS, OP 23, 2 VOLS.	HEI
CORRETTE, M.-BLOCK. 6 SONATAS, OP 2	NOM
CORRETTE, M. SONATE # 1,OP 21A	B&V
COUPERIN, F.-SCHMITZ. CONCERTO IN G MA	B&N
COUPERIN, F.-RUF. DUO IN G MA	SCH

2 FLUTES - 200

```
COUPERIN, F.-SCHMITZ.  MUSIK FUR FLOTE                              B&N
COUPERIN, F.  SUITE #1                                             TP
CROFT, W.-HUNT.  SONATA IN D M1                                   S&C
CSUPOR(ED).  DUOS FOR BEGINNERS                                   EMB
DAHL, I.  VARIATIONS ON A SWEDISH FOLKTUNE.  FL,AFL               JB
DANCES FROM THE TIME OF BACH.                                     FRH
DAQUIN, L.-NAZZI.  COUCOU, LE                                     MB
DAVENPORT, L.  3 DUETS                                            SF
DEVIENNE, F.-MOYSE.  AIR WITH VARIATIONS                          INT
DEVIENNE, F.  6 CELEBRATED SONATAS                                EDM
DEVIENNE, F.-BAUM.  6 DUETS, OP 75/2                              B&N
DEVIENNE, F.  6 DUETS, OP 82                                      EDK
DEVIENNE, F.-NAGEL.  3 DUETS,OP 18/4-6                            HEI
DEVIENNE, F.  6 DUETTE, OP 83                                     HUG
DEVIENNE, F.-BOHME.  6 DUETTINOS, OP 82                           PET
DEVIENNE, F.  6 DUO CONCERTANS, OP 83                             EDK
DEVIENNE, F.  DUOS,OP 75,2 VOLS                                   B&V
DEVIENNE, F.-WIENANDT.  38 DUOS                                   SO
DEVIENNE, F.  6 EASY DUETS,OP 82                                  INT
DEVIENNE, F.-KALMAR.  18 KLEINE FLOTENDUETTE                      SCH
DEVIENNE, F.-MOSKOVITZ.  24 PROGRESSIVE DUETS                     SO
DEVIENNE, F.-WIENANDT.  SICILIANO                                 SO
DEVIENNE, F.-WIENANDT.  SONATA #2 IN C MA                         SO
DEVIENNE, F.-WIENANDT.  SONATA #6                                 SO
DEVIENNE, F.  SONATINA #1 IN D MA                                 PET
DEVIENNE, F.  SONATINA #2 IN F MA                                 PET
DEVIENNE, F.  SONATINA #4 IN D MI                                 PET
DEVIENNE, F.  SONATINE #3 IN G MA                                 PET
DEVIENNE, F.  SONATINE IN D MA                                    EDH
DEVIENNE, F.  SONATINE IN F MA                                    EDM
DEVIENNE, F.  SONATINE IN G MA                                    EDH
DEVIENNE, F.  SONATINES #1,2,3.  2FL,B AD LIB                     EV
DEXTER, H.  AU CLAIR DE LA LUNE                                   PET
DEXTER, H.  COUNTRY DIALOGUES                                     PET
DIETHELM, C.  DUET, OP124                                         S-V
DOFLEIN(ED).  BICINIEN.20 FANTASIES                               SCH
DOPPELBAUER, J.  7 LITTLE DUETS                                   LDO
DORAN, M.  SONATINA                                               WI
DRESSLER, R.  3 DUOS, OP 46/1-3, IN C MA, G MI, A MA              EDH
DROUET, L.-QUAKERNAAT.  2 AIRS                                    B&V
DROUET, L.  GRANDS DUOS BRILLANS & FACILES, OP 74/1               EDH
DROUET, L.  GRANDS DUOS BRILLANS & FACILES, OP 74/2               EDH
DROUET, L.  GRANDS DUOS BRILLANS & FACILES, OP 74/3               EDH
DUBOIS, P.  BERCEUSE ET RONDO CAPRICCIOSO                         ALE
DZIEWULSKA, M.  DUETTI                                            PWM
ECKERT, M.  WISPS                                                 ACA
EDMONDSON, J.  LITTLE SUITE                                       KN
EHRLICH, A.  TESTIMONY(1962)                                      ISR
EISENHAUER, W.  LEARN TO PLAY DUETS                               AL
ERIKSSON, G.  FLOJTDUETTER                                        NOR
ESCHER, R.  SONATA, OP 8 (1944)                                   SD
EXCOFFIER.  FANTASIA-GRACIOSO                                     EV
FAURE, G.  PAVANE, OP 50                                          HE
FELD, J.  5 INVENTIONS                                            ALE
FESCH, W. DE-STEINBECK.  8 DUETS (OP 11)                          EUL
FESCH, W. DE-DOFLEIN.  3 LEICHTE SONATEN                          SCH
FESCH, W. DE.  SONATAS, OP 9                                      PET
FESCH, W. DE-RUF.  6 SONATAS, OP 9                                B&N
FILAS, T.  INTERVAL DUETS                                         CA
FILIPPI, A. DE.  7 MODES                                          GEN
FINGER, G-RODEMANN.  2 SONATAS                                    HMO
FINGER, G.-HARF.  LEICHTE DUETTE                                  HEI
```

FINGER, G.-BERGMANN. SONATA IN C MA	S&C
FINGER, G.-HUNT. SONATA IN G MA, OP 2/6	S&C
FISCHER, J.-NAGEL. 7 DIVERTIMENTI	EUL
FISCHER, J.C.-RUF. 3 DIVERTIMENTI	RC
FLOTHUIS, M. SONATA, OP 76/2 (1975). FL,AFL	SD
FORTNER, W. 9 INVENTIONEN UND EIN ANHANG	SCH
FOX, F. BEC-3	SS
FRANK M. CLASSICAL IMPROVISATION	KN
FREUNDLICH, R.(ARR). 4 OLD DANCES	RC
FRIEDRICHSEN, J.M.-BLOCK. GRANDFATHER'S DUET BOOK 1	NOM
FUERSTENAU, A.(STEINBECK). 3 CONCERTANTE DUOS	EUL
FUERSTENAU, A. 6 DUETS, OP137, 2 VOLS.	EDK
FUERSTENAU, A. 6 DUETS,OP137,2 VOLS	INT
FUERSTENAU, A. 3 DUOS	EUL
FUERSTENAU, A. GRANDS DUOS CONCERTANT, OP 36/1, 36/2, 36/3	EDH
FUERSTENAU, A. 48 LITTLE FLUTE DUETS	HE
FUERSTENAU, C. 6 DUETS	EDH
FUERSTENAU, C. 3 DUOS,OP 2	EDH
GABRIELSKI, W. GRAND DUO CONCERTAN #1, G	EDH
GABRIELSKI, W. GRAND DUO CONCERTAN, D MI	EDH
GAGLIANO, G. DITTICO #1 (ARIA E TOCCATA)	EDI
GAGRIELSKI, W. GRAND DUO CONCERTAN IN A MA	EDH
GARIBOLDI, G. DUOS GRADUES,OP145	ALE
GARIBOLDI, G. 6 EASY DUETS	EDK
GARIBOLDI, G. 6 MELODIC DUETS, OP145 IN C MA	CF
GEBAUER, F. DUET #2	EUL
GEFORS, H. INVENTION, OP 5 (1972)	STI
GENIN, P. GRAND DUO CONCERTANT,OP 51	BIL
GENZMER, H. SONATA IN F SH MI	SCH
GEORGE, T. 6 CANONIC SONATAS	SO
GEORGE, T. DUET (PATADAH)	ACC
GERAEDTS, J. 4 INVENTIES(1943)	SD
GERAEDTS, J. 6 STUDIES IN TOONGESLACHTEN (1962) 1&2FL	SD
GERBIGUIER, T. 6 DUETS,OP 59	EDK
GEUSS-BIRKNER. 8 DUETS	HMO
GIBBONS, O. 6 FANTASIAS,2 VOLS.	PET
GIESBERT, F.(ED). DUOS OF ENGLISH MASTERS	NV
GILLAM, R. DUET #1	MAN
GLOCKNER, G. VARIATIONS ON THREE POLISH FOLK SONGS	PM
GODFREY, K. DOUBLE PLAY	PO
GOODMAN, J. MUSIC	GEN
GOORHUIS, R. 5 MINIATURES (1977)	SD
GOTTSCHALK, A. PHASES	SS
GRENSER, K.-WIENANDT. GRAND DUO	PO
GRIEG, E.-THAULOW. BUTTERFLIES	MC
HANDEL-DAQUIN/ARLEN. 2 FLUTE DUETS	KN
HANDEL, G. ALLEGRO(SONATA #2)	CF
HANDEL, G.-DART. DUO	S&C
HANDEL, G.-DISHINGER. EXCERPTS (SONATA IN C MI)	SP
HANDEL, G.-LAIDLAW. SONATA IN E MI	SPR
HARVEY, P. GRADED STUDY DUETS	BH
HASSE, J.-NAGEL. 13 DUETTE	HEI
HASSE, J.-NAGEL. 20 KLEINE DUETTE	MV
HATTORI, K. DIALOGUE	SO
HAUBENSTOCK-RAMATI, R. INTERPOLATIONS	UE
HAUSER, M.-HAAS. SONG WITHOUT WORDS	RU
HAYDN, F.-RAMPAL. 6 DUOS CONCERTANTS	BIL
HAYDN, F.-WIENANDT. 6 DUOS, 2 VOLS	PO
HAYDN, F.-WALTHER. ECHO	WZ
HAYDN, F. ECHO	EDK
HAYDN, F.-WIENANDT. MINUET IN D MA	SO
HAYDN, F.-GODFREY. SURPRISE! SURPRISE!	PO

2 FLUTES - 200

HAYDN,F.-RAMPAL. DUET #3,IN F MA	INT
HEMPEL,C. 10 DUETTE	MV
HERMANN, R. FLUTE WILLOW	CF
HERSANT. KLAGE (PLAINTE)	ALE
HINDEMITH, P. KANONISCHE SONATINE, OP 31/3	SCH
HOFFMEISTER, F.-PAULER. 3 DUETS, OP 30	EUL
HOFFMEISTER, F.-RAMPAL. 3 DUETS, OP 31	INT
HOSMER, J. 4 DUOS	M&M
HOTTETERRE, J.-RUF/ZOLLER. SUITE IN B MI	HSM
HOVHANESS, A. PASTORAL & FUGUE (1973)	AMP
HUBER, K.-ARTAUD. OISEAUX D'ARGENT	EMT
HUGUES, L.-VEGGETTI. LA SCUOLA DEL FLAUTO,OP 51,3 VOLS	RC
HUMPHREYS, D. CHILDREN'S SUITE	SP
JELINEK, H. KANONS,OP 15/6(1950)	UE
JEPPSON, K. 3 PETITESSER (1972)	STI
JUST, J. 6 DUETTINOS, OP 3	EDH
KELLNER, D.-WIENANDT. GAVOTTE ANCIENNE	SO
KERR, H. 3 DUOS	EAM
KETTING, P. PARTITA(1936)	SD
KNAPE, W. 2 SUITES	WMS
KOECHLIN, C. SONATE,OP 75	EDS
KOEHLER, E. 40 PROGRESSIVE DUETS, OP 55,2 VOLS	EDK
KOEHLER, E. PROGRESSIVE DUETS,OP 55,2 VOLS	WZ
KOEHLER, E. 40 PROGRESSIVE DUETS,OP 55,2 VOLS	CF
KOEHLER, E.-DROUET. 6 SONATINAS, OP 96,AND 3 DUOS CONCERTANTS	EDK
KOEHLER, E.-DROUET. 6 SONATINES, 3 DUOS CONCERTANTS	SO
KOLZ, E.(ED). GALANTE MENUETTE	LDO
KONIETZNY, H. PAS DE DEUX(1968)	GBV
KRAKAMP, E. CONCERT SUITE,OP139	EDM
KREBS. CONTEMPLATION	OP
KUFFNER, J. DUO CONCERTANS, OP 84/1,2, IN G AND D MA	EDH
KUHLAU, F. 3 BRILLIANT DUETS, OP 13BIS	EDK
KUHLAU, F. 3 BRILLIANT DUETS, OP 80	EDK
KUHLAU, F. 3 BRILLIANT DUETS, OP102	EDK
KUHLAU, F.-VEGGETTI. 3 BRILLIANT DUETS,OP 80	RC
KUHLAU, F.-BARON. DUET, OP 80/1	ETP
KUHLAU, F.-BAKER. 3 DUETS, OP 10	ETP
KUHLAU, F.-VEGGETTI. 3 DUETS, OP 10	RC
KUHLAU, F. 3 DUETS, OP 10	EDK
KUHLAU, F. 3 DUETS, OP 10	INT
KUHLAU, F. 3 DUETS,OP 80	CF
KUHLAU, F. 3 DUETS,OP 80	INT
KUHLAU, F. 3 DUOS BRILLANTS, OP 81	EDK
KUHLAU, F. 3 DUOS BRILLANTS, OP110/1-3	SPR
KUHLAU, F. 3 DUOS BRILLANTS,OP 13 BIS	BIL
KUHLAU, F. 3 DUOS BRILLANTS,OP 81	CF
KUHLAU, F. 3 DUOS BRILLANTS,OP 81	INT
KUHLAU, F. 3 DUOS BRILLANTS,OP102	BIL
KUHLAU, F. 3 DUOS BRILLANTS,OP102	CF
KUHLAU, F. 3 DUOS BRILLANTS,OP102	INT
KUHLAU, F.-BAKER. 3 DUOS CONCERTANTES, OP 87	ETP
KUHLAU, F. 3 DUOS CONCERTANTS, OP 87	EDK
KUHLAU, F. 3 DUOS CONCERTANTS, OP 87	INT
KUHLAU, F. DUOS CONCERTANTS,OP 10	PET
KUHLAU, F. 3 DUOS CONCERTANTS,OP 10	CF
KUHLAU, F. 3 DUOS, OP 10	BIL
KUHLAU, F. 3 DUOS, OP 57 BIS (PUB SEPARATELY)	BIL
KUHLAU, F. 3 DUOS, OP 57 BIS	EDK
KUHLAU, F. 3 DUOS,OP 80	BIL
KUHLAU, F. 3 DUOS,OP 80	PET
KUHLAU, F. 3 DUOS,OP 81	BIL
KUHLAU, F. 3 DUOS,OP 81	PET

```
KUHLAU, F.  3 GRAND DUETS CONCERTANT, OP 87                      CF
KUHLAU, F.  3 GRAND DUETS,OP 39                                  CF
KUHLAU, F.  3 GRAND DUOS, OP 39                                  EDK
KUHLAU, F.  3 GRAND DUOS,OP 39                                   INT
KUHLAU, F.  3 GRANDS DUOS CONCERTANTS, OP 87 (PUB SEPARATELY)    BIL
KUHLAU, F.  3 GRANDS DUOS, OP 39 (PUB SEPARATELY)               BIL
KUHLAU, F.-BAKER.  3 GRANDS DUOS, OP 39                          ETP
KUMMER, G.  3 DUETS, OP132                                       EDK
KUMMER, G.(K).  3 DUETS,OP132                                    INT
KUMMER, G.(K).  DUOS CONCERTANTS,OP  9                           EDH
KUMMER, G.-HERICHE.  3 DUOS FACILES,OP 74                        BIL
KUMMER, G.  3 PETITS DUOS,OP 20                                  BIL
KUMMER, G.(K).  SONATINA,OP 36/3                                 EDM
KUTSCH, B.  JUNGE FLOTIST, DER                                   WZ
LANG, I.  DUO(1963)                                              EMB
LASSO, O. DI-OCHS.  7 FANTASIES                                  FRH
LATEEF, Y.  DUET, OP100/1                                        EAM
LATEEF, Y.  MUSIC                                                FAM
LAX, F.  TWILIGHT CAROL POLKA, OP112.  2PIC                      CF
LENDVAY, K.  4 DUETTI                                            EMB
LETNAN, J.  STYRI SKICE(1963)                                    SHF
LIBAEK, S.  6 MOODS                                              SN
LICHT, D.  3 PIECES                                              M&M
LINCKE, P.-WALTERS.  THE GLOWWORM                                RU
LOCATELLI, P.-RUF.  2 DUETS,OP  4/4&5                            SCH
LOCATELLI, P.-RUF & ZOLLER.  SONATA IN D MA,OP  1/6             HSM
LOCATELLI, P.-SCHLENGER.  SONATA IN E MI                         WZ
LOCATELLI, P.  SONATA, E                                         EDK
LOCATELLI, P.-RUF.  6 SONATAS,OP  4,VOL.1(1-3)                   RC
LOCATELLI, P.-WUMMER.  SONATE IN E MI                            INT
LOEBNER, R.  WINDVOGEL UBER OKLAHOMA                             HG
LOEILLET, J.-RUF.  6 DUETS,OP  5,2 VOLS                          SCH
LOEILLET, J.-RUF.  3 DUETS                                       SCH
LOEILLET, J.-HANSON.  SONATA IN D MI                             GAL
LOEILLET, J.-BLOCK.  6 SONATAS, 2 VOLS                           MR
LOEILLET, J.  SONATE IN E MI(NO.942)                             EV
LOEILLET, J.  SONATE IN G MI(NO.943)                            EV
LOEILLET, J.-POULTEAU.  SONATE, OP  5/1                          ALE
LOEILLET, J.-POULTEAU.  SONATE, OP  5/2                          ALE
LOEILLET, J.-POULTEAU.  SONATE, OP  5/3                          ALE
LOEILLET, J.-POULTEAU.  SONATE, OP  5/4                          ALE
LONQUICH, H.  MUSIK IN DIE STILLE (1976)                        HG
LORENZO, L. DE.  SUITE MODERNA,OP 83                             PET
LOTZ, H.  9 FLUTE DUETS                                          MV
LUENING, O.  3 DUETS                                             NVM
LUENING, O.  SONORITY CANON                                      GA
MAASZ, G.  DUO IN G MA                                           MV
MAGANINI, Q.  COUPERIN SUITE                                     EDM
MAGANINI, Q.  2 HUMMING BIRDS                                    EDM
MAGANINI, Q.  IN THE BEGINNING                                   EDM
MAGANINI, Q.  PETITE SUITE CLASSIQUE                             EDM
MAHAUT, A.-HEUWEKEMEIJER.  6 SONATE DA CAMERA,2 VOLS             EDH
MAROS, M.  MONONOME (1971).  2BFL                                STI
MARTINU, B.  DIVERTIMENTO                                        EES
MATTHESON, J.-HUNT.  SONATA, OP 1/ 1 (D MI)                      S&C
MATTHESON, J.-HUNT.  SONATA, OP 1/ 2 (F MA)                      S&C
MATTHESON, J.-HUNT.  SONATA, OP 1/11 (B-FLAT MA)                S&C
MATTHESON, J.-HUNT.  SONATA, OP 1/12 (A MI)                      S&C
MICHAEL, F.  GINKO(1968),OP 23/1                                 BRH
MIEG, P.  PIECES POUR 1, 2 ET 3 FLUTES                           HUG
MIGOT, G.  6 PETITS PRELUDES,2 VOLS                              ALE
MILLS, C.  SUITE FOR 2 FLUTES SOLI                               ACA
```

MOLS, R. 20 MODERN DUETS	ETP
MONTECLAIR, M. DE-VIOLLIER. CONCERTO #1 IN D MA	HEI
MONTECLAIR, M. DE-VIOLLIER. CONCERTO #2 IN E MI	HEI
MONTECLAIR, M. DE-VIOLLIER. CONCERTO #3 IN G MA	HEI
MONTECLAIR, M. DE. CONCERTO #3	PET
MONTECLAIR, M. DE-FROTSCHER. 6 CONCERTOS, 2 VOLS	WMS
MOURET, J.-AUBANEL. 12 AIRS A CHANTER ET A DANSER	GA
MOURET, J.-VIOLLIER. 6 SONATAS, 2 VOLS.	HEI
MOZART, W.-TIPTON. DUET, OP 75/1	ETP
MOZART, W.-HADDEN. 17 DUETS (MAGIC FLUTE)	NOM
MOZART, W.-BARGE. DUETS,OP 74/1 IN D MA	PET
MOZART, W.-BARGE. DUETS,OP 74/2 IN E MI	PET
MOZART, W.-BARGE. DUETS,OP 74/3 IN D MA	PET
MOZART, W. 6 DUETS,OP 75,2 VOLS	CF
MOZART, W.-BARGE. 6 DUETTE, K.V.156(1-3)	WZ
MOZART, W.-WEHSENER. 6 DUETTE,K.V. 157(4-6)	WZ
MOZART, W.-BRAUN. MAGIC FLUTE, THE	UE
MOZART, W.-BRAUN. MARRIAGE OF FIGARO, THE	UE
MOZART, W.-JODE. 4 MIRROR CANONS	MV
MUCZYNSKI, R. 6 DUOS, OP 34	GS
MULOT, A. SUITE DANS LE STYLE ANCIEN,OP 13	DUR
NAUDOT, J.-RUF. BABIOLES,OP 10,2 VOLS	SCH
NAUDOT, J.-TAYLOR. SONATA	RC
NAUDOT, J.-BLOCK. 6 SONATAS, OP 5	NOM
NAUDOT, J.-HOCKNER,W&H. 6 SONATAS,2 VOLS	SIM
NAUDOT, J. 6 SONATAS	BRH
NELHYBEL, V. SHORT STORIES	EAM
OLSEN, S. INVENTION	NM
URBAN, M. SONATINE	MB
PAISIBLE, J.-RUF. 6 DUETS, OP 1, 2 VOLS	SCH
PAISIBLE, J.-HUNT. SONATA, OP 1/1 (D MI)	S&C
PAISIBLE, J.-HUNT. SONATA, OP 1/2 (F MA)	S&C
PAISIBLE, J.-HUNT. SONATA, OP 1/4 (G MI)	S&C
PAISIBLE, J.-HUNT. SONATA, OP 1/5 (C MA)	S&C
PASSMORE, J. ADAGIO & ALLEGRO, OP 2	CF
PATACHICH, I. 3 QUADRI	FS
PELZ, W. MINUET PETITE	BE
PETRASSI, G. DIALOGO ANGELICO (1948)	ESZ
PISK, P. SUITE, OP 80	PET
PLA, J.-LEBERMANN. 6 SONATAS	SCH
PLEYEL, I.-STEINBECK. 12 DUETS, 4 VOLS	LDO
PLEYEL, I.-RAMPAL. 3 DUOS CONCERTANTS, OP 68	INT
POLGAR, T. SONATINA (1971)	CAN
POLIN, C. TELEMANICON	SS
POPP, W.-SOUSSMANN, H. EASY DUETS	CF
POPP, W. MELODIC SUITE, OP281	EDM
PORRET, J. 12, OP648 EASY DUOS	HE
PORTA, B.-WIENANDT. 2 DUOS FOR EQUAL INSTRUMENTS	TP
POSKIN, P. INVENTIE EN FUGA	MAU
PRESSER, W. 7 DUETS	TRI
PUHAKKA, J. DUO, OP 14/1	FIN
QUANTZ, J.-TIPTON. DUETS, OP 2/1-2	ETP
QUANTZ, J.-WUMMER. 6 DUETS, OP 2, 2 VOLS.	INT
QUANTZ, J.-MUELLER. 6 DUETS, OP 2, 2 VOLS	BRH
QUANTZ, J. 3 DUETS, OP 2	EDK
QUANTZ, J.-WITTGENSTEIN. 6 DUETS, OP 2	GS
QUANTZ, J.-NAGEL. 6 DUETS, OP 5, 2 VOLS	HEI
QUANTZ, J.-RUF & ZOLLER. SONATA IN A MI, OP 2/2	HSM
QUANTZ, J.-LASOCKI. 6 SONATAS, OP 2	NOM
RAPHAEL, G. KANONISCHE SUITE, OP 47/5	WMS
RAPHLING, S. VARIATIONS	EDM
REICHA, A.-MOYSE. 3 ROMANCES, OP 21	INT

REICHA, A.-POOR. 3 ROMANCES	ETP
REICHA, A.-POLNAUER. 3 ROMANZEN, OP 21	SCH
REICHA, A.-NAGEL. VARIATIONS, OP 20	EUL
REICHA, A.-POLNAUER. VARIATIONS, OP 20	PET
RIEDT, F.-SONNTAG. DUETT IN F MA	HEI
RIPPERT, J. FIRST COLLECTION OF NOELS AND BRUNETTES	ALE
ROSSI, M.-MOYSE. ANDANTINO & ALLEGRO	INT
ROSSINI, G.-FORSTER. 12 WALTZES	EUL
ROUSSAKIS, N. 6 SHORT PIECES	AB
ROWE, P. (ARR). FUN FOR FLUTES. 2FL,OPT PF	PO
ROYER-NAZZI. ZAIDE, LA	MB
RUF, H. (ED). 2 DUOS ALTER ENGLISCHER MEISTER	S&C
RYTERBAND, R. DIALOG	HUG
SACCHINI, A. ANDANTINO GRAZIOSO (RENAUD)	CF
SAGVIK, S. 14 KORTA BAGATELLDUETTER, OP 69 (1976)	STI
SAMMARTINI, G.-BLOCK. 6 SONATAS, OP 4	NOM
SARO, H. STUDIES IN CANON FORM	CF
SCARLATTI-MARIANO. DUETS	WMI
SCHADE, W. 20 EASY & PROGRESSIVE DUETS	CF
SCHAEFFER, D. FLUTES TWO	PO
SCHICKELE, P. SMALL WORLD, A (1962)	CAN
SCHNEIDER, G. 3 DUOS CONCERTANT, OP 78	EUL
SCHNEIDER, W. SONATA	MV
SCHNEIDER, W. 2 SONATINES	MV
SCHWARTZ, E. SIBLING SUITE	MEP
SEGERHAMMER. LITTLE CASCADE WALTZ	PO
SHIELD, W. SPORTSMAN'S RHAPSODY, THE	EDH
SHORT, D. CONFIGURATIONS. FL,AFL	ZA
SOLLBERGER, H. 2 PIECES	M&M
SOULE, E. 3 DUETS	MAN
SOUSSMAN, H.-DOEPPLER. 12 PIECES, OP 47	INT
SOUSSMANN, H.-GOLDBERG. DUETS	ETP
SOUSSMANN, H.-TILLMETZ. 12 DUETS, OP 53	INT
SOUSSMANN, H. 12 LIGHT PIECES, OP 47	EDM
SOUSSMANN, H.-DOPPLER. 12 PIECES, OP 47	EDK
STAMITZ, C. (K). 3 DUETS, OP 27	INT
STAMITZ, K.-GLODER. 6 DUETS, OP 27, 2 VOLS.	B&N
STAMITZ, K.-BORMANN. 6 DUETS, OP 27, 2 VOLS	NV
STAMITZ, K. 3 DUETS, OP 27	EDK
STEINBRENNER, W. BICINIUM	ALB
STEKL, K. MUSIC, OP126	FS
STRONGIN, T. 4 DUOS	TP
SULPIZI, F. CECI...CELA...ET AUTRES CHOSES, OP 17. PIC,FL	EBE
SZERVANSKY, E. SUITE (1956)	EMB
TAKEMITSU, T. MASQUE-CONTINU/INCIDENTAL	EDS
TAKEMITSU, T. MASQUE-INCIDENTAL # 2	EDS
TCHEREPNIN, A. DUO, OP108	BEL
TELEMANN, G. DRESDEN DUETS IN E MI, A MA, & E MA	B&N
TELEMANN, G. DRESDEN DUETS IN G MA, A MI, & B MI	B&N
TELEMANN, G.-BARON. DUET IN D MA	ETP
TELEMANN, G.-BUDDE. 6 DUETS	MV
TELEMANN, G.-LOEWER. 6 DUETS	B&V
TELEMANN, G.-DISHINGER. EXCERPTS (SONATA IN G MA)	SP
TELEMANN, G.-DISHINGER. EXCERPTS (SONATA IN G MI)	SP
TELEMANN, G.-DISHINGER. EXCERPTS (SUITE IN A MI)	SP
TELEMANN, G. MARBURG DUETS IN B FL MA, C MI, & E FL MA	B&N
TELEMANN, G. MARBURG DUETS IN F MI, B FL MA, & E MA	B&N
TELEMANN, G.-DAVENPORT. PARTITA IN E MI	M&M
TELEMANN, G.-BERGMANN. SONATA IN B FL MA	S&C
TELEMANN, G.-BERGMANN. SONATA IN C MA	S&C
TELEMANN, G.-BERGMANN. SONATA IN D MI	S&C
TELEMANN, G.-RUF & ZOLLER. SONATA IN E MI, OP 2/5	HSM

2 FLUTES - 200

TELEMANN, G.-HUNT. SONATA IN F MA	S&C
TELEMANN, G.-BERGMANN SONATA IN G MA	S&C
TELEMANN, G.-CHAMPION. SONATA IN G MI	S&C
TELEMANN, G. SONATAS IN CANON FORM, OP 5	INT
TELEMANN, G. SONATAS IN CANON FORM, OP 5	PET
TELEMANN, G.-RICHERT. 6 SONATAS IN CANON, OP 5	SCH
TELEMANN, G.-JODE. 6 SONATAS IN CANON	MV
TELEMANN, G.-RAMPAL. 6 SONATAS, OP 2 (DRESDEN DUETS)	INT
TELEMANN, G.-HAUSSWALD. SONATAS, OP 2, 2 VOLS	B&N
TELEMANN, G.-HAUSSWALD. SONATAS, OP 5, 2 VOLS	B&N
TELEMANN, G.-RAMPAL. 6 SONATAS, SERIES #2 (MARBURGER DUETS)	INT
TELEMANN, G.-PAUBON. 6 SONATAS, 2 VOLS.	BIL
TELEMANN, G.-RAMPAL. 6 SONATAS, 2 VOLS.	INT
TELEMANN, G. 6 SONATAS, 2 VOLS.	FRH
TELEMANN, G.-RIKKO. 6 SONATAS, 2 VOLS	TP
TELEMANN, G.-MOYSE. 6 SONATAS	GS
TERSCHAK, A. 12 CHARACTERISTIC PIECES	EDM
TERSCHAK, A. DUOS PROGRESSIFS, OP 70	CF
THEVET. 100 EXERCISES RYTHMIQUES	ALE
TILLMETZ, R. 12 EXERCISES IN MODERN RHYTHM, OP 54	WZ
TILLMETZ, R. 12 EXERCISES ON MODERN RHYTHMS, OP 54	EDK
TOESCHI, C.-LEBERMANN. 6 DUETS, OP 11, 2 VOLS	SCH
TREMBLOT DE LA CROIX. 10 INVENTIONS	ALE
TULOU, J. 6 DUET ETUDES	EDM
TULOU, J. 3 DUETS, OP104	EDK
TULOU, J. 3 DUOS, OP 14	EDH
TULOU, J. 3 DUOS, OP 14	UE
TULOU, J. 24 DUOS, 9 VOLS	HLE
TULOU, J. 3 EASY DUETS, OP102	EDK
TULOU, J. 3 EASY DUETS, OP102	INT
TULOU, J. 3 EASY DUETS, OP103	EDK
TULOU, J. 3 EASY DUETS, OP103	INT
TULOU, J. 3 EASY DUETS, OP104	INT
TULOU, J. 3 EASY DUETS, OP193	EV
TULOU, J.-RAMPAL. 3 GRAND DUOS, OP 72	INT
TURK, D.-DISHINGER. CUCKOO	SP
TWINN, S. (ED). 12 OLD ENGLISH SONGS	GAL
ULRICH, J. 5 (1966) DUETS	WH
VALENTINE, R.-RUF. 4 DUETS, OP 6/1-4	SCH
VALENTINE, R.-NAGEL. 3 SONATAS, OP 14	HEI
VALENTINE, R.-GLAZER. 4 SONATAS	CF
VALENTINE, R.-PETER. 6 SONATAS	MRL
VAN BOOM, J. 6 PIECES	HE
VAN VACTOR, D. DUETTINO (1974)	RR
VAN VACTOR, D. SUITE (1934)	RR
VANHAL, J.-BRAUN. 6 DUETS, VOLS. 1 AND 2	UE
VIGNE, P. DE LA. FLEURS, LES	EUL
VIGNE, P. DE LA-RUF. 3 LEICHTE SUITEN	RC
VIVALDI, A.-DISHINGER. GLORIA	SP
WAHREN, K. PAS DE DEUX	ROB
WALCKIERS, E. 3 DUOS CONCERTANS, OP 1/1-3	EDH
WANHAL, J.-BRYAN. 6 DUETTI, 2 VOLS.	UE
WEBER-OSTLING. DUETS, 2 VOLS	BE
WENDEL, M. DUET (1948)	EUL
WENDLING, J.-HEUWEKEMEIJER. DUETTO, OP 4/1-3	EDH
WIENANDT, E. (ED). MINUET & GAVOTTE	SO
WILDER, A. SUITE. AFL,BFL	MAR
YOFFE, S. AFFETUOSO	ISR
YUASA, J. INTERPENETRATION	TP
ZACHERT, W. 6 SUITEN IM ALTEN STIL	WZ
ZANETTOVICH, D. PIECES EN DUOS... TCHECOSLOVAQUES	ALE
ZEHM, F. 6 CAPRICEN	SCH

2 FLUTES - 200

ZEHM, F. NEUE DUETTSTUDIEN	SCH
ZIRNBAUER, H. (ED). BICINIEN	SCH
ZUCKERMAN, M. REUNION	ACA

2 FLUTES (COLLECTIONS)-201

ARNOLD, J. SELECTED DUETS, 2 VOLS.	ASH
BARGE, W.(ED). HEITERES AUS ALTER ZEIT	WZ
BEEKUM, J. VAN. INSTRUMENTAL DUETS, 2 VOLS.	HU
CAREY. FLUTE DUET ALBUM	BE
CSUPOR, L.(ARR). FLUTE DUOS	EMB
FLEURY, L. OEUVRES ORIGINALES DES XVII ET XVIII SIECLES	ALE
FLOTENDUOS FUR ANFANGER.	EUL
FLOTENDUOS, 3 VOLS.	EUL
FODOR, A.(ED). WERKE DEUTSCHER KOMPONISTEN	EMB
GATTI, G.(ED). COMPOSIZIONI PER 2 FLAUTI	EBE
GATTI, G.(ED). 15 DUETS BY CONTEMPORARY COMPOSERS	EBE
GEARHART, L. FLUTE SESSIONS	SH
GUENTHER, F. MASTERWORKS FOR 2 FLUTES, 2 VOL	BE
HODGSON(ARR). FLUTE ALBUM, 2 VOLS	PET
JENEY, Z.(ED). FLOTENDUOS, 3 VOLS.	EMB
JODE, F.(ARR). MEISTERKANONS	MV
JOHEN, K. & G. WIERZEJEWSKI (ARR). TANZE AUS BACHS ZEIT	FRH
KAPLAN, D. (ARR). GOTHAM COLLECTION OF DUETS	SPR
LIST-PRETSCH(EDS). OLD & NEW DUETS, 2 VOLS	FRH
MARTIN & PIZZUTO(ARR). MUSIC OF THE RENAISSANCE	KN
MATHER, B.(ED). 3 OPERA DUETS	CF
MOYSE, L. ALBUM OF FLUTE DUETS	GS
MOYSE, L. 30 EASY DUETS	M&M
MOYSE, M. ALBUM OF 30 CLASSICAL DUETS	INT
OLD AND NEW DUETS, 2 VOLS.	EDK
SCHAEFFER, D. (ARR). DUETS ARE FUN	PO
SCHAEFFER, D. (ARR). 21 RHYTHMIC DUETS	PO
STOUFFER, P.(ARR). SIX FOR TWO	KN
STOUFFER, P. (ARR). ALBUM OF 10 BAROQUE COMPOSITIONS	HE
VOXMAN, H. (ARR). SELECTED DUETS, 2 VOLS	RU
WIENANDT, E.(ARR). 11 FLUTE DUETS	PO
WYE, T.(ED). FLUTE DUETS, 2 VOLS.	CHE

2 OBOES-202

AMY, G. JEUX	UE
ARNELL, R. 5 INVENTIONS	HI
ARRIEU, C. 3 DUOS FACILES	BIL
AUBERT, J.-HARF. PETITS CONCERTS,LES, 2 VOLS.	HEI
BABELL, W. BOUREE	BE
BACH-MAGANINI. CANON (SONATA IN F MI)	CF
BACH, W.F. DUO SONATA	EDM
BACON, E. COCK FIGHT, THE	BR
BEETHOVEN, L. VAN. ALLEGRO & MINUET	EDM
BERGT, C.-DEGEN. DUET #1 IN C MA	HEI
BERGT, C.-DEGEN. DUET #2 IN F MA	HEI
BERGT, C.-DEGEN. DUET #3 IN B FL MA	HEI
BLAVET, M.-RUF. 2 DUETS, OP 1/5 & 6	SCH

```
BLAVET, M.-RUF.  6 SONATAS, OP  1, VOL 1 (1-3)                  RC
BOISMORTIER, J.-HARF.  6 EASY DUETS, OP 11, 2 VOLS.             OHN
BOISMORTIER, J.-RUF.  6 EASY DUETS, OP 17, 2 VOLS              SCH
BOISMORTIER, J.-BEECHEY.  2 SONATAS, OP  2/3,4                  OX
BONVALET.  CLAIRIERE, LA- LA PINEDE                             EV
BOUTRY, R.  TOCCATA, SARABAND & JIG                            ALE
BUCQUET, P.  SUITE #1                                          EDM
BUCQUET, P.  SUITE #2                                          EDM
BUTTERWORTH, N.  3 DIALOGUES                                   PET
CHAGRIN, F.  6 DUETS                                            NO
CHANCE, N.  DUOS II.  OB,EHN                                    SS
CHEDEVILLE, N.-UPMEYER.  2 PASTORALSONATEN IN C MI & C MA       NV
CLODOMIR, P.  12 DUOS                                           HE
CORRETTE, M.  6 SONATAS, OP  2                                 NOM
DAVENPORT, L.  3 DUETS                                          SF
DECHIFFRAGE DU MANUSCRIT.                                      HLE
DEVIENNE, F.  6 CELEBRATED SONATAS                             EDM
DEXTER, H.  AU CLAIR DE LA LUNE                                PET
DEXTER, H.  COUNTRY DIALOGUES                                  PET
FRIEDRICHSEN, J.-BLOCK.  GRANDFATHER'S DUET BOOK 1             NOM
GARNIER, F.-GERLACH.  ANFANGER-DUETTE (METHODE)               FRH
GEBAUER, F.  DUET #2                                           EUL
GRAHN, U.  FOR 2 ENGLISH HORNS (1968).  2EHN                   STI
GRAHN, U.  LITEN SERENADE (1965)                               STI
HALLAUER, D.  3 LEICHTE STUCKE                                  MV
HARVEY, P.  GRADED STUDY DUETS                                  BH
KAPLAN, D. (ARR).  GOTHAM COLLECTION OF OBOE DUETS            SPR
KAZACSAY, T.  2 DUETTE, OP113 (1956).  OB,EHN                  EMB
KENNAWAY, L.  TANDEM                                            BH
KUFFNER, J.  27 DUETS                                          M&M
LACOUR, G.  SUITE EN DUO                                       BIL
LANCEN, S.  TWINS, THE                                         PET
LOEILLET, J.-RUF.  6 DUETS, OP  5, 2 VOLS                      SCH
LOEILLET, J.-RUF.  3 DUETS                                     SCH
LOEILLET, J.-POULTEAU.  SONATA, OP  5/1                        ALE
LOEILLET, J.-POULTEAU.  SONATA, OP  5/2                        ALE
LOEILLET, J.-POULTEAU.  SONATA, OP  5/4                        ALE
LUFT, H.  24 ETUDES IN DUET FORM                               CF
LUFT, J.-STEINS.  12 ETUDES, OP 11                            B&B
MADERNA, B.  DIALODIA                                          RC
MAGANINI, Q.  IN THE BEGINNING                                EDM
MAGANINI, Q.  PETITE SUITE CLASSIQUE                          EDM
MALIGE, F.  6 ZWEISTIMMIGE INVENTIONEN                        FRH
MARCONI, L.  COLLAGE PER UN DUO                               EDI
MIGOT, G.  PASTORALE                                          ALE
MOEVS, R.  DUO.  OB,EHN                                       EES
MONTECLAIR, M. DE.  6 CONCERTI, 2 VOLS                        PET
MOZART, L.  4 SHORT PIECES                                     HE
NAUDOT, J.-RUF.  BABIOLES, OP 10, 2 VOLS                      SCH
OWEN, D. (ARR).  21 DUETS                                      KN
PAISIBLE, J.-RUF.  6 DUETS, OP  1, 2 VOLS                     SCH
PAULSON, G.  DUBBEL RORBLADSGLADJE, OP 84 (1955).  OB,EHN     STI
PLA, J.-LEBERMANN.  6 SONATAS                                 SCH
PLEYEL, I.-VOXMAN.  3 DUOS                                    NOM
POLIN, C.  TELEMANICON                                         SS
PORRET, J.  12 EASY DUOS, OP648                                HE
PORTA, B.-WIENANDT.  DUO                                       TP
PORTA, B.-WIENANDT.  2 DUOS                                    TP
PRESSER, W.  7 DUETS                                           TP
RAPHLING, S.  DUOGRAMS                                        EDM
REGT, H. DE.  METAMORPHOSES, OP 39 (1974).  OB,EHN            SD
RHYS, S.  6 INVENTIONS                                         OX
```

2 OBOES-202

RICHARDSON, A. SONATINA. 2OB	NOM
RUF, H. (ED). 2 DUOS ALTER ENGLISCHER MEISTER	S&C
SAMMARTINI, G. SONATA, OP 1/6	M&M
SARO, H. STUDIES IN CANON FORM	CF
SCHAEFFER, D. (ARR). DUETS ARE FUN	PO
SCHAEFFER, D. (ARR). 21 RHYTHMIC DUETS	PO
SELLNER, J. 12 DUOS, 3 VOLS	EV
SINGER, S. 2 SONATAS	M&M
SOLLBERGER, H. TWO OBOES TROPING	M&M
STOKER, R. LITTLE SUITE	PET
STOUFFER, P. ALBUM OF 10 BAROQUE COMPOSITIONS	HE
TAKAHASHI, Y. OPERATION EULER	PET
THEVET. EXERCICES RYTHMIQUES	ALE
ULRICH, J. 5 DUETS (1966)	WH
VIGNE, DE LA-RUF. 2 LITTLE SUITES	RC
VIGNE, P. DE LA. FLEURS, LES	EUL
WARDROP, L. 2-PART INVENTIONS. OB,EHN	UNI
WHITTENBERG, C. IAMBI IN TWO PARTS	M&M
WILDER, A. SUITE. OB,EHN	MAR
WUORINEN, C. BICINIUM	PET

2 OBOES (COLLECTIONS)-203

INSTRUMENTAL DUETS, 2 VOLS.	HU
STOUFFER, P.(ARR). SIX FOR TWO	KN
SZEKELY, E. & T. SZESZLER(ED). OBOE DUOS FOR BEGINNERS	EMB

2 CLARINETS-204

ARMA, P. DIVERTIMENTO #10	CHP
ARMA, P. 3 TRANSPARENCES	HLE
ARNELL, R. 5 INVENTIONS	HI
BACH, C.P.E.-MC GINNIS. DUET	INT
BACH, C.P.E.-STEPHAN. DUET IN C MA, WQ 142	B&N
BACH, C.P.E.-MARX. 2 DUETS	TP
BACH, J.S.-SIMON. BACH FOR THE CLARINET, PT. II	GS
BACH, J.S.-LUISETTI. BACH INVENTIONS	SF
BACH, J.S.-FOTE. 4 BACH PRELUDES. CL,BCL	KN
BACH, J.S. CANON #4	EDM
BACH, J.S.-LANGENUS. CLARINET DUOS	CF
BACH, J.S.-TOMEI. DUO CONCERTO	PO
BACH, J.S.-DISHINGER. EXCERPTS (SONATA IN C MA)	SP
BACH, W.F.-MAGANINI. CANON (SONATA IN F MI)	CF
BACH, W.F.-DE SMET. DUO #1	B&V
BACH, W.F. DUO SONATA	EDM
BACON, E. COCK FIGHT, THE	BR
BARRET, A.-TOLL. 12 DUETS	CF
BARTOK, B.-SUCHOFF. 23 PROGRESSIVE DUETS	BH
BASSETT, L. CLARINET DUETS	UNI
BAVICCHI, J. 5 DIALOGUES	OX
BECK, J. SPIEL	MV
BEETHOVEN, J. 6 EASY DUETS	HE
BEETHOVEN, L. VAN-HILTON. ALLEGRO & MINUET	RD
BEETHOVEN, L. VAN. ALLEGRO & MINUET	EDM

BEETHOVEN, L. VAN-MINOR. 2 BEETHOVEN SONATAS	SH
BEETHOVEN, L. VAN-BERLINSKI. CLARINET DUETS	TP
BEETHOVEN, L. VAN. 3 DUOS	SPR
BEETHOVEN, L. VAN-TOLL. RONDO (PATHETIQUE SONATA)	CF
BEETHOVEN, L. VAN-GRISEZ. SYMPHONY #1	ALE
BEETHOVEN, L. VAN-GRISEZ. TRIO #1 IN B FL MA	ALE
BEETHOVEN, L. VAN-GRISEZ. TRIO, OP 11	CF
BEHR, F.-DISHINGER. MENUETTO	SP
BELLINI, V. DUET (NORMA)	CF
BENDER, H.-COCHRANE. 4 CLARINET DUOS, OP 30	CF
BENJAMIN, T. AFTER-DINNER PIECES	SO
BENNETT, R. CROSSTALK	UE
BENTON, D. SERIAL STRAINS	SS
BENTON, D. SHORT SERIAL SUITE	SS
BERBIGUIER, T. 6 EASY DUETS	EDM
BERR, F.-LANCELOT. 20 PETITS DUOS	BIL
BERRY, W. 2 CANONS	EV
BLANK, A. 4 MINIATURES	AMP
BLANK, A. 3 ONE-NOTERS	ACA
BLUNT, M. 3 CONTRASTS	JE
BOEHM, F. 12 PETITS DUOS, OP 5	BIL
BORGHI, L.-WIENANDT. 5 CLARINET DUOS	SO
BORGHI, L.-WIENANDT. DIVERTIMENTO	TP
BORODIN, A. INTRODUCTION & ALLEGRO VIVO	HE
BOTH, H. TANZ- UND JAZZ- DUETTE	EAM
BOUFIL, J.-WESTON. GRAND DUO, OP 2/1	FEM
BRANDENBURG. ASH GROVE, THE	CF
BRAUN, Y. 4 EASY PIECES (1974)	ISR
BREPSANT, E. 15 DUETS, 3 VOLS	CF
BROWN, J. CHALUMEAU CANONS	TP
BUCQUET, P. SUITE #1	EDM
BUCQUET, P. SUITE #2	EDM
BUSCHMANN, R. MINIATURES FUR ZWILLINGE (1969)	GBV
BUTTERWORTH, N. 3 DIALOGUES	PET
BUTTERWORTH, N. THEME & VARIATIONS	RC
CADOW, P. ELEGIE UND RONDO	PGM
CAHUZAC, L.-LANCELOT. SONATE CLASSIQUE #1	BIL
CAHUZAC, L. SONATE CLASSIQUE #2 (AFTER WORKS OF GEBAUER)	BIL
CAVALLINI, E. 3 GRAND ARTISTIC DUETS	CF
CAVALLINI, E. 2 GRAND DUETS	CF
CAZDEN, N. 10 CONVERSATIONS, OP 34	SPR
CHAGRIN, F. 6 DUETS	NO
CHEDEVILLE-DEN AREND. AINE, L'	HE
CHILDS, B. MUSIC; THAT IT MIGHT BE..., A	SS
CLARINET ALBUM #1.	PET
CLARINET ALBUM #2.	PET
CLARKE, J.-DISHINGER. AIR	SP
CLERGUE, J. MELODIE- EN BALANCELLE	EV
CLODOMIR, P. 12 DUOS	MOL
COCKSHOTT, G. VARIATIONS ON A PASSEPIED OF HANDEL	SF
CORI, C. BACH LITERATURE DUETS	SF
CORI, C. (ARR). MELODY DUETS, BK #2	KPM
COUPERIN, F.-DISHINGER. MENUETTO	SP
COUPERIN, F. SUITE I	TP
CRAGUN, J. 8 CONCERT DUETS	RU
CRAWFORD-SEEGER, R. DIAPHONIC SUITE #3	AB
CROFT-ECCLES-DISHINGER. SARABANDE & MENUET	SP
CRUSELL, B.-MICHAELS. DUO I IN D MI	HSM
CRUSELL, B.-MICHAELS. DUO II IN C MA	HSM
CRUSELL, B. 3 DUOS	MT
CRUSELL, B.-CHAPMAN. PROGRESSIVE DUET #1 IN F MA	PET
CRUSELL, B.-CHAPMAN. PROGRESSIVE DUET #2 IN D MI	PET

```
CRUSELL, B.-CHAPMAN.  PROGRESSIVE DUET #3 IN C MA          PET
CUNNINGHAM, M.  SONATINA                                   SS
DA-OZ, R.  10 MINIATUREN                                   HEI
DAHL, I.  5 DUETS (1970)                                   JB
DAVENPORT, L.  3 DUETS                                     SF
DAVIDSON, J.  TWO PART INVENTION                           PMP
DAWE, M.  SEASONS, THE                                     CRA
DE FILIPPI, A.  AXIOMS                                     GEN
DE LULLI-ERICKSON.  CHOPSTICKS                             EJ
DEASON, D.  POLARITY.  CL,BCL                              SS
DECHIFFRAGE DU MANUSCRIT.                                  HLE
DELGUIDICE, M.  20 DUOS FACILES                            BIL
DEPELSENAIRE, J.  GARDES FRANCAISES                        EFM
DEPELSENAIRE, J.  PASTOURELLE- L'ARGYROMETRE               EV
DEPELSENAIRE, J.  REVERENCE                                EFM
DEVIENNE, F.  6 CELEBRATED SONATAS                         EDM
DEVIENNE, F.-STEINBECK.  DUO CONCERTANT IN E-FLAT, OP 67/3 LDO
DEVIENNE, F.-STEINBECK.  DUO CONCERTANT, OP 67/1           LDO
DEVIENNE, F.-LEBERMANN.  DUOS, OP 69/1 & 2                 SCH
DEVIENNE, F.-LEBERMANN.  DUOS, OP 69/3                     SCH
DEXTER, H.  AU CLAIR DE LA LUNE                            PET
DEXTER, H.  COUNTRY DIALOGUES                              PET
DIEMENTE, E.  3 PIECES                                     SS
DOMAZLICKY, F.  3 DUETS, OP  3 (1953)                      HU
DONIZETTI, G.  SONATA                                      PET
DUBOIS, P.  6 CAPRICES                                     ALE
DUBOIS, P.  18 DUOS PROGRESSIFS                            BIL
DVORAK, A.-ERICKSON.  HUMORESQUE                           EJ
EISENHAUER, W.  LEARN TO PLAY DUETS                        AL
ELTON, A.  SHORT SONATA                                    CHE
ERICKSON, E.  FESTIVE MOOD                                 EJ
ESCHER.  GROSSES DUO, OP120                                EUL
ESCHER.  7 KLEINE DUOS, OP122                              EUL
FESCH, W. DE.  ANDANTE & MENUET                            HE
FRANCK, C.  TO LITTLE CHILDREN                             HE
FRANK, A.  DUO                                             SS
FRANK, A.  SUITE                                           OX
FREED, I.  DIVERTIMENTO                                    AB
GAMBARO, G.-PAULER.  3 DUOS, OP 10                         PET
GARBARINO, G.  DIALOGHI. 20 DUETTI                         RC
GAY, E.-LANCELOT.  16 DUOS CLASSIQUES                      BIL
GAY, E.-LANCELOT.  20 PETITS DUOS                          BIL
GEBAUER, E.  DUO #5                                        HEU
GEBAUER, F.  DUETTO #2                                     EUL
GEBAUER, F.-WOJCIECHOWSKI.  6 DUOS, OP  2                  HSM
GHYS, J.-ERICKSON.  AMARYLLIS                              EJ
GOLDMAN, R.  SONATINA                                      BH
GRAZIOLI-ROCERETO.  MINUETTO (SONATA IN G MA)             VO
GRIEVE.  SHERLOCK HOLMES SUITE                             WAT
GRIMS-LAND-EBBE.  POLYFON POLKA-POLONAISE (1977)          STI
HAJDU, M.  CLARINET DUETS (1951)                          EMB
HANDEL, G.  ALLEGRO (SONATA #2)                           CF
HANDEL, G.  BAROQUE DUET #3                               HE
HANDEL, G.-DISHINGER.  EXCERPTS (SONATA IN C MI)          SP
HARVEY, J.  STUDIES                                        NO
HARVEY, P.  GRADED STUDY DUETS, 2 VOLS                    BH
HARVEY, P.  SATIRICAL SUITE                               S&C
HAYDN, F.-VOXMAN.  6 DUETS, 2 VOLS                        MR
HAYDN, F.  SONATA IN D MA                                 EDM
HAYDN, F.-GRISEZ.  SONATAS #5 & 6                         CF
HAYDN, F.-SKOLNIK.  WITCHES' CANON, THE                   EDM
HEIM, N.  FESTIVAL SUITE.  CL,BCL                         SMO
```

HEIM, N. SUITE	KN
HEMPEL, C. MINERALI. 8 STUCKE	MV
HESS, W. 5 DUOS, OP 64	PET
HEUSSENSTAMM, G. 8 SHORT DUETS	WI
HOFMANN, W. 5 INVENTIONS	PET
HOLSTEIN, J. DUETTISTES, LES	ALE
HOOK, J.-CURWIN. GUIDA DI MUSICA	CA
HOVEY, N. SUPPLEMENTARY DUETS	BE
HOVHANESS, A. SONATA, OP297	PI
HUFFNAGLE, H. RHYTHM DUETS	SF
HUFFNAGLE, H. STREAMLINED DUETS, 2 VOLS	SF
HYAMS, A. 7 MICRO-ORGANISMS	SO
KAUFMANN, A. CONCERTINO #2, OP 86	LDO
KIBBE, M. SONATA	SH
KIETZER, R. 4 DUETS IN SYMPHONIC STYLE, OP 94, 2 VOLS.	EDK
KIETZER, R. DUETTE, OP 94, 3 VOLS	WZ
KIMBELL, M. 5 DIALOGUES	MAN
KLAUSS, N. INVENTION	KN
KLERK, J. DE. KLEINE PARTITA	MOL
KLOSE, H. 3 CONCERT DUETS	EDM
KLOTZMAN, A. FUN	MC
KOECHLIN, C. IDYLLE	CHM
KOEHLER, M.-SNAVELY. 14 PROGRESSIVE DUETS	SH
KOLB, B. REBUTTAL	PET
KOLMAN, P. SONATA CANONICA. CL,BCL	SHF
KRAFT, L. LITTLE SUITE	TP
KREITH, K.-SUPPAN. DUETTE	FS
KREJCI, M. MOMENTKY	ART
KREUTZER, C.-BALASSA. DUETTO IN C MA	EMB
KREUTZER, C. DUO IN C MA	EUL
KREUTZER, K.-MICHAELS. DUO IN C MA	HSM
KROEPSCH, F. 5 DUETS	CF
KROEPSCH, F. 5 DUOS	EM
KUEFFNER, J.-WIENANDT. DUET #3	PO
KUEFFNER, J.-DRUCKER. 24 EASY DUETS	INT
KUFFNER, J. 50 PROGRESSIVE DUETS	CF
KUHLAU, F. 3 DUETS, OP 81	CF
KUNZ, A. FUN FOR 2 (1964). 2BCL	CAN
KUPFERMAN, M. 4 DOUBLE FEATURES	GEN
KURTZ, S. 3 IMPRESSIONS	LYA
KUSZING. KLARINETTENMUSIK FUR ANFANGER	EMB
LA VIOLETTE, W. DUET ALBUM	BE
LACOUR, G. SUITE EN DUO	BIL
LAJOVIC, A. DIALOGUE	EDD
LANCEN, S. TWINS, THE	PET
LANESE, T. ELEMENTARY DUETS	SO
LANGENUS, G. STUDIES AND DUOS	CF
LASSO. O. DI-KRIVIN. SONGS	EM
LAZARUS, H. 3 CONCERT DUETS	CF
LAZARUS, H. 24 EASY & PROGRESSIVE DUETS ON OPERATIC MELODIES	CF
LAZARUS, H. 20 EASY PROGRESSIVE DUETS	CF
LAZARUS, H. 3 GRAND ARTISTIC DUETS	CF
LAZARUS, H.-DE VILLE. 3 GRAND CONCERT DUETS	CF
LEFEVRE, X.-LANCELOT. 6 DUOS	BIL
LEFEVRE, X. 6 PETITS DUOS FACILES	BIL
LESTER, L. CLARINET TWOSOME	CF
LETELLIER, R. 14 NOUVEAUX DUOS ET TRIOS	EDR
LETELLIER, R. RECUEIL DE DUOS ET TRIOS	EDR
LEWIN, G. TWO OF A KIND	BH
LIDHOLM, I. INVENTION (1954). CL,BCL	STI
LIJNSCHOTEN, V. 4 CANONS	T-M
LUEDEKE, R. 15 INVENTIONS	SS

MAGANINI, Q.	CANONICO ESPRESSIVO	EDM
MAGANINI, Q.	COUPERIN SUITE	EDM
MAGANINI, Q.	IN THE BEGINNING	EDM
MAGANINI, Q.	PETITE SUITE CLASSIQUE	EDM
MAGNANI, A.	6 DUETTI CONCERTANT	CF
MAGNANI, A.	SONATA	CF
MAILLOT, J.	12 DUOS PROGRESSIFS, 3 VOLS.	EMT
MALIGE, F.	7 DUOS	FRH
MAMLOK, U.	8 EASY DUETS	ACA
MAMLOK, U.	SONATINA	ACA
MANNINO, F.	FEUILLES D'AUTOMNE, LES	EDI
MARCO, T.	HOQUETUS (1973)	EEC
MASCHAYEKI, A.	9 EXPRESSIONEN. CL,BCL	UE
MAZAS, J.	DUETS	SF
MAZAS, J.	DUO	HE
MAZAS, J.	PETIT DUOS #S 1, 2, 3, 5	MOL
MC CABE, J.	BAGATELLES	NO
MC LUCKIE, I. (ED).	12 BELOW B	BH
MENDELSSOHN, F.-GRISEZ.	DUO CONCERTANT, OP114	ALE
MERCIER.	DUO CURIEUX	EDR
MIASKOVSKY, N.-LESTER.	FUGUE IN A CLASSIC STYLE. CL,BCL	WI
MINOR-FARNSWORTH.	FUN DUETS	SH
MIRANDOLLE, L.	3 DUOS	ALE
MORTENSEN, F.	3 PIECES, OP 22/3	NM
MOSER, C.	VARIAZIONI DIATONIQUE	GZ
MOSZKOWSKI, M.-ERICKSON.	SPANISH DANCE, OP 12/1	EJ
MOZART, L.	16 DUETS	EMB
MOZART, L.	4 SHORT PIECES	HE
MOZART, W.-FREEMAN.	CLARINET DUET #4	SF
MOZART, W.-WIENANDT.	DUET #2	PO
MOZART, W.-WIENANDT.	DUET #3	PO
MOZART, W.-KURKIEWICZ.	3 DUETS (K. 367-369)	PWM
MOZART, W.-HODGSON.	DUETS, OP 70/ 7, 8	PET
MOZART, W.-HODGSON.	DUETS, OP 70/ 9, 10	PET
MOZART, W.-HODGSON.	DUETS, OP 70/11, 12	PET
MOZART, W.-TENNEY.	6 DUETS, OP 70, 2 VOLS	CF
MOZART, W.-MAGNANI.	6 DUETS, OP 77, 2 VOLS	CF
MOZART, W.	6 DUETS, 2 VOLS.	EDK
MOZART, W.-DRUCKER.	6 DUETS, 2 VOLS	INT
MOZART, W.-HASKINS.	12 DUETS	OX
MOZART, W.	DUO, K487	MOL
MOZART, W.-LANGENUS.	3 DUOS	CF
MOZART, W.-SCHNEIDER.	KEGELDUETTE, K. 487	MV
MOZART, W.-TOLL.	PIANO SONATA #4, EXCERPT	CF
MOZART, W.-DAHM.	3 SONATAS	VO
MOZART, W.	SONATE #1	MOL
MOZART, W.	TRIO #7 (K498)	CF
MOZART, W.-MINOR.	6 VIENNESE SONATINAS	SH
MUELLER, I.-SIMON.	6 EASY DUETS, OP 41	INT
MUELLER, I.	6 EASY DUOS, OP 41	EM
MUTTER, G.	DIVERTIMENTO	MV
NAUMANN, J.	DUO	HE
NAUMANN, J.	PETIT DUO	MOL
NELHYBEL, V.	EPISODES	EAM
NEVIN, M.-HOLZMAN.	INVENTIONS	AMP
ORTOLANI, O.	MORE (THEME FROM MONDO CANE)	EM
OSTERC, S.	SONATINE (1929)	HG
OSTRANDER, A.	FIRST PALS	EDM
OWEN, D. (ARR).	21 DUETS	KN
PADEREWSKI, I.-ERICKSON.	MINUET	EJ
PAISNER, B.	SWING DUETS	SF
PATACHICH, I.	DUETTINO	FS

PATACHICH, I. PETITE SUITE	ALE
PELLEGRINI, E. SONATINA	OR
PELZ, W. CANDLELIGHT WALTZ	BE
PELZ, W. FIRESIDE REVERIES	BE
PELZ, W. GRADUATION WALTZ	PO
PERIER, A. STUDY-CAPRICES IN THE FORM OF DUETS	ALE
PERSICHETTI, V. SERENADE #13	EV
PIERCE, A. JOB 22:28	SS
PIERCE, A. MY LADY HUNDSON'S PAVANE	SS
PLEYEL, I.-GLAZER. DUETS #1 & 2	OX
PLEYEL, I. 6 DUETS, OP 8	CF
PLEYEL, I.-SUPPAN. 6 DUETTE	MV
PLEYEL, I.-GEBAUER/WIENANDT. DUO IN D MI	SO
PLEYEL, I.-GEBAUER/WIENANDT. DUO IN F MA	SO
PLEYEL, I.-SIMON. DUOS, OP 14/1-3	EM
PLEYEL, I. 6 LITTLE DUETS	CF
PORRET, J.-MARIVAUX. CONTEST DUO #13	MOL
PORRET, J.-NELSON. CONTEST DUO #14	MOL
PORRET, J. CONTEST DUO #7	MOL
PORRET, J. DUO DE CONCOURS #8	MOL
PORRET, J. 12 EASY DUOS	MOL
PORRET, J. 12 PROGRESSIVE DUETS, OP254	MOL
PORRET, J. LA VOISIER. CONTEST DUO #12	MOL
PORTA, B.-WIENANDT. DUO	TP
PORTA, B.-WIENANDT. 2 DUOS	TP
POULENC, F. SONATA. A & B FL CL	CHE
PRANZER, J.-LANCELOT. DUO #1 (3 DUOS CONCERTANTS)	EMT
PRANZER, J.-LANCELOT. DUO #2 (3 DUOS CONCERTANTS)	EMT
PRANZER, J.-LANCELOT. DUO #3 (3 DUOS CONCERTANTS)	EMT
PRANZER, J.-LANCELOT. 4TH DUO CONCERTANT	EMT
PRANZER, J.-LANCELOT. 5TH DUO CONCERTANT	EMT
PRANZER, J.-LANCELOT. 6TH DUO CONCERTANT	EMT
PURCELL-BLOW/DISHINGER. INTRADA AND AIR	SP
PURCELL, H.-DISHINGER. GAVOTTE	SP
PURCELL, H.-WRIGHT. PRELUDE	PO
RAINER, G. MINIATUREN FUR ZWILLINGE	B&N
RAMEAU, J.-DISHINGER. MENUET (SUITE #1)	SP
RAPHLING, S. SONATINA	EDM
RATHBURN, E. CONVERSATION (1956)	CAN
RICKER, R. 10 DUETS FOR THE 20TH CENTURY CLARINETIST	AU
RIMSKY-KORSAKOV, N.-GNESIN. CANZONETTA; TARANTELLA	MR
ROLLA, A. VIRTUOSO STUDY	EDM
ROSSI-ROCERETO. ANDANTINO IN A FL MA	VO
RUSSELL, R. ABSTRACT #1	GEN
SARLIT, H. (COMP). 20 ETUDES DE DECHIFFRAGE	GS
SARLIT, H. (COMP). 20 ETUDES DE DECHIFFRAGE	SCF
SARO, H. STUDIES IN CANON FORM	CF
SAYGUN, A. SEZISLER (INTUITIONS)	PI
SCARLATTI, D.-ROSENTHAL. DUETS FROM PIANO SUITES	TP
SCARLATTI, D.-SKOLNIK. NEAPOLITAN SUITE	EDM
SCARLATTI, D.-WRIGHT. PASTORALE	PO
SCHAEFFER, D. CLARINETS TWO	PO
SCHNEIDER, W. 30 DUETTE	MV
SCHNEIDER, W. HEITERES DIVERTIMENTO	SCH
SCHNEIDER, W. PARTITA	BA
SCHNEIDER, W. SONATA	MV
SCHUBERT, F. 5 LITTLE DUETS, VERSION B	TP
SCHUBERT, F.-ERICKSON. MARCH MILITAIRE	EJ
SCHULLER, G. DUO SONATA. CL,BCL	AMP
SCHUMANN, R. FAIRY TALES, OP132	CF
SCHWADRON, A. PROGRESSIVE ENSEMBLE STUDIES, VOL. 1	KN
SCHWARTZ, E. 4 STUDIES	GEN

2 CLARINETS-204

SEMLER-COLLERY, J. PIECE DE CARACTERE	BIL
SESTAK, Z. SONATA (1967)	ART
SIEGRIST, B. TRUCS ET SL-FLAT	EFM
SIENNICKI, E.-HITE. LET ME TELL IT	SO
SIMEONOV, B. INVENTION	WAT
SIMEONOV, B. 3 STUDIES	CAN
SIRULNIKOFF, J. SUITE (1952)	CAN
SMITH, W. CLARINET DUO	MJ
SOBECK, J. DUET, OP 8	CF
SOUFFRIAU, A. SONATE	EBR
SOUSSMANN, H. 12 LIGHT PIECES	EDM
SPINO, P. FIRST DUETS	STM
STADLER, A.-MICHAELS. DUO IN F MA	HSM
STARK, R.-SIMON. 4 DUETS	INT
STARK, R. SONATA #1 IN E FL MA	CF
STEKL, K. KLEINE DUO-MUSIK	MV
STERN, R. LITTLE BIT OF MUSIC, A	NVM
STOKER, R. LITTLE SUITE	PET
TELEMANN, G.-KELL. 6 CANONIC SONATAS	INT
TELEMANN, G.-DISHINGER. EXCERPTS (SONATA IN G MA)	SP
TELEMANN, G.-DISHINGER. EXCERPTS (SONATA IN G MI)	SP
TELEMANN, G.-DISHINGER. EXCERPTS (SUITE IN A MI)	SP
THEVET. 100 EXERCICES RYTHMIQUES	ALE
THOMAS, R. 4 DUETS FOR YOUNG MUSICIANS	GA
TOLL, R. 2 DUETS IN CANONIC TREATMENT	CF
TROJE-MILLER, N. CHINESE CHECKERS	BE
TULL, F. 5 INVENTIONS	BH
TULOU, J. 6 DUETS	EDM
TURK, D.-DISHINGER. CUCKOO	SP
TWINN, S. 6 OLD ENGLISH SONGS	GAL
TWINN, S. (ARR). 12 OLD WELSH SONGS	PET
ULRICH, J. 5 DUETS (1966)	WH
VAN LYN SCHOOTEN, H. 4 CANONS	HE
VIVALDI, A.-DISHINGER. GLORIA	SP
VIVALDI, A. SONATA DA CAMERA	EDM
VOGEL, J.-MICHAELS. DUO IV IN D MI	HSM
WAHLICH, M. 10 EASY DUETS	HUG
WARDROP, L. TWO PART INVENTIONS. CL,ACL	UNI
WEBER, C. VON. GRAND DUO CONCERTANTE, OP 48	CF
WEHNER, W. 20 MODERN DUETS	SO
WIEDEMANN, L. DUETS, VOLS. 2 & 3 OF CLARINET STUDIES	BRH
WIEDEMANN, L. 30 EASY & MELODIOUS DUETS	SIM
WIEDEMANN, L. 30 EASY DUETS, 2 VOLS	CF
WILDER A. 7 DUETS	MAR
WILDER, A. 7 EASY DUETS	MAR
YOST, M.-MICHAELS. DUO #4 IN A MI	HSM
YOST, M.-MICHAELS. DUO II IN F MA	HSM
YOST, M.-VOXMAN. 6 DUOS, OP 5/1-3	MR
YOST, M. 6 FAVORITE DUETS, OP 12	M&M
ZEHM, F. KLARINETTEN IM DUETT	SCH

2 CLARINETS (COLLECTIONS)-205

ALBUM OF SHORT EASY PIECES, 2 VOLS.	EDK
ARNOLD, J. SELECTED DUETS, 2 VOLS	ASH
AYRES, T. (ARR). 6 CONCERTANTE DUETS	SH
AYRES, T. (ARR). 30 DUETS	SH
AYRES, T. (ARR). INTERMEDIATE DUOS	SH

18

2 CLARINETS (COLLECTIONS)-205

BACH, J.S.-SIMON. BACH FOR THE CLARINET, PART II	GS
BAY, C. CLARINET VIRTUOSI CONCERT DUETS, 2 VOLS	MUC
BECKER, H. (ED). CLARINET DUETS	BRH
BEEKUM, J. VAN. EASY DUETS	HU
BERKES, K.(ED). CLARINET DUOS, 3 VOLS	EMB
BURGSTAHLER, E. (ARR). DUETS FOR CLARINETS	PO
COMRADES' REPERTORY.	CF
ELKAN, H. CLASSICAL ALBUM	HE
FORBES & FRANK, A. 2 CLARINETS, 2 VOLS	OX
FRANK, A. & W. FORBES. 30 EASY CLASSICAL DUETS	OX
GABUCCI, A. (ARR). 50 DUETTI	CAR
GEARHART, L. CLARINET SESSIONS	SH
GIAMPIERI, A. (ARR). 26 PEZZI DI CELEBRI AUTORI	RC
GLASENAPP, F. (ED). DUETS	FRH
GORNSTON, D. & H. HUFFNAGLE(ARR). STANDARD CLARINET DUETS	SN
JOOSEN, B. 20 EENVOUDIGE KLASSIEKE DUETTEN	MOL
KAPLAN, D. (ARR). GOTHAM COLLECTION	SPR
KRTICKA (ARR). DUETTE AUS TSCHECHISCHEN OPERN	ART
KRTICKA, S. ALBUM DER KOMPOSITIONEN FUR 2 KLARINETTEN	ES
LINDEMAN, B.(ARR). CONCERT MASTERS ON THE HIT PARADE	PO
LURIE-NEUFELD (ARR). CLASSICS FOR CLARINETS	CF
MERRIMAN, L. (ARR). DUET CLASSICS, BK #1	SO
OSTLING-WEBER. DUETS, 2 VOLS	BE
RICHTER, C. (ARR). DUETS FOR CLARINETS, 2 VOLS	CF
RICHTER, C. (ED)-CHRISTOFFERSEN. KLARINETTEN-DUOS	FRH
ROSENTHAL, C. (ARR). CLARINET DUOS	EM
ROSENTHAL, C. (TR). 15 EASY DUETS	KPM
SCHAEFFER, D. (ARR). DUETS ARE FUN	PO
SCHAEFFER, D. (ARR). 21 RHYTHMIC DUETS	PO
SCHNEIDER & HETSCHKO(ED). DUETTE FUR ANFANGER	FRH
SCHNEIDER, W. KLASSISCHE SPIELSTUCKE	B&N
STOUFFER, P. ALBUM OF 10 BAROQUE COMPOSITIONS	HE
STOUFFER, P. (ARR). SIX FOR TWO	KN
TIROLER VOLKSMUSIK AUS DEM ZILLERTAL. 2CL,GUIT AD LIB	B&N
VI CAN SPELA, VOL #4.	NOR
VOXMAN, H. (ARR). DUETTIST FOLIO	RU
VOXMAN, H. (ARR). SELECTED DUETS, 2 VOLS	RU
WESTON, P. (ED). ALBUM OF DUETS, 3 VOLS	S&C
WESTON, P. (ARR). CLASSICAL ALBUM	BH

2 BASSOONS-206

ALMENRAEDER, W. 2 DUOS, OP 8	SPR
BARRETTE-MUELLER. 6 DIVERTIMENTI, OP 1	HEI
BECKWITH, J. 4 PIECES (1951)	CAN
BLANK, A. 2 BAGATELLES (1962)	SS
BLOCK, R. (ARR). BASS CLEF GALANT	NOM
BOISMORTIER, J.-THOMPSON. BAROQUE DUOS	SH
BOISMORTIER, J. 9 PETITE SONATES, OP 66	BE
BOISMORTIER, J. 9 PETITE SONATES, OP 66	CP
BOISMORTIER, J.-RUYSSEN. SONATA #1 IN G MA	GAL
BOISMORTIER, J.-RUYSSEN. SONATA #2 IN D MI	GAL
BOISMORTIER, J.-O'DONOVAN. 2 SONATAS, OP 14/1,2	OJE
BOISMORTIER, J. 6 SONATES, OP 14	BE
BOISMORTIER, J. 6 SONATES, OP 14	CP
BOISMORTIER, J. 6 SONATES, OP 40	CP
BOUTRY, R. PRELUDE, PASTORAL & TARANTELLA	ALE
BOZZA, E. DUETTINO	ALE

BROWN, R. SONATA	WI
BUCQUET, P. SUITE IN G MI	EDM
CAUSSINUS, V. 6 CONCERT DUOS, OP 14	SPR
CONCONE, G.-OSTRANDER. 5 DUETS	KN
COSTE, G. FANTAISIE INSTRUMENTALE	HEU
COUPERIN, F.-BAZELAIRE. CONCERT	ALE
COUPERIN, F.-RUF. DUO IN G MA	SCH
DECHIFFRAGE DU MANUSCRIT.	HLE
DEVIENNE, F.-HESS. DUOS CONCERTANTS, OP 3	EK
DEVIENNE, F.-ALLARD. 6 DUOS CONCERTANTS, OP 3, 2 VOLS.	BIL
DIEPPO. VIRTUOSO STUDIES	EDM
DUBOIS, P. SONATINA	ALE
ERBACH-NOACK. 6 DUOS	B&N
FARAGO, M. 4 DUETS, OP 27	B&V
GABRIELI, D. CANON	KAW
GASTYNE, S. DE. LA CORBUSIERE (1968)	FER
GEBAUER, F.-WOJCIECHOWSKI. 3 AUSGEWAHLTE DUOS, OP 44	HSM
GOODMAN. 2 STUDIES	PET
GUIGNON, J. SONATAS, OP 2	EK
GUILLEMANT, B.-MUELLER. 6 SONATAS, OP 3	HEI
HOUDY, P. CANON	ALE
JANCOURT, E. 3 GRANDES SONATES	BIL
JANCOURT, E.-COLLINS. SONATA #1	BE
JANCOURT, E.-COLLINS. SONATA #2	BE
KEYES. BASSOONERIES	WI
KLEINKNECHT, W. 3 SONATAS	M&M
KONT, P. DUO	LDO
KUNZ, A. FUN FOR TWO (1964)	CAN
MALIGE, F. 7 DUOS	FRH
MANCINELLI, D.-RUF. 2 SONATEN	RC
MATEJ, J. 10 ZWEISTIMMIGE INVENTIONEN	ES
MOZART, W.-POWELL. 11 MOZART DUETS	SH
MOZART, W.-BAZELAIRE. SONATA	ALE
MOZART, W. SONATA IN B FL MA	SO
MUELLER, P. 35 DUETS	SPR
OZI, E. 6 GRANDES SONATES, 2 VOLS	EDH
OZI, E.-MUCCETTI. 6 GRANDI SONATE	RC
OZI, E. 2 PETITES SONATES, 2 VOLS	EDH
OZI, E. 3 SMALL SONATAS	FRH
PACHELBEL, J.-BROWN. VERSETS	WI
PLEYEL, I.-KLITZ. RONDO IN B-FLAT	JB
PORRET, J. 12 EASY DUOS, OP648	MOL
PRESSER, W. 7 BASSOON DUETS	JB
QUANTZ, J.-LASOCKI. 6 SONATAS, OP 2	NOM
RAPHLING, S. SONATINA	EDM
REGNER, H. SPIELHEFT 1	PGM
ROTH, M. BASSOON DUETS	AEP
SATZENHOFER, J.-KOVAR. 24 DUETS	INT
SCHNEIDER, G.-SHARROW. 3 DUETS	INT
SCHNEIDER, G.-PISCHKITL. DUETTE FUR TIEFE INSTRUMENTE	FRH
SIENNICKI, E. DUET #1	SPR
SIENNICKI, E. DUET #2	SPR
SIENNICKI, E. 2 DUETS (1965)	OJE
STAHULJAK, M. INVENTIONS	KAW
STOKER, R. 4 DIALOGUES	PET
STOVER, F. 3 TRIFLES	SS
SZELENYI, I. SUITE	EMB
TELEMANN, G.-OROMSZEGI. 6 KANONSONATEN	EMB
TELEMANN, G. SONATA #1	M&M
TELEMANN, G. SONATA #2	M&M
TELEMANN, G. SONATA #4	M&M
TICCIATI, N.-SOLLOWAY. VOI, CHE SAPETE	PET

2 BASSOONS-206

TOESCHI, C.-LEBERMANN. 6 DUETS, OP 11,2 VOLS.	SCH
TOMASI, H. CROQUIS	ALE
UBER, D. 10 CONCERT DUETS	EDM
ULRICH, J. 5 DUETS (1966)	WH
VAUBOURGOIN, M. 12 CANONS	BIL
WEELINK, K. MOVEMENT IN A CLASSICAL STYLE	KAW

2 BASSOONS (COLLECTIONS)-207

BLUME, O. (ARR). 12, 2 VOLS DUETS	INT
BLUME, O. (ARR). 12 MELODIOUS DUETS	CF
DUETTE FUR FAGOTTE.	FRH
FAGOTT-DUOS.	EUL
GLASENAPP-KARL (ED). DUETS	FRH
OROMSZEGI(ED). FAGOTTDUOS	EMB
SIENNICKI, E. (ARR). GOTHAM COLLECTION	SPR

2 SAXOPHONES-208

AUBERT, J.-LONDEIX. SUITE	ALE
BACH, J.S. CANON #4. ASAX,TSAX	EDM
BACH, J.S.-DISHINGER. EXCERPTS (SONATA IN C MA)	SP
BACH, J.S.-TEAL 15 TWO-PART INVENTIONS	TP
BACH, W.F. DUO SONATA	EDM
BEETHOVEN, L. VAN. ALLEGRO & MINUET	EDM
BERBIGUIER, T. 6 EASY DUETS	EDM
BERNARDS, B. 10 INSTRUKTIVE DUOS	WZ
BOUVARD, J. 21 MINI DUETTE	BIL
BUCQUET, P. SUITE #1	EDM
BUCQUET, P. SUITE #2	EDM
BUMCKE, G. 38 DUOS (OP 43)	ABE
BUTTERWORTH, A. 3 DIALOGUES	PET
CHAGRIN, F. 6 DUETS	NU
CHAUVET, G. 15 ETUDES	COM
CLARISAXO. ASAX(SOP SAX),TSAX(CL)	HU
CLERGUE, J. PRIMAVERA-VOLUTE	EV
CRAGUN, J. 8 CONCERT DUETS	RU
DE LULLI-ERICKSON. CHOPSTICKS	EJ
DESCHAMPS, J. SONATINE	BIL
DEVIENNE, F. 6 CELEBRATED SONATAS	EDM
DUBOIS, P. 6 CAPRICES	ALE
ELLIS, R. DIXIELAND DUET. ASAX,TSAX	KN
ERICKSON, E. FESTIVE MOOD	EJ
FERLING, W.-GEE. DUO CONCERTANTE #1, OP 13	PO
FIVE FOR PLEASURE.	OP
GATTI, D.-IASILLI. 30 PROGRESSIVE DUETS	CF
GOSSEC, F. OVERTURE	HE
HANDEL, G.-DISHINGER. EXCERPTS (SONATA IN C MI)	SP
HANSEL, A.-SANSONE. CONCERTINO, OP 80. ASAX,TSAX	SO
HAYDN, F.-SKOLNIK. WITCHES' CANON, THE. ASAX,TSAX	EDM
HINDEMITH, P.-RASCHER. CONCERTPIECE	M&M
HUFFNAGLE, H. RHYTHM DUETS	SF
KLERK, J. DE. KLEINE PARTITA	MOL
KLOSE, H. 6 DUETS	CF

```
KOCH, E. VON.  DIALOGUE (1975).  SSAX,ASAX                    STI
KUHLAU, F.-TEAL.  CONCERT DUETS, OP 10.  ASAX,ASAX(TSAX)      TP
LACOUR, G.  SUITE EN DUO                                      BIL
LAMB, J.  6 BAREFOOT DANCES                                   M&M
LANCEN, S.  TWINS, THE                                        PET
LAZARUS, H.-TRAXLER.  GRAND ARTISTIC DUETS                    BE
LECLAIR, J.-LONDEIX.  SONATA IN C MA                          ALE
LECLAIR, J.-LONDEIX.  SONATA IN D MA                          ALE
LECLAIR, J.-LONDEIX.  SONATA IN F MA                          ALE
LETELLIER, R.  NOUVEAUX DUOS & TRIOS                          EDR
LUFT, J.  24 ETUDES IN DUET FORM                             CF
MAGANINI, Q.  CANONICO ESPRESSIVO.  ASAX,TSAX                 EDM
MAGANINI, Q.  IN THE BEGINNING                                EDM
MAGANINI, Q.  PETITE SUITE CLASSIQUE                          EDM
MASSIAS, G.  DIALOGUES                                        BIL
MOROSCO, V.  6 CONTEMPORARY ETUDES IN DUET FORM               ETP
MOZART, L.  4 SHORT PIECES                                    HE
MOZART, W.-AUSLENDER.  SONATA IN B FL MA.  TSAX,BAR SAX       WI
NAUMANN, J.  DUO                                              HE
NIEHAUS, L.  JAZZ CONCEPTION                                  CC
PADEREWSKI, I.-ERICKSON.  MINUET                              EJ
PAISNER, B.  SWING DUETS                                      KPM
PELZ, W.  BALLAD                                              BE
PORRET, J.-INGRESS.  9TH DUO DE CONCOURS.  ASAX,TSAX          HE
PORRET, J.  12 PROGRESSIVE DUETS, OP254                       MOL
PORTER, C.-SEARS.  NIGHT AND DAY                              WB
PRESSER, W.  7 DUETS                                          TP
RAPHLING, S.  DUOGRAMS                                        EDM
ROCHOW, E.  DUETS                                             RBM
RUGGIERO, G.  3 PIECES                                        ALE
SCHMIDT, W.  12 CONCERT DUETS                                 WI
SELLNER, J.  12 DUOS, 3 VOLS                                  EDC
SELLNER, J.  12 DUOS, 4 VOLS                                  BIL
SIX FOR PLEASURE.                                            OP
SOUSSMANN, H.  12 LIGHT PIECES                                EDM
TELEMANN, G.-DISHINGER.  EXCERPTS (SONATA IN G MA)            SP
TELEMANN, G.-DISHINGER.  EXCERPTS (SONATA IN G MI)            SP
TELEMANN, G.-DISHINGER.  EXCERPTS (SUITE IN A MI)             SP
THEVET.  EXERCISES RYTHMIQUES                                 ALE
TURK, D.-DISHINGER.  CUCKOO                                   SP
TWINN, S.  OLD ENGLISH SONGS                                  PET
ULRICH, J.  5 DUETS (1966)                                    WH
VALLIER, J.  ANDANTINO-SCHERZANDO                             COM
VEREECKEN, B.  16 ARTISTIC DUETS                              RU
VIVALDI, A.DISHINGER.  GLORIA                                 SP
```

2 SAXOPHONES (COLLECTIONS)-209

```
ARNOLD, J.  SELECTED DUETS, 2 VOLS.                          ASH
CORI, C.(ARR).  MELODY DUETS, BK #2                          KPM
DUETS FOR SAXOPHONE.                                        HU
GEE H.(ARR).  SAX DUETS.  ASAX,TSAX                         PO
GUREWICH, J.  17 CLASSIC DUETS                              CF
KAPLAN, D. (ARR).  GOTHAM COLLECTION                        SPR
LETELLIER, L. (ARR).  RECUEIL DE DUOS ET TRIOS              EDR
OSTLING-WEBER.  DUETS, 2 VOLS                               BE
SCHAEFFER, D. (ARR).  DUETS ARE FUN                         PO
SCHAEFFER, D. (ARR).  21 RHYTHMIC DUETS                     PO
```

STOUFFER, P.(ARR).   ALBUM OF 10 BAROQUE COMPOSITIONS   HE
STOUFFER, P.(ARR).   SIX FOR TWO   KN
VOXMAN, H. (ARR).   SELECTED DUETS, 2 VOLS   RU

2 PARTS: WOODWINDS-210

ALEXANDER, J. BRACE OF DUETS, A. CL,BSN   GEN
AMES, W. 2 SKETCHES. FL,BSN   ACA
ANDRIESSEN, J. AULOS (1959). FL,OB   SD
APPLEBAUM, S. DESCRIPTIVE DUETS, 2 VOLS. 2WW   CC
APPLEBAUM, S. SWINGING DUETS. 2WW   CC
ARBATSKY, Y. FROM A TO Z. FL,CL   M&M
ARCHER, V. SUITE (1947). CL,BSN   CAN
ARMA, P. 3 TRANSPARENCES. FL(OB),CL   HLE
ARRIEU, C. 3 DUOS FACILE. FL,BSN   BIL
BACH, C.P.E.-COOLIDGE. CANTABILE. FL(OB),BSN   KN
BACH, J.S.-DEDRICK. TWO PART INVENTIONS(12, 13). CL,BSN(BCL) KN
BACH, J.S.-DEDRICK. TWO PART INVENTIONS(3, 14). CL,BSN(BCL)   KN
BACH, J.S.-DEDRICK. TWO PART INVENTIONS(4, 10). CL,BSN(BCL)   KN
BACH, W.F. DUO SONATA. FL,OB(CL)   EDM
BAINES, F. COMIC VARIATIONS. CL,BSN   JE
BALBATRE, L. NOEL WITH 4 VARIATIONS. FL,CL(BSN)   EDM
BALBO, G. 3 ETCHINGS. FL(OB),CL   SF
BAUER, M. IMPROVISATION, OP 25/2. OB,CL   PET
BAVICCHI, J. 6 DUETS, OP 27. FL,CL   OX
BECK, F. FANFARE. FL,CL   AMC
BECK, J. KAMMERMUSIK. CL,BSN   MV
BEETHOVEN-POULTEAU. DUO #1. CL,BSN   ALE
BEETHOVEN-POULTEAU. DUO #2. CL,BSN   ALE
BEETHOVEN, L. VAN. 3 DUETS. CL,BSN   EDK
BEETHOVEN, L. VAN. 3 DUETS. CL,BSN   INT
BEETHOVEN, L. VAN. 3 DUETS. FL,CL   SO
BEETHOVEN, L. VAN-GOHLER. DUO #1 IN C MA. CL,BSN,PF AD LIB BRH
BEETHOVEN, L. VAN-GOHLER. DUO #2 IN F MA. CL,BSN,PF AD LIB BRH
BEETHOVEN, L. VAN. DUO #2. CL,BSN   EM
BEETHOVEN, L. VAN-POULTEAU. DUO #3. CL,BSN   ALE
BEETHOVEN, L. VAN-GOHLER. DUO #3 IN B FL MA   BRH
   CL,BSN,PF AD LIB
BEETHOVEN, L. VAN. DUO #3. CL,BSN   EM
BEETHOVEN, L. VAN-MEDERACKE. 3 DUOS. CL,BSN   FRH
BEETHOVEN, L. VAN-SIBER. 3 DUOS. CL,BSN   FRH
BEETHOVEN, L. VAN-WILDGANS. 3 DUOS. CL,BSN   LDO
BEETHOVEN, L. VAN. 3 DUOS. CL,BSN   MR
BEETHOVEN, L. VAN. 3 DUOS. OB,BSN   NOM
BEETHOVEN, L. VAN. 3 DUOS. CL(OB,FL),BSN   SPR
BENJAMIN. FOUR BY TWO. CL,BSN   SO
BENNETT, ROBERT RUSSELL. SUITE. FL,CL   WB
BERGER. 3 DUETS. 2WW   BE
BERKOWITZ. 10 DUETS. 2 TREBLE INSTR   BT
BESOZZI, C.-SCIANNAMEO. SONATA. OB,BSN   SPR
BESOZZI, C.-VOXMAN. SONATA IN C MA. OB,BSN   NOM
BEYER, J. 4 PIECES. OB,BSN   AMC
BEYER, J. SUITE #3. CL,BSN   AMC
BEYER, J. SUITE. OB,CL   AMC
BINKERD, G. DUO. FL,OB   BH
BISHOFF, R. DUO, OP 3. FL,CL   LDO
BLANK, A. 4 BAGATELLES. OB,CL   SS
BLANK, A. BICINIUM II. CL,BSN   ACA

BLANK, A. BICINIUM. OB,BSN	ACA
BLEZARD, W. 3 DIVERSIONS. CL,BSN	CP
BOCCHERINI, L.-SCIANNAMEO. SONATA. CL,BSN	SPR
BONVALET. SOUVENIR-CANZONE. FL,CL	EV
BORRIS, S. DUO, OP116/1 (1964). FL,OB	GBV
BOTTENBERG, W. SONATA (1960). FL,CL	CAN
BOZZA, E. CONTRASTES I. FL,BSN	ALE
BOZZA, E. CONTRASTES II. OB,BSN	ALE
BOZZA, E. CONTRASTES III. CL,BSN	ALE
BOZZA, E. 3 MOUVEMENTS. FL,CL	ALE
BOZZA, E. SONATINA. FL,BSN	ALE
BRANDON, S. SONATINA (1971). OB,BSN	MAN
BROD, H.-LANGATTE. SONATA #1. OB,BSN(VC)	BIL
BROWN, N. 4 PIECES. FL,CL	TP
BUCKMANN, R. 8 ZWEISTIMMIGE SATZE. 2 LIKE INSTR	PG
BURKHARD, W. SERENADE (1953). FL,CL	B&N
CAMPBELL. RAGGED DIVERSION #2. CL,BSN	KN
CARAVAN, R. 3 MODAL DANCES. CL(SOP SAX),BAR SAX	ETH
CARTAN, J. SONATINE. FL,CL	HEU
CHAMBERS, S. DUO. FL,CL	GA
CHARPENTIER, J. ANTIENNE. FL,CL	ALE
CHILDS, B. BARNARD II. OB,BSN	ACA
CHILDS, B. DUO. FL,BSN	ACA
CHILDS, B. LOCATION OF MUSIC,THE. FL,CB	CF
CLARKE, H. GAME THAT 2 CAN PLAY, A. FL,CL	WI
CLODOMIR, P. 12 DUOS. 2WW	MOL
CORTES, R. DUO. FL,OB	EV
CRANMER, P. VARIATIONS ON A FRENCH TUNE. FL,CL	NO
CROSSE, G. 3, OP 3 INVENTIONS. FL,CL	OX
CYTRON, W. DANCES FOR TWO TREBLES	M&M
DANFELT, D. DIVERTIMENTO. FL,CL	SH
DEAK, C. DUO SUITE. FL,CL	CHE
DEFOSSEZ, R. DUO. CL,BSN	EBR
DEVIENNE-STEINBECK. DUO #6 IN F MA. CL,BSN	EUL
DEVIENNE, F. DUO #4. CL,BSN	EUL
DIJK, J. VAN. DUO (1952). CL,BSN	SD
DOBRZYNSKI, I. DUO. CL,ASAX	KAW
DONAHUE, R. 5 CANONIC DUETS. FL,CL	TP
DONATELLI, V. DUET #1. OB(FL),CL	WI
DONATELLI, V. DUET #2. OB(FL),CL	WI
DUBOIS, P. PETITE SUITE. FL,BSN	ALE
DUBOIS, P. TRETEAUX, LES. FL,SAX	ECH
EDMONDSON, J. LITTLE SUITE. FL,OB	KN
EKLUND, H. SMAPRAT (1965). FL,CL	STI
ELY, R. ACCURACY IN RYTHM. 2WW	WM
ERB, D. CONVERSATION (1963). FL,OB	CAN
ERIXON, P. DUO, OP 9(1964). CL,EHN	STI
ERIXON, P. LENTO OCH ALLEGRO, OP 3(1964). CL,BSN	STI
ESTRADE-GUERRA D', O. SONATINE PASTORALE. OB,CL	JOB
EVANS, R. DUET SUITE (1965). FL(OB),CL	BER
FARRAND, N. DUO. OB,BSN	ACA
FELD, J. DUO (1964). FL,BSN(BCL)	ALE
FENNER, B. SUITE. FL,BSN	SS
FERNANDEZ, O. 3 INVENTIONS-SERENADES. CL,BSN	SN
FIALA, J. DUO CONCERT. FL(OB),BSN	EK
FIALA, J. DUO CONCERTANTA IN F MA. OB,BSN	OJE
FIALA, J.-READ. DUO CONCERTANTE # 1 IN F MA & # 2 IN C MA FL(OB),BSN	NOM
FRANK. 3 SHORT DUOS. FL,CL	BO
FREUND, D. PAS DE DEUX. CL,BSN	SS
FURRER-MUNCH, F. DIALOG (1970). OB,CL	EMO
GABAYE, P. SONATINA. FL,BSN	ALE

```
GALLON, N.  SONATA.  FL,BSN                                        ALE
GARNIER, FL-STEINBECK.  DUO CONCERTANT, OP  4/4.  OB,BSN           EUL
GATES, E.  ODD METER DUETS.  2 TREBLE INSTR                        SF
GEARHART, L.  BASS CLEF SESSIONS.  2BSN                            SH
GEARHART, L.  DUET SESSIONS.  2 TREBLE CLEF INSTR                  SH
GEBAUER, F.-WOJCIECHOWSKI.  6 DUOS CONCERTANTS, OP  8.  CL,BSN     HSM
GENIN, P.  GRAND DUO CONCERTANT, OP 51.  FL,OB(CL)                 BIL
GENZMER, H.  SONATA.  FL,OB                                        SCH
GHENT, E.  2 DUOS.  FL(OB),CL                                      OX
GINASTERA, A.  DUO.  FL,OB                                         TP
GLASER, W.  LITEN DUETT (1967).  OB,CL                             STI
GOODMAN, J.  JADIS (IN DAYS OF YORE).  FL,BSN                      GEN
GOULD, M.  DUO.  FL,CL                                             CA
GRABNER, H.  KLEINE SERENADE, OP 47/1.  FL,BSN                     KIS
GRAHN, U.  CHANSON (1969).  FL,CL                                  STI
GRAHN, U.  DIALOG (1969).  FL,CL                                   STI
GRAMATGES, H.  PRELUDE & INVENTION.  CL,BSN                        HE
GRANT, P.  PRELUDE & CANONIC PIECE.  FL,CL                         ACA
GRIMM, C.  ALLA SARABANDA.  CL,BSN                                 SO
GROOT, C. DE.  SERENADE (1949).  OB,BSN                            SD
GRUNDMAN, C.  WALTZ & INTERLUDE.  FL,CL                            BH
GYRING, E.  10 CANONS FOR 2 & 3 WOODWINDS.  #2.  FL,DB            ACA
HAAN, S. DE.  DIVERTIMENTO.  CL,BSN                                PET
HAIEFF, A.  3 BAGATELLES.  OB,BSN                                  BR
HALL, R.  2 DIVERSIONS.  FL,BSN                                    BH
HARRIS, A.  ORIGINAL DUETS.  2WW                                   CC
HART, W.  INTERLUDE.  FL,BSN                                       SPR
HARTZELL, E.  WORKPOINTS I.  FL,BSN                                LDO
HARVEY, P.  ALL AT SEA.  OB,CL                                     BH
HARVEY, P.  GRADED STUDY DUETS.  FL,OB                             BH
HASQUENOPH, P.  SONATA ESPRESSA.  CL,BSN                           EES
HAUBIEL, C.  PASTORAL.  OB,BSN                                     WI
HAUFRECHT, H.  DIALOGUES.  FL,CL                                   ACA
HAUFRECHT, H.  OVERTURE FOR A NEW YEAR.  FL,CL                     ACA
HAWKINS, J.  8 MOVEMENTS (1966).  FL,CL                            CAN
HAYDN, F.  3 SONATAS.  FL,CL                                       EDM
HAYDN, F.-SKOLNIK.  WITCHES' CANON, THE.  FL,CL                    EDM
HEDWALL L.  SONATIN (1964-75).  FL,OB                              STI
HEDWALL, L.  DUO (1952).  CL,BSN                                   STI
HEDWALL, L.  5 EPIGRAMS (1959).  FL,CL                             NOR
HEDWALL, L.  LITEN DUO (1975).  FL(OB,CL),BSN                      STI
HEDWALL, L.  VARIATIONER OCH FUGA (1975).  FL,OB                   STI
HEINICHEN, J.-STEINBECK.  SONATE IN C MI.  OB,BSN                  BRH
HEKSTER, W.  DIALOGUES.  FL,CL                                     SD
HENRY, O.  3 SERIAL DUETS.  FL,CL                                  AMC
HESSENBERG, K.  LU-DI SUITE.  FL,CL                                WZ
HEUSSENSTAMM, G.  AMBAGES, OP 29.  FL,CL                           SS
HOFFDING, F.  DIALOGUES.  OB,CL                                    WH
HOFFMEISTER, F.-SCHONERT.  3 DUOS, OP 38.  FL,OB                   FRH
HOFMANN, L.-BIBA.  DIVERTIMENTO IN C MA.  FL,BSN                   EUL
HOSKINS, W.  INVENTION FOR 2 WOODWINDS.  FL,CL                     ACA
HOVHANESS, A.  PRELUDE & FUGUE, OP 13.  OB(FL),BSN                 PET
HOVHANESS, A.  SONATA, OP302.  OB,BSN                              PI
HOVHANESS, A.  SUITE, OP 21 (1937).  EHN,BSN                       PET
HOVHANESS, A.  SUITE, OP 23.  OB,BSN                               PET
HUGHES, K.  SECOND CHANCE.  FL,OB                                  WI
HYAMS, A.  PRELUDE, BLUES AND FUGUE.  FL,CL                        SO
JACOB, G.  3 INVENTIONS.  FL,OB                                    GA
JACOB, G.  3 LITTLE PIECES.  OB,BSN                                MR
JOHANNES, J.  SONATINE.  OB,BSN                                    EDH
JOHNSON, H.  SERENADE.  FL,CL                                      NVM
JOLIVET, A.  SONATINE (1961).  FL,CL                               BH
```

```
JOLIVET, A.  SONATINE (1963).  OB,BSN                          BH
JONES, K.  3 IMPROMPTUS.  CL,BSN                               AU
KAPLAN, L.  2-PART INVENTION.  CL,BSN                          PMP
KARKOFF, M.  DUO, OP 3 (1951).  CL,BSN                         STI
KAY, U.  SUITE.  FL,OB                                         MC
KELLER, H.  5 PIECES.  CL,BSN                                  AMP
KELTERBORN, R.  INCONTRI BREVI (1967).  FL,CL                  B&N
KETTERING, E.  15 CAROLS.  2WW                                 CON
KEULER, J.  PICCOLA PARTITA.  CL,BSN                           EMB
KIBBE, M.  3 CANONS.  FL,CL                                    SS
KISIELEWSKI, S.  SUITE.  FL,CL                                 PWM
KLERK, A. DE.  SARABANDE EN SICILIENNE.  FL,OB                 EDH
KNELLWOLF, J.  DUETS, 4 VOLS.  2INSTR                          HUG
KOCSAR, M.  UNGARESCA.  2WW                                    EMB
KOECHLIN, C.  SONATINE MODALE, OP155.  FL,CL                   EME
KONDOROSSY, L.  SERENADE.  OB,BSN                              AMC
KONIETZNY, H.  ISOMETRISCH-ISORHYTHMISCH.  2WW                 B&N
KONIG, H.  DUO.  FL,CL                                         PGM
KOUGUELL, A.  3 PIECES.  OB,BSN                                AMC
KRENEK, E.  SONATINA, OP 92/2B (1942).  FL,CL                  B&N
KUBIK, G.  5 BIRTHDAY PIECES.  FL,CL                           JB
KUMMER, G.  2 DUETS, OP 46.  FL,CL                             CF
KUMMER, G.  2 DUOS CONCERTANTS, OP 46.  FL,CL                  BIL
KUNERT, K.-ADAMS.  SONATA IN G MA, OP 15.  FL,OB              VO
KUNERT, K.  SONATA, OP 15A.  FL,OB                            ETB
KUNERT, K.  SONATA, OP 20.  CL,BSN                            FRH
KUNZ, A.  FUN FOR TWO (1964).  BSN,BCL                         CAN
KUPFERMAN, M.  AVAILABLE FORMS (1966).  CL,BSN               GEN
KUPFERMAN, M.  4 CHARADES.  FL,CL                              GEN
KUPFERMAN, M.  4 CONSTELLATIONS.  FL,CL                        GEN
KUPFERMAN, M.  DUO DIVERTIMENTO.  CL,BSN                       GEN
KUPFERMAN, M.  SHORT SHRIFT.  PIC,CL                           SER
KURZ, W.  VARIATIONENSUITE (1953).  CL,BSN                     LDO
LACOME, P.  PASSEPIED.  OB(FL),BSN(VC)                         DUR
LANGER, H.  TAKT UND RHYTHMUS.  2WW                            HEI
LEAHY, M.  4 SHORT SKETCHES.  OB,BSN                           MAN
LEES, B.  3 DUOS (1969).  FL,CL                                BH
LEICHTLING, A.  NACHTMUSIK.  BCL,BSN                           SS
LEICHTLING, A.  NACHTMUSIK, OP 36.  BCL,CBSN                   AMC
LEMELAND, A.  5 PORTRAITS, OP 49.  CL,ASAX                     BIL
LEVINE, B.  DUET.  AFL,EHN                                     MAN
LEVY, F.  DUO.  CL,BSN                                         SS
LEWIN, G.  CARIBBEAN SKETCHES.  FL,CL                          BH
LEWIN, G.  3 LATIN AMERICAN IMPRESSIONS.  FL,CL               BH
LINN, R.  5 PIECES.  FL,CL                                     SH
LOWRY, R.  FARCE AND FANTASY.  FL,CL                           SO
LUNDE, I.  L'ECOLE, OP 11, A.  OB,CL                           SH
MAASZ, G.  5 INVENTIONS.  FL,CL                                MV
MAGANINI, Q.  AIR & DOUBLE.  OB,CL                             CF
MAGANINI, Q.  BOA CONSTRICTOR & THE BOBOLINK.  FL,BSN        CF
MAGANINI, Q.  CANONICO ESPRESSIVO.  FL,CL(BSN)               EDM
MAGANINI, Q.  COUPERIN SUITE.  FL,OB(CL)                      EDM
MAGANINI, Q.  PETITE SUITE CLASSIQUE.  FL,OB(CL)             EDM
MANGS, R.  6 BAGATELLEN.  FL,CL                                STI
MARCONI, L.  COLLAGE PER UN DUO.  OB,CL                        EDI
MARGOLA, F.  PARTITA.  FL,OB                                   EDI
MARIATTI, F.  3 PEZZI.  OB,BSN                                 EDI
MARTELLI, H.  5 IMAGES, OP110.  OB,BSN                         EES
MASSIAS.  DIALOGUE.  2WW                                       BIL
MAVES, D.  DUET.  FL,CL                                        CAN
MC KUSICK, H.  ATONAL DUETS.  2WW                             CC
MELILLO, P.  DUO.  FL,BSN                                      AMC
```

MELLNAS, A. VAXLINGAR. FL/PIC,CL/BCL	EMF
MICHAEL, E. SONATINE (1962). FL,CL	RC
MICHALSKY, D. SONATINA. FL,CL	JB
MIGOT, G. SUITE EN 3 MOUVEMENTS. FL,CL	B&N
MONACO, R. 5 SHORT PIECES. FL,CL	SH
MORIGI, A.-VOXMAN. DUO. OB,BSN	NOM
MOSZUMANSKA-NAZAR, K. 5 DUETS. FL,CL	PWM
MOYLAN, W. DUET. CL,BSN	SS
MOZART, W. 12 DUETS, K487. 2WW	EDK
MOZART, W.-HASKINS. 12 DUETS. OB,CL	OX
MOZART, W.-SIMON. 12 DUOS. 2WW	EM
MOZART, W. 12 DUOS. 2WW	BRH
MOZART, W.-SMITH. 12 EASY DUETS, K487. 2WW	GS
MOZART, W.-DAHM. 3 SONATAS. FL(OB),CL	VO
MUELLER, F. EASY DUETS. 2 TREBLE CLEF INSTR	UNI
MULLINS, H. DUETS. FL,CL	CF
MUSGRAVE, T. IMPROMPTU. FL,OB	CHE
MYERS, R. 3 INVENTIONS. ASAX,BSN	SS
NAUMANN, J.-BORMANN. DUETT IN B FL MA. OB,BSN	HSM
NAUMANN, S. DUO (1948). CL,BSN	STI
NELHYBEL, V. COUNTERPOINT #1. CL,ASAX	JER
NELHYBEL, V. 4 DUETS. 2WW	GEN
NIKODOMOWICZ, A. 5 DIALOGUES. FL,BSN	PWM
NIXON, R. 4 DUOS. FL(OB),CL	TP
OLLER, J. DUO (1936). FL,CL	EBL
OTT, J. 5 PIECES (1968). FL,CL	CU
OTTEN, L. DUO (1965). FL,BSN	SD
OWEN, B. 2 TWO-PART INVENTIONS. 2WW	OP
PARIK, I. HUDBA PRE TROCH. FL(OB),CL	SHF
PAULSON, G. DUO, OP 84 (1955). OB,EHN	STI
PEARSON, W. 3 PASTORAL FUGUES. FL,OB	BH
PHILLIPS, G. SUITE. OB,CL	S&C
PIRANI, O. IMPRESSIONE GROTESCA. CL,BSN	EBE
PIRANI, O. MOMENTO DINAMICO, STUDIO. CL,BSN	EBE
PISK, P. DUO, OP106. CL,BSN	ACA
PLUMBY. PICTURE OF A HUNT. FL(OB),BSN	BE
PORRET, J.-MARIVAUX. 13TH DUO DE CONCOURS. CL,TSAX	HE
PORRET, J.-NELSON. 14TH DUO DE CONCOURS. CL,TSAX	HE
POULENC, F. SONATA. CL,BSN	CHE
POULTEAU, P. SONATINE. CL,BSN	ALE
PRESSER, W. 5 DUETS. OB,BSN	TP
PUTSCHE,T. 3 STUDIES. FL,CL	SS
QUERAT, M. LIED-CANONICA. FL(OB),ASAX	COM
RACUSEN, D. CANONIC ETUDES. 2WW	SH
RANSOM, D. PAVANNE. FL,CL	WM
RANSOM, D. PRELUDE & SAMBA. FL,CL	WM
RAPHLING, S. SONATINA. FL,CL	EDM
RAPHLING, S. VARIATIONS. FL,CL	EDM
REGT, H. DE. MUSICA, OP 28 (1973). FL,CL	SD
REGT, H. DE. MUSICA, OP 31 (1973). OB,CL	SD
REGT, H. DE. PASTORALE, OP 43 (1974-75). FL,OB	SD
REIZENSTEIN, F. DUO, OP 38. OB,CL	LEN
RIEGGER, W. 3 CANONS, OP 9/2. FL,CL	TP
RIEGGER, W. DUO, OP 35, #1. FL,OB	TP
RIEGGER, W. DUO, OP 35, #2. FL,CL	TP
RIEGGER, W. DUO, OP 35, #3. OB,CL	TP
RIETI, V. CANON. CL,BSN	GEN
RIEUNIER. ANTIENNE. FL,CL	ALE
RIVIER, J. DUO. FL,CL	BIL
ROCHBERG, G. DUO. OB,BSN	TP
ROY, K. DUO. FL,CL	TP
RUSSELL, R. DUO. FL,CL	GENI

SAEYS, E. SUITE. FL,BSN	MAU
SAVNIK, V. INVENTIONS. CL,BSN	KAW
SCARLATTI, D.-SKOLNIK. NEAPOLITAN SUITE. FL,CL	EDM
SCARMOLIN, A. DUET TIME. 2WW	LU
SCHEIDT, S.-SCHWADRON. BICINIUM (CANTIO SACRA). FL,CL	PMP
SCHMIDT, W. DUO WITH CADENZAS. OB,CL	WI
SCHNEIDER, W. SONATINE. OB,BSN	MV
SCHONBERG, S. DIALOGUES (1960). FL,CL	CHE
SCHONBERG, S. DUO (1959). CL,BSN	STI
SCHRODER, H. MUSIC. FL,BSN	ROB
SCHWADRON, A. 2 CONTRAPUNTAL DUOS. OB,BSN	PMP
SCHWADRON, A. DUO,. CL,OB	PMP
SCHWARZ, I. BACHATTI. FL,CL	SMO
SCHWARZ, I. CHOPINESQUE. FL,CL	SMO
SCHWARZ, I. DIALOGUE. FL,CL,OPT.DANCERS	SMO
SCHWARZ, I. HIGH ON A CLAUDE. FL,CL	SMO
SCHWARZ, I. KLOZARTINA. FL,CL	SMO
SCHWARZ, I. LYRIC PIECE. FL,CL	SMO
SCHWARZ, I. VARIATIONS ON A FOLK TUNE. FL,CL	SMO
SCHWEIZER, K. KLAPPENTEXTE. 5 STUCKE (1976). FL/PIC,OB/EHN	B&N
SEEGER, P. 10 DUOS. 2WW	FS
SEHLBACH, E. DUO, OP 53/2. FL,OB	MV
SEMERAK, O. DIALOGUE DE TIMBRE (1965). FL,BSN	CHF
SILVERMAN, F. CONVERSATIONS. AFL,CL	SS
SINGER, S. CEDAR LAKE. FL,CL	CF
SMITH, L. 2 DUETS. CL,BSN	ACA
SMITH, R. DUO. FL(OB),BSN	AMC
SMITH, S. FACES. OB,CL	SMI
SMITH, W. JAZZ SET. FL,CL	MJ
SMITH, W. 5 PIECES. FL,CL	MJ
SOUFFRIAU, A. SONATE. FL,CL	MAU
SOULE, E. 5 DUETS. FL,BSN	MAN
STAHULJAK, M. INVENTIONS. CL,BSN	KAW
STEARNS, P. NOCTURNE. FL,CL	ACA
STEARNS, P. 3 SHORT STUDIES. OB,CL	ACA
STEFANSSON, F. DUO. OB,CL	B&B
STEVENS, H. 6 CANONS. 2WW	ACA
STEVENS, H. 5 DUOS. FL,CL	PI
STEWART, D. CONCERT DUET, OP 8. FL,BCL	EDS
STRANG, G. 5 PIECES. FL,CL	AMC
STUCKY, S. MOVEMENTS III. FL,CL	SH
SUTER, R. DUETTI. FL,OB	HEI
SWACK, I. 4 BURLESQUES. FL,CL	SH
SWEELINCK-SCHWADRON. 2 CONTRAPUNTAL DUOS. OB,BSN	PMP
SYDEMAN, W. DUO. CL,TSAX	SS
SYDEMAN, W. MUSIC. OB,CL	SN
SZALOWSKI, A.-CRAY. DUO. FL,CL	SF
TAUSCH, F.-PAULER. 3 DUOS, OP 21. CL,BSN	EUL
TAUSCH, F.-VOXMAN. 3 DUOS, OP 21. CL,BSN	MR
TEPPER. SUITE. CL,BSN	MC
THARICHEN, W. DUO, OP 47. FL,OB	B&B
TURK, D.-DISHINGER. CUCKOO. FL(OB),CL	SP
TUSTIN, W. 30 DUETS. 2WW	SN
TUTHILL, B. DUO, OP 18/2 (1940). CL,BSN	SPR
TUTHILL, B. SONATINE IN CANON. FL,OB(CL)	TP
UDOW, M. BULLRUSHES. OB,BSN	ACA
VAN VACTOR, D. CANONS ON VARIOUS INTERVALS, # 1(1974) FL,OB	RR
VELLEKOOP, G. LISTEN TO OUR RECORDERS. 2WW	GAL
VELLEKOOP, G. (ARR). 6 SUITES. 2WW	GAL
VILLA-LOBOS, H. BACHIANAS BRASILERIAS #6. FL,BSN	AMP
VILLA-LOBOS, H. CHOROS #2 (1924). FL,CL	EES

2 PARTS: WOODWINDS-210

VILLA-LOBOS, H. DUO (1957). OB,BSN	EES
VOGEL, R. SUITE IN G MA. OB,BSN	TRI
WALKER, R. 3 MINIATURES. FL,CL	KN
WALTER, J. CANONS IN THE CHURCH MODES. 2WW	EDK
WANEK, F. 3 BURLESKE STUCKE. FL,BSN	SCH
WEAVER. 7 DIALOGUES. FL,CL	SH
WEBER, A. SONATINA. FL,BSN	ALE
WEEGENHUISE, J. 3 PEZZI (1954). FL,CL	SD
WEINER, I. DUO. FL,OB	AMC
WEINZWEIG, J. INTERMISSIONS. FL,OB	SN
WELANDER, S. DIVERTIMENTO (1962-63). 2WW	STI
WELANDER, S. LITEN FUGA OCH DIALOG OVER BACH (1970). CL,BSN	STI
WELANDER, S. SONATIN (1966). CL,BSN	STI
WELIN, K. SERMO MODULATUS (1960). FL,CL	STI
WHITE, D. SUITE. OB,CL	SO
WIGGLESWORTH, F. DUO. OB,CL	TP
WILDBERGER, J. RENCONTRES. FL/PIC,CL/E FL CL/BASSET HN	HG
WILLIAMS, E. ARTISTIC DUETS. 2WW	CC
WILLIAMS, E. EASY DUETS. 2WW	CC
WOLPE, S. SUITE IM HEXACHORD. OB,CL	M&M
WRIGHT, M. A DUE (1974). FL,CL	B-B
WUENSCH, G. 6 DUETS, OP 53 (1971). FL,CL	CAN
ZETTERKVIST, H. CANON PER MOTU CONTRARIO (1967). CL,BSN	STI
ZONN, P. DANCE SET. CL,BSN	ACA

2 PARTS: WOODWINDS (COLLECTIONS)-222

ANDRAUD, A. (ARR). DUOS CONCERTANTS, SERIES #1. FL(OB),CL	SO
ANDRAUD, A. (ARR). DUOS CONCERTANTS, SERIES #2. FL(OB),CL	SO
ANDRAUD, A. (ARR). DUOS CONCERTANTS, SERIES #3. FL(OB),CL	SD
DUETS. FL(OB),CL	HU
ELKAN, H. DUET ALBUM. FL(OB,CL),BSN	HE
FRANK, M. (ARR). 20 DUETS. OB(FL,CL),BSN(BCL)	SF
FRANK, M. (TR). 20 EASY WOODWIND DUETS. FL(OB,CL),BSN(CL)	KPM
HENDERSON-STOUTAMIRE(ARR). CLASSIC DUETS. 2WW	PO
KAPLAN, D. (ARR). GOTHAM COLLECTION. FL,OB	SPR
LEWIS-WIDMER. BEGINNING DUETS. 2WW	BE
LITTLE, L. GREAT DUETS, 2 VOLS. 2WW	PO
NELSON, B. (ARR). ADVANCED DUETS, 3 VOLS. 2WW	CC
SCHAEFFER, D. CHRISTMAS DUETS. 2WW	PO
SCHAEFFER, D. DUETS ARE FUN. 2WW	PO
SCHAEFFER, D. 21 RHYTHMIC DUETS. 2WW	PO
SCHAEFFER, D. (ARR). PROGRAM DUETS. FL,CL	PO
STOUFFER, P. DUET ALBUM. FL,OB	HE
STOUTAMIRE-HENDERSON. DUETS FOR ALL. 2WW	PO
VOXMAN, H.(ARR). 78 DUETS, 2 VOLS. FL,CL	RU
WALN, G. (ARR). WALN DUETS. FL,CL	KJ

2 PARTS: WOODWIND-BRASS (INCL HORN)-231

BACH, JAN. 4 TWO-BIT CONTRAPTIONS. FL,HN	MEP
BALDWIN, D. DIVERTIMENTO. FL,TU	AM
BARSAM, Y. 3 ENCORE PIECES. BSN,HN	IMP
BEYER, J. DUET. OB,TU	AMC

BOUCARD, M. SUITE CHAMPETRE. FL,HN	BIL
CHILDS, B. HORN & OBOE MUSIC. OB,HN	ACA
DEVIENNE, F.-MAYHAN. DUETS. FL(OB,CL),HN(BSN)	GS
DOBRZYNSKI, I.-KURKIEWICZ. DUET. CL,HN	PWM
DOBRZYNSKI, I.-LELOIR. DUO IN E FL MA. CL,HN	KAW
DUVERNOY, F.-LELOIR. 3 SONATAS. HN,BSN(VC)	KAW
ERIXON, P. DIVERTIMENTO, OP 11 (1964). OB,HN	STI
ERIXON, P. PHANTASY, OP 13 (1964). CL,TRB	STI
EVERETT, T. DUOS. CL,TRB	SS
FAVRE, G. PNYX. FL,HN	EMT
FUCHS, G.-KLOCKER/HENKE. DUO, OP 5. CL,HN	PET
HARTLEY, W. DUET. FL,TU	TP
HAZZARD, P. DUET. CL,HN	SS
HEWITT, H. 9 PRELUDES. FL,TRB	MAN
JOHANSON, S. SYSKONS TYCKE (1973). CL,TRB	STI
JOHNSEN, H. SUITE, OP 41. FL,HN	NM
KOECHLIN, C. 4 LITTLE PIECES, OP173. CL,HN	EES
MAGANINI, Q. BOA-CONSTRICTOR AND THE BOBOLINK, THE. PIC,TU	EDM
MAKOVECKY, J.-WEELINK. DUO CONCERTANT #1. CL,HN	KAW
MOZART, W.-WEELINK. DUO. HN,BSN	KAW
OLSEN, S. NOCTURNE, OP 57/2. FL,HN	NM
OTT, J. 5 DUETS. OB,HN	CU
PABLO, L. DE. PARDON (1972). CL,TRB	EDS
POLIN, C. DEATH OF PROCRIS, THE. FL,TU	SS
PRESSER, W. 5 DUETS. OB,TRB	TRI
RICE, T. CARLSON'S KIT. CL,TPT	SS
SCHWADRON, A. SHORT SUITE. CL,TRB	KN
STECKL, K. MUSIK, OP 82A. E FL CL,HN	PGM
STICH-PUNTO, J.-LELOIR. SONATA. HN,BSN	KAW
SYDEMAN, W. DUO. CL,HN	SS
TAYLOR, C. DUO. ASAX,TRB	ACA
TELEMANN, G.-HARTLEY. 3 DANCES IN A MI. FL,TU	EP
THOMAS, D. VOICES. CL,TPT	EAM
VAUGHAN, R. QUATTRO BICINIE. CL,TU	AM
WILDER, A. DUETS. BSN,HN	MAR
WILDGANS, F. 3 INVENTIONEN. CL,HN	LDO

2 PARTS: WOODWIND-STRING-233

ABENDROTH, W. DIVERTIMENTO, OP 5. FL,VA	WMS
ACKER, D. DUO (1975). FL/AFL,VC	HG
ALEXANDER, J. 3 INVENTIONS. OB,VA	GEN
ALSINA, C. UNITY, OP 31 (1973). CL,VC	ESZ
AMES, W. DUO. FL,VA	ACA
ARMA, P. 3 TRANSPARENCES. CL,VN	HLE
BACH, C.P.E. DUET IN G MA. FL,VN	INT
BACH, C.P.E. DUET. FL,VN	HU
BACH, C.P.E. 2 DUETS. FL,VN	EDK
BACH, C.P.E. 2 DUETS. OB,VN	TP
BACH, C.P.E.-STEPHAN. DUO IN E MI WQ 140. FL,VN	B&N
BACH, C.P.E.-STEPHAN. 2 DUOS. FL,VN	NV
BACH, J.C.-NAGEL. 3 SONATAS IN D,G, AND C MA. FL,VN	SCH
BACH, W.F. DUO SONATA. CL,VN	EDM
BAEYENS, A. PIRANESI. FL,VC	EME
BALASSA, S. DIMENSIONI, OP 8 (1966). FL,VA	EMB
BARSKOVS, O. SONATA #2. FL,VC	MKE
BECK, C. SONATINA. FL,VN	EES
BENTZON, J. INTERMEZZO. CL,VN	CHE

BEREZOWSKY, N.   DUO.   CL,VA   AMC
BERG, G.   POUR CLARINETTE ET VIOLON (1959).   CL,VN   SPD
BEZANSON, P.   5 MINIATURES.   CL,VC   ACA
BISCHOF, R.   THEMA UND / VARIATIONEN, OP 4.   OB,VC   LDO
BIZET, G.   LITTLE DUET IN C MI (1874).   BSN,VC   MR
BLANK, A.   VARIATIONS.   CL,VA   SS
BOGUSLAWSKI, E.   IMPROMPTU.   FL,VA   PWM
BOND, V.   CAN(N)ONS.   CL,VN   SS
BORGULYA, A.   4 DUETTI.   FL,VA   EMB
BORNEFELD, H.   CHORALSONATE "AUF MEINEN LIEBEN GOTT".   FL,VN   B&N
BROD, H.-GILLET.   6 SONATAS.   OB,VC   HLE
BUNGE, S.   DUO (1966).   FL,VC   SD
BUSCH, A.   HAUSMUSIK, OP 26/1.   CL,VN   BRH
BUSCH, A.   HAUSMUSIK, OP 26/2.   CL,VN   BRH
CALABRO, L.   5 DUOS.   CL,VC   EV
CAMPAGNOLI, B.   DUET IN D MA.   FL,VN   B&V
CANNABICH, C.-HOCKNER/TWARZ.   6 DUETS, 2 VOLS.   FL,VA   SIM
CAPDEVIELLE, P.   SONATINA PASTORALE.   FL,VA   EFM
CHAMBERS, S.   ONE PLUS ONE.   FL,DB   AMC
CHUGUNOV, Y.   12 STUDIES.   SAX,DB   MKE
CLARKE, R.   HAPPENINGS.   FL,DB   MAN
COCKELL, R.   SUITE.   OB,VN   CAN
COUPERIN, F.-SCHMITZ.   MUSIK FUR FLOTE.   FL,VN   B&N
CRAWFORD-SEEGER, R.   DIAPHONIC SUITE #2.   BSN,VC   AB
CRAWFORD-SEEGER, R.   DIAPHONIC SUITE #4.   OB,VC   AB
CROSSE, G.   VARIATIONS.   OB,VC   OX
DANZI, F.-SONNTAG.   3 DUETS, OP 64.   FL,VC   HSM
DAVID, J.   SONATE, OP 32/1.   FL,VA   BRH
DAVID, J.   SONATE, OP 32/4.   CL,VA   BRH
DAVID, T.   SONATINE (1958).   FL,VA   LDO
DEGEN, H.   SONATA.   FL,VA   SIM
DIETTER, C.-READ.   SONATA VI.   BSN,VC   NOM
DORAN, M.   SONATINA.   FL,VC   WI
DUKELSKY, V.   ETUDE.   VN,BSN   MC
ECKERBERG, S.   DUO.   FL,VC   STI
ECKHARDT-GRAMATTE, S.   DUO CONCERTANTE (1956).   FL,VN   CAN
EDER, H.   DUO.   FL,VN   BRH
ETLER, A.   DUO.   OB(FL,VN),VA(CL)   NVM
FARAGO, M.   4 DUETS, OP 27.   VA(VC),BSN   HE
FELCIANO, R.   SPECTRA.   PIC/AFL/FL,DB   ECS
FRANCO, J.   SONATINA.   FL,VA   ACA
FRANCO, J.   6 VARIATIONS.   FL,VA   ACA
FRANK, A.   DIVERTIMENTO.   BFL,DB   SS
FREUDENTHAL, O.   12 VERANDERUNGEN.   OB,VA   EAM
FRICKER, P.   3 ARGUMENTS, OP 59 (1969).   BSN,VC   AB
GAL, H.   DIVERTIMENTO, OP 90/1.   BSN,VC   ABE
GALLAHER, C.   4 PIECES.   CL,VC   SP
GARLICK, A.   DUO.   FL,VA   SS
GEBAUER, F.   DUO CONCERTANTE, OP 16/3.   CL,VN   MR
GENIN, P.   GRAND DUO CONCERTANT.   FL,VN   BIL
GENZMER, H.   DIVERTISSEMENT.   FL,VN   PET
GERAEDTS, J.   3 (1943) INVENTIES.   FL,VN   SD
GILMORE, B.   DUO (1969).   FL,VA   SS
GODFREY, D.   BALLADE.   CL,VN   ACA
GRAVES, M.   WATERCOURSE.   BSN,DB   SS
GUIGNARD.   32 SHORT DUETS.   FL,VC   PET
GYRING, E.   DUO.   CL,VA   ACA
GYRING, E.   DUO #2.   CL,VA   ACA
HABER, L.   6 MINIATURES.   FL,VN   GEN
HALLNAS, H.   SPEL FOR TVA.   CL,VA   EMF
HAMILTON, I.   SERENATA.   CL,VN   TP
HANDEL, G.-GUIGNARD.   8 STUCKE.   FL,VC   S-V

```
HAUBENSTOCK-RAMATI, R.  MULTIPLE #5 (1970).  1WW,1STR         UE
HAYDN, F.  3 SONATAS.  FL,VA                                  EDM
HEKSTER, W.  MONOLOGUES & CONVERSATION (1970).  ASAX,VC       SD
HERMANSON, A.  A DUE VOCI.  AFL,VA                            EMF
HESS, W.  SONATA, OP 78.  VA,BSN                              EUL
HINDEMITH, P.  2 DUETS.  CL,VN                                SCH
HINDEMTH, P.  STUCKE (1942).  BSN,VC                          SCH
HOFFMEISTER, F.-DRUNER.  DUO IN F MA.  FL,VA                  PET
HONEGGER, A.  PRELUDE (3 CONTREPOINTS, #1).  OB,VC            CHE
HUYBRECHTS, A.  SONATINE (1934).  FL,VA                       CBD
HYE-KNUDSEN, J.  2 CHAMBER DUETS.  FL,VC                      CHE
JACOB, G.  MINIATURE SUITE.  CL,VA                            MR
JEZ, J.  VERSES.  OB,VA                                       EDD
JOHNSON, R.  SONATA.  AFL,VC                                  OX
JOHNSTON, B.  DUO.  FL,DB                                     M&M
JOLAS, B.  REMEMBER.  EHN,VC                                  HEU
KARDOS, I.  DUO.  CL,VC                                       GEN
KARLINS, M.  BIRTHDAY MUSIC #2.  FL,DB                        MEP
KASBERGEN, M.  CHACONNE.  FL,DB                               SD
KAUDER, H.  SONATA (1958).  CL,VN                             SS
KELTERBORN, R.  4 MINIATUREN.  OB,VN                          GBV
KENINS, T.  FANTASY-VARIATIONS (1967).  FL,VA                 CAN
KENINS, T.  SERENADE (1973).  OB,VC                          CAN
KLEPPER, W.  SONATA.  FL,VA                                   EMU
KOERPPEN, A.  DUO.  FL,VN                                     MV
KORTE, K.  RONDINO.  OB,VN                                    AU
KRAUS, J.-WINTER.  SONATA IN D MA.  FL,VA                     B&N
KUPFERMAN, M.  GARDEN OF MY FATHER'S HOUSE.  CL,VN            GEN
KUPFERMAN, M.  THREE FOR TWO.  CL,VN                          GEN
KUUSISTO, I.  DUO (1957).  FL,VC                              MT
LACOME, P.  PASSEPIED,.  BSN,VN                               DUR
LANGER, H.  3 DUETTE (1975).  CL,VC                           HG
LESSARD, J.  MUSIC FOR THE WEDDING.  FL,VN                    ACA
LEWIS, P.  DUET.  FL,VC                                       ACA
LIANI, D.  CJANTIS.  FL,VC                                    GZ
LINN, R.  DUO.  CL,VC                                         SH
LIPKIN, M.  SUITE (1961).  FL,VC                              CHE
LUCK, R.  VERANDERUNGEN...OBERPFALZISCHEN TANZ.  VN,BSN       HG
LUCKE, G.  KLEINER DIALOG (1966).  CL,VA                      GBV
LUYKENAAR, C.  DUO (1974).  OB,DB                             SD
MAASZ, G.  DUO IN C MA.  FL,VN                                MV
MACONCHY, E.  CONVERSATIONS.  CL,VA                           CA
MAES, J.  SONATINE (1934).  FL,VA                             CBD
MAGANINI, Q.  CANONICO ESPRESSIVO.  FL,VC                     EDM
MAMLOK, U.  SINTRA.  AFL,VC                                   ACA
MANN, I.  3 BAGATELLES, OP 3 (1951).  CL(VA),VC               CAN
MARTINO, D.  5 FRAMMENTI.  OB,DB                              M&M
MATYS, J.  INVENCE (1969).  FL,VC                             CHF
MATYS, J.  QUIPS.  CL,VN                                      PAN
MEIJERLING, C.  UGLY HOWLING MONKEY (1978), THE.  BAR SAX,VN  SD
METRAL, P.  ALLEGRETTO (DISPARATES) (1961).  OB,VA            EDT
MICHAEL, F.  6 MINIATURES, OP 31/1.  CL(AFL),VA              WZ
MIEG, P.  DUO (1977).  FL,VA                                  EUL
MIGOT, G.  6 PETITS PRELUDES, 2 VOLS.  FL,VN                  ALE
MIMAROGLU, I.  PIECE FUTILE.  CL,VC                           SS
MOGILL, L.  12 DUETS.  FL(OB),VA                              HE
MOLIQUE, B.-RAMPAL/GINGOLD.  CONCERTANTE.  FL,VN             INT
MOYSE, L.  4 DANCES.  FL,VN                                   M&M
MOZART, W.-KORDA.  SONATA IN B FL MA, K292.  BSN,VC          LDO
MOZART, W.  SONATA IN B FL MA, K292.  BSN,VC                 EDK
MOZART, W.  SONATA, K292.  BSN,VC                            INT
MOZART, W.  SONATE IN B FL MA, K292.  BSN,VC                 BRH
```

```
NESSLER, R.  POISSONS MAGIQUES (1968), LES.  FL,VC                LDO
NEUBAUER, F.-MOYSE.  4 PIECES.  FL,VA                             GS
NIELSEN, C.  FAITH & HOPE.  FL,VA                                 CHE
NORDGREN, E.  SONATIN.  CL,VN                                     EMF
ORLAND, H.  PERPETUUM MOBILE.  FL,VC                              SS
PABLO, L. DE.  SOIREE (1972).  CL,VN                              EDS
PAPORISZ, Y.  PICCOLI DUETTI.  FL,VA                              IMP
PARRIS, R.  DUO.  FL,VN                                           ACA
PEDERSEN, P.  RICERCARE (1958).  CL,VN                            CAN
PITFIELD, T.  DUETTO.  CL,VA                                      SS
PRAAG, H. VAN.  KLEINE SUITE (1936).  FL,VN                       SD
PRAAG, H. VAN.  VOORSPEL, INTERMEZZO EN SCHERZO (1943).  CL,VC    SD
PRESSER, W.  SERENADE.  FL,VA                                     OP
RAPHAEL, G.  DIVERTIMENTO, OP 74.  ASAX,VC                        BRH
RAPHAEL, G.  KAMMERMUSIK, OP 47/6, DUO IN E FL MA.  CL,VN         B&N
REGT, H. DE.  MUSICA, OP 20 (1972).  FL,VC                        SD
REGT, H. DE.  MUSICA, OP 47 (1975).  FL,VA                        SD
RICE, T.  SONATINA.  PIC,DB                                       SS
RONSHEIM, J.  FRAGMENT (1964).  FL,DB                             B-B
ROOS, R. DE.  QUATTRO PER DUE.  OB,VA                             PET
ROSEN, J.  SONATA.  CL,VC                                         ACA
ROUSSEL, A.  DUO.  BSN,DB                                         DUR
SCARMOLIN, A.  3 PIECES.  FL,VA                                   AMC
SCHICKELE, P.  LITTLE WELCOME SERENADE, A.  FL,VN                 EV
SCHILLING, H.  SUITE EN MINIATURE (1964).  VN,BSN                 BRH
SCHMITT, M.  4 STUCKE.  CL,VC                                     MV
SCHONBERG, S.  5 PIECES.  CL,VC                                   CHE
SCHRODER, H.  DUO-SONATE.  FL,VA                                  FRH
SCHRODER, H.  MUSIC.  OB,VN                                       ROB
SETER, M.  EPIGRAMS (MITCHTAMIM) (1970).  FL,VC                   ISR
SIMEONOV, B.  2 INVENTIONS (1974).  FL,VA                         CAN
SIMONS, N.  DESIGN GROUPS #2.  FL,DB                              TP
SKOLD, Y.  SONATIN.  FL,VA                                        EMF
SMIT, L.  SUITE (1938).  OB,VC                                    SD
SMITH, W.  SUITE.  CL,VN                                          OX
SPISAK, M.  DUETTO CONCERTANTE.  BSN,VA                           RC
STAEMPFLI, E.  DUO (1974).  OB,VA                                 HUG
STALLAERT, A.  BESTIARE.  ASAX,VC                                 BIL
STEARNS, P.  DUO.  AFL,DB                                         ACA
STEARNS, P.  DUO.  CL,VC                                          AMC
STOUFFER, P.  DUET ALBUM.  FL(OB),VN                              HE
STOUT, A.  3 CANONS, OP 61A.  FL,VC                               ACA
SUTER, R.  IMPROVISATION.  OB,VA                                  HEI
SWICKARD, R.  4 DUETS.  FL,VA                                     SS
SYDEMAN, W.  DUO (1959).  FL,DB                                   SS
SYDEMAN, W.  DUO.  CL/BCL,DB                                      PET
SYDEMAN, W.  VARIATIONS.  VA,BSN                                  AMC
SZABO, F.  SERENADE.  FL,VA                                       EMB
TATE, P.  SONATA.  CL,VC                                          OX
TATTON, M.  2 DUETS, ECLOGUE, DISPUTE.  FL,VA                     AMC
TATTON, M.  TWO BY TWO.  FL,VA                                    AMC
TAUSINGER, J.  ETUDEN.  FL,VC                                     CHF
TAUTENENHAN, G.  GREELEY VARIATIONS.  BSN,VN                      SS
TAUTENENHAN, G.  OPTIONS I.  FL,DB                                SS
TELEMANN, G.-ERMELER.  DUET IN G MA.  FL,VN                       B&N
TELEMANN, G.  DUET IN G.  FL,VN                                   INT
TELEMANN, G.-LOEWER.  6 DUETS.  FL,VN                             B&V
TELEMANN, G.-MICHAEL.  SONATA IN A.  FL,VA                        WZ
THOMSON, V.  SERENADE.  FL,VN                                     SN
TROMBLY, P.  IN EGALE.  OB,VC                                     ACA
VALDAMBRINI, F.  19 MOVEMENTS.  FL,VA                             UE
VALLEE, G.  MENUET & RIGODON.  FL(OB),VC                          GD
```

```
VILLA-LOBOS, H.  ASSOBIO A JATO.  FL,VC                              SN
VIVIER, C.  POUR VIOLON ET CLARINETTE.  CL,VN                        CAN
WATKINSON, J.  FANFARE TO UNVEIL.  FL,VC                             MAN
WHITTENBERG, C.  COMPOSITION.  FL,DB                                 ACA
WIGGLESWORTH, F.  DUO.  OB,VA                                        TP
WISZNIEWSKI, Z.  DUO.  FL,VA                                         HMO
XENAKIS, I.  CHARISMA (1971).  CL,VC                                 EDS
YAVELOW, C.  EXPLANATION OF 1 MECHANICAL MAN, AN.  CL,VC             ACA
ZANETTOVICH, D.  AIRS DE LA RENAISSANCE ESPAGNOLE.  BSN,VC           ALE
ZUR, M.  DISCUSSIONS.  CL,VN                                         SS
```

2 PARTS INCLUDING HARP-238

```
ALIPRANDI, P.  PAYSAGES.  CL,HP                                      CHP
ALWYN, W.  NAIADES (FANTASY SONATA).  FL,HP                          BH
ANDRIESSEN, H.  PADOVANA DI DON CHISIOTTE.  FL,HP                    SD
ANGERER, P.  OBLECTATIO VESPERTINA.  FL,HP                           LDO
BADINGS, H.  CAVATINA (1952).  AFL,HP                                SD
BAMERT, M.  5 APHORISMS.  FL,HP                                      SS
BEECROFT, H.  3 PEZZI BREVI.  FL,HP                                  UE
BEMBERG, H.  DANSE GREQUE.  FL,HP                                    HLE
BENVENUTI, A.  MORCEAU (EN FORME DE...) (1977).  FL,HP               BRU
BERNIER, R.  SONATE A DEUX (1939).  FL,HP                            CBD
BERTHOMIEU, M.  5 NUANCES.  FL,HP                                    SEM
BONDON, J.  SWING #1.  FL,HP                                         EES
BOZZA, E.  2 IMPRESSIONS.  FL,HP                                     ALE
BRESGEN, C.  4 CAPRICCIOS.  FL,HP                                    LDO
BRETTINGHAM SMITH, J.  TWO TIMES PAST, OP 18.  FL,HP                 B&B
BROECKX, J.  PETITE SUITE.  FL,HP                                    EME
BUSSER, H.  NOCTURNE.  FL,HP                                         HLE
CHOU, WEN-CHUNG.  3 FOLK SONGS.  FL,HP                               PET
CONSOLI, M.  INTERACTIONS #3.  FL,HP                                 ACA
CUNNINGHAM, M.  PHASES.  BCL,HP                                      SS
DAMASE, J.  SONATE.  FL,HP                                           HLE
DODGSON, S.  DUO.  FL,HP                                             CA
DOMAZLICKY, F.  POLNI KVITI (1962).  OB,HP                           CHF
DONIZETTI, G.-MEYLAN.  SONATE.  FL,HP                                PET
DRESDEN, S.  SONATA.  FL,HP                                          EDS
DUREY, L.  NICOLIOS ET LA FLUTE.  FL,HP                              BIL
EBEN, P.  ORDO MODALIS (1964).  OB,HP                                CHF
ERVIN, K.  5 LITTLE PIECES.  OB,HP                                   SS
FIALA, G.  SONATA BREVE (1972).  CL,HP                               CAN
FLOSMAN, O.  ROMANZA E SCHERZO.  FL,HP                               ART
FOLPRECHT, Z.  KLEINE SUITE IN ALTEM STIL (1937).  FL,HP            PAN
FONTYN, J.  FILIGRANE.  FL,HP                                        JOB
FRANCAIX, J.  5 PICCOLI DUETTI.  FL,HP                               SCH
GOTKOWSKY, I.  EOLIENNE.  FL,HP                                      BIL
HESS, W.  3 TONSTUCKE, OP 79.  FL,HP                                 EUL
HILSE, B.  SUITE, OP 6.  FL,HP                                       WZ
HLOBIL, E.  ARIA E RONDO.  OB,HP                                     CHF
HOLLIGER, H.  MOBILE (1962).  OB,HP                                  SCH
HOVHANESS, A.  GARDEN OF ADONIS, OP245, THE.  FL,HP                  PET
IBERT, J.  ENTR'ACTE.  FL,HP                                         ALE
JACQUET, H.  ELEGIE.  FL,HP(PF)                                      EES
JACQUET, H.  POUR UN PETIT CHIEN CLOWN.  FL,HP(PF)                   EES
JIRKO, I.  DIVERTIMENTO (1966).  FL,HP                               CHF
JOLIVET, A.  ALLA RUSTICA.  FL,HP                                    BH
JOLIVET, A.  CONTROVERSIA.  OB,HP                                    BIL
```

JONAK, Z. MIM (1965). FL,HP	ES
JONGEN, J. DANCE LENTE. FL,HP(PF)	CHE
KAPR, J. DIALOGE. FL,HP	ES
KARAS, RUDOLF. SUITE (1967). OB,HP	CHF
KARKOFF, M. 2 IMPRESSIONER, OP 36 (1958). FL,HP	STI
KELLY, R. SONATA. OB,HP	ACA
KELTERBORN, R. MONODIE #1 (1976). FL,HP	HUG
KOHN, K. SOUVENIRS #2. OB,HP	CF
KRUMPHOLTZ, J.-ZINGEL. SONATA IN F MA. FL,HP(PF)	B&N
KUBIZEK, A. SONATA, OP 24B. FL,HP	LDO
LASALA, A. POEMA DEL PASTOR COVA. FL,HP	RC
LAUBER, J. 4 DANSES MEDIEVALES, OP 45. FL,HP	WZ
LEEUW, T. DE. RIME (1974). FL,HP	SD
LEHMANN, H. SPIELE. OB,HP	SCH
LEMELAND, A. CAPRICCIO, OP 43. CL,HP	BIL
LINDE, B. DANS (1952). FL,HP	STI
LORA, A. 2 SKETCHES (1960). FL,HP	AMP
LOUCHEUR, R. DIALOGUES. FL,HP	EFM
LUNDQUIST, T.. INTUIZIONE/VARANING. FL,HP	STI
MELARTIN, E. SONATA (1920). FL,HP	FIN
METRAL, P. RAPSODIE (1965). FL,HP	EDT
MIEG, P. MORCEAU ELEGANT. FL,HP	S&B
MIGOT, G. PREMIER LIVRE DE DIVERTISSEMENTS FRANCAIS, LE CL,HP	ALE
MIROGLIO, F. FLUCTUANCES (1961). FL,HP,PERC AD LIB	ESZ
MOUQUET, J. DANSE GREQUE. FL,HP	HLE
MOUQUET, J. DIVERTISSEMENT GREC. FL,HP	HLE
MOURANT, W. ELEGY. FL,HP	ACA
MOZART, W.-FLOTHUIS. CADENZA TO CONCERTO, K299. FL,HP	B&V
MOZART, W.-HOUDY. CADENZAS FOR THE CONCERTO, K299. FL,HP	ALE
MOZART, W.-JONGEN. CADENZAS TO CONCERTO, K299. FL,HP	HE
MOZART, W.-PILLNEY. CADENZAS TO CONCERTO, K299. FL,HP	WZ
MOZART, W.-REINECKE. 3 CADENZAS TO CONCERTO, K299. FL,HP	BRH
NIELSEN, C. FOG IS LIFTING, THE. FL,HP	CHE
NOWKA, D. 7 ESQUISSES. FL,HP	VNM
OBROVSKA, J. SYMBIOZY. FL,HP	ART
ODSTRCIL, K. REFLEXY (1964). FL,HP	ART
PADOVANO, A. BERCEUSE. FL,HP	EBE
PELEMANS, W. SONATE. FL,HP	MAU
PERSICHETTI, V. SERENADE #10. FL,HP	EV
POLIN, C. SONATA #2. FL,HP	AMC
POLIN, C. SONATA. FL,HP	SS
PRAAG, H. VAN. SONATINE (1955). CL,HP	SD
PROCUREUR, J. ROSE DE NOEL. FL,HP	ECH
RAMOVS, P. IMPULSIONS (1967). OB,HP	HG
RAMOVS, P. 3 LITTLE PASTORALS. FL,HP	EDD
RAPHAEL, G. SONATINE, OP 65/2 (1948). OB,HP(PF)	BRH
REINER, K. 2 COMPOSIZIONI (1962). OB,HP	ART
ROMITI. SUITE. FL,HP	SO
ROREM, N. BOOK OF HOURS. FL,HP	BH
ROTA, N. SONATA. FL,HP	RC
SAGNIER. PETITE SUITE ARMORICAINE. FL,HP	ALE
SAUGUET, H. BARCAROLLE. BSN,HP	CHM
SLAVICKY, K. INTERMEZZI MATTUTINI. FL,HP	ART
SMITH, J. TWO TIMES PAST. FL,HP	B&B
SMUTNY, J. 3 STUCKE (1969). OB,HP	B&N
SOUKUP, V. POHADKA (1955). FL,HP	CHF
SPELMAN, T. RONDO. FL,HP	CHE
STAEMPFLI, E. DUO (1965). FL,HP	B&B
STRENS, J. 2 IMPROMPTUS, OP 33. FL,HP	HE
TAIRA, Y. EVEIL. OB,HP	ERR
TAIRA, Y. STRATUS. FL,HP	ERR

2 PARTS INCLUDING HARP-238

TAUSINGER, J. AVVENTURE, LE (1965). FL,HP	ART
TAUTENHAHN, G. ELEGY. TSAX,HP	SS
TON-THAT, T. NIEM. FL,HP	EMT
ULTAN, L. MEDITATION. FL,HP	SS
VALLIER, J. SUITE. FL,HP	EFM
VAN NOSTRAND, B. VENTILLATION MANUAL. FL/AFL,HP	ACA
VIGNATI, M. POETICKE KUSY. FL,HP	CHF
VIGNATI, M. POETICKE SKLADBY. FL,HP	CHF
VOSS, F. NOTTURNO (1958). OB,HP	BRH
VRIES ROBBE, W. DE. SONATA (1949). FL,HP	SD
VRIES ROBBE, W. DE. SONATA #2 (1975). FL,HP	SD
VRIES-ROBBE, W. DE. SONATA. FL,HP	B&V
WERNER, J. 3 RITOURNELLES. FL,HP	EMT
WILLIAMS, D. SONATINA. BSN,HP	AMC
WISSMER, P. SONATINE- CROISIERE. FL,HP	BIL
YUN, I. DOPPELKONZERT (1977). OB,HP	B&B
ZAMARA, A. CAPRICCIETTO. FL,HP(PF)	LDO
ZANETTOVICH, D. NOCTURNE ET PANTOMIME. FL,HP	ALE
ZECCHI, A. DIVERTIMENTO. FL,HP	EDB
ZINGEL, R. KLEINE SERENADE, EINE. FL,HP	ETB
ZUCKERT, L. DOS IMPROVISACIONES (1968). FL,HP	CAN

2 PARTS INCLUDING GUITAR-239

ALBERT, R. IMAGENES DEL SOLITARIO. 6 PIECES. FL,GUIT	UME
ALBINONI, T. SONATA IN A MI. FL(OB),GUIT	WZ
ALTE MUSIK. FL,GUIT	EMB
ANONYMOUS-SCHALLER. GREENSLEEVES TO A GROUND. FL(OB),GUIT	LDO
ANTONIOU, T. DIALOGUE, OP 19 (1963). FL,GUIT	EMO
ASRIEL, A. 5 INVENTIONS. TSAX,GUIT	ISR
AZPIAZU, J. SONATE BASQUE. FL,GUIT	WZ
BACH, J.S.-TOWER. BADINERIE (SUITE #2). FL,GUIT	BHL
BACH, J.S.-THOMATOS. SONATA #1, BWV 1033. FL, GUIT	WZ
BACH, J.S.-UHLMANN. SONATA #3 IN E MA, BWV 1035. FL,GUIT	BRH
BACH, J.S.-RAGNOSSIG. SONATA #4 IN C MA (S 1033). FL,GUIT	EES
BACH, J.S. SONATA IN C MA. FL,GUIT	EMB
BALLOU, E. DIALOGUES. OB,GUIT	ACA
BANTAI/KOVACS/NAGY. ALYE MUSIK. FL,GUIT	EMB
BARLOW, F.-COTTE. PAVANE. FL,GUIT	HLE
BARON, E. 2 CONCERTI. FL,GUIT	NO
BARON, E.-BEHREND. CONCERTO #2. FL,GUIT	WZ
BARON, E.-DIRKX. DUET IN G MA. FL,GUIT	BHL
BARON, E. DUETTO. FL,LUTE	B&N
BARON, E.-MEUNIER. SONATA. FL,GUIT	BRH
BARON, E. SUITE. FL,GUIT	HE
BARTOLOZZI, B. AUSER (1973). OB,GUIT	ESZ
BAUER, R. 3 PIECES. SSAX,GUIT	CAN
BECKER, G. CON BUEN AYRE. FL(OB),GUIT	WZ
BEETHOVEN, L. VAN-SCHEIT. SONATINE. FL,GUIT	LDO
BEHREND, S. TRIPTYCHON (1970). FL(OB),GUIT	WZ
BEHREND, S. HAIKU-SUITE. FL,GUIT	WZ
BEHREND, S. LEGNANIANA. FL,GUIT	WZ
BENARY, P. FANTASIEN. FL,GUIT	MV
BERGMAN, E. DIALOGUE. FL,GUIT	FIN
BLAVET, M.-CASTET. 8 PIECES. FL,GUIT	ALE
BONNARD, A. SONATINE BREVE. FL,GUIT	ALE
BOSKE, J. LEAVE SOMETHING UNEXPLAINED (1975). FL,GUIT	SD
BOUSCH, F. COMME CHANTE LA SOURCE. FL,GUIT	HEU

```
BOZZA, E.   BERCEUSE ET SERENADE.  FL,GUIT                    ALE
BOZZA, E.   POLYDIAPHONIE.  FL,GUIT                           ALE
BOZZA,E.   3 PIECES.  FL,GUIT                                 ALE
BRAGA, G.   SERENATA.  FL(OB,EHN,CL,BSN),GUIT                 DUR
BRAUN, G.   SONATINE.  OB(FL),GUIT                            WZ
BRESGEN, C.  5 MINIATUREN.  FL,GUIT                           WZ
BURKHARD, W.  SERENADE, OP 71/3 (1944).  FL,GUIT             B&N
CALATAYUD, B.  DIVERTIMENTOS.  FL,GUIT                        UME
CALL, L. DE(SALDARELLI).  VARIAZIONI.  FL,GUIT               ESZ
CAMPRA, A.-KOVATS.  MENUET VIF & GIGUE.  OB(FL),GUIT         EES
CAROSO, F.-BEHREND.  BALLETTO.  FL,GUIT                       WZ
CARULLI, F.-THOMATOS.  FANTASIA, OP337.  FL,GUIT             HEI
CARULLI, F.-NAGEL.  NOCTURNE, OP190.  FL,GUIT                BRH
CARULLI, F.-NAGEL.  SERENADE, OP109/1.  FL,GUIT             S&C
CARULLI, F.-NAGEL.  SERENADE, OP109/6.  FL,GUIT             SCH
CARULLI, F.  5 SERENADES.  FL,GUIT                           CFV
CASTELNUOVO-TEDESCO, M.  SONATINA, OP205 (1965).  FL,GUIT    EES
CASTET, F.(ARR).  4 PIECES (FITZWILLIAM VIRGINAL BOOK)       ALE
   FL,GUIT
CHIEREGHIN, S.  4 TEMPI.  FL,GUIT                             GZ
CHOPIN, F.-SPALDING.  NOCTURNE, OP POSTH..  FL,GUIT          PMP
CHOPIN, F.-SPALDING.  PRELUDE IN E MI.  FL,GUIT             PMP
CHOPIN, F.  PRELUDE, OP 28/14.  FL,GUIT                      BRM
CILENSEK, J.  SONATA.  FL,GUIT                               EDK
CILENSEK, J.  SONATE (1950).  FL,GUIT                        BRII
CONSTANT, F.  CANTILENE.  FL,GUIT                            EES
CONSTANT, F.  CONTRASTES.  FL,GUIT                           EES
CONSTANT, F.  ONDE.  FL,GUIT                                 EES
COUPERIN, F.-KOVATS.  PETITS MOULINS A VENT, LES.  OB(FL),GUIT  EES
COX, H.  3 PIECES.  FL,GUIT                                   HE
DALLINGER, F.  SONATINE.  FL,GUIT                            LDO
DAVID, J.  VARIATIONEN, OP 32/2.  FL,LUTE                    BRH
DE JONG, M.  SUITE, OP127.  FL,GUIT                           HE
DE MEYER, C.  MELODIE.  FL,GUIT                               HE
DEBUSSY, C.  1ST ARABESQUE.  CL,GUIT                         BRM
DEBUSSY, C.  DANSE.  CL,GUIT                                 BRM
DELAVIGNE-CASTET.  FLEURS, LES.  FL,GUIT                     ALE
DEMILLAC.  PETITE SUITE MEDIEVALE.  FL,GUIT                  ALE
DENISOV, E.  SONATA.  FL,GUIT                                HSM
DERUNGS, G.  FANTASIA, OP 28/3.  CL,GUIT                     S-V
DESPORTES, E.  PASTORALE JOYEUSE.  FL,GUIT                   BRM
DESPORTES, E.  PASTORALE MELANCOLIQUE.  FL,GUIT             BRM
DESPORTES, E.  RONDE.  FL,GUIT                               BRM
DIABELLI/SCHUBERT-GOTZE.  TANZE.  FL,GUIT                     PM
DIABELLI, A.-SCHEIT.  DUO IN A MA.  FL,GUIT                  LDO
DIABELLI, A.-SCHEIT.  DUO IN D.  FL,GUIT                     LDO
DIABELLI, A.-NAGEL.  3 PIECES.  FL,GUIT                      BRH
DIABELLI, A.  POTPOURRI FROM BEETHOVEN.  FL,GUIT            BHL
DIABELLI, A.  SERENADE, OP 99.  FL,GUIT                      SIM
DIETHELM, C.  SERENATA NOTTURNA, OP119.  FL,GUIT            S-V
DJEMIL.  PETITE SUITE MEDIEVALE.  FL,GUIT                    ALE
DORAN, M.  SUITE.  FL,GUIT                                    WI
DOWLAND, J.-CASTET.  MY LORD CHAMBERLAIN: HIS...TITRE        ALE
   FL,GUIT
DRAPER, P.(TR).  GUITAR/FLUTE DUETS.  FL,GUIT                HY
DUARTE, J.  SONATINE, OP 15.  FL,GUIT                        B&V
DUCKWORTH, W.  AN IMAGINARY DEATH DANCE.  OB,GUIT            SS
ERBSE, H.  3 STUDIEN, OP30.  FL,GUIT                         LDO
FAURE, G.-SILVERMAN.  SICILIENNE.  FL,GUIT                    BE
FAURE, G.  SICILIENNE.  FL,GUIT                              BRM
FELD, J.  2 DANCES.  FL,GUIT                                 ALE
FLAGELLO, N.  BURLESCA.  FL,GUIT                             GEN
```

FREUNDLICH, R. 5 LITTLE MELODIES. FL,GUIT   BE
FUERSTENAU, C.-NAGEL. 12 STUCKE, OP 16. FL,GUIT   BRH
FUERSTENAU, K.-HUMANN. 12 ORIGINALKOMPOSITIONEN, OP 35   NV
  FL,GUIT
FUERSTENAU, K.-NAGEL. STUCKE, OP 37. FL,GUIT   HEI
FURSTENAU, K.-NAGEL. 12 STUCKE, OP 38. FL,GUIT   SCH
FURSTENAU, K.-BEHREND. SUITE, OP 34. FL,GUIT   WZ
FURSTENAU, K.-BEHREND. SUITE, OP 35. FL,GUIT   WZ
GEBAUER, M.-NAGEL. POLONAISE. FL,GUIT   BRH
GELLI, V.-THOMATOS. 2 DIVERTIMENTI. FL,GUIT   TP
GEMINIANI, &. SONATA IN E MI. OB(FL),GUIT   WZ
GENIN, P.-MADDOX. CARNIVAL OF VENICE, THE. FL,GUIT   SO
GIULIANI, M.-THOMATOS. DIVERTIMENTO. FL,GUIT   WZ
GIULIANI, M.-NAGEL. DUETTE FACILE, OP 77. FL,GUIT   SCH
GIULIANI, M.(SALDARELLI). DUETTINO. FL,GUIT   ESZ
GIULIANI, M. DUETTINO FACILE, OP 77. FL,GUIT   RS
GIULIANI, M.-NAGEL. GRAN DUETTO CONCERTANTE, OP 52. FL,GUIT   SCH
GIULIANI, M. GRAND SERANADE, OP 82. FL,GUIT   BRH
GIULIANI, M. GROSSE SONATE, OP 85. FL,GUIT   WZ
GIULIANI, M.(SALDARELLI). MESTO GEMITO. FL,GUIT   ESZ
GIULIANI, M.(SALDARELLI). SERENATA. FL,GUIT   ESZ
GOEPFERT, K.-WOJCIECHOWSKI. SONATE, OP 13. BSN,GUIT   B&B
GOSSEC, J. TAMBOURIN. FL,GUIT   BRM
GREEN, H. 3 CAVATINAS. FL,GUIT   PMP
GREENWOOD & ROSENBLUM(TR). ROSEWOOD BOOK, THE. FL,GUIT   CF
GRETRY, A.-GATTI. ENTR'ACTE. FL,GUIT   EBE
GRIFFITHS, J. CONVERSATION PIECE. FL,GUIT   WZ
GRIFFITHS, J. 2 OPPORTUNITIES. FL,GUIT   WZ
HALLNAS, H. 3 DIALOGER (1971). FL,GUIT   STI
HAND, F. 4 EXCURSIONS. FL,GUIT   BH
HANDEL, G.-AZPIAZU. SONATA #2 IN G MI. FL,GUIT   WZ
HANDEL, G.-SCHEIT. SONATA IN A MI, OP 1/4. FL(OB),GUIT   LDO
HANDEL, G.-SCHEIT. SONATA IN C MA. FL(OB),GUIT   LDO
HANDEL, G.-ZANOSKAR. SONATA IN D MA. FL,GUIT   HSM
HANDEL, G.-SCHALLER. SONATA IN D MI. FL(OB),GUIT   LDO
HANDEL, G. SONATA IN E MI. FL,GUIT   BRH
HANDEL, G.-SCHALLER. SONATA IN F MA. FL(OB),GUIT   LDO
HANDEL, G. SONATA IN F MA. FL,GUIT   FRH
HANDEL, G.-SCHEIT. SONATA IN G MI. FL(OB,GUIT   LDO
HAUG, H. CAPRICCIO (1963). FL,GUIT   EES
HEER, H. DE. SONATINA #3 (1975). FL,GUIT   SD
HEER, H. DE. SONATINE (1967). FL,GUIT   SD
HEER, H. DE. SONATINE #2. FL,GUIT   SD
HEKSTER, W. 5 MOMENTS OF DAY (1977-78). FL/AFL,GUIT   SD
HENZE, B. VOLKSLIEDER UND -TANZE AUS ALLER WELT, 3 VOLS.   WZ
  FL,GUIT
HENZE, B. (ARR). STERNE UBER STILLEN STRASSEN. FL,GUIT   FRH
HEUCKERATH-HESSEN. IMPRESSION. FL(OB),GUIT   B&V
HEUCKERATH-HESSEN. SONG AND DANCE. FL(OB),GUIT   B&V
HODDINOTT, A. ITALIAN SUITE. FL,GUIT   OX
HOVHANESS, A. SUITE, OP291. ASAX,GUIT   PI
HOVHANESS, A. SUITE, OP300. FL,GUIT   AB
IBERT, J. ENTR'ACTE. FL,GUIT   ALE
JELINEK, H. OLLAPOTRIDA, OP 30 (1957). FL,GUIT   EMO
JENNI, D. MUSIC FOR FRIENDS, #2. FL,GUIT   AMP
JOPLIN, S.-BOYDSTON. ENTERTAINER, THE. FL,GUIT   GS
KAISER, D. RITOURNELLE. FL,GUIT   ALE
KARP(ARR). NINETEENTH CENTURY MASTERPIECES. FL,GUIT   GS
KESSNER, D. 6 APHORISMS. CL,GUIT   BE
KLEBE, G. RECITATIVO, ARIA E DUETTO, OP 44. FL,GUIT   B&B
KOCH, E. VON. CANTO E DANZA (1975). FL,GUIT   STI
KOLZ, E. KLEINE VARIATIONEN. FL,GUIT   LDO

```
KOMTER, J.  ANDANTE IN D MA (REV 1973).  FL,GUIT          SD
KOMTER, J.  DIVERTIMENTO IN G MA (1943).  FL(VN),GUIT      SD
KONT, P.  BALLADE.  FL,GUIT                                LDO
KONT, P.  SUITE EN PASSANT.  FL,GUIT                       EES
KORINEK, M.  KONCERTNA FANTAZIA.  FL,GUIT                  SHF
KOVATS, B.  SONATINA (1948).  OB,GUIT                      EMO
KRATOCHWIL, H.  SUITE, OP101.  FL,GUIT                     LDO
KREJCI, M.  SERENATA.  FL,GUIT                             ART
KRETSCHMAR, W.-BEHREND.  MUSIC IN C MA.  FL,GUIT           WZ
KROPFREITER, A.  TANZ-BALLADE.  FL,GUIT                    LDO
KUFFNER, J.-BEHREND.  DRITTES POTPOURRI, OP103.  FL,GUIT   WZ
KUFFNER, J.  SERENADE.  FL,GUIT                            MV
KUFFNER, J.-HENKE.  2 SERENADES, OP 20, 49.  FL,GUIT       HEI
KUHLAU-RAGOSSNIG.  DIVERTISSEMENT IN G MA, OP 68 #5.  FL,GUIT  RC
KUMMER, G.  NOCTURNE.  FL,GUIT                             FRH
LARUELLE, J.  ESQUISSE & TOCCATA.  FL,GUIT                 S&C
LAUFFENSTEINER, W.-SCHALLER.  DUETTO IN A MA.  FL(OB),GUIT LDO
LECLERC, M.  3 BLUETTES.  FL,GUIT                          HE
LEUKAUF, R.  ALTSPANISCHE SUITE.  FL,GUIT                  HEI
LOCATELLI, P.-BROJER.  SONATA IN G MA.  FL(OB),GUIT        LDO
LOCATELLI, P.-SCHEIT.  SONATA IN G MA.  FL,GUIT            LDO
LOEILLET, J.-BROJER.  SONATA IN A MI, OP  1/1.  OB,GUIT    LDO
LOEILLET, J.-BROJER.  SONATA IN G MA, OP  1/3.  OB,GUIT    LDO
LOEILLET, J.  SUITE IN E MI.  OB(FL),GUIT                  NO
LUCK, H.  KLEINE VORTRAGSSTUCKE.  FL,GUIT                  FRH
MACE, T.-CASTET.  PRELUDE.  FL,GUIT                        ALE
MANCINI, F.-PINSCHOF.  SONATA #4 IN A MI.  FL,GUIT         WZ
MARGOLA, F.  SONATA #4.  FL,GUIT                           GZ
MARTINI, C.  GAVOTTE.  FL,GUIT                             JB
MIGOT, G.  SONATE.  FL,GUIT                                EMT
MOLINO, F.  NOCTURNE #2, OP 38.  FL,GUIT                   BRH
MOLINO, G.-HENZE.  NOCTURNO, OP 37.  FL,GUIT               WZ
MOYSE, L.(TR).  LITTLE PIECES.  FL,GUIT                    GS
MOYZES, A.  SONATINA, OP 75.  FL,GUIT                      SHF
MOZART, W.-BEHREND.  4 KLEINE STUCKE.  FL,GUIT             WZ
MOZART, W.  4 SHORT PIECES.  FL,GUIT                       NO
NODA, T.  NAGARE.  FL,GUIT                                 ALE
OBROVSKA, J.  SUITE IM ALTEN STIL.  FL,GUIT               ART
OCHS, G. (ARR).  NEUES SPIELBUCHLEIN.  FL,GUIT             FRH
OCHS, G. (ARR).  SPIELBUCHLEIN.  FL,GUIT                   FRH
PARIK, I.  EPITAF #2.  FL,GUIT                             SHF
PAUBON, P.  SUITE.  FL,GUIT                                ALE
PELEMANS, W.  KLEIN DUO.  FL,GUIT                          MAU
PEPUSCH, J.-KOVATS.  SONATA.  OB,GUIT                      EES
PEPUSCH, J.-SCHALLER.  SONATA IN D MI.  FL(OB),GUIT        LDO
PEPUSCH, J.-BROJER.  SONATA IN F MA.  FL(OB),GUIT          LDO
PEPUSCH, J.-BROJER.  SONATA IN G MA.  FL(OB),GUIT          LDO
PEPUSCH, J.-SCHEIT.  SONATA IN G MA.  OB,GUIT              LDO
PERGOLESI, G.-KOVATS.  SICILIANO.  OB(FL),GUIT             EES
PESSARD, E.  ANDALOUSE.  FL,GUIT                           BRM
PFISTER, H.  BALLADE.  CL,GUIT                             EUL
PILSS, K.-SCHEIT.  SONATINA (1942).  OB,GUIT              LDO
POSKIN, P.  3 PRELUDES.  FL,GUIT                           MAU
PRAAG, H. VAN.  COMPLAINTE.  OB,GUIT                       B&V
PRAAG, H. VAN.  DUETTINO.  OB,GUIT                         B&V
PRAEGER, H.  INTRODUCTION, THEME AND VARIATIONS.  FL,GUIT  BRH
PRIETO, C.  SOLO A SOLO (1968).  FL,GUIT                   EDA
PURCELL, H.-BEHREND.  SUITE.  FL,GUIT                      HEI
RAUTAVVARA, E.  SONATA.  FL,GUIT                           FIN
RAVEL, M.-KETCHUM/SEGAL.  PIECE EN FORME DE HABANERA.  FL,GUIT  ALE
RECHBERGER, H.  SONATINE.  OB,GUIT                         FIN
REGT, H. DE.  MUSICA, OP 21 (1972).  FL,GUIT              SD
```

REICHARDT, J.-SCHMIDT. 6 PIECES. FL(OB),GUIT	WZ
RICCHI, M.(ARR). FAMOUS SONATAS, 2 VOLS.. FL,GUIT	EBE
RODRIGUEZ, A. IMAGENES DEL SOLITARIO. FL,GUIT	UME
ROREM, N. ROMEO & JULIET. FL,GUIT	BH
ROVICS, H. SERENADE. FL,GUIT	ACA
SAMMARTINI, G. SONATA IN G. OB,GUIT	WZ
SATIE, E.-PELLERITE. GYMNOPEDIES #3. FL,GUIT	ZA
SAUGUET, H. 6 PIECES FACILE. FL,GUIT	ALE
SCHEIT, K.(ARR). LEICHTE STUCKE AUS ALT-ENGLAND. FL,GUIT	LDO
SCHICKELE, P. 3 PIECES. WINDOWS. FL,GUIT	AB
SCHICKELE, P. WINDOWS,(1966). CL,GUIT	AB
SCHMIDT, A. MEISTERWERKE DER ENGLISCHEN KLASSIK (C) FL(OB),GUIT	WZ
SCHNEIDER, O. SUITE, OP 20. FL,GUIT	LDO
SCHRODER, H. MUSIC. FL,GUIT	ROB
SCHUMANN, R. CANCION DE CUNA. FL,GUIT	UME
SCHWARZ, M. SONATINA. FL,GUIT	PM
SHAUGHNESSY, R. DUO. FL,GUIT	SS
SIEGL, O.-RAGOSSNIG. SONATA. FL,GUIT	WZ
SIMONIS, J. NOCTURNE, OP 23 (1972). FL,GUIT	CBD
SINGER, L. MUSICA A DUE (1965). OB,GUIT	ESZ
SPRONGL, N. SUITE. FL,GUIT	EES
STINGL, A. 5 STUCKE, OP 34. FL,GUIT	WZ
SULZER, B. MUSICA TONALIS #2. FL,GUIT	LDO
SUTER, R. MUSIC (1975). FL,GUIT	EUL
TAUTENHAHN, G. ELEGY. FL,GUIT	SS
TELEMANN, G.-CASTET. 9 CANONS MELODIEUX. FL,GUIT	ALE
TELEMANN, G.-KAMMERLING. PARTITA #2 IN G MA. FL(OB),GUIT	LDO
TELEMANN, G.-KAMMERLING. PARTITA #5 IN E MI. FL(OB),GUIT	LDO
TELEMANN, G.-BEHREND. SONATA IN A MI. FL(OB),GUIT	WZ
TELEMANN, G. SONATA IN A MI. FL(OB),GUIT	NO
TELEMANN, G.-WENSIECKI. SONATA IN F MA. FL,GUIT	FRH
TERZAKIS, D. CHRONIKO. FL,ELECGUIT	UE
TILLENIUS, L. INTERLUDIUM IN E MI (1976). FL,GUIT	STI
TOGNI, C. 5 PEZZI (1975/76). FL,GUIT	ESZ
TRUHLAR, J. SONATINA SEMPLICE, OP 18. FL,GUIT	WZ
VACCHI, F. SUITE. FL,AMPLIFIED GUIT	EBE
VAN DEN BROECK, L. SLANGENBEZWEERDER, DE. FL,GUIT	MAU
VAN VACTOR, D. 5 SONGS (1974). FL,GUIT	RR
VERACINI, F.-SCHEIT. LARGO (OP 2/6). FL,GUIT	LDO
VERACINI, F.-SCHALLER. SONATE TERZA. AFL,GUIT	BRH
VILEN, A. UNO PEZZO. FL,GUIT	FIN
VILLA-LOBOS, H. DISTRIBUTION OF FLOWERS. FL,GUIT	BRM
VRIES ROBBE, W. DE. DANSE-ARIOSO-RONDEAU (1973). FL,GUIT	SD
VRIES ROBBE, W. DE. PAVANE-SARABANDE-GIGUE. FL,GUIT	SD
WEISS, F. KLEINE SUITE. FL,GUIT	LDO
WERDIN, E. CAPRIZIOSE IMPRESSIONEN. FL,GUIT	LDO
WESSMAN, H. DUO. FL,GUIT	FIN
WISSMER, P. SONATINA. FL,GUIT	EES
WOLF-FERRARI, E. ITALIAN INTERMEZZO. FL,GUIT	JOW
WORSCHECH, R. 12 GRANDS CLASSIQUES, VOL 1. FL,GUIT	COM
ZANETTOVICH, D. 5 BERCEUSES POPULAIRES. FL,GUIT	ALE
ZBINDEN, J. 4 MINIATURES, OP 14. FL,GUIT	SID
ZEHM, F. SERENADE. FL,GUIT	SCH

```
ABRAMSON, R.  NIGHTPIECE.  FL,PERC                              AMC
AMRAM, D.  HERACLES.  FL,PERC                                   PET
BACK, S.  FAVOLA (1962).  CL,PERC                               WH
BACK, S.  5 PRELUDIER (1966).  CL,PERC                          WH
BECK, J.  MOVIMENTO III (1975).  FL,VIB                         WZ
BREHM, A.  DIALOGUES.  BSN,PERC                                 EES
CABUS, P.  SONATE.  CL,PERC                                     MAU
CHILDS, B.  DAY SEQUENCE, THE: 2.  BCL,PERC                     ACA
CUNNINGHAM, M.  INCANTATION.  AFL,CEL(PF)                       SS
DAHL, I.  DUETTINO CONCERTANTE (1966).  FL,PERC                 AB
DE BERADINIS, J.  INTERLUDE.  -B,VIB                            SS
DE BERADINIS, J.  4 MINIATURES.  FL,VIB                         SS
DUBOIS, P.  CIRCUS PARADE.  ASAX,PERC                           ALE
DVORACEK, J.  MEDITATION.  CL,PERC                              PAN
FINK, S.  IMPRESSION #1.  FL,VIB                                RS
FINK, S.  TRIO OSTINATO.  CL,PERC                              SIM
FROCK, G.  VARIATIONS.  FL,PERC                                 SO
GASTYNE, S. DE.  SUMI-E, OP 74,A.  FL,MAR                       FER
GESENSWAY, L.  8 MINIATURES.  FL,PERC                           TP
GILBERT.  PERCUSSINET.  CL,PERC                                 KN
HARTZELL, E.  MONOLOGUE 5. VARIANTS (1965).  ASAX(TSAX),PERC    LDO
HAZZARD, P.  SONATA #2.  CL,MAR                                 SS
HELBERGER, H.  MUSIC (1978).  CL,VIB                            EHE
HEUSSENSTAMM, G.  DOUBLE SOLO.  CL,PERC                         SS
JENTZSCH, O.  ZUSAMMENGE & UGTES (1969).  OB,PERC              HMO
KEETMAN, G.  STUCKE.  FL,DR                                     SCH
KILLMAYER, W.  3 DANCES.  OB,PERC                               SCH
KOLB, B.  HOMAGE TO K. JARRETT & G. BURTON.  FL,VIB            BH
KOPELENT, M.  CANTO INTIMO (1964).  FL,VIB                      EMO
KRAFT, L.  LINE DRAWINGS.  FL,PERC                              EDK
LA ROSA, M.  THE ANCIENT OF ANCIENTS.  BSN,PERC               SS
LACOUR, G.  DIVERTISSEMENT.  ASAX,PERC                          BIL
LAZAROF, H.  ASYMPTOTES.  FL,VIB                                AMP
MAROS, M.  IZE.  FL,PERC                                        NM
MARTTINEN, T.  ALFA (1962).  FL,PERC                            MT
MYERS, R.  FANTASY DUOS.  ASAX,PERC                             ARM
NAUMANN, S.  RISPOSTE I (1956).  FL,PERC                        ESU
POLOLANIK, Z.  MUSICA SPINGENTA III (1962).  BCL,PERC           ART
RAXACII, E.  IMAGINARY LANDSCAPE (1968).  FL,PERC               SD
REGT, H. DE.  MUSICA OP 12, (1972).  FL,PERC                    SD
SARY, L.  SONANTI #2.  FL/AFL/PIC,PERC                          EMB
SIENNICKI, E.  JOURNEY,.  BSN,PERC                              LMP
TAUTENHAHN, G.  SONATA.  CL,MAR                                 SS
TERPSTRA, K.  PLURI-INTERPRETABLE (1972).  FL,PERC             SD
TOMASI, H.  TOMBEAU DE MIREILLE, LE                             ALE
     FL(OB),TAMBOURINE (DR,PF)
TOWER, J.  BRIMSET.  FL,PERC                                    ACA
URQUHART, D.  PUNCTUS.  FL,PERC                                 SS
VALK, A.  CIRCLES.  ASAX,PERC                                   B&V
VRIES ROBBE, W. DE.  BIRDS (1975).  FL,PERC                     SD
VRIES ROBBE, W. DE.  BLACK BIRDS (1972).  FL,PERC             SD
VRIES ROBBE, W. DE.  PETITS RONDEAUX (1972).  FL,VIB          SD
WALACINSKI, A.  INTROSPECTIONS (1964).  CL,PERC               AP
```

41

2 PARTS INCLUDING TAPE-243

AGER, K. GLASTRAUM. CL/BCL,TAPE	EMO
ANTUNES, J. FLAUTATUALF. FL,TAPE	ESZ
AUSTIN, L. JB, LARRY AND( ). ASAX,TAPE	DOR
AUSTIN, L. QUADRANTS: EVENT COMPLEX #6. FL,TAPE	AB
AUSTIN, L. QUADRANTS: EVENT COMPLEX #7. CL,TAPE	AB
BEERMAN, B. POLYGRAPH #1. CL,TAPE	ACA
BEERMAN, B. POLYGRAPH #3. CL,TAPE	ACA
BEERMAN, B. POLYGRAPH #5. FL,TAPE	ACA
BERLIN, D. INTERACTIONS. FL,TAPE	MAN
BIGGS, J. INVENTION. FL,TAPE	MF
BODIN, L. PRIMARY STRUCTURES (1976). BSN,TAPE	STI
BOOGAARD, B. VAN DEN. KOSMOI (1974-75). OB,TAPE	SD
BOONE, C. COOL GLOW OF RADIATION, A. FL,TAPE	EDS
BOOREN, J. VAN DEN. SPIEL I (1969). OB,TAPE	SD
BOTTJE, W. MODALITIES #2 (1970). CL,TAPE	ECK
BOTTJE, W. 4 PASTORALES OF SEASON AND TIME. FL,TAPE	ACA
BRAUN, P. ESSAY (1960-69). OB,TAPE	HG
BROWN, A. SOUNDSCAPES 3. SAX,TAPE	SS
BRUYNEL, T. DIALOGUE #1 (1976). BCL,TAPE	SD
BRUYNEL, T. INTRA I (1971). BCL,TAPE	SD
BRUYNEL, T. SOFT SONG (1974). OB,TAPE	SD
CORY, E. TEMPI. CL,TAPE	ACA
CUSTER, A. FOUND OBJECTS #6. FL/AFL/PIC,TAPE	GEN
DAVIDOVSKY, M. SYNCHRONISMS #1. FL,TAPE	M&M
DIEMENTE, E. DIMENSIONS #3. SAX,TAPE	SS
DIEMENTE, E. FOR LADY DAY. FL(OB,EHN,CL,SAX,BSN),TAPE	SS
DIEMENTE, E. MIRRORS #5. CL,TAPE	BOW
DITTRICH, P. ACTION-REACTION (1976). OB,TAPE	HG
DOBROWOLSKI, A. MUSICA. OB,TAPE	HMO
DOLIN, S. SONATA #2 (1973). FL,TAPE	CAN
DRUCKMAN, J. ANIMUS #3. CL,TAPE	BH
EISMA, W. PRAU LAS CAGLIAS (1977). VERMEULENFLUTE,TAPE	SD
EVANS, S. EACH TOLLING SUN. ASAX,TAPE,ACTRESS	DOR
FELCIANO, R. NOOSPHERE #1. AFL,TAPE	ECS
FELCIANO, R. SOUNDSPACE FOR MOZART. FL,TAPE	ECS
FRANCO, J. DIPTYCH. FL,TAPE	ACA
FRANCO, J. TRITTICO CAPRICCIOSO. ASAX,TAPE	ACA
FULKERSON, J. PATTERNS #1(1971). FL,TAPE	EMO
GHEZZO, D. MUSIC. FL,TAPE	SS
GRAHN, U. PACE. FL,TAPE	SS
GRANT, J. DUO #1. SAX,TAPE	DOR
GRANT, W. VARIED OBSTINACY. ASAX,TAPE	ACA
GRIPPE, R. ELECTRA GLIDE. CL,TAPE	ER
GRIPPE, R. SITUATION #1 (1976). BCL,TAPE	ER
HANNAY, R. PIED PIPER. CL,TAPE	SS
HANSON, S. PLAY POWER #1 (1976). BCL,TAPE	STI
HELLERMANN, W. ONE INTO ANOTHER. EHN,TAPE	ACA
HEUSSENSTAMM, G. SAXOCLONE (1971). SAX,TAPE	SS
HEWITT, H. SAXERCISES. SAX,TAPE	MAN
HOLLIGER, H. CARDIOPHONIE. 1WW,TAPE	SCH
HORVIT, M. ANTIPHON #2. CL,TAPE	SH
HORVIT, M. ANTIPHON. ASAX,TAPE	DOR
KARKOSCHKA, E. IM DREIECK. FL,TAPE	UE
KOCH, &. 3 DANCE EPISODES. ASAX,TAPE	SS
KORTE, K. DIALOGUE!. ASAX,TAPE	GA

2 PARTS INCLUDING TAPE-243

```
KORTE, K.  REMEMBRANCES.  FL,TAPE                                    EV
LAZAROF, H.  CADENCE #5.(1972).  FL,TAPE                             B&B
LEEUW, T. DE.  MOUNTAINS (1977).  BCL,TAPE                           SD
LORRAIN, D.  ANGELUS (1971), L'.  CL,TAPE                            CAN
LUCAS, T.  METAMUSIC.  FL,TAPE                                       SS
MADERNA, B.  MUSICA SU DUE DIMENSIONI (1957).  FL,TAPE              ESZ
MAMANGAKIS, N.  PARASTASIS.  FL,TAPE                                 HG
MC CLELLAN, R.  OCCURRENCES.  FL,TAPE                                SS
MEFANO, P.  PERIPLES (1978).  SAX,TAPE                              EDS
MICHAEL, F.  OKTOPUS, OP 29/5.  FL,TAPE                              WZ
MICHAELSON, C.  PALAEMON.  CL,TAPE                                  EAM
MICHEL, W.  DEKLAMATION.  FL,TAPE                                   B&N
MICHEL, W.  MULTIPLIKATIONSSPIEL (1975).  FL,ELECTRONIC AIDS        B&N
MILLER, E.  PIECE FOR CLARINET & TAPE.  CL,TAPE                     ACA
MORYL, R.  CHAMBERS #2.  ASAX,TAPE                                  ACA
MOSS, L.  EVOCATION AND SONG.  ASAX,TAPE                             CF
NELSON, L.  FLUTE THING.  FL,TAPE                                    CF
NELSON, L.  MUSIC.  CL,TAPE                                          CF
OAKES, R.  DIALOGUE.  FL,TAPE                                        SS
OLAN, D.  COMPOSITION (1976).  CL,TAPE                              ACA
OLIVE, J.  STUDY #3.  CL,TAPE                                       ACA
PERSSON, B.  FYRHANDIG INVENTION (1966).  FL,TAPE                   STI
PERT, M.  EOASTRION, OP 30.  E FL CL,TAPE                           JOW
PINKHAM, D.  HE SCATTERS THE SNOW.  CL,TAPE                         ECS
PLAETNER, J.  NOCTURNE (1963).  FL,TAPE                              WH
RAUSCH, C.  PARA GERARDO (PHONOS #2).  FL,TAPE                       ZA
RAXACH, E.  CHIMAERA (1974).  BCL,TAPE                               SD
REICHBERGER, H.  MAYENZEIT OHNE NEIDT.  FL,TAPE                      MT
SCHWARTZ, E.  DIALOGUE #2.  CL,TAPE                                  CF
SIEDERT, W.  FLUTE BY FLUTE.  FL,TAPE                               ROB
SKVOR, F.  DUET IN A MI.  FL,HP                                     CHF
STEINKE, G.  4 DESULTORY EPISODES (1972-73).  OB,TAPE               SS
STINE, R.  HEAVEN TREE, THE.  FL,TAPE                                ZA
SULPIZI, F.  LUCANY, OP 25.  FL,TAPE                                EBE
SYDEMAN, W.  PIECE.  CL,TAPE                                         SS
SZATHMARY, Z.  MONOLOG (1971).  FL,TAPE                             HMU
TANENBAUM, E.  TRANSFORMATIONS.  FL,TAPE                            ACA
TROMBLY, P.  KINETICS #3.  FL,TAPE                                  ACA
UNGVARY, T.  AKONEL #2 (1976).  FL,TAPE                              ER
URQUHART, D.  EXCHANGES.  CL,TAPE                                    SS
WHITTENBERG, C.  STUDY.  CL,TAPE                                    ACA
WYATT, S.  FOUR FOR FLUTE.  FL,TAPE                                  ZA
ZONN, P.  SONORUM #3.  PIC,TAPE                                     ACA
```

3 FLUTES-300

ALBISI, A. MINIATURE SUITE #1	CF
ALBISI, A. MINIATURE SUITE #2	CF
ANDERSON, L. PENNY WHISTLE SONG	BE
ANDRE, J. ORIGINAL TRIO, OP 27	BE
ANDRE, J. TRIO, OP 29	EDH
ANDRIESSEN, J. PETIT CONCERT CHAMPETRE	HU
ANDRIEU, J.-DISHINGER. FIFRES, LES	SP
APOTHELOZ, J. PIPEAUX D'ARGENT, LES	EMP
ARENSKY, A.-WOOD. CUCKOO, THE	HE
BACH, J.S.-BERLINSKI. 3 & 4 PART CANONS & ROUNDS	TP
BACH, J.S.-MC LEOD. MY HEART EVER FAITHFUL	S&
BADINGS, H. SUITE #2	HU
BARAB, S. LITTLE SUITE	BH
BARAB, S. SONATINA	BH
BARRERE, G. 2 SHORT PIECES	CF
BARTOK, B.-DISHINGER. DANCE OF THE SLOVAKS	SP
BECK, F. TRIO #1	AMC
BECK, F. TRIO #2	AMC
BEEKUM, J. VAN. MINI TRIOS	HU
BEETHOVEN, L. VAN-SPIEGEL. ALLEGRO FOR A FLUTE CLOCK	OX
PIC,2FL	
BEETHOVEN, L. VAN-ANDRAUD. GRAND TRIO, OP 87	SO
BEETHOVEN, L. VAN-MC LIN. MENUET IN G MA	PO
BEETHOVEN, L. VAN-FETHERSTON. RONDO	BE
BEETHOVEN, L. VAN-FETHERSTON. THEME & VARIATIONS, OP 25	BE
BENJAMIN, T. 4 PIECES	SO
BERBIGUIER, T. 3 GRANDS TRIOS, OP 40/1-3	EDM
BERBIGUIER, T.-WIENANDT. TRIO FOR FLUTES, OP 51/1	SO
BERBIGUIER, T.-WIENANDT. TRIO FOR FLUTES, OP 51/2	SO
BERBIGUIER, T.-WIENANDT. TRIO FOR FLUTES, OP 51/3	SO
BOISMORTIER, J. CARILLON	HEU
BOISMORTIER, J.-KOCH. SONATA IN D MA	MV
BOISMORTIER, J.-BERGMANN. SONATA IN F MA, OP 7/1	S&C
BOISMORTIER, J. SONATA, OP 7/4	BIL
BOISMORTIER, J.-DOFLEIN. 6 SONATAS, OP 7, 2 VOLS	SCH
BOISMORTIER, J. (RAWSKY). SONATA, OP 7/1	BH
BOISMORTIER, J. (RAWSKY). SONATA, OP 7/5	BH
BOOREN, JO VAN DEN. EQUILIBRIO. PIC,FL,AFL	SD
BROOKE, A. THREE MUSKETEERS	CF
BUCHTEL, F. PIPERS 3	KJ
BYRNE, A. INTRODUCTION, BLUES & FINALE	PET
CACAVAS, J. FLUTES 3	CF
CACAVAS, J. SHIMMERING FLUTES	SO
CALL, L. DE. TRIO, OP 31	EDH
CALMEL. CLAIR MATIN-PASTORALE	EV
CAMERON, R. KYRIE (MANTRA)	ZA
CARLS. CELEBRATION	S&
CASTEREDE, J. FLUTES EN VACANCES	ALE
CASTLE, A. FLUTOCYCLE	KN
CAVALLY, R. FLUTE FAMILY SKETCH. PIC,FL,AFL	SO
CHAUBET, G. PRELUDE & JACASSERIE	BIL
CHERUBINI, L.-GODFREY. FUGUE IN G MA	PO
CLASSENS, H. DANZA SCHERZETTINO	COM
CONSTANTINO, J. DANCE OF THE DRESDEN DOLL	PO
CORBEEL, R. SUITE	MAU

3 FLUTES-300

CORELLI, A.-MORRIS. SARABANDE & CORRENTE	PO
COSTANZO-WIENANDT. TRIO #1	SO
COSTANZO-WIENANDT. TRIO #2	SO
COSTANZO-WIENANDT. TRIO #3	SO
COSTANZO-WIENANDT. TRIO #4	SO
COUPERIN, F.-DISHINGER. RONDEAU	SP
CRIST, B. OLD SPANISH MELODY	HE
CRIST, B. TAP DANCE	HE
DEMACHI, G.-STEINBECK. TRIO #1 IN G MA	LDO
DEVIENNE, F.(STEINBECK). TRIO #3 IN C MA	EUL
DEVIENNE, F. TRIO #5	SIM
DEVIENNE, F.-STEINBECK. TRIO IN D MA	EUL
DEVIENNE, F. TRIO	PET
DEVIENNE, F. 6 TRIOS, OP 19, 2 VOLS	EDH
DEVIENNE, F.-RAMPAL. 6 TRIOS, 2 VOLS	BIL
DEVIENNE, F.-WUMMER. 6 TRIOS, 2 VOLS	INT
DIETTER, C.-LIST. 10 STUCKE	FRH
DILLON, R. JUNANBE	BH
DROUET, J. 3 TRIOS, OP 33	EDH
DUFAY, G.-DARVAS. 10 SONGS	EMB
DUSSEK, F.-SCHULTZ/HAUSER. NOTTURNO	SCH
ERDMANN, H. TRIO II	HSM
ERRANTE, B. 3 TRIO ETUDES	SH
FARNABY, R.-DISHINGER. NOBODYES GIGGE	SP
FELD, J. PETIT DIVERTISSEMENT	ALE
FETHERSTON-MORRIS. IN THE FOREST	BE
FILIPPI, A. DE. SERENADE	GEN
FINGER, G.-BERGMANN. SUITE #1	S&C
FINGER, G.-BERGMANN. SUITE #2	S&C
FOSTER-MILLER. TIOGA WALTZ	BE
FRANK, M. 3 GROOVY FLUTES	BO
FUERSTENAU, A.-WUMMER. TRIO, OP118	INT
GABRIELSKY, J.-ANDRAUD. GRAND TRIO, OP 31	SO
GARCIA, M. CANCIONES POPULARES DE ESPANA	JB
GIBBS, C. HARLEQUINADE	PET
GRABNER, H. MUSIC (1956)	KIS
GRAUN, C.-JANETZKY. TRIO	FRH
GRAUPNER, C. SUITE IN F MA	PET
GREAVES, T. DANCE TRIOS	JE
GREAVES, T. FLUTE TRIOS	JE
GRIEG, E.-GUENTHER. GRANDMOTHER'S MINUET	BE
GRUNDMAN, C. FLUTATION	BH
GUBBY, R. SUITE	BH
GUENTHER, R. FOLK DANCE	BE
GUENTHER, R. PETIT RONDEAU, LE	BE
HAAGER, M. MUSIC FOR 3 INSTRUMENTS, OP 6A	AMP
HANDEL, G.-DISHINGER. BOURREE (ROYAL FIREWORKS SUITE)	SP
HANDEL, G.-MC LEOD. EXULTATION	S&
HANDEL, G.-SCHAEFFER. LITTLE FUGUE	PO
HANDEL, G.-DISHINGER. TRIO & MENUET	SP
HAUBIEL, C. IN THE DORIAN MODE	OP
HAUBIEL, C. IN THE LYDIAN MODE	OP
HAUBIEL, C. IN THE PHRYGIAN MODE	OP
HAYDN, F.-ECK. ALLEGRO DECISO. 2FL,AFL(CL)	BD
HAYDN, F.-OSTLING. ALLEGRO GIOCOSO	BE
HAYDN, F.-SCHAEFFER. CONCERTO IN D MA	PO
HAYDN, F.-SPIEGL. FLUTE CLOCK SONATAS	OX
HAYDN, F.-MANIFOLD. 2 PIECES FOR CLOCKWORK ORGAN	AU
HAYDN, F.-TAYLOR. RONDO SCHERZANDO	BE
HAYDN, F.-RAMPAL. 3 TRIOS	INT
HEISS, J. 4 MOVEMENTS	BH
HERMANN, R. FLUTE WILLOW	CF

45

3 FLUTES-300

HODGSON. FANFARES	HI
HOFFMEISTER, F.-HOCKNER. TERZETTO	OHN
HOFFMEISTER, F.-BIBAL. TRIO IN D MA	LDO
HOOK, J. SONATA IN G MA, OP 83/4	BH
HOOK, J.-VOXMAN. 6 TRIOS, OP 83	RU
HOVHANESS, A. SPIRIT OF INK, THE, OP230	PET
HUBER, K.-ARTAUD. OISEAUX D'ARGENT	EMT
HUMMEL, J.-DISHINGER. ALLEGRETTO	SP
JACOBS, G. INTRODUCTION & FUGUE. PIC,FL,AFL	JE
JEMNITZ, S. FLOTENTRIO #2	EMB
KARKOSCHKA, E. IM DREIECK	UE
KEITH, G. SCHERZO & CONTINUO	AMC
KUFFNER, J. TRIO, OP 34	EDH
KUHLAU, F. GRAND TRIO, OP 86, VOL I,, IN G MA	EDK
KUHLAU, F. GRAND TRIO, OP 86, VOL II, IN D MA	EDK
KUHLAU, F. GRAND TRIO, OP 86, VOL III, IN E FL MA	EDK
KUHLAU, F.-RAMPAL. GRAND TRIO, OP 90	INT
KUHLAU, F. GRAND TRIO, OP 90	BIL
KUHLAU, F. GRAND TRIO, OP 90	EDK
KUHLAU, F. 3 GRANDS TRIOS, OP 86, PUB SEPARATELY	BIL
KUHLAU, F.-RAMPAL. TRIO, OP 86/1	INT
KUHLAU, F.-RAMPAL. 3 TRIOS, OP 13	INT
KUHLAU, F. 3 TRIOS, OP 13	BIL
KUMMER, F. TRIO #6, OP 56	EDK
KUMMER, G. CONCERT TRIO, OP 24	EDM
KUMMER, G. TRIO #6, OP 59	WZ
KUMMER, G. TRIO BRILLANT IN D MA, OP 58	CF
KUMMER, G. TRIO BRILLANT, OP 58	EDH
KUMMER, G. TRIO IN A MA, OP 59	CF
KUMMER, G. TRIO IN C MA, OP 53	CF
KUMMER, G. TRIO IN G MA, OP 24	CF
KUMMER, G.-DOEPPLER. TRIO, OP 24	INT
KUMMER, G. TRIO, OP 24	EDH
KUMMER, G. TRIO, OP 30	EDH
LANCEN, S. 12 OLD FRENCH SONGS	PET
LANGLEY, J. TRIO	PET
LARSON. VALSE	TM
LEEUWEN, A. VAN. SONATINA IN THE OLD STYLE	CF
LIADOV, A.-WESTON. MOSQUITO DANCE	HE
LIADOV, A.-WADE. MUSICAL SNUFF BOX	CF
LINKE, N. COLORATURA	HG
LORENZO, L. DE. I TRE VIRTUOSI, OP 31	WZ
MAGANINI, Q. 3 LITTLE KITTENS	EDM
MAGANINI, Q. TRIPLE PLAY	EDM
MARIE, G.-MC LIN. CINQUANTINE, LA	PO
MATTHESON, J.-HUNT. SONATA IN B FL MA, OP 1/6	S&C
MATTHESON, J.-HUNT. SONATA IN C MA, OP 1/5	S&C
MATTHESON, J.-HUNT. SONATA IN C MI, OP 1/4	S&C
MATTHESON, J.-HUNT. SONATA IN F MA, OP 1/8	S&C
MATTHESON, J.-HUNT. SONATA IN F MI, OP 1/10	S&C
MATTHESON, J.-HUNT. SONATA IN G MA, OP 1/7	S&C
MATTHESON, J.-HUNT. SONATA IN G MI, OP 1/3	S&C
MATTHESON, J.-HUNT. SONATA IN G MI, OP 1/9	S&C
MATTHEWS, D. KING'S PIPES, THE	WJ
MC KAY, F. LYRIC POEM	BA
MC KAY, G. 4 SEASONS	BA
MERCADANTE, S. 3 SERENADES	BE
MIEG, P. PIECES POUR 1, 2 & 3 FLUTES	HUG
MORRIS-FETHERSTON. MORNING SCENES	BE
MOZART-VESTER. 5 PIECES	UE
MOZART, W.-GUENTHER. ALLEGRO (DIVERTIMENTO #3, KV229)	SO
MOZART, W.-GUENTHER. ALLEGRO & MENUETTO	BE

MOZART, W.-GUENTHER. ALLEGRO CONCERTANTE	BE
MOZART, W.-GUENTHER. LARGHETTO & MENUETTO	BE
MOZART, W.-GUENTHER. MENUETTO (DIVERTIMENTO #3, KV229)	SO
MOZART, W.-GUENTHER. RONDO	BE
MOZART, W.-VESTER. 5 STUCKE	UE
NELHYBEL, V. CASTLE MUSIC	EAM
NEUMANN, H. GRAND TRIO, OP 14	CF
NOVAK. PANISCI FISTULA (3 PRELUDES)	GZ
OSTLING, A. YANKEE DOODLE DANDIES	BE
PAINTER, P. TRIO (SEMPLICIA)	AMC
PAYNE, F. TOCCATA	SH
PEARSON, W. PASTORELLA	HI
PETZ, J.-SCHULTZ/HAUSER. SYMPHONIA	SCH
PORTER, R. BEAVER CREEK	HE
PRESSER, W. SUITE (1961)	TP
QUANTZ, J.-SALKELD. SONATA A 3	S&C
QUANTZ, J.-LASOCKI. SONATA IN D MA (K 46) & SONATINA IN D MA	NOM
QUANTZ, J.-WUMMER. SONATA IN D MA	INT
QUANTZ, J.-RUF. SONATA IN F MA, OP 3/6	HEI
QUANTZ, J.-DOFLEIN. SONATE IN D MA	B&N
QUANTZ, J. SUITE IN D MA	EUL
QUANTZ, J.-DELIUS. TRIO IN D MA	EUL
RAMEAU, J.-CHAUBET. 2 PIECES	BIL
RAYMOND, L. DIVERTISSEMENT	WI
REICHA, A. TRIO, OP 26	M&M
REIF, P. TRIO (1971)	SS
ROUGERON. 3 PIECES EN TRIO	BIL
ROUSE, C. SUBJECTIVES IX. 3FL,OPT TAPE	ACA
SAGVIK, S. 3 TRIOS, OP 68 (1976)	STI
SCARLATTI, D.-STEIN. 6 SONATAS	MV
SCARMOLIN, A. PETITE SUITE	BA
SCHNEIDER, W. SUITE CAPRICIEUSE	MV
SKOLNIK, W. 3 CANONIC TUNES	EDM
SMITH, R. INTRADA	SH
SOLOMON, E. 2 ESCAPADES	SO
STEFFES, G. HOLIDAYS	HL
STOKER, R. ROUNDS & CANONS	PET
SZERVANSKY, E. TRIO	EMB
TCHAIKOVSKY, P.-GUENTHER. DANCE OF THE REED FLUTES 3FL,PF OPT	SO
TCHAIKOVSKY, P.-OSTLING. DANCE OF THE REED FLUTES	BE
TCHEREPNIN, A. TRIO, OP 59	BEL
THEVET. 100 EXERCICES RYTHMIQUES	ALE
TOMASI, H. 3 PASTORALES	ALE
TULOU, J.-RAMPAL. TRIO, OP 65	INT
WALCKIERS, E. GRAND TRIO, OP 93/1	EDM
WALCKIERS, E. GRAND TRIO, OP 93/2	EDM
WALCKIERS, E. GRAND TRIO, OP 93/3	EDM
WALN, G. (ARR). CLASSIC FANTASY	KJ
WALTER, F. SKIZZEN	WZ
WEISS, F. 5 SKIZZEN	LDO
WIENANDT, E. 3 EASY CANONS	SO
WIGGLESWORTH, F. TRIO	ACA
ZANDER, H. 5 BAGATELLES	MV
ZILLER, D. DIVERTIMENTO IN C MA. 2FL,AFL	BRH

3 FLUTES (COLLECTIONS)-301

CACAVAS, J.(ARR). 30 PLUS-FLUTE TRIOS	BE
ELKAN, H. (ARR). ENSEMBLE TRIO ALBUM	HE
GEARHART, L. (ARR). FLUTE SESSIONS	SH
GUENTHER, R. (ARR). TRIO ALBUM FOR FLUTES	BE
HUDADOFF, I. (ARR). 24 FLUTE TRIOS	PO
SCHAEFFER, D.(ARR). 12 TRIOS	PO
SCHAEFFER, D.(ARR). 10 WOODWIND TRIOS	PO
STUART, H. (ARR). BMCO FAMOUS FLUTE TRIOS	BT
VOXMAN, H. (ARR). CHAMBER MUSIC FOR FLUTES	RU
WYE, T.(ED). FLUTE TRIOS	CHE

3 OBOES-302

AMY, G. JEUX	UE
BACH, J.S.-BERLINSKI. TRIO ALBUM	TP
BERLINSKI, H. CANONS & ROUNDS	TP
BOISMORTIER, J.-DOFLEIN 6 SONATAS, OP 7, 2 VOLS	SCH
BYRNE, A. INTRODUCTION, BLUES & FINALE	PET
CHILDS, B. CHANGES	ACA
ELKAN, H. ENSEMBLE TRIO ALBUM	GA
GIBBS, A. HARLEQUINADE	PET
HODGSON. FANFARES	HI
JACOBSON, I. 3 ODES	BE
KEANE, D. CARPOPHAGOUS CANON #4	LMP
LANCEN, S. OLD FRENCH SONGS	PET
LANGLEY, J. TRIO	PET
MAGANINI, Q. TRIPLE PLAY	EDM
MAGANINI, Q. TROUBADOURS	EDM
RAPHLING, S. SUITE IN MODERN STYLE	EDM
SELLNER, J. 6 EASY EXERCISES	M&M
STOKER. MUSIC FOR 3 OBOES	MC
STOKER, R. ROUNDS & CANONS	PET
TAKAHASHI, Y. OPERATION EULER	PET
THEVET. 100 EXERCICES RYTHMIQUES	ALE

3 CLARINETS-304

ARTOT, J. 12 TRIOS	CF
BACH, C.P.E. ALLEGRO. 2CL,BCL	CST
BACH, C.P.E.-SUTTON. 6 LITTLE MARCHES	NO
BACH, J.S.-BIGELOW. 3 BACH CHORALES	KN
BACH, J.S.-SIMON. BACH FOR THE CLARINET, PART III	GS
BACH, J.S.-SCHWADRON. CANON PERPETUUS	PMP
BACH, J.S. CANONICAL FUGUE. CL,ACL,BCL	EDM
BACH, J.S.-SCHWADRON. FUGA CANONICA. 2CL,BCL	WI
BACH, J.S.-DISHINGER. GAVOTTE (FRENCH SUITE #5). 2CL,BCL(CL)	SP
BACH, J.S.-GUENTHER. GAVOTTE IN G MI	BE

```
BACH, J.S.-COCHRANE.  15 3-PART INVENTIONS.  2CL,BCL(CL)      CF
BACH, J.S.-DISHINGER.  SARABANDE.  2CL,BCL                    SP
BACH, J.S.  SICILIANO                                         EDM
BACH, J.S.-KLEYMEER.  SUITE.  2CL,BCL                         B&V
BACH, J.S.-DANSBY.  TERZETTO (CANTATA #38)                    KN
BANCO, G.  SONATINE                                           EHE
BARAT, J.  PETITS RATONS LAVEURS, LES                        ECH
BARTOK, B.-DISHINGER.  DANCE OF THE SLOVAKS.  CL,ACL,BCL      SP
BARTOS, J.  DIVERTIMENTO #7                                   FS
BEEKUM, J. VAN.  PREMIERE                                     HU
BEEKUM, J. VAN.  2 SONATINAS                                  HU
BEEKUM, J. VAN.  TRIPHONIA                                    HU
BEETHOVEN, L. VAN-WALN.  ADAGIO CANTABILE (OP 87)             KJ
BEETHOVEN, L. VAN-HARRIS.  ALLEGRETTO (TRIO, OP  2)           CF
BEETHOVEN, L. VAN-HENRIED.  ALLEGRO (OP 87)                  WB
BEETHOVEN, L. VAN-LOTTERER.  MENUETT & FINALE, OP 87         FS
BEETHOVEN, L. VAN-VOXMAN.  MENUETTO & FINALE (OP 87)         RU
BEETHOVEN, L. VAN.  MINUET IN G MA                           CF
BEETHOVEN, L. VAN-MERRIMAN.  PRELUDE & FUGUE.  2CL,BCL       SO
BEETHOVEN, L. VAN-WALN.  PRESTO (OP 87)                      KJ
BEETHOVEN, L. VAN-GORDON.  SCHERZO (TRIO, OP 87).  2CL,BCL(CL) KJ
BEETHOVEN, L. VAN-HARRIS.  TRIO (ADAGIO CANTABILE), OP 87    CF
BEETHOVEN, L. VAN.  TRIO IN E FL MA                          MOL
BEETHOVEN, L. VAN-SUTTON.  TRIO, OP 87                       NO
BERGENFELD.  CHROMA-TRIX                                     TM
BERGENFELD.  TWO MOODS                                       TM
BERLINSKI, H.  CANONS & ROUNDS                              TP
BIGGS, J.  3 CANZONI                                        CPR
BOEHM, T.-DISHINGER.  PRESTO                                SP
BOOREN, J. VAN DEN.  SONATA (1962)                          SD
BOUFFIL, J.  GRAND TRIO, OP  8                              CF
BOUFFIL, J.  TRIO, OP  8/1                                  EDK
BOUFFIL, J.-NUDERA.  TRIOS                                  EDK
BOUFFIL, J.  3 TRIOS, OP  7, PUB SEPARATELY                 CF
BOUFFIL, J.-GETSPIELER.  3 TRIOS, OP  7                     BIL
BOUFFIL, J.-JANETZKY.  3 TRIOS, OP  8                       FRH
BRANDENBURG.  ASH GROVE, THE                                CF
BRENET.  MELANCOLIE                                         EV
BROOKS, K.  10 TRIOS FOR DEVELOPING CLARINET TECHNIQUE      BH
BROWN, J.  CHALUMEAU CANONS                                 TP
BROZAK, D.  KOROZE (1977)                                   SD
BUCHTEL, F.  COMRADES                                       BA
BUECHE, G.  FUGUE                                           CF
BURTON-DISHINGER.  ALLEGRETTO                               SP
BUSCH, C.  CONTENTMENT                                      CF
BUSCH, C.  FROLIC                                           CF
BUSCH, C.  JOYFULNESS                                       CF
BUSCH, C.  SOLITUDE                                         CF
BUTTERWORTH, N.  THREE TIMES THREE                          CA
BUTTS, C.  DESERT DANCES                                    PO
BYRNE, A.  INTRODUCTION, BLUES & FINALE                     PET
CACAVAS, J.  CLARINETS 3                                    CF
CALMEL.  PETITE MARCHE-CHANSON D'AUTOMNE                    EV
CARROLL, B.  VELOCITY                                       AU
CHANDLER.  EUDORA                                           PO
CHERUBINI, L.-DE KLERK.  CANON                              HE
CLARKE, R.  SCHERZANDO                                      MAN
CLEBER-FRANK.  RICKSHAW RIDE                                SF
CLEMENTI-KUHLAU/TERVOORT.  TRIO                             MOL
COHEN, S.  HAUNTED HOUSE                                    BE
COHEN, S.  MADRIGAL.  2CL,BCL                               BE
COLBY.  THREE BLIND MICE                                    WB
```

CONSTANTINO, J. 3 FUGUES	PO
CONSTANTINO, J. PASSACAGLIA	PO
COOKE, A. SUITE	OX
COUPERIN, F.-DISHINGER. RONDEAU. 2CL,BCL(CL)	SP
COUPERIN, F.-BALENT. TRIO SONATA	PO
COX, C. DIVERTISSEMENT	HE
COX, C. PRELUDE	HE
DANCLA, C.-WALN. TUNEFUL TRIO	KJ
DANDRIEU, J.-DISHINGER. FIFRES, LES	SP
DANDRIEU, J.-SEAY. TOURBILLONS, LES. 2CL,BCL	SPR
DE SCHRIJVER, K. SUITE A 3	HE
DERVAUX. ADAGIO	BIL
DEVIENNE, F. TRIO	HE
DONATO, A. 3 PIECES	TP
DUBANOWICZ, W. MUSICAL PICTURES	PWM
DUFAY, G.-DARVAS. 10 SONGS	EMB
ENDRESEN, R. WOODWIND MOODS	RU
ENDRESEN, R. WOODWIND REVELS	RU
ERRANTE, B. TERZETTO IN G MI	PO
EYSER, E. SERENATA (1973)	STI
EYSER, E. TRIOLETTO (1973)	STI
FABER, J. 6 MELODIES IN ANCIENT STYLE	CF
FABER, J.-HUNT. SUITE, "PARTIES SUR LES FLEUNT DOUS A 3"	S&C
FELDERHOF, J. TRIO (1968)	SD
FLEMING, R. 2-PIECE SUITE, A (1958). 2CL,BCL	CAN
FORSYTH, M. MELANCHOLY CLOWN, THE (1967). E FL CL,CL,BCL	ECK
FOURCHOTTE. MARCHE	BIL
FRANGKISER, C. LAVIOLETTES, LES	BH
FUCHS, F. MUSIC, OP 94	LK
FURSTENAU, A.-WIENANDT. 3 TRIOS (PUB SEPARATELY)	SO
FUSSELL, C. 3 INVENTIONS (1959). E FL CL,CL,BCL	CAN
GALUPPI, B.-DISHINGER. GIGA	SP
GARLICK, A. 2 TRIOS	SS
GARUN, C.-DE SMET. TRIO	OX
GAY, E. 15 MINATURES, 2 VOLS	BIL
GAY, E. 10 PETITES PIECES CLASSIQUES, 2 VOLS	BIL
GEE, H. FUGUE IN BAROQUE STYLE	PO
GIBBONS, O. FANTASIA FOR 3	EDM
GIBBS, A. HARLEQUINADE	PET
GLASER, W. FYRA KORTA STYCKEN	NOR
GLOBOKAR, V. DISCOURS IV	PET
GLUCK, C. GAVOTTE	CF
GORDON, P. CALLING ALL CLARINETS	KJ
GOSSEC, F.-PHILLIPS. TAMBOURIN	KN
GRAUPNER, C.-HUNT. SUITE #1	S&C
GRAUPNER, C.-HUNT. SUITE #2	S&C
GRUDZINSKI, C.-KURKIEWICZ. PRELUDE & FUGUE	PWM
GUENTHER, R. CANZONE AMABILE	BE
HALLORAN, D. 5 MINIATURES	SO
HALLORAN, D. TRIO	SO
HANDEL, G.-MORRIS. BAROQUE TUNE	PO
HANDEL, G.-DISHINGER. BOURREE (ROYAL FIREWORKS SUITE) 2CL,BCL	SP
HANDEL, G. BOURREE	CF
HANDEL, G.-LAWTON. OVERTURE IN C MA	OX
HANDEL, G.-WILLIAMS. SONATA	SO
HANDEL, G. SONATA IN D MA	TP
HANDEL, G.-DISHINGER. TRIO & MENUET	SP
HARVEY, P. 4 EASY TRIOS	S&C
HASSLER, H.-LEONARD. 2 SHORT PIECES	BE
HAUPTMANN-EVERTSE. TRIO	T-M
HAYDN, F.-HARRIS. ADAGIO (SYMPHONY # 99)	KPM

```
HAYDN, F.-SUTTON.  4 CLOCK PIECES                               NO
HAYDN, F.-MERRIMAN.  DIVERTIMENTO.  2CL,BCL                     SO
HAYDN, F.-VOXMAN.  DIVERTIMENTO IN E FL MA                      RU
HAYDN, F.-LOTTERER.  DIVERTIMENTO IN F MA                       FS
HAYDN, F.-VOXMAN.  MENUET & ALLEGRO                             RU
HAYDN, F.  MINUETTO (DIVERTIMENTO #1)                           PO
HAYDN, F.-MANIFOLD.  2 PIECES FOR CLOCKWORK ORGAN               AU
HERBERT, V.-OSTLING.  MELODIES MODISTE                          BE
HEUGTEN, H. VAN.  MELODIC STUDIES                               HU
HODGSON.  FANFARES                                             HI
HOLM, P.  TO SVENSKE VISER                                      WH
HOLM, P.  VIDEVIDEVIT                                           WH
HOLM, P.  VILDGAESSENE                                          WH
HOOK, J.  SONATA                                               HE
HOOK, J.-CURWIN.  SONATINAS                                     CA
HOOK, J.-CURWIN.  SUITE FOR 3                                   CA
HOVHANESS, A.  ST NERSES THE GRACEFUL                           AB
HUBNER, W.  BRUMMKREISEL, DER                                   EDK
HUMMEL-HAYDN/DISHINGER.  2 ALLEGRETTOS                          SP
HUMMEL, J.F.  TRIO IN B FL MA                                   SIM
JABLONSKI, H.  3 MINIATURES                                     PWM
JANNOCH, H.  BRUMMKREISEL, DER.  3CL,PF AD LIB                  FRH
JETTEL, R.  MODERNE KLARINETTIST IN PRAXI, DER, 17 STUDIEN      JOW
JETTEL, R.  THEMA & VARIATIONEN                                 LDO
KABALEVSKY, D.-SCHAEFFER.  DANCE (OP 27)                        PO
KABALEVSKY, D.-SCHAEFFER.  PARADE                               PO
KANETSCHEIDER, A.  SERENADE NACH DEUTSCHEN VOLKSLIEDERN         EHE
KARG-ELERT, S.-WALN.  TRIO IN D MI                              KJ
KATZ, E.  3 CANONIC DANCES                                      SF
KOLASINSKI, J.  LITTLE SUITE                                    PWM
KOLB, B.-BROWN.  VERSETS.  2CL,BCL                              WI
KONIG, H.  5 KLEINE SATZE                                       PGM
KONIG, H.  KLEINE SUITE                                         LDO
KRATOCHVIL, J.  SUITE                                           ES
KROMMER, F.-MYSLIK.  VARIATIONS ON A THEME OF PLEYEL            EK
KUHMSTEDT, P.  MIKRONETTEN                                      MV
KUMMER, G.  TRIO, OP 24                                         CF
KUMMER, G.  TRIO, OP 53                                         CF
KUMMER, G.  TRIO, OP 58                                         CF
KUMMER, G.  TRIO, OP 59                                         CF
KURTZ, S.  SUITE                                               LYA
LAMB, P.  PASTORAL                                             BH
LANCEN, S.  OLD FRENCH SONGS                                    PET
LANGLEY, J.  TRIO                                              PET
LEONARD.  SARABANDE & WALTZ                                     BE
LESTER, L.  3 PIECES                                           WI
LINN, R.  FANFARES                                             SH
LOEFFLER, E.  HEITERE TANZSUITE                                 FS
LOEFFLER, E.  SPIELMUSIK                                        FS
LOEVENDIE, T.  3 PEZZI (1968)                                   SD
LOTTI, A.-EVERTSE.  VERE LANGUORUS                              T-M
LUBIN, E.  SCHERZO #1                                           SF
LUIGI'S POLKA.                                                 SLP
LULLY, J.-DISHINGER.  GAVOTTE                                   SP
MAGANINI, Q.  3 LITTLE KITTENS                                  EDM
MAGANINI, Q.  TRIPLE PLAY                                       EDM
MAGANINI, Q.  TROUBADOURS                                       EDM
MARCO, T.  HOQUETUS (1973)                                      EEC
MARIE, G.-MC LIN.  CINQUANTAINE, LA                             PO
MATTHEUS LE MAISTRE-EVERTSE.  DOMINUS NOSTER CASTELLUM          T-M
MC KAY, F.  AT THE PUPPET SHOW                                  BA
MC KAY, F.  BLUE TAPESTRY                                       BA
```

MC KAY, F. TRAIL TO SUNNY POINT	BA
MELILLO, P. CLARINET TRIO	AMC
MENDELSSOHN, F. LIFT THINE EYES & CAST THY BURDEN	KJ
MEYER. VARIATIONS SUR UN THEME CLASSIQUE. 3CL(FL OR OB,2CL)	ALE
MICHALSKY, D. DIVERTIMENTO. CL,ACL,BCL	WI
MIHALOVICI, M. SONATA, OP 35. E FL CL,CL,BCL	EDS
MILLER, E. 3 PIECES	M&M
MILLS, D. MARCH, MADRIGAL & SCHERZO	BE
MORITZ, E. DIVERTIMENTO	TP
MOZART-GRIEG/TCHAIKOVSKY/GEE. 3 TRIOS	PO
MOZART, W. 2 ADAGIOS	OX
MOZART, W.-WHEWELL. DIVERTIMENTI	OX
MOZART, W.-GEE. DIVERTIMENTO #4, K439B	SP
MOZART, W. ECCO QUEL FIERO ISTANTE, K436. 2CL,BCL	GS
MOZART, W. MI LAGNERO TACENDO, K437. 2CL,BCL	GS
MOZART, W.-OSTLING. MINUET & TRIO	BE
MOZART, W.-NEUFELD. SERENADE IN B FL MA	WI
MOZART, W.-DE KORT. SONATINE	T-M
MOZART, W.-FINCH. 2 THEMES & VARIATIONS, K547, K547A	OX
MOZART, W.-DAHM. TRIO. 2CL,BCL(BSN)	VO
MULLER, J. COMPTINES	MAU
NELHYBEL, V. RUSTIC DANCES	EAM
NELHYBEL, V. 9 TRIOS FOR CLARINET	BE
NEUMANN, F. 5 STUCKE	LDO
NORDEN, H.-MC CATHREN. MINIATURE SUITE	BA
NUDERA, A. 2 DIVERTIMENTOS	EDK
OPITZ, E. SONATINE	FS
OSTLING, A. ALOUETTE CLARINETTE	BE
OSTRANDER. SUITE FOR 3	EDM
PALA, J. PRELUDE & SCHERZO	HE
PARADIES, P.-DISHINGER. GRAZIOSO	SP
PARTITA.	FRH
PATACHICH, I. 4 STUCKE	FS
PEDLEY, D. 5 FOLK TUNES	KPM
PELZ, W. THREE OF A KIND	BE
PHILLIPS, I. 6 SHORT ARRANGEMENTS	OX
PIKET, F. LEGEND & JOLLITY	SF
PLEYEL, I.-PAULSON. TRIO IN C MA	PO
PLEYEL, I.-HARRIS. 6 TRIOS (OP 8)	CF
POLK, M. 3 SHORT DIALOGUES	SH
POOT, M. TERZETTO	ALE
PRAAG, H. 4 SHORT PIECES (1968). 2CL,BCL	SD
PRESSER, W. 3 ROUNDS	TP
PRESSER, W. 3 WHITE SPIRITUALS	TRI
PURCELL, H. CHACONNE	EDM
RAMEAU, J.-DE FILIPPI. HEN, THE. 2CL,BCL	HE
REGNER, H. HEITERES IDYLL	PGM
REGNER, H. MUSIKALISCHE BILDER	PGM
REGNER, H. 8 SPIELSTUCKE	MV
REID, A. SKETCHES OF YOUTH	KN
RUELLE, F. ROMANCE	EBR
RUSSEL-SMITH, G. ALICE & THE MAD HATTER	BH
RUSSELL, A. TRIO IN E FL MA. E FL CL,CL,BCL	RH
RYAN, P. (ARR). 3 COUPERIN MOVEMENTS	CA
SAEYS, E. LENTO & ALLEGRO	MAU
SAMYN, N. 5 TRIOS, PUB SEPARATELY	BIL
SAVAGE. MOMENTO GIOJOSO	CF
SCARLATTI-SCHWADRON. PASTORALE. 2CL,BCL	KN
SCARLATTI-WALN. PASTORALE	KJ
SCARLATTI-DE JESU. SONATA #1	HL
SCARLATTI-DE JESU. SONATA #2	HL
SCARLATTI-DE JESU. SONATA #3	HL

SCARLATTI-DE JESU. SONATA ALLEGRISSIMO	HL
SCHAEFFER, D. ENCORE	PO
SCHAEFFER, D. (ARR). ANCIENT FUGUE	PO
SCHALK, C. RICERCARE ON AN OLD ENGLISH MELODY	CON
SCHEIFFES, H. 4 SHORT PIECES FROM OLD MASTERS	HE
SCHNEIDER. ALTHOLLANDISCHE TANZ-SUITE	B&N
SCHNEIDER, W. ERSTES KLARINETTENSPIEL	SCH
SCHRAMM, H. EPISODES	AMC
SCHUBERT, F.-DISHINGER. GERMAN DANCE. CL,ACL,BCL	SP
SCHUBERT, F.-DISHINGER. MENUETTO	SP
SCHUBERT, F. TRIO MOVEMENT	GAL
SCHWADRON, A. PROGRESSIVE ENSEMBLE STUDIES, VOL II	KN
SEEGER, P. KLARINETTENMUSIK	FS
SEEGER, P. 7 SPIELSTUCKE	PGM
SEMLER-COLLERY, J. TERZETTO	EES
SERINI, G.-PILGRIM. ARIA & GIUGE	BH
SHANKS, E. SONATA OF MOODS & HUMORS	WB
SIENNICKI, E. ACT III	BA
SIMPSON, J. DIVERTIMENTO	KPM
SIQUIET, C. MENUET	MAU
SKOLNIK, W. 3 CANONIC TUNES	EDM
SNAVELY, J. WOODWIND SERENADE	PO
SOBAJE, M.(ARR). GREENSLEEVES	KN
STARER, R. SERENADE	SN
STEIN, L. TRIO	TP
STEKL, K. MUSICA SEMISERIA, OP 92	FS
STIEBLER, E. STADIEN (1964). E FL CL,CL,BCL	EMO
STOKER, R. ROUNDS & CANONS	PET
STOUFFER, D. TOCCATA	PO
TARTINI, G. 2 TRIO SONATAS	EDM
TCHEREPNIN, A. MARCH FOR 3 TRUMPETS	EM
TCHEREPNIN, A. TRIO	EM
TERMOS, P. SEMANTIC HEDONISM (1976)	SD
TERVOORT, L. HOFMANNIANA	HE
THEVET. 100 EXERCICES RYTHMIQUES	ALE
THOMPSON (ED). 7 PIECES FROM A MUSIC BOOK OF 1826	AMP
TORRENGA, B. TRIO (1978). 2CL,BCL/BSN	SD
TOWNSEND, D. BALLET SUITE	PET
TRIEBENSEE, J. TRIO IN B FL MA	EK
TUTHILL, B. INTERMEZZO. 2CL,ACL	CF
TUTHILL, B. SCHERZO	CF
TUTHILL, B. TRIO	SPR
VAN SLYCK, N. 12 FOR 3 (1973). 2CL,BCL	SO
VERRALL, J. INTRODUCTION & RONDINO	ACA
VERRALL, J. SUITE	ACA
VIVALDI, A. SONATA DA CAMERA	EDM
VOGT, G.-VOXMAN. ADAGIO RELIGIOSO	RU
WALKER, R. JEUNESSE	BE
WALKER, R. RONDO SCHERZANDO	PO
WALKER, R. SCHERZINO	TM
WALKER, R. TRIO IN B FL MA	BE
WALKER, R. TRIO IN D MI	CRE
WALTER, F. 6 STUCKE, 2 VOLS	WZ
WATERSON, J. GRAND TRIO CONCERTANTE #1 IN G MI	CF
WATERSON, J. GRAND TRIO CONCERTANTE #1	BH
WEELKES. GAY TUNE, A	EDM
WEIJERS, J. CONCERTINO	T-M
WELANDER, S. PRELUDIUM (1961)	STI
WENTH, J.-MYSLIK. PETITE SERENADE CONCERTANTE	EK
ZACHAU, F.-DISHINGER. CHORALE	SP
ZEISL, E. GREEK MELODY	BE
ZENONI, B.-SMIM. SINFONIA A TRE	EDM

3 CLARINETS (COLLECTIONS)-305

BOURNE (ARR). BOURNE TRIO ALBUM	BO
BROOKS, K.(ARR). CLASSICAL ALBUM	BH
CACAVAS, J.(ARR). 30 PLUS-CLARINET TRIOS	BE
CLARINET TRIOS.	CA
DELGIUDICE, M.(ARR). 20 DUOS & TRIOS FACILES & PROGRESSIFS	EDR
ELKAN, H. (ARR). ENSEMBLE TRIO ALBUM	HE
GAY, E.(ARR). 18 GRANDS MORCEAUX CLASSIQUES EN TRIOS, 2 VOLS	BIL
GAY, E.(ARR). 15 MINIATURES, 2 VOLS	BIL
GAY, E. (ARR). 10 PETITES PIECES CLASSIQUES	B&V
GEARHART, L. (ARR). CLARINET SESSIONS	SH
HAUGHTON, P.(ARR). 10 CLARINET TRIOS	OX
HAUGHTON, P. (ARR). 12 CLARINET TRIOS	OX
KNIGHT, V. (ARR). 10 TRIOS	GS
KRATOCHVIL, J. (ED). TRIOS TSCHECHISCHER KLASSIKER	ES
LAWTON, S.(ARR). CLARINET TRIOS	OX
LETELLIER, R. 14 NOUVEAUX DUOS & TRIOS	EDR
LETELLIER, R. RECUEIL DE DUOS & TRIOS	EDR
MULLER-MEDEK, W. (ARR). KLEINE STUCKE ALTER MEISTER, 2 VOLS	PGM
ROSENTHAL, C.(ARR). CLARINET TRIOS (18TH CENTURY)	EM
ROSENTHAL, C.(ARR). CLARINET TRIOS FROM CORELLI TO BEETHOVEN	EM
ROSENTHAL, C.(ARR). CLARINET TRIOS-RUSSIAN	EM
SCHAEFFER, D. (ARR). CLARINET TRIO ALBUM	PO
SCHAEFFER, D. (ARR). ENCORE (12 TRIOS)	PO
SCHNEIDER, W.(ARR). TRIOSPIEL NACH ALTEN MEISTERN	MV
SCHNEIDER, W. (ARR). ALLERLEI ALTE MARSCHWEISEN, 2 VOLS	PGM
SCHWADRON, A.(ARR). PROGRESSIVE ENSEMBLE STUDIES, VOL 2	KN
STUART, H. CLARINET CLASSICS	SH
VERRALL, P. CAMEOS FOR CLARINET	KPM
VERRALL, P. CLARINETS IN CHORUS	RS
VERRALL, P. CLARINETS IN CONCERT	KPM
VOXMAN, H. (ARR). CHAMBER MUSIC FOR 3 CLARINETS, 2 VOLS	RU
WESTON, P.(ARR). 8 CLARINET TRIOS	S&C

3 BASSOONS-306

ALFVEN, H. BOURREE	CGM
BACH, J.S.-MILLER. CHORALES, 2 VOLS	EP
BACH, J.S.-BERLINSKI. TRIO ALBUM	TP
BERGT, A. TRIO	FRH
BOZZA, E. DIVERTISSEMENTS	ALE
BUEL, C. 4 3-PART CANONS (1978)	OJE
CHASE, A. 4 TRIOS	COR
DONDEYNE. POUR SE DIVERTIR	BIL
DUBOIS. OUVERTURE, SERENADE AMICALE	BIL
DUBOIS. SARABANDE POUR UNE TORTUE. PASSEPORT DU GALANT	BIL
GIBBONS, O. SILVER SWAN, THE	AM
HAAN, S. DE. MARCH- WALTZ- QUASI ADAGIO	HI
HARTLEY, G. BASSOON TRIO	JE
HARTLEY, G. ROUND THE MULBERRY BUSH	JE
JACOBSON. 3 BAGATELLES	BE
KUMMER, G.-GLASENAPP/KARL. 24 TRIOS, OP 11 & 13	FRH

```
MATEJ, J.   10 DREISTIMMIGE INVENTIONEN                      ES
MULDER, E.   TRIO IN CONTRAPUNTISCHE STIJL (1942)           SD
PRESSER, W.   TRIO                                          TRI
SNOSKO-BOROVSKY, A.   SCHERZO, OP. 13                       INT
SURDIN.   A LA BASSOON                                      CAN
VACHEY, H.   MENUET                                         ALE
VRIES ROBBE, W. DE.   VARIATIONS                            SD
WALTER, F.   TROLLERIEN                                     WZ
```

3 SAXOPHONES-308

```
ALBRIGHT, W.   DOO-DAH.   3ASAX                                      DOR
BACH, J.S.-SCHMIDT.   FUGUE XXI.   SOP SAX,ASAX,BAR SAX              WI
BACH, J.S.-DEDRICK.   3 PART INVENTION #8                           KN
   SOP SAX,ASAX,BAR SAX
BACH, J.S.-ALEXANDER.   PRAELUDIUM IX                               S&
BARAT, J.   PORCELAINES DE SAXE, LES.   3ASAX                       ECH
BARTOK, B.-DISHINGER.   DANCE OF THE SLOVAKS.   2ASAX,TSAX          SP
BAUZIN, P.   DIVERTIMENTO.   2ASAX,TSAX                             HLE
BEETHOVEN, L. VAN(HILTON).   CI DAREM LA MANO, LA                   RD
BEETHOVEN, L. VAN.   FUGUE.   2ASAX,TSAX¬                           EDM
BEETHOVEN, L. VAN-TEAL.   TRIO, OP 87                               EQM
   SOP SAX(ASAX),ASAX(TSAX),TSAX(BAR SAX)
BERTOUILLE, G.   PRELUDE & FUGUE (1955).   SOP SAX,ASAX,BAR SAX     CBD
BEVIN-RIPPE.   BROWNING.   ASAX,TSAX,BAR SAX                        DOR
BOEHM, T.-DISHINGER.   PRESTO.   2ASAX,TSAX                         SP
BOURNE-LEIDZEN.   BOURNE TRIO ALBUM.   2ASAX,TSAX                   BO
BOUVARD, J.-GOURDET.   4 DANSES                                     BIL
BOUVARD, J.   12 PIECES BREVES                                      BIL
BRENET, T.   FLANERIE.   2ASAX,ASAX(BAR SAX)                        EV
BROSH, T.   MISTERIOSO.   2ASAX,TSAX                                MAN
BROWN, A.   SURFACE TEXTURES.   2ASAX,TSAX                          SS
BROWN, R.   FUGUE.   ASAX,TSAX,BAR SAX                              WI
BUSCHMANN, R.   EINFACH FUR DREI.   2ASAX,TSAX                      FS
BUTTS, C.   MODERATO & ALLEGRO.   3ASAX                             SH
BUTTS, C.   MODERATO & SCHERZO.   2ASAX,ASAX(TSAX)                  KN
BUTTS, C.   TRIO.   3SAX                                            PO
CECCONI, M.   AUBADE- DANSE.   3ASAX                                EV
CHERUBINI, L.-DE KLERK.   CANON.   SOP SAX,ASAX,TSAX                HE
CHERUBINI, L.   CANON.   SOP SAX,ASAX,TSAX                          MOL
CLARK.   SEICENTO.   2ASAX,TSAX                                     EDM
COUPERIN, F.-DISHINGER.   RONDEAU.   2ASAX,TSAX                     SP
CRAEN, N.-RIPPE.   ST. ASCENDERO IN GAELUM.   ASAX,TSAX,BAR SAX     DOR
DEPELSENAIRE, J.   DIVERTISSEMENT.   3ASAX                          COM
DORN, K.(ARR).   PAVAN.   ASAX,                                     DOR
DORN, K.(ARR).   SI DORMIERO.   ASAX,TSAX,BAR SAX                   DOR
DORN, K.(ARR).   TART ARA.   ASAX,TSAX,BAR SAX                      DOR
FARNABY, R.-DISHINGER.   NOBODYES GIGGE                             SP
GEE, H.   FUGUE IN BAROQUE STYLE.   2ASAX,TSAX                      PO
GIBBONS, O.-CLARK.   FANTASIA FOR 3.   2ASAX,TSAX                   EDM
GIBBS, A.   HARLEQUINADE.   3SAX                                    PET
HANDEL, G.-DISHINGER.   BOURREE.   2ASAX,TSAX                       SP
HANDEL, G.-DISHINGER.   TRIO & MENUET.   2ASAX,TSAX                 SP
HAUPTMANN, M.   TRIO.   SOP SAX,ASAX,TSAX                           HE
HAYDN, F.-DISHINGER.   GAVOTTE.   2ASAX,TSAX                        SP
HOOK, J.-GEE.   ANDANTE & RONDO (TRIO #6).   2ASAX,TSAX(ASAX)       PO
HOOK, J.-VOXMAN.   6 TRIOS.   3SAX                                  RU
HUMMEL, J.-DISHINGER.   GAVOTTE.   ASAX,TSAX,BAR SAX                SP
```

```
ISAAC, H.  BENEDICTUS.  ASAX,TSAX,BAR SAX                    DOR
LAMB, J.  MADRIGAL                                           AMP
LETELLIER, R.  PIECE RECREATIVE.  3ASAX(3TSAX)              EDR
LOTTI, A.-EVERTSE.  VERE LANGUORUS.  2ASAX,TSAX             T-M
MAGANINI, Q.  3 LITTLE KITTENS.  3SAX                       EDM
MAGANINI, Q.  TRIPLE PLAY.  3SAX                            EDM
MAGANINI, Q.  TROUBADORS.  2ASAX,TSAX                       EDM
MAILLOT, J.  TRIO.  ASAX,TSAX,BAR SAX                       EFM
MATTHEUS LE MAISTRE-EVERTSE.  DOMINUS NOSTER CASTELLUM      T-M
   2ASAX,TSAX
MORLEY, T.-DISHINGER.  ALMAN                                SP
MOZART, W.  AVE VERUM CORPUS.  2ASAX,TSAX                   EDM
MOZART, W.-DE KORT.  SONATINE.  3SAX                        T-M
MOZART, W.  SONATINE.  SOP SAX,ASAX,TSAX                    MOL
MURPHY.  NOTTURNO.  ASAX,TSAX,BAR SAX                       WI
OSTRANSKY, L.  3 MINIATURES.  2ASAX,TSAX                    RU
OSTRANSKY, L.  PEASANT DANCE.  2ASAX,TSAX                   RU
OSTRANSKY, L.  2 PORTRAITS.  2ASAX,TSAX                     RU
PARADIES, P.-DISHINGER.  GRAZIOSO                           SP
PRESSER, W.  TRIO.  2ASAX,TSAX                              TRI
PURCELL, H.-ROSENTHAL.  FANTASIA #3.  ASAX,TSAX,BAR SAX     WI
RAPHLING, S.  SUITE IN MODERN STYLE.  3SAX                  EDM
RIPPE, A.(ARR).  KATZENPFOTE, DIE.  ASAX,TSAX,BAR SAX       DOR
SCARLATTI-ALEXANDER.  SONATA IN C MA                        S&
SCHONFELDER-RIPPE.  MICH HAT GROB UMBEGEN.  ASAX,TSAX,BAR SAX  DOR
SKOLNIK, W.  3 CANONIC TUNES.  2ASAX,TSAX                   EDM
TAYLOR, P.  BACH GOES TO SEA.  ASAX,TSAX,BAR SAX            JE
THEVET.  100 EXERCICES RYTHMIQUES                           ALE
TOEBOSCH, L.  THEMA MET VARIATIES, OP 42 (1952).  3SAX      SD
VOGT, G.  ADAGIO RELIGIOSO                                  BIL
ZENONI, B.  SINFONIA A TRE.  ASAX,TSAX,BAR SAX              EDM
```

3 SAXOPHONES (COLLECTIONS)-309

```
GEE, H.(ARR).  12 SAXOPHONE TRIOS.  2ASAX,ASAX(TSAX)        PO
LETELLIER, R.  14 NOUVEAUX DUOS & TRIOS                     EDR
LETELLIER, R.(ARR).  RECUEIL DE DUOS ET TRIOS              EDR
VOXMAN, H. (ARR).  CHAMBER MUSIC FOR 3 SAXOPHONES.  2ASAX,TSAX  RU
```

3 PARTS: WOODWINDS-310

```
ALBISI, A.  MINIATURE SUITE #2.  FL,2CL                     CF
ALDEN, J.  VARIATIONS ON "WALTZING MATILDA".  FL,2CL        OX
ANDRAUD, A.(ARR).  18 TRIOS.  FL,OB(FL),CL                  SO
ANDRIESSEN, J.  TRIO (1957).  FL,OB,BSN                     SD
ANDRIESSEN, L.  AANLOOP EN SPRONGEN (1961).  FL,OB,CL       SD
ANONYMOUS.  TUBA GALLICALLIS.  EHN,2BSN                     HEU
ANTONI, T.  2 EASY FANFARES.  FL,OB,CL                      CM
ANTONI, T.  3 ENCORES.  FL,OB,CL                            CM
APOSTEL, H.  BAGATELLES, OP 20.  FL,CL,BSN                  UE
ARCHER, V.  DIVERTIMENTO (1949).  OB,CL,BSN                 CAN
ARDEVOL, J.  SONATA #4.  2OB,EHN                            SN
ARMA, P.  3 (1949) MOUVEMENTS.  OB,CL,BSN                   EMT
ARNOLD, M.  DIVERTIMENTO, OP 37.  FL,OB,CL                  PAT
```

```
ARNOLD, M.   TRIO.  FL,CL,BSN                                        PAT
ARRIEU, C.   TRIO IN C MA.  OB,CL,BSN                                APH
ARTOT, J.   12 TRIOS.  FL(CL),CL,ACL(ASAX)                           CF
ASHTON, J.   A TONAL TRIO.  FL,CL,BSN                                SS
AURIC, G.   TRIO.  OB,CL,BSN                                         COM
BAAREN, K, VAN.  TRIO (1936).  FL,CL,BSN                             SD
BACH, J.C.-MAGANINI.  ALLEGRETTO PIACEVOLE.  FL,CL,BSN               CF
BACH, J.S.   ADAGIO.  FL,OB,BSN                                      CST
BACH, J.S.   ALLEGRETTO.  FL(OB),CL,BSN                              CST
BACH, J.S.   ALLEGRO.  FL,OB,BSN                                     CST
BACH, J.S.   BIST DU BEI MIR.  CL,ASAX,TSAX,                         HE
BACH, J.S.-SCHWADRON.  FUGA CANONICA.  2CL,BSN                       WI
BACH, J.S.-ANDRAUD.  2 GAVOTTES.  FL,OB,CL                           SO
BACH, J.S.-JOHNSON.  GOLDBERG VARIATIONEN.  OB(FL),CL,BSN            HI
BACH, J.S.-HIRSCH.  I CALL UPON THY NAME O JESUS.  OB,CL,BSN         CF
BACH, J.S.-JOHNSON.  INVENTIONEN.  OB(FL),CL,BSN                     HI
BACH, J.S.-COCHRANE.  15 3-PART INVENTIONS.  FL,CL,ACL(BCL)          CF
BACH, J.S.   15 3-PART INVENTIONS                                    CF
    FL(OB,CL),OB(CL),BSN(BCL,CL)
BACH, J.S.-ANTONI.  2-PART INVENTIONS.  OB,CL,BSN                    CM
BACH, J.S.-SEAY.  3 3-PART INVENTIONS.  2OB,EHN                      SPR
BACH, J.S.-WELLER.  JESU, JOY OF MAN'S DESIRING.  FL,OB,BSN          BNA
BACH, J.S.-MORSCH.  LITTLE BACH SUITE #1.  FL,CL,BSN                 TP
BACH, J.S.-MORSCH.  LITTLE BACH SUITE #2.  FL,CL,BSN                 TP
BACH, J.S.   PRELUDE & FUGUE.  OB,CL,BSN                             EDL
BACH, J.S.-ATKINS.  PRELUDE IN C MI.  OB,CL,BSN                      WI
BACH, J.S.-WELLER.  SHEEP MAY SAFELY GRAZE.  FL,OB,BSN               BNA
BACH, J.S.   SINFONIA IN A MI.  FL,OB,BSN                            BE
BACH, J.S./MOZART-MAROS.  ADAGIO E FUGA.  OB(FL),CL,BSN              EMB
BADEN, C.   TRIO.  FL,OB,CL                                          HLY
BADINGS, H.   TRIO #2 (1943).  OB,CL,BSN                             SD
BADINGS, H.   TRIO #4A (1946).  2OB,EHN                              SD
BAEYENS, A.   CONCERTINO.  OB,CL,BSN                                 EME
BAILEY, M.   2 STRUCTURES.  OB,EHN,BSN                               ACA
BAINES, F.   DIVERTIMENTO.  FL,CL,BSN                                JE
BAKER, M.   5 EPIGRAMS (1965).  2CL,BSN                              CAN
BAKSA, R.   RUNNING TUNE, LULLABY & MARCH.  FL,OB,CL                 SH
BAKSA, R.   TRIO.  FL,CL,BSN                                         AB
BALLIF, C.   TRIO.  OB,CL,BSN                                        ECH
BARRAUD, H.   TRIO.  OB,CL,BSN                                       EDL
BARTOK, B.-DISHINGER.  BAGATELLE #6, OP 6.  FL,OB,BSN                SP
BARTOK, B.-DISHINGER.  DANCE OF THE SLOVAKS.  FL,OB,BSN              SP
BARTOS, F.   TRIO (1958).  OB,CL,BSN                                 ART
BARTSCH, C.   SUITE.  OB,CL,BSN                                      MAU
BAUERNFEIND, H.   GAY PLAY.  FL,CL,BSN                               LDO
BAUERNFEIND, H.   HEITERE MUSIK.  OB,CL,BSN                          LDO
BAUMANN, H.   DIVERTIMENTO.  OB,CL,BSN                               HSM
BAUR, J.   KONTRAPUNKTE.  FL,EHN,BSN                                 BRH
BAURLE, J.   6 LEICHTE STUCKE.  2FL,OB                               GBV
BECHERT, P.   TRIO, OP 29.  FL,CL,BSN                                ETB
BECK, J.   TRIO.  FL,CL,BSN                                          MV
BEDEN, C.   TRIO.  FL,OB,CL                                          HLY
BEETHOVEN, L. VAN-ELKAN.  BAGATELLE, OP 33/2.  FL,CL(OB),BSN         HE
BEETHOVEN, L. VAN.  EXCERPTS FROM RONDO (SONATA PATHETIQUE)          CF
    2CL,BSN( ASAX,ACL)
BEETHOVEN, L. VAN.  GRAND TRIO IN C MA, OP 87,.  OB,FL,ASAX          BIL
BEETHOVEN, L. VAN-TUSTIN.  MINUET IN G MA.  FL,OB,CL                 BE
BEETHOVEN, L. VAN.  MINUET IN G MA, #2.  2CL,BSN                     CF
BEETHOVEN, L. VAN.  PETIT TRIO.  OB,CL,BSN                           CF
BEETHOVEN, L. VAN-MORRIS.  RONDO (SONATINA IN F MA)                  PO
    FL,OB(FL),CL
BEETHOVEN, L. VAN-GRANT.  SCHERZO, OP 9/3.  OB,CL,BSN                BO
```

```
BEETHOVEN, L. VAN-STACY. TRIO IN C MA, OP 87. 2OB,EHN          INT
BEETHOVEN, L. VAN. TRIO IN C MA, OP 87. 2OB,EHN               BH
BEETHOVEN, L. VAN. TRIO IN C MA, OP 87. 2OB,EHN               BRH
BEETHOVEN, L. VAN. TRIO IN C MA, OP 87. 2OB,EHN               EDK
BEETHOVEN, L. VAN. TRIO IN C. 2OB,EHN                         NOM
BEETHOVEN, L. VAN-LANGENUS. TRIO, OP 87. FL,OB,CL             CF
BEETHOVEN, L. VAN-WILDGANS. TRIO, OP 87. 2OB,EHN              LDO
BEETHOVEN, L. VAN. TRIO, OP 87. 2OB,EHN                       PET
BEETHOVEN, L. VAN-STEIN. VARIATIONEN. 2OB,EHN                 BRH
BEETHOVEN, L. VAN-STACY. VARIATIONS ON "LA CI DAREM"          INT
   2OB,EHN
BEETHOVEN, L. VAN. VARIATIONS ON "LA CI DAREM". OB,CL,BSN     MR
BENNETT, R.R. TRIO (1965). FL,OB,CL                           UE
BENTLEY, A. (ARR). TRIOS OF THE 16TH CENTURY                  CA
   FL(OB,CL),OB(CL),SAX(B SN)
BENTZON, J. RACCONTO #3, OP 31. OB,CL,BSN                     WH
BENTZON, J. SONATINE, OP 7. FL,CL,BSN                         WH
BERGER, J. DIVERTIMENTO. 3 TREBLE INSTR                       BR
BERLINSKI, H. BACH TRIO ALBUM. 2FL(2OB),BSN                   TP
BERTHELEMY, N. RONDO POUR RIRE. 2CL,BSN(TSAX)                 BIL
BERTOUILLE, G. PRELUDE & FUGUE (1957). OB,CL,BSN              CBD
BESOZZI, A.-MARX. SONATA A TRE IN F MA, OP 7/6. 2OB,BSN       M&M
BETTS, L. PRELUDE, PASTORAL & DANCE (1949). FL,EHN,BSN        CAN
BIALOSKY, M. SUITE. FL,OB,CL                                  WI
BIALOSKY, M. VARIATIONS ON AN ELIZABETHAN LUTE THEME          SS
   FL,OB,BSN
BIERSACK, A. DIVERTIMENTO. FL,CL,BSN                          SCH
BIGGS, J. WOODWIND TRIO. FL,CL,BSN                            CPR
BLAKE, N. TRIO, OP 18. 2OB,EHN                                JE
BLAND, E. TRIO. FL,CL,BSN                                     AMC
BLANK, A. 3 RELATED PIECES. FL,CL,BSN                         ACA
BLEZZARD, W. PAIR OF PIECES, A. 2FL,CL                        KPM
BLIN, L. GRUPETTINO. CL,ASAX,TSAX                             GA
BLOMDAHL, K. TRIO (1938). OB,CL,BSN                           WH
BOCCHERINI, L.-WALN. TERZETTO. FL,OB(CL),CL                   KJ
BODER, G. TRIO, OP 1. OB,CL,BSN                               ABE
BOHUN, L. DE. AMERICAS TRIO, THE. FL,CL,BSN                   ARF
BOIS, ROB DU. TRIO (1961). FL,OB,CL                           SD
BONNEAU, P. 3 NOELS ANCIENS. OB,EHN(CL),BSN                   ALF
BOOREN, J. VAN DEN. TRIO, OP 2 (1960). OB,CL,BSN             SD
BORRIS, S. PARTITA, OP 92/1. FL,2CL                           MV
BORRIS, S. SONATINA PER TRE, OP 45/1. 3WW                     S-W
BORRIS, S. SUITE, OP 92/2. 2CL,BSN                            MV
BOTTENBERG, W. TRIO (1961-63). FL,CL,BSN                      CAI
BOUCARD, M. TRIADE. OB,CL,ASAX                                BI
BOURGUIGNON, F. SUITE EN TRIO, OP 80 (1944). OB,CL,BSN        CB
BOUTRY, R. DIVERTISSEMENT. OB,CL,BSN                          AL
BOVE, J. ANDANTE & ALLEGRO. 2CL,BCL(BSN)                      MC
BOYCE, W. ANDANTE DOLCE. FL(OB),CL,BSN                        CS
BOZZA, E. SERENADE EN TRIO. FL,CL,BSN                         AL
BOZZA, E. SUITE BREVE EN TRIO. OB,CL,BSN                      AL
BRAHMS, J.-DANSBY. LILAC HILLSIDES. OB(CL),2CL                KN
BRASHER, J. DIADELPHOS. FL,CL,BSN                             WI
BRAVNICAR, M. TRIO QUASI FANTASIA. FL,CL,BSN                  ED
BRERO, C. TRIO (1935). FL,CL,BSN                              RC
BRETTINGHAM SMITH, J. WIND IN THE REEDS, OP 12 (1975)         B&
   OB,CL,BSN
BRICCETTI, T. PARTITA, OP 9 (1956). OB,CL,BSN                 CA
BROGUE, R. TRIO. OB,CL,BSN                                    AM
BRONS, C. SERENATA II (1965). OB,CL,BSN                       SD
BROSH, T. DIALOGUE. 3WW                                       SH
BROTONS, S. SUITE A TRES. FL,OB,CL                            EF
```

BROWN. PARMI LES PRES. FL,OB,CL		EV
BROWN, C. TRIO. OB,CL,BSN		BIL
BRUGK, H. ZUM VORTRAG. 3B FL OR E FL INSTR		PGM
BRUNS, V. TRIO, OP 49. OB,CL,BSN		BRH
BUCHTEL, F. WOOD NYMPHS. FL,OB,CL		KJ
BUCHWALD, R. TRIO (1967/73). FL,CL,BSN		DEU
BUECHE, G. FUGUE. 2CL,BSN		CF
BULL, E. 3 BUCOLIQUES. OB,CL,BSN		APH
BULLING, B. SUITE, OP 30. FL,OB(CL),BSN		ETB
BUTTS, C. TRIO. FL,2CL		PO
CADOW, P. KLEINE SUITE. OB(FL),OB,EHN		ETB
CALDARA, A. DAS DO-RE-MI. 28 KANONS. 3WW		MV
CAMARA, J. SUITE. FL,CL,BSN		SN
CAMBINI, G.-VOXMAN. TRIO, OP 45/6. FL,OB,BSN		MR
CAMBINI, G. 2 TRIOS, OP 45. FL,OB,BSN		EUL
CANTELOUBE, J. RUSTIQUES. OB,CL,BSN		EDL
CARION, F. BAGATELLES, OP 19. FL,OB,CL		EBR
CARION, F. LIED. 2OB,EHN		EBR
CARMAN. PETIT RONDO. 2CL,BSN		CF
CARMEL, D. TERZETTINO. FL,CL(OB),BSN		IMP
CARTER, E. CANON IN MEMORIAM IGOR STRAVINSKY. 3WW		AMP
CARULLI, B.-STEPHAN. TRIO IN C MA, OP 1. 2CL,BSN		S&C
CAZDEN, N. TRIO #2, OP 40. FL,OB,CL		SPR
CHAMBERS, S. REFLECTIONS. FL,OB,CL		AMC
CHEDEVILLE, N. SCHERZO. FL,OB,CL		EDM
CHEMIN-PETIT, H. TRIO IM ALTEN STIL. OB,CL,BSN		MRL
CLEMENTI, A. 3 PICCOLI PEZZI (1955). FL,OB,CL		ESZ
CLEMENTI, A. TRIPLUM (1960). FL,OB,CL		ESZ
CLEMENTI, M.-ELKAN. SONATINA, OP 36/3. FL,CL(OB),BSN		HE
COHEN, S. MADRIGALE. 2CL,BSN		BE
CONSTANT, M. TRIO. OB,CL,BSN		CHE
CORELLI, A. AIR & DANCE. FL,OB,CL		EDM
CORELLI, A.-AUSLENDER. CHAMBER SONATA, OP 2/2. OB,CL,BSN		WI
CORELLI, A.-SCHAEFFER. PRAELUDIUM. FL,OB(FL),CL		PO
CORROYEZ, G. 26 PIECES CONCERTANTES EN TRIOS. 3WW		EDR
CORTES, R. DIVERTIMENTO. FL,CL,BSN		PI
COUPERIN, F.-ELKAN. BACCHANALES, LES. FL,CL(OB),BSN		HE
COUPERIN, F. KLEINE SUITE. FL,OB,BSN		EMB
COYNER, L. TERTIUM QUID. FL,CL,BCL		ACA
CRUFT, A. 3 BAGATELLES, OP 50. FL,OB,CL		BH
CRUFT, A. 3, OP 70 MINIATURES. OB(CL),CL,BSN(BCL)		CA
CUNNINGHAM, M. SERENADE. CL,BSN,SAX		SS
D'HOIR, J. VARIATIES OP "EEN KIND IS GEBOREN". OB,CL,BSN		MAU
DAESON, D. ENTROPY. FL,CL,BSN		SS
DANDRIEU, J.-SEAY. TOURBILLONS, LES. OB(FL),CL,BSN(BCL)		SPR
DANIELS, M. 3 OBSERVATIONS, OP 41. OB(FL),CL,BSN		CF
DAVIDSON, J. ROW #1. FL,2CL		PMP
DAVIS, D. PREFACE & FUGUE. FL,OB,BSN		AMC
DAVIS, D. TRIO. FL,2CL		AMC
DE ROYE, E. TRIO. OB,CL,BSN		EME
DECADT, J. TRIO. OB,CL,BSN		MAU
DEFOSSEZ, R. TRIO (1946). OB,CL,BSN		CBD
DELMOTTE, C. TRIO. OB,CL,BSN		MAU
DELVAUX, A. TRIO (1948). OB,CL,BSN		CBD
DESPREZ, F. PRELUDE & DANSE. OB,CL,BSN		EBR
DESSAU, P. 3 PIECES. 2CL,BSN		DEU
DEVIENNE, F.-DE KLERK. SONATINE #1. 2FL,BSN(VC)		EDH
DEVIENNE, F.-DE KLERK. SONATINE #2. 2FL,BSN(VC)		EDH
DEVIENNE, F.-DE KLERK. SONATINE #3. 2FL,BSN(VC)		EDH
DEVIENNE, F.-DE KLERK. SONATINE #4. 2FL,BSN(VC)		EDH
DEVIENNE, F.-MEERWEIN. TRIO IN A MI, OP 61/3. FL,CL,BSN		PET
DEVIENNE, F.-VOXMAN. TRIO IN E FL MA, OP 75/3. 2CL,BSN		NOM

```
DEVIENNE, F.  TRIO.  2CL,TSAX                                   MOL
DEVIENNE, F.-BALASSA.  6 TRIOS (#4).  2CL,BSN                   EMB
DEVIENNE, F.-BALASSA.  3 TRIOS, OP 61.  FL,CL,BSN              EUL
DEVIENNE, F.  3 TRIOS.  FL,CL,BSN                              EMB
DOBROWOLSKI, A.  TRIO (1956).  OB,CL,BSN                        AP
DODGE, C.  SOLOS & COMBINATIONS (1964).  OB,FL,CL             B-B
DOMAZLICKY, F.  TRIO (1953).  FL,CL,BSN                         ES
DONAHUE, R.  TRIO.  FL,OB,CL                                   MAN
DONDEYNE, D.  SUITE D'AIRS POPULAIRES.  OB,CL,BSN             EMT
DOPPELBAUER, J.  TRIO (1962).  2CL,BSN                         LDO
DOPPELBAUER, J.  TRIO (1965).  OB,CL,BSN                       LDO
DOPPELBAUER, J.  TRIO #1 (1963).  FL,OB,CL                     LDO
DRESDEN, S.  KLEIN TRIO (1912).  2OB,EHN                       DEW
DRESDEN, S.  KLEIN TRIO, (1921).  2OB,EHN                       SD
DREYFUS, G.  TRIO, OP  1.  FL,CL,BSN                            JB
DUBOIS, P.  TRIO D'ANCHES.  OB,CL,BSN                          ALE
DUFAY, G.-DARVAS.  10 CHANSONS.  3 MELODY INSTR               EMB
DUREY, L.  DIVERTISSEMENT.  OB,CL,BSN                          CHM
DUSSEK-ELKAN.  CANZONETTA.  FL,CL(OB),BSN                       HE
DUSSEK, F.  PARTHIA IN C MA.  2OB,BSN                           ES
DUSSEK, F.-KOMOROUS.  6 PARTHIAS, 2 VOLS.  2OB,BSN            ECK
DUYCK, G.  DIVERTISSEMENT.  OB,CL,BSN                          MAU
ECKHARDT-GRAMATTE, S.  TRIO (1967).  FL,CL,BSN                CAN
ECKLEBE, A.  BLASERTRIO (1975).  OB(FL),CL,BSN                 HG
EDER, H.  WAECHTER-DIVERTIMENTO (1959).  FL,CL,BSN            OHN
EISMA, W.  AFFAIRS #3.  OB,CL,BSN                               SD
ELER, A.-VOXMAN.  TRIO, OP 9/1.  FL,CL,BSN                    NOM
ELIEZER, B.  KLEINE SUITE (1952).  FL,CL,BSN                   HG
ELKUS, J.  5 SKETCHES.  2CL,BSN                                AME
ERDMANN, D.  MINIATUREN (1972).  OB,CL,BSN                     HG
ESCHER, P.  DIVERTISSEMENT, TRIO.  OB,CL,BSN                  EHE
ESCHER, R.  TRIO D'ANCHES (1946), OP  4.  OB,CL,BSN           SD
ETLER, A.  3 PIECES.  3 TREBLE INSTR                          GAL
ETLER, A.  SUITE (1960).  FL,OB,CL                            AMP
EWERS, J.  TRIO, OP  2.  OB,CL,BSN                             LK
FASCH, J.-WOJCIECHOWSKI.  SONATA IN F MA.  2OB,BSN           HSM
FAVRE, G.  GOUACHES.  OB,CL,BSN                               DUR
FELDERHOF, J.  RONDO (1960).  OB,CL,BSN                        SD
FELDERHOF, J.  THEMA MET VARIATIES (1944).  OB,CL,BSN         SD
FERNANDEZ, O.  2 INVENCOES SERESTEIRAS.  FL,CL,BSN            PI
FERROUD, P.  TRIO IN E MA.  OB,CL,BSN                         DUR
FILIPPI, A. DE.  CORYDON SUITE.  FL,CL,BSN                    GEN
FINE, A.  DANCE PIECE #2.  2FL,OB                             AMC
FLEGIER, A.-VOXMAN.  CONCERT SUITE.  OB,CL,BSN                RU
FLEMING, R.  A 2 PIECE SUITE (1959).  OB,CL,BSN              CAN
FLOTHIUS, M.  NOCTURNE, OP 22 (1941).  FL,OB,CL              CHE
FLOTHUIS, M.  NOCTURNE, OP 11 (1941).  FL,OB,CL               SD
FONTYN, J.  7 LITTLE PIECES (1956).  OB,CL,BSN               GS
FORET, F.  SUITE EN TRIO.  OB,CL,BSN                          BIL
FORSYTH, M.  MELANCHOLY CLOWN, THE (1967).  FL,CL,BSN        ECK
FORTNER, W.  SERENADE (1945).  FL,OB,BSN                     SCH
FRANCAIX, J.  DIVERTISSEMENT.  OB,CL,BSN                      SCH
FRANCK, M.  TRIO D'ANCHES, #2.  OB,CL,BSN                     EMT
FRANCL, J.  TRIO.  OB,CL,BSN                                  CHF
FRANGKISER, C.  INVENTRIOLE.  2CL,BSN                          BE
FRANK, M.  WIND TRIO #2.  OB,CL,BSN                           EMT
FREISTADT, M.  WOODWIND TRIO, OP 38.  3WW                     AMC
FRID, G.  DUBBELTRIO, OP 73 (1967).  FL/PIC,OB/EHN,BSN/CBSN  SD
FRITTER, J.  8 RONDELS.  FL,CL,BSN                             UE
GARDONYI, Z.  3 RONDOS.  FL,OB,BSN                            WZ
GARSCIA, J.  THEME WITH VARIATIONS, OP 35.  FL,CL,BSN        PWM
GASTYNE, S. DE.  TRIO, OP 65 (1970).  OB,CL,BSN              FER
```

```
GATTERMEYER, H.  TRIO, OP 62/2.  OB,CL,BSN                        LDO
GERAEDTS, J.  DIVERTIMENTO #1 (1943).  OB,CL,BSN                  SD
GERAEDTS, J.  DIVERTIMENTO #2 (1946).  OB,CL,BSN                  SD
GERSCHEFSKI, E.  TRIO ("AMERICA" VARIATIONS), OP 44/4            ACA
   FL,CL,BSN
GESSNER, J.  ADAGIO & ALLEGRO.  WW TRIO                           S&
GETHEN, F.  SCHERZO.  OB,CL,BSN                                   EMI
GIANELLA, L.-WIENANDT.  NOCTURNE IN G MA, OP 28/1.  2FL,BSN      SO
GIBBONS, O.-CLARK.  FANTASIA FOR 3.  FL,OB,CL                     EDM
GIBBONS, O.  SILVER SWAN, THE.  3WW                               AM
GILTAY, B.  SONATA A TRE (1953).  OB,CL,BSN                       SD
GLASS, P.  DIVERTIMENTO (1958).  FL,CL,BSN                        CAN
GOEB, R.  SUITE.  FL,OB,CL                                        SN
GOETHALS, L.  FANTASIA EN HUMORESKE (1975).  2OB,EHN             CBD
GOLESTAN, S.  PETITE SUITE BUCOLIQUE.  OB,CL,BSN                 DUR
GOODENOUGH, F.  WOODWIND TRIO.  FL,OB,BSN                         ACA
GOODMAN, A.  KLEINE SUITE.  FL,OB,CL                              MRL
GOODMAN, J.  5 BAGATELLES.  FL,CL,BSN                             GEN
GORNER, H.  TRIO, OP 24.  FL,OB,CL                                ABE
GOULD, E.  DISCIPLINES.  OB,CL,BSN                                EV
GRAAP, L.  DIVERTIMENTO (1964).  FL,OB,BSN                        DEU
GRABNER, H.  TRIO (1951).  OB,CL,BSN                              KIS
GRAHN, U.  TRIO.  FL,OB,CL                                        SS
GRIEG, E.-ELKAN.  RIGAUDON, OP 40/5.  FL,CL,BSN                   HE
GRIEND, K. VAN DE.  TRIO (1929).  OB,CL,BSN                       SD
GROOT, H. DE.  SOUVENIR SUD AMERICAN.  OB,CL,BSN                  EBR
GROOT, H. DE.  VARIATIONS ON "AUPRES DE MA BLONDE".  OB,CL,BSN    EBR
GROOT, H. DE.  VARIATIONS.  OB,CL,BSN                             HU
HAAN, ST. DE.  TRIO.  FL,CL,DCN                                   SCH
HABASH, J.  ADAGIO & RONDO.  FL,CL,BSN                            BO
HABERLING, A.  KLEINES TRIO.  2CL,BSN                             MV
HABERLING, A.  3 TANZE.  B FL,E FL, OR C INSTR                    PGM
HAJDU, M.  TRIO.  2FL,CL                                          EMB
HALL, C.  PETITE SUITE.  FL,CL,BSN                                OR
HANDEL, G.-CHRISTENSEN.  BOUREE.  FL(OB),CL,BSN                   KN
HANDEL, G.-ELKAN.  FIREWORKS SUITE.  FL,CL(OB),BSN               HE
HANDEL, G.-ELKAN.  FUGUE (CELLO SONATA #2).  FL,CL(OB),BSN       HE
HANDEL, G.-MORSCH.  LITTLE HANDEL SUITE.  FL,OB(CL),BSN          TP
HANDEL, G.-BUSTO.  MINUET.  OB,CL,BSN                             CF
HANDEL, G.  RIGAUDON, BOURREE & MARCH.  2OB,BSN,DR OPT           MR
HANDEL, G.-WILLIAMS.  SONATA.  OB(FL),CL,BSN                      SO
HANDEL, G.  TRIO #2 IN D MI.  2OB,BSN                             EDK
HANDEL, G.-SCHWADRON.  TRIO: THEME & VARIATIONS (CHACONNE)       PMP
   OB,CL,BSN
HANNA, J.  TRIO.  FL,CL,BSN                                       SPR
HARBISON, J.  4 PRELUDES.  FL,OB(FL),CL(OB,FL)                    M&M
HARCOURT, D'.  RHAPSODIE PERUVIENNE.  OB,CL,BSN                   HLE
HARRIS, A.  4 PIECES.  3 TREBLE INSTR                             BR
HARRIS, R.  CONCERT ETUDES.  EHN,CL,ASAX                          SS
HARTMANN, E.  7 STUCKE.  OB D'AMORE,EHN,BSN                       ROB
HASSELMANN, V.  KLEINE GAVOTTE.  2FL,CL                           FS
HASSELMANN, V.  MENUETT.  3WW                                     EHE
HAUTA-AHO, T.  TRIO #1.  FL,OB,BSN                                FIN
HAYDN, F.-SCHAEFFER.  SCHERZANDO.  FL,OB,CL                       PO
HAYDN, M.-SUTTON.  4 MINUETS.  2CL,BSN                            NO
HEDWALL, L.  TRIO (1962).  FL,CL,BSN                              STI
HEININE, P.  SUITE.  FL,OB,CL                                     FIN
HEKSTER, W.  ECHOES OF SUMMER (1975).  OB/EHN,CL/BCL,BSN         SD
HEKSTER, W.  REED MUSIC (1970).  OB,CL,BSN                        SD
HEMBERG, E.  TIO VARIATIONER (1960).  OB,CL,BSN                   STI
HEMEL, O. VAN.  TRIO (1959).  FL,OB,BSN                           SD
HENNESSY, S.  TRIO, OP 54.  2CL,BSN                               EES
```

```
HERMANS, N.   DIVERTIMENTO PICCOLO, OP  2 (1948).   OB,CL,BSN        SD
HESS, W.   TRIO, OP 75.   2CL,BSN                                    EUL
HEUSSENSTAMM, G.   CANONOGRAPH I.   3WW                              SS
HEUSSENSTAMM, G.   7 ETUDES, OP 17.   OB,CL,BSN                      WI
HLOBIL, E.   TRIO.   OB,CL,BSN                                       CHF
HOFFER, P.   KLEINE SUITE (1944).   OB,CL,BSN                        HSM
HOFFER, P.   THEMA MIT VARIATIONEN (1944).   OB,CL,BSN               HSM
HOMS, J.   TRIO (1954).   FL,OB,BCL(BSN)                             SS
HORVIT, M.   LITTLE SUITE.   FL,CL,BSN                               SH
HOSKINS, W.   PRELUDE & FUGUE.   OB,CL,BSN                           ACA
HOVEY, H.   7 PIECES.   FL,CL,OB                                     BH
HUMMEL, B.   MOMENTS MUSICAUX.   OB,CL,BSN                           SIM
HUSA, K.   2 PRELUDES.   FL,CL,BSN                                   ALE
IBERT, J.   5 PIECES EN TRIO.   OB,CL,BSN                            EDL
IKONOMOV, B.   TRIO #2 (1968).   OB,CL,BSN                           HG
ILIEV, I.   TRIO #3, OP 69 (1968).   OB,CL,BSN                       HG
IM, K.   SUITE.   FL,CL,BSN                                          ES
IPPOLITOV-IVANOV, M.   2 KIRGHIZ SONGS.   OB,CL,BSN                  TP
JACKSON, D.   MIKROKOSMOS "M"- DANCE SUITE.   FL,CL,BSN              MAN
JACOB, G.   2 PIECES.   2OB,EHN                                      GAL
JANACEK, L.   BLAUKEHLCHEN-MARSCH.   PIC,FL,CL                       ES
JEMNITZ, S.   WOODWIND TRIO, OP 70 (1958).   FL,OB,CL                EMB
JOHANNES, J.   INTRODUCTIE EN FUGA (1968).   OB,CL,BSN               SD
JOHANSON, S.   CACCIA (1968).   FL,CL,TSAX                           STI
JOHANSON, S.   LYRISK SVIT (1953).   OB,CL,BSN                       STI
JOLY, D.   TRIO.   OB,CL,BSN                                         EMT
JONES.   THREE BY THREE.   3WW                                       SH
JONG, M. DE.   TRIO, OP126 (1961).   OB,CL,BSN                       CBD
JONGEN, J.   TRIO.   OB,CL,BSN                                       SO
JUON, P.   ARABESKEN, OP 73 (1940).   OB,CL,BSN                      MRL
JURDZINSKI, K.   DIVERTIMENTO (1956).   2CL,BSN                      AP
KALLSTENIUS, E.   PICCOLO TRIO SERIALE, OP 47 (1956)                 STI
   FL,EHN,CL
KARG-ELERT, S.   TRIO IN D MI, OP 49/1.   OB,CL,EHN                  EDK
KARKOFF, M.   TRIO PICCOLO, OP 55 (1961).   FL,CL,BSN                STI
KASANDSHIEV, V.   KLEINE SUITE (1956).   OB,CL,BSN                   HG
KAUFFMAN, G.-MARX.   CHORALE PRELUDE.   OB,CL,BSN                    M&M
KEANE, D.   CARPOPHAGOUS CANON #4.   3 DOUBLE REED INSTR             LMP
KELDORFER, R.   TRIO.   FL,CL,BSN                                    LDO
KELKEL, M.   DIVERTIMENTO, OP  3.   OB,CL,BSN                        RC
KENDELL, I.   VARIATIONS ON A LONDON STREET CRY                      CHE
   3 MELODY INSTR
KENINS, T.   PRELUDE & SCHERZO (1949).   FL,CL,BSN                   CAN
KERSTERS, W.   BERCEUSE EN HUMORESQUE, OP  8.   OB,CL,BSN            MAU
KETTING, P.   TRIO (1929).   FL,CL,BSN                               SD
KIBBE, M.   TRIO.   OB,EHN,OB D'AMORE                                SS
KIBBE, M.   VARIATIONS ON A THEME OF MOZART.   2OB,EHN               SS
KLEIN, R.   3 CHORALES FOR ADVENT, CHRISTMAS & NEW YEARS            HEI
   2FL(2OB),BS N
KLEIN, R.   FESTTAGSMUSIKEN. CHORALE & LIEDER.   FL,OB,BSN          HEI
KLEIN, R.   SERENADE.   OB,CL,BSN                                    HEI
KNIGHT, M.   SELFISH GIANT SUITE.   FL,CL,BSN(TRB)                   TP
KOCHAN, G.   DIVERTIMENTO, OP 12.   FL,CL,BSN                        PET
KOCSAR, M.   DIVERTIMENTO (1956).   OB,CL,BSN                        EMB
KOECHLIN, C.   TRIO D'ANCHES.   OB,CL,BSN                            SEM
KOECHLIN, C.   TRIO.   FL,CL,BSN                                     EDS
KOEPKE, P.   BADINAGE.   FL,OB(FL),CL                                RU
KOETSIER, J.   6 BAGATELLEN, OP 16/2 (1937).   OB,CL,BSN            SD
KOGOJ, M.   EPISODES.   FL,CL,BSN                                    EDD
KONIETZNY, H.   KLEINE KAMMERMUSIK #2 (1947).   OB,CL,BSN           EMO
KONOWALSKI, B.   MINI-RONDO.   OB,CL,BSN                             PWM
KORINEK, M.   TRIO, A (1962).   2OB,EHN                              SHF
```

```
KOSKEY, G.   FUGUE.   3WW                                        AMC
KOTSCHAU, J.-VOXMAN.   DIVERTIMENTO IN B FL MA.   FL,CL,BSN      RU
KOTSCHAU, J.   DIVERTIMENTO.   FL,CL,BSN                         PET
KOUMANS, R.   TRIO, OP 30.   OB,CL,BSN                           SD
KOWALSKI, J.   DIVERTIMENTO.   FL,OB,BSN                         SHF
KRAFT, L.   SHORT SUITE.   FL,CL,BSN                             GEN
KRATOCHVIL, J. (ED).   TRIOS TSCHECHISCHER KLASSIKER            ES
   2OB(2CL),BSN
KRATOCHWIL, H.   PARTITA RITMICA, OP 92                          LDO
   FL(CL),OB(CL),CL(BCL,BSN)
KREJCI, I.   BLASERTRIO (1935).   OB,CL,BSN                      CHF
KREUTZER, R.-WIENANDT.   TRIO.   OB(FL),CL,BSN                   PO
KRIENS, C.   RONDO DES LUTINS.   FL,OB,CL                        CF
KROMMER, F.   VARIATIONS ON A THEME BY PLEYEL.   2OB,EHN         EK
KUBIK, G.   LITTLE SUITE.   FL,2CL                               HA
KUBIZEK, A.   KLEINE TANZ-SUITE.   3MELODY INSTR                 LDO
KUBIZEK, A.   4 PIECES.   FL(OB),CL,BSN(BCL)                     BRH
KUHLAU, F.-TUSTIN.   ALLEGRO (OP 20/2).   FL,CL,BSN(BCL)         SPR
KUHLAU, F.-TUSTIN.   SONATINA (OP 20/1).   FL,OB,CL              SPR
KUMMER, K.-VOXMAN.   TRIO IN F MA.   FL,CL,BSN                   RU
KUNERT, K.   TRIO IN C MI.   FL,CL,BSN                           BRH
KUNERT, K.-ADAMS.   TRIO IN C MI, OP  7.   FL,CL,BSN             VO
KUNZ, A.   FUN FOR 3 (1964).   FL,CL,BCL(BSN)                    CAN
KURTZ, J.   2 STUDIES.   FL,CL,BSN                               CAN
KURZBACH, P.   TRIO.   OB,CL,BSN                                 PET
LACHOWSKA, S.   TRIPTYCH (1964).   FL,CL,BSN                     AP
LARSON, VALSE.   3WW                                            TM
LE SIEGE, A.   DIALOGUE.   OB,EHN,BSN                            SS
LEDERER, J.   ROKOKO-SUITE, OP 43.   FL,CL,BSN                   ETB
LEFEVRE, J.-STEINBECK   TRIO IN B FL MA.   2CL,BSN               EMB
LEGLEY, V.   TRIO, OP 11 (1942).   OB,CL,BSN                     CBD
LEGRENZI, G.   BONACOSSA.   FL(OB),CL,BSN                        CST
LEGRENZI, G.   FINI, LA.   FL(OB),CL,BSN                         CST
LEGRENZI, G.   SECCA SOARDA, LA.   FL(OB),CL,BSN                 CST
LEHMANN, H.   TRACTUS (1971).   FL,OB,CL                         SCH
LEMAIRE.   MINI-TRIO.   OB,CL,BSN                                BIL
LEMELAND, A.   DIVERTISSEMENT, OP 45.   FL,CL,ASAX               BIL
LEMELAND, A.   PASTORALE.   OB,CL,BSN                            BIL
LESUR, D.   SUITE.   OB,CL,BSN                                   EDL
LIDL, V.   DIVERTIMENTO (1951).   FL,CL,BSN                      CHF
LIMMERT, E.   SERENADE (1962).   FL,OB,BSN                       BRH
LOCKWOOD, N.   THREE.   FL,OB,CL                                 ACA
LOLOV, V.   SUITE, OP 10 (1947).   FL,CL,BSN                     HG
LORENZO, L. DE.   TRIO ECCENTRICO, OP 76.   FL,CL,BSN            PET
LORENZO, L. DE.   TRIO ROMANTICO, OP 78.   FL,OB,CL              PET
LOUCHEUR, R.   PORTRAITS.   OB,CL,BSN                            BIL
LUENING, O.   SUITE FOR DIVERSE HIGH & LOW INSTRUMENTS           GA
   2TREBLE1BASS
LULLY, J.-MULLER.   AIRS DE TABLE.   OB,CL,BSN                   MAU
LUTOSLAWSKI, W.   TRIO (1944-45).   OB,CL,BSN                    AP
LUTYENS, E.   TRIO, OP 52.   FL,CL,BSN                           S&C
MACHAUT, G.   DOUBLE HOQUET.   3WW                               EDL
MAEGAARD, J.   TRIO (1950).   OB,CL,BSN                          SPD
MAES, J.   MINIATURE TRIO.   OB,CL,BSN                           HE
MAESSEN, A.   CASSATION (1958).   OB,CL,BSN                      SD
MAESSEN, A.   TRIO (1956).   FL,CL,BSN                           SD
MAGANINI, Q.   ARS CONTRAPUNCTUS.   FL,CL,BSN                    EDM
MAGANINI, Q.   HAVANA.   FL,CL,BSN                               CF
MAGANINI, Q.   ISTANBOUL.   FL(OB),CL,BSN                        CF
MAGANINI, Q.   3 LITTLE KITTENS.   FL,OB,CL                      EDM
MAGANINI, Q.   RUBIA, LA.   OB,CL,BSN                            CF
MAGANINI, Q.   VIENNA WALTZ.   FL,CL,BSN                         CF
```

```
MAJO, E.  TRIO.  2CL,BSN                                              FS
MAKLAKIEWICZ, T.  BIBLICAL TRIPTYCH.  2CL,BSN                        PWM
MAKSYMIUK, J.  TRIO.  OB,CL,BSN                                      PWM
MANIET, R.  CONCERT D'ANCHES.  OB,CL,BSN                             MAU
MANIET, R.  TRIO D'ANCHES I.  OB,CL,BSN                              MAU
MANIET, R.  TRIO D'ANCHES II.  OB,CL,BSN                             MAU
MARCELLO-ROCERETO.  TOCCATA IN C MI.  2CL,BSN                        VO
MAREZ OYENS, T. DE.  SWATCHES TRIO.  FL,OB,BSN                       HU
MARIASSY & VIGH(ARR).  CHAMBER MUSIC II.  FL(OB),CL,BSN              EMB
MAROS, R.  SERENATA (1951).  OB,CL,BSN                               EMB
MARTELLI, H.  TRIO, OP 45.  OB,CL,BSN                                BIL
MARTINI, J.-HIRSCH.  GAVOTTE.  OB,CL,BSN                             CF
MARTINON, J.  SONATINE #4.  OB,CL,BSN                                BIL
MARTINU, B.  4 MADRIGALE (1937).  OB,CL,BSN                          EES
MASON, J.  CANONIC DEVICE.  2CL,BSN                                  OP
MAXWELL.  TRIO.  FL,CL,BSN                                           WI
MAYR, A.  LITTLE SUITE.  FL,OB,BSN                                   AMP
MAYR, G.  12 BAGATELLES.  FL,CL,BSN                                  AB
MAYR, S.  BAGATELLE A TRE.  FL,CL,BSN                                EK
MC BRIDE, R.  FUGUE.  OB,2CL                                         ACA
MC BRIDE, R.  VARIATIONS ON VARIOUS POPULARISMS.  CL,EHN,BSN         ACA
MC CALL, H. (ARR).  INSTRUMENTAL HYMN FAVORITES.  3WW                CF
MC KAY, F.  AT THE PUPPET SHOW.  OB,CL,CL(BCL,BSN)                   BA
MC KAY, F.  BLUE TAPESTRY.  OB,CL,CL(BCL,BSN)                        BA
MC KAY, F.  TRAIL TO SUNNY POINT.  FL,OB,CL                          BA
MECHAM, K.  TRIO.  OB,CL,BSN                                         ECS
MELARTIN, E.  TRIO.  FL,CL,BSN                                       FIN
MELLNAS, A.  DIVERTIMENTO.  FL,CL,BSN                                STI
MENDELSSOHN, F.  LIFT THINE EYES & CAST THY BURDEN.  FL,OB,CL        KJ
MENGELBERG, K.  TRIO (1940).  FL,OB,BSN                              SD
METRAL, P.  PETITE SUITE.  OB,CL,BSN                                 CF
MEULEMANS, A.  TRIO (1933).  OB,CL,BSN                               EBR
MEULEMANS, A.  TRIO #2 (1960).  OB,CL,BSN                            CBD
MICHEL (YOST)-VOXMAN.  TRIO #1.  2CL,BSN(BCL)                        RU
MIGOT, G.  THRENE.  OB,CL,BSN                                        ALE
MIGOT, G.  TRIO.  OB,CL,BSN                                          ALE
MIHALOVICI, M.  TRIO, OP 71.  OB,CL,BSN                              A&S
MIKODA, B.  TRIO, OP 7.  OB,CL,BSN                                   CHF
MILHAUD, D.  PASTORALE.  OB,CL,BSN                                   CHM
MILHAUD, D.  SUITE D'APRES CORRETTE.  OB,CL,BSN                      EDL
MILLER, M.  IN-TALK (1975).  2OB,EHN                                 CAN
MOESCHINGER, A.  5 CAPRICCI (1960).  FL,CL,BSN                       HEI
MOESCHINGER, A.  CAPRICCI E DANZE.  OB,CL,BSN                        HUG
MOLLICONE, H.  TRIO.  FL,CL,BSN                                      ACA
MOORTEL, A. VAN DE.  TRIO #1.  OB,CL,BSN                             MAU
MOORTEL, L. VAN DE.  DIVERTIMENTO I.  OB,CL,BSN                      MAU
MOORTEL, L. VAN DE.  DIVERTIMENTO III.  OB,CL,BSN                    MAU
MORITZ, E.  DIVERTIMENTO, OP150.  FL,CL,BSN                          WZ
MOSER, F.  TRIO, OP 38.  2OB,EHN                                     BOS
MOSS, P.  TRIO.  OB,CL,BSN                                           PWM
MOZART, W.-ELKAN.  ADAGIO (SONATINA #5).  FL,CL(OB),BSN             HE
MOZART, W.-ELKAN.  ALLELUIA.  FL,CL(OB),BSN                         HE
MOZART, W.-HASSELMANN.  ANDANTE GRAZIOSO.  2FL,CL                   FS
MOZART, W.-MARX.  CANON,.  2CL,BSN                                  M&M
MOZART, W.-MORSCH.  CONTREDANSE & MINUET.  FL,CL,BSN                TP
MOZART, W.  DIVERTIMENTI #4, #5, IN B FL MA, K439B.  2CL,BSN        MR
MOZART, W.  5 DIVERTIMENTI, K229 (PUB SEPARATELY).  2CL,BSN         BRH
MOZART, W.-THURSTON.  DIVERTIMENTO #1.  2CL,BSN                     BH
MOZART, W.-WIENANDT.  DIVERTIMENTO #1.  2CL,BSN                     PO
MOZART, W.  DIVERTIMENTO #1, K229.  2CL,BSN                         EDK
MOZART, W.-KURKIEWICZ.  DIVERTIMENTO #2.  2CL,BSN                   PWM
MOZART, W.-THURSTON.  DIVERTIMENTO #2.  2CL,BSN                     BH
```

```
MOZART, W.  DIVERTIMENTO #2, K229.  2CL,BSN                       EDK
MOZART, W.-WIENANDT.  DIVERTIMENTO #2, K439B.  OB(CL),CL,BSN      PO
MOZART, W.  DIVERTIMENTO #3 IN B FL MA, K439B.  2CL,BSN           MR
MOZART, W.  DIVERTIMENTO #3, K229.  2CL,BSN                       EDK
MOZART, W.-WIENANDT.  DIVERTIMENTO #3, K439B.  OB(CL),CL,BSN      PO
MOZART, W.  DIVERTIMENTO #6 IN B FL MA, K439B.  2CL,BSN           MR
MOZART, W.  DIVERTIMENTO #6, K229.  2CL,BSN                       H-V
MOZART, W.  DIVERTIMENTO.  FL(OB),CL,BSN                          CST
MOZART, W.  DIVERTIMENTO, KV229/1.  2CL,BSN                       HU
MOZART, W.  DIVERTIMENTOS #4 & #5, K229.  2CL,BSN                 EDK
MOZART, W.  5 DIVERTISSEMENTS, K439 (SOLD SEPARATELY)             EDL
   OB,CL,BSN
MOZART, W.-WOJCIECHOWSKI.  KANONISCHES ADAGIO, KV410             HSM
   2BASSET HN,BSN
MOZART, W.-MULLER.  PIECES.  3WIND INSTR                         MAU
MOZART, W.-TRINKAUS.  RONDO (8TH VIOLIN SONATA).  FL,CL,BSN      CF
MOZART, W.-IRMER/MARGUERRE.  SERENADE #1, KV439B.  2OB,BSN       B&N
MOZART, W.-IRMER/MARGUERRE.  SERENADE #2, KV439B.  2OB,BSN       B&N
MOZART, W.-IRMER/MARGUERRE.  SERENADE #3, KV439B.  2OB,BSN       B&N
MOZART, W.-IRMER/MARGUERRE.  SERENADES #4, #5, KV439B            B&N
   2OB,BSN
MOZART, W.-SCHEIFES.  SONATINE.  2CL,BAR SAX                     MOL
MOZART, W.-DAHM.  TRIO.  FL(OB),CL,BSN(BCL)                      VO
MUCZYNSKI, R.  FRAGMENTS.  FL,CL,BSN                             SH
MULDER, E.  FUGA #7 (1940).  FL,CL,BSN                           SD
MULDER, H.  TRIO, OP 17 (1960).  FL,EHN,BSN                      SD
MUSGRAVE, T.  IMPROMPTU #2.  FL,OB,CL                            CHE
NABERT.  METABOLE #1 & #2.  FL,OB,BSN                            EV
NAGAN, Z.  ISRAELI MINIATURES.  OB,EHN,BSN                       IMP
NAGAN, Z.  SERENADE FOR LISA.  FL,OB,BSN                         IMP
NAZARIAN, A.  DIVERTIMENTO.  FL,CL,BSN                           GZ
NEMIROFF, I.  PERSPECTIVES.  FL,OB,BSN                           M&M
NEMIROFF, I.  VARIATIONS TO A THEME.  FL,OB,BSN                  M&M
NEWMAN-TAYLOR.  RONDO BRILLANTE.  FL,OB,BSN                      BE
NILSSON, B.  20 GRUPPEN.  PIC,OB,CL                              UE
NORDGREN, E.  SERENATA A TRE, OP 77 (1966-68).  FL,CL,BSN        STI
NOWAK, L.  SOUNDSCAPE.  FL,CL,BSN                                ACA
OLDFIEDL, A.  TRIO.  FL,OB,CL                                    MUC
OLIVADOTI, J.  DIVERTIMENTO.  FL,OB,CL                           RU
OLSEN, S.  SUITE, OP 10.  FL,OB,CL                               HLY
ORLAND, H.  FUGHETTA.  FL,CL,BSN                                 SS
ORREGO-SALAS, J.  DIVERTIMENTO.  FL,OB,BSN                       SN
OSTERC, S.  WOODWIND TRIO.  FL,CL,BSN                            EDD
OSTRANSKY, L.  TRIO IN G MI.  FL,OB,CL                           RU
OTTEN, L.  TRIO.  FL,CL,BSN                                      SD
OWEN, B.  TRIO.  OB,CL,BSN                                       OR
PACHERNEGG, A.  3 ENNSTALER MENUETTE.  CL(FL,OB),CL,BSN          FS
PACHERNEGG, A.  HIRTENMUSIK.  FL,2CL                             FS
PACIORKIEWICZ, T.  REED TRIO (1963).  OB,CL,BSN                  AP
PACIORKIEWICZ, T.  TRIO STROIKOWE.  OB,CL,BSN                    EM
PAHOR, K.  DIVERTIMENTO.  FL,OB,BSN                              EDD
PALLASZ, E.  PAINTED TOWER.  FL,CL,BSN                           PWM
PARFREY, R.  TRIO.  OB,CL,BSN                                    JE
PARIK, I.  MUSIC FOR 3.  FL,OB,CL                                SHF
PASQUINI, B.-ROCERETO.  SONATA.  2CL,BSN                         VO
PATTERSON, P.  WIND TRIO.  FL,OB(CL),BSN                         JOW
PAUBON, P.  COLLOQUE A 3.  FL,OB,CL                              BIL
PEDERSEN, P.  WOODWIND TRIO #1 (1956).  FL,CL,BSN               CAN
PEDERSEN, P.  WOODWIND TRIO #2 (1957).  FL,CL,BSN               CAN
PEETERS, F.  TRIO, OP 80.  FL,CL,BSN                            PET
PELEMANS, W.  TRIO #2.  OB,CL,BSN                               MAU
PELEMANS, W.  TRIO #3.  OB,CL,BSN                               MAU
```

PELEMANS, W. TRIO. 2OB,EHN	MAU
PERCEVAL, J. SERENATA. FL,CL,BSN	SN
PESCETTI, G.-ELKAN. PRESTO. FL,CL(OB),BSN	HE
PETKOV, D. 3 POLYPHONE STUCKE (1953). FL,CL,BSN	HG
PETRASSI, G. TRE PER SETTE (1966)	ESZ
FL/AFL/PIC,OB/EHN,E FL CL/CL	
PETTERSSON, A. FUGA IN E MA. OB,CL,BSN	STI
PEZEL, J.-BLOCK. 18 PIECES. 2OB,BSN	NOM
PFEIFFER, G.-ANDRAUD. MUSETTE. OB,CL,BSN	SO
PFEIFFER, G. MUSETTE, OP 47/1. OB,CL,BSN	EDS
PHILLIPS, G. PASTORALE. FL,OB,CL	PET
PHILLIPS, I. 6 SHORT ARRANGEMENTS. CL,OB,BSN	OX
PIERNE, P. BUCOLIQUE VARIEE. OB,CL,BSN	BIL
PIETRZAK, B. TRIO (1964). OB,CL,BSN	PWM
PIJPER, W. TRIO (1927). FL,CL,BSN	SD
PIKET, F. TRIO. FL,CL,BSN	SF
PISTON, W. 3 PIECES (1926). FL,CL,BSN	AMP
PLATZ, R. FOR ROLF. OB,CL,BSN	EMO
PLEYEL, I. TRIO #2 IN C MA. FL,CL,BSN	MR
PLEYEL, I.-BLOCK. TRIO IN B FL MA, OP 20/1. 2CL,BSN	NOM
PLEYEL, I.-HENKE/KLOCKER. TRIO IN E FL MA. 2CL,BSN	PET
PLEYEL, I.-VOXMAN. TRIO IN E FL MA, OP 20/2. 2CL,BSN	MR
PLEYEL, I. TRIO, OP 20/1. 2CL,BSN	MR
POESSINGER, F. TRIO IN F MA. 2OB,EHN	EK
POLIN, C. TOWER SONATA. FL,CL,BSN	SS
PONSE, L. TRIO (1941). FL,CL,BSN	SD
POOT, M. BALLADE. OB,CL,BSN	EES
POOT, M. DIVERTIMENTO. OB,CL,BSN	EES
POSPISIL, J. 3 INVENCIE. FL,CL,BSN	SHF
PRAAG, H. VAN. FANTASIA A 3 (1956). FL,OB,BSN	SD
PRESSER, W. TRIO. 2OB,EHN	TRI
PRZYBYLSKI, B. PERMUTARE. OB,CL,BSN	PWM
PUCCINI, G.-STEBBING. MUSETTA'S WALTZ SONG	RC
QUINET, M. POLYPHONIES (1971)	CBD
PIC/FL/AFL,OB/EHN,E FL CL/CL/BCL	
QUINET, M. TRIO (1967). OB,CL,BSN	CBD
RAMEAU, J.-DE FILIPPI. HEN, THE. FL,OB,BSN	HE
RAUSCH, C. TRIO, OP 3. FL,CL,BCL	ACA
RAZZI, F. INVENZIONE A 3 (1964). OB,E FL CL,BCL	ESZ
REDEL, M. MOBILE (1976). OB,CL,BSN	B&B
REGER, M.-SCHWADRON. CANON IN D MI. FL,CL,BSN(BCL)	KN
REGNER, H. DIVERTIMENTO. FL,2CL	OHN
REGNER, H. SPIEL. 2CL,BSN	SCH
REGNER, H. SPIELHEFT II. 3 B FL INSTR	PGM
REGT, H. MUSICA (1971). OB,EHN,HECKELPHONE	SD
REGT, H. DE. MUSICA, OP 5 (1970). OB,CL,BSN	SD
REGT, H. DE. MUSICA, OP 25 (1973). 3WW	SD
REGT, H. DE. MUSICA, OP 27 (1973). FL,OB,CL	SD
REGT, H. DE. MUSICA, OP 36 (1974). 2OB,EHN	SD
REINER, K. TERZETTI (1971). OB,CL,BSN	CHF
REINHARDT, B. 4 SCHERZI. OB,CL,BSN	IMP
REIZENSTEIN, F. TRIO, OP 39. FL,CL,BSN	LEN
RIBARI, A. 5 MINIATUREN. FL,CL,BSN	EMB
RIETI, V. PRELUDE. FL,CL,BSN	GEN
RIISAGER, K. CONVERSAZIONE, OP 26A. OB,CL,BSN	PET
RIMSKY-KORSAKOV, N.-RUGGIERO. SCHERZO (TSAR SULTAN)	GZ
FL,CL,BSN	
RIVIER, J. PETITE SUITE. OB,CL,BSN	SEM
RONTGEN, J. TRIO, OP 86. FL,OB,BSN	ALS
ROOS, R. DE. 4 PEZZI (1971). OB,CL,BSN	SD
ROPARTZ, J. ENTRATA A SCHERZETTO. OB,CL,BSN	EDS
ROSENBERG, H. TRIO (1927). OB,CL,BSN	STI

```
ROSSI, S.   3 SINFONIAS.  FL,OB,CL                                      SO
ROUSSEAU, N.   3 JOUETS, OP 53 (1955).  OB,CL,BSN                       CBD
ROZMANN, A.   5 PEZZI (1963/75).  FL,CL,BSN                             STI
RUDZINSKI, Z.   TRIO.  2CL,BSN                                          PWM
RUEFF, J.   3 PIECES.  OB,CL,BSN                                        ALE
RUELLE, F.   AUTOUR DU CHATEAU.  OB,CL,BSN                              MAU
RUELLE, F.   ROMANCE.  SOP SAX,2CL                                      EBR
RYBAR, J.   TRIO (1968).  FL,CL,BSN                                     CHF
RYCHLIK, J.   RELAZIONI (1963).  AFL,EHN,BSN                            ART
RYGER, A.   TRIO (1957).  FL,CL,BSN                                     ISR
SALBERT, D.   MUSIK FUR 3.  OB,CL,BSN                                   MV
SALIERI, A.   DANSE (TARARE).  FL,OB,CL                                 EDM
SALOMON, K.   ELEGIE & TANZ.  OB,2FL                                    IMP
SAMTER, A.   SKETCH.  OB,CL,BSN                                         ROB
SAMYN, N.   5 TRIOS (PUB SEPARATELY).  2CL,ASAX                         BIL
SAUGUET, H.   TRIO.  OB,CL,BSN                                          EDL
SAVNIK, V.   FUGHETTA.  FL,OB,BSN                                       KAW
SCARMOLIN, A.   BARCAROLLE & PETITE HUMORESQUE.  2CL,BSN(BCL)           LU
SCARMOLIN, A.   GHOSTLY TALE, A.  OB,CL,BSN                             BA
SCHAEFFER, D. (ARR).   GRANT US PEACE.  FL,OB(FL),CL                    PO
SCHAEFFER, D. (ARR).   10 WOODWIND TRIOS.  FL,OB(FL),CL                 PO
SCHALK, C.   RICERCARE ON AN OLD ENGLISH MELODY.  2FL,CL               CON
SCHICKELE, P.   COMMEDIA.  2OB,BSN                                      TP
SCHIFF, H.   DIVERTIMENTO.  OB,CL,BSN                                   LDO
SCHISKE, K.   TRIO SONATA, OP 41 (1954).  2OB,BSN                       LDO
SCHLEMM, G.   TRIO.  OB,CL,BSN                                          ETB
SCHMIDT, W.   PRELUDE & FUGUE.  FL,CL,BSN                               WI
SCHMIT, C.   TRIO (1945).  OB,CL,BSN                                    CBD
SCHNEIDER, W.   TRIOSPIEL NACH ALTEN MEISTERN.  FL,OB,CL                MV
SCHOEMAKER, M.   SUITE CHAMPETRE (1940).  OB,CL,BSN                     CBD
SCHOONENBEEK, K.   SEANCE A 3 (1973).  OB,CL,BSN                        SD
SCHRODER, H.   DIVERTIMENTO.  FL,EHN,BSN                                PET
SCHUBERT, F.-GREENE.   TRIO MOVEMENT.  2CL,BSN                          GAL
SCHUMANN, R.-SEAY.   SUITE.  OB(FL),CL,BSN                              SPR
SCHWADRON, A.   TRIO.  OB,CL,BSN                                        PMP
SCLATER, J.   TRIO.  FL,CL,BSN                                          WI
SEEGER, P.   KLEINES KONZERT ZU DRITT.  3 B FL INSTR                    PGM
SEHLBACH, E.   5 BAGATELLEN, OP119.  FL,OB,BSN                          MV
SEMLER-COLLERY, J.   DIVERTISSEMENTS.  OB,CL,BSN                        SEM
SEREBRIER, J.   SUITE CANINA.  OB,CL,BSN                                SN
SERMILA, J.   3 PEZZI PICCOLI.  2CL,BSN                                 FIN
SHAPERO, H.   3 PIECES.  WW TRIO                                        SN
SHERARD.   ADAGIO & ALLEGRO.  FL(OB),CL,BSN                             CST
SHOSTAKOVITCH, D.   PRELUDES.  FL,CL,BSN                                EDM
SICHLER, J.   TRIO D'ANCHES.  OB,CL,BSN                                 COM
SIENNICKI, E.   PONY RIDE.  FL,CL,BSN(BCL)                              LU
SIENNICKI, E.   POPULATION ZERO.  FL,CL,BSN(BCL)                        LU
SIMEONOV, B.   MAX & MORITZ (1952).  OB,CL,BSN                          CAN
SKOLNIK, W.   3 CANONIC TUNES.  FL,OB,CL                                EDM
SLAVICKY, K.   TRIO (1937).  OB,CL,BSN                                  ART
SMIT, A.   TRIO.  OB,CL,BSN                                             MAU
SMITH, L.   TRIO FOR WOODWINDS.  OB,CL,BSN                              ACA
SODERHOLM, V.   PRELUDIUM OCH FUGA (1970).  FL,OB,BSN                   STI
SORENSON, T.   TRIO #1, OP 19.  FL,CL,EHN                               STI
SORENSON, T.   TRIO #2, OP 33 (1959).  FL,CL,BSN                        STI
SOUFFRIAU, A.   TRIO, OP 49.  OB,CL,BSN                                 MAU
SPERRY.   PEACH TREE.  3WW                                              TM
SPISAK, N.   SONATINA (1946).  OB,CL,BSN                                AP
SPRATT, J.   3 MINIATURES.  OB(FL),CL,BSN                               SPR
SREBOTNJAK, A.   SERENATA.  FL,CL,BSN                                   EDD
STACHOWIAK, L.   CHILDREN'S TRIO.  OB,CL,BSN                            PWM
STALLAERT, A.   EPITAPHES ET BAGATELLAS (1967).  OB,CL,BSN             SD
```

3 PARTS: WOODWINDS-310

```
STARY, K.   SUITE.   FL,OB(CL),BSN                                    HE
STEARNS, P.   5 SHORT PIECES.   OB,CL,BSN                             ACA
STEFFEN, W.   TRIO, OP 2.   OB,CL,BSN                                 B&B
STEINER, G.   SUITE (1958).   FL,CL,BSN                               SS
STEVENS, H.   TRIO.   FL,CL,BSN                                       ACA
STIEBER, H.   SPIELMUSIK #1.   2OB,BSN                                FRH
STIEBER, H.   SPIELMUSIK #2.   2FL,CL                                 FRH
STOCK, D.   ICICLES.   PIC,OB,E FL CL                                 ACA
STRAVINSKY, I.   PASTORALE.   FL,CL,BSN                               EDM
STRIETMAN, W.   DIVERTISSEMENT D'ANCHES.   OB,CL,BSN                  SD
STRINGFIELD, L.   CHIPMUNKS.   FL,CL,BSN                              EDM
SURTEL, M.   TRIO, OP 10 (1978-79).   FL,CL,BSN                       SD
SUTER, R.   DIVERTIMENTO (1955).   OB,CL,BSN                          EMO
SUTHOFF-GROSS, R.   FETZEN.   FL,OB,CL                                MV
SVARA, D.   WOODWIND TRIO.   FL,CL,BSN                                EDD
SWIDER, J.   LYRICAL MINIATURES.   OB,CL,BSN                          PWM
SYDEMAN, W.   TRIO.   3 TREBLE INSTR                                  SS
SZALOWSKY, A.   TRIO.   OB,CL,BSN                                     CHE
SZEKELY, E.   DIVERTIMENTO (1958).   OB,CL,BSN                        EMB
SZONYI, E.   5 ALTE TANZE.   OB,CL,BSN                                EMB
TALMELLI, A.   BACCANALE.   FL,CL,BSN                                 EDI
TANSMAN, A.   SUITE.   CL,OB,BSN                                      EES
TAPKOFF, D.   GRENOUILLE PRESOMPTUEUSE, LA, 3 CONTES MUSICAUX         ALE
    PIC,OB(EHN),CL(BCL),NAR AD LIB
TAYLOR, P.   CARRY ON BACH.   OB,CL,BSN                               JE
TCHAIKOVSKY, P.-TUSTIN.   HUMORESQUE, OP 10/2.   FL,OB,CL             BE
TCHEREPNIN, N.   DIVERTIMENTO.   FL,OB,BSN                            BEL
TELEMANN, G.-POLNAUER.   60 MINUETS.   FL(OB),OB,CL                   CF
THIRIET, M.   LAIS ET VIRELAIS.   OB,CL,BSN                           SEM
TOCH, E.   SONATINETTA, OP 84.   FL,CL,BSN                            BE
TOMASI, H.   CONCERT CHAMPETRE.   OB,CL,BSN                           HLE
TOPLIFF, R.   REFLECTIONS.   2CL,BSN                                  TP
TRIEBENSEE, J.   TRIO IN B FL MA.   2OB,EHN                           EK
TRIEBENSEE, J.   VARIATIONS ON A THEME OF HAYDN.   2OB,EHN            EK
TUBA GALLICALLIS.   EHN,2BSN                                          HEU
TUSTIN, W.   PASTORALE MODERNE.   FL,OB,CL                            BA
TUSTIN, W.   TARANTELLA.   FL,OB,CL                                   BA
TUSTIN, W.   WALTZING WOODWINDS.   FL,OB,CL                           BA
URBANNER, E.   8 APHORISMEN.   FL,CL,BSN                              LDO
VACHEY, H.   4 INSTANTANES.   OB,CL,BSN                               ALE
VALLIER, J.   TRIO D'ANCHES.   OB,CL,BSN                              ECH
VEIT, G.   KASSATION.   2CL,BSN                                       FS
VELDEN, R. VAN DER.   DIVERTIMENTO (1957).   OB,CL,BSN               CBD
VELLERE, L.   BAGATELLES.   OB,CL,BSN                                 MAU
VEREMANS, M.   TRIO #1 (1953).   OB,CL,BSN                            EME
VERESS, S.   SONATINA (1931).   OB,CL,BSN                            ESZ
VERHAAR, A.   TRIO, OP 38 (1949).   FL,OB,CL                          SD
VIECENZ.   TRIO.   2OB,EHN                                            FRH
VILLA-LOBOS, H.   TRIO.   OB,CL,BSN                                   EES
VILLA-LOBOS, H.   TRIO.   OB,CL,BSN                                   INT
VITALI-WIENANDT.   3 DANCES.   OB(FL),CL,BSN                          PO
VIVALDI, A.-OUBRADOUS.   CONCERTO #25 IN G MI.   FL,OB,BSN            EMT
VIVALDI, A.   CONCERTO IN G MI, F XII/4.   FL,OB,BSN                  RC
VIVALDI, A.-RAMPAL.   CONCERTO IN G MI, P402.   FL,OB,BSN             INT
VIVALDI, A.   GIGA.   FL(OB),CL,BSN                                   CST
VOGEL, W.   TERZETT.   FL/PIC,CL,BSN                                  S-V
VOGLER, E.   KLEINE STADT, DIE (1962).   FL,CL,BSN                    BRH
VOGT, G.   ADAGIO RELIGIOSO.   2OB(2CL),EHN(ASAX)                     BIL
VON KREISLER, A.   LITTLE TRIO.   2OB,EHN                             SO
VON KREISLER, A.   PASTELS.   FL,OB(FL),CL                            SO
VOORN, J.   TRIO (1975).   OB,CL,BSN                                  SD
VOXMAN, H. (ARR).   CHAMBER MUSIC FOR 3 WOODWINDS, VOL I             RU
    FL,OB(FL),CL
```

```
VOXMAN, H. (ARR).  CHAMBER MUSIC FOR 3 WOODWINDS, VOL II        RU
   FL,CL,BSN(B CL)
VREDENBURG, M.  TRIO (1965).  OB,CL,BSN                          SD
WAHREN, K.  EN 3 COULEURS (1977).  OB(FL),CL,BSN               B&B
WAILLY, P.-VOXMAN.  AUBADE.  FL,OB,CL                            RU
WAILLY, P.  AUBADE.  FL,OB,CL                                   EDS
WAILLY, P.  AUBADE.  FL,OB,CL                                    SO
WALKER, R.  BAGATELLE.  FL,OB,CL                                AMP
WALKER, R.  BALLET DANCE.  FL,OB,CL                              BA
WALKER, R.  CARAVAN.  FL,OB,CL                                   TM
WALKER, R.  SPRING DANCE.  FL,OB(CL),CL                          KN
WALSHE, M.  TRIO PASTORALE.  FL,OB,CL                            JE
WALTER, F.  EPISODEN.  2OB,EHN                                   WZ
WALTER, J.  CANONS IN THE CHURCH MODES.  3WW                    EDK
WALTHEW, R.  TRIOLET IN E FL MA.  OB,CL,BSN                      BH
WARFIELD, G.  2 FOR 3.  FL,OB(CL),CL                             BE
WASHBURN, R.  3 PIECES.  FL,CL,BSN(BCL)                          OX
WATERS, C.  SERENADE.  OB,CL,BSN                                PET
WAXMAN, D.  TRIO.  OB,CL,BSN                                     GA
WEBER, A.  TRIO D'ANCHES.  OB,CL,BSN                            ALE
WEEGENHUISE, J.  TRIO D'ANCHES (1973).  OB,CL,BSN               SD
WEINER, K.  3 PIECES, OP 20.  FL,EHN,CL                          UE
WEIS, F.  MUSIC (1928).  FL,CL,BSN                              SPD
WELANDER, S.  PRELUDIUM (1966).  FL,CL,BSN                      STI
WELANDER, S.  PRELUDIUM EFTER ETT SYNAGOGALT TEMA (1955).  3WW  STI
WELANDER, W.  DIVERTIMENTO.  OB,CL,BSN                          STI
WELLER (ARR).  ASH GROVE,THE.  FL,OB,BSN                        BNA
WELLER (ARR).  TIS A GIFT TO BE SIMPLE.  FL,OB,BSN             BNA
WELLER, D.(ARR).  ASH GROVE, THE.  FL,OB,BSN                   BNA
WELLER, D.(ARR).  TIS A GIFT TO BE SIMPLE.  FL,OB,BSN          BNA
WENNIG, H. (ARR).  VOLKSLIEDSATZE.  OB,CL,BSN                   FRH
WENTH, J.  DIVERTIMENTO IN B FL MA.  2OB,EHN                     EK
WENTH, J.  PETITE SERENADE CONCERTANTE.  2OB,EHN                 EK
WENTH, J.  SERENADE IN C MA.  2OB,EHN                            EK
WENTH, J.  VARIATIONS ON A THEME BY PAISIELLO.  2OB,EHN          EK
WERNER, J.  TRIO.  OB,CL,BSN                                    BIL
WESTERING, P.  SONATINE (1966).  FL,EHN,BSN                      SD
WIJDEVELD, W.  TRIO, OP 64 (1958).  FL,OB,BSN                    SD
WILDBERGER, J.  TRIO (1952).  OB,CL,BSN                         EMO
WILDER, A.  SUITE.  OB,CL,BSN                                   MAR
WILDGANS, F.  KLEINES KAMMERTRIO.  OB,EHN,BSN                   LDO
WILDGANS, F.  KLEINES TRIO.  FL,CL,BSN                          LDO
WILHELMER, A.  2 KLEINE SATZE.  3 B FL INSTR                    PGM
WILSON, D.  STABILE 11.  3WW                                    ACA
WISEMAN, C.-LEACH.  TRIO.  2FL,BSN                              ROP
WISSMER, P.  SERENADE.  OB,CL,BSN                               EDC
WLADIGEROFF, P.  TRIO (1951).  FL,CL,BSN                         HG
WOESTIJNE, D. VAN DE.  DIVERTIMENTO (1941).  OB,CL,BSN          CBD
WOLFL, J.-SCHROEDER.  2 TRIOS.  2CL,BSN                         EUL
WORTH-TUSTIN.  MUSIC BOX.  FL,OB,CL                              BA
YOST, M.-SCHULTZ/HAUSER.  TRIO IN F MA.  2CL,BSN               SCH
YUN, I.  RONDELL (1975).  OB,CL,BSN                            B&B
ZAGWIJN, H.  TRIO (1944).  FL,OB,CL                              SD
ZAGWIJN, H.  TRIO #2 (1949).  FL,OB,CL                           SD
ZANABONI, G.  PICCOLA SUITE.  OB,CL,BSN                          GZ
ZBINDEN, J.  TRIO, OP 12.  OB,CL,BSN                            HLE
ZEHM, F.  TRIO CAPRICCIOSO.  FL,OB,BSN                          ROB
ZELENKA, I.  RITOURNELLES (1975).  FL,OB,BSN                    EDT
ZENTNER, J.  SUITE.  3WW                                        ERM
ZIERITZ, G. VON.  KAPRIOLEN.  OB,CL,BSN                         R&E
ZIPOLI, D.-JOHNSON.  ITALIAN AIRS & DANCES.  OB,CL,BSN          BH
ZOELLER, C.  AUF DER ALM PASTORALE.  2CL,BSN                    BH
```

ZULAWSKI, W. ARIA CON VARIAZIONI (1950). FL,CL,BSN   PWM

3 PARTS: 2 FLUTES-KEYBOARD-311

ABACO, E. TRIO SONATA, OP 3/2 IN F MA. 2FL,BC	PET
ABEL, C.-SONNTAG. SONATA, OP 16/1 IN G MA. 2FL,BC	HEI
ABEL, C.-SONNTAG. SONATA, OP 16/4 IN C MA. 2FL,BC	HEI
ADAM, A. O HOLY NIGHT	RU
ADAMS, S.-DE LAMATER. HOLY CITY, THE	RU
ARMA, P. 3 RESONANCES	BIL
BACH, C.P.E.-JOHNEN. 12 KLEINE STUCKE, WQ 82	PET
BACH, C.P.E. 12 LITTLE PIECES, W 81	PET
BACH, C.P.E. 12 LITTLE PIECES	EDK
BACH, C.P.E.-WALTHER. TRIO IN E FL MA	WZ
BACH, C.P.E. TRIO IN E MA. 2FL,BC	WZ
BACH, C.P.E. TRIO IN E MA, WQ162	EDK
BACH, J.C.-MOYSE. DIVERTISSEMENT	SO
BACH, J.C.-NAGEL. TRIO IN G MA. 2FL,BC	WMS
BACH, J.C. TRIO. 2FL,BC	MV
BACH, J.S. CONCERTO, BWV1057	EDK
BACH, J.S.-LAWTON. SHEEP MAY SAFELY GRAZE	OX
BACH, J.S.-CRUSSARD. SONATA. 2FL,BC	ECS
BACH, J.S. SONATA IN G MA	HA
BACH, J.S.-RABAUD. SONATA IN G MA, BWV1039	DUR
BACH, J.S. SONATE IN G MA, BWV1039	BRH
BACH, J.S.-SEIFFERT. TRIO IN G MA. 2FL,BC	BRH
BACH, J.S.-SEIFFERT. TRIO IN G MA, BWV1039	B&N
BACH, J.S.-BELAUBRE. TRIO SONATA. 2FL,BC	BIL
BACH, J.S.-LANDSHOFF. TRIO SONATA #2 IN G MA. 2FL,BC	PET
BACH, J.S.-SCHMITZ/SCHNEIDER. TRIOSONATE IN G MA, BWM1039	B&N
BACH, W.F.-VAN LEEUWEN. SONATE IN D MA	WZ
BACH, W.F.-SEIFFERT. TRIO (ALLEGRO) IN A MI. 2FL,BC	BRH
BACH, W.F. TRIO #1 IN D MA. 2FL,BC	EDK
BACH, W.F. TRIO #1 IN D MA. 2FL,BC	INT
BACH, W.F. TRIO #2 IN D MA. 2FL,BC	EDK
BACH, W.F. TRIO #2 IN D MA. 2FL,BC	INT
BACH, W.F. TRIO #3 IN A MI. 2FL,BC	INT
BACH, W.F. TRIO IN A MI. 2FL,BC	EDK
BACH, W.F.-SEIFFERT. TRIO IN D MA, #1. 2FL,BC	BRH
BACH, W.F.-SEIFFERT. TRIO IN D MA, #2. 2FL,BC	BRH
BARNARD, G. GLORIANA,. 2 D FL PIC,PF	CF
BARRE, M. DE LA-VIOLLIER. SONATA V. 2FL,BC	HEI
BEAUMONT. CON AMORE	CEN
BECKERATH, A. SONATINA	S&C
BEETHOVEN, L. VAN-SPIEGL. ADAGIO FOR A FLUTE CLOCK	OX
BEETHOVEN, L. VAN. MOONLIGHT SONATA (ADAGIO)	CEN
BELLINI, V. DUET (NORMA)	CF
BELLINZANI, P. TRIO SONATAS IN E MI, B-FLAT MA AND F MI	MV
BENDA, F.-RAMPAL. TRIO IN G MA	INT
BENDA, F.-RUF. TRIOSONATE IN G MA. 2FL,BC	HEI
BENT, R. SWISS BOY,. 2PIC,PF	CF
BERLIOZ, H.-BUTTERWORTH. TRIO (THE CHILDHOOD OF CHRIST)	CA
BERLIOZ, H.-BRAUN. TRIO	UE
BERLIOZ, H. TRIO OF THE YOUNG ISHMAELITES	EDM
BERLIOZ, H.-RICHTER. TRIO, OP 25	WZ
BISCARDI, C. TENZONE	TP
BIZET, G. ADAGIETTO	EDM
BIZET, G. ARAGONAISE	EDM

```
BIZET, G.   CARILLON (L'ARLESIENNE)                                    EDM
BIZET, G.   ENTR'ACTE                                                  EDM
BIZET, G.   MINUET                                                     EDM
BIZET, G.   MINUET #2                                                  EDM
BIZET, G.-ANDRAUD.  3 PIECES                                           SO
BOEHM, T.-PELLERITE.  3 DUETS.  FL,AFL,PF                              ZA
BOISMORTIER, J.-RUF.  CONCERTO IN A MI                                 RC
BOISMORTIER, J.-RUF.  CONCERTO IN C MA                                 RC
BOISMORTIER, J.-HIBY.  SONATA IN G MA, OP 34/2.  2FL,BC                HEI
BOISMORTIER, J.-GOURRIER.  3 SUITES                                    GA
BOISMORTIER, J.-RUF.  TRIO-SONATE IN F MA.  2FL,BC                     SCH
BOISMORTIER, J.-RUF.  TRIO-SONATE IN G MA.  2FL,BC                     SCH
BONNER, E.   OVER THE HILLS                                            EDM
BONONCINI, G.-GIESBERT.  7 SUITES, 2 VOLS                              SCH
BORODIN, A.   SOLICITUDE                                               EDM
BOUSQUET, N.   GOLDEN ROBIN POLKA.  2 D FL PIC,PF                      CF
BRITTEN, B.   GEMINI VARIATIONS                                        GS
BROWN, T.   FRECKLES & FLOWERS                                         KN
BUCHTEL, F.   BONITA                                                   BE
BUCHTEL, F.   2 IMPS                                                   KJ
BURGHARDT, H.   PARTITA BREVIS II                                      B&N
BURKHARD, W.   CANZONA, OP 76A (1947)                                  B&N
CALIFANO, A.-BRINCKMANN/MOHR.  SONATA A TRE IN G MA.  2FL,BC           B&N
CASTELLO, D.-BLOCK.  SONATAS NOS. 3 & 4.  2FL,BC                       NOM
CHEDEVILLE, N.   SCHERZO                                               EDM
CHELLERI, F.-MOHR.  SONATA IN E MI.  2FL,BC                            MV
CHON.  DOUBLE TOOTIN' FLUTES                                           RU
CHRISTENSEN, J.   HOLIDAY ON ICE                                       KN
CIMAROSA, D.  OUDRADOUS.  CONCERTANTE                                  EMT
CIMAROSA, D.-MOYSE.  CONCERTO IN G MA                                  SO
CIMAROSA, D.-PICCIOLI.  CONCERTO IN G MA                               INT
CIMAROSA, D.-RAMPAL.  CONCERTO IN G MA                                 JB
CIMAROSA, D.-WOLLHEIM.  CONCERTO IN G MA                               B&B
CONLEY, L.   DIALOGUE                                                  KN
CONLEY, L.   REFLECTIONS                                               KN
CORBETT, W.-DAWES.  SONATA IN G MI                                     S&C
CORBETT, W.   3 SONATAS.  2FL,BC                                       PET
CORELLI, A.   AIR & DANCE                                              EDM
CORELLI, A.   GAVOTTE & GIGUE                                          EDM
CORELLI, A.   GIGUE                                                    EDM
CORELLI, A.-MOECK.  SONATA #2.  2FL,BC                                 S&C
CORELLI, A.   SONATA DA CAMERA, OP  2/1,5,7.  2FL,BC                   PET
CORRETTE, M.-RUF.  CONCERTO IN A MA, OP  3/3.  2FL,BC                  SCH
COUPERIN, F.-HIGGINBOTTOM.  ESPAGNOLE, L'.  2FL,BC                     MR
DANSBY, E.   DANDY DUO                                                 KN
DEMERSSEMAN, J.   BALLADINE                                            BIL
DEVIENNE, F.-LASOCKI.  SYMPHONIE CONCERTANTE IN G MA, OP 76            MR
DIJK, J. VAN.  SUITE (1956)                                           SD
DONIZETTI, G.   SEXTETTE (LUCIA DI LAMMERMOOR)                        CF
DOPPLER, F.-EPHROSS.  ANDANTE & RONDO                                  SO
DOPPLER, F.-RAMPAL.  ANDANTE & RONDO, OP 25                            INT
DOPPLER, F.   ANDANTE & RONDO, OP 25                                   MR
DOPPLER, F.-ADORJAN.  CONCERTO IN D MI                                 BIL
DOPPLER, F.-ADORJAN.  DUETTINO HONGROIS, OP 36                         BIL
DOPPLER, F.   HUNGARIAN PHANTASY, OP 35                                MR
DOPPLER, F.-EPHROSS.  VALSE DI BRAVURA                                 SO
DOPPLER, F.   VALSE DI BRAVURA, OP 33                                  MR
DOPPLER, F. & K.   RIGOLETTO-FANTAISIE, OP 38                          BIL
DOPPLER, F. & K.   SOUVENIR DE PRAGUE, OP 24                           MR
DORNEL, L.-RUF.  SUITE IN D MI                                         SCH
EASY FLUTE SOLOS OR DUETS.  2FL,PF                                     MS
ENDRESEN, R.   PRAIRIE WARBLERS                                        RU
```

3 PARTS: 2 FLUTES-KEYBOARD-311

```
ENDRESEN, R.   PROMENADE                                          RU
ENDRESEN, R.   2 FLIERS, THE                                      RU
ERBACH, F.-SCHULTZ.   3 DIVERTISSEMENTS MELODIEUX.   2FL,BC       SCH
ERDMANN, V.   MOBILE                                             MV
EVENING WITH VIVALDI, AN.                                         B3
EXAUDET, J.   COUR DE LA MARQUISE, LA                            EDM
FABRE, C.-HARRIS.   REVERIE                                       CF
FABRE, C.   REVERIE #2                                            CF
FELDERHOF, J.   SHORT STORY                                       HU
FESCH, W. DE-RUF.   CONCERTO IN G MA, OP 10/8                    SCH
FESCH, W. DE.   3 SONATAS, OP 12/1/3.   2FL,BC                   PET
FESCH, W. DE-NOSKE.   SONATE, OP 12/1-3                          EDH
FESCH, W. DE-SCHROEDER.   3 SONATEN, OP 7/2,4,8.   2FL,BC        HEI
FESCH, W. DE-SCHOUWMAN.   TRIOSONATEN, OP 12/1-3.   2FL,BC       B&N
FILTZ, A.-SONNTAG.   SONATA, OP 2/3 IN G MA.   2FL,BC            HEI
FILTZ, A.-SONNTAG.   SONATA, OP 2/4 IN D MA.   2FL,BC            HEI
FLOTOW, F.-BUCHTEL.   AH! SO FAIR (MARTHA)                        KJ
FOCKING, H.   SONATA, OP 1/2.   2FL,BC                           EDH
FOSTER, S.-TR. MAGANINI.   VILLAGE FESTIVAL, A                   EDM
FOTE, R.   TUTTI FLUTI                                           KN
FRESCOBALDI, G.-DAVID.   5 CANZONI PER SONAR.   2FL,BC           SCH
FRID, G.   12 METAMORPHOSEN, OP 54 (1957)                        SD
FURSTENAU, A.   RONDO BRILLANT, OP102                            EDH
FURSTENAU, A.   RONDO BRILLIANT                                  EDM
FURSTENAU, A.   UNION, L', OP115                                 MR
GALUPPI, B.-SCHROEDER.   CONCERTO IN E MI                        HEI
GARLICK, A.   2 TRIO MANUSCRIPTS.   2FL,HPCD                     SS
GAUBERT, P.   DIVERTISSEMENT GREC.   2FL,PF(HP)                  ALE
GEBAUER, F.-WEELINK.   TRIO #2 IN C MI.   CL,HN,BSN              KAW
GENZMER, H.   SONATA                                            S&C
GIOVANNINI, C.   THEME FOR A QUIET DAY                           ETP
GOSSEC, F.-MAGANINI.   GAVOTTE                                    CF
GOUNOD, C.-LAUBE.   AVE MARIA                                     CF
GRAF ZU ERBACH, F.-ERBRECHT.   DIVERTISSEMENT MELODIEUX         KIS
   2FL,BC
GRAUN, C.-KOLBEL.   SONATE IN E FL MA.   2FL,BC                  B&N
GRAUN, C.-GERLACH.   TRIOSONATE IN F MA.   2FL,BC                HMO
GRAUN, K.-STADELMANN.   TRIOSONATE IN D MA.   2FL,BC             LEU
GRAUPNER, C.   CANON IN F MA.   2FL(2OB),BC                      MV
GRAUPNER, C.   CONCERTO #35                                      EUL
GRAUPNER, C.-ROTTLER.   CONCERTO IN E MI                         LEU
GRIEG, E.   TO SPRING                                            CEN
GRONEMAN, A.   SONATA, OP 2/2                                    HE
GROOMS, C. (ARR).   DARK EYES (RUSSIAN SONG)                     CEN
HANDEL, G.-GLASER.   ALLEGRO (SONATA #2)                          CF
HANDEL, G.-SEIFFERT.   CHAMBER TRIO # 8 IN G MI                  BRH
   2FL(2OB)(FL,OB),BC
HANDEL, G.-SEIFFERT.   CHAMBER TRIO #13 IN G MI.   2FL(2OB),BC   BRH
HANDEL, G.-SEIFFERT.   CHAMBER TRIO #14 IN G MI.   2FL(2OB),BC   BRH
HANDEL, G.-SEIFFERT.   CHAMBER TRIO #19 IN G MA.   2FL,BC        BRH
HANDEL, G.-BELL/CUCKSTON.   SONATA IN E MI                       PET
HANDEL, G.-PARKINSON.   TRIO SONATA IN G MI.   2FL,BC            OX
HANDEL, G.-NAGEL.   TRIOSONATE IN E MI                           SCH
HANDEL, G.   TRIOSONATE.   2FL,BC                                B&V
HANDEL, G.-SCHNEIDER.   TRIOSONATEN, OP 5.   2FL,BC              BA
HARRIS, F.   2 BUCKAROOS                                         LU
HARRIS, F.   2 LARKS                                             LU
HARRIS, F.   2 MARIONETTES                                       LU
HARRIS, F.   PETITE MAZURKA                                      LU
HASSE, J.-SCHENK.   SONATA A 3 IN D MA, OP 3/6.   2FL,BC         LDO
HASSE, J.   SONATA IN C MA.   2FL,BC                             HU
HASSE, J.-FROTSCHER.   TRIO SONATA IN D MA.   2FL,BC             NV
```

```
HASSE, J.-WALTHER.  TRIO SONATA IN G MA.  2FL,BC            WZ
HASSE, J.-RUF.  TRIO-SONATE IN E MI                        SCH
HASSE, J.-RUF.  TRIO-SONATE IN G MA                        SCH
HAVLICEK, L.  2 CANARIES                                   PO
HAYDN, F.  6 GERMAN DANCES                                 HU
HAYDN, F.  OXEN MINUET                                     CF
HEILBUT, P.  MUSIZIERBUCH                                  HUG
HOTTETERRE, J.-HECHLER.  SUITE IN C                        HMO
HOTTETERRE, J.  TRIO SONATAS, OP  3/1, 2                   EUL
HOTTETERRE, J.  TRIO SONATAS, OP  3/3, 4                   EUL
HOTTETERRE, J.  TRIO SONATAS, OP  3/5, 6                   EUL
HOTTETERRE, J.-LASOCKI/BLOCK.  3 TRIO SONATAS, OP 3/1-3    NOM
    2FL,BC
HOTTETERRE, J.-LASOCKI/BLOCK.  3 TRIO SONATAS, OP 3/4-6    NOM
    2FL,BC
HOTTETERRE, J.-RUF.  TRIO-SONATE IN G MI, OP  3/1          SCH
HOTTETERRE, J.-RUF.  TRIOSONATE IN D MA, OP  3/2.  2FL,BC  SCH
HURNIK, I.  TRIO.  2FL,HPCD                                CHF
JACCHINI, G.  TRIO SONATA, OP  5/3, IN G MA.  2FL,BC       PET
JOMELLI, N.  TRIOSONATE                                    FRH
KENNEDY-HARRIS.  STAR OF THE EAST                          LU
KESNAR, M.  PETIT RIEN, UN                                 EDM
KLEINKNECHT, J.-HOFFMANN.  SONATA IN G MA.  2FL,BC         MV
KLEINKNECHT, J.  SONATA IN G                               MV
KLING, H.-CATLIN.  TWO LITTLE BULFINCHES POLKA.  2PIC,PF   CF
KOEHLER, E.-WYE.  VALSE DES FLEURS                         JE
KREBS, J.-NAGEL.  TRIO IN D MA.  2FL,BC                    WMS
KREBS, J.-NAGEL.  TRIO IN E MI.  2FL,BC                    WMS
KREBS, J.-RUF.  TRIO-SONATE IN B MI.  2FL,BC               SCH
KREBS, J.-ERBRECHT.  TRIOSONATE IN B MI.  2FL,BC           KIS
KUHLAU, F.-RAMPAL.  TRIO, OP119                            INT
KUHLAU, F.  TRIO, OP119                                    BIL
KUTSCH, B.  JUNGE FLOTIST, DER                             WZ
LABITZKY, A.  HERD GIRL'S DREAM, THE                       CF
LE MARE, E.-MAGANINI.  ANDANTINO                           CF
LECLAIR, J.-RUF.  RECREATION DE MUSIQUE #2, OP  8.  2FL,BC B&N
LECLAIR, J.  SONATE A 3                                    HU
LESTER, L.  CRIMSON BLUSHES                                CEN
LINDE, H.  TRIO.  FL,AFL,PF                                SCH
LINICKE, J.  OVERTURE IN C MA.  2FL,BC                     PET
LINICKE, J.-RUCKER.  2 SUITEN                              MIT
LINICKE, J.  2 SUITES                                      PET
LOCATELLI, P.-CRUSSARD.  SONATA.  2FL,BC                   ECS
LOCATELLI, P.  SONATE A TRE.  2FL,BC                       HU
LOCATELLI, P.-RIEMANN.  TRIO IN G MA, OP  3/1.  2FL,BC     BRH
LOCATELLI, P.  TRIO IN G MA, OP  3/1.  2FL,BC              INT
LOCATELLI, P.-ALBRECHT.  TRIO SONATA IN D MI, OP  5/5.  2FL,BC  KIS
LOCATELLI, P.-ALBRECHT.  TRIO SONATA IN G MA, OP  5/1.  2FL,BC  KIS
LOCATELLI, P.-ALBRECHT.  TRIO-SONATE IN C MA, OP  5/4.  2FL,BC  KIS
LOCATELLI, P.-RUF.  TRIO-SONATE IN E MA, OP  5/3.  2FL,BC  SCH
LOCATELLI, P.-KOLBEL.  TRIOSONATE, OP  5/1, IN G MA.  2FL,BC  HEI
LOEILLET, J.-BEON.  SONATA IN E MI                         INT
LOEILLET, J.  SONATA IN E MI                               HLE
LOEILLET, J.  SONATA IN E MI, OP  1 #6                     MR
LOEILLET, J.-BLOCK.  SONATA IN G MA, OP  1 #2              MR
LOEILLET, J.-BEON.  SONATA IN G MI                         INT
LOEILLET, J.  SONATA IN G MI                               EDK
LOEILLET, J.  SONATA IN G MI                               HLE
LOEILLET, J.-BEECHEY.  2 SONATAS, OP  5/1, 4               OX
LOEILLET, J.-POULTEAU.  SONATE EN TRIO IN B MI, OP  2/8    ALE
    2FL,BC
LOEILLET, J.-SCHROEDER.  TRIOSONATE IN G MA, OP  1/2.  2FL,BC  MV
```

LOEILLET, J.B. SONATA A 3, #17	CF
LOEILLET, J.B.-RUF. TRIO SONATA IN D MA, OP 1/4. 2FL,BC	SCH
LOEILLET, J.B.-RUF. TRIO SONATA IN E MI, OP 1/6. 2FL,BC	SCH
LOEILLET, J.B.-RUF. TRIO SONATA IN G MA, OP 1/2. 2FL,BC	SCH
LOEILLET, J.B.-RUF. TRIOSONATE IN G MA, OP 2/12. 2FL,BC	B&N
LUENING, O. SUITE. 2FL,PF,VC AD LIB	SER
LULLY, J.-RIKKO. FRENCH DANCES	M&M
LULLY, J.-MATTHES. 20 STUCKE	HUG
MAGANINI, Q. TWINS	CF
MAGANINI, Q. (ARR). CONCERT ALBUM	EDM
MAGANINI, Q. (ARR). PARIS SOIR	EDM
MARTINI, J. PLAISIR D'AMOUR	EDM
MC CAUGHEY, W. ENCHANTED ISLE	CF
MICHAEL. NEPENTHES RAJAH (1970), OP 23. FL,AFL,PF	B&N
MONDONVILLE, J. SONATA IN G MA	EDS
MONTI, V. CSARDAS	CF
MORE EASY FLUTE SOLOS.	MS
MOYSE, L.(ARR). 40 SHORT DUETS FOR BEGINNER FLUTISTS	GS
MOZART, W. 8 MENUETS, K315A	HU
NARDINI, P. SHEPHERD'S PIPES	EDM
NARDINI, P.-GUMBEL. TRIO IN C MA. 2FL,BC	B&N
OFFENBACH, J.-BUCHTEL. BARCAROLLE (TALES OF HOFFMANN)	KJ
PACKER, W. SEA BREEZE	KN
PAISIBLE, J.-FRIEDRICH. SONATAS #1-5 (PUB SEPARATELY)	S&C
PEPUSCH, J.-RUF. TRIO SONATA IN B FL MA. 2FL,BC	SCH
PEZ, J. TRIO SONATA IN C MA. 2FL,BC	PET
PONCE, M.-MAGANINI. ESTRELLITA	CF
POPULAR FLUTE.	HY
PROWO, P.-FRIEDRICH. SONATA A 3, #5	S&C
PROWO, P.-FRIEDRICH. SONATA A 3, #6	S&C
PUCCINI, G.-STEBBING. MUSETTA'S WALTZ SONG	RC
PUCCINI, G.-STEBBING. VISSI D'ARTE, VISSI D'AMORE	BE
PURCELL, D.-RUF. TRIO-SONATE IN D MI. 2FL,BC	SCH
PURCELL, H.-BERGMANN. CHACONNE	S&C
PURCELL, H.-FINK. 2 SYMPHONIES. 2FL,BC	ECS
PURCELL, H.-BERGMANN. 3 SYMPHONIES	S&C
PURCELL, H.-JUST. TRIOSTUCKE. 2FL,BC	SCH
QUANTZ, J.-VOXMAN/BLOCK. CONCERTO #1 IN G MI	MR
QUANTZ, J.-CRUSSARD. SONATA. 2FL,BC	ECS
QUANTZ, J. SONATA ANDANTE	CF
QUANTZ, J.-SONNTAG. SONATA IN D MA. 2FL,BC	HEI
QUANTZ, J.-SONNTAG. SONATA IN D MI. 2FL,BC	HEI
QUANTZ, J.-SONNTAG. SONATA IN G MA. 2FL,BC	HEI
QUANTZ, J. SONATE EN TRIO. 2FL,HPCD	HUG
QUANTZ, J.-KOCH. TRIO IN A MI. 2FL(2OB),BC	MV
QUANTZ, J.-LASOCKI-MADDEN. TRIO SONATA IN C MI (K33). 2FL,BC	NOM
QUANTZ, J.-RUF. TRIO SONATA IN D MA	RC
QUANTZ, J.-LASOCKI-MADDEN. TRIO SONATA IN E MI (K28). 2FL,BC	NOM
QUANTZ, J. TRIO SONATA IN E MI. 2FL,BC	BRH
QUANTZ, J.-ERBRECHT. TRIOSONATE IN A MI. 2FL,BC	KIS
QUANTZ, J.-PISTORIUS. TRIOSONATE IN F MI. 2FL,BC	HSM
QUANTZ, J.-RUF. TRIOSONATE IN G MA. 2FL,BC	B&N
RACHMANINOFF, S. POLKA ITALIENNE	EDM
RAMEAU, J. RIGODON DE DARDANUS	EDM
RENOSTO. MIXAGE	RC
RICKER. ORIENTAL DANCE	PO
RONTGEN, J. LAMENTO (1956)	SD
ROSAS, J. OVER THE WAVES	CEN
ROSSINI, G. POWER ETERNAL (STABAT MATER)	KJ
SAINT-SAENS, C. MY HEART AT THY SWEET VOICE	CEN
SALIERI, A. DANSE (TARARE)	EDM
SAMMARTINI, G.-RAMPAL. 6 SONATAS, OP 6, 2 VOLS	INT

```
SAMMARTINI, G.-GIESBERT.  12 SONATAS, 3 VOLS.  2FL,BC        SCH
SARGENT-BARRINGTON.  NIP & TUC.  2PIC,PF                     CF
SCHAEFFER, D. (ARR).  CHRISTMAS DUETS                        PO
SCHICKHARDT, J.  SONATA #6                                   HMP
SCHMITT, J.-GOTTRON.  CONCERTO IN G MA, OP 15                B&N
SCHUBERT, F.-FRANK.  MOMENT MUSICAL                          S&
SCHUBERT, F.  SERENADE                                       CEN
SCHULTZE, J.-FRIEDRICH.  OUVERTURE I IN F MA                 S&C
SCHULTZE, J.-MOECK.  OUVERTURE II IN B MA                    S&C
SCHULTZE, J.-MOECK.  OUVERTURE III IN A MI                   S&C
SCHULTZE, J.-FRIEDRICH.  SUITE                               S&C
SEGERHAMMAR, R.  LITTLE CASCADE WALTZ                        PO
SEHLBACH, E.  KLEINES KONZERT IN EINEM SATZ                  MV
SERRADELL.  GOLONDRINA, LA                                   CEN
SHOSTAKOVICH, D.  DUET (KING LEAR)                           GS
SIMEONE, H.  FLUTE COCKTAIL                                  SH
SROM, K.  CONCERTINO                                         PAN
STAMITZ, A.-LEBERMANN.  CONCERTO IN G MA                     SCH
STOLZEL, G.  SONATA I IN D MA.  2FL,BC                       HU
STOLZEL, G.-FROTSCHER.  TRIOSONATE IN G MA.  2FL,BC          HSM
SULLIVAN, A.-BENNETT/WYE.  TWILIGHT                          JE
SYDEMAN, W.  STUDY (1956)                                    SS
TCHAIKOVSKY, P.  SUITE (ALBUM FOR CHILDREN)                  EDM
TELEMANN, G.-OUBRADOUS.  CONCERTO.  2FL,BC                   EMT
TELEMANN, G.-MEYEROLBERSLEBEN.  CONCERTO IN A MA             HUG
TELEMANN, G.  CONCERTO IN B FL MA                            CFV
TELEMANN, G.-MOYSE.  CONCERTO IN E MI                        GS
TELEMANN, G.-DRATHS.  KLEINE TRIO-SATZE                      SCH
TELEMANN, G -SCHREITER.  SONATA                              INT
TELEMANN, G.-SCHREITER.  SONATA IN A MA.  2FL,BC             BRH
TELEMANN, G.-FUSSAN.  SONATA IN F MA.  2FL,BC                SCH
TELEMANN, G.-MONKEMEYER.  SONATA IN G MI.  2FL,BC            SCH
TELEMANN, G.-NAGY.  SUITE IN E MI                            EMB
TELEMANN, G.(SCHNEIDER).  3 TRIETTI E III SCHERZI, 3 VOLS    BRH
   2FL,BC
TELEMANN, G.  TRIO SONATA IN C MA.  2FL,PF                   BRH
TELEMANN, G.  TRIO SONATA IN C MA.  2FL,BC                   EDK
VALENTINE, R.-PEARSON.  TRIO SONATA IN A MI.  2FL,BC         S&C
VALENTINE, R.-PEARSON.  TRIO SONATA IN C MA.  2FL,BC         S&C
VALENTINE, R.-PEARSON.  TRIO SONATA IN D MI                  S&C
VALENTINE, R.  3 TRIO SONATAS.  2FL,BC                       MRL
VIOTTI, G.-RAMPAL.  CONCERTO IN A MA                         INT
VIVALDI, A.-GHEDINI.  CONCERTO IN C MA                       INT
VIVALDI, A.-RAMPAL.  CONCERTO IN C MA                        JB
VIVALDI, A.-SCHROEDER.  CONCERTO, OP 47/2, IN C MA, P76      EUL
VIVALDI, A.  GIGA                                            EDM
VRIES ROBBE, W. DE.  BUMBLE BEES (1975).  FL,VERMEULEN FL,PF SD
WAGNER, R.-ROBERTS.  SONG TO THE EVENING STAR (TANNHAUSER)   CF
WENDELGELST, H.  FACE THE MUSIC, 3 VOLS                      HU
WESLEY, S.-COBBE.  TRIO IN F MA                              OX
WILLIAMS, W.-DART.  SONATA IN IMITATION OF BIRDS.  2FL,BC    OX
WILLSON, M.  76 TROMBONES                                    BT
WOOD.  LET 'ER GO                                            CEN
YASHIRO, A.  SONATA                                          TP
ZAGWIJN, H.  PASTORALE & SCHERZO                             PET
ZIMMERMAN.  PLAY A SONG OF AMERICA                           TP
ZIMMERMAN.  PLAY A SONG OF CHRISTMAS                         TP
```

3 PARTS: 2 OBOES-KEYBOARD-312

ALBINONI, T.-GIEGLING. CONCERTO A 5, OP 9/ 3	MR
ALBINONI, T.-GIEGLING. CONCERTO A 5, OP 9/ 6	MR
ALBINONI, T.-GIEGLING. CONCERTO A 5, OP 9/ 9	MR
ALBINONI, T.-GIEGLING. CONCERTO A 5, OP 9/12	MR
ALBINONI, T. CONCERTO IN C MA, OP 7/2	EUL
ALBINONI, T.-KOLNEDER. CONCERTO IN C MA, OP 7/5	EUL
ALBINONI, T.-KOLNEDER. CONCERTO IN F MA, OP 9/3	EUL
BACH, J.S.-HINDERMANN. TRIO SONATA IN B MI. 2OB D'AMORE,BC	HUG
BARRE, M. DE LA-VIOLLIER. SONATE V IN G MA. 2OB,BC	HEI
BELLINZANI, P. TRIOSONATEN IN E MI, B-FLAT MA AND F MI	MV
BODINUS, S.-KOCH. TRIOSONATE #1. 2OB,BC	MV
BOISMORTIER, J.-RUF. CONCERTO IN A MI	RC
BOISMORTIER, J.-RUF. CONCERTO IN C MA	RC
BOISMORTIER, J.-RUF. TRIO SONATA IN F MA. 2OB,BC	SCH
CASTELLO, D.-BLOCK. SONATAS 3 & 4. 2OB,BC	NOM
CORELLI, A. SONATE IN A MI, OP 4/5. 2OB,BC	HU
CORELLI, A. SONATE IN F MA, OP 4/7. 2OB,BC	HU
FASCH, J. SONATA A 3 IN E MI. 2OB(2FL),BC	MV
FINGER, G.-HOLMAN. SONATA IN B FL MA. 2OB,BC	NOM
FIORILLO, F.-STEINBECK. SINFONIA CONCERTANTE IN F MA	EUL
GARSCIA, J. TRIFLES, OP 42	PWM
HANDEL, F. KAMMERTRIO #1 IN B FL MA. 2OB,BC	BRH
HANDEL, G. KAMMERTRIO #2 IN D MI. 2OB,BC	BRH
HANDEL, G. KAMMERTRIO #4 IN F MA. 2OB,BC	BRH
HANDEL, G. KAMMERTRIO #6 IN D MA. 2OB,BC	BRH
HANDEL, G. SONATA IN D MA	INT
HANDEL, G. SONATA IN D MI	INT
HANDEL, G. SONATA IN E FL MA	INT
HANDEL, G. SONATA IN G MI, OP 2/2. 2OB,BC	INT
HANDEL, G.-FLESCH/BERNSTEIN. 6 SONATAS. 2OB,BC	DEU
HEINICHEN, J.-JANETZKY. SONATA A 3 IN C MI. 2OB,BC	WMS
HEINICHEN, J. SONATA A 3. 2OB,HPCD	FRH
HEINICHEN, J.-RUF. TRIOSONATE IN C MI. 2OB,BC	SCH
HOTTETERRE, L. LE ROMAIN. 6 TRIO SONATAS, OP 3. 2OB,BC	NOM
HOVHANESS, A. SONATA, OP130. 2OB,ORG	PET
LOEILLET, J.-POULTEAU. SONATE EN TRIO, OP 2/8. 2OB,BC	ALE
LULLY, J. FRENCH DANCES	M&M
PALA, J. 3 MINIATUREN	MOL
PEPUSCH, J.-RUF. TRIO-SONATE IN B FL MA. 2OB,BC	SCH
PEPUSCH, J.-ERBRECHT. TRIOSONATE IN D MA. 2OB,BC	KIS
PEPUSCH, J.-ERBRECHT. TRIOSONATE IN F MA. 2OB(2FL),BC	KIS
PEPUSCH, J.-RUF. TRIOSONATE IN F MA. 2OB,BC	SCH
PEPUSCH, J.-ERBRECHT. TRIOSONATE IN G MA. 2OB(2FL),BC	KIS
PEZEL, J.-DOV. 6 SONATINAS (NOS.1,2,3,7,9,11). 2OB,BC	NOM
QUANTZ-RUF. TRIO SONATA IN E MI. 2OB,BC	SCH
QUANTZ, J.-RUF. TRIO SONATA IN D MA	RC
QUANTZ, J.-RUF. TRIOSONATE IN E MI. 2OB,BC	SCH
QUANTZ, J.-RUF. TRIOSONATE IN G MA. 2OB,BC	B&N
ROMAN, J. SONATA A TRE	CHE
SAMMARTINI, G.-LAUSCHMANN. CONCERTO	FOR
SCHAEFFER, D. (ARR). CHRISTMAS DUETS	PO
SINGER, S. CONCERTO IN D MI	M&M
STOLZEL, G.-OSTHOFF. TRIOSONATE IN F MI. 2OB,BC	B&N
STRADELLA, A.-KOLNEDER. SINFONIA A 3. 2OB,BC	SCH
TELEMANN, G.-DRATHS. KLEINE TRIO-SATZE	SCH
VIVALDI, A.-HOMOLYA. CONCERTO IN A MI, F. VII/8	EMB

```
VIVALDI, A.-NAGY.  CONCERTO IN C MA, F. VII, #3          EMB
VIVALDI, A.  CONCERTO IN D MI, P302                      MR
VIVALDI, A.-SCHROEDER.  CONCERTO, P 85 (F. VII/3, OP 53/1)  EUL
VIVALDI, A.-LUND.  TRIOSONATA IN G MI.  2OB,BC           MR
ZAGWIJN, H.  PASTORALE & SCHERZO                         PET
ZIMMERMAN(ARR).  PLAY A SONG OF CHRISTMAS                TP
```

3 PARTS: 2 CLARINETS-KEYBOARD-313

```
ADAM, A.-HOLMES.  CANTIQUE DE NOEL                       RU
ADAM, A.  O HOLY NIGHT                                   RU
ADAMS, S.-GLENN.  HOLY CITY                              BH
ADAMS, S.-DE LAMATER.  HOLY CITY, THE                    RU
ADAMS, S.  HOLY CITY, THE                                HE
ALBENIZ, I.-FRANK.  2 PIECES FROM ESPANA                 OX
ALETTER, W.  RENDEZVOUS                                  BOS
ANDRE, P.  CONCERTINO                                    BIL
ARDITI, L.  BACIO, IL (THE KISS)                         CEN
BACH, C.-AMBROSIO.  SPRING'S AWAKENING                   CF
BACH, J.S.-TOMEI.  DUO CONCERTO                          PO
BALBATRE, L.  NOEL                                       EDM
BARNARD, G.  GLORIANA                                    CF
BARNARD, G.  MERRIMENT POLKA                             CF
BARNARD, G.  MERRIMENT POLKA                             WAT
BARNARD, C.  PUNCH & JUDY                                BA
BEAUMONT.  CON AMORE                                     CEN
BEETHOVEN, L. VAN.  ALLEGRO & MINUET.  CL,BCL,PF         EDM
BEETHOVEN, L. VAN-TRINKAUS.  MINUET                      CF
BEETHOVEN, L. VAN-HARRIS.  MINUET IN G MA                CF
BEETHOVEN, L. VAN.  THEME (SYMPHONY #2)                  CEN
BEETHOVEN, L. VAN.  TRIO, OP 11.  CL,BCL,PF              CF
BELLINI, V.-SAMBIN.  DUET (LA SONNAMBULA)                EDS
BELLINI, V.-LEWIS.  HEAR ME NORMA.  E FL CL(CL),E FL CL,PF  CF
BENDA.  INTRODUCTION & DANCE                             EDM
BENNETT, D.  CLARINET CAROUSEL                           SO
BENT, R.  SWISS BOY,.  E FL CL(CL),E FL CL,PF            CF
BIZET, G.  CARILLON                                      EDM
BIZET, G.  ENTR'ACTE (CARMEN)                            EDM
BIZET, G.  PRELUDE (SCENE BOHEMIENNES)                   MOL
BIZET, C.  SERENADE ESPAGNOLE                            EDM
BORODIN, A.  INTRODUCTION EN ALLEGRO VIVO                MOL
BORSCHEL, E.(ARR).  BLASER-FAVORITEN                     B&N
BOUSQUET, N.-BETTONEY.  GOLDEN ROBIN POLKA               CF
BRAGA, G.  ANGELS SERENADE                               CF
BRAHE, M.-GLENN.  BLESS THIS HOUSE                       BH
BRAHMS, J.-HARRIS.  FAMOUS WALTZ, OP 39/15               CF
BRAHMS, J.  HUNGARIAN DANCE #5                           CF
BRAHMSTEDT.  FRIVOLITIES (CONCERT POLKA)                 RU
BRAHMSTEDT.  SOUVENIR OF VENICE                          RU
BROWN, T.  PERPETUAL COMMOTION                           KN
BRUNIAU, A.  TOI ET MOI                                  BIL
BUCHTEL, F.  MARIANINA                                   KJ
BUCHTEL, F.  MERRY HEARTS                                KJ
BUCHTEL, F.  MEXICAN CLAPPING SONG                       KJ
BUCHTEL, F.  TIRITOMBA                                   KJ
BUCHTEL, F.  TWO IMPS                                    KJ
BUCHTEL, F.  TWO PALS                                    KJ
BUCHTEL, F.  WALTZ "ALPHENS"                             KJ
```

BUOT-PILLEVESTRE. CHANSON DES NIDS, LA	ALE
CHAMINADE, C. SCARF DANCE	CEN
CHEDEVILLE, N. SCHERZO	EDM
CHERUBINI, L. AVE MARIA	CF
CHOPIN, F. PRELUDES, OP 28/7,20	CEN
CHRISTOPHE. GRAND DUO	T-M
CIRRI, G. ARIOSO	EDM
CORELLI, A. AIR & DANCE	EDM
CORELLI, A. GAVOTTE & GIGUE	EDM
CORELLI, A. GIGUE	EDM
D'AUVERGNE, B. PLAINS OF PEACE	BOS
DAHM, P. PARIS SOIR	EDM
DAHM, P. (ARR). CONCERT ALBUM	EDM
DAME, E. CONTES DE GRAND-MERE	MAU
DANSBY, E. DANDY DUO	KN
DE LAMATER, E. (ARR). ADESTE FIDELIS	RU
DE VILLE, P. SWISS BOY, THE	CF
DEBUSSY, C. MANDOLINE	EDM
DELBECQ. DANS LES MONTAGNES	MOL
DELBECQ. FANTASIE DUO	MOL
DEPELSENAIRE, J. INCANTATIONS	EV
DEVIENNE, F. CONCERTO	EMB
DI CAPUA, E. O SOLE MIO (MY SUNSHINE)	CEN
DONIZETTI, G.-DE VILLE. SEXTETTE (LUCIA DI LAMMERMOOR)	CF
DORADO-WHEELER. 2 FRIENDS	VO
DVORAK, A. HUMORESQUE	CEN
EASY CLARINET SOLOS.	HY
EASY CLARINET SOLOS OR DUETS.	HY
ELGAR, E.-TRINKAUS. SALUT D'AMOUR	CF
ENDRESEN, R. PEPPERINO	RU
ENDRESEN, R. PRAIRIE WARBLERS	RU
ENDRESEN, R. PROMENADE	RU
ENDRESEN, R. TWO FLYERS, THE	RU
FABRE, C.-HARRIS. REVERIE	CF
FABRE, C.-HARRIS. REVERIE #2	CF
FABRE, C. REVERIE #2	BIL
FILAS, T. CLARINET ECHOES	CF
FILAS, T. DOUBLE OR NOTHING	CF
FIORILLO, F.-STEINBECK. SINFONIA CONCERTANTE IN F MA	EUL
FLOTOW, F.-BUCHTEL. AH! SO FAIR (MARTHA)	KJ
FRANCK-CLUWEN. AUX PETITS ENFANTS	T-M
GHYS, J.-HARRIS. AMARYLLIS & COUNTRY GARDENS	LU
GILLAM, R. CONVERSATION #1	MAN
GILLAM, R. SONATA #1	MAN
GIORDANI, T. 18TH CENTURY AIR, AN	EDM
GLUCK, C.-DAVIS. SPIRIT DANCE	RU
GODARD, B.-TRINKAUS. BERCEUSE (JOCELYN)	CF
GOSSEC, F.-RUYSSEN. ANDANTINO	GAL
GOSSEC, F.-ROCHON. OVERTURE	MOL
GOUNOD, C.-DE VILLE. FLOWER SONG (FAUST)	CF
GRIEG, E. WATCHMAN'S SONG, OP 12/3	CEN
GROOMS, C. (ARR). DARK EYES (RUSSIAN SONG)	CEN
GROOMS, C. (ARR). TWO GUITARS (RUSSIAN SONG)	CEN
HANDEL, G. ADAGIO & ALLEGRO	INT
HANDEL, G.-GLASER. ALLEGRO (SONATA #2)	CF
HARRIS, F. ANDANTE & GAVOTTE	LU
HARRIS, F. GAY MINUET	LU
HARRIS, F. 2 MARIONETTES	LU
HASSE, J. CANZONE	EDM
HAYDN, F. OXEN MINUET	CF
HEUBERGER, R. MIDNIGHT BELLS	FO
HILL. DANCE CHROMATIQUE	KJ

HOFFMEISTER, F. CONCERTO IN E FL MA		MR
HOLMES, G.(ARR). AULD LANG SYNE. E FL CL(CL),E FL CL,PF		CF
HOLMES, G. AULD LANG SYNE		CF
HOOK, J.-CURWIN. GUIDA DI MUSICA		CA
HOWELL. RUSTIC DANCE		CEN
HUMMEL, H. (ARR). CLARINET POLKA		RU
ILJINSKY, A. BERCEUSE		CEN
KAMMELL, A.-THOMPSON/EADES. NOTTURNO #2		CA
KENDALL, R. 6 CLARINET DUETS		VO
KENNEDY, H. STAR OF HOPE (REVERIE)		CEN
KETELBEY, A. SANCTUARY OF THE HEART		BOS
KIEFER, W. ELENA POLKA. E FL CL,CL,PF		BA
KING, K. NIGHT IN JUNE, A		BA
KING, K. NIGHT IN JUNE, A		WAT
KLING, H.-CATLIN. TWO LITTLE BULFINCHES POLKA, E FL CL(CL),E FL CL, PF		CF
KREISLER, F.-LEIDZEN. LIEBESFREUD		FO
KREISLER, F.-LEIDZEN. RONDINO ON A THEME OF BEETHOVEN		FO
KREISLER, F.-LEIDZEN. SCHON ROSMARIN		FO
KROMMER, F. CONCERTO IN E FL MA, OP 35		MR
LABITZKY, T. DREAM OF THE SHEPHERDESS		CEN
LABITZKY, T. HERD GIRL'S DREAM, THE		CF
LAKE, M. ANNIE LAURIE		CF
LAWRENCE. TANDEM		PO
LAWTON, S. BOOK OF CLARINET DUETS, A		OX
LEMARE, E.-TRINKAUS. ANDANTINO		CF
LEMARE, E. CATHEDRAL MEDITATION		CEN
LESTER. CRIMSON BLUSHES		CEN
LIDDLE, S. HOW LOVELY ARE THY DWELLINGS		BH
LINCKE, P.-WALTERS. GLOWWORM, THE		RU
LISZT, F. LOVE DREAMS (LIEBESTRAUM)		CEN
LOEILLET, J.-BLOCK. SONATA IN F MI, OP 2/5		NOM
LOTTI, A. ARIETTA		EDM
LOUMEY. SHADOWS ON THE WATER		CEN
LURIE-NEUFELD (ARR). CLASSICS FOR CLARINETS		CF
MACIEJEWSKI, S. STUBBORN CLARINET, THE		PWM
MARSAL, E. NANINE		CF
MARTINI, J. PLAISIR D'AMOUR		EDM
MASSENET, J.-TRINKAUS. ELEGY		CF
MASSENET, J. UNDER THE LINDEN TREES		EDM
MASTALIR, J. TRIO CONCERTANTE (1940). CL,BASSET HN,PF		CHF
MEACHAM-HUMMEL. AMERICAN PATROL		RU
MENDELSSOHN, F. CONCERT PIECE #1 IN F MI, OP113		EDK
MENDELSSOHN, F.-HUNT. CONCERT PIECE IN F MI, OP113		S&C
MENDELSSOHN, F.-SIMON. CONCERTPIECE #1 IN F MI, OP113		INT
MENDELSSOHN, F.-SIMON. CONCERTPIECE #2 IN D MA, OP114		INT
MENDELSSOHN, F. EVENING SONG		HE
MENDELSSOHN, F. ICH WOLLT'MEINE LIEB ERGOSSE SICH		HE
MENDELSSOHN, F.-KREISELMAN. KONZERTSTUCK #1, OP113 CL,BCL,PF		M&M
MENDELSSOHN, F.-KREISELMAN. KONZERTSTUCK #2, OP114 CL,BCL,PF		M&M
MENDELSSOHN, F. KONZERTSTUCK, OP113. CL,BASSET HN,PF		M&M
MENDELSSOHN, F. KONZERTSTUCK, OP114. CL,BASSET HN,PF		M&M
MENDELSSOHN, F. KONZERTSTUCKE #1, OP113. CL,BASSET HN,PF		BRH
MENDELSSOHN, F. KONZERTSTUCKE #2 IN D MI, OP114 CL,BASSET HN,PF		BRH
MENDELSSOHN, F.-MICHAELS. 2 KONZERTSTUCKE, OP113-114		HSM
MENDELSSOHN, F. MAIGLOCKCHEN UND DIE BLUMELEIN		HE
MENDELSSOHN, F.-DAVIS. NOCTURNE		RU
MENDELSSOHN, F.-TRINKAUS. NOCTURNO (MID-SUMMER NIGHTS DREAM)		CF
MENDELSSOHN, F. O WIE SELIG IST DAS KIND		HE

```
MENDELSSOHN, F.-TRINKAUS.  ON WINGS OF SONG                      CF
MENDELSSOHN, F.  SONG WITHOUT WORDS #48                          CEN
MEYERBEER, G.-TRINKAUS.  CORONATION MARCH (THE PROPHET)          CF
MEYERBEER, G.-LAZARUS.  ROBERT LE DIABLE                         CF
MONTI, V.  CSARDAS                                               CF
MOZART, W.-TOLL.  EXCERPT FROM PIANO SONATA #2                   CF
MOZART, W.  MINUET & TRIO (SYMPHONY IN E FL MA)                  CEN
MOZART, W.-FRANK.  PRESTO (SINFONIA CONCERTANTE)                 OX
MOZART, W.-PHILLIPS.  RONDO (SERENADE IN B FL MA)                OX
MOZART, W.-DE SMET.  TRIO, K498                                  PET
MULLER-WESTON.  SYMPHONIE CONCERTANTE IN E FL, OP 23             FEM
NARDINI, P.  SHEPHERD'S PIPES                                    EDM
NEVIN, E.-HUMMEL.  NARCISSUS                                     RU
OFFENBACH, J.-BUCHTEL.  BARCAROLLE (TALES OF HOFFMANN)           KJ
OFFENBACH, J.-DAVIS.  BARCAROLLE                                 RU
PADEREWSKI, I.-TRINKAUS.  MINUET A L'ANTIQUE                     CF
PAGANINI, N.-FALCONE.  PERPETUAL MOTION, OP 11                   SO
PALA, J.  BONJOUR                                                M&M
PALA, J.  3 MINIATUREN                                           M&M
PAQUE, J.  DUO DE LA NORMA, #2                                   SCF
PERFECT, A.  TWO LITTLE CHUMS.  E FL CL(CL),E FL CL,PF           CF
PERFECT, A.  TWO LITTLE CHUMS;                                   CF
PILLEVESTRE, J.  ANCHES REBELLES, LES                            ALE
PILLEVESTRE, J.  IDYLLE BRETONNE                                 ALE
PILLEVESTRE, J.  MOUVEMENT PERPETUEL, LE                         ALE
PLEYEL, I.  6 DUETS, OP  8                                       CF
POPULAR CLARINET.                                                HY
PORRET, J.  DUO DE CONCOURS #7                                   EDR
PORRET, J.  DUO DE CONCOURS #8                                   EDR
PUCCINI, G.-STEBBING.  VISSI D'ARTE, VISSI D'AMORE               RC
RACHMANINOFF, S.  VOCALISE                                       EDM
RAMEAU, J.  RIGODON DE DARDANUS                                  EDM
RANGER, A. (ARR).  COUNTRY GARDENS                               CF
RANGER, A. (ARR).  WREATH OF HOLLY, A                            CF
RAPHLING, S.  SQUARE DANCE                                       EDM
RAVEL, M.-WALTERS.  PAVANE                                       RU
RAVEL, M.  PAVANE POUR UNE INFANTE DEFUNTE                       EDM
RIMSKY-KORSAKOFF, N.  SONG OF INDIA                              CEN
ROSAS, J.  OVER THE WAVES                                        CEN
SAINT-SAENS, C.-TRINKAUS.  SWAN, THE                             CF
SARGENT.  NIP & TUC,.  E FL CL(CL),E FL CL,PF                    CF
SAUPE.  AIR VARIE                                                SCF
SCHAEFFER, D. (ARR).  CHRISTMAS DUETS                            PO
SCHOLTES.  SWISS BOY                                             WAT
SCHONHERR, M.  IM DUETT                                          LK
SCHUBERT, F.  AVE MARIA                                          HE
SCHUMANN, R.-DAVIS.  MELODY, OP 68/1                             RU
SCHUMANN, R.  SOLDIER'S MARCH, OP 68/2                           CEN
SIBELIUS, J.-TRINKAUS.  VALSE TRISTE (KUOLEMA)                   CF
SIMEONOV, B.  INVENTION                                          WAT
SINGERLING.  CLARINET POLKA                                      T-M
SIQUIET, C.  QUAND 2 CLARINETTES SE RENCONTRENT                  MAU
SLECHTA, T.  FATHER OF WATERS                                    CF
SMETANA, B.-HARRIS.  POLKA (BARTERED BRIDE)                      LU
SMITH-HOLMES.  DRINK TO ME ONLY WITH THINE EYES,                 CF
   E FL CL(CL),E FL CL ,PF
SMITH-HOLMES.  OLD BLACK JOE,.  E FL CL(CL),E FL CL,PF           CF
SMITH & HOLMES.  THROUGH SHADOWED VALES                          BA
SMITH, C.  FROM DAY TO DAY                                       CF
SMITH, C.  HELEN                                                 CF
SMITH, C.  LIFE'S LIGHTER HOURS                                  BA
SMITH, C.  ON PLEASURE BENT                                      CF
```

3 PARTS: 2 CLARINETS-KEYBOARD-313

```
SMITH, C.  SPIRIT OF JOY, THE.  E FL CL(CL),E FL CL,PF          CF
SOUSA, J.-WALTERS.  STARS & STRIPES FOREVER, THE               RU
SPENCER, J.  SILVATONES.  E FL CL(CL),E FL CL,PF               CF
SPENCER, J.  SILVATONES;                                       CF
STAIGERS, D.  HAZEL                                            CF
STAMITZ, C.-LEBERMANN.  CONCERTO IN B FL MA                    PET
STEEN.  NOCTURNE IN E FL MA                                    WAT
STRAUSS, J.-BETTONEY.  TALES FROM THE VIENNA WOODS, OP325      CF
STRAUSS, J.-JOLLIFF.  TRITSCH-TRATSCH POLKA                    RU
STRAUSS, O.-HARRIS.  WALTZ DREAM, A                            LU
STRAVINSKY, I.  BERCEUSE                                       EDM
STRAVINSKY, I.  DANCE OF THE BALLERINA                         EDM
STRAVINSKY, I.  DANCE OF THE PRINCESSES                        EDM
STRAVINSKY, I.  PASTORALE                                      EDM
TAYLOR, L.  MINOR & THE MAJOR POLKA, THE                       HL
TCHAIKOVSKY, P.-TRINKAUS.  CHANT SANS PAROLES                  CF
TCHAIKOVSKY, P.-HUMMEL.  CONCERTO IN B FL MI                   RU
TCHAIKOVSKY, P.  3 PIECES                                      EDM
TELEMANN, G.  CONCERTO IN D MI.  2CL(2CHALUMEAUX),PF           MR
TENAGLIA, A.  ARIA ANTICA                                      EDM
THOME, F.  SIMPLE AVEU                                         CF
TITL, A.  SERENADE                                             CF
VIVALDI, A.-SCHWADRON.  CORRENTE                               KN
VIVALDI, A.  GIGA                                              EDM
WAGNER, R.-TRINKAUS.  SONG TO THE EVENING STAR (TANNHAUSER)    CF
WAGNER, R.-TRINKAUS.  WALTHER'S PRIZE SONG (DIE MEISTERSINGER) CF
WALLACE, W.-GRUENWALD.  CAVATINA (MARITANA)                    CF
WALTERS, H.  SHINDIG (FOLK SONG FANTASY)                       RU
WALTERS, H. (ARR).  WHEN THE SAINTS GO MARCHING IN             RU
WARREN, D.  GRENADILLA CAPRICE                                 LU
WEBER & OSTLING.  DUETS, 2 VOLS                                BE
WEBER, C. VON-DAVIS.  HUNTERS' CHORUS                          RU
WERKMEISTER.  SOUVENIR DE SFAX                                 EDR
WESTON, P.  CLASSICAL ALBUM                                    BH
WHEELER.  MEDITATION                                           VO
WHITE, C.  PETITE SUITE,.  E FL CL,ACL,PF                      SF
WOOD.  LET 'ER GO                                              CEN
ZIMMERMAN (ARR).  PLAY A SONG OF CHRISTMAS                     TP
```

3 PARTS: 2 BASSOONS-KEYBOARD-314

```
CAROLO.  SONATA #1 IN B FL MA                                  MR
COUPERIN, F.  GOUTS REUNIS, LES, VOL 3.  2BSN,BC              MR
JANCOURT, E.  3 GRANDES SONATES                               BIL
SCHIFFELHOLZ, J.  TRIO IN G MA                                MR
SELMA Y SALAVERDE, B. DE-KASTNER.  CANZON A 2 BASSI.  2BSN,BC  SCH
```

3 PARTS: 2 SAXOPHONES-KEYBOARD-315

```
ADAM, A.  O HOLY NIGHT.  2ASAX,PF                             RU
ADAMS, S.-DE LAMATER.  HOLY CITY, THE.  2ASAX,PF             RU
ALDRICH.  LOVE & FLOWERS.  ASAX,TSAX,PF                       CEN
ANDRE, P.  ROMANCE D'AUTOMNE.  2ASAX,PF                       EDR
ARDITI, L.  BACIO, IL (THE KISS).  ASAX,TSAX(ASAX),PF         CEN
```

3 PARTS: 2 SAXOPHONES-KEYBOARD-315

```
BACH, J.S.-GOUNOD.  AVE MARIA.  ASAX,TSAX,PF                          CEN
BACH, J.S.-SIBBING.  DUET (CANTATA #78).  2ASAX,PF                    DOR
BARNHOUSE, C.  SILVER LINING.  ASAX,TSAX,PF                           BA
BEAUMONT.  CON AMORE.  ASAX,TSAX(ASAX),PF                             CEN
BEETHOVEN, L. VAN-TRINKAUS.  MINUET.  ASAX,ASAX(TSAX),PF              CF
BEETHOVEN, L. VAN-HARRIS.  MINUET IN G MA.  2TSAX,PF                  CF
BEETHOVEN, L. VAN.  MINUET IN G MA.  ASAX,TSAX(ASAX),PF              CEN
BEETHOVEN, L. VAN.  MOONLIGHT SONATA (ADAGIO)                         CEN
    ASAX,TSAX(ASAX),PF
BELLINI, V.  DUET (NORMA).  2SAX,PF                                   CF
BENT, R.  SWISS BOY.  2ASAX,PF                                        CF
BLEGER, A.  SOUVENIR DE VALENCE.  2TSAX,PF                            MOL
BORODIN, A.  SOLICITUDE.  ASAX,TSAX,PF                                EDM
BRAGA, G.  ANGEL'S SERENADE.  ASAX,TSAX,PF                            CEN
BRAGA, G.  ANGEL'S SERENADE.  ASAX,TSAX,PF                            CF
BRAHMS, J.-HARRIS.  FAMOUS WALTZ, OP 39/15.  2SAX,PF                  CF
BUCHTEL, F.  BLUE TAIL FLY.  2ASAX,PF                                 KJ
BUCHTEL, F.  FAIR ARE THE MEADOWA.  2ASAX,PF                          KJ
BUCHTEL, F.  ROVING MINSTRELS.  ASAX,TSAX,PF                          KJ
BUCHTEL, F.  SKYLARKS.  ASAX,TSAX,PF                                  KJ
BUCHTEL, F.  TIRITOMBA.  2ASAX,PF                                     KJ
BUCHTEL, F.  TWO PALS.  2ASAX,PF                                      KJ
BUCHTEL, F.  WALTZ "SIBYL".  2ASAX,PF                                 KJ
BUCHTEL, F.  WOODLAND WHISPERS.  2ASAX,PF                             KJ
BUTTERFIELD, N.  WHEN YOU & I WERE YOUNG.  ASAX,TSAX,PF               CEN
CHEDEVILLE, N.  SCHERZO.  ASAX,TSAX,PF                                EDM
CLODOMIR, P.  12 DUOS.  2TSAX,PF                                      HE
CONKLIN.  HANDY ANDY.  2SAX,PF                                        CF
CUNNINGHAM, M.  TRIO #3, OP 59.  SOP SAX,ASAX,PF                      EQM
DANKS, H.  SILVER THREADS AMONG THE GOLD.  ASAX,TSAX,PF               CEN
DE LAMATER, E. (ARR).  ADESTE FIDELIS.  2ASAX,PF                      RU
DESCHAMPS, J.  SONATINE.  2ASAX,PF                                    BIL
DI CAPUA, E.  O SOLE MIO (MY SUNSHINE).  ASAX,TSAX(ASAX),PF          CEN
DONIZETTI, G.  LUCIA DI LAMMERMOOR.  ASAX,TSAX,PF                     CEN
DRIGO, R.  SERENADE.  ASAX,TSAX,PF                                    CEN
DRIGO, R.-SAENGER.  VALSE BLUETTE.  2ASAX,PF                          CF
DVORAK, A.  HUMORESKE.  ASAX,TSAX(ASAX),PF                            CEN
EASY SAXOPHONE SOLOS.  2SAX,PF                                        HY
EASY SAXOPHONE SOLOS OR DUETS.  2SAX,PF                               HY
ELGAR, E.  SALUT D'AMOUR.  ASAX,TSAX,PF                               CEN
EMMETT, D.  DIXIE'S LAND.  2SAX,PF                                    MCK
FABRE, C.-HARRIS.  REVERIE.  2ASAX,PF                                 CF
FABRE, C.  REVERIE #2.  2ASAX,PF                                      CF
FAURE, J.  RAMEAUX, LES (THE PALMS).  ASAX,TSAX,PF                    CEN
FOSTER, S.-BROOKE.  COME WHERE MY LOVE LIES DREAMING                  CF
    2TSAX,PF
FOTE, R.  AMIGOS.  2ASAX,PF                                           KN
GIORDANI, G.  18TH CENTURY AIR, AN.  ASAX,TSAX,PF                     EDM
GODARD, B.-TRINKAUS.  BERCEUSE (JOCELYN).  ASAX,ASAX(TSAX),PF         CF
GODARD, B.  LULLABY (JOCELYN).  ASAX,TSAX,PF                          CEN
GORNER, H.  CONCERTINO, OP 31.  ASAX,TSAX,PF                          FRH
GRIEG, E.  I LOVE YOU.  ASAX,TSAX,PF                                  CEN
GRIEG, E.  TO SPRING.  ASAX,TSAX(ASAX),PF                             CEN
GROOMS (ARR).  FAMOUS SCOTCH AIRS, VAR..  ASAX,TSAX,PF               CEN
GROOMS (ARR).  HOME FAVORITES, VAR..  ASAX,TSAX,PF                    CEN
GROOMS (ARR).  NEAPOLITAN FAVORITES, VAR..  ASAX,TSAX,PF             CEN
GROOMS (ARR).  OCEAN ECHOES, VAR..  ASAX,TSAX,PF                      CEN
GROOMS (ARR).  PLANTATION ECHOES, VAR..  ASAX,TSAX,PF                CEN
GROOMS (ARR).  TWO GUITARS (RUSSIAN SONG).  ASAX,TSAX(ASAX),PF       CEN
HARRIS, F.  2 BUCKAROOS.  2ASAX(2TSAX),PF                             LU
HARRIS, F.  2 MARIONETTES.  2TSAX,PF                                  LU
HARRIS, F. (ARR).  OLD REFRAIN, THE & DARK EYES.  2ASAX,PF            LU
```

```
HAYDN, F.  OXEN MINUET.  2ASAX,PF                              CF
HERBERT, V.-HARRIS.  GYPSY LOVE SONG.  2ASAX,PF               LU
HEUBERGER, R.-KREISLER/LEIDZEN.  MIDNIGHT BELLS.  2ASAX,PF    FO
HOLMES, G. (ARR).  AULD LANG SYNE.  ASAX(TSAX),ASAX(TSAX),PF  CF
IASILLI, G.  GOLDIE.  2SAX,PF                                  CF
KENNEDY, H.  STAR OF HOPE (REVERIE).  ASAX,TSAX(ASAX),PF      CEN
KESNAR, M.  PETIT RIEN, UN                                    EDM
KIEFER, W.  ELENA POLKA.  TSAX(ASAX),TSAX,PF                  BA
KING, K.  NIGHT IN JUNE                                       BA
KLICKMANN, F.  SWEET HAWAIIAN MOONLIGHT.  2SAX,PF             MCK
KLICKMANN, F.  TRAIL TO LONG AGO.  2SAX,PF                    MCK
KOCH, E. VON.  CONCERTO PICCOLO.  SSAX,ASAX,PF               EMF
LACK, T.  IDILIO.  ASAX,TSAX,PF                               CEN
LAKE, M. (ARR).  ANNIE LAURIE.  ASAX(TSAX),ASAX(TSAX),PF     CF
LANGE, G.  BLUMENLIED (FLOWER SONG).  ASAX,TSAX,PF           CEN
LEMARE, E.  ANDANTINO.  ASAX,ASAX(TSAX),PF                    CF
LEMARE, E.  CATHEDRAL MEDITATION.  ASAX,TSAX(ASAX),PF        CEN
LEONCAVALLO, R.  ARIOSO (PAGLIACCI).  ASAX,TSAX,PF           CEN
LEYBACH, I.  NOCTURNE #5 IN G MA.  ASAX,TSAX(ASAX),PF        CEN
LISZT, F.-SMITH.  LIEBESTRAUM.  TSAX(ASAX),TSAX,PF           BA
LISZT, F.-SMITH.  LIEBESTRAUM;.  2ASAX,PF                     BA
LISZT, F.  LOVE DREAMS (LIEBESTRAUM).  ASAX,TSAX(ASAX),PF    CEN
MASSENET, J.-TRINKAUS.  ELEGY.  ASAX,ASAX(TSAX),PF           CF
MENDELSSOHN, F.  EVENING SONG.  2TSAX,PF                      T-M
MENDELSSOHN, F.  ICH WOLLT' MEINE LIEBE ERGOSSE SICH         T-M
   2TSAX,PF
MENDELSSOHN, F.  MAIGLOCKCHEN UND DIE BLUMELEIN.  2TSAX,PF   HE
MENDELSSOHN, F.-TRINKAUS.  NOCTURNO (MID-SUMMER NIGHTS DREAM) CF
   ASAX,A SAX(TSAX),PF
MENDELSSOHN, F.  O WIE SELIG IST DAS KIND.  2TSAX,PF         HE
MENDELSSOHN, F.-TRINKAUS.  ON WINGS OF SONG                   CF
   ASAX,ASAX(TSAX),PF
MENDELSSOHN, F.  SPRING SONG.  ASAX,TSAX,PF                  CEN
MEYERBEER, G.-TRINKAUS.  CORONATION MARCH (THE PROPHET)       CF
   ASAX,ASAX(TS AX),PF
MOLLOY, J.  LOVE'S OLD SWEET SONG.  2SAX,PF                  MCK
MORE EASY SAXOPHONE SOLOS.  2SAX,PF                           HY
MOREL.  NORWEGIAN CRADLE SONG.  ASAX,TSAX,PF                 CEN
MOZART, W.  AVE VERUM CORPUS.  ASAX,TSAX,PF                  EDM
OFFENBACH, J.-BUCHTEL.  BARCAROLLE (TALES OF HOFFMAN)         KJ
   2ASAX,PF
OFFENBACH, J.  BARCAROLLE (TALES OF HOFFMANN).  ASAX,TSAX,PF CEN
OFFENBACH, J.  BARCAROLLE (TALES OF HOFFMANN).  2ASAX,PF     CF
OFFENBACH, J.  BARCAROLLE (TALES OF HOFFMANN).  2SAX,PF      MCK
PADEREWSKI, I.-TRINKAUS.  MINUET A L'ANTIQUE                  CF
   ASAX,ASAX(TSAX),PF
PALA, J.  3 MINIATURES.  2TSAX,PF                             HE
PAQUE, J.  DUO DE LA NORMA, #7.  2TSAX,PF                    S&C
PERFECT, A.  TWO LITTLE CHUMS.  2ASAX,PF                      CF
PERGOLESI, G.  SICILIAN AIR.  ASAX,TSAX,PF                   EDM
PONCE, M.  ESTRELLITA.  2ASAX,PF                              CF
PORRET, J.  INGRES.  ASAX,TSAX,PF                            MOL
PORRET, J.  JENNER.  ASAX,TSAX,PF                            MOL
RAMEAU, J.  RIGODON DE DARDANUS.  ASAX,TSAX,PF              EDM
RANGER, A.  WREATH OF HOLLY, A.  ASAX(TSAX),ASAX(TSAX),PF    CF
RIMSKY-KORSAKOFF, N.  SONG OF INDIA.  ASAX,TSAX(ASAX),PF     CEN
SAINT-SAENS, C.  CYGNE, LE (THE SWAN).  ASAX,TSAX,PF         CEN
SAINT-SAENS, C.  MY HEART AT THY SWEET VOICE                 CEN
   ASAX,TSAX(ASAX),PF
SAINT-SAENS, C.-TRINKAUS.  SWAN, THE.  ASAX,ASAX(TSAX),PF    CF
SCHUBERT, F.  AVE MARIA.  2TSAX,PF                            HE
SCHUBERT, F.  SERENADE.  ASAX,TSAX,PF                        CEN
```

SIBELIUS, J.-TRINKAUS. VALSE TRISTE (KUOLEMA)		CF
ASAX,ASAX(TSAX),PF		
SIBELIUS, J. VALSE TRISTE. ASAX,TSAX,PF		CEN
SLECHTA, T. FATHER OF WATERS. 2SAX,PF		CF
SMETANA, B.-HARRIS. POLKA (BARTERED BRIDE). 2TSAX,PF		LU
SMIM, P. (ARR). DUET ALBUM. ASAX,ASAX(TSAX),PF		EDM
SMIM, P. (ARR). PARIS SOIR. ASAX,TSAX,PF		EDM
SMITH, C. AMONG THE SYCAMORES. TSAX(ASAX),TSAX(ASAX),PF		BA
SMITH, C.-HOLMES, G. BELIEVE ME IF ALL		CF
ASAX(TSAX)ASAX(TSAX),PF		
SMITH, C. CALL OF THE SEA. TSAX(ASAX),TSAX,PF		BA
SMITH, C.-HOLMES, G. CARIBBEAN, THE		CF
ASAX(TSAX),ASAX(TSAX),PF		
SMITH, C.-HOLMES, G. DRINK TO ME ONLY WITH THINE EYES		CF
ASAX(TSAX),A SAX(TSAX),PF		
SMITH, C. HELEN. ASAX(TSAX),ASAX(TSAX),PF		CF
SMITH, C. IMOGENE. 2TSAX,PF		BA
SMITH, C. ITALIANA. TSAX(ASAX),TSAX,PF		BA
SMITH, C. MILADY'S PLEASURE. TSAX(ASAX),TSAX(ASAX),PF		BA
SMITH, C. MY SONG OF SONGS. ASAX(TSAX),ASAX(TSAX),PF		CF
SMITH, C.-HOLMES, G. OLD BLACK JOE. ASAX(TSAX),ASAX(TSAX),PF		CF
SMITH, C. ON PLEASURE BENT. ASAX(TSAX),ASAX(TSAX),PF		CF
SMITH, C. RAINBOW HUES. TSAX(ASAX),TSAX(ASAX),PF		BA
SMITH, C. SMITHSONIAN. TSAX(ASAX),TSAX(ASAX),PF		BA
SMITH, C. SPIRIT OF JOY, THE. ASAX(TSAX),ASAX(TSAX),PF		CF
SMITH, C. TRUMPETER, THE. 2TSAX,PF		BA
SMITH, C. & HOLMES, G. ITALIANA. 2ASAX,PF		BA
SMITH, C. & HOLMES, G. MASSA'S IN THE COLD COLD, GROUND		BA
TSAX(ASAX) ,TSAX(ASAX),PF		
SMITH, C. & HOLMES, G. SILVER THREADS AMONG THE GOLD		BA
TSAX(ASAX),TS AX(ASAX),PF		
SMITH, C. & HOLMES, G. THROUGH SHADOWED VALES		BA
TSAX(ASAX),TSAX,PF		
SMITH, C. & HOLMES, G. WAYFARER, THE		BA
TSAX(ASAX),TSAX(ASAX),PF		
SPENCER, F. SILVATONES. 2ASAX,PF		CF
STAIGERS, D. HAZEL. ASAX,ASAX(TSAX),PF		CF
STRAUSS, O.-HARRIS. WALTZ DREAM, A. 2TSAX,PF		LU
SULLIVAN, A. LOST CHORD, THE. ASAX,TSAX,PF		CEN
TCHAIKOVSKY, P.-TRINKAUS. CHANT SANS PAROLES		CF
ASAX,ASAX(TSAX),PF		
THOMAS. ROMANCE. ASAX,TSAX,PF		CEN
THOME, F. SIMPLE AVEU (CONFESSION). ASAX,TSAX,PF		CEN
TITL, A. SERENADE. ASAX,TSAX,PF		CF
TOSTI, F. GOOD-BYE. ASAX,TSAX,PF		CEN
TRINKAUS, G. LAMENT. ASAX,ASAX(TSAX),PF		CF
VERDI, G. CELESTE AIDA (AIDA). ASAX,TSAX,PF		CEN
VERDI, G. DONNA E MOBILE, LA. ASAX,TSAX,PF		CEN
VERDI, G. MISERERE, IL TROVATORE. ASAX,TSAX,PF		CEN
VOGT. BOAT SONG. ASAX,TSAX,PF		CEN
VOGT. DREAM WALTZ. ASAX,TSAX,PF		CEN
VOGT. REMEMBRANCE. ASAX,TSAX,PF		CEN
VOGT. SAX-O-MOAN. ASAX,TSAX,PF		CEN
VOGT. SAXOMOLA. ASAX,TSAX,PF		CEN
VOGT. SAXONADE. ASAX,TSAX,PF		CEN
WAGNER, R. BRIDAL CHORUS (LOHENGRIN). 2SAX,PF		MCK
WAGNER, R. ROMANCE (TANNHAUSER). ASAX,TSAX,PF		CEN
WAGNER, R.-TRINKAUS. SONG TO THE EVENING STAR TANNHAUSER		CF
ASAX,ASAX(TSAX),PF		
WAGNER, R. WALTHER'S PRIZE SONG (DIE MEISTERSINGER)		CF
ASAX,ASAX(TSAX),PF		
WILSON. MOONLIGHT ON THE HUDSON, OP 60. ASAX,TSAX,PF		CEN

```
WILSON.  WAYSIDE CHAPEL, THE.  ASAX,TSAX,PF                        CEN
WOOD.  LET 'ER GO.  ASAX,TSAX(ASAX),PF                             CEN
YRADIER, S.  DOVE, THE (LA PALOMA).  ASAX,TSAX,PF                  CEN
YRADIER, S.  PALOMA, LA.  ASAX,TSAX,PF                             CF
ZINDARS, E.  QUIDDITY.  2ASAX,PF                                   AMC
```

3 PARTS: WOODWINDS (COLLECTIONS)-322

```
ISTVAN, M.(ED).  CHAMBER MUSIC FOR BEGINNERS.  2WW,PF          BH
MONKEMEYER, H.(ARR).  TRICINIEN DES 17. JAHRHUNDERTS.  2OB,EHN  PEL
OSTRANDER(ARR).  DUET ALBUM.  FL,BSN,PF                        EDM
PARR(ARR).  BACH-HANDEL ALBUM.  OB,CL,BSN                      HI
SCHAEFFER, D.(ARR).  SELECT TRIOS.  FL,CL,BSN                  PO
SCHAEFFER, D.(ARR).  12 TRIOS.  FL,OB(FL),CL                   PO
STOUTAMIRE, A. & K. HENDERSON.  TRIOS FOR ALL.  3WW            PO
THORPE, R.(ARR).  6 SHORT CLASSICS.  2CL,BSN                   KPM
VERRALL, P.(ARR).  OLD ENGLISH MUSIC.  OB(CL),CL,BSN           OX
```

3 PARTS: WOODWIND-KEYBOARD-327

```
ADAMS, S.-DE ROOY.  HOLY CITY, THE.  2B FL INSTR,PF           MOL
ADDISON, J.  TRIO.  FL,OB,PF                                  GA
ADOLPHUS, M.  TRIBRACH.  FL,CL,PF                             ACA
ALLEGRA, S.  SONATA IN UN TEMPO.  FL(CL),BSN,PF               CAR
ANDRIESSEN, H.  CANZONE (1965).  FL,OB,PF                     SD
ANDRIESSEN, H.  THEMA MET VARIATIES (1953).  FL,OB,PF         SD
ANDRIESSEN, J.  TRIO #1 (1955).  FL,OB,PF                     SD
ARCHER, V.  SONATA.  FL,CL,PF                                 CAN
ARVIN, A.  3 SEASONS.  FL,CL,PF                               CA
ASHTON, J.  TRIO.  CL,BSN,PF                                  SS
AUBIN, T.  CALME DE LA MER, LE.  FL,CL,PF                     ALE
AUCLERT, P.  TRIO #2.  FL,CL,PF                               APH
BACH, C.P.E.-WALTHER.  PASTORALE IN A MI.  OB(FL),BSN,BC      WZ
BACH, C.P.E.-SIMON.  6 PIECES.  CL,BSN,PF                     PI
BACH, C.P.E.-BALASSA.  6 SONATAS.  CL,BSN,BC                  EMB
BACH, C.P.E.  6 SONATAS.  CL,BSN,PF                           INT
BACH, C.P.E.  6 SONATES.  CL,BSN,PF                           B&V
BACH, C.P.E.  TRIO #1 IN D MA.  FL,CL,PF                      INT
BACH, C.P.E.  TRIO #2 IN A MI.  FL,CL,PF                      INT
BACH, C.P.E.  TRIO #3 IN G MA.  FL,CL,PF                      INT
BACH, J.C.  DIVERTISSEMENT.  FL,OB,PF                         SO
BACH, J.S.  ANDANTE (TRIO SONATA).  FL,OB,PF                  OX
BACH, J.S.-MARX.  CANONIC TRIO.  FL,OB,PF                     M&M
BACH, J.S.-LANGENUS.  CONCERTO #3 IN D MI.  FL,CL,PF          CF
BACH, W.F.  SICILIANO.  OB,BSN,PF                             M&M
BAKSA, R.  TRIO.  FL,BSN,PF                                   AB
BAMERT, M.  TRIO.  FL,CL,PF                                   SS
BARNARD, G.  GLORIANA.  FL,CL,PF                              CF
BARNES, M.  CONCERTO GROSSO.  FL,CL,PF                        CAN
BEETHOVEN, L. VAN-GOHLER.  DUOS.  CL,BSN,PF                   BRH
BEETHOVEN, L. VAN-TRINKAUS.  MENUET.  2WW,PF                  CF
BEETHOVEN, L. VAN-BADURA/SKODA.  TRIO.  FL,BSN,PF             BRH
BEETHOVEN, L. VAN.  TRIO IN G MA.  FL,BSN,PF                  INT
BEETHOVEN, L. VAN.  TRIO, OP 38.  CL,BSN(VC),PF               MR
```

```
BENT, R.  SWISS BOY.  FL,CL,PF                                      CF
BERLIOZ, H.  TRIO OF THE YOUNG ISHMAELITES.  FL,OB(CL),PF           EDM
BEVAN, C.  PARIS 1890'S.  3 ESQUISSES.  FL/PIC,OB,HPCD              EMI
BISHOP, H.-LAX.  LO! HERE THE GENTLE LARK.  FL,CL,PF                CF
BIZET, G.  ADAGIETTO.  FL,CL,PF                                     EDM
BIZET, G.  ARAGONAISE.  FL,OB(CL),PF                                EDM
BIZET, G.  CARILLON.  FL,CL,PF                                      EDM
BIZET, G.  ENTR'ACTE.  FL,CL,PF                                     EDM
BIZET, G.  MINUET #2.  FL,CL,PF                                     EDM
BIZET, G.  MINUET.  FL,OB(CL),PF                                    EDM
BIZET, G.  3 PIECES.  FL,CL,PF                                      SO
BIZET, G.  SERENADE ESPAGNOLE.  FL,CL,PF                            EDM
BLAKE, H.  FANTASY ALLEGRO.  FL(OB,CL),BSN,PF                       CA
BLAKE, H.  TRIO.  FL,CL,PF                                          CA
BLATNY, P.  3 SATZE (1962).  FL,BCL,PF                              CHF
BLOCH, E.  CONCERTINO.  FL,CL,PF                                    GS
BOEDIJN, G.  FOLKLORISCHE SUITE, OP 87 (1937).  FL,OB,PF            SD
BOIS, R. DU.  HIS FLOW OF SPIRITS (1979).  FL,BCL,PF               SD
BOISMORTIER, J.-RUF.  CONCERTO IN A MI.  FL,OB,BC                   RC
BOISMORTIER, J.-RUF.  CONCERTO IN C MA.  FL,OB,BC                   RC
BOISMORTIER, J.-RUF.  SONATE IN E MI, OP 37/2.  OB,BSN(VC),BC       B&N
BOISMORTIER, J.-RUF.  TRIO SONATA IN A MI.  OB,BSN(VC),BC           SCH
BOISMORTIER, J.  TRIO SONATA IN A MI, OP 37/5.  FL(OB),BSN,BC       MR
BORGULYA, A.  TRIO.  FL,BSN,PF                                      GEN
BORODIN, A.  SOLICITUDE.  FL,OB(CL),PF                              EDM
BORRIS, S.  RHAPSODIE, OP103.  OB,BSN,HPCD                          S-V
BORRIS, S.  TRIO, OP 90.  OB,BSN,PF                                 S-V
BORRIS, S.  TRIO, OP116/1B (1965).  FL,OB,PF                        B&N
BORTOLOTTI, M.  PARENTESIS (1968).  CL,BSN,PF                       ESZ
BOTTENBERG, W.  TRIO (1963-64).  FL,CL,PF                           CAN
BOTTJE, W.  TRIO SONATE (1958).  FL,BSN,PF                          CO
BOUSQUET, N.-BROOKE.  GOLDEN ROBIN POLKA.  FL,CL,PF                 CF
BRAGA, G.  ANGEL'S SERENADE.  FL,ASAX(TSAX,CL),PF                   CF
BRAHMS, J.-HARRIS.  FAMOUS WALTZ, OP 39/15.  FL,CL,PF               CF
BRAHMS, J.  HUNGARIAN DANCE #5.  CL,ASAX(FL),PF                     CF
BRECK, E.  (ARR).  CHRISTMAS JOYS.  2WW,PF                          CF
BREVAL, J.  SYMPHONIE CONCERTANTE IN F MA, OP 31.  FL,BSN,PF        MR
BROGUE, R.  SONATINA.  FL,CL,HPCD                                   AMC
BRUNIAU, A.  TOI ET MOI (FANTAISIE-DUO).  OB,CL,PF                  BIL
BUCHTEL, F.  ENCHANTMENT.  FL,CL,PF                                 KJ
BUCHTEL, F.  ROVING MINSTRELS.  FL,CL,PF                            KJ
BUCHTEL, F.  SKYLARKS.  FL,CL,PF                                    KJ
BUSH, G.  TRIO.  OB,BSN,PF                                          NO
CANINO, B.  IMPROMPTU #1 (1969).  FL,OB,PF                          ESZ
CARRIERE, G.  AIR MEDIEVAL.  SOP SAX(TSAX),CL,PF                    EDR
CASTELLO.  QUARTA SONATA A DUE                                      SH
    2C OR B FL TREBLE OR BASS INSTR,BC
CHEDEVILLE, N.  SCHERZO.  FL,OB(CL),PF                              EDM
CHERUBINI, L.  AVE MARIA.  FL,CL,PF                                 CF
CIMA, G.-WEAST.  SONATA A TRE.  2WW,PF                              PO
CIMAROSA, D.  CONCERTO IN G MA.  FL,OB,PF                           SO
CIRRI, M.  ARIOSO.  FL,CL,PF                                        EDM
CLIQUET-PLEYEL.  CHANT D'ESPERANCE.  CL,BSN,PF                      EV
CORELLI, A.  AIR & DANCE.  FL,OB(CL),PF                             EDM
CORELLI, A.  GAVOTTE & GIGUE.  FL,OB(CL),PF                         EDM
CORELLI, A.  GIGUE.  FL,CL,PF                                       EDM
CORY, E.  TRIO.  FL/PIC,OB/EHN,PF                                   ACA
CUNNINGHAM, M.  TRIPLE SONATA.  FL,CL,PF                            SS
DAMASE, J.  TRIO.  FL,OB,PF                                         HLE
DANSBY, E.  DANDY DUO.  FL,OB,PF                                    KN
DAVID, F.  THOU BRILLIANT BIRD.  FL,CL(OB),PF                       CF
DEBUSSY, C.  IL PLEURE DANS MON COEUR.  FL,CL,PF                    EDM
```

```
DEBUSSY, C.  MANDOLINE.  FL,CL,PF                                    EDM
DEPELSENAIRE, J.  SUR L'ALBAICIN.  OB,FL(CL),PF                      EV
DESSAU, P.  VARIATIONS ON "HAB MEIN WAGEN VOLLGELADEN"               PET
    CL,BSN,PF
DESTENAY, E.  TRIO, OP 27.  OB,CL,PF                                 HAM
DEVIENNE, F.-MARIASSAY.  SYMPHONIE CONCERTO #2 IN C MA               EUL
    OB(CL),BSN,PF
DIAMOND, D.  PARTITA.  OB,BSN,PF                                     SN
DIEMER, E.  MOVEMENT.  FL,OB,ORG                                     CF
DIJK, J. VAN.  CANZON ALL CAPRICCIO (1958).  OB,BSN,PF               SD
DODGSON, S.  TRIO.  OB,BSN,PF                                        CA
DONIZETTI, G.  MAD SCENE (LUCIA DI LAMMERMOOR).  FL,CL,PF            CF
DONIZETTI, G.  SEXTET (LUCIA DI LAMMERMOOR).  FL,CL,PF               CF
DONIZETTI, G.-PAULER.  TRIO IN F MA.  FL,BSN,PF                      PET
DRING, M.  TRIO.  FL,OB,PF                                           JOW
DUBOIS, P.  DOUBLE CONCERTINO.  OB,BSN,PF                            ALE
DUBOIS, P.  TRETEAUX, LES.  FL,ASAX,PF                               ECH
DUKELSKY, V.  TRIO THEME WITH VARIATIONS.  FL,BSN,PF                 BH
DUVERNOY, F.  TRIO #1.  FL(CL),OB(HN),PF                             HE
DUVERNOY, F.  TRIO #2.  FL(CL),OB(HN),PF                             HE
DVORKIN, J.  SUITE.  OB,BSN,PF                                       AMC
EBEN, P.  MUSIC.  OB,BSN,PF                                          CHF
ELGAR, E.-TRINKAUS.  LOVE'S GREETING.  2WW,PF                        CF
ELLIOT, W.  6 FRENCH SONGS OF THE 15TH CENTURY.  OB,BSN,PF           SO
EMMANUEL, M.  SONATA.  FL,CL,PF                                      HLE
EXAUDET, J.  COUR DE LA MARQUISE, LA.  FL,CL,PF                      EDM
EYSER, E.  TRIPIKO II (1974).  FL,CL,PF                              STI
FABRE, C.-HARRIS.  REVERIE.  CL,SAX(FL),PF                           CF
FABRE, C.-HARRIS.  REVERIE #2.  CL,SAX(FL),PF                        CF
FASCH, J.-BRAUN.  CONCERTO IN E MI.  FL,OB,PF                        EUL
FAURE, C.  EN PRIERE.  FL,CL,PF                                      EDM
FELDERHOF, J.  SUITE (1974).  FL,OB,PF                               SD
FINGER, B.-KRATOCHVIL.  ADAGIO (SONATA IN F MA).  FL,BCL,PF          ES
FINGER, G.-HOLMAN.  SONATA IN C MA, OP 5/10.  OB,BSN,BC              NOM
FOSTER, S.-BROOKE.  COME WHERE MY LOVE LIES DREAMING                 CF
    FL,CL,PF
FOSTER, S.  VILLAGE FESTIVAL, A.  FL,CL,PF                           EDM
FREEDMAN, H.  VARIATIONS (1965).  OB,FL,HPCD                         CAN
FRICKER, P.  TRIO, OP 35 (SERENADE #2).  FL,OB,PF                    SCH
FRID, G.  CHEMINS DIVERS, OP 75 (1968).  FL,BSN,PF                   SD
FUCHS, J.-CRUSSARD.  SINFONIA.  FL,OB,BC                             HUG
FUX, J.  NURNBERGER PARTITA.  FL,OB,BC                               MV
GALUPPI, B.-RUF.  TRIOSONATE IN G MA.  FL,OB,BC                      B&N
GANNE, L.-WEELINK.  EXTASE.  CL,BSN,PF                               KAW
GAUBERT, P.  TARENTELLE.  FL,OB,PF                                   E&C
GENIN, P.  GRAND DUO CONCERTANT, OP 51.  FL,OB(CL),PF                BIL
GEORGE, G.  SONATA.  FL,CL,PF                                        CAN
GERBER, R.  SUITE (1948).  FL,OB,PF                                  EUL
GILSON, P.  TRIO.  OB,CL,PF                                          M&M
GIORDANI, G.  18TH CENTURY AIR, AN.  FL,CL(BSN),PF                   EDM
GLASER, W.  TRIO (1953).  CL,BSN,PF                                  STI
GLINKA, M.-OUBRADOUS.  TRIO PATHETIQUE.  CL,BSN,PF                   EMT
GLINKA, M.  TRIO PATHETIQUE.  CL,BSN,PF                              INT
GLINKA, M.  TRIO PATHETIQUE.  CL,BSN(VC),PF                          MR
GODARD, B.-TRINKAUS.  BERCEUSE (JOCELYN).  2WW,PF                    CF
GODRON, H.  STOTINIANA (1960).  OB,BSN,PF                            SD
GOOSSENS, E.  PASTORAL & HARLEQUINADE.  FL,OB,PF                     ALE
GORNER, H.  DUO, OP 37.  CL,BSN,BC                                   PET
GOUNOD, C.-LAUBE.  AVE MARIA.  FL,CL,PF                              CF
GRUBER, H.  BOSSA NOVA, OP 21E.  FL,BSN,PF                           LDO
GRUNDMAN, C.  WALTZ & INTERLUDE.  FL,CL,PF                           BH
GYRING, E.  TRIO.  CL,BSN,PF                                         ACA
```

```
HA, J.  TRIO.  FL,CL,PF                                            MAN
HAIEFF, A.  3 BAGATELLES.  OB,BSN,HPCD(PF)                         BR
HALETZKI, P.  FATHER & SON.  PIC,BSN(ASAX),PF                      S&C
HANDEL, G.-GLASER.  ALLEGRO (SONATA #2).  FL,CL,PF                 CF
HANDEL, G.-SEIFFERT.  KAMMERTRIO #24 IN F MA.  OB,BSN,BC           BRH
HARTZELL, E.  TRIO (1969).  FL,BCL(BSN),PF                         LDO
HASSE, J.  CANZONE.  FL,CL,PF                                      EDM
HAYDN, F.-FISCHER.  CAPRICCIETTO.  FL,OB(CL),PF                    FOR
HAYDN, F.-ROBBINS/LANDON.  5 LYRE CONCERTI.  FL,OB,PF              LDO
HAYDN, F.  OXEN MINUET.  FL(CL),CL(ASAX,SAX),PF                    CF
HAYDN, F.  TRIO #29 IN F MA.  FL(CL),BSN(VC),PF                    CF
HAYDN, F.  TRIO #31 IN G MA.  FL,BSN(VC,BCL),PF                    CF
HEAD, M.  TRIO.  OB,BSN,PF                                         JE
HEINICHEN, J.-HAUSSWALD.  SONATA IN G MA.  FL,OB,BC                BRH
HEINICHEN, J.-JANETZKY.  TRIO-SONATE IN F MA.  FL(OB),OB,BC        WMS
HEINIO, M.  TRIO.  OB,BSN,HPCD                                     FIN
HERTEL, J.-WINSCHERMANN.  PARTITA I IN C MA.  OB,HPCD,BC           HSM
HERTEL, J.-WINSCHERMANN.  PARTITA II IN F MA.  OB,HPCD,BC          HSM
HERTEL, J.-WINSCHERMANN.  PARTITA III IN D MI.  OB,HPCD,BC         HSM
HETU, J.  TRIO (1960).  FL,OB,HPCD                                 CAN
HOLST, G.  FUGAL CONCERTO, A.  FL,OB,PF                            NO
HONEGGER, A.  CONCERTO DA CAMERA (1948).  FL,EHN,PF               EDS
HONEGGER, A.  PETITE SUITE.  2INSTR IN C,PF                        CHM
HONEGGER, A.  PETITE SUITE.  2WW,PF                                HSM
IBERT, J.-HOEREE.  ARIA.  FL(OB),CL(VN),PF                         ALE
IMBRIE, A.  SERENADE.  FL,OB,PF                                    SH
ISAAC, M. (ARR).  SACRED MUSIC.  2WW,PF                            CF
JABLONSKI, H.  SUITE.  OB,BSN,PF                                   PWM
JACOB, G.  TRIO.  FL,OB,PF                                         OX
JANCOURT, E.  CONCERTINO.  OB,BSN,PF                               BIL
JOHNSON, J.  TRIO.  FL,OB,PF                                       GA
JONES, K.  SONATA DA CAMERA (1957).  FL,OB,HPCD                    CAN
JONES, K.  SONATA DA CHIESA (1967).  FL,OB,HPCD                    CAN
KAHMANN, C.  DANCES.  FL,OB,PF                                     AMC
KALINNIKOV, V.  CHANSON TRISTE.  FL,CL(BSN),PF                     EDM
KALLIWODA, J.  CONCERTINO.  FL,OB,PF                               MR
KARLINS, M.  CELEBRATION.  FL,OB,HPCD                              ACA
KARLINS, M.  MUSIC.  OB,BCL,PF                                     ACA
KAUFFMANN, G.-GORE.  6 CHORALES.  OB,CL(TPT),ORG                   CON
KEMPIS, N. A.  SYMPHONIA A 3 IN D.  OB,BSN(VC),BC                  NOM
KENNAWAY, L.  DOWNSTREAM.  OB,CL,PF                                HI
KENNEDY-HARRIS.  STAR OF THE EAST.  FL,CL,PF                       LU
KETTING, O.  THEMA EN VARIATIES (1958).  CL,BSN,PF                 SD
KETTING, P.  SONATA (1936).  FL,OB,PF                              SD
KIESEWETTER, P.  SZENEN (1968).  FL,OB,PF                          GBV
KING, K.  NIGHT IN JUNE.  FL,CL,PF                                 BA
KLAUSS, N.  FUGUE IN C MA.  FL,CL,PF                               SO
KLEINKNECHT, J.-WEISS.  SONATA IN C MI.  FL,OB(VN),BC              DEU
KOETSIER, J.  TRIO, OP 13/1 (1936).  FL,OB,PF                      SD
KOETSIER, J.  TRIO, OP 81 (1978).  FL,BSN,PF                       SD
KOPSCH, J.  TRIO.  OB,CI,PF                                        M&M
KOPSCH, J.  TRIO.  OB,CL,PF                                        UE
KRAUSS.  ALLEGRO.  FL,CL,PF                                        MOL
KREBS, J.-RUF.  TRIOSONATE IN G MA.  FL,OB,BC                      HEI
KREIN, M.  TRIO.  CL,BSN,PF                                        MKE
KREUTZER, K.-SCHUTZ.  TRIO, OP 43.  CL,BSN,PF                      FRH
KUMMER, K.  2 DUETS, OP 46.  FL,CL,PF                              CF
KUNAD, R.  COMMEDIA "DIE EHE" (1969).  OB,BSN,PF                   DEU
KURI-ALDANA, M.  CANTARES.  FL,CL,PF                               MR
LABITZKY, T.  HERD GIRL'S DREAM, THE.  FL,CL,PF                    CF
LACOMBE, P.  SERENADE, OP 47.  FL,OB,PF                            INT
```

```
LALLIET, T.   TERZETTO.  OB,BSN,PF                                    HAM
LANGLEY, J.   INVOCATION & DANCE.  FL,OB,PF                           HI
LAVALLEE, C.-BOURDON.  BUTTERFLY, THE.  FL,CL,PF                      CF
LECLAIR, J.-FISCHER.  SARABANDE & TAMBOURIN.  FL,CL(OB),PF            FOR
LEEUW, T. DE.  TRIO (1952).  FL,CL,PF                                 SD
LEIGH, W.   TRIO.  FL,OB,PF                                           OX
LEMARE, E.-TRINKAUS.  ANDANTINO.  2WW, PF                             CF
LEVY, F.   SUITE.  FL,BSN,HPCD                                        SS
LOEILLET, J.-BLOCK.  SONATA IN F MI, OP  1 #1.  FL,OB,PF              MR
LOEILLET, J.-BLOCK.  SONATA IN G MI, OP  1 #3.  FL,OB,PF              MR
LOEILLET, J.-ERMELER/KLUGE.  TRIOSONATE IN F MA, OP  2/2              HEI
   FL,OB(FL),B C
LOEILLET, J.B.  COURANTE.  FL,CL,PF                                   EDM
LOEILLET, J.B.  SONATA IN C MI.  FL,OB,PF                             HLE
LOEILLET, J.B.  SONATA IN C MI.  FL,OB,PF                             INT
LOEILLET, J.B.  SONATA IN D MI.  FL,OB,PF                             HLE
LOEILLET, J.B.  SONATA IN D MI.  FL,OB,PF                             INT
LOEILLET, J.B.-BERGMANN.  TRIO SONATA IN F MA, OP  1/1                S&C
   FL,OB,PF
LONDON, E.   TRIO.  FL,CL,PF                                          MJ
LOVREGLIO, D.-BELLISON.  DUO CONCERTANTE.  FL,CL,PF                   MC
LUCAS, L.   AUBADE.  BSN,HN,PF                                        CHE
LUNDE, I.   ELEGI, OP 5.  OB,CL,PF                                    KN
MAGANINI, Q.   BOA CONSTRICTOR, THE, & THE BOBOLINK.  FL,BSN,PF       CF
MAGANINI, Q.   CONCERT ALBUM.  FL,CL,PF                               EDM
MAGANINI, Q.   MOONLIGHT ON THE PAINTED DESERT.  FL,CL,PF             EDM
MAGANINI, Q.   PARIS SOIR.  FL,CL,PF                                  EDM
MAI, P.   COMMEDIA "DIE EHE".  OB,BSN,PF                              DEU
MAREZ OYENS, T. DE.  INTER-TIMES (1977).  OB,BSN,PF                   SD
MARGOLA, F.   LONGOBARDA, LA.  FL,OB,PF                               GZ
MARIE, G.   DANS LA CALME NUIT.  OB,CL,PF                             HLE
MARIE, G.   DIALOGUE TENDRE.  OB,CL,PF                                HLE
MARIE, G.   EN SE JOUANT.  OB,CL,PF                                   HLE
MARIE, G.   FEUILLES AU VENT.  OB,CL,PF                               M&M
MARSAL, E.-LAUBE.  NANINE.  FL,CL,PF                                  CF
MARTELLI, H.   CONCERTO.  CL,BSN,PF                                   HMO
MARTIN, D.  5 SKETCHES (1961).  OB,BSN,PF                             CAN
MARTINI, G.-BALLOLA.  CONCERTO IN G MA.  FL,CL,BC                     ESZ
MARTINI, J.   PLAISIR D'AMOUR.  FL,OB(CL),PF                          EDM
MASSENET, J.-TRINKAUS.  ELEGY.  2WW, PF                               CF
MASSENET, J.   UNDER THE LINDEN TREES.  FL,CL(BSN),PF                 EDM
MASSENET, J.-LEONARD.  UNDER THE LINDENS                              TP
   OB(CL),CL(ASAX,TSAX,BSN),PF
MASSEUS, J.   INTRODUCTIE EN ALLEGRO, OP 19 (1952).  OB,CL,PF         SD
MATHE, O.  SAUFERSONNE, DIE (1970).  FL,BSN,ACC                       EMO
MATHIAS, W.   DIVERTIMENTO.  FL,OB,PF                                 OX
MATSUDAIRA, Y.   ORBITS 1,2,3 (1960).  FL,CL,PF                       ESZ
MAYER, W.  CELEBRATION.  FL,CL,PF                                     AMC
MC CAUGHEY, W.  ENCHANTED ISLE.  FL,CL,PF                             CF
MC KAY.  INSTRUMENTAL DUO SUITE.  2WW,PF                              WI
MENDELSSOHN-TRINKAUS.  ON WINGS OF SONG.  2WW,PF                      CF
MENDELSSOHN, F.   CONCERTPIECE #1 IN F MI, OP113.  CL,BSN,PF          INT
MENDELSSOHN, F.   CONCERTPIECE #2 IN D MI, OP114.  CL,BSN,PF          INT
MENDELSSOHN, F.   ICH WOLLT' MEINE LIEB' ERGOSSE SICH                 T-M
   2WIND INSTR,PF
MENDELSSOHN, F.-TRINKAUS.  NOCTURNO.  2WW,PF                          CF
MENDELSSOHN, F.   SPRING SONG.  FL,CL,PF                              CF
MERSSON, B.   KLEINE SUITE, OP 10.  FL,OB,PF                          HG
MESTRES-QUADRENY, J.  INVENCIONS MOVLIS I (1960).  FL,CL,PF           SS
METZLER, F.   TRIO PASTORALE (1959).  OB,BSN,HPCD                     HG
MEYERBEER, G.-TRINKAUS.  CORONATION MARCH (THE PROPHET)               CF
   2WW,PF
```

```
MILNE, J.  SCHERZETTO.  OB(CL),BSN,PF                              CHE
MONONEN, S.  TRIO.  FL,BSN,PF                                      FIN
MOORE, T.  POEM.  FL,SAX,PF                                        AMC
MORAWETZ, O.  TRIO (1960).  FL,OB,HPCD(PF)                         CAN
MOSKOWSKI, M.  SERENADE, OP 15/1.  FL,CL,PF                        CF
MOZART, W.-NAUMANN.  2, K252, K240 DIVERTIMENTI.  OB,BSN,PF        BRH
MOZART, W.-ROTHWELL.  DIVERTIMENTO (KV240 & KV252)                 CHE
    OB(CL,FL),BSN,PF
MOZART, W.-SCHWEDLER.  PHANTASIE F EINE ORGELWALZE                 WZ
    FL,OB(FL),PF
MOZART, W.  RONDO (SERENADE IN B FL MA).  FL,CL,BSN AD LIB,PF      OX
MOZART, W.-COLLINS.  SPRING RONDO, A (K320).  FL,OB,PF             BOS
MOZART, W.-HOFFMANN.  WIENER SERENADEN, K439B.  2WW,PF             MV
MULLER.  CONCERTANTE.  2WW,PF                                      BIL
MUSGRAVE, T.  TRIO.  FL,OB,PF                                      CHE
NANCARROW, C.  SARABANDE & SCHERZO.  OB,BSN,PF                     AMC
NARDINI, P.  SHEPHERD'S PIPES.  FL,OB(CL),PF                       EDM
NILSSON, B.  20 GRUPPEN.  OB,CL,PF                                 UE
OSIECK, H.  VARIATIES OVER VIER WEVERKENS (1968)                   SD
    FL,OB/EHN,PF
OTTEN, L.  MUSETTE ET PASTOURELLE (1955).  FL,OB,PF               SD
PADEREWSKI, I.-TRINKAUS.  MINUET.  FL,BSN,PF                       CF
PADEREWSKI, I.-TRINKAUS.  MINUET A L'ANTIQUE.  2WW,PF              CF
PAQUE, J.  DUO DE LA NORMA, #1.  CL,BSN,PF                         SCF
PAULSON, G.  DIVERTIMENTO, OP113 (1961).  OB,EHN,PF                STI
PELEMANS, W.  SONATE I.  FL,OB,PF                                  MAU
PELEMANS, W.  SONATE II.  FL,OB,PF                                 MAU
PENTLAND, B.  CANZONA (1961).  FL,OB,HPCD                          CAN
PEPUSCH, J.  TRIO SONATA IN G MI.  FL,OB,BC                        PET
PERGOLESI, G.  SICILIAN AIR.  FL,CL,PF                             EDM
PFISTER, H.  MOBILI A TRE.  FL,CL,PF                               PET
PINOS, A.  KARIKATUREN.  FL,BCL(BSN),PF                            ES
PITFIELD, T.  TRIO.  OB,FL(BSN),PF                                 GAL
PITFIELD, T.  VARIEGATIONS.  FL,OB,PF                              CA
PLATTI, G.-VOXMAN.  TRIO SONATA IN G MA.  FL,OB,BC                 MR
POELMAN, R.  MUSIC (1974).  FL,BSN,PF                              SD
POLIN, C.  SYNAULIA II.  FL/AFL,CL/BCL,PF                          SS
PORRET, J.  KLEBER.  CL,ASAX,PF                                    MOL
PORRET, J.  LAVOISIER.  CL,ASAX,PF                                 MOL
PORRET, J.  MARIVAUX.  CL,TSAX,PF                                  MOL
PORRET, J.  NELSON.  CL,TSAX,PF                                    MOL
POULENC, F.  TRIO.  OB,BSN,PF                                      CHE
PRAAG, H.  FANTASIA CONCERTANTE (1957).  FL,BSN,PF                 SD
PREVOST, A.  TRIPTYQUE (1962).  FL,OB,PF                           CAN
QUANTZ, J.-FISCHER.  GAVOTTE (DER RUHMESTEMPEL).  FL,CL(OB),PF     FOR
QUANTZ, J.-BERGMANN.  TRIO SONATA IN C MA.  FL,OB,BC               SCH
QUANTZ, J.-LASOCKI.  TRIO SONATA IN C MI.  FL,OB,BC                MR
QUANTZ, J.  TRIO SONATA IN C MI.  FL,OB,PF                         EDK
QUANTZ, J.-RUF.  TRIO SONATA IN D MA.  FL,OB,BC                    RC
QUANTZ, J.-LASOCKI-MADDEN.  TRIO SONATA IN G MA (K 45)             NOM
    FL(OB),BSN(VC),BC
QUANTZ, J.-BLUMENTHAL.  TRIO-SONATE IN C MI.  FL,OB(FL),PF         WZ
QUANTZ, J.-RUF.  TRIOSONATE IN G MA.  FL,OB D'AMORE,BC             HEI
QUENSEL, A.  ENTR'ACTE, OP 12.  FL,CL,PF                           CF
RACHMANINOFF, S.  POLKA ITALIENNE.  FL,CL,PF                       EDM
RACHMANINOFF, S.  VOCALISE.  FL,CL(BSN),PF                         EDM
RAMEAU, J.-FISCHER.  MENUETT & PASSEPIED (CASTOR & POLLUX)         FOR
    FL,CL(OB),PF
RAMEAU, J.  RIGODON DE DARDANUS.  FL,CL,PF                         EDM
RAPHLING, S.  SQUARE DANCE.  FL,CL,PF                              EDM
RAVEL, M.  PAVANE POUR UNE INFANTE DEFUNTE.  FL,CL,PF              EDM
RAWSTHORNE, A.  SONATINA.  FL,OB,PF                                OX
```

```
REGT, H. DE.  MUSIC, OP 32 (1973-74).  FL,EHN,HPCD            SD
REGTEREN ALTENA, L. VAN.  DIVERTIMENTO.  FL,OB,PF             SD
REIZENSTEIN, F.  TRIO IN A MA, OP 25.  FL,OB,PF              LEN
RICHTER, F.-NAGEL.  TRIO IN G MA.  FL,OB,BC                  WMS
ROBBINS, G.  BAGATELLE.  FL,OB,PF                             EV
ROBBINS, G.  PASTORALE.  FL,OB,PF                             EV
ROETSCHER, K.  RISSER-TRIO, OP 29.  CL,BSN,PF               B&B
ROSSEAU, N.  RAPSODIE, OP 81 (1958).  FL,BSN,PF             CBD
ROVICS, H.  CYBERNETIC STUDY #2.  CL,BSN,PF                   SS
RUDZINSKI, W.  CANZONETTA (1940).  FL,OB,PF                   AP
RUYNEMAN, D.  AMATERASU (1953).  FL,OB,HPCD                   SD
SABON.  CLOCHES BLEUES, LES.  2WW,PF                         BIL
SABON.  HELVETIE.  2WW,PF                                    BIL
SAINT-SAENS, C.-BROOKE.  SERENADE.  FL,CL,PF                  CF
SAINT-SAENS, C.-TRINKAUS.  SWAN, THE.  2WW,PF                 CF
SAINT-SAENS, C.  TARANTELLA, OP  6.  FL,CL,PF               INT
SAINT-SAENS, C.  TARANTELLE, OP  6.  FL,CL,PF               EDK
SAINT-SAENS, C.  TARENTELLE, OP  6.  FL,CL,PF               DUR
SALIERI, A.  DANSE (TARARE).  FL,OB,PF                      EDM
SALIERI, A.-WOJCIECHOWSKI.  KONZERT IN C MA.  FL,OB,PF      PET
SAMBIN, V.  DUO DE LA SOMNAMBULE.  OB,CL,PF                 EDS
SANDRE, G.  SOUS LA FEUILLEE.  FL,CL,PF                     E&C
SAYGUN, A.  TRIO, OP 56.  OB,CL,PF                           SN
SCHAFER, R.  DIVISIONS FOR BAROQUE TRIO (1963).  FL,OB,HPCD CAN
SCHENKER, F.  TRIOBALLADE (1968).  OB,BSN,PF               DEU
SCHLEMM, G.  BURLESKE.  E FL CL,BSN,PF                      PGM
SCHMITT, F.  SONATINE EN TRIO, OP 85.  FL,CL,PF            DUR
SCHOLLUM, R.  TRIO, OP 45.  FL,BSN,PF                       LDO
SCHOLLUM, R.  TRIO, OP 71.  OB,CL,PF                        LDO
SCHOUWMAN, H.  TRIO, OP 30 (1944).  OL,BON,PF               OD
SCHUMANN, R.-PARROTT.  ETUDE.  OB(FL),CL,PF                  CA
SCHUYT, N.  SONATA A TRE (1954).  OB,BSN,PF                  SD
SCHWARTZ, E.  TRIO.  FL,CL,PF                                BT
SGRIZZI, L.  ELEGIA E SCHERZO.  FL,BSN,PF                   EDB
SHOSTAKOVITCH, D.-ATOUMYAN.  4 WALTZES.  FL,CL,PF            MR
SIBELIUS, J.-TRINKAUS.  VALSE TRISTE (KUOLEMA).  2WW,PF      CF
SLECHTA, T.  FATHER OF WATERS.  FL,CL,PF                     CF
SOMERS, H.  THEME FOR VARIATIONS.  2WW,PF                   BER
SONTAG, H.  EVENING SERENADE, AN.  FL,ASAX(TSAX,CL),PF       CF
SPENCER, J.  SILVATONES.  FL(CL),ASAX(CL),PF                 CF
SPIEGLER.  CANZON A 2.  BSN,OB(FL),BC                        MR
STAM, H.  TROPIC.  FL,OB,PF                                  SD
STAMITZ, K.-WOJCIECHOWSKI.  DOUBLE CONCERTO IN B FL MA      HSM
   CL,BSN,PF
STANLEY, J.-FINCH.  TRIO MOVEMENT.  FL,OB,PF               S&C
STEIN, L.  TRIO.  CL,ASAX,PF                                DOR
STILL, W.  MINIATURES BASED ON AMERICAN FOLK SONGS.  FL,OB,PF OX
STOKER, R.  4 MINIATURES.  FL,CL,PF                          CA
STRAUSS, J.-BETTONEY.  TALES FROM THE VIENNA WOODS, OP325    CF
   FL,CL,PF
STRAUSS, R.  DUET CONCERTINO.  CL,BSN,PF                     BH
STRAUSS, R.  ZUEIGNUNG.  FL,BSN(CL),PF                      EDM
STRAVINSKY, I.  BERCEUSE.  FL,CL,PF                         EDM
STRAVINSKY, I.  DANCE OF THE BALLERINA (PETROUCHKA).  FL,CL,PF EDM
STRAVINSKY, I.  DANCE OF THE PRINCESSES.  FL,CL,PF          EDM
STRAVINSKY, I.  PASTORALE.  FL,CL,PF                        EDM
STRINGFIELD, L.  MORNING.  FL,CL,PF                         EDM
STRINGFIELD, L.  TO A STAR.  FL,CL,PF                       EDM
STUHEC, I.  SONATA A TRE.  CL,BSN,PF                        EDD
SUTER, R.  SONATINA (1966).  OB,BSN,HPCD                    HUG
SYDEMAN, W.  TRIO (1968).  BCL,BSN,PF                        SS
SZELENYI, I.  TRIO.  FL,BSN,PF                              EMB
```

```
TCHAIKOVSKY, P.-TRINKAUS.  CHANT SANS PAROLES.  2WW,PF          CF
TCHAIKOVSKY, P.  3 PIECES.  OB,CL,PF                            EDM
TCHAIKOVSKY, P.  SUITE (ALBUM FOR CHILDREN).  FL,CL,PF          EDM
TCHEREPNIN, I.  CADENZAS IN TRANSITION.  FL,CL,PF               BEL
TELEMANN, G.  CONCERTO #2.  FL,OB,PF                            GD
TELEMANN, G.-HAVEMANN.  CONCERTO IN G MA.  FL,OB D'AMORE,PF     PET
TELEMANN, G.  SONATA IN A MI.  FL,OB,BC                         INT
TELEMANN, G.  SONATA IN C MI.  FL,OB,BC                         INT
TELEMANN, G.-RUF.  SONATA IN E FL MA.  OB,HPCD,BC               SCH
TELEMANN, G.-HOFMANN.  SONATA IN E MI.  FL,OB,BC                B&N
TELEMANN, G.-RUF.  SONATE IN D MI.  FL,OB,BC                    B&N
TELEMANN, G.-SEIFFERT.  TRIO (TAFELMUSIK II, #4).  FL,OB,BC     BRH
TELEMANN, G.-LAUSCHMANN.  TRIO IN C MI.  FL,OB,BC               FOR
TELEMANN, G.  TRIO IN C MI.  FL,OB,PF                           SO
TELEMANN, G.-HINNENTHAL.  TRIO IN E MI.  FL,OB,BC               B&N
TELEMANN, G.-SCHEURICH/BRAUN.  TRIO SONATA IN A MI             HSM
   FL,HPCD,BC
TELEMANN, G.-WOEHL.  TRIO SONATA IN C MI (ESSERCIZII MUSICI)   PET
   FL,OB,BC
TELEMANN, G.-TOETTSCHER-SCHOLZ.  TRIO SONATA IN E FL MA        HSM
   OB,HPCD,BC
TELEMANN, G.  TRIO SONATA IN E MI.  FL,OB,BC                    EDK
TELEMANN, G.-RUF.  TRIO SONATA IN F MA.  OB,BSN(VC),BC          SCH
TELEMANN, G.-RUF.  TRIO-SONATE IN A MA (ESSERCIZII MUSICI)     SCH
   FL,HPCD OBL,BC
TELEMANN, G.-RUETZ.  TRIOSONATE IN B FL MA.  FL,HPCD,BC         B&N
TEMPLETON, A.  TRIO IN D MI.  FL,OB,PF                          SH
TENAGLIA, A.  ARIA ANTICA.  FL,CL,PF                            EDM
THILMAN, J.  4 GESPRACHE.  FL,BCL,PF                            PET
THOMAS, A.  FEAR NO MORE THE HEAT O' TH' SUN (1975)            MAR
   CL,BSN,HPCD
THOME, F.  SIMPLE AVEU.  FL,CL,PF                               CF
TITL/BUCHTEL.  SERENADE.  FL,CL,PF                              KJ
TITL, A.  SERENADE.  FL(CL),SAX(CL,OB),PF                       CF
TOLL, R.  PALS.  FL,ASAX,PF                                     CF
TRINKAUS, G.  LAMENT.  FL(WW),BSN(WW),PF                        CF
VERHAAR, A.  TRIO, OP 18 (1940).  FL,OB,PF                      SD
VILLA-LOBOS, H.  FANTAISIE CONCERTANTE.  CL,BSN,PF              EES
VIVALDI, A.-LASOCKI.  CONCERTO IN G MA, F. XII/36 (P129)       MR
   OB,BSN,PF
VIVALDI, A.  CONCERTO IN G MI, P402.  FL(CL),OB,BC             JB
VIVALDI, A.  GIGA.  FL,CL(OB),PF                                EDM
VIVALDI, A.-SCHROEDER.  SONATA A DUE IN A MI.  FL,BSN,BC       HEI
VIVALDI, A.  SONATA IN A MI, F. XV/1.  FL,BSN,BC               RC
VLIET, H.  SCHERZO (1969).  FL,EHN,PF                           SD
VON KREISLER, A.  TRIO SONATA.  FL,OB(FL),PF                   SO
VORLOVA, S.  SERENATA DESTA, OP 58 (1962).  FL,BCL,PF          CHF
WAGNER, R.-TRINKAUS.  SONG TO THE EVENING STAR.  2WW,PF        CF
WAGNER, R.-TRINKAUS.  WALTHER'S PRIZE SONG (MEISTERSINGER)     CF
   2WW,PF
WALLACE, W.-GRUENWALD.  CAVATINA (MARITANA).  FL,CL,PF         CF
WECKERLIN, J.  PASTORALE.  FL,OB,PF                             HEU
WEISGARBER, E.  SONATINE.  FL,CL,PF                             COR
WERNICK, R.  QUADRIGNOMES.  FL(VN),BSN(VC),PF                  BE
WHITE, D.  6 MINIATURES.  CL,BSN,PF                             SH
WILDER, A.  SUITE #1.  CL,BSN,PF                                MAR
WILDER, A.  SUITE #2.  CL,BSN,PF                                MAR
WILDER, A.  SUITE.  FL,CL,PF                                    MAR
WILLIAMS, D.  SUITE.  OB,CL,PF                                  RH
WUENSCH, G.  TRIO, OP  1.  CL,BSN,PF                           CAN
YEVSEYEV, S.  BURLESQUE, OP 70.  CL,BSN,PF                     MKE
ZACHOW, F.-SEIFFERT.  KAMMERTRIO IN F MA.  FL(OB),BSN,BC       KIS
```

```
ZACHOW, F.   TRIO.  FL,BSN,BC                                    EDK
ZAGWIJN, H.  PASTORALE (1937).  FL,OB,PF                         SD
ZAGWIJN, H.  PASTORALE E SCHERZO (1951).  FL,OB,HPCD             SD
ZAGWIJN, H.  SONATA (1950).  FL,CL,HPCD                          SD
ZAGWIJN, H.  TRIO (1952).  OB,CL,PF                              SD
ZANINELLI, L.  WINTER MUSIC.  FL,CL,PF                           ZA
ZILCHER, H.  3 STUCKE.  FL,PF,ACC                                HOH
```

3 PARTS: WOODWIND-KEYBOARD (COLLECTIONS)-329

```
COMRADES' REPERTORY.                                            CF
DEARNLEY, C. (ARR).  MORE EASY PIECES.  2FL(OB,CL,BSN),PF       CHE
EASY TO PLAY PIECES.  2FL(2CL,2ASAX),PF                         ASH
INTERMEDIATE PIECES,.  2CL(2ASAX),PF                            ASH
MASTERS OF THE BAROQUE.  2FL,BC                                 PET
NIEDERSACHSISCH DORFTANZE.  2OB(2CL),BC                         MV
OSTRANDER, A.  DUET ALBUM;.  FL,BSN,PF                          EDM
OSTRANDER, A.  DUET ALBUM,.  2CL,PF                             EDM
TRINKAUS, G. (ARR).  WORLD'S BEST-KNOWN PIECES.  2WW,PF         CF
```

3 PARTS: WOODWIND-BRASS (INCL HORN)-331

```
AMRAM, D.  TRIO.  BSN,TSAX,HN                                   PET
BJORKMAN, R.  LITEN MUSIK (1972).  FL,BSN,HN                    STI
BLEZARD, W.  4 SUITE PIECE.  FL(CL),CL,HN(BSN)                  EMI
BOCK, I. & A. JANETSKY.  10 PIECES.  BSN,2HN                    FRH
BOTTJE, W.  TRIO SONATE.  FL,HN,BSN                             CO
BRINGS, A.  BURLETTE.  FL,CL,TRB                                SS
BRIXEL, F.  COMMEDIA DELL'ARTE.  FL,CL,HN                       MV
CHAILLEY, J.  SUITE DU XV SIECLE                                ALE
    OB(EHN),HN,BSN(VA),TABOR AD LIB
CHILDS, B.  3 PLAYERS I.  CL,BSN,HN                             ACA
COWELL, J.  TRIO.  CL,BSN,HN                                    COR
DELMOTTE, C.  TRIO.  OB,CL,HN                                   MAU
DEVIENNE, F.-LELOIR.  TRIO #1 IN C MA.  CL,BSN,HN               KAW
DEVIENNE, F.-LELOIR.  TRIO #2 IN F MA.  CL,BSN,HN               KAW
DEVIENNE, F.-LELOIR.  TRIO #3 IN D MI.  CL,BSN,HN               KAW
DEVIENNE, F.  TRIO.  CL,BSN,HN                                  HE
DIAMOND, A.  TRIO.  FL,CL,TPT                                   GEN
DRESSEL, E.  TRIO MINIATURE.  CL,BSN,HN                         R&E
DUVERNOY, F.-LELOIR.  TRIO #1 IN F MA.  CL,BSN,HN               KAW
DUVERNOY, F.-LELOIR.  TRIO #2 IN E FL MA.  CL,BSN,HN            KAW
DUVERNOY, F.-LELOIR.  TRIO #3 IN F MA.  CL,BSN,HN               KAW
EMMERT, A.-HOCKNER.  TRIO IN E MA.  BSN,2HN                     SIM
GEBAUER, E.  3 TRIOS.  CL,HN,BSN                                KAW
GEBAUER, F.  TRIO #1 IN F.  CL,HN,BSN                           KAW
GEBAUER, F.-LELOIR.  TRIO #3 IN F MA.  CL,HN,BSN                KAW
GLASS, P.  DIVERSIONS (1960).  2FL,TRB                          CAN
GRAUN, K.  TRIO #1 IN D MA.  OB,BSN,HN                          M&M
GRAUN, K.  TRIO #1 IN G MA.  CL,BSN,HN                          M&M
GRAUN, K.  TRIO #2 IN E MI.  OB(CL),BSN,HN                      M&M
GROSSI, P.  COMPOSITION #3 (1958).  CL,BSN,HN                   AMP
GROSSI, P.  COMPOSIZIONE #3 (1959).  CL(VA),BSN(VC),HN(BCL)     BRU
HANDEL G.-HAAS.  OUVERTURE (SUITE).  2CL,HN                     SCH
```

```
HANDEL, G.-COOPERSMITH/LA RUE.  SONATA IN D MA.  2CL,HN(CL)        TP
HAYDN, F.-WEELINK.  DIVERTIMENTO #16.  CL,HN,BSN                   KAW
HAYDN, F.-WERNER.  DIVERTIMENTO TRIO.  CL,HN,BSN(VC)               CA
HAYDN, F.  DIVERTIMENTO, OP100.  CL,HN,BSN                         KAW
HEKSTER, W.  WINDSONG II (1970).  FL,ASAX,TPT                      SD
HELMSCHROTT, R.  INVENTION (1967).  CL,BSN,TRB                     GBV
HOLEWA, H.  LAMENTI (1976).  ASAX,BSN,CT                           STI
HORROD, N.  TRIO.  HN,TRB,BSN                                      KAW
JACOBSOHN, G.  ADAGIO & ALLEGRO.  OB,CL,HN                         ISR
KARG-ELERT, S.  TRIO, OP 49/1.  OB,CL,HN                           FRH
KEE, C.  12 ORIGINAL TRIOS.  ASAX,TSAX,TPT                         HE
KRATOCHVIL, J.  TRIO (1958).  CL,BSN,HN                            CHF
LEVY, F.  TRIO.  CL,BSN,HN                                         COR
LEYE, L.  SUITE.  2HN,BSN                                          KAW
LICKL, J.-STEINBECK.  TRIO IN E FL MA.  CL,HN,BSN                  EUL
LICKL, J.  TRIO IN E FL MA.  CL,HN,BSN                             B&V
LICKL, J.  3 TRIOS.  CL,BSN,HN                                     PET
LYBBERT, D.  TRIO FOR WINDS.  CL,HN,BSN                            PET
MAXWELL, C.  TRIO.  FL,BSN,HN                                      SS
MICHALSKY, D.  TRIO CONCERTINO.  FL,OB,HN                          WI
MOZART, W.  ADAGIO, K580A.  EHN,2HN(2CL)                           EK
MOZART, W.  TRIO.  2CL,HN                                          PWM
OTTEN, L.  DIVERTIMENTO #2 (1963).  FL,BSN,HN                      SD
PANNIER, O.  TRIO #2 IN E FL MA, OP 40.  CL,HN,BSN                 ETB
PARRIS, R.  4 PIECES.  CL,BSN,HN                                   ACA
PHILLIPOT, M.  TRIO INACHEVE.  FL,CL,TRB                           EDS
PLATTI, G.  SONATA.  CL,BSN,HN                                     COR
POLIN, C.  KLWRK DIURNAL, A.  ASAX,BSN,HN                          DOR
POLLOCK, R.  TRIO #2 (1969).  OB,BSN,TPT                           B-B
PRUNTY, W.  TRIO ALLEGRO.  CL,TPT,TRB                              ACC
REICHA, A.-LELOIR.  TRIOS, OP 92, 2 VOLS.  2HN,BSN                 KAW
ROBERTS, W.  MINIATURES.  CL,HN,BSN                                COR
ROBERTS, W.  WALK IN THE COUNTRY, A.  CL,BSN,HN(CL)                COR
SABATINI, G.  PUPPET WALTZ.  CL(OB),BSN,HN                         COR
SCHUMANN, G.  MINIATUR-TRIO.  OB,HN,BSN                            S-V
THURNER, E.  TRIO, OP 56.  CL,HN,BSN                               ETB
VERRALL, J.  DIVERTIMENTO.  CL,HN,BSN                              ACA
VIECENZ, H.  TERZETT.  2OB,HN                                      FRH
WALLACE, W.  DIVERSIONS II.  FL,HN,BSN                             CAN
WALLNER, A.  5 BAGATELLEN.  2CL,HN                                 FS
WALLNER, A.  IN MODO CLASSICO.  2CL,HN                             FS
WEBER, C.M. VON.  FREISCHUTZ, DER.  CL,BSN,HN                      SO
WEIGL, V.  BRIEF ENCOUNTERS.  OB(EHN),CL,HN                        ACA
WILDER, A.  MOOSACAGLIA.  OB,BSN,HN                                MAR
```

3 PARTS: WOODWIND-STRING-333

```
AESCHBACHER, W.  TRIO, OP 72.  FL,VA,DB(VC)                        HEI
AGERSNAP, H.  INTERLUDIUM (1936).  FL,VN,VC                        SPD
AHLGRIMM, H.  DIVERTIMENTO.  FL,VN,VA                              MRL
AMBROSIUS, H.  3 PRELUDES & FUGUES.  FL,2VN                        PET
AMES, W.  TRIO.  OB,VN,VC                                          ACA
ANDERSEN, K.  TRIO, OP 5.  FL,CL,VC                                EDK
ANDERSEN, K.  TRIO, OP 5.  FL,CL,VC                                NOR
ANDRIESSEN, H.  SERENADE.  FL,VN(OB),VC(BSN)                       HU
ANTONIOU, T.  TRIO, OP 14 (1961).  FL,VA,VC                        EMO
ARCHER, V.  DIVERTIMENTO #2 (1957).  OB,VN,VC                      CAN
ARDEVOL, J.  SONATA #1.  OB,CL,VC                                  SN
```

```
ARDEVOL, J.  SONATA #2.  2FL,VA                                        SN
ARNOLD, M.  TRIO.  FL,BSN,VA                                          CF
ASCOUGH, R.  TRIO.  FL,CL,VN                                          EXM
BACEWICZ, G.  TRIO (1935).  OB,VN,VC                                  PWM
BACH, C.P.E.-WALTHER.  10 KLEINE TRIOS, WQ 82, 193.  2FL,VN           WZ
BACH, J.C.-MARGUERRE.  SONATA IN F MA.  FL,VN,VC                      HMO
BACH, J.C.-NAGEL.  TRIO IN C MA.  2FL,VC                              MV
BACH, J.S.  21 SELECTED PIECES.  2FL(2OB),VC(BSN)                     SCH
BACH, J.S.-COCHRANE.  15 3-PART INVENTIONS.  2CL,VC                   CF
BACH, W.F.-ERMELER.  TRIO IN G MA.  2FL,VA                            B&N
BACH, W.F.E.  TRIO IN G MA.  2FL,VA                                   EDK
BADINGS, H.  TRIO #5 (1947).  FL,VN,VA                                SD
BAER, W.  5 SATZE.  CL,VN,VC                                          S-V
BALLIF, C.  TRIO, OP 35/2.  FL,OB,VC                                  B&B
BALORRE, C.  TRIO.  OB,VA,VC                                          HAM
BARTSCH, C.  SUITE EN TRIO.  FL,VA,DB                                 MAU
BEALE, J.  3 MINIATURES, OP  3.  OB,CL,VC                             ACA
BEETHOVEN, L. VAN.  SERENADE IN D MA, OP 25.  FL,VN,VA                BRH
BEETHOVEN, L. VAN-GERLACH.  SERENADE, OP 25.  FL,VN,VA                GHE
BEETHOVEN, L. VAN.  SERENADE, OP 25.  FL,VN,VA                        EDK
BEETHOVEN, L. VAN.  SERENADE, OP 25.  FL,VN,VA                        INT
BEETHOVEN, L. VAN.  SERENADE, OP 25.  FL,VN,VA                        PET
BEETHOVEN, L. VAN.  TRIO IN C MA, OP 87.  2OD,VA                      BRH
BEETHOVEN, L. VAN.  TRIO, OP 87.  2FL,VA                              INT
BENKER, H.  SERENADE.  FL,VN,VA                                       MV
BENTON, D.  STATELY DANCES.  AFL,VA,VC                                SS
BESOZZI, C.-STENZL.  6 TRIOS.  OB,VN,VC(BSN)                          EUL
BEYER, J.-HOCKNER.  PARTITA #1.  FL,VN,VC                             ABE
BEYER, J.-HOCKNER.  PARTITA #2.  FL,VN,VC                             ABE
BIALAS, G.  TRIO (1946).  FL,VA,VC                                    B&N
BINKERD, G.  TRIO.  CL,VA,VC                                          BH
BJERRE, J.  MOSAIQUE MUSICALE (1936).  FL,VN,VC                       SPD
BJERRE, J.  MOSAIQUE MUSICALE #3.  FL,VN,VC                           WH
BJERRE, J.  SERENADE.  FL,OB,VA                                       SPD
BLUMER, T.  TRIO, OP 55.  CL,VN,VC                                    SIM
BOIS, R. DU.  2 PIECES.  FL,OB,VC                                     SD
BOIS, R. DU.  SUMMER MUSIC.  ASAX,VN,VC                               SD
BOOREN, J. VAN DEN.  AKIROB 1972.  FL,VN,VA                           SD
BURRIS, S.  VILLANELLEN, OP 97.  FL,VN,VC                             S-V
BOTTJE, W.  MUSIC FOR A JOYOUS OCCASION III.  2FL,VC                  ACA
BRAAL, A. DE.  GIOCOSO (1972).  FL,VN,VA                              SD
BRAAL, A. DE.  TRIO (GIOCOSO).  FL,VN,VA                              SD
BREUER, P.  SERENADE.  2FL,DB                                         HG
BROWN, J.  TRIO.  FL,CL,VC                                            ACA
BROWN, R.  TRIO.  FL,CL,VA                                            WI
BUGGY, B.  TRIO.  FL,VN,VA                                            AU
BUSCH, A.  HAUSMUSIK, OP 26/3.  CL,VN,VC                              BRH
CAMBINI, G.-SCHULTZ/HAUSER.  TRIO #5 IN F MA; TRIO #6 IN G MA         SCH
    2FL,VA
CAMBINI, G.-NAGEL.  TRIO, OP  3/6.  2FL,VC                            EUL
CAMBINI, G.-DOUGLAS.  3 TRIOS, OP 26/1-3.  FL,VN,VA                   NOM
CHADABE, J.  PRELUDE TO NAPLES.  FL,CL,VC                             CPE
CHAMBERS, S.  ABSTRACTIONS FOR 3.  FL,OB,VC                           AMC
CHEVREUILLE, R.  TRIO, OP 90 (1968).  FL,VA,VC                        CBD
CHRISTIANSEN, A.  TRIO.  FL,VA,VC                                     WH
COLACO OSORIO-SWAAB, R.  SUITE (1940).  FL,VN,VA                      SD
COPE, D.  5 PIECES.  FL,BSN,VN                                        SS
CUSTER, A.  PERMUTATIONS.  CL,VN,VC                                   GEN
DAHL, I.  CONCERTO A TRE.  CL,VN,VC                                   JB
DANZI, F.-RAMPAL.  TRIO #1, OP 71.  FL,VN,VC                          INT
DANZI, F.-RAMPAL.  TRIO #2, OP 71.  FL,VN,VC                          INT
DANZI, F.-SONNTAG.  TRIO IN D MA, OP 71/3.  FL,VN,VC                  B&N
```

DANZI, F.-SONNTAG. TRIO IN E MI, OP 71/2. FL,VN,VC	B&N
DANZI, F.-PETERS. TRIO, OP 71/1. FL,VN,VC	HEI
DANZI, F. TRIO, OP 71/2 IN E MI. FL,VN,VC	PET
DANZI, F. TRIO, OP 71/3 IN D MA. FL,VN,VC	PET
DANZI, F. 2 TRIOS, OP 71/7, 2. FL,VN,VC	EDK
DANZI, F.-JANETZKY. 2 TRIOS, OP 71. FL,VN,VC	FRH
DAVID, J. TRIO, OP 30. FL,VN,VA	BRH
DAVID, J. TRIO, OP 73. AFL,VN,VC	BRH
DAVID, T. TRIO, OP 1/1. FL,VN,VA	BRH
DAVID, T. TRIO, OP 8. FL,VN,VA	BRH
DAVIDOVSKY, M. JUNCTURES. FL,CL,VN	EM
DELLA PERUTI, C. SOUNDINGS. FL,CL,VC	MAN
DELNOOZ, H. DIVERTIMENTO. FL,CL,VN	SD
DEVIENNE, F. SONATINE IN D MA. 2FL,VC	EDH
DEVIENNE, F. SONATINE IN D MI. 2FL,VC	EDH
DEVIENNE, F. SONATINE IN F MA. 2FL,VC	EDH
DEVIENNE, F. SONATINE IN G MA. 2FL,VC	EDH
DIJK, J. VAN. DIVERTIMENTO (1941). CL,VA,VC	SD
DOPPELBAUER, J. DIVERTIMENTO (LEOBNER TRIO) (1971). FL,VN,VC	LDO
DOPPELBAUER, J. MINIATURES. FL,VA,VC	LDO
DOPPELBAUER, J. TRIO (1967). OB,VA,VC	LDO
DUBOIS, P. 5 MOUVEMENTS BREFS. FL,VA,DB	MAU
DURE, R. TRIO. FL,CL,VC	AMC
EKLUND, H. SMALL SERENADE. CL,VN,DB	CHE
ERBACH, F. DIVERTISSEMENT MELODIEUX IN G MI. 2FL,VC	EDK
ERDMANN, H. TRIO III. AFL,CL,VC	HSM
ETLER, A. SONATA. OB,CL,VA	NVM
FARKAS, F. SERENADE (1965). FL,2VN	EMB
FELD, J. TRIO (1963). FL,VN,VC	ART
FIORILLO, F. TRIO, OP 29/1. FL,VN,VA	ABE
FRITCHIE, W. COMO PARK SUITE. FL,CL,VC	SS
FUX, J.-CRUSSARD. SINFONIA. FL,OB,DB	ECS
GAL, H. HUYTON-SUITE, OP 92. FL,2VN	SIM
GAL, H. SERENADE, OP 93. CL,VN,VC	SIM
GAL, H. TRIO SERENADE, OP 88. FL,VN,VC	SIM
GAL, H. TRIO, OP 94. OB,VN,VA	SIM
GASSMANN, F.-NAGEL. DIVERTIMENTO IN G MA. FL,VN,VC	MV
GASSMANN, F.-ALBRECHT. TRIO SONATA IN A MA. FL,VN,VA	KIS
GASSMANN, F.-ALBRECHT. TRIO SONATA IN B FL MA. FL,VN,VA	KIS
GASSMANN, F.-ALBRECHT. TRIO SONATA IN C MA. FL,VN,VA	KIS
GASSMANN, F.-ALBRECHT. TRIO SONATA IN D MA. FL,VN,VA	KIS
GASSMANN, F. TRIO SONATA IN D MA. FL,VN,VA	EDK
GASSMANN, F.-ALBRECHT. TRIO SONATA IN E FL MA. FL,VN,VA	KIS
GASSMANN, F.-ALBRECHT. TRIO SONATA IN G MA. FL,VN,VA	KIS
GEBAUER, F. TRIO, OP 33/3. BSN,VN,VC	MR
GIANELLA, L. NOCTURNE IN G MA. 2FL,VC	SO
GILLAM, R. THEME IN C MA. 2CL,VC	MAN
GILSE, J. VAN. TRIO. FL,VN,VA	ALS
GIORDANI, T.-JANETZKY. TRIO IN G MA. FL,VA,VC	PM
GIORDANI, T.-SCHULTZ/HAUSER. 6 TRIOS, OP 12, 2 VOLS FL,VA,VC	SCH
GRAF, F.-ERMELER. TRIO IN D MA. FL,VN,VC	HEI
GROFE, F. TABLE D'HOTE. FL,VN,VA	KJ
GURKOV, V. 3 IRONIES. FL,VA,VC	MKE
HANDEL, G.-SCHWADRON. THEME & VARIATIONS (CHACONNE IN G MA) CL,VN,BSN	PMP
HAWORTH, F. TRIO. FL,SAX,VC	CAN
HAYDN, F. DIVERTIMENTI IN A MA & G MA. FL,VN,VC	MV
HAYDN, F.-JANETZKY. DIVERTIMENTO IN D MA. FL,VA,VC	PM
HAYDN, F. LONDON TRIO. 2FL,VC	HU
HAYDN, F.-BALET. 4 LONDON TRIOS, HOB IV,1-4. 2FL,VC	B&N
HAYDN, F. 4 LONDON TRIOS. 2FL,VC	EDK

HAYDN, F. 4 LONDON TRIOS. 2FL,VC	INT
HAYDN, F. 4 LONDON TRIOS. 2FL,VC	SO
HAYDN, F.-KOLBEL. TRIO IN D MA. FL,VN,VC	HEI
HAYDN, F. TRIO IN D MA. FL,VN,VC	PET
HAYDN, F. TRIOS, OP 11/4-6. FL,VN,VC	B&V
HAYDN, F. 3 TRIOS, OP 11/4-6. FL,VN,VC	MR
HAYDN, F. 3 TRIOS, OP 11/4-6. FL,VN,VC	PET
HAYDN, F. 6 TRIOS, OP100, 2 VOLS. FL,VN,VC	WZ
HAYDN, F. 3 TRIOS. 2FL,VC	EDK
HAYDN, F. 3 TRIOS. FL,VN,VC	GS
HAYDN, M.-RAINER. DIVERTIMENTO IN C MA. OB,VA,VN	LDO
HEDWALL, L. TRIO (1945). FL,VA,VC	EMF
HEINICHEN, J. TRIO SONATA. OB,VA DA GAMBA,VC	EDK
HEISS, H. MUSIKALISCHES GASTGESCHENK. FL,VN,VC	WMS
HEKSTER, W. INCENTER (1970). FL,OB,VC	SD
HENNESSY, W. TRIO, OP 70. FL,BSN,VN	EES
HERBST, R. TANZE NACH VOLKSMELODIEN, OP 15A. CL,VN,VC	ETB
HESPOS, H. FAHL-BRUCHIG (1971)	EMO
BASSET HN,VC,PICC HECKELPHONE	
HESS, W. DIVERTIMENTO, OP 82. FL,VN,VA	EUL
HEUSSENSTAMM, G. TRIO, OP 3 (1959). CL,VN,VC	SS
HOBSON, B. TRIO (1966). CL,VN,VC	B-B
HODDINOTT, A. NOCTURNES & CADENZAS. CL,VN,VC	OX
HOLST, G.-HOLST. TERZETTO (1925). FL,OB,VA(CL)	CHE
HONEGGER, A. CHORAL A 3 VOIX (3 CONTREPOINTS #2). EHN,VN,VC	CHE
HORST, A. VAN DER. THEME, VARIATIONS ET FUGUE, OP 76 (1957)	SD
FL,VN,VA	
HRISANIDE, A. TRIO (1958). VN,VA,BSN	HG
HUBER, K. 6 MINIATUREN. CL,VN,VC	HEI
HUBNER, W. CAPRICCIOSO. FL,VN,VA	BRH
HUMEL, G. TRIO (1964). FL,VA,VC	B&B
HUSA, K. EVOCATIONS DE SLOVAQUIE. CL,VA,VC	SCH
JEMNITZ, A. FLUTE TRIO, OP 19. FL,VN,VA	EDK
JEMNITZ, A. TRIO, OP 19. FL,VN,VA	WZ
JETTEL, R. TRIO IN C MI. CL,VN,VA	LDO
JOHNSON, T. ACTION MUSIC I. FL,VA,DB	AMP
JOSEPHS, W. TRIO, OP 50. FL,VN,VC	CA
JUON, P. DIVERTIMENTO, OP 34. CL,2VA	EDK
JUON, P. DIVERTIMENTO, OP 34. CL,2VA	MRL
KALLSTENIUS, E. LYRISK SVIT, OP 55. FL,SAX(CL),VC	EMF
KALLSTENIUS, E. PICCOLO TRIO SERIALE, OP 47. CL,VN,VA	EMF
KALLSTENIUS, E. TRIO DIVERTENTE, OP 38. FL,VN,VA	EMF
KANITZ, E. NOTTURNO. FL,VN,VA	NVM
KARDOS, I. GROTESQUE. FL/PIC,VC,DB	GEN
KARKOFF, M. MINIATYRSVIT #1, OP 34A. FL,CL,VA	EMF
KARKOFF, M. MINIATYRSVIT #2, OP 34B. OB,BSN,VN	EMF
KARKOFF, M. SERENATA, OP 61A. FL,VN,VA	EMF
KAUDER, H. TRIO #1 (1936). FL,OB,VA(HN)	SS
KAUDER, H. TRIO #2 (1960). FL,OB,VA(HN)	SS
KELTERBORN, R. LYRISCHE KAMMERMUSIK (1959). CL,VN,VA	B&N
KEMPE, H. TRIO SENZA PRETESE. CL,VA,VC	EMF
KERKHOF, F. TRIO. FL,VN,VA	B&V
KIBBE, M. TRIO. FL,VN(CL),BSN(VC)	SS
KOERPPEN, A. SERENADE IN F MA (1952). FL,VN,VA	BRH
KONT, P. SERENATA A TRE, OP 61/1. FL,VN,VA	LDO
KOPPEL, H. DIVERTIMENTO PASTORALE, OP 61 (1955). OB,VA,VC	SPD
KORN, P. ALOYSIA SERENADE, OP 19. FL,VA,VC	ABE
KOSA, G. TRIO. FL,VA,VC	EMB
KOUTZEN, B. MUSIC. ASAX,BSN,VC	AMP
KREBS, J. TRIO SONATA IN B MI. 2FL,VC	EDK
KREUTZER, C. TRIO. 2CL,VA	PET
KROMMER, F. 13 PIECES, OP 47. 2CL,VA	PET

```
KROMMER, F.   13 STUCKE, OP 47.  2CL,VA                          EK
KUNERT, K.   TRIO IN D MA, OP  5.  FL,VN,VC                      ETB
KUNERT, K.   TRIᴖ  OP 5.  FL,VN,VC                               PG
LEGLEY, V.   SE̅  .DE, OP 44/3 (1957).  FL,VN,VC                  CBD
LERICH, R.   TRIᴖ IN C MA.  FL,2VN                               MRL
LEVI, P.   5 PROGRESSIONS.  FL,CL,VA                             ACA
LEVY, F.   SERENADE.  FL,CL,VC                                   SS
LINDE, B.   VINJETTSVIT (1959).  OB,VA,VC                        EMF
LINDLEY, R.   TRIO.  BSN,VA,VC                                   M&M
LINKE(ARR).   TANZE AUS 5 JAHRHUNDERTEN.  FL,2VN                 HEI
LUNDBORG, E.   TRIO.  FL,VN,VC                                   ACA
MAIGUASHCA, M.   UBUNGEN (1972).  CL,VN,VC                       FEE
MANN, L.   PARTITA, OP 28 (1972).  VN,BSN(FL),VC                 CAN
MANN, L.   TOCCATA ALLA BAROCCO, OP 15 (1956).  FL,CL,VC         CAN
MANN, L.   TRIO, OP  6 (1952).  FL,CL,VC                         CAN
MANNINO, F.   LITTLE MUSIC FOR 3 FRIENDS, A.  FL,VN,VA           EDI
MARKEVITCH, I.   SERENADE.  CL,VN,BSN                            SCH
MARTEAU, J.   TERZETTO, OP 32.  FL,VN,VA                         SIM
MC CABE, J.   MOVEMENTS, OP 29.  CL,VN,VC                        NO
MELLNAS, A.   SONATA A TRE.  FL,VN,VA                            EMF
MESTRES-QUADRENY, J.   DIVERTIMENTO "LA RICARDA" (1962)          SS
    FL,CL,DB
MEYER, J.   VARIATIONS ON A THEME OF PAGANINI.  PIC,CL/BCL,VA    ZA
MEYEROVICH, M.   TRIO.  FL,VN,VA                                 MKE
MIMAROGLU, I.   CONJECTUS 2.  FL,CL,VC                           SS
MOSS, L.   WINDOWS.  FL,CL,DB                                    SS
MOZART, W.   ADAGIO (K356).  FL,OB,VA                            PET
MOZART, W.   ADAGIO FOR GLASHARMONIKA.  FL,OB(FL),VA             WZ
MOZART, W.-SCHWEDLER.   ANDANTE IN F MA FUR EINE WALZE           WZ
    FL,OB(FL),VA
MYERS, R.   TRIO.  ASAX,BSN,VC                                   ARM
MYSLIVECEK, J.   SONATA IN B FL MA.  FL(OB),VN,VC(BSN)           EUL
MYSLIVECEK, J.   SONATA, OP  1/3.  FL,VN,VC                      CHF
MYSLIVECEK, J.   TRIO IN B FL MA, OP  1/4.  FL,VN,VC             EDK
MYSLIVECEK, J.   TRIO.  FL,VN,VC                                 BRH
MYSLIVECEK, J.-RIEMANN.   TRIO, OP  1/4.  FL,VN,VC,PF AD LIB     INT
NEDBAL, M.   KLEINES TRIO.  CL,BSN,VC                            LDO
NEMIROFF, I.   VARIATIONS TO A THEME.  FL,OB,VC                  M&M
NEUBAUER, F.-BORMANN.   TRIO IN C MA, OP  3/3.  FL,VN,VA         HSM
NEUBAUER, F.-NAGEL.   TRIO IN D MA.  2FL,VC                      EUL
NOWAK, L.   TRIO.  CL,VN,VC                                      ACA
OLAN, D.   STARTING WINTER.  FL,CL,VN                            ACA
OVANIN, N.   LARGHETTO.  CL,VN,VC                                MAN
PARSCH, A.   POETICA #4 (1970).  FL,BCL,DB                       CHF
PEHRSON, J.   ENTELECHIES.  CL,2VA                               SS
PELEMANS, W.   TRIO.  FL,VA,DB                                   MAU
PEPUSCH, J.   SONATA DA CAMERA IN G MI.  FL,VN,VC                EDK
PETERSON, W.   PHANTASMAGORIA.  FL,CL,DB                         SS
PHILIPP, F.   SERENADE, OP 23.  FL,VN,VA                         ABS
PHILLIPS, B.   HUNTINGDON TWOS & THREES.  FL,OB,VC               GA
PICHL, V.-KLEMENT.   2 DIVERTIMENTI.  FL,VN,VC                   ES
PLEYEL, I.-NAGEL.   TRIO #1 IN G MA, OP 73.  FL,VN,VC            EUL
POOT, M.   CONCERTINO (1963).  FL,VN,VC                          CBD
PORCELIJN, D.   SHADES (1975).  FL,VN,VA                         SD
PORTER, Q.   LITTLE TRIO.  FL,VN,VA                              NVM
RACEK, F.   EINE KLEINE HAUSMUSIK.  FL(OB),VN,VA                 LDO
RAPHAEL, G.   TRIO (1940) IN B MA, OP 48.  FL,VN,VA              B&N
READ, T.   5 SKETCHES.  FL,CL,VA                                 ACA
REGER, M.-SCHNIRLIN.   SERENADE #1, OP 77A.  FL,VN,VA            B&B
REGER, M.   SERENADE #2, OP141A.  FL,VN,VA                       PET
REGER, M.   SERENADE, OP 77A.  FL,VN,VA                          EDK
REGER, M.   SERENADE, OP 77A.  FL,VN,VA                          INT
```

```
REGT, H.   POEME, OP 63 (1979).  FL,VN,VA                          SD
REICHA, A.-PAULER.   TRIO IN G MA.  FL,VN,VC                       EUL
REICHA, A.-FORSTER.   18 VARIATIONS & A FANTASY IN G MA, OP 51     EUL
    FL,VN,VC
REIMANN, A.   CANZONI E RICERCARI.  FL,VA,VC ·                     SCH
RICHTER, N.   SERENADE (1945).  FL,VN,VA                           SD
RIGEL, A.-KOCH.   TRIO #4 IN F MA.  FL,VN,VC                       HUG
RIISAGER, K.   SERENADE.  FL,VN,VC                                 CHE
ROHWER, J.   TRIO.  OB,VN,VA                                       MV
ROJO, J.   MUSICA SOBRE UNOS MODULOS.  2FL,VA                      EDA
ROLLA, A.   CONCERTINO.  VA,VC,BSN                                 AB
ROMBERG, H.-PAULER.   TRIO (INTERMEZZI CONCERTANT),OP  7           EUL
    FL,VN,VC
ROOSEVELT, J.   SERENADE.  OB,VA,VC                                ACA
ROSENBERG, H.   SERENAD, OP 82.  FL,VN,VA                          EMF
ROSENBERG, H.   TRIO.  FL,VN,VA                                    CHE
ROUSSEL, A.   TRIO, OP 40.  FL,VA,VC                               DUR
SAIKKOLA, L.   TRIO.  FL,VA,DB                                     FIN
SALOMON, K.   ELEGIE UND TANZ.  OB,2VN                             HEI
SCHADEWITZ, C.   SERENADE, OP 49.  FL,VN,VA                        ETB
SCHADEWITZ, C.   SERENADE, OP 49.  FL,VN,VC                        PGM
SCHMIDT, W.   SONATA BREVE.  FL,CL,VA                              WI
SCHMITT, J.   TRIO IN G MA.  FL,VN,VC                              CHE
SCHOONENBEEK, K.   ARAGARA (1974).  FL,VN,VA                       SD
SCHULHOFF, E.   CONCERTINO.  FL,VA,DB                              EDK
SCHWANTNER, J.   ENTROPY.  SOP SAX,BCL,VC                          DOR
SCHWARTZ, E.   TRIO.  FL,CL,VC                                     GEN
SCHWEIZER, K.   2 SATZE UBER BEWEGLICHE ZEITMASSE (1962)           EMO
    FL,VN,VA
SENSTIUS, K.   SERENADE, OP 36 (1952).  OB,VA,BSN                  SPD
SHOSTAKOVITCH, D.   PRELUDES.  FL,VN,VC                            EDM
SIEGL, O.   TRIFOLIUM, OP145.  FL,OB,VA                            FRH
SIGTENHORST MEYER, B. VAN.   TRIO, OP 49 (1952).  FL,VN,VA         ALS
SIMEONOV, B.   4 MOMENTS.  FL,VA,VC                                WAT
SIRULNIKOFF, J.   TRIO (1959).  CL,VN,VC                           CAN
SKOLD, Y.   SERENAD, OP 25.  FL,VN,VA                              EMF
SOMERS, H.   TRIO (1950).  FL,VN,VC                                CAN
SORENSON, T.   SERENATA PER TRE (1966).  FL,VA,VC                  STI
SPERGER, J.-BIBA.   DIVERTIMENTO IN D MA.  FL,VA,VC                EUL
STAMITZ, C.-SCHNAPP.   TRIO IN G MA.  2FL,VC                       B&N
STAMITZ, C.   TRIO IN G MA.  2FL,VC                                EDK
STEARNS, P.   MAY 27TH, 1956.  FL,CL,VC                            AMC
STEARNS, P.   SUMMER NOCTURNE.  CL,VN,VC                           AMC
STEARNS, P.   TRIO.  FL,BCL,DB                                     ACA
STERN, A.   VARIATIONS ON "ES WOLLT EIN SCHNEIDER WANDERN"         HUG
    FL,VN,VA
STEWART, R.   TRIO #4.  FL,VN,VC                                   ACA
STRINGFIELD, L.   CHIPMUNKS.  FL,VN,VC                             EDM
SUCK, C.-ROTHWELL.   TRIO.  OB,VN,VC                               CHE
SULYOK, I.   TRIO.  FL,VN,VC                                       EMB
SUTER, R.   INVENTIONS 1956.  FL,VN,VC                             HEI
SYDEMAN, W.   2 SHORT PIECES & FINALE.  CL,VN,DB                   AMC
SYDEMAN, W.   TRIO (1957).  CL,VN,DB                               SS
SYDEMAN, W.   TRIO.  FL,VN,DB                                      M&M
SZCZENIOWSKI, B.   TRIO #2 (1960).  2FL,VC                         CAN
SZERVANSZKY, E.   TRIO (1951).  FL,VN,VA                           EMB
TANENBAUM, E.   TRIO.  FL,VC,DB                                    ACA
TARTINI, G.   2 TRIO SONATAS.  FL,VN,VA(VC)                        EDM
TCHEREPNIN, A.   TRIO (1960).  FL,VN,VC                            EUL
TELEMANN-FLEISCHHAUER.   TRIOSONATE D MA.  2FL(VN),BC              DEU
TELEMANN, G.-POLNAUER.   6 MINUETS (7 FOIS 7 & 1)                  CF
    FL(OB),VA(CL),BSN(V C)
```

3 PARTS: WOODWIND-STRING-333

TELEMANN, G.-POLNAUER. 6 MINUETS.(7 FOIS 7 & 1). OB,CL,VC   CF
TELEMANN, G.-POLNAUER. 6 MINUETS;(7 FOIS 7 & 1)   CF
 OB,VN,VL(VA)
TELEMANN, G.-POLNAUER. 6 MINUETS,(7 FOIS 7 & 1)   CF
 FL,VA(CL),BSN(VC)
THIELE, S. SERENADE (1969). FL,VN,VC   DEU
THILMAN, J. TRIO PICCOLO, OP 90. AFL,BCL,VA   PET
THOMPSON, R. SUITE. OB,CL,VA   ECS
TOMASI, H. INCA PASTORAL. FL,2VN   ALE
TRINKAUS, G. 16 ORIGINAL & TRANSCRIBED COMPOSITIONS   CF
 FL(OB,VN),VN(C L),BSN(VC)
TURCHI, G. TRIO (1945). FL,CL,VA   ESZ
VILLA ROJO, J. MUSICA SOBRE UNOS MODULOS (1969). 2FL,VA   EDA
VIVALDI, A. CONCERTO IN D MA. FL,VN,BSN   M&M
VIVALDI, A. CONCERTO IN D MA, F. XII/7. FL,VN,BSN   RC
VOORN, J. TRIO "NAKUPENDA". FL,VN,VA   SD
VRANEK, G. PICCOLO TRIO. PIC,VN,VC   CHF
WAGNER, J. SERENADE. OB(FL,CL),VN,VC   SN
WANHAL, J.-BALASSA. TRIOS, OP 20/1-3. CL,VN,VC(BSN)   EMB
WEBER, B. CONCERTINO, OP 11B. CL,VN,VC   ACA
WEBER, E. VON-HOCKNER. TRIO. OB,BSN,VA   ABE
WEIS, F. SONATINA. FL,VN,VC   PET
WEISGARBER, E. DIVERTIMENTO. CL,VN,VA   COR
WEISS, A. TRIO. FL,VA,VC   AMC
WELANDER, S. SONATIN I GAMMAL STIL. CL,VN,VC   EMF
WENDLING, J.-NAGEL. TRIO IN G MA, OP 2/1. FL,VN,VC   EUL
WERNICK, R. TRIO. CL,VN,VC   BE
WHITTENBERG, C. TRIO DIVERTIMENTO. FL/PIC,BSN,VA   ACA
WILDGANS, F. KLEINE HAUS-UND SPIELMUSIK. FL,VN,VC   LDO
YUN, I. TRIO (1972/73). FL,OB,VN   B&B
ZECHLIN, R. TRIO. OB,VA,VC   PET
ZENDER, H. SERENADE (1956). FL,VN,VC   BRH
ZIPP, F. BEFIEHL DU DEIN WEGE (CHORALE MUSIC). OB,VN,VA   PET
ZONN, P. PERIPHRASIS. OB,CL,VC   ACA

3 PARTS: WOODWIND-BRASS-STRING-334

ADASKIN, M. DIVERTIMENTO #3 (1965). VN,HN,BSN   CAN
BALLIF, C. TRIO, OP 35/3. CL,HN,VN   B&B
BORTOLOTTI, M. STUDI (1960). CL,VA,HN   ESZ
CHAUN, F. TRIO, EINLADUNG ZUM HAPPENING. CL,HN,DB   CHF
CUMMINGS, C. BONE SONGS. CL,TPT,DB   ACA
DANZI, F.-WOJCIECHOWSKI. TRIO, OP 24. VN,HN,BSN   ABE
EVERETT, T. 3 COMMENT. TSAX,TRB,DB   SS
FARKAS, F. 3 TANZPARAPHRASEN. FL,VA,HN   EMB
GHENT, E. TRIALITY I & II. VN,TPT,BSN   OX
GODFREY, D. TRIO. CL,VA,HN   ACA
GOLDMANN, F. SO UND SO (1972). EHN,DB,TRB   DEU
JEZ, J. NOMOS II. CL,VC,TRB   EDD
KALLSTENIUS, E. TRIO SVAGANTE, OP 51. CL,HN,VC   EMF
KAM, D. GO. CL,TRB,VC(DB)   SMI
LAUCK, T. TRIO (1974/75). CL,VC,TRB   EMO
LEHMANN, H. REGIONS III. CL,TRB,VC   SCH
PENNISI, F. TRIO (1968). FL,HN,DB   ESZ
POESSINGER, F.-BIBA. TRIO, OP 28. FL,VA,HN   EUL
RAPHAEL, G. SONATINE, OP 65/4. VN,HN,BSN   BRH
SCHULLER, G. TRIO (1948). OB,HN,VA   AMP
SCHWARTZ, E. MUSIC. OB,TPT,VC   GEN

```
SMITH, L.   SUITE FOR TRIO.   CL,TPT,VN                              ACA
STEARNS, P.  TRIO VARIATIONS.  BCL,TPT,VA                            ACA
STEWART, R.  TRIO #5.  CL,TRB,VA                                     ACA
WATKINSON, J.  TRIO IN 3.  FL,VA,HN                                  MAN
WOLFF, C.  TRIO I.  FL,TPT,VC                                        PET
YANNAY, Y.  PRE FIX-FIX-SUFFIX.  BSN,HN,VC                           MEP
```

3 PARTS: WOODWIND-BRASS-KEYBOARD-335

```
BARBOTEU, G.  ESQUISSE.  FL,HN,PF                                    ECH
BEETHOVEN, L. VAN-TRINKAUS.  MENUET.  CL(FL,SAX),TPT(TRB),PF         CF
BELLINI, V.-LEWIS.  HEAR ME NORMA.  CL(SAX),TPT(TRB),PF             CF
BEZANSON, P.  TRIO.  CL,HN,PF                                        ACA
BIZET, G.  SERENADE ESPAGNOLE.  FL(OB),TPT,PF                        EDM
BOHM, C.-HAMILTON.  CALM AS THE NIGHT.  CL(FL),HN,PF               CF
COPLAND, A.  QUIET CITY (1940).  OB(EHN),TPT,PF                      BH
COWELL, J.  TRIO.  CL,HN,PF                                          COR
DE VILLE, P.  SWISS BOY, THE.  CL(SAX),TPT,PF                        CF
DEPELSENAIRE, J.  DIALOGUE.  ASAX,TPT,PF                             EMT
DERUNGS, G.  SUITE, OP 70.  FL,HN,ORG                                S-V
DONIZETTI, G.-DE VILLE.  SEXTET (LUCIA).  CL,TPT,PF                  CF
DOPPLER, F.-HOSMER.  SOUVENIR DU RIGI, IDYLLE, OP 34                 CF
    CL(FL),TPT(HN), PF
DUVERNOY, F.-LELOIR.  TRIO #1 IN C MA.  FL(CL),HN,PF                KAW
DUVERNOY, F.-LELOIR.  TRIO #2 IN F MA.  FL(CL),HN,PF                KAW
ELGAR, E.-TRINKAUS.  LOVE'S GREETING                                 CF
    BSN(CL,FL,SAX),TRB(TPT),PF
FELIX, V.  SONATA DA REQUIEM.  BCL,HN,PF                             PAN
FINGER, G.  SONATA IN C.  OB,TPT,BC                                  MR
FISHER, S.  INVOLUTION.  PIC,TPT,HPCD                                AMC
GODARD, B.-TRINKAUS.  BERCEUSE (JOCELYN)                             CF
    BSN(CL,FL,SAX),TRB(TPT),PF
GOUNOD, C.-DE VILLE.  FLOWER SONG (FAUST).  CL,TPT,PF                CF
GRAIN, U.  TENSTA EMOTIONS (1971).  CL,TRB,PF                        STI
HARTLEY, W.  DOUBLE CONCERTO.  ASAX,TU,PF                            JB
HERTEL, J.  CONCERTO A 6 IN E FL MA.  OB,TPT,PF                      MR
HERZOGENBERG.  TRIO IN D MA, OP 91.  OB,HN,PF                        MR
HESSEN, A. VON.  TRIO, OP 3.  CL,HN,PF                               SIM
HINDEMITH, P.  CONCERTO (1949).  BSN,TPT,PF                          SCH
HOLMES, G. (ARR).  AULD LANG SYNE.  ASAX(TSAX,CL),TPT(TRB),PF        CF
JOHNSTON, D.  LEGENDE.  CL,HN,PF                                     FS
KAHN, R.  SERENADE, OP 73.  OB(CL),HN,PF                             M&M
KAHN, R.  SERENADE, OP 73.  OB,HN,PF                                 SIM
KAUDER, H.  TRIO (1951).  FL,HN,PF                                   SS
KAUDER, H.  TRIO #1 (1929).  OB,HN,PF                                SS
KAUDER, H.  TRIO #2 (1946).  OB,HN,PF                                SS
KLING, H.  OLIFANT EN MUG.  PIC,TRB,PF                               MOL
KOWALSKI, J.  MINIATURY.  CL,HN,PF                                   SHF
LAKE, M. (ARR).  ANNIE LAURIE.  ASAX(TSAX,CL),TPT(TRB),PF            CF
LEMARE, E.-TRINKAUS.  ANDANTINO.  BSN(CL,FL,SAX),TRB(TPT),PF         CF
MANNINO, F.  SONS ENCHANTES.  FL,HN,PF                               EDI
MASSENET, J.-TRINKAUS.  ELEGY.  BSN(CL,FL,SAX),TPT(TRB),PF           CF
MENDELSSOHN, F.-TRINKAUS.  NOCTURNO                                  CF
    BSN(CL,FL,SAX),TRB(TPT),PF
MENDELSSOHN, F.-TRINKAUS.  ON WINGS OF SONG                          CF
    BSN(CL,FL,SAX),TRB(TPT), PF
MEYERBEER, G.-TRINKAUS.  CORONATION MARCH (THE PROPHET)              CF
    BSN(CL,FL,SA X),TRB(TPT),PF
```

```
MILLS, C.  SERENADE, OP 68.  FL,HN,PF                          ACA
OSTRANDER, A.  DUET ALBUM.  FL,HN,PF                           EDM
PADEREWSKI, I.-TRINKAUS.  MINUET A L'ANTIQUE                   CF
   BSN(CL,FL,SAX),TRB(TPT) ,PF
PEZEL, J.  BICINIA 75.  BSN,TPT,BC                             MR
PRESSER, W.  JOREPI.  CL,TRB,PF                                TRI
RANGER, A. (ARR).  WREATH OF HOLLY, A                          CF
   ASAX(TSAX,CL),TPT(TRB),PF
REINECKE, C.  TRIO IN A MI, OP188.  OB,HN,PF                   BRH
REINECKE, C.  TRIO IN A MI, OP188.  OB,HN,PF                   EDK
REINECKE, C.  TRIO IN A MI, OP188.  OB,HN,PF                   INT
REINER, K.  ZEICHNUNGEN (1970).  CL,HN,PF                      ART
RIVIER, J.  CONCERTO.  ASAX,TPT,PF                             BIL
SAINT-SAENS, C.-BROOKE.  SERENADE.  FL,HN,PF                   CF
SAINT-SAENS, C.-TRINKAUS.  SWAN, THE                           CF
   BSN(CL,FL,SAX),TRB(TPT),PF
SCHULLER, G.  SONATA (1941).  CL,HN,PF                         MAR
SCHUMANN, R.-BUCHTEL.  VOICE OF LOVE.  FL,HN,PF                KJ
SCHWARTZ, E.  DIVERTIMENTO.  CL,HN,PF                          GEN
SIBELIUS, J.-TRINKAUS.  VALSE TRISTE (KUOLEMA)                 CF
   BSN(CL,FL,SAX),TRB(TP T),PF
SMITH, C.-HOLMES, G.  BELIEVE ME IF ALL                       CF
   ASAX(TSAX),TPT(TRB),PF
SMITH, C.-HOLMES, G.  CARIBBEAN, THE.  ASAX(TSAX),TPT(TRB),PF  CF
SMITH, C.  DE DIE IN DIEM.  ASAX(TSAX,CL),TPT(TRB),PF          CF
SMITH, C.-HOLMES, G.  DRINK TO ME ONLY WITH THINE EYES         CF
   CL(ASAX,TSAX ),TPT(TRB),PF
SMITH, C.  HELEN.  ASAX(TSAX,CL),TPT(TRB),PF                   CF
SMITH, C.-HOLMES, G.  OLD BLACK JOE                            CF
   CL(ASAX,TSAX),TPT(TRB),PF
SMITH, C.  ON PLEASURE BENT.  ASAX(TSAX,CL),TPT(TRB),PF        CF
SMITH, C.  SPIRIT OF JOY; THE.  ASAX(TSAX,CL),TPT(TRB),PF      CF
SONTAG.  EVENING SERENADE, AN.  FL(CL),HN,PF                   CF
STAIGERS, D.  HAZEL.  CL(ASAX,TSAX),TPT(TRB),PF                CF
STEINKE, G.  TRICINIUM (1972).  ASAX,TPT,PF                    SS
STEWART, F.  TOCCATA SONORA.  FL,TRB,PF                        SS
STOUFFER, P.  CONCERTINO FOR 2.  CL,TPT,PF                     HE
STRAVINSKY, I.  DANCE OF THE BALLERINA.  FL,TPT,PF             EDM
STRAVINSKY, I.  DANCE OF THE PRINCESSES.  FL,HN,PF             EDM
TCHAIKOVSKY, P.-TRINKAUS.  CHANT SANS PAROLES                  CF
   BSN(CL,FL,SAX),TRB(TPT ),PF
TELEMANN, G.-ANDRE.  CONCERT IN C MA.  OB,TPT,PF               B&V
TITL, A.-BUCHTEL, F.  SERENADE.  FL,HN,PF                      KJ
TITL, A.-DE VILLE.  SERENADE.  CL,HN,PF                        CF
TITL, A.  SERENADE.  FL,HN,PF                                  MOL
TOVEY, D.  TRIO, OP 8.  CL,HN,PF                               MR
TRINKAUS, G.  LAMENT.  BSN(CL,FL,SAX),TRB(TPT),PF              CF
VAZZANA, A.  TRIO.  CL,HN,PF                                   AMC
WAGNER, R.-TRINKAUS.  SONG TO THE EVENING STAR                 CF
   CL(FL,SAX),TPT(TRB),P F
WAGNER, R.-TRINKAUS.  WALTHER'S PRIZE SONG                     CF
   BSN(CL,FL,SAX),TRB(TPT),P F
WASHBURN, G.  SOLITUDES FOR MUSIC.  ASAX,TPT,PF                SS
WEIGL, V.  CHERRY TREE, THE- VERSION II.  OB(FL),HN,PF         ACA
WILDER, A.  SUITE.  CL,HN,PF                                   MAR
WIRKANDER, B.  TITLE (1975).  FL,TPT,PF                        STI
```

```
ABEL, K.-BEECHEY.  SONATA IN E MI.  FL,VC,PF              OX
ABEL, K.  6 SONATAS, OP 5, 2 VOLS.  FL,VC,HPCD           EDH
ABEL, K.-MOBIUS.  TRIOSONATE IN C MA.  FL,VN,BC          HMO
ABENDROTH, W.  SONATINA, OP 39.  FL,VN,HPCD              SIM
ACILU, A.  LIM-TRIO (1976).  CL,VN,PF                    EEC
ACKER, D.  GLOSSEN (TRIO #2) (1968).  CL(FL),VC,PF(HPCD)  B&B
ADASKIN, M.  TRIO (1970).  FL,VC,PF                      CAN
ALBICASTRO, H.  SONATA, OP 1/3 IN B MI.  FL,VN,BC        PET
ALLENDE-BLIN, J.  SILENCES INTERROMPUS (1968/70).  CL,DB,PF   HG
ALTMANN, E.  SUITE IM ALTEN STIL, OP 14.  FL,VN,PF      FRH
AMES, W.  EMANATION.  FL,VA,PF                           ACA
ANDERSON, T.  5 BAGATELLES.  OB,VN,HPCD                  ACA
ANDRIESSEN, H.  PASTORALE (1942).  FL,VN,PF              SD
ANDRIESSEN, J.  TRIO (1965).  CL,VC,PF                   SD
ANDRIESSEN, J.  TRIO #2 (1955).  FL,VA,PF                SD
ANGERER, P.  CHANSON GAILLARDE.  OB,VC(BSN),HPCD(PF)     LDO
APPLEBAUM, E.  MONTAGES.  CL,VC,PF                       CHE
ARCHDUKE RUDOLPH.  TRIO.  CL,VC,PF                       MR
ARMENIAN, R.  PROGRESSIONS I (1972).  FL,VC,PF           CAN
AUCLERT, P.  TRIO.  FL,VA,PF                             RC
BABER, J.  TRIO.  OB,VA,PF                               CO
BACH, C.P.E.-WALTHER.  12 KLEINE STUCKE.  FL,VN,PF       WZ
BACH, C.P.E.-BRAUN.  SONATA IN D MA.  FL,VN,PF           PET
BACH, C.P.E.  SONATA IN G MI.  OB,VC,PF                  BRH
BACH, C.P.E.  SONATA.  FL,VN,BC                          EDK
BACH, C.P.E.  TRIO #1 IN D MA.  FL,VA,PF                 INT
BACH, C.P.E.  TRIO #2 IN A MI.  FL,VA,PF                 INT
BACH, C.P.E.  TRIO #3 IN G MA.  FL,VA,PF                 INT
BACH, C.P.E.  TRIO IN B FL MA.  FL,VN,BC                 INT
BACH, C.P.E.-ERMELER.  TRIO IN B MI.  FL,VN,BC           WZ
BACH, C.P.E.  TRIO IN F MA.  BSN,VA,PF                   INT
BACH, C.P.E.  TRIO SONATA IN B FL MA, WQ161.  FL,VN,BC   EDK
BACH, C.P.E.  TRIO SONATA IN B MI, WQ143.  FL,VN,BC      EDK
BACH, C.P.E.-WALTHER.  TRIO SONATA IN D MA.  FL,VN,BC    WZ
BACH, C.P.E.-WALTHER.  TRIO SONATA IN G MA, WQ144.  FL,VN,BC   WZ
BACH, C.P.E.-LORENZ/TSCHIERPE.  TRIO SONATE II.  FL,VN,PF   WZ
BACH, C.P.E.  TRIOSONATA IN G MA.  FL,VN(FL,OB),PF       B&V
BACH, C.P.E.-DURR.  TRIOSONATE IN A MA.  FL,VN,BC        HMO
BACH, C.P.E.-WALTHER.  TRIOSONATE IN A MI, WQ148.  FL,VN,BC   WZ
BACH, C.P.E.-RUF.  TRIOSONATE IN C MA, WQ147.  FL,VN,BC  B&N
BACH, C.P.E.  TRIOSONATE IN D MA, WQ151.  FL,VN,BC       H-V
BACH, C.P.E.-DURR.  TRIOSONATE IN D MI.  FL,VN,BC        HMO
BACH, J.C.-FROTSCHER.  SONATA IN A MA.  FL,VN,BC         HSM
BACH, J.C.-NAGEL.  SONATA IN C MA.  FL,VN,PF             SCH
BACH, J.C.-SMITH.  6 SONATAS, OP 2/1-6: PUB SEPARATELY   LDO
    FL,VC,PF
BACH, J.C.-SCHUNEMANN.  TRIO #2 IN C MA.  FL,VN,PF       KIS
BACH, J.C.-NAGEL.  TRIO IN B FL MA.  FL,VN,BC            WMS
BACH, J.C.-NAGEL.  TRIO IN C MA.  FL,VN,BC               MV
BACH, J.C.-KOELBEL.  TRIO SONATA IN B FL MA.  FL,VN,PF   HUG
BACH, J.C.F.-RUF.  SONATE IN D MA.  FL,VC,PF             B&N
BACH, J.S.-BOERINGER.  ADAGIO & AFFETUOSO.  FL,VN,PF     AUG
BACH, J.S.-SEIFFERT.  CONCERTO IN C MI.  OB,VN,PF        INT
BACH, J.S.  CONCERTO IN C MI.  OB,VN,PF                  GS
BACH, J.S.  CONCERTO IN C MI.  OB,VN,PF                  PET
```

```
BACH, J.S.-SOMMER.  CONCERTO IN C MI, BWV1060.  OB,VN,PF          B&N
BACH, J.S.-BERNER.  CONCERTO IN C MI, S1060.  OB,VN,PF            SCH
BACH, J.S.-SCHNEIDER.  CONCERTO IN D MI.  VN,OB,PF                BRH
BACH, J.S.  KANONISCHES TRIO, BWV1040.  OB(FL),VN,BC             B&B
BACH, J.S.-GOUNOD.  MEDITATION (AVE MARIA).  FL(OB,CL),VC,PF     PET
BACH, J.S.-GERLACH.  SONATA IN C MA (BWV1027, 1039).  FL,VA,BC   SCH
BACH, J.S.-HERMANN.  SONATA IN C MI.  FL,VN,PF                   INT
BACH, J.S.-HERMANN.  SONATA IN G.  FL,VN,PF                      INT
BACH, J.S.-RABAUD.  SONATA IN G MA, BWV1038.  FL,VN,PF           DUR
BACH, J.S.  SONATA IN G MA, BWV1038.  FL,VN,PF                   BRH
BACH, J.S.-MEYLAN.  SONATA IN G MI, BWV1030B                     PET
   FL,VA DA GAMBA,HPCD
BACH, J.S.-HINDERMANN.  SONATE A TRE IN G MI.  OB,VA,BC          HUG
BACH, J.S.-DAVID.  2 SONATEN IN C MA & D MA.  FL,VN,PF           BRH
BACH, J.S.-SEIFFERT.  TRIO (THE MUSICAL OFFERING).  FL,VN,BC     BRH
BACH, J.S.-RABAUD.  TRIO #8, BWV1079.  FL,VN,PF                  DUR
BACH, J.S.  TRIO SONATA (MUSICAL OFFERING).  FL,VN,BC            EDK
BACH, J.S.  TRIO SONATA & CANON PERPETUUS, BWV1079.  FL,VN,BC    GHE
BACH, J.S.-LANDSHOFF.  TRIO SONATAS #3 IN G MA & #4 IN C MI      PET
   FL,VN,BC
BACH, J.S.-MOYSE.  3 TRIO SONATAS.  FL,VN,BC                     GS
BACH, J.S.-FROTSCHER.  6 (ORGELTRIOS), 2 VOLS TRIO SONATAS       PET
   FL(OB),VN ,BC
BACH, J.S.-WALTHER.  TRIOSONATE IN G MI.  FL,VN,BC               WZ
BACH, W.F.-SEIFFERT.  SONATA IN B FL MA.  FL,VN,PF,VC AD LIB     INT
BACH, W.F.  SONATA IN F MA.  FL,VN,BC                            PET
BACH, W.F.  SONATA.  FL,VN,BC                                    EDK
BACH, W.F.  TRIO IN B FL MA.  FL(VN),VN,BC                       BRH
BACK, S.  SENTIRE.  FL,VC,PF                                     NOR
BAKSA, R.  TRIO IN A MA.  CL,VC,PF                               AB
BANCQUART, A.  POSSIBLES.  CL,VN,PF                              JOB
BARLOW, F.  SONATINE.  FL,VN,PF                                  HLE
BARTOK, B.  CONTRASTS.  CL,VN,PF                                 BH
BECERRA-SCHMIDT, G.  TRIO.  FL,VN,PF                             SN
BEETHOVEN, L. VAN-TRINKAUS.  MENUET.  FL(OB,CL,BSN),VN(VC),PF    CF
BEETHOVEN, L. VAN.  TRIO #4, OP 11.  CL,VC,PF                    GAL
BEETHOVEN, L. VAN.  TRIO #4, OP 11.  CL,VC,PF                    GS
BEETHOVEN, L. VAN.  TRIO IN B FL MA, OP 11.  CL,VC(VA),PF        BRH
BEETHOVEN, L. VAN.  TRIO IN B FL MA, OP 11                       CF
   CL(FL),VA(BSN,BCL,VC),PF
BEETHOVEN, L. VAN.  TRIO IN B FL MA, OP 11.  CL,VC,PF            INT
BEETHOVEN, L. VAN.  TRIO IN B FL MA, OP 11.  CL,VC,PF            PET
BEETHOVEN, L. VAN.  TRIO IN E FL MA, OP 38.  CL,VC,PF            INT
BENARY, P.  TRIO.  CL,VC,PF                                      MV
BENDA, F.  SONATA.  FL,VC,BC                                     ART
BENNETT, R.  COMMEDIA II.  FL,VC,PF                              NO
BENTZON, J.  RACCONTO #4, OP 45.  EHN,VN,PF                      WH
BERG, A.  ADAGIO (CHAMBER CONCERTO).  CL,VN,PF                   UE
BERGER, W.  TRIO IN G MI, OP 94.  CL,VC,PF                       MR
BERGER, W.  TRIO IN G MI, OP 94.  CL,VC,PF                       PET
BEYER, J.-GRONEFELD.  PARTITA IN C MA.  FL,VN,BC                 LEU
BIALAS, G.  MOMENTS MUSICAUX III (1975/76).  CL,VC,PF           HG
BIZET, G.  ADAGIETTO.  FL,VN(VA,VC),PF                           EDM
BIZET, G.  ARAGONAISE.  CL,VN,PF                                 EDM
BIZET, G.  MINUET.  FL,VN(VA),PF                                 EDM
BIZET, G.  SERENADE ESPAGNOLE.  FL,VN(VA),PF                     EDM
BLOCH, E.  CONCERTINO.  FL,VA,PF                                 GS
BLOMDAHL, K.  TRIO.  CL,VC,PF                                    S&C
BLUME, J.  MUSIK.  CL,VC,PF                                      MV
BOEDDECKER, P.-SEIFFERT.  SONATA SOPRA "LA MONICA".  VN,BSN,BC   KIS
BOIS, R. DU.  DOG NAMED BOO, THE, HAS A MASTER CALLED LOBO       SD
   CL,VN,PF
```

```
BOISDEFFRE, R. DE.  POEM PASTORALE.  OB,VC,PF                    EDK
BOISMORTIER, J.-RUF.  CONCERTO IN A MI.  FL(OB),VN,BC            RC
BOISMORTIER, J.-RUF.  SONATA IN E MI, OP 37/2                   B&N
   FL(OB),VA DA GAMBA,BC
BOISMORTIER, J.-RUF.  TRIOSONATE IN A MI, OP 37/5.  FL,VC,BC    SCH
BONSEL, A.  MUSICA.  FL,VC,PF                                    SD
BORGULYA, A.  TRIO.  CL,VN,PF                                    EMB
BORODIN, A.  SOLICITUDE.  FL,VA(VC),PF                          EDM
BOURGEOIS, E.  AIR DE BALLET.  FL,VC,PF                         HLE
BOUVARD, J.  3 PIECES BREVES EN TRIO.  FL,VN,PF                 BIL
BRAAL, A. DE.  PASTORALE EN SCHERZO (1946).  FL,VN,PF           SD
BRAAL, A. DE.  TRIO (1976).  FL,VC,PF                           SD
BRAGA, G.  SERENATA, LA.  FL,VC(VN),PF                          DUR
BRAHMS, J.  BERCEUSE.  FL,VN,PF                                 HAM
BRAHMS, J.  TRIO IN A MI, OP114.  CL,VC,PF                      BRH
BRAHMS, J.  TRIO IN A MI, OP114.  CL,VC,PF                      INT
BRAHMS, J.  TRIO, OP114.  CL,VC,PF                              EDK
BRAHMS, J.  TRIO, OP114.  CL,VC,PF                             GHE
BRAHMS, J.  TRIO, OP114.  CL,VC,PF                              PET
BRINGS, A.  DIVERTIMENTO.  FL,VA,HPCD                            SS
BROGUE, R.  QUODLIBET.  FL,VC,HPCD                              AMC
BROGUE, R.  TRIO.  CL,VN,PF                                     AMC
BRONS, C.  CONCERTINO (1977).  CL,VN,PF                          SD
BROOKS, R.  TRIO.  OB,VA,PF                                     ACA
BRUCH, M.-LINDEMANN.  CONCERTO, OP 88.  CL,VA,PF                 RS
BRUCH, M.  8 PIECES, OP 83.  CL,VA,PF (PUB SEPARATELY)          SIM
BRUCH, M.  8 STUCKE, OP 83.  CL,VA,PF                           B&N
BUBALO, R.  SOUNDPOSTS.  CL,VN,PF                                LU
BUXTEHUDE, D -PEYROT & REBUFFAT.  SONATA IN F MA.  FL,VC,BC     EDS
BUXTEHUDE, D.-MOYSE.  SONATA IN C MA  FL,VC,PF                   GS
BUXTEHUDE, D.-PEYROT & REBUFFAT.  SONATA IN G MA.  FL,VC,BC     EDS
CALIFANO, A.-BRINCKMANN/MOHR.  SONATA A TRE IN G MA.  FL,VN,BC  B&N
CALLHOFF, H.  5 EPISODES (1970/71).  FL,VC,PF                    HG
CAMBINI, G.-STEINBECK.  TRIO IN F MA.  OB,VN,HPCD              EUL
CAMMAROTA, P.  ARIOSO & FUGUE.  FL,VN,PF                        EDB
CASTALDI, P.  CLAUSOLA (1961/68).  PIC/FL/AFL,VN/VA,PF/ACC      ESZ
CHAMPAGNE, C.  SUITE MINIATURE (1958).  FL,VC,HPCD(PF)         CAN
CIMA-GREBE.  SONATA #3 IN A MA.  OB,VN,BC                       HSM
CIMA-GREBE.  3 SONATAS (1610).  OB,VN,BC                        HSM
CLEMENTI, M.-SAUER/HARNEST.  TRIO IN D MA, OP 22/1.  FL,VC,PF   WMS
CLOSTRE, A.  CONCERTO.  FL,VN,PF                                EMT
CORELLI, A.  GAVOTTE & GIGUE.  CL,VN,PF                         EDM
CORELLI, A.  GIGUE.  FL,VN(VA),PF                               EDM
CORRETTE, M.  SONATA IN D MI, OP 13.  FL,VC,PF                   GA
CORRETTE, M.-BOULAY.  SONATILLE.  FL,VC,PF                      EMT
CORY, E.  TRIO.  CL,VC,PF                                       ACA
COUPERIN, F.-BOULAY.  ASTREE, L'.  OB,VN,BC                     EMT
COUPERIN, F.  ASTREE, L', SONATA.  FL,VC,PF                     EMT
COUPERIN, F.-BOULAY.  CONCERT ROYAL #4.  OB,VC,PF              EMT
COUPERIN, F.-LASOCKI.  CONCERTS ROYAUX I-IV                      MR
   FL(OB),VA DA GAMBA,BC
COUPERIN, F.  GOUTS REUNIS, LES.  FL(OB),GAMBA,BC               MR
COUPERIN, F.  GOUTS-REUNIS, LES, CONCERT #6.  FL,VC,PF         EMT
COUPERIN, L. -BOUVET.  2 SYMPHONIES.  FL,VC,BC                 EME
CRESTON, P.  PARTITA.  FL,VN,PF                                  BE
CRESTON, P.  SUITE, OP 56.  FL,VA,PF                             SH
CRUMB, G.  VOX BALAENAE FOR 3 MASKED PLAYERS (1971)            PET
   ELEC FL,ELEC VC ,ELEC PF
CUI, C.  5 PIECES, OP 56.  FL,VN,PF                             INT
CUSTER, A.  PASTORALE & HORNPIPE.  CL,VN,PF                     GEN
DADAK, J.  PARTITA (1967).  CL,VN,PF                            CHF
DALLINGER, F.  CONCERTINO.  CL,VN,PF                            LDO
```

DAMASE, J. NOCTURNE. FL,VC,PF	SEM
DAMASE, J. SONATE FOR CONCERT. FL,VC,PF	HLE
DAUTREMER, M. DUO-CONCERTINO. VN,BSN,PF	DUR
DAVIS. OLD KING COLE VARIATIONS. OB,VA,PF	WI
DAVISON, J. SUITE (1954). FL,VN,PF	CAN
DEBUSSY, C.(ALDER). ARABESQUES #1 & #2. FL,VN,PF	DUR
DEBUSSY, C. IL PLEURE DANS MON COEUR. FL,VA(VC),PF	EDM
DEBUSSY, C. MANDOLINE. FL,VA(VC),PF	EDM
DELA, M. SUITE (1954). FL,VC,PF	CAN
DELERUE, G. PRISME. SAX,VA,PF	EMT
DOHL, F. SOTTO VOCE (1973). FL,VC,PF	HG
DONIZETTI, G.-DE VILLE. SEXTET (LUCIA). FL,VN,PF	CF
DOPPLER, F.-HOSMER. SOUVENIR DU RIGI, IDYLLE, OP 34 FL,VC,PF	CF
DORAN, M. ANDANTE & ALLEGRO. FL,VC,PF	WI
DORAN, M. TRIO. FL,VC,PF	WI
DRIESSLER, J. SERENATA A TRE, OP 34/2. FL,VA DA GAMBA,PF	B&N
DUBOIS, P. SUITE. CL,VN,PF	MAU
DUBOIS, T. 2 PIECES EN FORME CANONIQUE. OB,VC,PF	M&M
DURUFLE, M. PRELUDE RECITATIF ET VARIATIONS, OP 3. FL,VA,PF	DUR
DUSSEK, J.-DELIUS. SONATA IN F MA, OP 65. FL,VC,PF	EUL
DUSSEK, J. TRIO. FL,VC,PF	MR
EARL OF KELLY. TRIO SONATA. OB,VN,BC	OX
EBERL, A. GRAND TRIO IN E FL MA, OP 36. CL,VC,PF	MR
ECKERBERG, S. TRIO CONCERTANTE (1966). FL,VC,PF	STI
EL-DABH, H. THULATHIYA. OB,VA,PF	PET
ELGAR, E.-TRINKAUS. LOVE'S GREETING. FL(OB,CL,BSN),VN(VC),PF	CF
ELLIS, D. TIME TRIP. FL,VN,PF	TP
ENDO, R. WANDERING FLAMES (1971). OB,VC,PF	ESZ
ERBSE, H. 12 APHORISMEN. FL,VN,PF	PET
EXAUDET, J. COUR DE LA MARQUISE, LA. FL,VN(VA),PF	EDM
EYCHENNE, M. CANTILENE & DANSE. ASAX,VN,PF	BIL
FANTAISIES SUR DES AIRS D'OPERAS. FL,VN,PF	HLE
FASCH, J.-WINSCHERMANN & BUCK. DOUBLE CONCERTO IN D MI OB,VN,PF	HSM
FASCH, J.-NAGEL. TRIO SONATA IN D MA. FL,VN,BC	EUL
FASCH, J.-GREBE. TRIO SONATA IN G MA. FL,VN,BC	HSM
FAURE, G. EN PRIERE. FL,VN(VA,VC),PF	EDM
FESCH, W. DE. SONATE A 3. FL,VN(FL,OB),PF	B&V
FINGER, G. SONATA A 5 IN B FL. OB,VN,BC	NOM
FINGER, G.-HOLMAN. SONATA IN C MA. OB(TPT),VN,BC	NOM
FODI, J. TRIO. FL,VA,HPCD	CAN
FONTANA, G. SONATA # 9. VN,BSN,BC	LDO
FONTANA, G. SONATA #10. VN,BSN,BC	LDO
FONTANA, G. SONATA #12. VN,BSN,BC	LDO
FORBES, S. PARTIA. CL,VC,PF	CA
FOSTER, S. VILLAGE FESTIVAL, A. FL,VN(VA),PF	EDM
FRANCAIX, J. MUSIQUE DE COUR. FL,VN,PF	SCH
FRANK, A. SONATA DA CAMERA. FL,VN,PF	AMC
FRANKEL, B. PEZZI PIANISSIMI, OP 41. CL,VC,PF	NO
FRANKEL, B. TRIO, OP 10. CL,VC,PF	GAL
FRANKEN, W. SERENADE (1958). FL,DB,PF	SD
FRITSCH, J. IM DUNKEL DEM WERDENDEN HERZEN (1973). OB,VA,ORG	FEE
FRITZ, G.-STEINBECK. SONATA IN D MA, OP 4/5. FL,VN,BC	EUL
FROMM, H. CHAG HA-MATSOT. FL,VC,HPCD	AB
FRUHLING, C. TRIO IN A MI, OP 40. CL,VC,PF	LEU
FURST, P. PETITIONEN, OP 51. CL,VA,PF	LDO
FUX, J.-HILLEMANN. SONATA A 3 IN D MI. FL(OB),VN,PF	HEI
GAL, H. TRIO, OP 97. CL,VN,PF	SIM
GANNE, L. EXTASE. FL,VC,PF	KAW
GARLICK, A. SUITE PER SALOTTO. OB,VA,HPCD	SS
GATTERMEYER, H. DIVERTIMENTO, OP114. CL,VA,PF	LDO

```
GAUBERT, P.  PIECE ROMANTIQUE.  FL,VC,PF                              HLE
GEBAUER, A.  5 MINIATUREN.  CL,VN,PF                                  B&V
GENIN, P.  GRAND DUO CONCERTANT, OP 51.  FL,VN,PF                     BIL
GENTILUCCI, A.  DIAGRAMMA (1970).  CL,VN,PF                           ESZ
GERHARD, F.  TRIO.  FL,VC,PF                                          WZ
GHEDINI, G.  MUSICHE PER 3 STRUMENTI.  FL,VC,PF                       RC
GHEZZO, D.  KANONES.  FL,VC,HPCD                                      SS
GILTAY, B.  4 MINIATURES (1972).  CL,VN,PF                            SD
GIORDANI, G.  18TH CENTURY AIR, AN.  FL,VN(VA,VC),PF                  EDM
GIORDANI, T.  18TH CENTURY AIR, AN.  CL,VN,PF                         EDM
GLASER, W.  BROLLOPSMUSIK (1966).  FL,VC,HPCD                         STI
GLASER, W.  KAMMARMUSIK (1952).  CL,VC,PF                             STI
GLICK, S.  TRIO (1958-59).  CL,VC,PF                                  CAN
GLUCK, C.-BOUVET.  SONATA IN G MI.  VN,FL,PF                          EES
GODARD, B.-TRINKAUS.  BERCEUSE (JOCELYN)                              CF
    FL(OB,CL,BSN),VN(VC),PF
GODRON, H.  SERENADE OCCIDENTALE (1942).  CL,VC,PF                    SD
GOEYVAERTS, K.  PIECE POUR 3 (1960).  FL,VN,PF                        CBD
GOODMAN, J.  TRIO.  FL,VN,PF                                          AMP
GOOSSENS, E.  5 IMPRESSIONS OF A HOLIDAY.  FL,VC,PF                   CHE
GOOSSENS, E.  4 SKETCHES, 2 VOLS.  FL,VN,PF                           CHE
GOUNOD, C.  BARCAROLLA.  FL,VC,PF                                     HLE
GOUNOD, C.  D'UN COEUR QUI T'AIME.  FL,VC,PF                          HLE
GOUNOD, C.-DE VILLE.  FLOWER SONG (FAUST).  FL,VN,PF                  CF
GRAUN, J.-KOLBEL.  SONATA IN G.  FL,VN,BC                             OHN
GRAUN, J.-RIEMANN.  TRIO IN F MA.  OB,VN,BC                           BRH
GRAUN, J.-FISCHER.  TRIO SONATA IN F MA.  FL,VN,BC                    WZ
GRAUPNER, C.-FLATTSCHACHER/FROTSCHER.  SONATA IN C MA                 B&N
    FL,VA D'AMORE, BC
GRAUPNER, C.-GOEBELS-KAMMERLING.  TRIOSONATE IN B FL MA              LEU
    FL,VA,BC
GRIFFIS, E.  SUITE FOR TRIO.  CL,VC,PF                                AMC
GROSS, R.  CHO-SEN VARIATIONS.  CL,VN,PF                              ACA
GURSHING, A.  TRIO.  FL,VC,ACC                                        PI
GYROWETZ, A.-ALBRECHT.  DIVERTISSEMENT IN A MA.  FL,VC,PF             KIS
HABER, L.  PARADE, BLUES & ALLEGRO.  FL,VN,PF                         GEN
HACQUART, C.  3 SONATEN (HARMONIA PARNASSIA).  FL,VN(FL,OB),PF        B&V
HAHN, R.  ROMANESQUE.  FL,VA,PF                                       HEU
HAIK-VENTOURA, S.  BEAU DIMANCHE, UN.  CL,VN,PF                       EMT
HANDEL, G.-SEIFFERT.  KAMMERTRIO #7 IN C MI.  FL,VN(VC),PF            BRH
HANDEL, G.-SIKORSKI.  SONATA #1 IN B FL MA.  OB,VN,BC                 PWM
HANDEL, G.-MONKEMEYER.  SONATA IN C MI.  FL,VN,BC                     SCH
HANDEL, G.  SONATA IN C MI, OP 2/1.  FL,VN,BC                         EDK
HANDEL, G.-MONKEMEYER.  SONATA IN F MA.  FL,VN,BC                     SCH
HANDEL, G.-KOLNEDER.  TRIO.  OB,VN,BC                                 SCH
HANDEL, G.  TRIO SONATA IN B FL MA.  OB,VN,BC                         EDK
HANDEL, G.-KRAUSE.  TRIO SONATA IN F MA, OP 2/5.  FL,VN,BC            SCH
HANDEL, G.-MOYSE.  4 TRIO SONATAS.  FL(OB),VN,PF                      GS
HANDEL, G.-HINNENTHAL.  TRIO SONATE IN B FL MA.  OB,VN,BC             B&N
HANNAY, R.  FANTOME.  CL,VA,PF                                        PET
HASSE, J.-WINSCHERMANN.  TRIO SONATA IN F MA.  OB,VN,BC               HSM
HAUBIEL, C.  IN THE FRENCH MANNER.  FL,VC,PF                          OP
HAUBIEL, C.  PASTORAL TRIO.  FL,VC,PF                                 OP
HAUBIEL, J.  IN THE FRENCH MANNER.  FL,VC,PF                          SS
HAUFRECHT, H.  CAPRICE.  CL,VA,PF                                     BO
HAYDN, F.-NAGEL.  CASSATION.  FL,VN,BC                                PET
HAYDN, F.-DAVID.  KLAVIERTRIO #30 IN D MA.  FL,VC,PF                  BRH
HAYDN, F.-DAVID.  KLAVIERTRIO #31 IN G MA.  FL,VC,PF                  BRH
HAYDN, F.  TRIO #28 IN D MA, HOB XV: 16.  FL,VC,PF                    LDO
HAYDN, F.-DAVID.  TRIO #29 IN F MA.  FL,VC,PF                         BRH
HAYDN, F.  TRIO #29 IN G MA, HOB XV: 15.  FL,VC,PF                    LDO
HAYDN, F.  TRIO #30 IN F MA, HOB XV: 17.  FL,VC,PF                    LDO
```

```
HAYDN, F.  TRIO IN G.  FL,VC,PF                              EDK
HAYDN, F.-BERGMANN.  TRIO, OP  2/4.  FL,VN,BC                SCH
HAYDN, F.-RAMPAL.  3 TRIOS IN F MA, D MA, G MA.  FL,VC,PF    INT
HAYDN, F.  TRIOS, H XV:15-17.  FL,VC,PF                      GHE
HAYDN, M.-BEYER.  SONATA IN G MA.  FL,PF,DB                  JB
HEINICHEN, J.-HAUSSWALD.  SONATA A TRE IN C MI              LDO
   OB,VA DA GAMBA(VA),BC
HEINICHEN, J.-WINSCHERMANN.  TRIO SONATA IN C MI           HSM
   OB(FL),VN,BC
HEINICHEN, J.  TRIO SONATA IN C MI.  OB,VA,BC              PET
HEKSTER, W.  CREDENCES OF SUMMER (1974).  CL,VN,PF         SD
HINDEMITH, P.  TRIO, OP 47.  HECKELPHONE(TSAX),VA,PF       SCH
HOBSON, M.  TRIO.  CL,VA D'AMORE,PF                        VA
HODGE, T.  3 SKETCHES.  FL,VN,PF                           CHE
HOFFER, P.  TRIOSONATE.  FL,VA,PF                          PET
HOLM, M.  TRANSITIONS II.  FL,VC,PF                        WH
HOMILIUS, G.-BLEJER.  KLEINES TRIO IN G MA.  FL,VN,BC      HG
HUBER, K.  ASCENSUS (1969).  FL,VC,PF                      SCH
HUBICKI (ARR.)  4 SCOTTISH & IRISH AIRS.  OB,VC,PF         S&C
HUMMEL, J.N.-PAULER.  TRIO IN A MA, OP 78.  FL,VC,PF       EUL
HUMMEL, J.N.  TRIO, OP 78.  FL,VC,PF                       MR
HUTCHESON, J.  RONDO BRILLANTE.  CL,VN,PF                  SS
HUYBRECHTS, A.  TRIO (1926).  FL,VA,PF                     CBD
IBERT, J.  ARIA.  FL,VN,PF                                ALE
IBERT, J.  2 INTERLUDES.  FL,VN,HPCD(HP)                  ALE
IMBRIE, A.  SERENADE.  FL,VA,PF                           SH
IMBRIE, A.  TO A TRAVELLER.  CL,VN,PF                     SH
INDY, V. D'.  TRIO, OP 29.  CL,VC,PF                      EV
INDY, V. D'.  TRIO, OP 29.  CL,VC,PF                      INT
IVES, C.  LARGO.  CL,VN,PF                                SN
JACHINO, C.  TRIO.  FL,VC,PF                              EDI
JACKSON, D.  THEME & VARIATIONS.  FL,VC,HPCD              MAN
JACOB, G.  TRIO.  CL,VA,PF                                MR
JACOBSON, J.  3 STYCKEN.  CL,VA,PF                        EMF
JACOBSON, M.  SUITE FOR 4 PIECES.  FL,VC,PF               GAL
JANITSCH, J.-KOLBEL.  SONATA IN F MA.  FL,VN,BC           HEI
JEPPESEN, K.  LITTLE SUMMER TRIO.  FL,VC,PF               CHE
JOHANSON, S.  MARINA SKISSER (1965).  FL,VC,PF            STI
JOHANSON, S.  TRIO.  CL,VC,PF                             EMF
JOHNSON, T.  TRIO.  FL,VC,PF                              AMP
JUON, P.  TRIO-MINIATUREN (OP 18, OP 24).  CL,VC,PF       MRL
KALINNIKOV, V.  CHANSON TRISTE.  FL,VA(VC),PF             EDM
KAUDER, H.  TRIO (1957).  CL,VA,PF                        SS
KAUFMANN, A.  DROSSER TRIO, OP101.  FL,VN,PF              LDO
KEISER, R.  SONATA A TRE.  FL,VN,BC                       EDK
KEISER, R.-SCHENK.  TRIOSONATE #2 IN G MA.  FL,VN,BC      B&N
KEISER, R.-SCHENK.  TRIOSONATE #3 IN D MA.  FL,VN,BC      B&N
KELLER, H.  REDUKTION.  FL,VC,HPCD                        S-V
KELTERBORN, R.  5 FANTASIEN.  FL,VC,PF                    B&N
KELTERBORN, R.  KAMMERMUSIK (1957).  FL,VN,PF             EMO
KEMPIS, N.-DOV.  SYMPHONIA AI, OP 3/XVIII.  VN,BSN,BC     NOM
KERR, H.  TRIO.  CL,VC,PF                                 TP
KEURIS, T.  MUSIC (1973).  CL,VN,PF                       SD
KHACHATURIAN, A.  TRIO.  CL,VN,PF                         MKE
KHACHATURYAN, A.  TRIO (1932).  CL,VN,PF                  PET
KHACHATURYAN, A.  TRIO.  CL,VN,PF                         CHM
KHACHATURYAN, A.  TRIO.  CL,VN,PF                         INT
KHACHATURYAN, A.  TRIO.  CL,VN,PF                         MC
KLEINKNECHT, J.-WEISS.  SONATA IN C MI.  FL,OB,BC         B&N
KLUGHARDT, A.  SCHILFLIEDER, OP 28.  OB,VA,PF             M&M
KNAB, A.  LINDEGGER LANDLER.  CL,VC,PF                    SCH
KOETSIER, J.  TRIO.  AFL,VA DA GAMBA,HPCD                 SD
```

```
KOETSIER, J.  TRIO, OP 13/2 (1937).  CL,VC,PF              SD
KOHLER, E.  AU VOL D'OISEAU, OP 98.  FL,VN,PF,VC AD LIB    WZ
KOMMA, K.  ESTAMPIE.  FL,VA,HPCD                           H-V
KORINGER, F.  SONATA PROFANA.  CL,VA,PF                    FS
KOUGUELL, A.  MELODIE & DANSE HEBRAIQUE.  FL,VC,PF         AMC
KOUNADIS, A.  4 PEZZI.  FL,VC,PF                           EDT
KRAFT, L.  TRIOS & INTERLUDES.  FL,VA,PF                   SER
KREBS, J.-RUF.  SUITE IN D MA.  FL,VN,BC                   SCH
KREBS, J.-RIEMANN.  TRIO IN D MA.  FL,VN,BC                BRH
KREBS, J.-NAGEL.  TRIO IN D MI.  FL,VN,BC                  MV
KREJCI, I.  TRIO (1936).  CL,DB,PF                         ART
KRENEK, E.  TRIO.  VN,CL,PF                                AMP
KREUTZER, C.  TRIO, OP 23/2.  FL,VC,PF                     WMS
KRUTZFELD, W.  RELATIONEN, OP 34 (1961).  FL,VA,PF         EMO
KUBIZEK, A.  TRIO, OP 26A.  CL,VC,PF                       LDO
KUHLAU, F.  TRIO, OP119.  FL,VN(VC),PF                     BIL
KUUSISTO, T.  CHRISTMAS SONATINE, OP 19.  FL,VN,PF         EDF
LANNOY, E.  GRAND TRIO, OP 15.  CL,VC,PF                   MR
LATEEF, Y.  TRIO.  FL,VC,PF                                FAM
LE CLAIR, J.-EITNER.  SONATE #8 IN D MA.  FL,VA(VC),PF     BRH
LECLAIR, J.(CRUSSARD).  SONATA.  FL,VC,BC                  ECS
LECLAIR, J.-POLNAUER.  SONATA, OP 9/2.  FL,VC,HPCD         CHE
LECLAIR, J.-BOUVET.  TRIO SONATA IN D MA, OP  2/8.  FL,VC,BC  EES
LECLAIR, J.-DOBEREINER.  TRIO SONATA IN D MA, OP  2/8      SCH
   FL,VA,BC
LEFEVRE, C.  BALLADE.  FL,VC,PF                            EDS
LEGE, G.  TRIO.  FL,VN,PF                                  MV
LEITERMEYER, F.  TIENTO (FANTASIE), OP 62.  CL,VA,PF       LDO
LEMARE, E.-TRINKAUS.  ANDANTINO.  FL(OB,CL,BSN),VN(VC),PF  CF
LENOT, J.  JULIAN TRIO.  FL,VC,PF                          EDS
LESSARD, J.  TRIO.  FL,VN,PF                               GEN
LEVINE, B.  INTRODUCTION & ALLEGRO.  FL,VN,PF              MAN
LEWIS, R.  TRIO (1966).  CL,VN,PF                          LDO
LIDL, V.  CANTUS VARIABILIS (1967).  CL,VN,PF              CHF
LINDE, B.  DIVERTIMENTO, OP 25.  FL,VC,PF                  EMF
LOCATELLI, P.-DRUNER/KLEIN.  TRIO #2 IN B FL MA.  FL(OB),VA,BC  LEU
LOEFFLER, C.  2 RHAPSODIES.  OB,VA,PF                      M&M
LOEILLET, J.  COURANTE.  CL,VN,PF                          EDM
LOEILLET, J.B.  COURANTE.  FL,VN(VA),PF                    EDM
LOEILLET, J.B.-RUF.  TRIO SONATA IN D MA, OP  1/4.  OB,VN,BC  SCH
LOEILLET, J.B.-RUF.  TRIO SONATA IN E MI, OP  1/6.  OB,VN,BC  SCH
LOEILLET, J.B.-RUF.  TRIO SONATA IN G MA, OP  1/2.  OB,VN,BC  SCH
LONGUE, A.  MELODIE.  CL,VN,PF                             MAU
LOTTI, A.  SONATA IN G MA.  FL,VC(VA),BC                   INT
LOTTI, A.  SONATA IN C MA.  FL,VC,BC                       WZ
LOTTI, A.  SONATA.  FL,VA DA GAMBA,BC                      EDK
LOTTI, A.-RUF.  TRIO IN A MA.  FL,VN,BC                    RC
LUDEWIG, W.  REFLEXIONEN (1975).  FL/AFL,VC,PF             B&B
LUENING, O.  TRIO #2.  FL,VC,PF                            PET
LUENING, O.  TRIO.  FL,VN,VC(BSN)AD LIB,PF                 GA
MAGANINI, Q.  CONCERT ALBUM.  FL,VN(VA),PF                 EDM
MAGANINI, Q.  MOONLIGHT ON THE PAINTED DESERT.  FL,VC,PF   EDM
MAINARDI, E.  TRIO (1967).  FL,VC,PF                       SCH
MANN, L.  MUSIC, OP 26 (1973).  CL,VA,PF                   CAN
MANZIARLY, M. DE.  TRIO.  FL,VC,PF                         DUR
MARAIS, M.-VEILHAN/ROBERT.  FOLIES D'ESPAGNE, LES          ALE
   FL,VA DA GAMBA,HPCD
MARAIS, M.-BOULAY.  SUITE #5 DI BRANI IN TRIO              EMT
   FL,VA DA GAMBA(VC),BC
MARTELLI, H.  TRIO, OP 77.  FL,VC,PF                       ECH
MARTINO, D.  TRIO.  CL,VN,PF                               ECS
MARTINU, B.  MADRIGAL-SONATE (1936).  FL,VN,PF             AMP
```

```
MARTINU, B.  PROMENADES (1940).  FL,VN,HPCD                    B&N
MARTINU, B.  TRIO (1944).  FL,VC,PF                            AMP
MARX, K.  TRIO, OP 61.  FL,VC,PF                               H-V
MASCITTI, M.  SONATA IN G MI.  FL,VC,BC                        EDS
MASCITTI, M.-RUF.  TRIO SONATA IN G MI, OP  6/15.  FL,VC,BC    SCH
MASON, D.  PASTORALE.  CL,VN,PF                                EDS
MASSENET, J.-TRINKAUS.  ELEGY.  FL(OB,CL,BSN),VN(VC),PF        CF
MASSEUS, J.  TRIO, OP  8 (1948).  FL,VN,PF                     SD
MATTEIS, M.-TILMOUTH.  SUITE IN G MI.  FL,VN,BC               S&C
MAYUZUMI, T.  METAMUSICA.  SAX,VN,PF                           PET
MC CABE, J.  SONATA (1969).  CL,VC,PF                          NO
MELLERS, W.  TRIO.  FL,VC,PF                                   NO
MENDELSSOHN, F.-TRINKAUS.  NOCTURNO.  FL(OB,CL,BSN),VN(VC),PF  CF
MENDELSSOHN, F.-TRINKAUS.  ON WINGS OF SONG                    CF
   FL(OB,CL,BSN),VN(VC),PF
MEYERBEER, G.-TRINKAUS.  CORONATION MARCH (THE PROPHET)        CF
   FL(OB,CL,BSN),VN(VC),PF
MICHAELIS, A.-SCHAFER.  3 SONATEN.  FL,VC,PF                   HG
MIGOT, G.  TRIO.  FL,VN,HPCD                                   EMT
MIHELCIC, S.  3 PIECES.  CL,VN,PF                              EDD
MILHAUD, D.  CONCERTO.  FL,VN,PF                               EDS
MILHAUD, D.  SUITE.  CL,VN,PF                                  EDS
MILLER, M.  TRIO FANTASY.  FL,VA,PF                            AMC
MILLER, M.  TRIO.  CL,VA,PF                                    CAN
MIMAROGLU, I.  TRIO (1961).  CL,VN,PF                          SS.
MORRISON, J.  JULIA STREET.  ASAX,DB,PF                        AMC
MOZART, L.-WEINMANN.  DIVERTIMENTO IN G MA.  FL(OB),VN,BC      EUL
MOZART, W.-WACHERNAGEL.  TRIO #4, KV498.  CL,VA,PF             MRL
MOZART, W.  TRIO #7, K498.  CL,VA,PF                           CF
MOZART, W.-ROPARTZ.  TRIO IN E FL MA, K498.  CL,VA,PF          DUR
MOZART, W.  TRIO IN E FL MA, K498.  CL,VA,PF                   INT
MOZART, W.  TRIO.  CL,VN,PF                                    GS
MOZART, W.-ADAMOWSKI.  TRIO, K498.  CL,VA,PF                   GS
MOZART, W.  TRIO, K498.  CL,VA,PF                              EDK
MOZART, W.  TRIO, K498.  CL,VA,PF                              GAL
MUCZYNSKI, R.  FANTASY TRIO, OP 26.  CL,VC,PF                  GS
MUNZING, A.  TRIO (1966).  CL,VN,PF                            STI
MYSLIVECEK, J.-RIEMANN.  TRIO IN B FL MA, OP  1/4.  FL,VN,PF   JB
NAGEL(ED).  SUITE IN D MI.  FL,VN,BC                           EUL
NAGEL(ED).  TRIO IN G MA.  FL,VN,BC                            MV
NAPOLI, C.  MOMENTI.  CL,VN,PF                                 EDI
NICULESCU, S.  TRIPLUM (1971).  FL,VC,PF                       EDS
NICULESCU, S.  TRIPLUM II (1974).  CL,VC,PF                    EDS
NIKOLAYEVA, T.  TRIO, OP 18.  FL,VA,PF                         MKE
NORGARD, P.  TRIO.  CL,VC,PF                                   CHE
OKOSAKA, K.  IRIAI.  CL,VC,PF                                  OV
OKUMURA, H.  JAHRESANFANG IN JAPAN (1969).  FL,VC,PF           GBV
OLIVER, H.  SAMSARA: A TRIO (1974).  CL,VC,PF                  AMC
OLSEN, P.  PROLANA, OP 33 (1955).  CL,VN,PF                    PET
ORTHEL, L.  OTTO ABBOZZI.  FL,VC,PF                            SD
OSIECK, H.  TRIO (1975).  FL,VC,PF                             SD
OSTRANDER, A.  DUET ALBUM.  FL,VC,PF                           EDM
OWEN, J.  SONATA IN BAROQUE STYLE.  FL,HPCD,DB                 SO
PADEREWSKI, I.-TRINKAUS.  MINUET A L'ANTIQUE                   CF
   FL(OB,CL,BSN),VN(VC),PF
PAPINEAU-COUTURE, J.  TRIO IN 4 MOUVEMENTS (1974).  CL,VA,PF   CAN
PAYNE, A.  PARAPHRASES & CADENZAS (1969).  CL,VA,PF           CHE
PAYNE, F.  2 CONTRASTS.  FL,VC,PF                              SS
PENN, W.  TRIO.  CL,VN,PF                                      SS
PEPUSCH, J.-RUF.  SONATA A TRE IN F MA.  FL,VN,BC              HEI
PEPUSCH, J.-ERBRECHT.  SONATA DA CAMERA IN G MI.  FL(OB),VN,BC KIS
PEPUSCH, J.-HAUSSWALD.  SONATA IN C MA.  FL,VN,BC              SCH
```

```
PEPUSCH, J.-RUF.  TRIO SONATA IN E MI.  FL,VA,BC              SCH
PEPUSCH, J.-NAGEL.  TRIO SONATA IN G MA.  FL,VN,BC            EUL
PEPUSCH, J.  6 TRIO SONATAS, 2 VOLS.  OB,VN,BC               EDK
PEPUSCH, J.-RUF.  TRIO-SONATE IN D MI.  FL,VA,BC             B&N
PEPUSCH, J.-RUF.  TRIOSONATE IN F MA.  FL,VN,BC              HEI
PEPUSCH, J.-HOFFMAN.  6 TRIOSONATEN, 2 VOL.  OB,VN,BC         BRH
PERGOLESI, G.  SICILIAN AIR.  FL,VN(VA,VC),PF                EDM
PEYROT, F.  TRIO, OP 7.  FL,VN,PF                            HEN
PHILIDOR, P.  SUITE.  FL,VC,PF                               EMT
PIERNE, G.  SONATA DA CAMERA, OP 48.  FL,VC,PF              DUR
PLATTI, G.-KOLBEL.  TRIO IN G MA.  FL,VN,BC                  HEI
PLESKOW, R.  MOVEMENT (1962).  FL,VC,PF                      SS
PLESKOW, R.  TRIO (1977).  FL,VC,PF                          ACA
PLEYEL, I.  GRAND TRIO, OP 29.  FL,VC,PF                     MR
PLEYEL, I.-ALBRECHT.  SONATA IN C MA, OP 16/2.  FL,VC,PF     KIS
PLEYEL, I.-ALBRECHT.  SONATA IN E MI, OP 16/5.  FL,VC,PF     KIS
PLEYEL, I.-ALBRECHT.  SONATA IN G MA, OP 16/1.  FL,VC,PF     KIS
PONCE, M.  ESTRELLITA.  FL,VN(VC),PF                         CF
POWELL, M.  IMPROVISATION.  CL,VA,PF                         GS
PROWO, P.-LAUSCHMANN.  SONATA.  OB,VC,HPCD                   FOR
QUANTZ, J.  TRIO IN F MA.  FL,VN,BC                          PET
QUANTZ, J.  TRIO IN F MA.  FL,VA D'AMORE,BC                  WZ
QUANTZ, J.-BERGMANN.  TRIO SONATA IN C MA.  FL,VN,BC         S&C
QUANTZ, J.  TRIO SONATA IN C MA.  FL,VN,BC                   EDK
QUANTZ, J.-SCHULTZ-HAUSER.  TRIO SONATA IN C MI.  FL,VN,BC   SCH
QUANTZ, J.-RUF.  TRIO SONATA IN D MA.  FL(OB),VN,BC          RC
QUANTZ, J.  TRIO SONATA IN D MA.  FL,VN,BC                   EDK
QUANTZ, J.-BERGMANN.  TRIO SONATA IN G MA.  OB,VC(BSN),HPCD  S&C
QUANTZ, J.-RUF.  TRIO SONATA IN G MI.  FL,VN,BC             HEI
QUANTZ, J  TRIO SONATA IN G MI.  FL,VN,BC                    BRH
QUANTZ, J.-PISTORIUS.  TRIOSONATE #33 IN E MI.  FL,VN,BC     HG
QUANTZ, J.-PISTORIUS.  TRIOSONATE IN B MI.  FL,VN,BC         HSM
QUANTZ, J.-SCHROEDER.  TRIOSONATE IN D MA.  FL,VN(FL,OB),BC  BRH
QUANTZ, J.-SEIFFERT.  TRIOSONATE IN D MA.  FL(OB),VN,BC      KIS
QUANTZ, J.-NAGEL.  TRIOSONATE IN E MI.  FL,VN,BC            MV
QUANTZ, J.-FRIEDRICHSEN/JONSSON.  TRIOSONATE IN G MA         HSM
   FL,OB D'AMORE,B C
QUANTZ, J.-RUF.  TRIOSONATE IN G MA.  FL,VN,BC              HEI
QUENTIN, J.-RUF.  SONATA IN E MI.  FL,VN(VA),PF             SCH
QUINET, M.  SONATE EN TRIO (1977).  FL,VC,PF                CBD
RABAUD, H.  ANDANTE & SCHERZO.  FL,VN,PF                     HEU
RACHMANINOFF, S.  VOCALISE.  CL,VN,PF                        EDM
RAMEAU, J.-PEYROT/REBUFFAT.  5 CONCERTI                      EDS
   FL,VC,HPCD (PUB SEPARATELY)
RAMEAU, J.-JACOBI.  PIECES DE CLAVECIN EN CONCERTS          B&N
   FL,VN,HPCD
RAMEAU, J.-HORUSITZKY.  PIECES DE CLAVECIN, KONZERT 1 & 2    EMB
   FL,VA(VN), HPCD
RAMEAU, J.-HORUSITZKY.  PIECES DE CLAVECIN, KONZERT 3, 4 & 5 EMB
   FL,VA(V N),HPCD
RAMEAU, J.  RIGODON DE DARDANUS.  CL,VN,PF                   EDM
RAPHAEL, G.  TRIO-SUITE, OP 44.  FL,VC,PF                    B&N
RAPHAEL, G.  TRIO, OP 70 (1950).  CL,VC,PF                   BRH
RAVEL, M.-ALDER.  MA MERE L'OYE.  FL,VC,PF                   DUR
RAVEL, M.  PAVANE POUR UNE INFANTE DEFUNTE.  CL,VN,PF        EDM
REGT, H. DE.  CIRCE, OP 44 (1975).  CL,VN(VA),PF            SD
REGT, H. DE.  MUSICA, OP 29 (1973).  FL,VC,HPCD             SD
REIF, P.  TRIO.  FL,VC,PF                                    SS
REINECKE, C.  TRIO IN A MA, OP264.  CL,VA,PF                B&N
REINECKE, C.  TRIO IN A MA, OP264.  CL,VA,PF                B&V
REINECKE, C.  TRIO IN B FL MA, OP264.  CL,VA(HN),PF         MR
REINECKE, C.  TRIO, OP264.  CL,VA,PF                        INT
```

REINECKE, C. TRIO, OP264. CL,VA,PF	RS
REINER, K. VOLNE LISTY (1969). CL,VC,PF	PAN
REINHOLD, O. KONZERTANTE MUSIC. FL,VA,PF	BRH
REYNOLDS, R. ACQUAINTANCES. FL,DB,PF	PET
RICHTER, F.-NAGEL. DIVERTIMENTO, OP 91. FL,VC,BC	WMS
RICHTER, F. SONATA DA CAMERA. FL,VC,PF	BRH
RICHTER, F.-WEIGART. SONATA IN G MA. FL,VC,PF	SCH
RIES, F. TRIO, OP 28 IN G MI. CL,VC,PF	RS
RIES, F. TRIO, OP 28. CL,VC,PF	MR
RIETI, V. PASTORALE E FUGHETTA. FL,VA,PF	GEN
ROGERS, B. BALLADE. VA,BSN,PF	SN
ROMAN, J.-VRETBLAD. 12 SONATAS. FL,VN,BC	STI
ROOS, R. DE. INCIDENZE (1967). FL,VC,HPCD	SD
ROREM, N. TRIO. FL,VC,PF	PET
ROSSEAU, N. TRIO, OP 60 (1956). FL,VC,PF	CBD
RUBINSTEIN, A. MELODIE. FL,VN,PF	HAM
RUDHYAR, D. 3 MELODIES. FL,VC,PF	SER
RUDINGER, G. DIVERTIMENTO IN G MI, OP ·75 VA(CL),TSAX(BCL,VC),PF	ABS
RUDOLF, ARCHDUKE. TRIO IN E FL MA. CL,VC,PF	MR
RYDMAN, K. 7 MINIATURES. FL,VA,PF	FIN
SAINT-SAENS, C. REVERIE DU SOIR. FL,VN(VA),PF	EDM
SAINT-SAENS, C.-BROOKE. SERENADE. FL,VC,PF	CF
SAINT-SAENS, C.-TRINKAUS. SWAN, THE. FL(OB,CL,BSN),VN(VC),PF	CF
SALBERT, D. KAMMERMUSIK. CL,VN,PF	MV
SALIERI, A. DANSE (TARARE). FL,VN(VA),PF	EDM
SARY, L. IMAGE. CL,VC,PF	EMB
SCHAPER. DIVERTIMENTO I. FL,VC,ACC	HOH
SCHERCHEN, T. TZOUE. FL(CL),VC,HPCD	UE
SCHMELZER, J.-JANETZKY. SONATA. VN,BSN,BC	FRH
SCHMIDT, E. DIVERTISSEMENT. FL,VN,PF	HEN
SCHNEBEL, D. ANSCHLAGE- AUSSCHLAGE. FL,VC,HPCD	S&C
SCHOLLUM, R. TRIO, OP 45. FL,VC,PF	LDO
SCHOONENBEEK, K. COMBINATIONS (1973). CL,VA,PF	SD
SCHROEDER, H. CONCERTINO. OB,VN,ORG	SCH
SCHROEDER, H. PIANO TRIO #3, OP 43. CL,VC,PF	SCH
SCHUMANN, R. FAIRY TALES, OP132. CL,VA,PF	CF
SCHUMANN, R. FAIRY TALES, OP132. CL,VA,PF	INT
SCHUMANN, R. MARCHENERZAHLUNGEN, OP132. CL,VA,PF	BRH
SCHWARTZ, E. TRIO. FL,VC,PF	CF
SCHWARZ-SCHILLING, R. DA JESUS. FL,VN,ORG	H-V
SCHWARZ-SCHILLING, R. JESUS AN DEM KREUZE STUND, DA FL,VN,ORG	SMO
SERMILA, J. COLOURS & CONTRASTS. FL,VN,PF	FIN
SIBELIUS, J.-TRINKAUS. VALSE TRISTE (KUOLEMA) FL(OB,CL,BSN),VN(VC), PF	CF
SIEGL, O. TRIO. CL,VC,PF	FS
SILSBEE, A. TRIALOGUE. CL,VN,PF	ACA
SIMEONOV, B. 4 MOVEMENTS. FL,VC,PF	WAT
SIMPSON, R. TRIO (1967). CL,VC,PF	LEN
SINGER, J. FROM THE GREEN MOUNTAINS. CL,VN,PF	EAM
SIRULNIKOFF, J. POLKA DOTS (1957). FL,VN,PF	CAN
SLAVICKY, K. TRIALOG (1966). CL,VN,PF	ART
SLAVICKY, M. LYRICAL MUSIC. FL,VN,HPCD	PAN
SMIT, L. TRIO (1938). CL,VA,PF	SD
SMITH, W. 4 PIECES. CL,VN,PF	MJ
SOLLBERGER, H. COMPOSITIONS. FL,VC,PF	ACA
SOLLBERGER, H. DIVERTIMENTO. FL,VC,PF	ACA
SOLO, C. GRAND SONATA, A, OP 31. FL,VC,PF	EDH
SPIEGLER. CANZON A 2. OB,VC,BC	MR
STACHOWSKI, M. AUDITION (1970). FL,VC,PF	PWM
STAMITZ, C. ANDANTINO. FL,VA,PF	EDM

```
STAMITZ, C.  TRIO #1, OP 14.  FL,VN,PF,VC AD LIB            INT
STAMITZ, C.-UPMEYER.  TRIO IN G MA, OP 14/1.  FL,VN,BC      B&N
STAMITZ, C.-HILLEMANN.  TRIOSONATE IN F MA, OP 14/5.  FL,VN,BC  BRH
STAMITZ, K.-BALASSA.  CONCERTO #4.  CL,VN(CL),PF            EMB
STAMITZ, K.  SONATA #1 IN G MA.  FL,VN,BC                   EDK
STAMITZ, K.-NAGEL.  TRIO IN G MI, OP 14/4.  FL,VC,HPCD      MV
STANLEY, J.-BOERINGER.  8 SOLOS, OP 1.  FL,VC,BC            CON
STANLEY, J.-BOERINGER.  6 SOLOS, OP 4.  FL(OB),VC(BSN),PF   CON
STARER, R.  TRIO.  CL,VC,PF                                 PI
STEFFEN, W.  TRIO, OP 37.  FL,VC,PF                         B&B
STILL, R.  CLARINET TRIO.  CL,VN,PF                         LEN
STOCKMEIER, W.  3 STUCKE.  FL,VA,ORG                        MV
STOLZEL, G.-WINSCHERMANN.  DOPPELKONZERT IN F MA.  OB,VN,PF HSM
STOLZEL, G.-HAUSSWALD.  SONATA.  FL,VN,BC                   BRH
STOLZEL, G.  SONATA IN G MA.  FL,VN,PF                      PET
STOLZEL, G.  SONATA.  OB,VN,BC                              BRH
STOLZEL, G.-HAUSSWALD.  SONATE IN G MA.  FL,VN,PF           B&N
STOLZEL, G.-FROTSCHER.  TRIO SONATA IN E MI.  FL(OB),VN,BC  BRH
STRAUCH(ARR).  WEIHNACHTLICHE KAMMERMUSIK.  FL,VN,BC        B&N
STRAUSS, R.  ZUEIGNUNG.  FL,VA(VC),PF                       EDM
STRAVINSKY, I.  BERCEUSE.  FL,VA(VC),PF                     EDM
STRAVINSKY, I.  DANCE OF THE PRINCESSES.  CL,VN,PF          EDM
STRAVINSKY, I.  SUITE (L'HISTOIRE DU SOLDAT).  CL,VN,PF     CHE
STRAVINSKY, I.  SUITE (L'HISTOIRE DU SOLDAT).  CL,VN,PF     INT
STRINGFIELD, L.  MORNING.  FL,VN(VA,VC),PF                  EDM
STROE, A.  REVER C'EST DESENGRENER (1970).  CL,VC,HPCD(PF)  EDS
SUK, J.  BAGATELLE.  FL,VN,PF                               SIM
SUK, J.  MIT DEM BLUMENSTRAUS IN DER HAND.  FL,VN,PF        ES
SYDEMAN, W.  FANTASY & 2 EPILOGUES (1964).  FL,VC,PF        SS
SYDEMAN, W.  TRIO (1961).  OB,VA,PF                         SS
SYDEMAN, W.  TRIO MONTAGNANA (1972).  CL,VC,PF              33
SZALONEK, W.  PROPORZIONI II.  FL,VC,PF                     SS
TAJCEVIC, M.  7 BALKAN DANCES.  CL,VC,PF                    JB
TAMANO, Y.  REACTION RELATIVISTE (1959).  CL,VN,PF          ESZ
TATE, P.  AIR & VARIATIONS.  CL,VN,PF                       OX
TAYLOR, C.  TRIO.  CL,VC,PF                                 ACA
TCHAIKOVSKY, P.-TRINKAUS.  CHANT SANS PAROLES              CF
    FL(OB,CL,BSN),VN(VC),P F
TCHAIKOVSKY, P.  SUITE (ALBUM FOR CHILDREN).  FL,VN(VA),PF  EDM
TCHEREPNIN, A.  KAMMERKONZERT IN D MA, OP 33.  FL,VN,PF     SCH
TELEMANN, G.  CONCERTO #2.  FL,VC,PF                        GD
TELEMANN, G.-HINNENTHAL.  CONCERTO IN A MA.  FL,VN,BC       B&N
TELEMANN, G.-HINNENTHAL.  CONCERTO IN A MI.  FL,VN,BC       B&N
TELEMANN, G.-HINNENTHAL.  CONCERTO IN B MI.  FL,VN,BC       B&N
TELEMANN, G.-HINNENTHAL.  CONCERTO IN D MA.  FL,VN,BC       B&N
TELEMANN, G.-HINNENTHAL.  CONCERTO IN E MI.  FL,VN,BC       B&N
TELEMANN, G.-HECHLER.  CONCERTO IN F MA.  OB,VN,BC          OHN
TELEMANN, G.-CRUSSARD.  SONATA.  OB,VN,BC                   ECS
TELEMANN, G.-RUF.  SONATA IN A MI.  FL,VA DA GAMBA(VC),PF   OHN
TELEMANN, G.-BRAUN.  SONATA IN C MI.  FL,VA DA GAMBA(VA,VC),PF  PET
TELEMANN, G.  SONATA IN C MI.  OB,VC,PF                     BRH
TELEMANN, G.-HINNENTHAL.  SONATA IN G MA.  FL,VN,BC         B&N
TELEMANN, G.-HOFMANN.  SONATA IN G MA.  OB,VN,BC            B&N
TELEMANN, G.-RUF.  SONATA IN G MA.  FL,VN,BC                B&N
TELEMANN, G.  SONATA IN G MI.  OB,VC,PF                     BRH
TELEMANN, G.-POULTEAU.  SONATE EN TRIO IN E MI.  OB(FL),VN,BC  ALE
TELEMANN, G.  SONATE EN TRIO.  OB,VN,BC                     HUG
TELEMANN, G.-HOFMANN.  SONATINA IN E MI.  OB,VN,BC          B&N
TELEMANN, G.  SUITE #2 IN B FL MA.  FL,VN,BC                EDK
TELEMANN, G.  SUITE #3 IN B MI.  FL,VN,BC                   EDK
TELEMANN, G.  SUITE #4 IN E MA.  FL,VN,BC                   EDK
TELEMANN, G.  SUITE #5 IN A MI.  FL,VN,BC                   EDK
```

```
TELEMANN, G.  SUITE #6 IN D MI.  FL,VN,BC                        EDK
TELEMANN, G.-HINNENTHAL.  SUITE IN A MI.  FL,VN,BC               B&N
TELEMANN, G.-HINNENTHAL.  SUITE IN B FL MA.  FL,VN,BC            B&N
TELEMANN, G.-HINNENTHAL.  SUITE IN B MI.  FL,VN,BC               B&N
TELEMANN, G.-HINNENTHAL.  SUITE IN D MI.  FL,VN,BC               B&N
TELEMANN, G.-HINNENTHAL.  SUITE IN E MA.  FL,VN,BC               B&N
TELEMANN, G.-HINNENTHAL.  SUITE IN G MA.  FL,VN,BC               B&N
TELEMANN, G.-SCHULTZ/HAUSER.  TRIO #1 IN B FL MA.  OB,VN,BC      CFV
TELEMANN, G.  TRIO #2 IN A MI.  FL,VN,BC                         CFV
TELEMANN, G.-SCHULTZ/HAUSER.  TRIO #3 IN G MA.  FL,VN,BC         CFV
TELEMANN, G.-RUETZ.  TRIO IN D MI.  FL,VN,BC                     SCH
TELEMANN, G.-UPMEYER.  TRIO IN F MA.  FL,VC(VA),BC              NV
TELEMANN, G.-RUETZ.  TRIO IN G MI.  FL,VN,BC                     SCH
TELEMANN, G.-LAUSCHMANN.  TRIO SONATA IN A MA                   HSM
   OB D'AMORE(OB),VN,BC
TELEMANN, G.  TRIO SONATA IN A MI (ESSERCIZII MUSICI)           PET
   FL,VN,BC
TELEMANN, G.-WINSCHERMANN.  TRIO SONATA IN C MI.  OB,VA,BC      HSM
TELEMANN, G.  TRIO SONATA IN C MI.  OB,VN,BC                     EDK
TELEMANN, G.-HUNT.  TRIO SONATA IN F MA.  FL,VN,PF,VC AD LIB    S&C
TELEMANN, G.-GREBE.  TRIO SONATA IN G MA.  FL,VN,BC             HSM
TELEMANN, G.-RUF.  TRIO SONATA IN G MI.  OB,VN,BC               SCH
TELEMANN, G.-TOTTCHER/GREBE.  TRIO SONATA IN G MI.  OB,VN,BC    HSM
TELEMANN, G.-HESS.  TRIOSONATE IN A MI.  FL,VN,BC               EUL
TELEMANN, G.-RUF.  TRIOSONATE IN B FL MA.  OB(FL),VN,BC         B&N
TELEMANN, G.-ERMELER/PASLER.  TRIOSONATE IN E MA.  FL,VN,BC     B&N
TELEMANN, G.-KOLBEL.  TRIOSONATE IN E MI.  FL,VN,BC             HEI
TELEMANN, G.-HESS.  TRIOSONATE IN F.  FL,VN,BC                  EUL
TELEMANN, G.-HOHNEN.  TRIOSONATE IN G MA.  FL,VN,BC             MV
TENAGLIA, A.  ARIA ANTICA.  CL,VN,PF                            EDM
THIELE, S.  PROPORTIONEN (1971).  OB,VC,PF                      DEU
TOVEY, D.  TRIO IN D MI, OP 14.  EHN,VN,PF                      M&M
TROMBLY, P.  TRIO DA CAMERA (1975).  FL,VC,PF                   ACA
TURNER, R.  DIVERSITIES (1967).  VN,BSN,PF                      CAN
TUROK, P.  TRIO, OP 38.  CL,VC,PF                               SS
UHL, A.  KLEINES KONZERT.  CL,VA,PF                             LDO
VALDAMBRINI, F.  QUARTINE (1971).  FL,VC,PF                     ESZ
VAN BOER.  PASTORALE.  FL,VC,PF                                 WAT
VAN NOSTRAND, B.  FANTASY MANUAL FOR URBAN SURVIVAL            ACA
   AFL,VC,PF
VANHALL, J.-WESTON/BERGMANN.  TRIO IN E FL MA, OP 20/5          S&C
   CL,VN,PF
VERACINI, A.-POLNAUER.  SONATA DA CAMERA, OP 3/2.  FL,VC,HPCD   CHE
VERHAAR, A.  TRIO-SONATE, OP 7 (1934).  FL,VC,PF               SD
VIVALDI, A.  CONCERTO IN D MA, F XII/43.  FL,VN,BC             RC
VIVALDI, A.-RAMPAL.  CONCERTO IN D MI, OP 27/5.  FL,VN,PF       INT
VIVALDI, A.-BARBE.  CONCERTO IN G MI.  FL,VN,BC                B&N
VIVALDI, A.-UPMEYER.  PASTORALE (OP 13/4).  FL,VC,BC           B&N
VIVALDI, A.  PASTORALE IN A MA, OP 13/4.  FL(OB),VC,PF         NV
VIVALDI, A.-UPMEYER.  PASTORALE, OP 13/4.  FL,VC,PF            INT
VIVALDI, A.  PASTORALE, OP 13/4.  FL,VC,BC                     EDK
VIVALDI, A.-FECHNER.  SONATA IN C.  OB,VN,ORG                  PET
VIVALDI, A.-NAGEL.  TRIOSONATE IN D MA.  FL,VN,BC              MV
WAGENSEIL, G.-SCHOLZ.  SONATA IN B FL MA.  CL,VN,BC            LDO
WAGNER, R.-TRINKAUS.  SONG OF THE EVENING STAR                 CF
   FL(OB,CL,BSN),VN(VC), PF
WAGNER, R.-TRINKAUS.  WALTHER'S PRIZE SONG                     CF
   FL(OB,CL,BSN),BN(VC),PF
WAHREN, K.  ART POUR L'ART, L' (1968).  FL,VC,PF               B&B
WARLAND.  ADAGIO.  CL,VC,PF                                    WI
WATKINSON, J.  TRIO, LARGO & ALLEGRO.  FL,VC,PF                MAN
WEBER, C.M. VON-WACKERNAGEL.  TRIO IN G MI, OP 63.  FL,VC,PF    MRL
```

```
WEBER, C.M. VON.  TRIO IN G MI, OP 63.  FL,VC,PF          INT
WEBER, C.M. VON.  TRIO, OP 63.  FL,VC,PF                  PET
WEISMANN, J.  KAMMERMUSIK, OP 86.  FL,VA,PF               B&N
WERNER, F.  CONCERTINO.  FL,VC,PF                         DUR
WERNER, G.-MODER.  CONCERTO A TRE IN G MA.  FL,VN,BC      LDO
WESTRUP, J.  DIVERTIMENTO.  BSN(TSAX),VC,PF               GA
WHEAR, P.  TRIO VARIATIONS.  CL,VC,PF                     LU
WIDOR, C.  SERENADE.  FL,VN,PF                            HAM
WIGY, F.  2 ESQUISSES.  FL,VN,PF                          MAU
WILDER, A.  TRIO.  FL,VC,PF                               MAR
WINKELHOLM, M.  TRANSITIONS II.  FL,VC,PF                 WH
WINTER, P. VON-MICHAELS/GUEDEL.  CONCERTINO.  CL,VC,PF    HSM
WOLPE, S.  TRIO.  FL,VC,PF                                M&M
WOOD, H.  TRIO, OP 3.  FL,VA,PF                           UE
WUORINEN, C.  PIECE FOR STEFAN WOLPE.  FL,VC,PF           M&M
WUORINEN, C.  TRIO (1961).  FL,VC,PF                      ACA
WUORINEN, C.  TRIO #2.  FL,VC,PF                          PET
WUORINEN, C.  TRIO #3.  FL,VC,PF                          PET
ZANINELLI, L.  ARIOSO.  FL,VC,PF                          SH
ZELINKA, J.  PODLETI.  CL,VN,PF                           CHF
ZEMLINSKY, A.  TRIO IN D MI, OP 3.  CL,VC,PF              SIM
ZEMLINSKY, A.  TRIO, OP 3 (D MI).  CL,VC;PF               MR
ZENDER, H.  MUJI NO KYO (1975)                            B&B
    FL,VN(VC),PF/ELEC ORG,V AD LIB
ZENDER, H.  TRIFOLIUM (1966).  FL,VC,PF                   B&B
ZIEMZARIS, I.  TRIO.  FL,VC,PF                            MKE
ZILCHER, H.  TRIO IN A MI, OP 90.  CL,VC,PF               B&N
```

3 PARTS INCLUDING HARP-338

```
ALBRECHTSBERGER, J.-WILHEIM.  PARTITA.  FL,VC,HP             EMB
ARMA, P.  DIVERTIMENTO #2.  FL,VC,HP                         EMT
AUSTIN, J.  ORPHEUS & THE MAENADS.  FL,VA,HP                 ACA
BACEWICZ, G.  TRIO (1965).  OB,HP,PERC                       PWM
BACH, C.P.E.-PIERRE.  2 MENUETS & 1 POLONAISE.  FL,VA,HP     EMT
BACKES, L.  BALLADE.  FL,HP,PF                               S-V
BADINGS, H.  TRIO #10 (1977).  AFL,VA,HP                     SD
BALLIF, C.  TRIO, OP 35/1.  FL,BSN,HP                        ECH
BARON, M.  ELEGY.  FL,VC,HP                                  MB
BAX, A.  ELEGIAC TRIO.  FL,VA,HP                             CHE
BEERMAN, B.  POLYGRAPH VI.  FL,HP,TAPE                       ACA
BERLIOZ, H.  JEUNES ISMAELITES, DES.  2FL,HP                 EDK
BERLIOZ, H.  TRIO DES JEUNES ISMAELITES.  2FL,HP            EDC
BERLIOZ, H.  TRIO OF THE YOUNG ISHMAELITES.  FL,OB,HP       EDM
BERLIOZ, H.  TRIO.  2FL,HP                                   WZ
BERNIER, R.  TRIO (1942).  FL,VC,HP                          CBD
BOIS, R. DU.  PASTORALE 2 (1960; REV. 1969).  OB,CL,HP       SD
BONDON, J.  SOLEIL MULTICOLORE, LE.  FL,VA,HP               EES
BOTTJE, W.  REFLECTIONS.  FL,HP,TAPE                         ACA
BOZIC, D.  SONATA IN COOL #3.  FL,BCL,HP                    EDD
BROTT, A.  3 ON A SPREE (1963).  FL,OB,HP                    CAN
BUCZYNSKI, W.  TRIO/74 (1974).  BCL,DB,HP                    CAN
CALL, L. DE (VON).  SERENADE, OP 75.  FL,VA,GUIT            CFV
CAMPOLIETI, L.  TRIO IN D MI.  FL,VA,HP                      GZ
CHAN, P.  SUITE (1975).  FL,VA,HP                            B-B
CHARPENTIER, J.  MOUVEMENT.  FL,VC,HP                        ALE
COLACO OSORIO-SWAAB, R.  TRIO #4 (1956).  CL,VC,HP           SD
CONSTANTINIDES, D.  COMPOSITION.  FL,HP,PERC                 SS
```

3 PARTS INCLUDING HARP-338

CORAL, G. 5 PEZZI (1973). FL,HP,HPCD   ESZ
COWELL, H. TRIO. FL,VN,HP   PET
DAMASE, J. DOUBLE CONCERTO. .FL,HP,PF   EMT
DAMASE, J. TRIO. FL,VC,HP   HLE
DARMSTADT, H. TRIO (1973). OB,VA,HP   HG
DEBUSSY, C. SONATE. FL,VA,HP   DUR
DENISOV, E. CANON EN MEMOIRE STRAVINSKY. FL,CL,HP   HG
EDLER, R. VARIANTEN (1962). FL,HN,HP   EDT
EISLER, H. SONATENSATZ, OP 49. FL,OB,HP   DEU
FRANCO, J. TRIO. FL,VC,HP   ACA
GAUBERT, P. DIVERTISSEMENT GREC. 2FL,HP   ALE
GELBRUN, A. CONCERTO FANTASIA (1963). FL,HP,PF   ISR
GENZMER, H. TRIO. FL,VA,HP   PET
GERSTEL, O. PETITE MUSIQUE DE NUIT. FL,VC,HP   IMP
GUBITOSI, E. COLLOQUI. FL,VC,HP   EDI
GUILLOU, J. COLLOQUES #3. HP,OB,PERC   ALE
HIBBARD, W. BASS TROMBONE, BASS CLARINET, HARP. BCL,TRB,HP   ECS
HLAVAC, M. LYRICKE PRELUDIUM A CAPRICCIO (1964). FL,OB,HP   CHF
HOLLIGER, H. TRIO. OB,VA,HP   SCH
HOLOUBEK, L. TRIO, OP 21. FL,VN,HP   SHF
HOVHANESS, A. FIRDAUSE, OP252. CL,HP,PERC   AB
HOVHANESS, A. STARRY NIGHT, OP288. FL,HP,XYL   AB
HOWARD, R. TRILOGUE. ASAX,VA,HP   ARM
HUBER, K. SABETH (1966/67). AFL,EHN,HP   SCH
IBERT, J. 2 INTERLUDES. FL,VN,HP   ALE
JEZ, J. ASSONANCES. OB,HP,PF   EDD
JOLIVET, A. ALLA RUSTICA. 2FL,HP   BH
JOLIVET, A. PASTORALES DE NOEL. FL,BSN(VA,VC),HP   HEU
JONES, J. SONATE A 3. FL,VC,HP   EFM
JONGEN, J. 2 PIECES EN TRIO, OP 80 (1925). FL,VC,HP   CBD
KLEIMAN, S. FESTIVITY. FL,VA,HP   SS
KOECHLIN, C. EPITAPHE DE JEAN HARLOW, OP164. FL,ASAX,HP(PF)   EES
KRENEK, E. AULOKITHARA (1971/72). OB/EHN,HP,TAPE   B&N
LAJTHA, L. TRIO #1, OP 22. FL,VC,HP   ALE
LAJTHA, L. TRIO #2, OP 47. FL,VC,HP   ALE
LEIBOWITZ, R. SONATINA, OP 69 (1966). FL,VA,HP   B-B
LUEDEKE, R. 5 PIECES. FL,VC,HP   SS
MA'AYANI, A. IMPROVISATION VARIEE. FL,VN,HP   IMP
MARCLAND, P. METRES. AFL,VA,HP   EMT
MARTELLI, H. TRIO. FL,VC,HP   EES
MARTIN, F. PIECE BREVE (1957). FL,OB,HP   HUG
MATHIAS, W. ZODIAC TRIO, OP 70. FL,VA,HP   OX
MATTHUS, S. TRIO. FL,VA,HP   DEU
MC CULLOH, B. LAMENT. FL,HP,MAR   CF
MEULEMANS, A. SONATE (1948). FL,VA,HP   CBD
MEYER, K. HOMMAGE A NADIA BOULANGER. FL,HP,VA   PWM
MIGOT, G. CONCERT. FL,VC,HP   ALE
MIGOT, G. LIVRE DES DANCERIES, LE. FL,VC,HP(PF)   ALE
MIGOT, G. PREMIER LIVRE DE DIVERTISSEMENTS FRANCAIS, LE   ALE
   FL,CL,HP
MOZART, W.-SALZEDO. CONCERTO IN C MA, K299. FL,PF,HP   SO
MOZART, W. CONCERTO IN C MA, K299. FL,HP,PF   EDK
MOZART, W. CONCERTO, K299. FL,HP,PF   CF
MOZART, W.-BURCHARD. KONZERT IN C MA, K299. FL,HP,PF   BRH
NORDOFF, P. TRIO. FL,VA,HP   AMC
NUNES, E. IMPROMPTU POUR UN VOYAGE II. AFL,VA,HP   JOB
PACIORKIEWICZ, T. TRIO (1966). FL,VA,HP   PWM
PORADOWSKI, S. CONCERTO. FL,HP,PF   PWM
POSTON, E. TRIO. FL,CL,HP(PF)   CHE
RAPHAEL, G. SONATINE, OP 65/1. FL,VA,HP   BRH
RAWSTHORNE, A. SUITE. FL,VA,HP   OX
REGT, H. DE. PROTEUS, OP 38 (1974). FL,VA,HP   SD

116

3 PARTS INCLUDING HARP-338

RIEGGER, W. DIVERTISSEMENT. FL,VC,HP	PET
ROHOZINSKY, L. SUITE BREVE. FL,VA,HP	EDS
SCHAFFER, B. TRIO (1966). FL,VA,HP	PWM
SKVOR, F. VALSE MELANCOLIQUE. 2FL,HP	CHF
SMIT, L. TRIO. FL,VA,HP	EDS
STOUT, A. CAPRICCIO (1967). OB,HP,PERC	JB
STRAVINSKY, I. EPITAPHIUM (1959). FL,CL,HP	BH
SURINACH, C. TIENTOS. EHN,HP(PF),TIMP	AMP
TAKEMITSU, T. EUCALYPTS II. FL,OB,HP	EDS
TESSIER, R. "A". FL,HP,PERC	EFM
THILMANN. ASPEKTE. FL,VA,HP	PET
THIRIET, M. SUITE EN TRIO. FL,VA,HP	SEM
TON-THAT TIET. INCARNATIONS STRUCTURALES. FL,VC,HP	JOB
VELLONES, P. TRIO, OP 94. FL,OB(VA),HP	DUR
VOSS, F. SERENADE (1959). FL,VN,HP	BRH
WATSON, W. DIVERTIMENTO. FL,BSN,HP	LU
WEBER, B. AUBADE. FL,VC,HP	ACA
WEIGL, V. TRIALOGUE. FL,VA,HP(PF)	ACA
WILDER, A. SUITE. OB,HN,HP	MAR
WISZNIEWSKI, Z. TRIO (1963). OB,VA,HP	AP
WUORINEN, C. BASSOON VARIATIONS. BSN,HP,TIMP	PET
WUSTHOFF, K. NOCTURNO. FL,VA,HP	WZ
WYTTENBACH, J. 3 SATZE (1963). OB,HP,PF	SCH
YUASA, J. INTER-POSI-PLAY-TION II. FL,HP,PERC	SCH
ZAGWIJN, H. INTRODUZIONE EN SCHERZETTO (1940). FL,VA,HP	SD

3 PARTS INCLUDING GUITAR-339

ANDRIESSEN, J. SONATA DA CAMERA (1959). FL,VA,GUIT	SD
APOSTEL, H. KLEINES KAMMERKONZERT, OP 38. FL,VA,GUIT	LDO
APOSTEL, H. STUDIE(1958),OP 29. FL,VN,GUIT	LDO
BADINGS, H. TRIO #9 (1962). FL,VA,GUIT	SD
BAKER, D. FANTASY, SERENADE & FUGUE. FL,BSN,GUIT	SS
BALADA, L. TRESIS. FL,VC,GUIT	GS
BAUER, R. TRANSILIENCE. OB,VC,GUIT	CAN
BAUMANN, H.-BEHREND. SONATINE UBER FINNISCHE VOLKSLIEDER	WZ
OB,BSN,GUIT	
BERLIOZ, H.-BRAUN. TRIO. 2FL,GUIT	UE
BOIS, R. DU. NIGHT MUSIC (1968). FL,VA,GUIT	SD
BOIS, R. DU. PASTORALE II (1969). REC,FL,GUIT	SD
BUCK, O. SUMMER TRIO (1968). FL,VC,GUIT	CHE
BUCZYNSKI, W. TRIO/67. CL,DB,MANDOLIN	CAN
CALL, L. DE. TRIO, OP134. FL,VA,GUIT	EDK
CALL, L. DE (VON). NOTTURNO, OP 85. FL,VA,GUIT	CFV
CALL, L. DE (VON). NOTTURNO, OP 89. FL,VA,GUIT	CFV
CALL, L. DE (VON). NOTTURNO, OP 93. FL,VA,GUIT	CFV
CALL, L. DE (VON). TRIO, OP134. FL,VA,GUIT	WZ
CAMPO, F. PRELUDES, OP 51. FL,CL,GUIT	BE
CARULLI, F.-CHIESA. CONCERTO. FL,GUIT,PF	ESZ
CARULLI, F. NOTTURNO IN A MI. FL,VN,GUIT	CFV
CARULLI, F. NOTTURNO IN C MA. FL,VN,GUIT	CFV
CARULLI, F.-HERBST. TRE GRAN TRIO. FL,VN,GUIT	WZ
CARULLI, F.-BEHREND. 3 TRIOS, OP 9. FL,VN,GUIT	WZ
CASTELNUOVO-TEDESCO, M. ECLOGHE. FL,EHN,GUIT	GEN
CUMMINGS, C. DIVERTIMENTO AFTER STRAVINSKY. OB,VC,GUIT	ACA
DAUBE, J. TRIO IN D MI. FL,LUTE,PF	CFV
DAVID, J. SONATE, OP 26A (1940). FL,VA,GUIT	BRH
DE BERADINIS, J. 3 MOMENTS. 2FL,GUIT	SS

```
DELAS, J. DE.   TRIO (1971).  FL,GUIT,PERC                          HG
DIABELLI, A.-OUBRADOUS.  TRIO.  FL,VA,GUIT(HP)                      EMT
FORSYTH, M.  INTIMACIES.  FL,VA,GUIT                                CAN
GESZLER, G.  TRIO (1963).  FL,VC,GUIT                               EMB
HASSE, J.-BROJER.  TRIOSONATE IN C MA.  FL,VN,GUIT                  LDO
HASSE, J.-KAMMERLING.  TRIOSONATE IN C MA.  FL,VN,GUIT              LDO
HEALEY, D.  5 MINIATURE, OP200 (1962).  FL,CEL,MANDOLIN             CAN
HEER, H. DE.   TRIO (1975).  FL,VA,GUIT                             SD
HEINIO, M.  SUITE, OP 16/1.  FL,2GUIT                               FIN
HEINIO, M.  TRIO.  FL,VN,GUIT                                       EDF
HEKSTER, W.  RELIEF #5.  FL,GUIT,VA                                 SD
HIBBARD, W.  TRIO.  CL,VN,GUIT                                      AMC
JORNS, H.  7 FORMS, OP 15.  FL,HPCD,GUIT                            RS
KALMAR, L.  TRIO (1968).  FL,GUIT,MAR                               EMB
KOMTER, J.  TRIO-SONATINE (REV 1973).  FL,VA,GUIT                   SD
KONT, P.  TRIO.  FL,VA,GUIT                                         LDO
KOTONSKI, W.  TRIO (1960).  FL,GUIT,PERC                            AP
KOVACH, A.  TRIO #1, MUSIQUE D'AUTOMNE (1942).  FL,CL,GUIT          EUL
KREUTZER, J.-SCHEIT.  TRIO IN D MA, OP  9/3.  FL,VN,GUIT            LDO
KREUTZER, J.  TRIO, OP 16.  FL(VN),CL(VA),GUIT                      EDK
KREUTZER, J.  TRIO, OP 16.  FL,CL,GUIT                              WZ
KUFFNER, J.  NOTTURNO, OP110.  FL,VA,GUIT                           CFV
KUFFNER, J.  SERENADE, OP 21.  CL,VA,GUIT                           CFV
LEEUW, T. DE.  SCHELP (1964).  FL,VA,GUIT                           SD
LEGLEY, V.  TRIO, OP 55 (1959).  FL,VA,GUIT                         CBD
LOTTI, A.-BEHREND.  SONATE.  FL,VC,GUIT                             B&B
LUNDEN, L.  AFTONSTUND.  FL,OB,GUIT                                 EMF
MAASZ, G.  SUITE.  FL,VC,GUIT                                       HEI
MAR-CHAIM, J.  TRIO.  FL,VA,GUIT                                    IMP
MATIEGKA, W.-HUBER.  NOTTURNO, OP 21.  FL,VA,GUIT                   WZ
MATIEGKA, W.  SERENADE, OP 26.  FL,VA,GUIT                          WZ
MATIEGKA, W.  TRIO, OP 26.  FL,VA,GUIT                              EDK
MIYAKE, H.  MUSIK.  PIC,FL,GUIT                                     WZ
MOLINO, F.  TRIO, OP 45.  FL,VA,GUIT                                EDK
MOLINO, F.  TRIO, OP 45.  FL,VA,GUIT                                WZ
MOLLERS, C.  SERENADE.  FL,GUIT,PERC                                ROB
MORYL, R.  SUMMER'S MUSIC.  FL,OB,GUIT                              ACA
MOZART, W.-SCHMIDT.  FLOTENUHRSTUCK, ANDANTE (KV616)                WZ
   FL,VN,GUIT
MUSGRAVE, T.  SONATA.  FL,VN,GUIT                                   NO
PFISTER, H.  PREAMBOLO, ARIA E BALLO.  CL,DB,GUIT                   HEI
POLOLANIK, Z.  SCHERZO CONTRARIO.  CL,VN,GUIT                       GZ
PRAAG, H. VAN.  SONATA (1963).  OB,GUIT,PF                          SD
RAKUJAS, B.  PASTORAL TRIO.  FL,PF,GUIT                             DSS
RECHBERGER, H.  WAYS.  FL,2GUIT                                     FIN
REGT, H. DE.   MUSICA, OP 15 (1972).  FL,VA,GUIT                    SD
REGT, H. DE.   MUSICA, OP 18.  FL,GUIT,PERC                         SD
REGT, H. DE.   SILENUS EN BACCHANTEN, OP 42 (1974).  FL,OB,GUIT     SD
RICHTER, N.  TRIO (1935).  FL,VA,GUIT                               SD
RUYNEMAN, D.  REFLEXIONS #2.  FL,VA,GUIT                            SD
SANDELEWSKI, W.  TRIO.  FL,EHN,GUIT                                 PWM
SCHUBERT, F.-WALTER.  BELIEBTE WALZER & MOMENT MUSICAL             WZ
   2FL,GUIT
SKORZENY, F.  TRIO (1957).  FL,VA,GUIT                              LDO
STEINKE, G.  MUSIC FOR 3.  OB,GUIT,PERC                             SS
STREET, T.  VARIATIONS.  FL,VC,GUIT                                 GS
TAKEMITSU, T.  RING (1962).  FL,GUIT,LUTE                           EDS
TCHEREPNIN, I.  SOMBRES LUMIERES.  FL,VC,GUIT                       BEL
TELEMANN, G.-KAMMERLING.  TRIOSONATE IN E MI.  OB,VN,GUIT           LDO
TSUJII, E.  NAPTHA.  FL,VC,GUIT                                     TP
ULTAN, L.  EXPLORATIONS.  FL,DB,GUIT                                SS
WALTER, F.  4 KLEINE STUCKE.  2FL,GUIT                              WZ
```

3 PARTS INCLUDING GUITAR-339

```
WEBER, C.M. VON-SCHEIT.  MENUET & TRIO.  FL,VA,GUIT              LDO
WEBER, C.M. VON-BEHREND.  MENUETT (DONNA DIANA).  FL,VA,GUIT     B&B
WEBER, C.M. VON-BERGER.  MENUETT UND TRIO.  FL,VN(VA),GUIT       HEI
WESSMAN, H.  3 PIECES.  2FL,GUIT                                 FIN
WIGGLESWORTH, F.  SERENADE.  FL,VA,GUIT                          ACA
```

3 PARTS INCLUDING PERCUSSION-340

```
ARMA, P.  CELUI QUI DORT ET DORT.  BSN,XYL,PERC                 BIL
ATOR, J.  ENUFFISPLUNTEE.  SAX,PF,PERC                          SS
BACEWICZ, G.  TRIO (1965).  OB,HP,PERC                          PWM
BACK, S.  FAVOLA.  CL,PF,CEL                                    WH
BAGINSKI, Z.  VOYAGE TO THE OTHER SIDE.  FL,PF,PERC             PWM
BAMERT, M.  INTRODUCTION & TARANTELLA.  FL,PF,PERC              GS
BARCE, R.  CANADA-TRIO (1968).  FL,PF,PERC                      EDA
BENTZON, N.  CONCERTO, OP176.  CL,VN,PERC                       WH
BLOMDAHL, K.  DANS-SVIT #2.  CL,VC,PERC                         EMF
BOIS, R. DU.  PASTORALE III (1969).  CL,DB,BONGOS               SD
BON, W.  SUNPHONEION I, OP 22 (1968).  FL,VIB,PF                SD
BOYAMYAN, A.  MINIATURES.  OB,VC,PERC                           MKE
BRANT, H.  ICE AGE (1954).  CL,GLOCKENSPIEL,PF                  TP
BRUN, H.  TRIO.  FL,DB,PERC                                     SMI
BURGHAUSER, J.  POSSIBILITA.  CL,PERC,DULCIMER                  PAN
CAMPO, F.  TRES CUBITO.  FL/AFL,VA,PERC                         MFP
CHANCE, N.  DAYSONGS.  AFL,2PERC                                SS
CHIHARA, P.  BRANCHES.  2BSN,PERC                               PET
CHILDS, B.  MUSIC FOR....  PIC,OB,DR                            BER
CONSTANTINIDES, D.  COMPOSITION.  FL,HP,PERC                    SS
COWIE, E.  QUATTRO LIBRI DI PALLADIO (1975).  CL,PF,PERC        CHE
COYNER, L.  PIVA!.  ASAX,PERC,TAPE                              ACA
CUNNINGHAM, M.  COOL FANTASY FUGUE.  FL,DB,VIB                  SS
DE YOUNG, L.  TEXTURE.  FL,HPCD,PERC                            SS
DELAS, J.DE.  TRIO (1971).  FL,GUIT,PERC                        HG
DIEMENTE, E.  TRIO (1969).  FL,TPT,PERC                         SS
DOBOS, K.  INNERE BEWEGUNGEN.  CL,PF,PERC                       EMB
EISMA, W.  BECAUSE IT IS (1968).  OB,HPCD,PERC                  SD
ELLIS, M.  DREAM FANTASY, A.  CL(ASAX),TAPE,PERC                CF
EPSTEIN, A.  CANONS & POSTLUDE.  FL,BSN,PERC                    SS
EPSTEIN, A.  4 DIALOGUES.  FL,DB,PERC                           SS
ERIXON, P.  ELEGIA OCH ALLEGRO, OP 1 (1963).  OB,TPT,PERC       STI
FAHRES, M.  MINIMAL (1977).  BCL,PERC,TAPE                      EMO
FARBERMAN, H.  PROGRESSIONS.  FL,2PERC                          BR
FARBERMAN, H.  TRIO.  CL,VC,MAR                                 BR
FELD, J.  FANTAISIE CONCERTANTE.  FL,PF,PERC                    ALE
FENIGSTEIN, V.  6 FOLKSONGS.  FL,VC,DR                          EUL
FINNEY, R.  3 ACTS FOR 3 PLAYERS.  CL,PF,PERC                   PET
FISCHER, J.  7 .DOPISU SONATORUM.  FL,BCL,PERC                  PAN
FOX, F.  BEC-4.  FL,DB,PERC                                     SS
FRANKS, W.  HAIKU (1969).  FL,VC,PERC                           ISR
GASTYNE, S. DE.  ABACUS IN TRIO, OP 60 (1969).  BSN,HN,PERC     FER
GIEFER, W.  CANTI (1970).  FL,PF,PERC                           HG
GIEFER, W.  CHORALE (1973).  FL,ORG,PERC                        HG
GROSSKOPF, E.  NEXUS (1968).  FL,TAPE,PERC                      B&B
GRUNAUER, I.  MADRASHE.  FL,VN,PERC                             EMO
HALEN, W.  MEDITATION.  OB,PF,PERC                              SS
HARRISON, L.  CONCERTO #1.  FL,2PERC                            PET
HARTWELL, H.  3 X 3: AN EPIGRAM (1968).  CL,VA,VIB             CAN
HAUTA-AHO, T.  TRIO.  CL,DB,PERC                                FIN
```

```
HEIDER, W.   MUSIK IM DISKANT.  PIC,PF,PERC                         PET
HEINICK, D.   RITUAL.  CL,TPT,PERC                                  SS
HEISS, J.   CAPRICCIO (1976).  FL,CL,PERC                           AMC
HEUSSENSTAMM, G.   MUSIC FOR 3, OP 33.  BFL,PERC,VIB                SS
HEUSSENSTAMM, G.   POIKILOS, OP 32.  AFL,PERC,VIB                   SS
HIBBARD, W.   GESTURES.  FL,DB,PERC                                 AMC
HIRSCH.   KAMMERMUSIK.  FL,CL,PERC                                  PET
HOCH, P.   LIEDER FREMDER LANDER.  2CL,PERC                         SCH
HOLEWA, H.   CON 4 FLAUTI (1975).  PIC/FL/AFL/BFL,2PERC             STI
HOLLFELDER, W.   SERENADE.  FL,CL,PERC                              EDT
HOSKINS, W.   PRELUDE & DANCE FOR PVC.  PIC,CBSN,VIB                ACA
HOVHANESS, A.   FIRDAUSE, OP252.  CL,HP,PERC                        AB
HOVHANESS, A.   STARRY NIGHT, OP288.  FL,HP,XYL                     AB
HUMMEL, B.   LUDI A 3.  OB,PF,PERC                                  RS
JAGER, R.   CONCERTO.  ASAX,BRASS,PERC                              VO
JOHANSON, S.   TRIFONOGRAM (1970).  FL,CL,PERC                      STI
KALMAR, L.   TRIO (1968).  FL,GUIT,MAR                              EMB
KARKOFF, M.   TIO AFORISMER, OP104 (1971)                          STI
    PIC/FL/AFL/BFL,OB/OB D'AMO RE,PERC
KOHS, E.   NIGHT WATCH (1944).  FL,HN,TIMP                          TP
KROEGER, K.   TOCCATA.  CL,TRB,PERC                                 AB
KUCERA, V.   PANTA RHEI (1963).  FL,VIB,PERC                        CHF
LA ROSA, M.   COMING IN GLORY.  ASAX,TRB,VIB                        SS
LACHENMANN, H.   TRIO FLUIDO (1966).  CL,VA,MAR                     HG
LAMPERSBERG, G.   TRIO.  CL,VN,DR                                   UE
LEWIS, R.   OSSERVAZIONI I.  PIC/FL/AFL,PF,PERC                     TP
LINKE, N.   CHESAGE (PUZZLE #3) (1973).  PIC/FL,CL,PERC             HG
LINKE, N.   PERCUZZLE PUZZLE (PUZZLE #1) (1973).  CL,PERC,ORG       HG
LISCHKA, R.   KONTAKTE.  AFL,VIB,DB                                 DEU
MAES, J.   TRIO.  FL,VA,PERC                                        HE
MANNINO, F.   EPITAFFIO PER GLI AMICI SCOMPARSI.  AFL,PF,PERC       EDI
MARTTINEN, T.   DIVERTIMENTO, OP127.  OB,EHN,PERC                   FIN
MAVES, D.   OKTECHOS.  CL,HN,PERC                                   PET
MC CULLOH, B.   LAMENT.  FL,HP,MAR                                  CF
MERKELT(ED).   11 CELEBRATED MARCHES.  2FL,DR                       SIM
MICHAEL, E.   3 RITUELS.  2OB,PERC                                  ECH
MOLLERS, C.   SERENADE.  FL,GUIT,PERC                               ROB
MORYL, R.   SUNDAY MORNING.  ASAX,PERC,TAPE                         ACA
MOSS, L.   TOOT-SWEET.  OB,2PERC                                    SS
MOSZUMANSKA, K.   RENDITION.  FL,PERC,TAPE                          EM
NOON, D.   SONATA, OP 21.  CL,VIB,PF                                CF
OLIVEROS, P.   TRIO (1963).  FL,PERC,DB                             MEP
PAPP, L.   IMPRESSIONI.  FL,PF,GONG                                 EMB
PAUK, A.   MAGARU.  FL,VA,PERC                                      CAN
PERT, M.   ALPHA CENTAURI, OP 10.  FL,PERC,TAPE                     JOW
PERUTI, C.   CONFLUENCE.  CL,VN,PERC                                MAN
PIRANI, O.   REVERIE.  FL,VIB,CYMBAL                                EBE
PORENA, B.   NEUMI (1963).  FL,MAR,VIB                              ESZ
PRIN, Y.   MOBILE I.  OB/MUSETTE/EHN,PERC,TAPE                      ERR
PYLE, F.   SONATA FOR 3.  CL,PF,PERC                                SO
RAE, A.   SLEEP WHISPERING (1971).  AFL,PF,VIB                      CAN
REGT, H. DE.   MUSICA, OP 18.  FL,GUIT,PERC                         SD
REINER, K.   TRIO (1964).  FL,BCL,PERC                              ES
RUSSELL, A.   BRIGHT RITUAL.  FL,CL,PERC                            SS
SCHMIDT, W.   SEPTIGRAMS (1956).  FL,PF,PERC                        WI
SCHOLLUM, R.   MOSAIK, OP 75.  OB,PF,PERC                           LDO
SCHWARTZ, E.   OPTIONS II.  CL,PERC,TAPE                            MEP
SCHWARTZ, E.   SERENADE.  FL,DB,PERC                                SMI
SEYFRIT, M.   IN SEARCH OF.  CL,MAR,DB                              ACA
SILVERMAN, F.   FOR HIM.  FL,VC,VIB                                 SS
SIVIC, P.   INTERPUNKCIJE.  CL,PF,XYL                               EDD
STEFFEN, W.   TRIPLUM 72, OP 39.  FL,PF,PERC                        B&B
```

3 PARTS INCLUDING PERCUSSION - 340

```
STEINKE, G.   MUSIC FOR OBOE, CONTRABASS, PERCUSSION, A        SS
   OB,DB,PERC
STEINKE, G.   MUSIC FOR 3.   OB,GUIT,PERC                      SS
STOCK, D.   TRIPLE PLAY (1970).   PIC,DB,PERC                  MAR
STOUT, A.   CAPRICCIO (1967).   OB,HP,PERC                     JB
STUPPNER, H.   ANIMA (1977).   CL,VC,PERC                      EMO
SURINACH, C.   TIENTOS.   EHN,HP(PF),TIMP                      AMP
SYDEMAN, W.   TRIO (1963).   FL,DB,PERC                        SS
TAUTENHAHN, G.   EMOTIONS ON A NOTE #1.   CL,VA,PERC           SS
TAUTENHAHN, G.   TRIO #2.   EHN,TU,GLOCKENSPIEL                SS
TELEMANN, G.   SONATA IN A MI.   REC,OB,BC                     H-V
TESSIER, R.   "A".   FL,HP,PERC                                EFM
TESSIER, R.   TRIEDRE.   FL,VIB,ACC                            EFM
TOUMA, H.   ORIENTAL RHAPSODIE.   2FL,DR                       IMP
TROMBLY, P.   TRIO IN 3 MOVEMENTS.   FL/AFL,DB,PERC            ACA
VOGEL, R.   TEMPORAL LANDSCAPE.   FL,PF,PERC                   TRI
VRIES ROBBE, W. DE.   ETINCELLES.   FL,VN,VIB                  SD
WAHREN, K.   INCREASE (1971).   FL,ORG,MAR                     B&B
WAHREN, K.   SOUNDSCREEN (1975).   FL,2PERC                    B&B
WEBER, B.   NOCTURNO, OP 55.   FL,VC,CEL                       EMT
WEBER, B.   PRELUDE & NOCTURNE.   FL,VC,CEL                    TP
WHITTENBERG, C.   A DUE, OP 49.   FL/AFL,PIC,PERC              ACA
WHITTENBERG, C.   3 FORMS WITH VARIATIONS.   FL/AFL,DB,PERC    ACA
WUORINEN, C.   BASSOON VARIATIONS.   BSN,HP,TIMP               PET
YUASA, J.   INTER-POSI-PLAY-TION II.   FL,HP,PERC              SCH
ZINN, M.   SUSPENSIONS.   ASAX,BSN,VIB                         SS
```

3 PARTS INCLUDING RECORDER-342

```
BALLARD.   MIDWINTER FIRES.   REC,FL,PF                        BO
BOIS, R. DU.   PASTORALE II (1969).   REC,FL,GUIT             SD
CORMIER, C.-VOXMAN.   SONATINA NO.1 IN CMA.   2REC,BSN         NOM
DOPPELBAUER, J.   TRIO I.   REC,OB,CL                          LDO
FUX, J.-HOFFMANN.   NURNBERGER PARTITA.   REC,OB,BC            MV
FUX, J.-KUNTNER.   SINFONIA.   REC(FL),OB,BC                   B&N
GRAUN, C.-GERLACH.   TRIOSONATE IN F MA.   REC,OB,BC           HMO
KELLER, G.-LASOCKI/HOLMAN.   TRIO SONATA IN B FL MA.  OB,REC,BC  NOM
KETTING, P.   FANTASIA (1969).   REC,FL,HPCD                   SD
KUKUCK, F.   KAMMERMUSIK.   REC,OB,GAMBA                       MV
LINDE, H.   TRIO (1960).   REC,FL,PF                           SCH
LOEILLET, J.   SONATA A 3.   REC,OB,BC                         UE
LOEILLET, J.-BERGMANN.   TRIO SONATA, OP 1/1.   REC,OB,PF      SCH
LOEILLET, J.-ERMELER/KLUGE.   TRIO-SONATE IN F MA, OP 2/2      HEI
   REC,OB,BC
LOEILLET, J.-RUF.   TRIOSONATE, OP 1/1 IN F MA.   REC,OB,BC    HMO
LOEILLET, J.-RUF.   TRIOSONATE, OP 1/3 IN G MI.   REC,OB,BC    HMO
LOEILLET, J.-RUF.   TRIOSONATE, OP 1/5 IN C MI.   REC,OB,BC    HMO
LOEILLET, J.-RUF.   TRIOSONATEN, OP 2/2 IN F MA                B&N
   REC(FL),OB,BC
LOEILLET, J.-RUF.   TRIOSONATEN, OP 2/4 IN D MI                B&N
   REC(FL),OB,BC
LOEILLET, J.-RUF.   TRIOSONATEN, OP 2/6 IN C MI                B&N
   REC(FL),OB,BC
PEPUSCH, J.   TRIO SONATA IN G MI.   REC,OB,BC                 PET
PROWO, P.   TRIO SONATA IN C MI.   AREC,FL,BC                  HMP
QUANTZ, J.-BIRKE.   TRIOSONATE IN C MA.   REC,FL,BC            B&N
REUTER-HENSE.   9 PIECES FOR 3 WIND INSTRUMENTS.   REC,FL,VN   RS
SCHROEDER-HOFMANN.   SONATE IN C MI.   REC,OB,BC               B&N
```

3 PARTS INCLUDING RECORDER-342

```
SCHROEDER-HOFMANN.  SONATE IN F MA.  REC,OB,BC               B&N
SCHULTZE, J.-NAGEL.  SONATA.  REC,FL,BC                      MV
TELEMANN, G.-HOFMANN.  SONATA IN C MI.  REC,OB,BC           B&N
TELEMANN, G.-HOFMANN.  SONATA IN F MA.  REC,OB,BC           B&N
TELEMANN, G.-RODEMANN.  SONATA IN F MA.  REC,OB,BC          HMO
TELEMANN, G.-POULTEAU.  SONATE EN TRIO IN E MI.  REC,OB,BC  ALE
TELEMANN, G.-RUF.  TRIO SONATA IN A MI.  REC,OB,BC         SCH
TELEMANN, G.  TRIO SONATA IN C MI.  OB,REC,BC              PET
TELEMANN, G.-RAMPAL.  TRIO SONATA IN G MI.  REC,FL,PF      INT
TELEMANN, G.-RUETZ.  TRIOSONATE IN E MI.  REC(FL),OB,BC    B&N
TELEMANN, G.-FLEISCHHAUER.  TRIOSONATE IN F MA.  REC,OB,BC DEU
TELEMANN, G.-RUF.  TRIOSONATE IN F MA.  REC,OB,BC          PEL
TOEBOSCH, L.  MAYETMAR, OP 99 (1968).  REC,FL,HPCD          SD
VIVALDI, A.-LASOCKI.  CONCERTO IN G MI.  AREC,OB,BC         HMP
VIVALDI, A.  TRIO IN A MI.  REC(FL),BSN,BC                  MR
```

3 PARTS INCLUDING TAPE-343

```
BEERMAN, B.  POLYGRAPH VI.  FL,HP,TAPE                      ACA
BEERMAN, B.  REFLECTIONS.  CL,VC,TAPE                       ACA
BERGEIJK, G. VAN.  SONATE.  EHN,PF,TAPE                     SD
BOTTJE, W.  CELESTIAL MOTIONS.  2FL,TAPE                    ACA
BOTTJE, W.  REFLECTIONS.  FL,HP,TAPE                        ACA
BROWN, A.  ADDITIONS.  FL,TRB,TAPE                          SS
BRUYNEL, T.  LOOKING EARS (1972).  BCL,PF,TAPE             SD
COYNER, L.  PIVA!.  ASAX,PERC,TAPE                          ACA
COYNER, L.  SPIRAL.  CL,VC,TAPE                             ACA
DIEMENTE, E.  DIARY (PART II- 1972).  2ASAX,TAPE           DOR
ELLIS, M.  DREAM FANTASY, A.  CL(ASAX),TAPE,PERC           CF
ERIKSON, A.  MUSIC (1974).  FL,BFL,TAPE                    STI
FAHRES, M.  MINIMAL (1977).  BCL,PERC,TAPE                 EMO
GROSSKOPF, E.  NEXUS (1968).  FL,TAPE,PERC                 B&B
HEIDER, W.  KUNST-STOFF.  CL,PF,TAPE                        PET
HUGHES, K.  CHANCE #2.  FL,OB,TAPE                          WI
KRENEK, E.  AULOKITHARA (1971/72).  OB/EHN,HP,TAPE         B&N
MEESTER, L. DE.  SPIELEREI (1969).  FL,VC,TAPE             CBD
MELBY, J.  ZONNORITIES.  OB,CL,COMPUTER                     ACA
MICHAELSON, C.  GAME.  2FL,TAPE                             EAM
MOORE, C.  MUSEUM PIECE.  FL,VC,TAPE                        PI
MORTHENSON, J.  INTIMI.  BCL,BSN,TAPE                       ER
MORYL, R.  SUNDAY MORNING.  ASAX,PERC,TAPE                  ACA
MOSZUMANSKA NAZAR, K.  INTERPRETATIONS.  FL,PERC,TAPE      PWM
PERT, M.  ALPHA CENTAURI, OP 10.  FL,PERC,TAPE            JOW
PINKHAM, D.  FOR EVENING DRAWS ON.  EHN,ORG,TAPE           ECS
POLIN, C.  O, ADERYN PUR.  FL,SAX,TAPE                      SS
PRIN, Y.  MOBILE I.  OB/MUSETTE/EHN,PERC,TAPE             ERR
ROSS, W.  TOWARD THE EMPYREAN.  ASAX,TAPE,DANCER           DOR
SCHWARTZ, E.  ECHO MUSIC I.  CL,VA,TAPE                     CF
SCHWARTZ, E.  NINAS.  FL,OB,TAPE                            CF
SCHWARTZ, E.  OPTIONS II.  CL,PERC,TAPE                     MEP
TANENBAUM, E.  REMEMBRANCE.  FL,ASAX,TAPE                   ACA
TRAFFORD, E.  DESCENT TO PERIHELION.  OB,PF,TAPE          SS
VASQUEZ DIAS, A.  RAIZ (1977).  FL,PF,TAPE                 SD
```

4 FLUTES-400

```
ANDREWS, J.  ILLUSIONS                                          PO
ARNOLD, J.(ED).  FLUTE QUARTETS                                 MS
BACH, J.S.-BAKER.  ARIA                                         GS
BACH, J.S.-TROXELL.  MENUETTO & POLACCA(BRANDENBURG #1)         PO
BACH, J.S.-ECK.  MINUET                                         BE
BACH, J.S.  2 PRELUDES                                          HU
BARTOLOZZI, B.  SINAULODIA (1970)                               ESZ
BENEY.  CALLIGRAPHIES                                           ALE
BENNETT, R.R.  RONDO CAPRICCIOSO                                CA
BENTZON, N.  QUARTETTO TERTIO, OP385                            WH
BERTHOMIEU, M.  ARCADIE                                         SEM
BERTHOMIEU, M.  CHATS                                           BIL
BIZET, G.-BROOKE.  ANDANTE & MINUET                            CF
BIZET, G.-FREEDMAN.  SUITE(CARMEN)                              MC
BJORKMAN, R.  MINIATYR (1974)                                   STI
BLOCK, R.-P. NOTHNAGLE.  SOUND THE BRIGHT FLUTES                NOM
    PIC(FL),2FL,AFL
BOISMORTIER, J.-POULTEAU.  SONATA, OP 34/3                      ALE
BORNSCHEIN, F.-CELLARS.  FRENCH CLOCK, THE                      TP
BOTTENBERG, W.  DIVERTIMENTO(1968).  2FL/2PIC,FL,AFL            CAN
BOZZA, E.  2 ESQUISSES                                          ALE
BOZZA, E.  JOUR D'ETE A LA MONTAGNE (1953)                      ALE
BOZZA, E.  3 PIECES                                             ALE
BRAUN, G.  PORTRAIT #1 (1969)                                   GBV
BUTTS, C.  QUARTET                                              CII
BUTTS, C.  SONG                                                 BO
CHEVREUILLE, R.  MUSIQUE LILLIPUTIENNE, OP 22 (1942)            CBD
CHEYETTE & ROBERTS.  FOUR-TONE FOLIO, 3 VOL                     CF
COHEN, S.  DIVERTIMENTO                                         WI
CORELLI, A.  ALLEMANDA                                          EDM
CORELLI, A.-JOHNSON.  SARABANDA & GAVOTTA                       RU
DAHL, I.  SERENADE (1960)                                       BH
DAVISON, J.  CANZONA & CHORALE (1965)                          CAN
DE ELIAS.  4 UBERLIEFERTE MEXIKANISCHE MELODIEN                 RC
DESPORTES, Y.  ITALIAN SUITE                                    SO
DEURSEN, A. VAN.  3 BAGATELLES                                  HU
DILLON, B.  FLAUTISSIMO                                         PO
DITTERSDORF, C.-STEINBECK.  CASSATION IN D MA                   LDO
DITTERSDORF, K.-SCHULTZ/HAUSER.  NOTTURNO                       SCH
DUBOIS, P.  QUARTET                                             ALE
ECK, E.  QUARTET ALBUM                                          BE
ECK, E.  VALSETTE                                               BE
ELGAR, E.  SALUT D'AMOUR, OP 12.  3FL,AFL                       CF
FARRENC, J.-BROOK.  ANDANTE                                     CF
FETHERSTON, E.  VALSE STACCATO (RUBENSTEIN)                     BE
FRACKENPOHL, A.  DIVERTIMENTO                                   SH
FRESCOBALDI, G.-JOHNSON.  GALLIARD & COURANTE                   RU
FUERSTNER, C.  BERCEUSE                                         ZA
GABRIELSKI, W.  GRAND QUARTET                                   EDM
GALUPPI, B.  TOCCATA                                            EDM
GEARHART, L.  FLUTE SESSIONS                                    SH
GIANELLA, L.-IMBESCHEID.  QUARTET                               UE
GLUCK, C.-JOHNSON.  ANDANTE & CAPRICE                           RU
GLUCK, C.-EPHROSS.  LOVELY FIELDS SO GENTLE                     TP
GOSSEC, F.-ECK.  GAVOTTE                                        BE
```

```
GRIM, C.-CAVALLY.   SALUTE TO QUANTZ                            SO
GUILLEMAIN, G.-TAYLOR.   TAMBOURIN                              BE
HAYDN, F.-FRACKENPOHL.   DIVERTIMENTO                           SH
HAYDN, F.-SPIEGL.   FLUTE CLOCK SONATAS                         OX
HEKSTER, W.   STATEMENT (1974)                                  SD
HERMANN, R.   FLUTE WILLOW                                      CF
HERMANS, N.   IMPRESSIEFLITSEN (1967)                           SD
HERVIG, R.   3 PIECES                                           RU
HESSENBERG, K.   QUARTETTINO, OP 99                             WZ
HOLMES-LONG.   SYMPHONY ENSEMBLE SERIES                         RU
JESSEL, L.-CAVALLY.   PARADE OF THE WOODEN SOLDIERS             SO
JONGEN, J.   ELEGY                                             SO
JONGEN, J.   2 PARAPHRASES ON WALLOON CHRISTMAS CAROLS          SO
KELLER, H.   PUZZLE (1973)                                      HUG
KOEPKE, P.   AUTUMN IDYLL                                       RU
KOEPKE, P.   DANSE CAPRIOLE                                     RU
KOEPKE, P.   FOX FIRE                                           RU
KOHLER, E.   GRAND QUARTET, OP 92                               SO
KOHLER, E.-COCHRANE.   GRAND QUARTETTE, OP 92                   CF
KOHLER, E.-VOXMAN.   SCHERZO (QUARTET, OP 92)                   RU
KUHLAU, F.-ANDRAUD.   GRAND QUARTET, OP103                      SO
KUHLAU, F.   QUARTET IN E MA, OP103                             LIT
KUHLAU, F.-NAGEL.   QUARTET, OP103                              PET
KUHLAU, F.   QUARTET, OP103                                     EDK
KUHLAU, F.   QUATUOR IN E MA, OP103                             BIL
LANG, R.   CHORALE & SCHERZO                                    LN
LANG, R.   REVERIE & TARANTELLA.   3FL,AFL                      LN
LEEUWEN, A. VAN.   4 MINIATURES                                 SO
LEEUWEN, A. VAN(ARR).   TURKEY IN THE STRAW                     SO
LEGLEY, V.   QUATUOR, OP 14 (1943)                              CBD
LEMELAND, A.   ETAT D'HORIZON, 2: L'ETE                         BIL
LEVI, W.   FLUTE FLIRTATION                                     WIL
LIADOV, A.-EPHROSS.   MUSICAL SNUFF BOX                         TP
LORENZO, L. DE.   CAPRICCIO, OP 82/3                            PET
LORENZO, L. DE.   I SEGUACI DE PAN, OP 32                       WZ
LOUCHEUR.   DIVERTISSEMENT.   2FL/PIC,FL/PIC/AFL,FL/AFL/BFL     BIL
LOUVIER.   9 CARRES, AVEC 10 DIAPOSITIVES AD LIB                ALE
MAGANINI, Q.   BEGINNERS' LUCK                                  EDM
MAGANINI, Q.   PATROL OF THE WOODEN INDIANS (REALM OF DOLLS)    CF
MAGANINI, Q.   SHEPHERDS IN ARCADIA                             EDM
MAURICE, P.   SUITE                                             BIL
MC BRIDE, R.   SHUT UP, MOCKINGBIRD.   4PIC                     ACA
MC KAY, G.   CHORALE, AUBADE & NOEL                             SF
MC KAY, G.   CHRISTMAS MORNING SUITE                            SO
MC KAY, G.   LYRIC POEM                                         SO
MC KAY, G.   SONATINA GIOCOSA                                   BA
MC KAY, G.   SUITE MATINALE                                     BA
MC KAY, G.   SUITE PASTORALE                                    BA
MENDELSSOHN, F.-JOHNSON.   ANDANTE CON MOTO                     RU
MEULEMANS, A.   ANDANTE ET SCHERZO (1945)                       CBD
MOZART, W.-HIBY.   ANDANTE IN F MA (KV616)                      SCH
OTT, J.   SUITE                                                 CU
PACHELBEL-WALKER.   CANON AND GIGUE                             RU
PAUBON, P.   QUATUOR                                            BIL
PIETRAGRUA, G.-BLOCK.   2 CANZONE, OP1.   PIC(FL),2FL,AFL       NOM
PLEYEL, I.   2 RONDOS                                           HU
PRESSER, W.   SONG & MARCH                                      TRI
REICHA, A.-LEOPOLD.   MINUET (QUARTET, OP 12)                   WZ
REICHA, A.   QUARTET, OP 19                                     BIL
REICHA, A.   SINFONICA, OP 12                                   EDK
REICHA, A.   SINFONICO QUARTETTE                                CF
REICHA, A.   SINFONICO, OP 12                                   BIL
```

4 FLUTES - 400

```
REYNOLDS, R.  4 ETUDES.  PIC,2FL,AFL                              PET
RIMSKY-KORSAKOV, N.-KOEPKE.  SONG OF INDIA                        RU
RIMSKY-KORSAKOV, N.(JEANJEAN).  VOL DU BOURDON, LE                BIL
RUITER, W. DE.  QUARTET (1978)                                    SD
SCARLATTI-JOHNSON.  ARIA & MINUET                                 RU
SCARMOLIN, A.  FOUR OF A KIND                                     BA
SCHMITT, F.  QUATUOR, OP106                                       DUR
SCHUBERT, F.-JOHNSON.  MENUET & TRIO                              RU
SCHUMANN, R.  TRAUMEREI.  3FL,AFL                                 CF
SCHWARZ, I.  PARTHENIA                                            RU
SEVERN, A.  SCHERZO BRILLIANTE                                    BE
SOBAJE, M.(ARR).  ANGELS WE HAVE HEARD ON HIGH                    KN
SOLLBERGER, H.  GRAND QUARTET (IN MEMORIAM:FRIEDRICH KUHLAU)      M&M
SOLOMON.  QUATRO GIOCOSO                                          SO
SOUSSMAN, H.-PORTER.  QUARTET, OP 27/1                            SO
SPIES, C.  CANON                                                  BH
STARER, R.  CADENZA                                              MC
TAUTENHAHN, G.  QUARTET.  PIC,2FL,AFL                             SS
TCHAIKOVSKY, P.-JOHNSON.  CHANSON TRISTE                          RU
TCHEREPNIN, A.  QUARTET, OP 60                                    BEL
TELEMANN, G.-GATTI.  CACCIA, LA                                   EBE
TROMBLY, P.  CANTILENA.  PIC,FL,AFL,BFL                           ACA
VIVALDI, A.  GIGA                                                 EDM
VOORN, J.  DIVERTIMENTO (5 CONSTELLATIONS) (1978)                 SD
VOXMAN, H.(ARR).  QUARTET REPERTOIRE                              RU
WAGNER, J.-CAVALLY.  UNDER THE DOUBLE EAGLE.  3FL,AFL             SO
WALKER.  AMUSEMENT                                                KN
WALKER, R.  BERGOMASK                                            PO
WALKER, R.  2 LYRICAL PIECES                                      HL
WELIN, K.  ANCORA (1969).  PIC,FL,AFL,BFL                         STI
WOODFORDE-FINDEN, A.-JOHNSON.  KASHMIRI SONG                      RU
WOUTERS, A.-VOXMAN.  ADAGIO & SCHERZO                             RU
```

4 OBOES-402

```
AMY, G.  JEUX                                                     UE
BERLINSKI, H.  CANONS & ROUNDS.  4OB                              TP
CASTEREDE, J.  MUSIC FOR THE OBOE FAMILY                          PET
     OB,OB D,AMORE,EHN,HECKELPHONE
GALUPPI, B.  TOCCATA                                              EDM
MAGANINI, Q.  BEGINNERS' LUCK                                     EDM
MOULAERT, R.  ANDANTE, FUGUE ET FINAL                             CBD
     OB,OB D'AMOUR,EHN,HECKELPHONE
RAPHLING, S.  CONCERT SUITE.  4OB                                 EDM
RENOSTO, P.  AR-LOTH.  OB,EHN,OB D'AMORE,MUSETTE                  RC
SCHUYT, N.  ALLA NOTTURNA.  2OB,OB D,AMORE,EHN                    SD
ZAGWIJN, H.  SUITE (1951).  2OB,EHN,HECKELPHONE                   SD
```

4 CLARINETS-404

```
ABSIL, J.  QUATUOR                                               HLE
ALICE BLUE GOWN.                                                 B3
ALLEN, M.  PROGRESSIVE SUITE                                      BH
AMANI-DONATELLI.  ORIENTALE.  2CL,ACL(CL),BCL                     WI
```

ARMA, P. 7 TRANSPARENCES		HLE
ARNE, T.-BARR. 2 (CORRUS) DANCES. 2CL,ACL(CL),BCL(CL)		BE
ARRIEU, C. 5 MOUVEMENTS		BIL
ARTOT, J. 12 QUARTETTES. 2CL,ACL(CL),BCL(CL)		CF
AVNI, T. 2 PIECES (1965)		ISR
BACH-PACHELBEL/SCHWADRON. 2 PIECES. 2CL,ACL,BCL		KN
BACH, J.S.-AYRES. ANDANTE AND FUGHETTA. 2CL,ACL(CL),BCL(CL)		BA
BACH, J.S.-JOHNSON. BACH CHORALES		RU
BACH, J.S.-VANDRE. 15 BACH CHORALES		TM
BACH, J.S.-SIMON. BACH FOR THE CLARINET.PART 3		GS
BACH, J.S.-BRANDENBURG. BOURREE		CF
BACH, J.S.-ROSENTHAL. FUGA #9. 2CL,ACL,BCL		WI
BACH, J.S.-PENTZ. FUGUE #16 IN G MI. 2CL,ACL(CL),BCL(CL)		BE
BACH, J.S.-MCKAY. FUGUE #4. 2CL,ACL(CL),BCL(CL)		BA
BACH, J.S.-GORDON. FUGUE #7. 2CL,ACL(CL),BCL		KN
BACH, J.S.-CRABB. FUGUE IN G MI		SH
BACH, J.S.-STOUFFER. GAVOTTE. 2CL,ACL(CL),BCL(CL)		KN
BACH, J.S.-BARR. 2 (SUITE IN D MA) GAVOTTES 2CL,ACL(CL),BCL(CL)		BE
BACH, J.S.-AUSLENDER. JIG FUGUE, THE. 2CL,ACL,BCL		WI
BACH, J.S.-GRISEZ. LOURE		CF
BACH, J.S.-MAGANINI. PRELUDE #12. 2CL,ACL,BCL		EDM
BAGATINI. ODE TO HIAWATHA		BE
BAGLEY-HARRIS. THISTLEDOWN. 2CL,ACL(CL),BCL(CL)		CF
BARTOK, B.-GORDON. 3 FOLK DANCES. 2CL,ACL(CL),BCL		SO
BEETHOVEN, L. VAN-WILSON. ALLEGRO CON BRIO (OP 18/1) 2CL,ACL,BCL		CF
BEETHOVEN, L. VAN-HASSELMANN. DEUTSCHER TANZ		FS
BEETHOVEN, L. VAN-GUENTHER. HAPPY & SAD		BE
BEETHOVEN, L. VAN-AYRES. MINUET & MARCH. 2CL,ACL(CL),BCL(CL)		BA
BEETHOVEN, L. VAN-TOLL. RONDO EXCERPT (SONATA PATHETIQUE) 2CL,ACL(CL),BCL(CL)		CF
BEETHOVEN, L. VAN-OSTLING. SCHERZO & TRIO 2CL,ACL(CL),BCL(CL)		BE
BEETHOVEN, L. VAN-HITE. SCHERZO, OP 18/1. 3CL,BCL		SO
BEETHOVEN, L. VAN-LEMARC. ZWEITER SATZ (SONATA IN G MA)		T-M
BENNETT, D. ARGENTINE. 2CL,ACL,BCL		CF
BENNETT, D. CANDID CLARINETS		CF
BENNETT, D. CLARINET RHAPSODY. 2CL,ACL,BCL		CF
BENNETT, D. PRELUDE & SCHERZO		CF
BENNETT, D. WAY OF THE WASP. 2CL,ACL,BCL		CF
BERLINSKI, H. CANONS & ROUNDS		TP
BERTOUILLE, G. CONCERTINO (1977)		CBD
BIGOT, P. 3 SHORT PIECES		HE
BIZET, G. ADAGIETTO (L'ARLESIENNE)		MOL
BIZET, G. CARILLON. 2CL,ACL(CL),BCL		EDM
BLOCK, R. HOMAGE TO D. S.. 2CL,ACL,BCL		WI
BOCCHERINI, L.-LEMARC. MENUET		T-M
BOCHSA-SCHMIDT/VOXMAN. ANDANTE & MINUETTO		RU
BOHM, C.-VOXMAN. QUARTET IN F MA. 3CL,BCL(CL)		RU
BOHNE, R.-VOXMAN. ANDANTE (QUARTET IN D MA). 2CL,ACL,BCL		RU
BOIS, R. DU. BECAUSE IT IS (1973)		SD
BOWLES, R. SUITE		PO
BOZZA, E. SONATINE. E FL CL,2CL,BCL		ALE
BRADAC, J.-VOXMAN. BOHEMIAN SUITE		RU
BRAHMS, J.-WOOD. ALLEGRETTO GRAZIOSO		HE
BRAHMS, J.-BRANDENBURG. WALTZ		CF
BRAUN, R. DIVERTIMENTO		YM
BRAUN, R.(ARR). SONGS FROM YE OLDE ENGLAND		YM
BRONS, C. SERENATA III (1974)		SD
BUSCH, C. EVENING PROMENADE		CF
BUSCH, C. IN PLAYFUL MOOD		CF

```
BUSCH, C.  QUIETUDE                                                    CF
BUTTERWORTH, N.(ARR).  3 MOZART MOVEMENTS                              CA
BYRD, W.-SKOLNIK.  PAVANA                                              SO
CABUS, P.  CLARINET QUARTET                                            MAU
CABUS, P.  RAPSODIE                                                    MAU
CACAVAS, J.  IMPRESSIONS                                               SO
CACAVAS, J.  ROMANTICA                                                 SPR
CAILLIET, L.  YOUTHFUL ADVENTURE                                       SO
CARION, F.  PETITE PIECE                                               EBR
CARLES, M.  PRELUDE & DANCE                                            ALE
CARROLL, B.  ARGUMENT                                                  AU
CARTER, E.  CANONIC SUITE                                              AMP
CAURROY, E.D.  DOUBLE CANON                                            EDM
CAZDEN, N.  ROUND DANCE #6, OP 40.  2CL,ACL,BCL                        SPR
CHAMINADE, C.-DE BUERIS.  DANCE CREOLE.  2CL,ACL(CL),BCL(CL)           BE
CHOPIN, F.-SARBER.  MINUTE WALTZ                                       RU
CHOPIN, F.-LIEGL.  PRELUDE                                             CF
CHOPIN, F.-DAVID.  PRELUDE IN B FLAT MA.  2CL,ACL,BCL                  WI
COHEN, S.  ALABAMA SKETCHES                                            WB
CONLEY, L.  CHRISTMAS CAROL, A                                         KN
CORELLI, A.  ALLEMANDA.  2CL,ACL(CL),BCL(CL)                           EDM
CORELLI, A.  GAVOTTE & GIGUE.  2CL,ACL(CL),BCL(CL)                     EDM
CORELLI, A.-HARRIS.  GIGUE.  2CL,ACL(CL),BCL(CL)                       CF
CORELLI, A.  GIGUE.  2CL,ACL(CL),BCL(CL)                               EDM
CORELLI, A.-SKORNICKA.  PRALUDIUM                                      BE
CORELLI, A.(LEWIN).  PRELUDIO & GIGA (7TH SONATA).  3CL,BCL            BH
CORELLI, A.-JOHNSON.  SARABANDA & GAVOTTA                              RU
   2CL,ACL(CL),BCL(CL)
COX, H.  CONCERTINO                                                    MAU
CROSSE, W.  PETITE QUARTET                                             BH
CUI, C.-HARRIS.  ORIENTALE.  2CL,ACL(CL),BCL(CL)                       CF
D'HARCOURT & BENNETT.  PERUVIAN INCA MELODIES.  2CL,ACL,BCL            BE
DAHL, I.  SERENADE                                                     BH
DALLIN, L.  AUTUMN VIGNETTE.  2CL,ACL(CL),BCL(CL)                      BE
DALLIN, L.  FOUNTAINS AT DAWN                                          BE
DAMASE, J.  RITOURNELLES                                               HLE
DAVISON, J.  CANZONA & CHORALE (1965)                                  CAN
DE BUERIS, J.  GAVOTTE CAPRICE.  2CL,ACL(CL),BCL(CL)                   CF
DE COURSEY, R.  WIND ENCORES.  2CL,ACL(BSN),BCL(BSN)                   AMP
DE JESU, J.  AVE VERUM CORPUS.  2CL,ACL,BCL                            HL
DE JESU, J.  MENUETTO                                                  HL
DEBUSSY, C.-DONATELLI.  CLAIR DE LUNE.  2CL,ACL(CL),BCL                WI
DEBUSSY, C.-HOWLAND.  NOCTURNE.  2CL,ACL,BCL                           S&
DEBUSSY, C.-AGA.  PETIT NEGRE, LE.  E FL CL,CL,ACL,BCL                 ALE
DEEMER, C.  TEN LITTLE INDIANS.  2CL,ACL(CL),BCL(CL)                   BE
DEEMER, C.  TEPEE                                                      BE
DEEP PURPLE.                                                           B3
DENZA, L.-HARRIS.  FUNICULI-FUNICULA.  2CL,ACL(CL),BCL(ACL)           CF
DESPORTES, Y.  FRENCH SUITE                                            SO
DESPORTES, Y.  NORMANDIE SUITE                                         SO
DEWIT, A.-HARRIS.  HARVEST DANCE.  2CL,ACL(CL),BCL(CL)                 CF
DEWIT, A.-HARRIS.  HUNGARIAN FANTASIE.  2CL,ACL(CL),BCL(ACL)          CF
DEWIT, A.-HARRIS.  ON THE LAKE.  2CL,ACL(CL),BCL(CL)                   CF
DEWIT, A.-HARRIS.  POLONAISE #1.  2CL,ACL(CL),BCL(CL)                  CF
DEWIT, A.  SPANISH WALTZ.  2CL,ACL(CL),BCL(CL)                         CF
DEWIT, A.  SUMMERTIME.  2CL,ACL(CL),BCL(ACL)                           CF
DILLON, R.  ALLEGRETTO FESTOSO                                         BH
DILLON, R.  4 QUARTETS                                                 S&
DILLON, R.  SONG                                                       BH
DITTERSDORF, K. VON-BARR.  ANDANTE (QUARTET IN B FLAT MA)              LU
   2CL,ACL(CL)    ,BCL(CL)
DONATO, A.  PASTORALE & DANCE                                          GS
```

DONT, J.-WALN. LARGHETTO & SCHERZO	KJ
DORMOLEN, J. OUT-OF-DATE APPARATUS (1979). 3CL,BCL	SD
DUBOIS, P. QUARTET	ALE
DVORAK, A.(SPINK). 4 SLAVONIC DANCES. 3CL,CL(BCL)	OX
EKLUND, H. 4 TEMPERAMENTI (1965)	STI
ENCINAR, J. TUKUNA	EDA
END, J. 6 MINIATURES	KN
ENDRESEN, R. CLARINET QUARTET #1. 2CL,ACL(CL),BCL(CL)	BE
ERICKSON, E. AMERICAN DANCE	EJ
ERICKSON, E. NOVELETTE	EJ
ERICKSON, E. SCHERZO, OP 33	EJ
ERICKSON, E. SONGS SAILORS SING	EJ
ERICKSON, E. SUNSHINE & SHADOWS	EJ
ERICKSON, M.-WALN. PETITE SUITE	CF
FARKAS, F. ANTICHE DANSE UNGHERESI DAL SEC. XVII E-FLATCL,2CL,BCL	EMB
FARRENC, J.-BROOKE. ANDANTE. 2CL,ACL(CL),BCL(CL)	CF
FELDSHER, H. 2 FUGUES. 2CL,ACL,BCL	KN
FERNEYHOUGH. SONATINA. 3CL,BCL	PET
FLOTHUIS, M. CANZONE, OP 76/4 (1978)	SD
FODI, J. FOUR FOR FOUR, OP 20 (1968). 2CL,ACL,BCL	CAN
FOUR OF A KIND.	B3
FRANGKISER, C. AUTUMN SKIES. 2CL,ACL(CL),BCL(CL)	BE
FRANGKISER, C. DANCING NYMPHS. 2CL,ACL(CL),BCL(CL)	BE
FRANGKISER, C. EN ESCAPADES. 2CL,ACL(CL),BCL(CL)	BE
FRANGKISER, C. FUGUEREST. 2CL,ACL(CL),BCL(CL)	BE
FRANGKISER, C. MELODIE PETITE. 2CL,ACL(CL),BCL(CL)	PO
FRANGKISER, C. SNOWFLAKES. 2CL,ACL(CL),BCL(CL)	BE
FRANGKISER, C. THREE BLIND MICE. 2CL,ACL(CL),BCL(CL)	BE
FRESCOBALDI, G.-JOHNSON. GALLIARD & COURANTE. 3CL,BCL(CL)	RU
FROBERGER, J.-BALENT. CAPRICCIO	SP
GABRIELSKY, W.-ANDRAUD. GRAND QUARTET, OP 53/1	SO
GABRIELSKY, W.-ANDRAUD. GRAND QUARTET, OP 53/2	SO
GABRIELSKY, W.-ANDRAUD. GRAND QUARTET, OP 53/3	SO
GALUPPI, B.-MAGANINI. TOCCATA. 2CL,ACL,BCL	EDM
GANTVOORT-HILLER-WEHNER. CLASSIC QUARTET #2	PO
GARIGLIO, R. FANTASIE & FUGUE. 3CL,BCL	PO
GERSHWIN, G.-SEARS. LIZA. 3CL,BCL	WB
GLASER, W. FYRA KORTA STYCKEN (1968)	STI
GLASER, W. 2 KORTA STYCKEN (1972). 2CL,ACL,BCL	STI
GLAZOUNOV, A.-BETTONEY. IN MODO RELIGIOSO. 2CL,ACL,BCL	CF
GLUCK, C.-LIEGL. DANCE OF THE HAPPY SPIRITS	CF
GODARD, B.-DONATELLI. ANDANTE, OP 16. 2CL,ACL,BCL	WI
GOEB, R. SUITE IN FOLK STYLE	AMP
GORDON(ARR). ENGLISH DANCE SUITE	CF
GREEN, D. 4 CONVERSATIONS (1959)	AMP
GRIEG, E.-GORDON. ALBUM LEAF. 2CL,ACL,BCL	KN
GRIEG, E.-DONATELLI. AN DER WIEGE. 2CL,ACL,BCL	WI
GRIEG, E.-LIEGL. ASE'S DEATH (PEER GYNT SUITE #1)	CF
GRIEG, E.-CARINI. ELF DANCE	GS
GRIEG, E.-GUENTHER. ELFIN DANCE	BE
GRIEG, E.-DONATELLI. LAST SPRING. 3CL,BCL	WI
GRIEG, E.-DONATELLI. SARABANDE, OP 40/2. 2CL,ACL,BCL	WI
GROOT, H. DE. SUITE	HU
GRUNDMAN, C. BAGATELLE	BH
GRUNDMAN, C. CAPRICE. 2CL,ACL,BCL	BH
GUENTHER, R. RUSTIC SCHERZO	BE
GYRING, E. CAPRICCIO	ACA
GYRING, E. CHORALE	HE
HABERLING, A. NEW CHAMBER MUSIC	HE
HANDEL, G.-BARR. AIR (WATER MUSIC). 2CL,ACL(CL),BCL(CL)	LU
HANDEL, G.-BARR. BOURREE (WATER MUSIC). 2CL,ACL(CL),BCL(CL)	BE

HANDEL, G.-SCHAEFFER. HALLELUJAH CHORUS	PO
HANDEL, G.-STANG. HOW BEAUTIFUL ARE THE FEET (MESSIAH) 2CL,ACL(CL),BCL(CL)	CF
HANDEL, G.-STANG. LARGO (XERXES). 2CL,ACL,BCL	CF
HANDEL, G.-MOORE. PASTORALE. 2CL,ACL,BCL	WI
HANDEL, G.-LIEGL. SARABANDE	CF
HANDEL, G.-STANG. SINFONIA (MESSIAH). 2CL,ACL(CL),BCL(ACL)	CF
HARRIS, A.(ARR). FAREWELL TO CUCULLAIN. 2CL,ACL(CL),BCL(ACL)	CF
HARRIS, A.(ARR). 4 HEART SONGS. 2CL,ACL(CL),BCL(ACL)	CF
HARRIS, A.(ARR). SACRED MELODIES. 2CL,ACL(CL),BCL(ACL)	CF
HARRIS, A.(ARR). SCOTTISH AIRS. 2CL,ACL(CL),BCL(ACL)	CF
HARRIS, A.(ARR). SONGS OF AMERICA. 2CL,ACL(CL),BCL(ACL)	CF
HARVEY, P. FANTASIA	BH
HARVEY, P. QUARTET. 3CL,BCL	S&C
HAUBIEL, C. NOSTALGIA	OP
HAUBIEL, C. WILL O' THE WISP	OP
HAUSDORFER. SUITE	MOL
HAYDN, F.-GEIGER. ADAGIO	CF
HAYDN, F.-STOUFFER. ALLEGRO. 2CL,ACL,BCL	PO
HAYDN, F.-HITE. ALLEGRO, A (OP 74/3)	LU
HAYDN, F.-HASSELMANN. CHORAL ST. ANTHONY	FS
HAYDN, F.-WILLIAMS. EMPEROR VARIATIONS, OP 76/3. 2CL,ACL,BCL	SO
HAYDN, F.-MC CATHREN. FINALE (FAREWELL SYMPHONY)	KN
HAYDN, F.-LANG. GIPSY RONDO	LN
HAYDN, F.-MC CATHREN. MENUETTO (SYMPHONY #45)	SP
HAYDN, F.-HITE. MENUETTO & PRESTO (OP 1/1)	LU
HAYDN, F.-FELDSHER. MENUETTO & TRIO (SYMPHONY #88) 2CL,ACL,BCL	KN
HAYDN, F.-BRANDENBURG. MENUETTO AL ROVESCIO (SONATA #4)	CF
HAYDN, F.-TROXELL. RONDO (DIVERTIMENTO #1). 2CL,ACL,BCL	PO
HAYDN, F.-DE BUERIS. SERENADE. 2CL,ACL(CL),BCL(CL)	BE
HAZZARD, P. QUARTET #2	SS
HEINEMAN, J. VIEWS. E FL CL,CL,BASSET HN(TSAX),BCL(BAR SAX)	CPE
HEYER, F. QUARTET IN F MA	HL
HLOBIL, E. KAMMERMUSIK, OP 67 (1965). 2CL,BASSET HN,BCL	CHF
HOUDY, P. QUATRE A QUATRE	ALE
HOUNSELL(ARR). SUITE. 2CL,ACL,BCL	TM
HOVHANESS, A. DIVERTIMENTO, OP 61/5. 3CL,BCL	PET
HRUBY, F. FOR THE BIRDS	BH
HUBBELL, F. CANON BALL	OP
HUFFNAGLE. BLACK VELVET	SF
HUFFNAGLE. CHOPIN BALLADE	SF
HUNT, R. MOTO PERPETUO	BH
HURRELL, C. GALWAY PIPERS	RU
IPPOLITOV, I.-DE BUERIS. PROCESSION OF THE SARDAR	BE
JACOB, G. SCHERZETTO, PAVANE & GOPAK. 3CL,BCL(CL)	JE
JOHN'S TUNE.	SLP
JOHNSON, C. RED SUNSET	RU
JOHNSON, C. SNOW BIRDS	RU
JOHNSON, C. WHITE FORESTS	RU
JONES, C. 3 ALLEGROS	AMC
JONES, S. SUITE MODERNE	VO
JOPLIN, S.-SPINK. 4 RAGS	OX
KABALEVSKY, D.-GREEN. ALLEGRO (SONATINA #1). 2CL,ACL,BCL	YM
KAPLAN, D. COUNTRY STORY, A	BE
KARKOFF, M. 5 AFORISMER. 3CL,BCL	STI
KARKOFF, M. LITEN MUSIK, OP 74 (1965)	STI
KEITH, G. INTERLUDE	BH
KELDORFER, R. RICORDO DI FAETIS. 3CL,BCL	LDO
KERSTERS, W. KLEINE SUITE	MAU
KERSTERS, W. VARIATIONS OP THEMA VAN FARNABY, OP 41	CBD
KIBBE, M. SONATINA. 3C,BCL	SH

KIRNBERGER, J.(DISHINGER). GAVOTTE	SP
KLAUSS, N. CLOWNS, THE	TM
KNIGHTON, M. LITTLE MINUET	BH
KNIGHTON, M. QUARTET #1	BH
KRAEHENBUEHL, D. VARIATIONS. 3CL,BCL	AMP
KUHLAU, F.-ANDRAUD. GRAND QUARTET, OP103	SO
LANG, R. HUMORESKE	LN
LANG, R. NOCTURNE & TARANTELLE	LN
LAUBE, P.-HARRIS. ALSATIAN DANCE	CF
LECUONA, E.-GORDON. LA COMPARSA	EM
LEDUC, J. 3, OP 9BIS STUKJES	MAU
LEFEBVRE, C.-WALN. INTERMEZZO (SUITE #2)	KJ
LEFEBVRE, C.-WALN. PRELUDE. 2CL,ACL(CL),BCL	KJ
LEGRON, L. PETITE SUITE	BIL
LEONARD, B. CANZONETTA & SCHERZO	BE
LEONARD, B. DRINK TO ME ONLY WITH THINE EYES	BE
2CL,ACL(CL),BCL(CL)	
LEONARD, B. IDYL	BE
LEONARD, B. SENTIMENTAL NOCTURNE. 2CL,ACL(CL),BCL	BE
LEONI, C. CONCLAVE & FUGUE PATROL	PO
LEONI, C. SOUTHERN WALTZ. 2CL,ACL(CL),BCL	BE
LESTER, L.-BELL. FUN FOR 4 CLARINETS	CF
LEVI, W. FOUR FOR FUN	WIL
LEVI, W. WALKING LIGHTLY	WIL
LIADOW, A.-HAYDN, F./VOXMAN. SARABANDE & FINALE. 2CL,ACL,BCL	RU
LIEDBECK, S. SUITE (1945). 2CL,ACL,BCL	STI
LINDE, B. QUATUOR EN MINIATURE, OP 31 (1965)	STI
LONG, N. IN THE AQUARIUM	CF
LOWMAN, K. LOS ANGELES SKETCHES. 2CL,ACL,BCL	WI
MAC DOWELL, E.-HENDERSON. DESERTED FARM, A. 2CL,ACL(CL),BCL	KN
MAC DOWELL, E.-WOOD. INTERMEZZO. 2CL,ACL(CL),BCL	HE
MAC DOWELL, E.-ESTES. TO A WILD ROSE. 2CL,ACL,BCL	KN
MAC DOWELL, E.-ISAAC. TO A WILD ROSE	CF
MAC DOWELL, E.-MC KAY. 2 TONE POEMS. 2CL,ACL(CL),BCL(CL)	BA
MAC DOWELL, E.-HARRIS. WOODLAND SKETCHES	LU
2CL,ACL(CL),BCL(CL)	
MACBETH, A.-HARRIS. INTERMEZZO "FORGET ME NOT"	CF
2CL,ACL(CL),BCL(ACL)	
MAES, J. 4 CONTRASTES (1965)	CBD
MAGANINI, Q. BEGINNER'S LUCK	EDM
MAHLER, G.-LEONARD. IN PRAISE OF LOFTY INTELLECT	TP
2CL,ACL,BCL	
MANIET, R.-RUELLE. CUBA, SUITE-QUARTETT	EBR
MANIET, R.-RULST. HABANERA. 2CL,ACL(CL),BCL(CL)	EBR
MARCO, T. HOQUETUS (1973)	EEC
MARTINI, G.-DISHINGER. BOURREE	SP
MARTINI, P. PLAISIR D'AMOUR	EDM
MARTINO, D. 7 CANONI ENIGMATICI. 2CL,ACL(BASSET HN),BCL	TP
MARTINO, D. RISOLUZIONI	JB
MASSENET, J.-HENDERSON. ELEGY. 2CL,ACL(CL),BCL(CL)	KN
MASSENET, J.-HARRIS. LAST SLUMBER OF THE VIRGIN	CF
2CL,ACL(CL),BCL(ACL)	
MAYEUR, L.-VOXMAN. QUARTET #1. 2CL,ACL,BCL	RU
MC BRIDE, R. 2 MEXICAN FOLK SONGS	ACA
MC CATHREN, D.-NORDEN. INTRODUCTION, ROUND & FUGUE	KN
MC CATHREN, D. SCHERZINO	S&
MC KAY(ARR). 2 SCHUMANN SELECTIONS. 2CL,ACL,BCL	FZ
MC KAY, F. AMERICAN SKETCH. 2CL,ACL(CL),BCL(CL)	BA
MC KAY, F. CHROMATIC CAPRICE. 2CL,ACL(CL),BCL(CL)	BA
MC KAY, F. CLARINET QUARTETS. 2CL,ACL(CL),BCL(CL)	BA
MC KAY, F. MUSETTE. 2CL,ACL(CL),BCL(CL)	BA
MC KAY, F. ON THE BOULEVARD. 2CL,ACL(CL),BCL(CL)	BA

MC KAY, F.	PASTORAL. 2CL,ACL(CL),BCL(CL)	BA
MC KAY, F.	2 PROMENADES. 2CL,ACL(CL),BCL(CL)	BA
MC KAY, F.	SONG & DANCE. 2CL,ACL(CL),BCL(CL)	BA
MC KAY, F.	SUMMER ETCHING. 2CL,ACL(CL),BCL(CL)	BA
MC KAY, F.	WITH GAY SPIRIT. 2CL,ACL(CL),BCL(CL)	BA
MC KAY, F.	WOODS IN APRIL. 2CL,ACL(CL),BCL(CL)	BA
MC KAY, G.	AMERICAN PANORAMA	CF
MC KAY, G.	EPISODES. 2CL,ACL(CL),BCL(CL)	BA
MC KAY, G.	FIESTA MEJICANA	CF
MC KAY, G.	ON A PASTORALE THEME	TP
MC KAY, G.	5 PIECES. 2CL,ACL,BCL	WI
MENDELSSOHN, F.-DE BUERIS.	CANZONETTA. 2CL,ACL(CL),BCL(CL)	BE
MENDELSSOHN, F.-LANG.	CAPRICCIO #2	LN
MENDELSSOHN, F.-LANGENUS.	FOLK SONG. 2CL,ACL(CL),BCL(CL)	CF
MENDELSSOHN, F.-WHITNEY.	JOYOUS SONG, A	GS
MENDELSSOHN, F.	MENUET EN TRIO	MOL
MENDELSSOHN, F.-LANGENUS.	MORNING SONG. 2CL,ACL(CL),BCL(CL)	CF
MENDELSSOHN, F.-LANGENUS.	RETROSPECTION. 2CL,ACL(CL),BCL(CL)	CF
MENDELSSOHN, F.-HOWLAND.	RONDO CAPRICCIOSO. 2CL,ACL,BCL	S&
MENDELSSOHN, F.-DONATELLI.	SHEPHERD'S COMPLAINT, THE, OP 67/5	SPR
MENDELSSOHN, F.-HENDERSON.	SONG OF THE HEATHER	KN
2CL,ACL(CL),BCL		
MENDELSSOHN, F.-DONATELLI.	SPINNING SONG. 2CL,ACL,BCL	WI
MENDELSSOHN, F.-LANG.	TARANTELLE	LN
MEULEMANS, A.	SERENATA (1961)	CBD
MEYER, L.	REFLECTIONS	SO
MEYERBEER, G.-HARRIS.	CORONATION MARCH (THE PROPHET)	CF
2CL,ACL(CL),BCL(ACL)		
MILLER, R.	PRELUDE & SCHERZO, OP 20. 2CL,ACL(CL),BCL(CL)	BE
MOLLOY, A.-HARRIS.	KERRY DANCE. 2CL,ACL(CL),BCL(ACL)	CF
MORLEY, T.-SCHAEFFER.	CONTRASTS	PO
MOSZKOWSKI, M.-VOGNAR.	MARCH OF THE DWARFS, OP 53/4	WB
2CL,ACL,BCL		
MOZART, W.-LAUBE.	ADAGIO (CLARINET CONCERTO). 2CL,ACL,BCL	CF
MOZART, W.-WALN.	ALLEGRO (K464). 2CL,ACL(CL),BCL	KJ
MOZART, W.-MC LEOD.	ALLEGRO (K581)	S&
MOZART, W.-VOXMAN.	ALLEGRO (QUARTET, K157). 2CL,ACL,BCL	RU
MOZART, W.-HITE.	ALLEGRO VIVACE, K387. 2CL,ACL,BCL	SO
MOZART, W.	ALLELUIA. 2CL,ACL(CL),BCL(CL)	EDM
MOZART, W.-ROSENTHAL.	DIVERTIMENTI	EM
MOZART, W.-LEMARC.	DRITTER SATZ (SONATA IN C MA)	T-M
MOZART, W.-MC LEOD.	EINE KLEINE NACHTMUSIK	S&
MOZART, W.-TOLL.	EXCERPT FROM PIANO SONATA #10. 2CL,ACL,BCL	CF
MOZART, W.-SMITH.	LULLABY	PO
MOZART, W.-LIEGL.	MENUET (DON JUAN)	CF
MOZART, W.-HASSELMANN.	MENUETT	FS
MOZART, W.-GEE.	MENUETTO (DIVERTIMENTO #2)	SP
MOZART, W.-GEE.	MENUETTO	PO
MOZART, W.-STEPHENS.	MINUET (SYMPHONY IN E FL MA)	CF
2CL,ACL(CL),BCL(CL)		
MOZART, W.-SEAY.	MINUETTO (K282)	SPR
MOZART, W.-FELDSHER.	MOLTO ALLEGRO (K387). 2CL,ACL,BCL	KN
MOZART, W.-LEONARD.	ROMANZE	BE
MOZART, W.-TOLL.	RONDO (PIANO SONATA #1)	CF
MOZART, W.-GEE.	RONDO ALLA TURCA. 2CL,ACL,BCL	SO
MOZART, W.-NEUFELD.	SERENADE IN B FLAT MA	WI
MOZART, W.-BELLISON.	SUITE #2 IN G MA. 2CL,ACL,BCL	BE
MUSSORGSKY, M.-SKOLNIK.	MUSHROOMS	EDM
NAUMANN, S.	RUOLI, OP 1 (1959). 2CL,BCL,BASSET HN	STI
NIEHAUS, L.	DANCING TOY SOLDIERS	HIM
NIEHAUS, L.	MARCHE MAESTOSO	HIM
NIEHAUS, L.	MELODIQUE CANTABILE	HIM

4 CLARINETS-404

```
NIEHAUS, L.  TICK TOCK CLOCK                                          HIM
NORDEN, H.  DELICATE SOUNDS OF THE KING                              CF
NORDEN, H.-MC CATHREN.  RONDO IN F MA                               CF
NYQUIST.  3 BAGATELLES                                              BE
OLD RUGGED CROSS.                                                   B3
OSTLING, A.  POP GOES THE WOODWINDS.  2CL,ACL(CL),BCL(CL)          BE
OSTRANDER, A.  BAROQUE SUITE                                        EDM
OVER THE RAINBOW.                                                   B3
OWEN, H.  CHAMBER MUSIC                                             WI
OWINGS, J.  AUDITORIUM QUARTETS                                     CF
OWINGS, J.  LAMENTOSO.  2CL,ACL(CL),BCL(CL)                        BE
PALA.  QUARTET IN C MI                                              MOL
PALESTRINA, G.-MENDELSSOHN, F./SKORNICKA.  ALLELUIA & CHORAL       BE
PALESTRINA, G.-SCHAEFFER.  QUITE THEME, A                          PO
PELEMANS, W.  KWARTET                                              MAU
PELEMANS, W.  QUARTET #2                                           MAU
PERRY, G.  PETITE TOOT SUITE                                       CRE
PESTALOZZA, H.-BENNETT.  CIRIBIRIBIN                               WB
PIERNE, G.-GRISEZ.  MARCH OF THE LITTLE TIN SOLDIERS              CF
PIERSOL, F.  SCHERZO                                               HL
PIKET, F.  REFLECTION & CAPRICE                                    SF
PISK, P.  SUITE                                                    CF
PLEYEL, I.  ANDANTE & RONDO, OP 48/1.  2CL,2ACL(2CL)              CF
POOT, M.  LEGEND (1967)                                            CBD
PORTER, C.-SEARS.  BEGIN THE BEGUINE.  3CL,BCL                     WB
PORTER, R.  BEAVER CREEK                                           HE
POWELL, L.  QUARTET.  2CL,ACL,BCL                                  CF
PRESSER, W.  NOCTURNE.  3CL,BCL(CL)                                TRI
PRESSER, W.  SONG & WORKOUT                                        SO
PRIETOK C.  REFLEJOS (1973)                                        EEC
PUCCINI, G.-LEIDZEN.  MUSETTA'S WALTZ (LA BOHEME)                 BE
   2CL,ACL(CL),BCL(CL)
PUCCINI, G.-LEIDZEN.  ONE FINE DAY (MADAMA BUTTERFLY)             BE
   2CL,ACL(CL),BCL(CL)
PUCCINI, G.-LEIDZEN.  THEY CALL ME MIMI (LA BOHEME)              BE
   2CL,ACL(CL),BCL(CL)
PUCCINI, G.-LEIDZEN.  VISSI D'ARTE.  2CL,ACL(CL),BCL(CL)         BE
QUINET, M.  PETITE SUITE (1959)                                   CBD
RACHMANINOFF, S.-DONATELLI.  PRELUDE, OP 3/2.  2CL,ACL,BCL        WI
RAMEAU, J.-DE FILIPPI.  HEN, THE.  2CL,ACL(CL),BCL(CL)           HE
RAMEAU, J.-DONATELLI.  LE TAMBOURIN.  2CL,ACL,BCL                WI
RAPHLING, S.  SQUARE DANCE                                        EDM
RATHAUS, K.  COUNTRY SERENADE                                     BH
READY, E.  PETITE CLASSIQUE                                       CF
REGT, H. DE.  MUSICA, OP 22 (1972-73)                            SD
REINER, K.  MUSIC (1966)                                          CHF
RIMSKY-KORSAKOV, N.-DONATELLI.  FLIGHT OF THE BUMBLE BEE         WI
   2CL,ACL,BCL
RODEN, R.  BROOK, THE                                             CF
RODEN, R.  CERISE                                                 CF
RODEN, R.  SOUNDS OF THE SEA                                      BA
RODGERS, R.-SEARS.  BLUE ROOM, THE.  3CL,BCL                      WB
ROHINSKY, A.  CLARINET CHORALES                                   CF
ROSEN, J.  PETITE SUITE                                           SO
ROWLEY, A.  NOCTURNE                                              GA
RUITER, W. DE.  OFF & ON (1976).  4BCL                           SD
RUSCH, H.  CHACONNE                                               PO
SAINT-SAENS, C.-LEONARD.  MARCHE HEROIQUE                        BE
SANDERS, R.  IMP, THE.  2CL,ACL,BCL                              CF
SATIE, E.-DAVIDSON.  SPORTS & DIVERTISSEMENTS.  3CL,BCL          EDS
SCARLATTI-RYAN.  5 SCARLATTI SONATAS                             CA
SCARLATTI, A.-JOHNSON.  ARIA & MINUET.  3CL,BCL(CL)              RU
```

```
SCARMOLIN, L.  FOUR OF A KIND                                       BA
SCARMOLIN, L.  MERRYMAKERS.  2CL,ACL(CL),BCL(CL)                    BA
SCHAEFFER, D.(ARR).  CONTRASTS                                      PO
SCHAEFFER, D.  CONVERSATIONS                                        PO
SCHAEFFER, D.  FIFTEENTH CENTURY MADRIGAL                           PO
SCHAEFFER, D.(ARR).  QUIET THEME, A                                 PO
SCHARWENKA, X.-LIEGL.  ANDANTE                                      CF
SCHMUTZ, A.  ALLEGRO CAPRICCIOSO                                    CF
SCHMUTZ, A.  PRELUDIAL FANTASIA.  2CL,ACL,BCL                       FZ
SCHMUTZ, A.  SCHERZOSO                                              FZ
SCHOEMAKER, M.  VOLIERE (1961)                                      CBD
SCHROER, H.  VARIATIONS ON "ES BUREBUEBLI MAN-I-NID"               ERM
SCHUBERT, F.  CANTILENA-PRESTO                                     EDM
SCHUBERT, F.-WILLAMAN.  FINALE (QUARTET #6)                         GS
SCHUBERT, F.-DE BUERIS.  MENUET (FANTASIA, OP 78)                   BE
SCHUBERT, F.-DISHINGER.  MENUETTO                                   SP
SCHUBERT, F.-TUSTIN.  4 SCHUBERT WALTZES.  2CL,ACL(CL),BCL(CL)      BA
SCHUBERT, F.-DEL BUSTO.  THEME FROM D MI QUARTET                    CF
SCHUMAN, W.-TUSTIN.  QUARTETTINO                                    SN
SCHUMANN, G.  AUDIOGRAMME                                          S-V
SCHUMANN, R.  ALLEGRETTO (SONATA #1, OP105).  2CL,ACL,BCL           CF
SCHUMANN, R.-SIMON.  7 MINIATURES                                   BH
SCHWADRON, A.(ARR).  PROGRESSIVE ENSEMBLE STUDIES, VOL.3            KN
SCHWADRON, A.  WALTZ.  2CL,ACL,BCL                                  KN
SEARS, G.  LICORICE-STICK SUITE                                     CF
SEARS, G.  SERENADE IN F MA                                         PO
SEARS, J.  BUCKJUMPER SUITE                                         CA
SEMLER-COLLERY, J.  QUARTETTO                                      EES
SIBELIUS, J.-BEELER/RODE.  ANDANTE FESTIVO                          SN
SILCHER, F.-HARRIS.  LORELEY-PARAPHRASE.  2CL,ACL(CL),BCL(ACL)      CF
SIMON, E.(ARR).  3 MINUETS                                         EM
SIQUIET, C.  8 STUCKE                                             MAU
SITT, H.-LEONARD.  ALBUM LEAF                                       BE
SKINNER, 1.  CAPRICIETTA                                            BE
SMITH, T.  SUITE.  3CL,ACL(CL)                                      BA
STAMITZ-KESNAR.  ANDANTE.  2CL,ACL(CL),BCL(CL)                      CF
STARER, R.  CADENZA                                                 MC
STARK, R.-GEE.  ANDANTE & MARCIA (SERENADE, OP 55)                  SP
   2CL,ACL(CL),BCL
STEVENS, H.  2 PIECES                                               MF
STEWART, L.  6 SHORT PIECES                                        KPM
STONE, G.  JOYFUL FOUR                                              DG
STOUFFER.  TICK-TACK-TOE.  2CL,ACL(CL),BCL(CL)                      PO
STRAVINSKY, I.-DE FILIPPI.  BERCEUSE (FIREBIRD)                     HE
   2CL,ACL(CL),BCL(CL)
SUMMERS, S.  ALLEGRO BREVE.  2CL,ACL,BCL                            WI
SWACK, I.  ALLEGRO                                                  SH
TAKACS, J.  HOMAGE TO PAN, OP 87/1                                 LDO
TAYLOR, C.  3 NOVELTIES                                             CF
TCHAIKOVSKY, P.-DE BUERIS.  ANDANTE CANTABILE                       BE
   2CL,ACL(CL),BCL(CL)
TCHAIKOVSKY, P.-JOHNSON.  CHANSON TRISTE                            RU
TCHAIKOVSKY, P.-SKORNICKA.  OVERTURE "1812"                         BE
TCHAIKOVSKY, P.  SCHERZO.  2CL,ACL,BCL                              FZ
TCHAIKOVSKY, P.-GEE.  WALTZ (SYMPHONY #5)                           PO
TCHEREPNINE, N.  6 PIECES.  2CL,ACL(CL),BCL(CL)                    EDM
TELEMANN, G.  CACCIA, LA                                           EBE
TELEMANN, G.-VON KANNON.  CONCERTO A 4                             EM
TELEMANN, G.-SIMON.  CONCERTO FOR FOUR CLARINETS                   EM
THOME, F.-HARRIS.  PIZZICATO.  2CL,ACL(CL),BCL(ACL)                CF
THOMPSON, T.(ED).  CAPTAIN MORGAN'S MARCH & 6 OTHER PIECES         S&C
THOMPSON, T.(ARR).  6 TRADITIONAL TUNES, 2 VOLS                    CA
```

THOMSON, V. 5 PORTRAITS   GS
THORNTON, R. DIVERSION PROJECT   BD
TOLL, R.(ARR). 6 LITTLE GEMS FROM THE MASTERS   CF
TOMASI, H. 3 DIVERTISSEMENTS   ALE
TUFILLI, W. CHARM   BE
TURINI, G.-WIENANDT. FANFARE & PROCESSIONAL   SO
TUSTIN, W. ALLEGRO CON SPIRITO. 2CL,ACL(CL),BCL(CL)   BA
TUSTIN, W. CHEERFUL ELEGY. 2CL,ACL(CL),BCL(CL)   BA
TUTHILL, B. FUGUE, OP 10/4. 2CL,ACL,BCL   SPR
UHL, A. DIVERTIMENTO. 3CL,BCL   SCH
VAUGHAN WILLIAMS, R. 3 PRELUDES (HOUSEHOLD MUSIC)   OX
   3CL,BCL(CL)
VECCHI, O. CRICKET, THE. 2CL,ACL(CL),BCL(CL)   EDM
VELDEN, R. VAN DER. FANTAISIE (1967)   CBD
VELLERE, L. QUATUOR   MAU
VERDI, G.-HARRIS. QUARTET (RIGOLETTO). 2CL,ACL(CL),BCL(ACL)   CF
VILLA ROJO, J. 4 + ... (1970)   ESZ
VIOLEAU, R. ANDANTE   BIL
VIVALDI, A. GIGA. 2CL,ACL(CL),BCL(CL)   EDM
VIVALDI, A. SONATA DA CAMERA. 2CL,ACL(CL),BCL(CL)   EDM
WALCKIERS, E.-HARRIS. RONDO. 2CL,ACL(CL),BCL(ACL)   CF
WALKER, R. APPALACHIAN DANCE   PO
WALKER, R. AUBADE. 2CL,ACL(CL),BCL   KN
WALKER, R. CHASE OF THE CENTAURS. 2CL,ACL(CL),BCL(CL)   BA
WALKER, R. QUIET BROOK   KN
WALKER, R. SERBIAN DANCE   SPR
WALKER, R. VALSE-SCHERZO. 2CL,ACL(CL),BCL(CL)   BA
WATERSON, J.-LANGENUS. ANDANTINO & SCHERZO   CF
WATERSON, J.-ANDRAUD. GRAND QUARTET   SO
WEBER, C.M. VON-GEE. ADAGIO (CONCERTO #1)   LU
WEIGL-DANCLA/HARRIS. AIR VARIE. 2CL,ACL(CL),ACL(CL)   CF
WEINZWEIG, J. QUARTET. 3CL,BCL   MC
WHITE, C. SUITE SPIRITUAL   HE
WHITNEY, M. ROULADE   CF
WILKINSON, P. SUITE   NO
WILLBYE, J. ENGLISH MADRIGAL   PO
WISE, L. REED RHAPSODY   MAN
WRIGHT, M. CONSTANT FLOW, THE (1974). 3CL,BCL   B-B
YODER, P.(ARR). DRY BONES. 2CL,ACL(CL),BCL,PERC OPT   KJ
ZINGARELLI-WIENANDT. ADAGIO & ALLEGRO. 2CL,ACL,BCL   SO
ZONN, P. MOVEMENT   ACA
ZONN, P. 2 MOVEMENTS   ACA

4 CLARINETS (COLLECTIONS)-405

ARNOLD, J. CLARINET QUARTETS   HY
BURGSTAHLER, E.(ARR). LET'S PLAY QUARTETS   PO
GAY, E. 10 PETITES PIECES CLASSIOUE, 2 VOLS.   BIL
GEARHART, L. CLARINET SESSIONS. 2CL,ACL(CL),BCL(CL)   SH
GILET, R.(ARR). 10 QUATUORS FACILES   EDR
HOLMES, G.-LONG. SYMPHONY ENSEMBLE SERIES   RU
HUDADOFF, I.(ARR). 24 CLARINET QUARTETS. 3CL,BCL(CL)   PO
LOTTERER, G. 38 SELECTED SONGS   EDK
MC LIN, E.(ARR). FOR FOUR B FL CLARINETS   PO
MORSCH, J.(ARR). 12 CLARINET QUARTETS. 2CL,ACL,BCL   TP
OWINGS, J. QUARTET ALBUM   BE
ROSENTHAL, C. (ARR). CLARINET QUARTETTES   EM
▀▀▀▀ICKA, J.-RUSH. QUARTET ALBUM   BE

4 CLARINETS (COLLECTIONS)-405

STUART, H.(ARR). CLARINET CLASSICS	SH
VOXMAN, H.(ARR). ENSEMBLE CLASSICS, VOL 1	RU
2CL,ACL(CL),BCL(CL)	
VOXMAN, H. (ARR). ENSEMBLE CLASSICS, VOL 2. 2CL,ACL,BCL	RU
WILLAMAN, R.(ARR). 6 EASY EXCERPTS	GS
WOOD, C. ENSEMBLE ALBUM OF FAMOUS MELODIES	HE

4 BASSOONS-406

ADDISON, J. 4 MINIATURES	JE
AMES, W. 2 MOVEMENTS	ACA
BOTTJE, W. DANCES: SOLEMN & JOYOUS	ACA
BREHM, A. COLLOQUY & CHORALE	SER
CHILDS, B. QUARTET	ACA
DONDEYNE. POUR SE DISTRAIRE	BIL
DUBENSKY, A. PRELUDE & FUGUE	BE
DUBOIS. CHANSON LOINTAINE. SCHERZO SARCASTIQUE	BIL
DUBOIS, P. SCHERZO	ALE
FORSYTH, M. QUARTET 61 (1961)	CAN
FREEDMAN, H. QUARTET (1973)	CAN
GARTLEY, G. FANTASIA ON A BRITISH TEA SONG. 3BSN,CBSN	JE
HABA, A. QUARTET, OP 74 (1951)	CHF
HARDT. LULLABY & DANCE	TM
JOSTEN, W. CONCERTANTE MUSIC	HE
MAXWELL. IDYLS OF FOUR GOBLINS	WI
MENDELSSOHN, F.-WITTMAN/SMITH. EQUALE #3	LU
PRESSER, W. BAROQUE SUITE	TRI
PROKOFIEV, S. HUMOROUS SCHERZO	M&M
PROKOFIEV, S. HUMOROUS SCHERZO, OP 12/9	EDK
PROKOFIEV, S. HUMOROUS SCHERZO, OP. 12/9	SPR
RIDOUT, A. PIGS, A PRESENT FOR GORDON JACOB	JE
SCHUMAN, W. QUARTETTINO	SN
THIRIET, A. 3 OUVERTURES MINIATURES	BIL
WEAIT, C.(ARR). SUITE OF EARLY AMERICAN TUNES	CP
WILDER, A. SUITE	MAR

4 SAXOPHONES-408

ABBOTT, A. POEME	BIL
ABEL,C.-BRINK. ANDANTE (SYMPHONY #3)	T-M
ABSIL, J. 3 PIECES IN QUARTET, OP 35	HLE
ABSIL, J. QUARTET #1, OP 31	HLE
ABSIL, J. SUITE SUR DES THEMES ROUMAINS, OP 90 (1956)	CBD
AHLBERG, G. MOSAIK (1964)	STI
ALBENIZ, I.-MULE. 3 PIECES	ALE
ALBENIZ, I.-MULE. SEVILLA	TP
APPLEBAUM. QUARTET	SO
AREND, J. BOISMORTIER SUITE	MOL
AREND, J. SUITE ANTIQUE	MOL
ARMA, P. 7 TRANSPARENCES	HLE
ARNOLD, H. DITHYRAMB (1969)	ARM
ARTOT, J.-HARRIS. 12 QUARTETS. 2ASAX,TSAX,BAR SAX	CF
ASHFORD. AMERICAN FOLKSONG SUITE	SO
ASHTON, J. DIALOGUES, DISCOURSES	SS

4 SAXOPHONES-408

```
BACH, C.P.E.  RONDO                                              EQM
BACH, J.C.-CUNNINGHAM.  QUARTET, OP 17/6                         EQM
    SOP SAX,ASAX,TSAX,DB(BAR SAX
BACH, J.C.  SINFONIA IN B FLAT MA                               MOL
BACH, J.S.-HEKKER.  AIR (SUITE #3)                              T-M
BACH, J.S.-FOTE.  2 BACH PRELUDES                               KN
    SOP SAX(ASAX),ASAX,TSAX,BAR SAX
BACH, J.S.-GILET.  CELEBRE ARIA                                 EDR
BACH, J.S.  2 CHORALS                                           BIL
BACH, J.S.-ROSENTHAL.  FUGA IX                                  WI
BACH, J.S.-GORDON.  FUGUE #7                                    KN
BACH, J.S.-KASPRZYK.  FUGUE IN E MI                             ARM
BACH, J.S.(AUSLENDER).  FUGUE ON A THEME OF CORELLI             WI
BACH, J.S.-SCHMIDT.  FUGUE VII                                  WI
BACH, J.S.-AVIGNON.  3 INVENTIONS A DEUX VOIX                   EDR
BACH, J.S.-EVERTSE.  JESU, JOY OF MAN'S DESIRING                HE
BACH, J.S.-EVERTSE.  KORAALBEWERKING (CANTATA 147)             T-M
BACH, J.S.(STANTON).  LITTLE FUGUE IN G MI                      WI
BACH, J.S.-CHARLTON.  PRELUDE (PARTITA #3)                      SH
BACH, J.S.-CARSTEN.  PRELUDE & FUGUE #2                         BA
BACH, J.S.-EYMANN.  PRELUDE & FUGUE IN D MI                     CF
    2ASAX,TSAX,BAR SAX
BACH, J.S.-EYMANN.  PRELUDE & FUGUE IN E MI                     BE
    2ASAX,TSAX,BAR SAX
BACH, J.S.-EYMANN.  PRELUDE & FUGUE IN G MI                     BE
    2ASAX,TSAX,BAR SAX
BACH, J.S.  PRELUDE #4.  2ASAX,TSAX,BAR SAX(TSAX)              EDM
BACH, J.S.-JOHNSON.  SARABANDE & BADINERIE                      RU
    2ASAX,TSAX,BAR SAX
BACH, J.S.-HEMKE.  SARABANDE.  SOP SAX(ASAX),ASAX,TSAX,BAR SAX  SO
BACH, J.S.-STANTON.  SICILIANO, GIGUE & ARIA                    WI
BARBIER, R.  QUATUOR, OP 99 (1961)                             CBD
BARNBY, J.-THOMPSON.  SWEET & LOW.  2ASAX,TSAX,BAR SAX          AL
BARRAUD, H.  QUARTET                                            BH
BARTOK, B.-GORDON.  3 FOLK DANCES.  2ASAX,TSAX,BAR SAX          SO
BAUDRIER.  MES AMIS                                            MOL
BAUER, R.  SINCERE & HONEST APPEAL, A                          CAN
BAUER, R.  SOKASODIC                                           BER
BEEFTINCK, H.  QUARTET (1977)                                   SD
BEETHOVEN-FRASCOTTI.  ALLEGRO MOLTO QUASI PRESTO                RH
BEETHOVEN, L. VAN-GUENTHER.  BAGATELLE IN F MI                  SO
BEETHOVEN, L. VAN-TILLIARD.  LARGHETTO (SYMPHONY #2)           EDR
BEETHOVEN, L. VAN.  MENUET DE PRINTEMPS                        BIL
BENNETT, D.  SAX SOLILOQUY.  2ASAX,TSAX,BAR SAX                 SO
BENNETT, D.  SAXOPHONE SYMPHONETTE.  2ASAX,TSAX,BAR SAX         CF
BERNAUD, A.  QUATUOR                                           ERR
BERNIER, R.  SERINETTE                                         BIL
BERNIER, R.  SUITE POUR LE PLAISIR DE L'OREILLE (1973)         CBD
BERTHOMIEU, M.  RONDO (SUITE BREVE)                            HLE
BERTOUILLE, G.  PRELUDE ET FUGUE (1955)                        CBD
BEUGNIOT, J.  PIECES                                           EFM
BIZET, G.-CAILLIET.  ADAGIETTO.  2ASAX,TSAX,BAR SAX            BE
BIZET, G.-MARTIN.  ADAGIETTO DE L'ARLESIENNE                   EDR
BIZET, G.-CAILLIET.  INTERMEZZO (SUITE L'ARLESIENNE)           BE
    2ASAX,TSAX,BAR SAX
BIZET, G.-JOHNSON.  QUARTET DE L'ARLESIENNE                     RU
    2ASAX,TSAX,BAR SAX
BLANK, A.  COALITIONS II                                       ACA
BOCCHERINI, L.-CAILLIET.  MENUET                               SO
BOCCHERINI, L.  MENUET                                         MOL
BOCCHERINI, L.-MULE.  MINUETTO                                 BIL
BOCKEMUEHL, E.  CORTEGE                                         YM
```

```
BOEDIJN. G.  BADINAGE IN EEN KNOLLENLAND, OP163 (1961)        MOL
BOTS, R. DU.  18TH OF JUNE, THE (1974)                        SD
BOISMORTIER, J.  SUITE                                        HE
BOLZONI, G.-MULE.  MINUETTO                                   BIL
BOREL, R.  FUGATO IN F MA                                     BO
BOTTJE, W.  DANCES, SOLEMN & JOYOUS (1964)                    CO
   2ASAX,TSAX,BAR SAX
BOTTJE, W.  QUARTET #1 (1963)                                 CO
BOUCARD, M.  QUARTETT-SINFONIA                                BIL
BOYCE, W.  OVERTURE FOR HIS MAJESTY'S BIRTHDAY (1770)         MOL
BOZZA, E.  ANDANTE & SCHERZO                                  ALE
BOZZA, E.  NUAGES                                             ALE
BRAHMS, J.-MARTIN.  CELEBRE VALSE                             EDR
BRANDON, S.  CONCERT OVERTURE.  2ASAX,TSAX,BAR SAX            PO
BROTT, A.  3 ACTS FOR FOUR SINNERS (1961)                     CAN
BROTT, A.  SAXI-FONI-SATIES (1972)                            CAN
BROWN, A.  QUARTET #1                                         SS
BROWN, A.  QUARTET #2                                         SS
BROWN, R.  FUGUES                                             WI
CAILLIET, L.  CARNAVAL                                        SO
CAILLIET, L.  FANTASY & FUGUE ON O'SUSANNA                    SO
CAILLIET, L.  QUARTET FOR SAXOPHONES.  2ASAX,TSAX,BAR SAX     BE
CAIX D,HERVELOIS, L. DE-CLASSENS.  MARCHE DU CZAR, LA         COM
CALMEL, R.  QUATUOR                                           EFM
CARAVAN, R.  CANZONA.  2ASAX,TSAX,BAR SAX                     ETH
CASSEDAY, A.  QUARTET IN G MI.  2ASAX,TSAX,BAR SAX            BO
CHEYETTE, I.  VIENNESE LULLABY.  2ASAX,TSAX,BAR SAX           SH
CHOPIN, F.-DEDRICK.  CHOPIN FAVORITES                         KN
   SOP SAX(ASAX),ASAX,TSAX,BAR SAX
CHRISTENSEN, J.  COMEDY FOR SAXOPHONES.  2ASAX,TSAX,BAR SAX   KJ
CHRISTENSEN, J.  HEY RIDE!.  SOP SAX(ASAX),ASAX,TSAX,BAR SAX  KN
CLEMENTI, M.-EVERTSE.  CANON                                  T-M
CLERISSE, R.  CACHE-CACHE                                     ALE
CLERISSE, R.  CARAVAN                                         ALE
CLERISSE, R.  CHANSON DU ROUET                                ALE
CLERISSE, R.  INTRODUCTION & SCHERZO                          ALE
CLERISSE, R.  POLKA VALAISANE                                 EDR
CLERISSE, R.  SERENADE MELANCOLIQUE                           ALE
CONLEY, L.  DIVERSION #1                                      SP
CONLEY, L.  SONG & CAPRICE.  2ASAX,TSAX,BAR SAX              KN
CONSTANT, F.  4 SEQUENCES                                     HE
CORDELL, F.  GESTURES                                         JE
CORELLI, A.-JOHNSON.  SARABANDE & COURANTE                    RU
   2ASAX,TSAX,BAR SAX
COWELL, H.  SAILOR'S HORNPIPE.  2ASAX,TSAX,BAR SAX            SN
COYNER, L.  SAXIFRAGE                                         ACA
CROLEY, R.  7 MOMENTI (1967; REV 1972)                        AU
CROLEY, R.  TRE ESPRESSIONI (1969)                            ARM
CULVER, E.  2 VIGNETTES.  2ASAX,TSAX,BAR SAX                  KN
DAKIN, C.  PRELUDE & DANCE (1956)                             HI
DAMASE, J.  QUARTET                                           HLE
DEBUSSY, C.(TEAL).  ANDANTINO & VIF                           EQM
DEBUSSY, C.-MULE.  LITTLE NEGRO, THE                          ALE
DEBUSSY, C.(ZAJAC).  LITTLE SHEPHERD, THE/GOLLIWOG'S CAKEWALK EQM
DEBUSSY, C.  MAZURKA                                          EQM
DEDRICK, A.  WALTZ FOR FOUR.  2ASAX,TSAX,BAR SAX             KN
DEDRICK, C.  SENSITIVITY.  SOP SAX(ASAX),ASAX,TSAX,BAR SAX    KN
DEDRICK, R.  IMPRESSIONISM (THE MODERN ART SUITE)            KN
   SOP SAX(ASAX),ASAX,TSAX,BAR SAX
DEDRICK, R.  MYSTICISM (THE MODERN ART SUITE)               KN
   SOP SAX(ASAX),ASAX,TSAX,BAR SAX
DEDRICK, R.  PURISM & SURREALISM (THE MODERN ART SUITE)      KN
   SOP SAX(ASAX),ASAX,TSAX,BAR SAX
```

DEDRICK, R. REALISM (THE MODERN ART SUITE)   KN
    SOP SAX(ASAX),ASAX,TSAX,BAR SAX
DEDRICK, R. SAXSAFARI   KN
DELA, M. DIVERTIMENTO (1972). 2ASAX,2TSAX   CAN
DELAMARRE, P. QUATUOR POUR RIRE   BIL
DELAMONT, G. 3 ENTERTAINMENTS   KN
    SOP SAXNASAX),ASAX,TSAX,BAR SAX
DELBECQ, L. A BATONS ROMPUS   EDR
DELBECQ, L. A SAUTE-MOUTON   EDR
DELBECQ, L. IMPROMPTU   EDR
DELBECQ, L. 4 SAXOS EN RECREATION   EDR
DEPRAZ, R. QUARTET #2   EFM
DESENCLOS, A. QUARTET   ALE
DILLON, H. NIGHTSHADE. 2ASAX,TSAX,BAR SAX   BH
DONIZETTI, G.-DIETZE. SEXTET (LUCIA). 2ASAX,TSAX,BAR SAX   RU
DORFF, D. FANTASY, SCHERZO & NOCTURNE   SH
DRDLA, R.-HARGER. SOUVENIR. 2ASAX,TSAX,BAR SAX   BE
DU CAURROY-MAGANINI, Q. DOUBLE CANON   EDM
    2ASAX,TSAX,BAR SAX(TSAX)
DUBOIS, P. QUARTET   ALE
DUCKWORTH, W. REEL MUSIC   MEP
DURY, M. DIVERTISSEMENT, OP 5   EBR
DVORAK-RONKLIN. PRELUDE AND POLKA. SOP SAX,ASAX,TSAX,BAR SAX   RH
DVORAK, A.-DELBECQ. HUMORESQUE   EDR
DVORAK, A.-VEREECKEN. HUMORESQUE. 2ASAX,TSAX,BAR SAX   CF
DYCK, V. QUATUOR MODERNE "LEBLANC"   BIL
ELGAR, E.-BROOKE. SALUT D'AMOUR   CF
END, J. 2 MODERN SAXOPHONE QUARTETS. 2ASAX,TSAX,BAR SAX   KN
ERICKSON, F. RONDINO. 2ASAX,TSAX BAR SAX   BE
EYMANN. PRELUDE & FUGUE. 4ASAX   CF
EYSER, E. TRIS (1976)   STI
FARHART, H. DIVERTIMENTO   SO
FAURE, J.-BROOKE. PALMS, THE. 2ASAX,TSAX,BAR SAX   CF
FIALA, G. SAXOPHONE QUARTET #1 (1955;REV 1962)   CAN
FIALA, G. SAXOPHONE QUARTET #2 (1961)   BER
FICHER, J. QUARTET   SN
FLORENZO, L. SUD-AMERICA   EES
FONTAINE, F. CONCERTINO DE DINANT   SH
FORD, T. SUITE   MOL
FRACKENPOHL, A. CHORALE AND CANON. SOPSAX,ASAX,TSAX,BARSAX   TP
FRACKENPOHL, A. FANFARE, AIR & FINALE   SH
FRACKENPOHL, A.(TR). RAGTIME SUITE   SH
FRANCAIX, J. KLEINES QUARTETT   SCH
FRANK, M. CONVERSATION PIECE. 2ASAX,TSAX,BAR SAX   KN
FRESCOBALDI, G.(BLYTON). FUGUE IN G MI   KN
FRESCOBALDI, G.-AARON. GAGLIARDA. ASAX,2TSAX,BAR SAX   GS
FROBERGER, J.-BALENT. CAPRICCIO   SP
GABELLES, G. 2 PIECES   EDR
GABELLES, G. 3 PIECES   EDR
GABRIELI, G.(AXWORTHY). CANZONA NONI TONI A 12   DOR
GABRIELI, G.(AXWORTHY). CANZONA PER SONARE #2   DOR
GADE, N.-GEE. NOVELETTE, OP 19   PO
GALLAHER, C. QUARTET #2, OP 31   SP
GALUPPI, B. TOCCATA. 2ASAX,TSAX,BAR SAX(TSAX)   EDM
GASTYNE, S. DE. QUARTET, OP 53. 2ASAX,TSAX,BAR SAX   FER
GEORGE, G. QUARTET (1972)   CAN
GERAEDTS, J. MOTO PERPETUO (1968)   SD
GIBBONS, O.-HEMKE. FANTAZIA   SO
GILET. PROMENADE   EDR
GILET. QUARTET-VALSE   EDR
GLASER, W.-RASCHER. LITTLE PIECES, OP 8A   TP
    SOP SAX,2ASAX,TSAX

```
GLASER, W.   4 PIECES (1934)                                          TP
GLAZOUNOV, A.-EYMANN.  IN MODO RELIGIOSO                              BE
GLAZOUNOV, A.  QUARTET, OP109                                         BEL
GLUCK, C.-JOHNSON.  AIR DE BALLET (ALCESTE)                           RU
   2ASAX,TSAX,BAR SAX
GLUCK, C.-CLASSENS.  IPHIGENIE EN TAURIDE                             COM
GODARD, B.-BROOKE.  BERCEUSE.  2ASAX,TSAX,BAR SAX                     CF
GORDON, L.  3 MOVEMENTS                                               SH
GRETRY, A.  3 DANSES VILLAGOISES                                      MOL
GRIEG, E.-GORDON.  ALBUM LEAF, OP 12/7                                KN
GRIEG, E.-TAYLOR.  ELEGIE.  2ASAX,TSAX,BAR SAX                        BE
GRIEG, E.-LEONARD.  LAST SPRING, THE                                  BE
GRIEG, E.-JOHNSON.  MARCH OF THE DWARFS.  2ASAX,TSAX,BAR SAX          RU
GRIEG, E.-BROOKE.  NORWEGIAN DANCE.  2ASAX,TSAX,BAR SAX               CF
GRISONI, R.  QUARTET                                                  EK
GURLITT, C.-ADAMSKI.  LITTLE SUITE                                    PO
HANDEL, G.-HERVIG.  ADAGIO & ALLEGRO (CONCERTO IN B FL MA)            RU
   2ASAX,TSA X,BAR SAX
HANDEL, G.(STANTON).  2 ALLEGROS                                      WI
HANDEL, G.  BOURREE, AIR EN GAVOTTE                                   MOL
HANDEL, G.-EVERTSE.  KORAALBEWERKING (ST. JOHN'S PASSION)             T-M
HANDEL, G.-BROOKE.  LARGO.  2ASAX,TSAX,BAR SAX                        CF
HANDEL, G.  LARGO                                                     BIL
HANDEL, G.-LEMARC.  MENUET (BERENICE)                                 T-M
HANDEL, G.-WILLIAMS.  SARABANDA.  2ASAX,TSAX,BAR SAX                  SO
HANDEL, G.-JOHNSON.  SARABANDE & AIR.  2ASAX,TSAX,BAR SAX             RU
HANDEL, G.-GORDON.  SARABANDE                                         SO
HANDEL, G.  SARABANDE ET MENUET                                       MOL
HANDEL, G.(STANTON).  SONATA #1                                       WI
HANNIKEN, J.  BLUES & SCHERZO                                         HE
HARDT.  LULLABY & DANCE                                               TM
HARRIS, A.(ARR).  FAREWELL TO CUCULLAIN.  2ASAX,TSAX,BAR SAX          CF
HARRIS, A.(ARR).  4 HEART SONGS.  2ASAX,TSAX,BAR SAX                  CF
HARRIS, F.  VESPER MOODS.  2ASAX,TSAX,BAR SAX                         LU
HARTLEY, W.  SUITE (1972)                                             AU
HARVEY.  AGINCOURT                                                    NO
HARVEY, P.  THE HARFLEUR SONG                                         NO
HASQUENOPH, P.  SONATE A 4                                            EES
HAUBIEL, C.  FOR LOUIS XVI.  2ASAX,TSAX,BAR SAX                       BE
HAWORTH, F.  KERNWOOD SUITE (1972)                                    CAN
HAYDN, F.-HERVIG.  FINALE (QUARTET, OP 9/3)                           RU
   2ASAX,TSAX,BAR SAX
HAYDN, F.-JOHNSON.  MOVEMENT #3 (SYMPHONY #100)                       RU
   2ASAX,TSAX,BAR SAX
HAYDN, F.-STANTON.  QUARTET IN C MA, OP 75/3                          EQM
HEPPENER, R.  CANZONA                                                 SD
HERVIG, R.  DIVERTIMENTO #3.  2ASAX,TSAX,BAR SAX                      RU
HILL, J.  ENTOURAGE                                                   SS
HILLIARD, J.  SAXONATA.  2ASAX,TSAX,BAR SAX                           MC
HOLMES, G.  SPIRITUAL FANTASIA.  2ASAX,TSAX,BAR SAX                   RU
HOWLAND, R.  QUARTET #1                                               YM
HOWLAND, R.  QUARTET #2                                               GS
HUMPERDINCK, E.-JOHNSON.  CHILDREN'S PRAYER                           RU
   2ASAX,TSAX,BAR SAX
IBERT, J.  3 HISTOIRES                                               ALE
IN THE GARDEN.                                                        B3
JACOB, G.  QUARTET                                                    JE
JARNEFELT, A.-THOMPSON.  PRAELUDIUM.  2ASAX,TSAX,BAR SAX              AL
JEANJEAN, P.  QUARTET                                                 EDS
JOHNSON, W.  CHORALE-FANTASY.  2ASAX,TSAX,BAR SAX                     FZ
JOHNSON, W.  IMPROMPTU.  2ASAX,TSAX,BAR SAX                           BE
JOHNSON, W.  PASTORALE.  2ASAX,TSAX,BAR SAX                           BE
```

JOHNSON, W. VALSE MIGNONNE. 2ASAX,TSAX,BAR SAX		BE
JOHNSTON, M.-BONNELL. DEEP RIVER. 2ASAX,TSAX,BAR SAX		S&
JOHNSTON, M.-BONNELL. PROCESSION OF THE SARDAR 2ASAX,TSAX,BAR SAX		S&
JOLY, S. SEQUENCES		EFM
JONGBLOED, D. ROMANCE		T-M
JONGEN, J. QUATUOR, OP122 (1942)		CBD
JONGEN, L. DIVERTISSEMENT (1937)		CBD
KADERAVEK, M. INTRODUCTION & ALLEGRO		TP
KARLINS, M. BLUES. 2ASAX,TSAX,BAR SAX		TRI
KARLINS, M. QUARTET		SS
KARLINS, M. QUARTET #2		ACA
KAT, J. CONVULSIONS (1979)		SD
KESNAR, M. CAPRICCIO. 2ASAX,TSAX,BAR SAX		CF
KEURIS, T. QUARTET		SD
KIRCK, G. RESULTANTS		DOR
KIRNBERGER, J.-DISHINGER. GAVOTTE		SP
KLINGSOR, T. SERENADE		CHM
KNIGHT. QUARTET. 2ASAX,TSAX,BAR SAX		SO
KOCH, E. MINIATYRER (1970)		BRH
KOCH, F. ANACLETS		SS
KORTE, K. FACETS, 1970		SS
KOSCHAT, T.-LEONARD. MELODIE CELESTE. 2ASAX,TSAX,BAR SAX		BE
KREIN, M. VALSE CAPRICE		BH
KRIEGER, S. JOHANN KRIEGER SUITE		MOL
LACOUR, G. QUATUOR		BIL
LANCEN, S. INTERMEDE I		MOL
LANCEN, S. INTERMEDE II		MOL
LANCEN, S. RONDO CAPRICE		MOL
LANGE, G.-BROOKE. FLOWER SONG. 2ASAX,TSAX,BAR SAX		CF
LANTIER, P. ANDANTE ET SCHERZETTO		BIL
LEBEIRRE, O. STYRIENNE		T-M
LECLERCQ, E. INTRODUCTION & SCHERZANDO		MAU
LECLERCQ, E. PRELUDE & MOUVEMENT PERPETUEL		MAU
LEDUC, J. SUITE EN QUATUOR		SCH
LEGLEY, V. 5 MINIATURES, OP 54 (1958)		CBD
LEIBOWITZ, R. VARIATIONS		JOB
LEJET, E. MUSIQUE		EFM
LEMELAND, A. EPILOGUE NOCTURNE, OP 22		BIL
LEONARD, B.(ARR). OLD FRENCH SONG, AN. 2ASAX,TSAX,BAR SAX		BE
LEONARD, B. ROMANZA. 2ASAX,TSAX,BAR SAX		BE
LEONARD, B. SUMMER ROMANCE. 2ASAX,TSAX,BAR SAX		BE
LEVI, W. SAXOPHONE CANTABILE. 2ASAX,TSAX,BAR SAX		WIL
LEVY, F. ADAGIO AND SCHERZO		SS
LIADOW, A.-HARGER. MUSICAL SNUFF BOX. 2ASAX,TSAX,BAR SAX		BE
LINN, R. PRELUDE & DANCE		WI
LINN, R. QUARTET		WI
LOUP & FRANCOIS. QUATUOR IN G MI		EDR
LOVREGLIO, E. ANDANTE		EFM
MAC DOWELL, E.-PATRICK. 2 WOODLAND SKETCHES 2ASAX,TSAX,BAR SAX		TP
MACBETH, A.-BROOKE. INTERMEZZO "FORGET ME NOT" 2ASAX,TSAX,BAR SAX		CF
MACHAUT, G.(AXWORTHY). KYRIE		DOR
MAGANINI, Q. BEGINNER'S LUCK. 2ASAX,TSAX,BAR SAX(TSAX)		EDM
MANZO, S. 2 TEMPI		GZ
MARIE, G.-THOMPSON. GOLDEN WEDDING. 2ASAX,TSAX,BAR SAX		AL
MARSHALL, J. GOLDRUSH SUITE		SH
MASSENET, J.-THOMPSON. AIR DE BALLET (SCENES PITTORESQUES) 2ASAX,TSAX,BAR SAX		AL
MASSENET, J.-THOMPSON. MARCHE (SCENES PITTORESQUES) 2ASAX,TSAX,BAR SAX		AL

MAURICE, R. AURORE		MAU
MAURY, L. COCK OF THE WALK		WI
MAZELLIER, J. 10 FUGUES		HLE
MC BRIDE, R. GO-GO		ACA
MC BRIDE, R. NON-SLIP SOFT SOAP		ACA
MC BRIDE, R. WATCH YOUR DRIVIN' BABY--I'LL DO THE LOOKIN'		ACA
MC CARTY, F. 5 SITUATIONS		ARM
MC CAULEY, W. 5 MINIATURES (1972)		CAN
MC KAY, G. AMERICAN PANORAMA. 4EQUAL SAXES		CF
MC KAY, G. FIESTA MEJICANA. 4EQUAL SAXES		CF
MEIER, D. EPI		EFM
MENDELSSOHN, F.(TEAL). RONDO CAPRICCIOSO		EQM
MENDELSSOHN, F.(TEAL). SPINNING SONG		EQM
MENDELSSOHN, F.-BROOKE. SPRING SONG. 2ASAX,TSAX,BAR SAX		CF
MENDELSSOHN, F.-JOHNSON. WAR MARCH OF THE PRIESTS (ATHALIE) 2ASAX,TSAX,BAR SAX		RU
MENICHETTI, F. BOUQUET ORIENTAL (1934)		EDR
MERSSON, B. SUITE, OP 17		BRH
MEULEMANS, A. QUATUOR (1953)		CBD
MEYER. DIVERTISSEMENT		BIL
MICHALSKY, D. THREE TIMES FOUR		SH
MIELENZ, H.-VOXMAN. SCHERZO. 2ASAX,TSAX,BAR SAX		RU
MIGNION, R. PETIT ENFANT		ALE
MILLER, R. QUARTET #2. 2ASAX,TSAX,BAR SAX		PO
MILLOCKER, K. HERINNERINGEN		MOL
MISTAK, A. QUARTET		EQM
MORITZ, E. QUARTET. 2ASAX,TSAX,BAR SAX		SO
MOSKOWSKI, M.-HARGER. SPANISH DANCE. 2ASAX,TSAX,BAR SAX		BE
MOULAERT, R. ANDANTE, FUGUE ET FINAL (1907)		CBD
MOURANT, W. QUARTET		ACA
MOURANT, W. SCHERZO		ACA
MOZART, W. ADAGIO & MINUET		HE
MOZART, W. ALLEGRO (PIANO SONATA IN C MA)		HE
MOZART, W. AVE VERUM		BIL
MOZART, W. BERCEUSE		MOL
MOZART, W.-HOUTVAST. MENUET FAVORITE		MOL
MOZART, W.-LANG. MOVEMENT #1 (EINE KLEINE NACHTMUSIK) 2ASAX,TSAX,BARSAX		LN
MOZART, W.-CLASSENS. PETITE MUSIQUE DE NUIT		COM
MOZART, W. SONATE		MOL
MURPHY, L. CADENZAS & RECITATIVOS		WI
MURPHY, L. PRELUDE & CANON		WI
MURPHY, L. RONDINO		WI
MURPHY, L. SUITE		WI
MUSSORGSKY, M. MUSHROOMS. 2ASAX,TSAX,BAR SAX(TSAX)		EDM
NELHYBEL, V. 3 PIECES. 2ASAX,TSAX,BAR SAX		BE
NESTICO, S. STUDY IN CONTRASTS, A SOP SAX(CL),ASAX,TSAX,BAR SAX		KN
NEVIN, E.-THOMPSON. NARCISSUS. 2ASAX,TSAX,BAR SAX		AL
NIEHAUS, L. FUGUE		HL
NIEHAUS, L. FUSION		HL
NIEHAUS, L. HALLOWEEN FANTASY		HIM
NIEHAUS, L. MOSAICS		HL
NIEHAUS, L. ROMANTIC SKETCH		HIM
NIEHAUS, L. STORM, THE		HIM
NIEHAUS, L. SUMMER NOCTURNE		HIM
NIEHAUS, L. SYMPHONETTE		HIM
NIEHAUS, L. THEME & VARIATIONS		HIM
OFFENBACH, J. BARCAROLLE (TALES OF HOFFMANN) 2ASAX,TSAX,BAR SAX		CF
OSTLING, A. QUAR-TETE-A-TETE. 2ASAX,TSAX,BAR SAX		BE
OTTEN, L. QUARTET		SD

OTTOSON, D. SVIT. 2ASAX,TSAX,BAR SAX	STI
PACHELBEL-FRASCOTTI. CANON AND GIGUE. 3ASAX,BAR SAX	RH
PALESTRINA, G. ALMA REDEMPTORIS	EDR
PARERA, A.-WALTERS. EL CAPEO. 2ASAX,TSAX,BAR SAX	RU
PASCAL, C. QUATUOR	DUR
PATACHICH, I. QUARTET	GEN
PATTERSON, P. DIVERSIONS (1976)	JOW
PELEMANS, W. SAXOPHONE QUARTET	MAU
PERRAULT, M. QUATUOR (1953)	CAN
PETERSEN, T. MINIATURE SUITE. 2ASAX,TSAX,BAR SAX	KN
PETERSMA, W. SAXOPHONE QUARTET	SD
PICHAUREAU, C. RAFFLESIA	EFM
PIERNE, G.-MULE. CHANSON D'AUTREFOIS	ALE
PIERNE, G.-MULE. CHANSON DE LA GRAND'MAMAN	ALE
PIERNE, G.-NELSON. GUARDIAN ANGEL & SONG OF THE GRANDMOTHER	LU
PIERNE, G. INTRODUCTION & VARIATIONS	ALE
PIERNE, G.-MULE. MARCH OF THE LITTLE TIN SOLDIERS, OP 14/6	ALE
PIERNE, G.-MULE. VEILLEE DE L'ANGE GARDIEN, LA	ALE
PIERNE, P. 3 CONVERSATIONS	BIL
PLANQUETTE, R. CLOCHES DE CORNEVILLE	MOL
POOT, M. CONCERTINO (1962)	CBD
POOT, M. LEGENDE (1967)	CBD
POOT, M. SCHERZO (1941)	CBD
POUSSEUR, H. VUE SUR LES JARDINS INTERDITS	ESZ
PRESSER, W. WALTZ & SCHERZO. 2ASAX,TSAX,BAR SAX	SO
PROKOFIEV, S.-JOHNSON. ROMANCE & TROIKA. 2ASAX,TSAX,BAR SAX	RU
QUINET, M. POCHADES	BIL
RAFF, J.-LEONARD. CAVATINA	BE
RAMSOE, W.-VOXMAN. QUARTET #5, MOVEMENT #1	RU
2ASAX,TSAX,BAR SAX	
RAPHLING, S. CONCERT SUITE. 4ASAX	EDM
RATHBURN, E. 2 INTERPLAYS (1972)	CAN
REA, J. FANTAISIES &/ET ALLUSIONS (1969)	CAN
REBER, H.-FORET. BERCEUSE	BIL
REGT, H. DE. MUSICA PER 4 SASSOFONI	SD
REX, H.(ARR). SHENANDOAH. 2ASAX,TSAX,BAR SAX	BE
RICARD, C. BADINERIE	SO
RILEY. VISIONES	SO
RIMSKY-KORSAKOV, N.-MULE. VOL DU BOURDON, LE	BIL
RIMSKY-KORSAKOV, N.-EYMANN. NOTTURNO. 2ASAX,TSAX,BAR SAX	BE
RIVIER, J. GRAVE ET PRESTO	BIL
RODEN, R. SAX CRAFT	SO
RUEFF, J. CONCERT EN QUATUOR	ALE
RUELLE, F. PRELUDE	MAU
RUSHBY-SMITH, J. QUARTET	RS
SAINT-SAENS, C.-BROOKE. MY HEART AT THY SWEET VOICE	CF
2ASAX,TSAX,BAR SAX	
SAINT-SAENS, C.-BROOKE. SWAN, THE. 2ASAX,TSAX,BAR SAX	CF
SAUCIER, G. 2 PIECES. 2ASAX,TSAX,BAR SAX	KN
SAUTER. QUARTET #1	KN
SCARLATTI-HEMKE. SONATA #44	SO
SCARLATTI, A.-SCHMIDT. PRELUDE & FUGUE	WI
SCHARWENKA, X.-BROOKE. POLISH DANCE. 2ASAX,TSAX,BAR SAX	CF
SCHIBLER, A. QUARTET (1978)	EUL
SCHMIDT, W.-VAN DEN BRINK. FINALE (QUARTET #4)	MOL
SCHMIDT, W. PRELUDE & RONDO	WI
SCHMIDT, W. SUITE	WI
SCHMITT, F. QUATUOR, OP102	DUR
SCHMUTZ, A. INTRODUCTION, RECITATIVE & CHORALE	AMP
2ASAX,TSAX,BAR SAX(TSAX)	
SCHMUTZ, A. PRELUDE & FINALE. 2ASAX,TSAX,BAR SAX(TSAX)	AMP
SCHRIJVER, K. DE. DRIE-DELIGE SUITE	T-M

4 SAXOPHONES-408

```
SCHRIJVER, K. DE.  QUADRICHROMIE                                      HE
SCHUBERT, F.-TEAL.  ANDANTE (QUARTET, OP 29)                          EQM
SCHUBERT, F.-GILET.  CELEBRE MARCHE MILITAIRE                         EDR
SCHUBERT, F.(LEWIN).  MENUETTO (PIANO SONATA IN G MA)                 BH
SCHUBERT, F.-DISHINGER.  MENUETTO                                     SP
SCHUBERT, F.-THOMPSON.  MOMENT MUSICAL.  2ASAX,TSAX,BAR SAX           AL
SCHUBERT, F.-OSTLING.  SYMPHONIC THEME.  2ASAX,TSAX,BAR SAX           BE
SCHUMAN, W.-RASCHER.  QUARTETTINO.  2ASAX,TSAX,BAR SAX                SN
SCHUMANN, R.  REVERIE                                                 BIL
SCHUMANN, R.-RASCHER.  4 SHORT PIECES.  2ASAX,TSAX,BAR SAX            BE
SCHUMANN, R.-DEDRICK.  SONG & MARCH                                   KN
  SOP SAX(ASAX),ASAX,TSAX,BAR SAX
SCHWARZ, I.  CANZONE.  2ASAX,TSAX,BAR SAX                             RU
SCIORTINO, P.  DANSE PAIENNE                                          ECH
SEREBRIER, J.  MINUETTO                                               PI
SEREBRIER, J.  QUARTET                                                SN
SHRUDE, M.  QUARTET                                                   SO
SIBELIUS, J.-BEELER/ROPE.  ANDANTE FESTIVO                            SN
  2ASAX,TSAX,BAR SAX
SIMON, J.  ILLEGITIMATE CHILD, THE                                    DOR
SIMONIS, J.  BOUTADES                                                 BIL
SINGELEE, J.-LEFEBRE.  ALLEGRO DE CONCERT.  2ASAX,TSAX,BAR SAX        CF
SINGELEE, J.  QUARTET #1, OP 53                                       HE
SINGER, S.  ORIENTALE.  2ASAX,TSAX,BAR SAX                           CF
SINGER, S.  THEME & LITTLE FUGUE.  2ASAX,TSAX,BAR SAX                 CF
SKOLNIK, W.  4 IMPROVISATIONS.  2ASAX,TSAX,BAR SAX                    TRI
SMETSKY, J. DE-WHEAR.  MARCH OF THE SPANISH SOLDIERY                  LU
  2ASAX,TSAX,BAR SAX
SMITH, G  MOOD MUSIC I (1973)                                        EQM
SODERLUNDH, L.  IDEA I & II.  2ASAX,TSAX,BAR SAX                     STI
SODOMKA, K.  MUSICA                                                   CHF
SOUSA, J.-HARGER.  THUNDERER MARCH, THE.  2ASAX,TSAX,BAR SAX          BE
SPERRY.  CHORALE & FUGUE                                              TM
STARER, R.  LIGHT & SHADOW.  2ASAX,TSAX,BAR SAX                      MC
STEIN, L.  SUITE (1962).  2ASAX,TSAX,BAR SAX                          SO
STERN.  QUARTET                                                       SH
STRAESSER, J.  INTERSECTIONS V (A SAXOPHONE'S WORLD) (1974)           SD
STRAUSS, R.-JOHNSON.  ALLERSEELEN, OP 10/8                            RU
  2ASAX,TSAX,BAR SAX
SUTER, R.  JEUX A 4 (1976)                                            S-V
TAUTENHAHN, G.  QUARTET                                               SS
TCHAIKOVSKY, P.-MULE.  ANDANTE DU QUATUOR                             BIL
TCHAIKOVSKY, P.  LIEDER OHNE WORTE                                    MOL
TCHAIKOVSKY, P.  NUITS BIZARRE EN BARCAROLLE                          MOL
TELEMANN, G.-JOHNSON.  MENUET & POLONAISE (SUITE IN A MI)             RU
  2ASAX,TSAX,BAR SAX
TELEMANN, G.-JOHNSON.  OVERTURE BAROQUE (SUITE IN A MI)               RU
  2ASAX,TSAX,BAR SAX
THOMPSON(ARR).  OLD REFRAIN, THE.  2ASAX,TSAX,BAR SAX                 AL
THOMPSON(ARR).  SWING LOW, SWEET CHARIOT.  2ASAX,TSAX,BAR SAX         AL
TISNE, A.  ALIAGES                                                    BIL
TOKUNAGA, H.  QUARTET IN 12 FRAGMENTS                                 SO
TOSELLI, G.-HARGER.  SERENADE                                         HE
TUFILLI, W.  ROSE BLUSH.  2ASAX,TSAX,BAR SAX                          BE
TUTHILL, B.  QUARTET.  2ASAX,TSAX,BAR SAX                             SO
VECCHI, O.  CRICKET, THE.  2ASAX,TSAX,BAR SAX(TSAX)                   EDM
VELLONES, P.  AU JARDIN DES BETES SAUVAGES                            DUR
VELLONES, P.  CAVALIERS ANDALOUS, LES                                HLE
VELLONES, P.  DAUPHINS, LES                                           DUR
VELLONES, P.  PRELUDE & RONDO FRANCAIS                               HLE
VELLONES, P.  VALSE CHROMATIQUE                                      HLE
VERDI, G.  CELESTE AIDA.  2ASAX,TSAX,BAR SAX                          CF
```

```
VERDI, G.   QUARTET (RIGOLETTO).   2ASAX,TSAX,BAR SAX          CF
VIOLEAU, R.   SUITE CHINOISE                                   BIL
VIVALDI, A.   GIGA.   2ASAX,TSAX,BAR SAX(TSAX)                 EDM
VRIES, K. DE.   2 (1974) CHORALS                              SD
WAGEMANS, P.   QUARTET, OP 8 (1975)                            SD
WAGNER, R.-GORDON.   MARCH (TANNHAUSER).   2ASAX,TSAX,BAR SAX  KJ
WAHLBERG, R.   PRISMA                                          STI
WALKER, R.   ECLOGUE                                           CRE
WALKER, R.   4 FANCIES.   2ASAX,TSAX,BAR SAX                   BE
WALKER, R.   SUITE.   2ASAX,TSAX,BAR SAX                       KN
WALLACE, W.   INTRODUCTION & CHACONNE                          CAN
WALTER, D.   FINALE                                            KN
WALTER, D.   QUINTALISM                                        KN
WALTER, D.   TRANSITION                                        KN
WALTERS, H.   FAIR & WARMER.   2ASAX,TSAX,BAR SAX              RU
WALTERS, H.   I'M ON MY WAY.   2ASAX,TSAX,BAR SAX              RU
WALTERS, H.   PIZZA PARTY.   2ASAX,TSAX,BAR SAX                RU
WARLOCK, P.-BLYTON/MITCHELL.   2 COD PIECES                    THP
WEBER, C.M. VON-THOMPSON.   OBERON OVERTURE                    AL
   2ASAX,TSAX,BAR SAX
WILDER, A.   QUARTET                                          MAR
WILLIAMS, V.   PRELUDE & BEGUINE.   2ASAX,TSAX,BAR SAX         CF
WISE, L.   OSTINATO OPUS.   2ASAX,TSAX,BAR SAX                 MAN
WISSMER, P.   QUATUOR                                          EMT
YODER, P.(ARR).   DRY BONES.   2ASAX,TSAX,BAR SAX,PERC OPT     KJ
YODER, P.(ARR).   JERICHO.   2ASAX,TSAX,BAR SAX               KJ
YOSHIOKA, E.   ALLEGRO                                         AM
YOSHIOKA, E.   ARIA (ARIA & ALLEGRO)                           ARM
YRADIER, C.-BROOKE.   PALOMA, LA.   2ASAX,TSAX,BAR SAX         CF
ZAJAC, E.   5 MINIATURES                                       EQM
```

4 SAXOPHONES (COLLECTIONS)-409

```
ARNOLD, J. & C. LINDSAY.   SAXOPHONE QUARTETS                  HY
   2ASAX,TSAX,BAR SAX
BURGSTAHLER, E.(ARR).   13 SAXOPHONE QUARTETS                  PO
   2ASAX,TSAX,BAR SAX
CAILLIET, L.   QUARTET ALBUM.   2ASAX,TSAX,BAR SAX             BE
CLERISSE, R.(ARR).   RECUEIL DE QUATUORS CLASSIQUES            EDR
FIVE SAXOPHONE QUARTETS.                                       ETP
GEE, H.   4 SAXOPHONE QUARTETS.   2ASAX,TSAX,BAR SAX           PO
HAUTVAST (ARR).   MEISTER PERLEN                               T-M
HOLMES, G.& LONG.   SYMPHONY ENSEMBLE SERIES                   RU
   2ASAX,TSAX,BAR SAX
HUDADOFF, I.(ARR).   24 SAXOPHONE QUARTETS.   2ASAX,TSAX,BAR SAX  PO
RASCHER, S.(ARR).   COLLECTION                                 M&M
RASCHER, S. & L. PATRICK.   5 CENTURIES FOR SAX QUARTET        BO
RASCHER, S. & L. PATRICK.   MASTERPIECES FOR SAX QUARTET       BO
   2ASAX,TSAX,BAR SAX
STUART, H.(ARR).   SAXOPHONE CLASSICS.   2ASAX,TSAX,BAR SAX    SH
TEAL, L.(ARR).   10 SAXOPHONE QUARTETS.   2ASAX,TSAX,BAR SAX   DOR
VOXMAN, H.(ARR).   QUARTET REPERTOIRE.   2ASAX,TSAX,BAR SAX    RU
```

4 PARTS: WOODWINDS-410

```
ABBOTT, A.  SAXOPHONIES.  OB,CL,BSN,ASAX                        EFM
ABSIL, J.  4 ESQUISSES, OP154 (1971).  FL,OB,CL,BSN            CBD
ADOLPHUS, M.  QUARTET, OP 20.  FL,CL,OB,BSN                    ACA
ALEMANN, E.  3 MICROPOEMS.  FL,OB,CL,BSN                       SN
ALEXANDROVA, N.  SUITE.  FL,OB,CL,BSN                          MKE
ALLGEN, C.  FUGA.  FL,OB,CL,BSN                                STI
AMES, W.  QUARTET.  FL,OB,CL,BSN                               ACA
ARTOT, J.-HARRIS.  12 QUARTETS                                 CF
   CL,CL(ASAX),ASAX(CL,ACL),BSN(BCL,ASAX )
ARTOT, J.-HARRIS.  12 QUARTETTES.  FL,OB,CL,BSN               CF
AUGENBLICK, L.  SCHERZO IN C MA.  FL,OB,CL,BSN                WI
BABBITT, M.  WOODWIND QUARTET.  FL,OB,CL,BSN                  AMP
BACH, J.C.-MAGANINI.  ALLEGRO BRILLANTE.  FL,OB,CL,BSN        CF
BACH, J.S.-BANQUER.  ACH GOTT UND HERR, WIE GROSS UND SCHWER  CF
   FL,OB(CL),CL,BSN
BACH, J.S.-LEWIN.  BOURREE (3RD CELLO SONATA).  FL,OB,CL,BSN  BH
BACH, J.S.-DAMM.  BOURREE.  FL,OB,CL,BSN                      CF
BACH, J.S.-BANQUER.  CHORALE & PRELUDE ON ACH GOTT UND HERR   CF
   FL,2CL,BCL(BSN)
BACH, J.S.  FUGA II.  FL,OB,CL,BSN                            CST
BACH, J.S.  FUGA XXIII.  FL,OB,CL,BSN                         CST
BACH, J.S.-CAFARELLA.  FUGHETTA.  FL,OB,CL,BSN                VO
BACH, J.S.-MC KAY.  FUGUE #4.  FL,OB,CL,BSN(BCL)             BA
BACH, J.S.-SEAY.  FUGUE IN C MI.  FL,OB,CL,BSN               SPR
BACH, J.S.-HAHN.  FUGUE IN G MI.  FL,2CL,BSN                 CF
BACH, J.S.-KESSLER.  FUGUE XIV.  FL,OB,CL,BSN                RU
BACH, J.S.-COX.  GAVOTTE (FRENCH SUITE #5).  FL,OB,CL,BSN    BH
BACH, J.S.-GRISEZ.  LOURE.  FL,OB,CL,BSN                     CF
BACH, J.S.-WILKINSON.  4 PIECES.  FL,OB,CL,BSN               NO
BACH, J.S.-REED.  SARABANDE & DOUBLE.  OB,CL,CL(HN),BSN      KN
BAGLEY-HARRIS.  THISTLEDOWN.  FL,OB,CL,BSN                   CF
BAIRD, T.  DIVERTIMENTO (1956).  FL,OB,CL,BSN                AP
BARBIER, R.  PETITE SUITE, OP108 (1964)  FL,OB,CL,BSN        CBD
BARTOLOZZI, B.  CONCERTAZIONI A QUATTRO (1969).  FL,OB,CL,BSN ESZ
BAUMGARTNER, H.  QUARTET, OP 94.  FL,OB,CL,BSN               ACA
BEALE, D.  PATTERN STUDIES.  FL,OB,CL,BSN                    MAN
BECKER, H.  ANSBACHER QUARTETT.  OB,OB D'AMORE,EHN,BSN       PG
BECKERATH, A.  HEITERES SPIEL.  FL,OB(CL),CL,BSN             MV
BECKWITH, J.  QUARTET (1951).  FL,OB,EHN,BSN                 CAN
BEETHOVEN, L. VAN-HAHN.  CONTRA DANCE.  FL,OB(CL),CL,BSN     CF
BEETHOVEN, L. VAN-LAUBE.  MENUET (SYMPHONY #1).  FL,OB,CL,BSN CF
BEETHOVEN, L. VAN-TARLOW.  MENUETTO (OP 10/3).  FL,2CL,BSN   WB
BEETHOVEN, L. VAN-DAHM.  MINUET (SEPTET, OP 20).  FL,OB,CL,BSN CF
BEETHOVEN, L. VAN-CAFARELLA.  MINUET (SONATA, OP 22)         VO
   FL,OB,CL,BSN
BEETHOVEN, L. VAN-TOLL.  RONDO (SONATA PATHETIQUE)           CF
   2CL,ASAX(CL,ACL),BSN(BCL,ASAX)
BEETHOVEN, L. VAN-HAHN.  SCENE AT THE BROOK (SYMPHONY #6)    CF
   FL,OB,CL,BSN(BCL)
BEETHOVEN, L. VAN-BELLISON.  VARIATIONS ON A THEME (DON JUAN) BE
   FL,OB,CL,BSN
BENTLEY, A.(ARR).  SIXTEENTH CENTURY QUARTETS.  4WW INSTR    CA
BENTON, D.  QUARTET.  4WW                                    SS
BERBIGUIER, B.-WIENANDT.  THEME & VARIATIONS.  FL,3CL        PO
BERGER, A.  QUARTET IN C MA.  FL,OB,CL,BSN                   PET
```

```
BERNARD, J.   DIALOGUE D'ANCHES.  FL,OB,CL,BSN                          EFM
BERNET, D.   CAPRICES.  FL(OB),2CL,BSN                                  UE
BERTOUILLE, G.   PRELUDE ET FUGUE (1959).  FL,OB,CL,BSN                 CBD
BIBER, C.   SONATA.  2OB,2EHN                                           UE
BITSCH, M.   DIVERTISSEMENT.  FL,OB,CL,BSN                              ALE
BIZET, G.-BROOKE.   ANDANTE & MINUET (L'ARLESIENNE).  3FL,ACL           CF
BJELINSKI, B.   SCHERZI DI NOTTE.  FL,OB,CL,BSN                         HG
BLACHER, B.   DIVERTIMENTO (1951).  FL,OB,CL,BSN                        B&B
BLATNY, J.   SUITE.  2FL,CL,BSN                                         CHF
BLAZEK, Z.   DIVERTIMENTI (1946).  FL,OB,CL,BSN                         CHF
BLIN, L.   GRUPETTINO.  2CL,ASAX,TSAX                                   GA
BLINOV, Y.   RUSSIAN SCHERZO.  FL,OB,CL,BSN                             MKE
BOERINGER, J.   DANCE SUITE.  FL,OB,CL,BSN                              AMP
BOHM, C.-HAMILTON.   CALM AS THE NIGHT.  2CL,2BSN                       GA
BONNARD, A.   BIS, OP 42.  FL(CL),OB(CL),CL,SAX(CL)                     BIL
BORISSOV, L.   WELTRAUMSZENEN (1958).  FL,OB,CL,BSN                     HG
BOTTENBERG, W.   QUARTET (1960).  FL,2CL,BSN                            CAN
BOTTJE, W.   THREESOME FOR FOUR.  2FL,CL,BSN                            ACA
BOYCE, W.   ALLEGRO (SYMPHONY #3).  FL,OB,CL,BSN                        CST
BOYCE, W.   MARCATO.  FL,OB,CL,BSN                                      CST
BOYCE, W.   VIVACE.  FL,OB,CL,BSN                                       CST
BOZZA, E.   3 PIECES POUR UNE MUSIQUE DE NUIT.  FL,OB,CL,BSN            ALE
BOZZA, E.   SERENADE.  FL,OB,CL,BSN                                     ALE
BOZZA, E.   SONATINE.  FL,OB,CL,BSN                                     ALE
BRAHMS, J.-HUNTER.   3 EASY QUARTETS.  FL,OB,CL,BSN                     SCH
BRIDGE, F.   DIVERTIMENTI.  FL,OB,CL,BSN                                BH
BRUGK, H.   QUARTET, OP 32.  FL,OB,CL,BSN                               SIM
BUCHTEL, F.   ENCHANTED FOREST.  FL,OB,CL,BSN                           KJ
BUTTERWORTH, N.(ARR).   TUDOR SUITE.  FL(OB,CL),OB(CL),ASAX,BSN         CA
CABUS, P.   HOUTBLAZERSKWARTET.  FL,OB,CL,BSN                           MAU
CALABRESE, T.   BRASIL.  FL,OB,CL,BSN                                   ACA
CALDARA, A.   GRAVE.  FL,OB,CL,BSN                                      CST
CAMBERT, R.   OVERTURE, AN.  2OB,EHN,BSN                                CP
CARTER, E.   8 ETUDES & A FANTASY (1950).  FL,OB,CL,BSN                 AMP
CASTLE, A.   SUMMER SKETCHES.  2FL,2CL                                  KN
CAZDEN, N.   INSISTENCE, OP 40/2.  2OB,2BSN                             SPR
CAZDEN, N.   WALTZ, OP 40/1.  FL,OB,CL,BSN                              SPR
CECCONI, M.   SILENCES.  FL,OB,CL,BSN                                   EFM
CERVETTI, S.   DIVERTIMENTO.  OB,CL,BCL,BSN                             SN
CHAGRIN, F.   SERENADE- JOTTINGS FOR JEREMY                             NO
    FL,OB(FL),CL,BSN(CL)
CHAMINADE, C.-GUENTHER.   SCARF DANCE.  FL,OB,CL,BSN                    BE
CHINI, A.   3 CRIS POUR 4 (1974).  OB,CL,BSN,ASAX                       STI
CHOPIN, F.-TRINKHAUS.   POLONAISE MILITAIRE.  2CL,2BSN                  GA
CHRISTLIEB, D.(ARR).   3 PIECES.  2OB,EHN,BSN                           CP
CLAIR DE LUNE.  FL,OB,CL,BSN                                            B3
CLEMENTI, M.-EVERTSE.   CANON.  CL,CL(TSAX),CL(ASAX),BAR SAX            T-M
COLIN, G.   QUATUOR.  FL,OB,CL,BSN                                      MAU
CONSTANTINIDES, D.   QUARTET.  FL,OB,CL,BSN                             SS
COPPOLA, D.   QUARTET FOR WINDS.  FL,OB,CL,BSN                          KN
CORBEEL, R.   ANDANTE.  FL,OB,CL,BSN                                    MAU
CORELLI, A.   GAVOTTE & GIGUE.  FL,OB,CL,BSN                            EDM
CORELLI, A.   GIGUE.  FL,OB,CL,BSN                                      EDM
CORELLI, A.-HARRIS.   GIGUE,.  2CL,ASAX(ACL),BSN(BCL)                   CF
CORROYEZ, G.   NOUVELLE PETITE COLLECTION.  4WW                         EDR
CORROYEZ, G.(ARR).   20 PETITES PIECES CONCERTANTES.  4WW               EDR
CORROYEZ, G. (ARR).   PETITE COLLECTION POPULAIRE.  4WW                 EDR
COUPERIN, F.-MORRIS.   CANTUS FIRMUS.  FL,OB(FL),CL,BSN(BCL)            PO
COX, N.   MENUET.  FL,OB,CL,BSN                                         BH
CRAY, R.(ARR).   6 EASY TRANSCRIPTIONS.  FL,OB,CL,BSN                   SF
CSONKA, P.   FRENCH SUITE.  4WW                                         SN
CUI, C.-HARRIS.   ORIENTALE.  2CL,ASAX(ACL),BSN(BCL)                    CF
```

CUI, C. ORIENTALE. FL,OB,CL,BSN		CF
DE FILIPPI, A. HORNPIPE FOR A GAY DOLPHIN. FL,OB,CL,BSN		HE
DE FILIPPI, A. IN A NOSTALGIC MOOD. FL,OB,CL,BSN		HE
DE FILIPPI, A. MARCH OF THE LITTLE TUMBLERS. FL,OB,CL,BSN		HE
DE LASSUS, O.-CORBEEL. DOMINE CONVERTERE. FL,OB,CL,BSN		MAU
DE LASSUS, O.-CORBEEL. SOYONS JOYEUS. FL,OB,CL,BSN		MAU
DEBRAS, L. ROTATIONEN (1967). FL,OB,CL,BSN		SS
DELAMARTER, E. SKETCH BOOK IN EIRE. FL,OB,CL,BSN		SO
DELBECQ, L.(ARR). QUATUORS FAVORIS. 4WW		EDR
DELVAUX, A. SONATA A QUATTRO (1964). FL,OB,CL,BSN		CBD
DENZA, L.-HARRIS. FUNICULI-FUNICULA. FL,OB,CL,BSN		CF
DENZA, L.-HARRIS. FUNICULI-FUNICULA,		CF
2CL,ASAX(CL,ACL),BSN(BCL,ASAX)		
DEWIT, A.-HARRIS. HARVEST DANCE,. 2CL,ASAX(ACL),BSN(BCL)		CF
DEWIT, A.-HARRIS. HUNGARIAN FANTASIE		CF
2CL,ASAX(CL,ACL),BSN(BCL,ASAX)		
DEWIT, A.-HARRIS. ON THE LAKE,. FL,OB,CL,BSN		CF
DEWIT, A.-HARRIS. POLONAISE #1. 2CL,ASAX(ACL),BSN(BCL)		CF
DEWIT, A. SPANISH WALTZ,. FL,OB,CL,BSN		CF
DEWIT, A. SUMMERTIME,. 2CL,ASAX(CL,ACL),BSN(BCL,ASAX)		CF
DIEMER, E. MUSIC FOR WOODWIND QUARTET. FL,OB,CL,BSN		OX
DIONISI, R. PICCOLE COMPOSIZIONI. FL,OB,CL,BSN		EBE
DONOVAN, R. QUARTET. FL,OB,CL,BSN		NVM
DOPPELBAUER, J. QUARTET. FL,OB,CL,BSN		LDO
DUBOIS, P. THREE MUSKETEERS, THE. OB,CL,ASAX(CL),BSN		ALE
DURAND, E.(LEONARD). POMPONETTE. FL,OB(CL),CL,BSN(BCL)		BE
ECKHARDT-GRAMATTE, S. WIND QUARTET (1946)		CAN
FL,CL,BASSET HN,BCL		
ELGAR, E. SALUT D'AMOUR, OP 12. 3FL,ACL		CF
ENGELMANN, H. PERMUTAZIONI (1959), OP 20A. FL,OB,CL,BSN		A&S
ERBSE, H. QUARTET, OP 20. FL,OB,CL,BSN		PET
ERDMANN, D. DIVERTIMENTO. FL,OB,CL,BSN		S-V
ERDMANN, D. IMPROVISATION (1967). FL,OB,CL,BSN		HG
ERDMANN, D. VARIATIONS. FL,OB,CL,BSN		S-V
ERICKSON, F. SCHERZINO. FL,OB,CL,BSN		BE
ERIKSSON, N. QUARTETTO. FL,OB,CL,BSN		STI
ERIKSSON, N. RONDINO ALLA MARCIA (1962). FL,OB,CL,BSN		STI
ERIXON, P. RONDO, OP 2 (1963). FL,OB,CL,BSN		STI
ETLER, A. FRAGMENTS. FL,OB,CL,BSN		JB
EYSER, E. SERENATA II (1976). 2CL,2BSN		STI
FARKAS, F. NOTTURNO. 4WW		EMB
FARRENC, J.-BROOKE. ANDANTE. 3FL,ACL		CF
FERNEYHOUGH. SONATINA. 3CL,BSN		PET
FISCHER-ANDRAUD. BANQUET MUSIC. FL,OB,CL,BSN		SO
FISHMANN, M. 6 STUDIES IN SONORITIES. FL,OB,CL,BSN		CF
FLEGIER, A. QUATUOR. 2OB,2BSN		E&C
FONTYN, J. 5 MOSAICS. FL,OB,CL,BSN		GS
FRACKENPOHL, A. TOCCATA. 4WW		GS
FRAGALE, F. SPRIGHTLY FLIGHT. FL,OB,CL,BSN		AMC
FRANCAIX, J. QUARTET. FL,OB,CL,BSN		SCH
FRANK, M. CANON & FUGUE. FL,OB,CL,BSN(BCL)		KN
FRANK, M. PRELUDE & FUGUETTE. FL,OB,CL,BSN		SH
FREISTADT, M. WOODWIND QUARTET. FL,OB,CL,BSN		AMC
FRESCOBALDI, G.-KLAUSS. CANZONA. FL,OB,CL,BSN		TM
FRESCOBALDI, G.-ROCERETO. FUGUE IN C MI. FL,OB,CL,BSN		VO
FRICKER, P. 5 KANONS. 2FL,2OB(2CL)		KPM
FUCHS, F. SERENADE. FL,OB,CL,BSN		FS
FULEIHAN, A. ACROBATICS (HUMORISTIC PRELUDES). FL,OB,CL,BSN		SN
FULEIHAN, A. EXIT (HUMORISTIC PRELUDES). FL,OB,CL,BSN		SN
FULEIHAN, A. IN A BARNYARD (HUMORISTIC PRELUDES)		SN
FL,OB,CL,BSN		
FULEIHAN, A. OVERTURE (HUMORISTIC PRELUDES). FL,OB,CL,BSN		SN

```
FULEIHAN, A.  SERENADE FOR JUDY, A (HUMORISTIC PRELUDES)         SN
   FL,OB,CL,BSN
FURST, P.  BLASERQUARTETT, OP 40.  FL,OB,CL,BSN                  LDO
GADE, N.-GEE.  ROMANCE, OP 19.  FL(OB),2CL,BSN(BCL)             SP
GARLICK, A.  QUARTET.  FL,OB,CL,BSN                              SS
GENDELEV, D.  QUARTET ON RUSSIAN THEMES.  FL,OB,CL,BSN           MKE
GERBER, S.  WOODWIND QUARTET.  FL,OB,CL,BSN                      ACA
GERMAN, E.-DAHM.  PASTORALE DANCE.  FL,OB,CL,BSN                 CF
GHENT, E.  QUARTET.  FL,OB,CL,BSN                                OX
GIBBONS, O.-CRUFT.  2 CORANTOS.  FL,OB,CL,BSN                    BH
GIDEON, M.  DIVERTIMENTO.  FL,OB,CL,BSN                          ACA
GLAZOUNOV, A.-BETTONEY.  IN MODO RELIGIOSO                       CF
   2CL,ASAX (ACL),BSN(BCL)
GLAZOUNOV, A.  IN MODO RELIGIOSO.  FL,OB,CL,BSN                  CF
GOLDMANN, M.  HEVEL II.  FL,OB,CL,BSN                            EMT
GRIEG, E.-TAYLOR.  3 LITTLE PIECES.  FL,OB,CL,BSN               CF
GRUNAUER, I.  BLASERQUARTETT.  FL,OB,CL,BSN                      LDO
GYRING, E.  10 CANONS FOR 2 & 3 WOODWINDS.  FL,OB,CL,BSN         ACA
HABICHT, G.  QUARTETTINO (1969).  FL,OB,CL,BSN                   BRH
HALLAUER, D.  KLEINE SUITE.  FL/PIC,OB,CL,BSN                    SCH
HANDEL, G.  ALEXANDER IN SERVEUS OVERTURE.  FL,OB,CL,BSN         CST
HANDEL, G.  ALLEGRO.  FL,OB,CL,BSN                               CST
HANDEL, G.  CONCERTO.  FL,OB,CL,BSN                              CST
HANDEL, G.  FARAMONDO OVERTURE.  FL,OB,CL,BSN                    CST
HANDEL, G.-STANG.  HOW BEAUTIFUL ARE THE FEET (MESSIAH)         CF
   FL,OB,CL,BSN
HANDEL, G.-STANG.  HOW BEAUTIFUL ARE THE FEET                   CF
   2CL,ASAX(CL,ACL),BSN(B CL,ASAX)
HANDEL, G.-STANG.  LARGO.  2CL,ASAX(CL,ACL),BSN(BCL,ASAX)       CF
HANDEL, G.-COX.  3 MOVEMENTS.  FL,OB,CL,BSN                      NO
HANDEL, G.  OVERTURE IN PARNASSO IN FESTA.  FL,OB,CL,BSN         CST
HANDEL, G.-OSTLING.  PETITE FUGUE.  FL,OB,CL,BSN                 BE
HANDEL, G.  QUARTETTINO.  FL,OB,CL,BSN                           BRH
HANDEL, G.-GRISEZ.  RINALDO'S ARIA.  FL,OB,CL,BSN              CF
HANDEL, G.-STANG.  SINFONIA (MESSIAH).  FL,OB,CL,BSN            CF
HANDEL, G.-STANG.  SINFONIA.  2CL,ASAX(CL,ACL),BSN(BCL,ASAX)    CF
HANMER, R.  CUCKOO QUARTET.  2FL,2CL                             JE
HARRIS, A.  DIVERSION.  FL,OB,CL,BSN                             RON
HARRIS, A.(ARR).  FAREWELL TO CUCULLAIN.  FL,OB(CL),CL,BSN      CF
HARRIS, A.(ARR).  FAREWELL TO CUCULLAIN,.  CL,3ASAX             CF
HARRIS, A.(ARR).  4 HEART SONGS,.  CL,3ASAX                     CF
HARRIS, A.(ARR).  4 HEART/SONGS                                 CF
   2CL,ASAX(CL,ACL),BSN(BCL,ASAX)
HARRIS, A.(ARR).  SACRED MELODIES,.  FL,OB,CL,BSN              CF
HARRIS, A.(ARR).  SCOTTISH AIRS,.  FL,OB,CL,BSN                CF
HARRIS, A.(ARR).  SONGS OF AMERICA,.  FL,OB,CL,BSN             CF
HARTLEY, W.  WOODWIND QUARTET.  FL,OB,CL,BSN                     CRE
HAYDN, F.-GEIGER.  ADAGIO (PIANO SONATA).  FL,OB,CL(ASAX),BSN   CF
HAYDN, F.-SPEETS.  ADAGIO (QUARTET #29).  FL,OB(CL),ASAX,TSAX   T-M
HAYDN, F.-HAHN.  ALLEGRO CON BRIO (STRING QUARTET #4)          CF
   FL,OB(CL),CL,BSN
HAYDN, F.-SPEETS.  ANDANTE (OP 33/6)                           T-M
   FL(E FL CL),CL(ASAX),CL,TSAX
HAYDN, F.-OSTLING.  ANDANTE (SURPRISE SYMPHONY).  FL,OB,CL,BSN  BE
HAYDN, F.  FLUTE CLOCK SONATAS.  2FL,2CL                         OX
HAYDN, F.-SEAY.  MENUET.  FL,OB,CL,BSN                           SPR
HAYDN, F.-VON KREISLER.  MENUETTO & SCHERZANDO.  FL,OB,CL,BSN   SO
HAYDN, F.-BANQUER.  PRESTO SCHERZANDO (OP 20/4).  FL,OB,CL,BSN  MC
HAYDN, F.-SNIECKOWSKI.  QUARTET, OP 2/6.  23B,EHN,BSN           PWM
HAYDN, F.-HAHN.  THEME & VARIATIONS (EMPEROR QUARTET)          CF
   FL,OB,CL,BSN(BCL)
HEKSTER, W.  RELIEF #1 (1968).  FL,OB,CL,BSN                     SD
```

```
HEKSTER, W.  RELIEF #4.  FL,OB,CL,BSN                          SD
HELLERMAN, W.  LONG ISLAND SOUND                              MEP
HELM, E.  QUARTET.  FL,OB,CL,BSN                              SIM
HENDERSON-STOUTAMIRE.  QUARTETS FOR ALL.  4WW                 PO
HEUGTEN, H. VAN.  QUARTET.  CL,ASAX,TSAX,BAR SAX              HU
HILDEMANN, W.  SERENATA.  FL,OB,CL,BSN                        MV
HLOBIL, E.  QUARTET (1964).  FL,OB,CL,BSN                     CHF
HOUNSELL, H.  SUITE.  FL,OB,CL,BSN                            TM
HURNIK, I.  ESERCIZI (1963).  FL,OB,CL,BSN                    UE
IBERT, J.  2 MOUVEMENTS.  FL,FL(OB),CL,BSN                    ALE
JACOB, G.  4 OLD TUNES.  FL,OB,CL,BSN                         JE
JACOB, G.  SIMPLE SERENADE, A.  FL,OB,CL,BSN                  JE
JANACEK, L.-MUNCLINGER.  3 MORAVIAN DANCES.  FL,OB,CL,BSN     INT
JELINEK, H.  DIVERTIMENTO.  E FL CL,CL,BASSET HN,BCL          UE
JIRKO, I.  VIVAT VERDI, 4 OPER-IMPRESSIONEN (1969)            CHF
   FL,OB,CL,BSN
JONES, C.  LYRIC WALTZ SUITE.  FL,OB,CL,BSN                   PET
JOSEPHS, W.  5 FICTITIOUS FOLKSONGS.  FL,OB,CL,BSN            BH
JOSQUIN DES PRES.  VIVE LE ROY.  EHN, 3BSN                    HEU
KABALEVSKY, D.-SEAY.  CHILDRENS SUITE, OP 27.  FL,OB,CL,BSN   SPR
KABALEWSKI, W.  5 (1960) PIECES.  FL,OB,CL,BSN                AP
KANTOR, J.  SERENADE.  FL,OB,CL,BSN                           WI
KELDORFER, R.  QUARTET.  FL,OB,CL,BSN                         FS
KELLAM, I.  CASSATION.  FL,OB,CL,BSN                          GAL
KERSTERS, W.  VARIATIONS, OP 49 (1969).  FL,OB,CL,BSN         CBD
KINGMAN.  4 MINIATURES.  FL,OB,CL,BSN                         WI
KOETSIER, J.  3 PEZZI.  FL,OB,CL,BSN                          SD
KOHN, K.  DIVERTIMENTO.  FL,OB,CL,BSN                         AMC
KONDOROSSY, L.  LITTLE SUITE.  FL,OB,CL,BSN                   AMC
KOUGUELL, A.  SUITE FOR WOODWINDS.  FL,OB,CL,BSN              AMC
KOZHEVNIKOV, B.  2 PIECES (SONG-MARCH).  FL,OB,CL,BSN         MKE
KUHLAU, F.-CAFARELLA.  ALLEGRETTO GRAZIOSO (SONATINA, OP 55/3) VO
   FL,OB,CL,BSN
KUPKOVIC, L.  TREFFPUNKT.  4WW                                UE
KURKA, R.  7 MORAVIAN FOLK-SONGS.  FL,OB,CL,BSN               HY
LA CAPRIA, V.  NOTTURNINO.  FL,OB,CL,BSN                      FZ
LAJTHA, L.  4 HOMAGES.  FL,OB,CL,BSN                          ALE
LANDRY-GRISEZ.  MUSETTE.  FL,OB,CL,BSN                        CF
LAUBE, P.-HARRIS.  ALSATIAN DANCE.  FL,OB,CL,BSN              CF
LAUBER, J.  4 INTERMEZZI (1922).  FL,EHN,CL,BSN              HEN
LEEUWEN, A. VAN.  4 MINIATURES.  2FL,2CL                      SO
LEICHTLING, A.  QUARTET #2, OP 25.  FL,OB,CL,BSN              AMC
LEMELAND, A.  NOCTURNE.  FL,OB,CL,BSN                         EFM
LEMELAND, A.  NOCTURNE, OP 10.  OB,CL,ASAX,BSN                EFM
LEONARD, B.  IDYL.  FL,OB,CL,BSN                              BE
LEONARD, B.  NIGHTFALL.  FL,OB(CL),CL,BSN(BCL)               BE
LEONARD, B.  PALM DESERT NOCTURNE.  FL,OB,CL,BSN             BE
LEVI, W.  DANCE OF THE REEDS.  FL,2CL,BSN                    WIL
LIMMERT, E.  GRIECHISCHE ESSAYS (1965).  FL,OB,CL,BSN        BRH
LIMMERT, E.  SUITE EN MINIATURE.  FL,OB,CL,BSN               MV
LINDBOM, A.  KVARTETT (1948).  FL,OB,CL,BSN                  STI
LIPATTI, D.  AUBADE.  FL,OB,CL,BSN                           RON
LIPTAK, D.  ENCOUNTER II.  FL,OB,CL,BSN                      SS
LLOYD.  PUZZLE CANON.  OB,EHN,2BSN                           HEU
LORENZO, L. DE.  I QUATTRO VIRTUOSI, OP 80.  FL,OB,CL,BSN    PET
LOUVIER.  5 PORTRAITS & 1 IMAGE.  ASAX,OB,CL,BSN             ALE
LUENING, O.  BASS WITH THE DELICATE AIR.  FL,OB,CL,BSN       GA
LULLY, J.-TAYLOR.  COURANT.  FL,OB,CL,BSN                    BE
LUNETTA, S.  FREE MUSIC.  FL,OB,CL,BSN                       CPE
MAASZ, G.  FINCKENSCHLAG.  FL,OB,CL,BSN                      HSM
MACBETH, A.-HARRIS.  INTERMEZZO/"FORGET ME NOT".  FL,OB,CL,BSN CF
MALIPIERO, G.  SONATA A QUATTRO (1954).  FL,OB,CL,BSN        UE
```

```
MANIET, R.-RULST.  HABANERA.  2CL,ASAX,TSAX                        EBR
MANSON, E.  FUGUE.  FL,OB,CL,BSN                                   AMP
MAREZ OYENS, T. DE.  SUITE DU PETIT PRINCE (1972)                  SD
   FL,OB,CL,BSN
MARTIN, D.  RONDO FOR WOODWINDS (1960).  FL,OB,CL,BSN              CAN
MARTINI, J.  PLAISIR D'AMOUR.  FL,OB,CL,BSN                        EDM
MASSENET, J.-HARRIS.  LAST SLUMBER OF THE VIRGIN                   CF
   2CL,ASAX(CL,ACL),BSN(BCL,ASAX)
MASSENET, J.-WALTERS.  NOCTURNE (LA NAVARRAISE)                    RU
MASSIAS, G.  VARIATIONS.  OB,CL,ASAX,BSN                           BIL
MAZELLIER, J.  10 FUGUES.  FL,OB,CL,BSN                            HLE
MC BRIDE, R.  INTERWOVEN.  2CL,2BSN                                ACA
MC BRIDE, R.  TELEVISION SPECIAL.  2CL,2BSN                        ACA
MC CLELLAN, R.  3 MODES.  FL,2CL,BCL                               WI
MC KAY, F.  MUSETTE.  FL,OB,CL,BSN(BCL)                            BA
MC KAY, G.  3 NAUTICAL CHARACTERS.  FL,OB,CL,BSN(BCL)              BA
MC NICOL, R.  3 DANCES.  FL(CL),CL,OB(CL),BSN                      HI
MC NICOL, R.  QUARTET.  FL,OB,CL,BSN                               PET
MEEK, K.  SUITE.  FL,OB,CL,BSN                                     CAN
MEIER, D.  KUKLOS (1974).  OB,CL,BSN,ASAX                          EFM
MEIER, D.  KUKLOS.  FL,OB,CL,BSN                                   EFM
MEULEMANS, A.  QUATUOR (1962).  FL,OB,CL,BSN                       CBD
MEYERBEER, G.-HARRIS.  CORONATION MARCH.  FL,OB,CL,BSN             CF
MIELENZ, H.  SCHERZO.  FL,EHN,CL,BSN                               R&E
MIGOT, G.  3 PASTORALES.  FL,OB,CL,BSN                             EMT
MOLLOY, J.-HARRIS.  KERRY DANCE,                                   CF
   2CL,ASAX(CL,ACL),BSN(BCL,ASAX)
MONTANARI, N.  5 INVENZIONI.  FL,OB,CL,BSN                         EDI
MOULAERT, R.  ANDANTE, FUGUE ET FINAL                             CBD
   OB,OB D'AMOUR,EHN,HECKELPHONE
MOURANT, W.  HALLOWE'EN DANCE.  FL,OB,CL,BSN                       ACA
MOYSE, L.  SUITE, C.  2FL,CL,BSN                                   SO
MOZART, W.-LAUBE.  ADAGIO (CLARINET CONCERTO)                      CF
   2CL,ASAX(ACL),BSN(BCL)
MOZART, W.-MUNCLINGER.  ADAGIO & ALLEGRO, K594.  FL,OB,CL,BSN      INT
MOZART, W.-MUNCLINGER.  ADAGIO, K580A                              B&N
   EHN,CL,BASSET HN(CL),BSN
MOZART, W.-WOJCIECHOWSKI.  ADAGIO, K580A.  EH,2BASSET HN,BSN       HSM
MOZART, W.  ADAGIO, K580A.  EHN,2HN(2BASSET HN,2CL),BSN            EK
MOZART, W.  ALLEGRO (SONATA, K402).  FL,OB,CL,BSN                  CST
MOZART, W.-LEONARD.  ALLELUIA.  FL,OB,CL,BSN                       BE
MOZART, W.  ALLELUIA.  FL,OB,CL,BSN                                EDM
MOZART, W.-LANGENUS.  ANDANTE & MENUETTO.  FL,OB,CL,BSN            CF
MOZART, W.-MUNCLINGER.  ANDANTE IN F MA, K616.  FL,OB,CL,BSN       INT
MOZART, W.-GEE.  DIVERTIMENTO (K251).  FL,OB(FL),CL,BSN(BCL)       PO
MOZART, W.-HARRIS.  EXCERPT (PIANO SONATA #10).  FL,OB,CL,BSN      CF
MOZART, W.-TOLL.  EXCERPT (SONATA #4)                              CF
   2CL,ASAX(CL,ACL),BSN(BCL,ASAX)
MOZART, W.-MUNCLINGER.  FANTASY IN F MI, K608.  FL,OB,CL,BSN       INT
MOZART, W.  FUGA, K546.  FL,OB,CL,BSN                              CST
MOZART, W.-STEPHENS.  MINUET (SYMPHONY IN E FL MA)                 CF
   2CL,ASAX(ACL),BSN(BCL)
MOZART, W.-LENTZ.  QUARTET (K298).  FL,OB,CL,BSN                   TM
MOZART, W.  QUINTET, K581; DIVERTIMENTO #11, K251                  EDK
   FL,OB,CL,BSN
MOZART, W.-TOLL.  RONDO (PIANO SONATA #1)                          CF
   2CL,ASAX(CL,ACL),BSN(BCL,ASAX)
MOZART, W.-KESNAR.  RONDO.  FL,OB,CL,BSN(BCL)                      CF
MOZART, W.-BELLISON.  SUITE #2 IN G MA.  FL,OB,CL,BSN              BE
MUELLER, F.  SUITE FOR FOUR                                        UNI
   FL(OB,CL,TSAX),FL(OB,CL,TSAX),CL(ACL,ASAX),BSN(BCL)
MUFFAT, G.-PACQUET.  COURANTE.  FL,OB,CL,BSN                       EV
```

```
MUSIC FROM THE COURT OF THE SUN KING.  2OB,EHN,BSN            NOM
MUSSORGSKY, M.-SKOLNIK.  MUSHROOMS.  FL,OB,CL,BSN             EDM
NEMIROFF, I.  4 TREBLE SUITE.  2FL,2CL                        M&M
NIELSEN, C.-MANN.  HUMORESQUE BAGATELLES, OP 11.  FL,2CL,BSN  WH
NILSSON, B.  DEJA VU (1968).  FL,OB,CL,BSN                    CHE
ORLAND, H.  FUGA.  FL,OB,CL,BSN                               SS
PASQUINI, B.-ROCERETO.  SONATA II.  FL,OB,CL,BSN              VO
PAULSON, G.  LITEN SERENAD, OP 22.  FL,OB,CL,BSN              STI
PAULUS.  WIND SUITE.  4WW                                     SH
PELEMANS, W.  BLAZERSKWARTET.  FL,OB,CL,BSN                   MAU
PELEMANS, W.  ONDER DE APPELBOMEN.  FL,OB,CL,BSN              MAU
PIERNE, G.  MARCH OF THE LITTLE TIN SOLDIERS.  FL,OB,CL,BSN   CF
PILLIN, B.  SCHERZO.  FL,OB,CL,BSN                            WI
PISK, P.  ELEGY & SCHERZINO, OP 70/2.  OB,2CL,BSN             ACA
PISK, P.  LITTLE WOODWIND MUSIC, A.  OB,2CL,BSN               AMP
PLEYEL, I.  ANDANTE & RONDO; OP 48/1                          CF
   2CL,ASAX(CL,ACL),BSN(BCL,ASAX)
PLEYEL, I.  ANDANTE & RONDO, OP 48/1.  FL,OB,CL,BSN           CF
PLEYEL, I.  QUARTET IN E FL MA.  FL,2CL,BSN                   MR
POLDINI, E.-MUELLER.  POUPEE VALSANTE (DANCING DOLL)          CF
   FL,OB,CL,BSN
PONJEE, T.  QUATUOR D'ANCHES (1979).  OB,CL,ASAX,BSN          SD
POOT, M.  MUSIQUE (1964).  FL,OB,CL,BSN                       CBD
POOT, M.  PETITE MARCHE DE FETE (1938).  FL,OB,CL,BSN         CBD
POZAJIC, M.  3 PIECES.  2OB,EHN(HN),BSN                       KAW
POZAJIC, M.  3 SATZE.  2OB,EHN,BSN                            SIM
PRAAG, H. VAN.  KWARTET (1947).  FL,OB,CL,BSN                 SD
PRAAG, H. VAN.  3 (1958) SCHETSEN.  FL,OB,CL,BSN              SD
PROKOFIEV, S.  FLEETING MOMENTS, OP 22.  FL,OB,CL,BSN         CF
PROKOFIEV, S.  VISIONS FUGITIVES.  FL,OB,CL,BSN               M&M
PROVINCIALI, E.  DANSE VILLAGEOISE.  FL,OB,CL,BSN             EES
PUCCINI, G.-LEIDZEN.  ONE FINE DAY (MADAMA BUTTERFLY)         BE
   FL,OB,CL,BSN
PUCCINI, G.-LEIDZEN.  VISSI D'ARTE (TOSCA).  FL,OB,CL,BSN     BE
PURCELL, H.-EDMUNDS.  DIOCLESIAN.  FL,OB,CL,BSN               CF
PURCELL, H.-EDMUNDS.  KING JAMES II SUITE.  FL,OB,CL,BSN      CF
QUINET, M.  QUATUOR (1964).  FL,OB,CL,BSN                     CBD
RAE, A.  AUTUMN COLORS (1969).  OB,CL,BCL,BSN                 CAN
RAE, A.  IMPROVIZATIONS.  FL,OB,CL,BSN                        CAN
RALSTON, A.  NOCTURNE SENTIMENTALE.  FL,2CL,BSN(BCL)          BH
RAMEAU, J.-SOELLER.  GAVOTTE.  FL,OB,CL,BSN                   FZ
RAMEAU, J.-CORBEEL.  GAVOTTE EN RONDEAU.  FL,OB,CL,BSN        MAU
RAMEAU, J.-DAWN.  RIGAUDON.  FL,OB,CL,BSN                     BH
RAPHAEL, G.  QUARTET, OP 61 (1945).  FL,OB,CL,BSN             B&N
RAPHLING, S.  SQUARE DANCE.  FL,OB,CL,BSN                     EDM
RATHBURN, E.  WALTZ FOR WINDS (1949; REV 1955).  FL,OB,CL,BSN CAN
RATHBURN, E.  WALTZ FOR WINDS #2 (1949).  FL,OB,CL,BSN        CAN
RAVIN, I.  SONATINA FOR WOODWINDS.  FL,OB,CL,BSN              AMC
REGER, M.-BROWN.  FUGUE, OP 56/2.  FL,OB,CL,BSN               WI
RENZI, A.  5 BAGATELLE.  FL,OB,CL,BSN                         EDS
RIDOUT, A.  CONCERTANTE.  FL,OB,CL,BSN                        CA
RIEGGER, W.  3 CANONS, OP  9 (1930).  FL,OB,CL,BSN            TP
RIISAGER, K.  QUARTET, OP 40A (1941).  FL,OB,CL,BSN           SPD
ROECKEL-LEONARD.  AIR DU DAUPHIN.  FL,OB,CL,BSN               BE
ROGER, D.  3 MOUVEMENTS.  OB,CL,BSN,ASAX                      EFM
ROLAND-MANUEL, A.  RONDELS DE PERONNELLE D'ARMENTIERES 2      DUR
   2FL,CL,BSN
ROY, K.  STERLINGMAN SUITE.  FL,OB,CL,BSN                     TP
RUT, J.  KINDERSERENADE.  FL,OB,CL,BSN                        CHF
RYKER, R.  4 ELIZABETHAN PIECES, OP  7.  2FL,2CL              BER
SADLER, H.  QUARTETTINO.  FL,OB,CL,BSN                        B&N
SAMONOV.  SUITE.  FL,OB,CL,BSN                                CHM
```

```
SARKOZY, I.  SALMO E GIOCO.  FL,OB,CL,BSN                            EMB
SAVINA, C.  MUSICA PER SUONARE INSIEME, UNA (1975)                  EBE
   FL,OB,CL,BSN
SCARLATTI-ROSENTHAL.  SCARLATTIANA.  FL,OB(FL),CL,BSN(BCL)          WI
SCARLATTI-ROCERETO.  SONATA VIII IN F MA.  FL,OB,CL,BSN             VO
SCARLATTI, D.-LEWIN.  CATS FUGUE.  FL,2CL,BSN(BCL)                  BH
SCARMOLIN, A.  DANSE GROTESQUE.  FL,OB,CL,BSN(BCL)                  BA
SCARMOLIN, A.  SCHERZO.  FL,OB,CL,BSN                               CF
SCARMOLIN, A.  WILL O' THE WISP.  FL,OB,CL,BSN(BCL)                 BA
SCHENK, J.-STEINBECK.  QUARTET.  FL,2EHN,BSN                        LDO
SCHICKELE, P.  7 BAGATELLES.  FL,OB,CL,BSN                          EV
SCHILLING, H.  METAMORPHOSEN UBER EIN ALTES LIEBESLIED (1951)       BRH
   FL,OB,CL,BSN
SCHMIDT, W.  3 LITURGICAL PRELUDES.  FL,OB,CL,BSN                   WI
SCHMIT, C.  BURLESQUES (1964-65).  FL,OB,CL,BSN                     CBD
SCHMITT(ARR).  ALTE BLASERSATZE.  4 WINDS IN ANY COMBINATION        SCH
SCHUBERT, F.-HAHN.  MINUETTO (FANTASIA, OP 78)                      CF
   FL,OB(CL),CL,BSN
SCHUBERT, F.(FELDSHER).  6 WALTZES.  FL,OB,CL,BSN                   TM
SCHUMANN, R.-GRISEZ.  ALLEGRETTO (SONATA #1).  FL,OB,CL,BSN         CF
SCHUMANN, R.-CORBEEL.  LENTELIED.  FL,OB,CL,BSN                     MAU
SCHUMANN, R.-HOLER.  3 PIECES (ALBUM FOR THE YOUNG)                 BD
   FL,OB,CL,BSN
SCHUMANN, R.  TRAUMEREI.  3FL,ACL                                   CF
SCHURINK, B.  QUARTET (1975).  AFL,EHN,BCL,BSN                      SD
SCHUYT, N.  ALLA NOTTURNA.  2OB,OB D'AMORE, EHN                     SD
SCHWARTZ, G.  INTERNATIONAL FOLK SUITE.  ACL,BCL,BSN,TSAX           SO
SCHWEIZER, K.  KONVERSATIONSSZENE (1966).  FL,OB,E FL CL,BSN        EMC
SEHLBACH, E.  QUARTET, OP 91.  FL,OB,CL,BSN                         MV
SEYFRIT, M.  PORTAL.  OB,EHN,CL,BSN                                 ACA
SHERMAN, N.  TRADITIONS (1948).  FL,OB,CL,BSN                       CAM
SILCHER, F.-HARRIS.  LORELEY.  FL,OB,CL,BSN                         CF
SILCHER, F.-HARRIS.  LORELEY-PARAPHRASE                             CF
   2CL,ASAX(CL,ACL),BSN(BCL,ASAX)
SIMPSON, J.  3 BAGATELLES.  FL,OB,2CL                               KPN
SINGER, L.  NEW DIMENSIONS (1968).  FL,OB,CL,BSN                    ES2
SITSKY, L.  QUARTET.  FL,OB,CL,BSN                                  BH
SKLENICKA, K.  QUARTET (1967).  FL,OB,CL,BSN                        CH1
SONTAG, H.  QUARTET ON OLD TUNES.  FL,OB,CL,BSN                     TP
SORCE, R.  THEME & VARIATIONS.  FL,OB,CL,BSN                        STN
SOURIS, A.  CONCERT FLAMAND (1965).  FL,OB,CL,BSN                   CBN
SPINO, P.  WOODWIND QUARTET.  FL,OB,CL,BSN                          STN
SPISAK, M.  QUARTET (1938).  OB,2CL,BSN                             AP
STAMITZ-KESNAR.  ANDANTE.  2CL,ASAX(ACL),BSN(BCL)                  CF
STARER, R.  WOODWIND QUARTET.  FL,OB,CL,BSN                         MC
STEINER, H.  ICH HATT' EINEN KAMERADEN.  2CL,2BSN                   B&
STOLZEL, G.  ADAGIO.  FL,OB,CL,BSN                                  CS
STOLZEL, G.  ALLEGRO.  FL,OB,CL,BSN                                 CS
STONE, D.  MINSTREL'S GALLERY, THE.  FL,OB,CL,BSN                   BH
STONE, D.(ARR).  RENAISSANCE, LA                                    BH
   FL(OB,CL),OB(CL),BCL(CL),BSN
STRAESSER, J.  INTERSECTIONS V-1 (1977).  OB,BCL,ASAX,BSN           SD
STRANG, G.  VARIATIONS.  FL(OB),OB(CL),CL(EHN),BSN(BCL)             AC
STRAVINSKY, I.  PASTORALE.  FL,OB,CL,BSN                            ED
STROUD, R.  CAPRICCIO.  FL,OB,BCL,ASAX                              SS
STROUD, R.  SKETCH.  FL,OB,CL,BSN                                   SS
TANG, J.  A LITTLE SUITE.  4WW                                      SS
TARDOS, B.  DIVERTIMENTO.  FL,OB,CL,BSN                             SC
TARDOS, B.  QUARTETTINO.  FL,OB,CL,BSN                              EM
TAUSINGER, J.  COLLOQUIUM (1964).  FL,OB,CL,BSN                     AR
TAYLOR.  3 LITTLE PIECES FROM GRIEG.  FL,OB,CL,BSN(BCL)             CF
TCHAIKOVSKY, P.-HAMILTON.  CHANSON TRISTE.  2CL,2BSN                GA
```

4 PARTS: WOODWINDS-410

TELEMANN, G.-POLNAUER. 6 MINUETS (7 FOIS 7 & 1)	CF
FL,OB,CL,BSN	
TELEMANN, G. 6 MINUETS. FL(OB),OB(FL),CL,BSN	CHE
THOME, F.-HARRIS. PIZZICATO,. 2CL,ASAX(CL,ACL),BSN(BCL,ASAX)	CF
TURECHEK, E. DIVERTISSEMENT IN F MI. FL,OB,CL,BSN	WB
TUSTIN, W. IMPROVISATION. FL,OB,CL,BSN(BCL)	BA
TUTHILL, B. DIVERTIMENTO. FL,OB,CL,BSN	CF
UBER, D. 3 SKETCHES. FL,OB,CL,BSN	SN
VELLERE, L. QUARTETTO. FL,OB,CL,BSN	MAU
VERDI, G.-HARRIS. QUARTET. 2CL,ASAX(CL,ACL),BSN(BCL,ASAX)	CF
VERIKIVSKY, M. QUARTET. FL,OB,CL,BSN	MKE
VILLA-LOBOS, H. QUARTET. FL,OB,CL,BSN	EES
VIVALDI, A. ALLEGRO. FL,OB,CL,BSN	CST
VIVALDI, A. GIGA. FL,OB,CL,BSN	EDM
VOGEL, W. HORFORMEN (1974). FL,OB,CL,BSN	HG
VOIRIN. 2 PETITES PIECES (NOCTILUQUE,BATIFOLAGE)	ECH
FL,OB,CL,BSN	
VRIES ROBBE, W. QUARTETTO (1959). FL,OB,CL,BSN	SD
WALCKIERS, E.-BROOKE. RONDO. 3FL,CL	CF
WALCKIERS, E.-HARRIS. RONDO. 2CL,ASAX(CL,ACL),BSN(BCL,ASAX)	CF
WARREN, E. 3 PIECES FOR 4. FL,OB,CL,BSN	CM
WATERS, C. 2 MINIATURES. FL,OB,CL,BSN	PET
WATSON, W. SCHERZO FOR WINDS. FL,OB,CL,BSN	LU
WEAIT, C. 4 MARCHES FROM THE AMERICAN REVOLUTION. 2OB,2BSN	M&M
WEBER, A. EPODES. OB,CL,BSN,ASAX	EFM
WEIGL-DANCLA-HARRIS. AIR VARIE,	CF
2CL,ASAX(CL,ACL),BSN(BCL,ASAX)	
WEISGALL, H. LINES. FL,OB,CL,BSN	TP
WEISGALL, H. PASTORALE. FL,OB,CL,BSN	TP
WENTH, J.-MYSLIK. QUARTETTO CONCERTANTE IN B FL MA	EK
OB,EHN,CL,BSN	
WHITE, T. QUARTET. FL,OB,CL,BSN	SS
WIESLANDER, I. MISSOLOGI: LITEN SVIT. 2CL,2BSN	STI
WILKINSON, P. SUITE. FL(OB,CL),OB(CL),CL,BSN(CL)	NO
WILSON, K. NOCTURNE. FL,OB,CL,BSN	BE
WISZNIEWSKI, Z. KAMMERMUSIK I (1977). OB,OB D'AMORE,EHN,BSN	EMO
WITTINGER, R. CONCENTRATIONI (1965), OP 7. FL,OB,CL,BSN	BRH
WNUK, J. DOUBLE REED QUADRIPTYCH (1975). OB,EHN,BSN,DBSN	PWM
WUORINEN, C. SONATINA. FL,OB,CL,BSN	TP
WYMAN. CLARINETS JOYEUX, LES. 3CL,BSN	WB
ZANINELLI, L. BURLA & VARIATIONS. 4WW	SH
ZLATIC, S. BALUN, VOLKSTANZ AUS ISTRIEN. OB,EHN,BSN,ASAX	SIM
ZONN, P. COMPOSITIONS FOR QUARTET. FL,OB,CL,BSN	ACA

4 PARTS: 3 FLUTES-KEYBOARD-416

ALETTER, W.-ERICKSON. RENDEZVOUS	EJ
ANDERSEN, J.-WALTERS. SCHERZINO	RU
BARNARD, G. PALS, THE	KJ
BEETHOVEN, L. VAN-KLAUS. MENUET	KN
BOISMORTIER, B.-RUF. SONATE IN G MI. 3FL,BC	B&N
BOISMORTIER, J.-HIBY. SONATA IN G MA, OP 34/2. 3FL,BC	HEI
BONNER. OVER THE HILLS	EDM
BROWN, T. FRECKLES & FLOWERS	KN
BUCHTEL, F. AZURE SKIES	KJ
BUCHTEL, F. DANCING NYMPHS	KJ
BUCHTEL, F. ELF IN DANCE	KJ
CHASE, THE.	B3

CORELLI, A. ALLEMANDA	EDM
COURSE, W. HAPPY-GO-LUCKY	RU
CUNNINGHAM, M. HAIKU	SS
DAINTY MISS.	B3
DELIBES, L.-ERICKSON. CAPRICE	S&
DOLL DANCE.	B3
ERICKSON, E.(ARR). COUNTRY GARDENS	EJ
ERICKSON, F. CARNIVAL OF VENICE	S&
FILAS, T. 'ROUND & 'ROUND SHE GOES	AMC
FILAS, T. CHASE, THE	AMC
FOTE, R. TUTTI FLUTI	KN
FRACKENPOHL, A. FLUTE RAG	EM
FRACKENPOHL, A. FLUTE WALTZ. 3FL,PF,OPT GUIT,OPT DB	KN
FRANK, M. 3 DANCING FLUTES, THE	KN
FRANK, M. 3 GROOVY FLUTES, THE	BO
GRUNDMAN, C. FLUTATION	BH
HARRIS, F. PETITE MAZURKA	LU
HURRELL, C. GALWAY PIPERS	RU
HURRELL, C. GIRL FRIENDS, THE	RU
JOHNSON, C. DEBONAIRES, THE	RU
JOPLIN, S.-WALTERS. ENTERTAINER, THE	RU
JORDAN, J. LITTLE RED MONKEY	AMC
KENNEDY-HARRIS. STAR OF THE EAST	LU
KOEPKE, P. AUBADE	RU
KOEPKE, P. HARLEQUINADE	RU
LIADOW, A.-HANSON. MUSIC BOX, THE	LU
LITTLE RED MONKEY.	B3
MAC PERRIN. CAREFREE	BE
MAC PERRIN. FOOLIN' AROUND	BE
MAC PERRIN. JOLLY CAPERS	BE
MAC PERRIN. SOMETHIN'	BE
MC KAY, F. DANCER, THE	BA
MC KAY, F. HALLOWE'EN TIME	BA
MC KAY, F. SICILIANO	BA
MOYSE, L. 4 PIECES	GS
OLIVER-LUBETKIN. TROPICAL SERENADE	HL
OLIVER, R. AMERICAN FOLK SONG	HL
OSTERLING, E. BEGUINE FOR FLUTES	LU
OSTERLING, E. SAMBA FOR FLUTES	LU
OSTRANSKY, L. ARABESQUES	RU
OSTRANSKY, L. SPANISH RONDO	RU
POLDINI, E.-ERICKSON. DANCING DOLL, THE	EJ
PONCHIELLI, A.-ERICKSON. DANCE OF THE HOURS	EJ
PURCELL, H.-RING. CHACONNE. 3FL,PF,VC AD LIB	S&C
RIMSKY-KORSAKOFF, N.-WALTERS. FLIGHT OF THE BUMBLEBEE	RU
RORICH, C. BURLESKE, OP 64	WZ
SALIERI, A. DANSE (TARARE)	EDM
SCARLATTI, A. QUARTET IN F MA. 3FL,PF,BSN AD LIB	PET
SCARLATTI, A.-WOEHL. QUARTETTINO. 3FL,PF,VC AD LIB	PET
SIENNICKI, E. PONYTAIL POLKA	KJ
SIMEONE, H. FLUTE COCKTAIL	SH
TAYLOR, L. TRIO	HL
TCHAIKOVSKY, P.-ERICKSON. DANCE OF THE REED FLUTES	EJ
TCHAIKOVSKY, P.-MAGANINI. DANCE OF THE REED FLUTES	CF
TCHAIKOVSKY, P.-HUMMEL. DANSE DES MIRLITONS	RU
TCHAIKOVSKY, P.-FINLAYSON. NUTCRACKER SUITE 3FL,PF,OPT BELLS	BH
TURKEY IN THE RAW.	B3
UGGEN, E. PLAYWELL TRIO & QUARTET FOLIO	S&
VIVALDI, A.-ROWE. CORRENTE	KN
VIVALDI, A.-ROWE. GIGA	KN
VIVALDI, A. GIGA	EDM

4 PARTS: 3 FLUTES-KEYBOARD-416

VIVALDI, A.-ROWE. PRELUDIO	KN
VIVALDI, A.-ROWE. SARABANDA	KN
WALKER, R. CAPRICCIO	BA
WALKER, R. CORTEGE	BA
WALTERS, H. SAFARI	RU
WHITNEY, M.-WALTERS. MOSQUITOES' PARADE	RU
YANKEE DOODLE ON TOUR.	B3

4 PARTS: 3 CLARINETS-KEYBOARD-418

BARNARD, G. MERRIMENT POLKA	WAT
BEETHOVEN, L. VAN. THEME (SYMPHONY #2)	CEN
BIZET, G. CARILLON	EDM
BRAHMSTEDT, N. FRIVOLITIES	RU
BUCHTEL, F. SOFT SHOE DANCE	KJ
CAILLIET, L. DIVERTISSEMENT	HE
CAMPO, F. CONCERTINO, OP 32. E FL CL,CL,BCL,PF	WI
CHAMINADE, C. SCARF DANCE	CEN
CHEDEVILLE, N. SCHERZO	EDM
CHOPIN, F. PRELUDES, OP 28/7, 20	CEN
CORELLI, A. AIR & DANCE	EDM
CORELLI, A. ALLEMANDA	EDM
CORELLI, A. GAVOTTE & GIGUE	EDM
CORELLI, A. GIGUE	EDM
DAHM, P. CONCERT ALBUM	EDM
DAINTY DOLL.	B3
DIETERICH, M. CHANSON JOYEUSE	RU
DIETERICH, M. CHANSON TRISTE	RU
ESTES, A. CLARISTHENICS	KN
FABRE, C.-HARRIS. REVERIE #2	CF
FRANCK, C.-LEONARD. ALLEGRETTO	BE
GHYS, J.-HARRIS. AMARYLLIS & COUNTRY GARDENS	LU
GIBBONS, O. FANTASIA FOR 3	EDM
GRIEG, E. WATCHMAN'S SONG, OP 12/3	CEN
HARRIS, F. ANDANTE & GAVOTTE	LU
HEUBERGER, R.-KREISLER/LEIDZEN. MIDNIGHT BELLS	FO
HUBNER, W. BRUMMKREISEL & ANDERE KOMPOSITIONEN, DER	FRH
HUMMEL, H.(ARR). CLARINET POLKA	RU
ILJINSKY, A. BERCEUSE	CEN
JOHNSON, C. CAPRICE GRACIEUSE	RU
JOHNSON, C. SERENADE IMPROMPTU	RU
JOPLIN, S.-WALTERS. ENTERTAINER, THE	RU
KLAUSS, N. CAPE KENNEDY SKETCHES	KN
KOEPKE, P. EVENSONG	RU
KOEPKE, P. SHIVAREE	RU
KREISLER, F.-LEIDZEN. LIEBESFREUD	FO
KREISLER, F.-LEIDZEN. RONDINO ON A THEME OF BEETHOVEN	FO
KREISLER, F.-LEIDZEN. SCHON ROSMARIN	FO
LEONARD, B. MOON WALK	BE
LEONARD, B. TRIO CON BRIO	BE
LOTTI, A. ARIETTA	EDM
MAGANINI, Q. MILADY'S FAN	EDM
MARTINI, J. PLAISIR D'AMOUR	EDM
MARTINO, D. TRIPLE CONCERTO (1977). CL,BCL,CBCL,PF	DAN
MASSENET, J.-WALTERS. NOCTURNE (LA NAVARRAISE)	RU
MAZAS, J.-PAULSON. RONDO	PO
MC KAY, F. HALLOWE'EN TIME	BA
MENDELSSOHN, F. SONG WITHOUT WORDS #48	CEN

4 PARTS: 3 CLARINETS-KEYBOARD-418

```
MOZART, W.  MINUET & TRIO (SYMPHONY IN E FL MA)              CEN
NARDINI, P.  SHEPHERD'S PIPES                                EDM
OLIVADOTI, J.  AIR & TARANTELLA                              RU
OLIVADOTI, J.  DANCE IN OLDEN STYLE                          RU
OSTRANSKY, L.  PASTORALE & SCHERZO                           RU
OSTRANSKY, L.  WALTZ & BURLESK                               RU
RACHMANINOFF, S.  VOCALISE                                   EDM
RAPHLING, S.  SQUARE DANCE                                   EDM
RIMSKY-KORSAKOFF, N.-WALTERS.  FLIGHT OF THE BUMBLEBEE       RU
SAVAGE.  MOMENTO GIOJOSO                                     CF
SCARMOLIN, A.  BARCAROLLE & PETITE HUMORESQUE.  2CL,BCL,PF   LU
SCHOLTES.  WE THREE                                          WAT
SCHUMANN, R.  SOLDIER'S MARCH, OP 68/2                       CEN
SIENNICKI, E.  PONYTAIL POLKA                                KJ
TAYLOR, L.  POLKA-A-POCO                                     HL
TCHAIKOVSKY, P.-DAVIS.  DANSE DES MIRLITONS                  RU
UGGEN, E.  PLAYWELL TRIO & QUARTET FOLIO                     S&
VIVALDI, A.  GIGA                                            EDM
WHITNEY-WALTERS.  MOSQUITOES' DANCE, THE                     RU
```

4 PARTS: 3 SAXOPHONES-KEYBOARD-420

```
ALETTER, W.-ERICKSON.  RENDEZVOUS.  2ASAX,TSAX,PF           EJ
ARDITI, L.  IL BACIO (THE KISS)                             CEN
   ASAX,TSAX(ASAX),TSAX(ASAX),PF
BARNARD, G.  PALS, THE.  3ASAX,PF                           KJ
BARNES, C.  3 DEBONAIRS.  3SAX,PF                           VO
BEAUMONT.  CON AMORE.  ASAX,TSAX(ASAX),TSAX(ASAX),PF        CEN
BEETHOVEN, L. VAN.  MINUET IN G MA                          CEN
   ASAX,TSAX(ASAX),TSAX(ASAX),PF
BEETHOVEN, L. VAN.  MOONLIGHT SONATA (ADAGIO)               CEN
   ASAX,TSAX(ASAX),TSAX(ASAX),PF
DI CAPUA, E.  O SOLE MIO (MY SUNSHINE)                      CEN
   ASAX,TSAX(ASAX),TSAX(ASAX),PF
DVORAK, A.  HUMORESKE.  ASAX,TSAX(ASAX),TSAX(ASAX),PF       CEN
ERICKSON, E.(ARR).  COUNTRY GARDENS.  2ASAX,TSAX,PF         EJ
FRANK.  MINKA, MINKA.  2ASAX,TSAX,PF                        RU
GRIEG, E.  TO SPRING.  ASAX,TSAX(ASAX),TSAX(ASAX),PF        CEN
GROOMS, C.(ARR).  TWO GUITARS (RUSSIAN SONG)               CEN
   ASAX,TSAX(ASAX),TSAX(ASAX),PF
HARRIS, F.  3 CADETS.  2ASAX,TSAX,PF                        LU
HARRIS, F.  3 CUBS.  2ASAX,TSAX,PF                          LU
HARRIS, F.  GALLANT BRIGADIERS.  2ASAX,TSAX,PF             BA
HARRIS, F.(ARR).  OLD REFRAIN & DARK EYES, THE             LU
   2ASAX,TSAX(ASAX),PF
HARRIS, F.  3 SYNCOPATORS.  2ASAX,TSAX,PF                   LU
HARRIS, F.  THREE FOR THE SHOW.  2ASAX,TSAX(ASAX),PF        LU
HERBERT, V.-HARRIS.  GYPSY LOVE SONG.  2ASAX,TSAX,PF        LU
HEUBERGER, R.-KREISLER/LEIDZEN.  MIDNIGHT BELLS,.  3ASAX,PF FO
KENNEDY.  STAR OF HOPE (REVERIE)                            CEN
   ASAX,TSAX(ASAX),TSAX(ASAX),PF
LEMARE, E.  CATHEDRAL MEDITATION                            CEN
   ASAX,TSAX(ASAX),TSAX(ASAX),PF
LEYBACH, I.  NOCTURNE #5 IN G MA                            CEN
   ASAX,TSAX(ASAX),TSAX(ASAX),PF
LISZT, F.  LOVE DREAMS (LIEBESTRAUM)                        CEN
   ASAX,TSAX(ASAX),TSAX(ASAX),PF
MC CALL, H.  VALSE ELISE.  2ASAX,TSAX,PF                    LU
```

4 PARTS: 3 SAXOPHONES-KEYBOARD-420

```
MC KAY, F.   3 AMIGOS.   2ASAX,TSAX(ASAX),PF                    BA
MC KAY, F.   ANITA.   2ASAX,TSAX,PF                             BA
MC KAY, F.   3 CADETS.   2ASAX,TSAX(ASAX),PF                    BA
MC KAY, F.   CARMELA.   2ASAX,TSAX(ASAX),PF                     BA
MC KAY, F.   CHIQUITA.   2ASAX,TSAX(ASAX),PF                    BA
MC KAY, F.   HALLOWE'EN TIME.   2ASAX,TSAX,PF                   BA
MC KAY, F.   3 JESTERS.   2ASAX,TSAX(ASAX),PF                   BA
RAVEL, M.-WALTERS.   PAVANE.   2ASAX,TSAX,PF                    RU
RICHARDS, J.   TRIAD.   2ASAX,TSAX,PF                           BA
RIMSKY-KORSAKOFF, N.   SONG OF INDIA                            CEN
   ASAX,TSAX(ASAX),TSAX(ASAX),PF
SAINT-SAENS, C.   MY HEART AT THY SWEET VOICE                   CEN
   ASAX,TSAX(ASAX),TSAX(ASAX),PF
SCARMOLIN, A.   3 SWINGSTERS.   2ASAX,TSAX,PF                   LU
SCHAEFER, A.   TROUBADOURS.   3ASAX(2ASAX,TSAX),PF             CF
TCHAIKOVSKY, P.-HARRIS.   SWEET DREAMS.   2ASAX,TSAX,PF        LU
UGGEN, E.   PLAYWELL TRIO & QUARTET FOLIO                       S&
WALTERS, H.   FANTASY FOR THREE.   2ASAX,TSAX,PF               RU
WALTERS, H.   JIM DANDIES.   2ASAX,TSAX,PF                      RU
WOOD.   LET 'ER GO.   ASAX,TSAX(ASAX),TSAX(ASAX),PF            CEN
```

4 PARTS: WOODWIND-KEYBOARD-427

```
ABBADO, M.   RIVERBERAZIONI.   FL,OB,BSN,PF                     RC
ASPLUND, G.   KVARTETT, OP 6.   OB,CL,BSN,PF                    STI
BARATI, G.   QUARTET.   FL,OB,BSN,PF                            PET
BIZET, G.   3 PIECES.   FL,CL(OB),BSN,PF                        SO
BODINUS, S.-FISCHER.   SONATE.   2OB,BSN,PF                     PET
BONNER.   OVER THE HILLS.   FL,OB,CL,PF                         EDM
BOTTJE, W.   THREESOME FOR 4 (1949).   FL,OB,BSN,PF            ACA
BOUSCH, F.   AU-DELA DU REVE (1977).   OB,CL,BSN,PF           EMO
BROWN, R.   PHOENIX AVATARA.   OB,EHN,BSN,PF                    WI
CHEDEVILLE, N.   3CHERZO,.   FL,CL,BSN,PF                       EDM
CORELLI, A.   AIR & DANCE,.   FL,CL,BSN,PF                      EDM
CORELLI, A.   ALLEMANDA.   FL,CL,BSN,PF                         EDM
CORELLI, A.   GAVOTTE & GIGUE,.   FL,OB,CL,PF                   EDM
CORELLI, A.   GIGUE.   FL,OB,CL,PF                              EDM
COUPERIN, F.   CONCERTO #1.   OB,CL,BSN,PF                      GD
COUPERIN, F.-OUBRADOUS.   GOUTS REUNIS, LES:PREMIER CONCERT    GA
   OB,CL,BSN,PF
DELVAUX, A.   5 IMPROMPTUS (1949).   FL,OB,CL,PF              CBD
DEPELSENAIRE, J.   CONCERTO GROSSO IN E MI.   FL,OB,CL,PF      GD
DRESSEL, E.   CONCERTO.   OB,CL,BSN,PF                          R&E
EVANS.   5 VARIATIONS ON AN OLDE ENGLISHE AYRE                 SH
   FL,CL,BSN(BCL),PF
FASCH, J.-WOJCIECHOWSKI.   SONATA IN D MI.   2OB,BSN,BC        HSM
FESCH, W. DE-SCHROEDER.   SONATA IN D MA, OP 7/2.   2FL,BSN,BC  HEI
FESCH, W. DE-SCHROEDER.   SONATA IN E MI, OP 7/8.   2FL,BSN,BC  HEI
FESCH, W. DE-SCHROEDER.   SONATA IN G MI, OP 7/4.   2FL,BSN,BC  HEI
GARSCIA, J.   MINIATURES.   OB,2BSN,PF                          EM
GERSCHEFSKI, E.   "AMERICA" VARIATIONS FOR WINDS, OP 44/1      ACA
   FL,CL,BSN,PF
GERSCHEFSKI, E.   AMERICA VARIATIONS, OP 45/8.   OB,BSN,CBSN,PF  ACA
GILBERT, P.   INTERRUPTED SUITE.   CL,3PF                       PET
GILLAM, R.   PRELUDE IN B FL MA.   FL,2CL,PF                    MAN
GLANVILLE-HICKS, P.   CONCERTINO DA CAMERA.   FL,CL,BSN,PF     COM
GRUNENWALD, J.   FANTASIE ARABESQUE.   OB,CL,BSN,PF            EDS
HAIEFF, A.   SERENADE.   OB,CL,BSN,PF                           GEN
```

```
HANDEL, G.-SEIFFERT.   CHAMBER TRIO #1 IN B FL MA.   2OB,BSN,PF       BRH
HANDEL, G.-SEIFFERT.   CHAMBER TRIO #2 IN D MI.   2OB,BSN,PF          BRH
HASSE, J.   CONCERTO.   2OB,BSN,HPCD                                  BRH
HEINIO, M.   QUATTROFONIA, OP 29.   FL,OB,BSN,HPCD                    FIN
HOHENSEE, W.   SERENATA 3.   OB,CL,BSN,PF                             ISR
HOLMBOE, V.   QUARTETTO MEDICO.   FL,OB,CL,PF                         CHE
HONEGGER, A.   RHAPSODY.   2FL,CL,PF                                  EDS
HOVHANESS, A.   HANNA, OP101.   2CL,2PF                               PET
JANACEK, K.   KLEINES SYMPOSIUM (1959).   FL,CL,BSN,PF                CHF
KELLY, B.   NEW ORLEANS SUITE.   2OB,BSN,HPCD                         JE
KOSMA, J.   DIVERTISSEMENT.   FL,CL,BSN,PF                            EES
KRULL, D.   QUARTET (1957).   FL,CL,BSN,PF                            STI
LEAHY, M.   AGITATION.   OB,CL,BSN,PF                                 MAN
MAGANINI, Q.   TRIO ALBUM.   FL,OB,CL,PF                              EDM
MARTINI, J.   PLAISIR D'AMOUR.   FL,OB,CL,PF                          EDM
MATHIAS, W.   CONCERTINO.   FL,OB,BSN,HPCD                            OX
MC BRIDE, R.   RUDIMENTS OF RUGCUTTING.   2OB,BSN,PF                  ACA
MILHAUD, D.   SONATE.   FL,OB,CL,PF                                   DUR
NARDINI, P.   SHEPHERD'S PIPES.   FL,OB,CL,PF                         EDM
PAGANINI, N.-TUSTIN.   MOTO PERPETUO.   FL,OB,CL,PF                   SPR
PILLIN, B.   SUITE.   FL,OB,CL,ORG                                    WI
PONCHIELLI, A.   QUARTETTO.   FL,OB,CL,PF                             M&M
QUINET, M.   CONCERTINO (1960).   OB,CL,BSN,PF                        CBD
RALSTON, A.   3 ENGLISH FOLK TUNES.   FL,OB,CL,PF                     BH
RIETI, V.   SONATE.   FL,OB,BSN,PF                                    UE
RIMSKY-KORSAKOV, N.-HORSFALL.   FLIGHT OF THE BUMBLEBEE               CF
   FL,OB,CL,PF
SAINT-SAENS, C.   CAPRICE ON DANISH & RUSSIAN AIRS, OP 79            INT
   FL,OB,CL,PF
SAINT-SAENS, C.   CAPRICE ON DANISH & RUSSIAN AIRS, OP 79            M&M
   FL,OB,CL,PF
SAINT-SAENS, C.   CAPRICE SUR DES AIRS DANOIS ET RUSSES, OP 79       DUR
   FL,OB,CL,PF
SALIERI, A.   DANSE (TARARE).   FL,OB,CL,PF                          EDM
SCHMITT, F.   A TOUR D'ANCHES, OP 97.   OB,CL,BSN,PF                 DUR
SCHNEIDER, W.   HOHENHEIMER TANZE.   OB,CL,BSN,PF                    PET
SCHUBERT, F.   ENTR'ACTE (ROSAMUNDE).   FL,OB(CL),CL,PF              CF
SCHUBERT, F.-JOSPE.   IMPROMPTU, OP142/2.   FL,OB,CL,PF              CF
SIENNICKI, E.   PONYTAIL POLKA.   2CL,BSN,PF                         KJ
STAM, H.   SONATE (1959).   FL,OB,BSN,HPCD                           SD
TELEMANN, G.-SEIFFERT.   QUARTET IN D MI (TAFELMUSIK)                BRH
   BSN,2FL,BC
TELEMANN, G.-HINNENTHAL.   QUARTET IN D MI.   2FL,BSN,BC             B&N
TELEMANN, G.   TRIO IN C MI.   FL,CL,BSN,PF                          SO
THEILE, J.-HOLMAN.   SONATA A 4.   2OB,BSN,BC                        NOM
VACKAR, D.   QUARTET (1948).   OB,CL,BSN,PF                          CHF
VIVALDI, A.-SCHROEDER.   CONCERTO IN D MA (LA PASTORELLA)            HEI
   FL,OB,BSN,BC
VIVALDI, A.   CONCERTO IN G MI.   FL,OB,BSN,BC                       B&V
VIVALDI, A.-PALFALVI.   CONCERTO IN G MI, P402.   FL,OB,BSN,BC       EMB
VIVALDI, A.   CONCERTO, P402.   FL(CL),OB,BSN,BC                     MR
VIVALDI, A.-GHEDINI.   SONATA IN G MI.   FL,OB,BSN,PF                INT
ZELENKA, J.-SCHOENBAUM.   TRIOSONATE #2 IN G MI                      B&N
   2OB,BSN(VC),BC
ZELENKA, J.-SCHOENBAUM.   TRIOSONATE #4 IN G MI                      B&N
   2OB,BSN(VC),BC
ZELENKA, J.-SCHOENBAUM.   TRIOSONATE #5 IN F MA                      B&N
   2OB,BSN(VC),BC
ZELENKA, J.-SCHOENBAUM.   TRIOSONATE #6 IN C MI                      B&N
   2OB,BSN(VC),BC
```

4 PARTS: WOODWIND-BRASS
(INCL HORN)-431

```
APOSTEL, H.  QUARTET, OP 14.  FL,CL,BSN,HN                          UE
BACH, J.S.-HIRSCH.  FUGUE IN E FL MA.  FL,CL,BSN,HN                 CF
BACH, J.S.-CATELINET.  KUNST DER FUGE (CONTRAPUNCTUS I)             PET
   OB,CL,HN,BSN
BAINBRIDGE, S.  WIND QUARTET.  FL,CL,HN,BSN                         UMP
BARTOS, F.  ECOLE DES FEMMES (1936).  OB,CL,BSN,TPT                 CHF
BARTOS, J.  DIVERTIMENTO XV.  FL,CL,HN,BSN                          FS
BISCHOF, R.  QUARTET, OP 5.  FL,CL,HN,BSN                           LDO
BLUMER, T.  SERENADE & THEME & VARIATIONS, OP 34                    SIM
   FL,CL,HN,BSN
BOUSTEAD, A.  3 MADRIGALE.  FL,CL,BSN,HN                            MC
CHAVEZ, C.  SOLI.  OB,CL,BSN,TPT                                    BH
DEDRICK, C.  SENSITIVITY.  OB,CL,HN,BSN                             KN
DI LASSO, O.-CHEYETTE.  MATONA, LOVELY MAIDEN                       GA
   2CL,HN(ACL,ASAX,EHN,BSN),BSN(BAR SAX)
EHRENBERG, C.  QUARTET, OP 40.  OB,CL,BSN,HN                        ABE
ELER, A.-DIENSTBIER.  QUARTET IN D MI, OP 11/2.  FL,CL,HN,BSN       LEU
ELER, A.-DIENSTBIER.  QUARTET IN F MA, OP 11/1.  FL,CL,HN,BSN       LEU
ELER, A.-DIENSTBIER.  QUARTET IN F MA, OP 11/3.  FL,CL,HN,BSN       LEU
ELER, A.-STEINBECK.  QUARTET, OP 6/1.  FL,CL,HN,BSN                 EUL
EROD, I.  RICERCARE ED ARIA.  FL,OB,BCL,HN                          LDO
FENNELLY, B.  2 MOVEMENTS.  OB,CL,TPT,TRB                           ACA
FRESCOBALDI, G.-AARON.  GAGLIARDA.  OB(CL),CL,HN,BSN(BCL)           GS
FUTTERER, C.  QUARTET.  OB,CL,HN,BSN                                EK
GAMBARO, G.-BALASSA.  QUARTET #1 IN F MA.  FL,CL,HN,BSN             EMB
GAMBARO, G.  QUARTET #1 IN F.  FL,CL,HN,BSN                         B&V
GAMBARO, G.-BALASSA.  QUARTET #2 IN D MI.  FL,CL,HN,BSN             EMB
GAMBARO, G.-BALASSA.  QUARTET #3 IN G MA.  FL,CL,HN,BSN             EMB
GAMBARO, G.  QUARTET #3 IN G.  FL,CL,HN,BSN                         B&V
GARDONYI, Z.  DIVERTIMENTI UBER TANZWEISEN.  FL,CL,HN,BSN           WZ
GATTERMEYER, H.  QUARTET, OP 81/2.  OB,CL,HN,BSN                    LDO
GEBAUER, F.  QUARTET.  FL,CL,HN,BSN                                 EK
GRAINER.  DISCUSSIONS.  FL,CL,HN,BSN                                CA
GRIEG, E.-CAFARELLA.  NORWEGIAN DANCE, OP 47/28.  FL,OB,CL,HN       VO
HALL, J.  DIVERTIMENTO #3.  FL,OB,BSN,HN                            CA
HANDEL, G.-AARON.  CHACONNE.  OB,CL,HN(TRB),BSN(BCL)                GS
HARTLEY, W.  SONATA DA CAMERA.  OB,CL,BSN,TRB                       CRE
HAYDN, F.-AARON.  CAPRICCIO.  OB(CL),CL,HN(TRB),BSN(BCL)            GS
HAYDN, F.-HOCKNER.  DIVERTIMENTO.  2CL,2HN                          WH
HAYDN, F.-LANDON.  DIVERTIMENTO #4, HOB. II:14 (C).  2CL,2HN        LDO
HAYDN, F.-PATERSON/MOORE.  LARGO (QUARTET, OP 76/5)                 GAL
   2CL,BSN,HN
HAYDN, F.-JANETZKY.  12 NOCTURNOS IN D MA, HOB II:5.  2FL,2HN       PM
HAYDN, F.-PATERSON/MOORE.  POCO ADAGIO CANTABILE (OP 76/3)          GAL
   2CL,BSN,HN
HAYDN, F.-NAKAGAWA.  QUARTET #18, OP 3/5.  FL,CL,BSN,HN             AMP
HAYDN, M.-LAUSCHMANN.  DIVERTIMENTO IN D MA.  FL,OB,HN,BSN          EDK
HAYDN, M.-LAUSCHMANN.  DIVERTIMENTO IN D MA.  FL,OB,HN,BSN          FRH
HENNEBERG, A.  LITEN KVARTETT, OP 36.  FL,OB,HN,BSN                 STI
HERMANN, F.  ZUR UBUNG IM ZUSAMMENSPIEL, BK. #1.  OB,CL,BSN,HN      BRH
HERTEL, J.-SALLAGAR.  SONATA A QUATTRO.  2BSN,2HN                   OHN
HESSENBERG, K.  SERENADE, OP 89.  OB,CL,HN,BSN                      S&C
HODDINOTT, A.  DIVERTIMENTO.  OB,CL,BSN,HN                          OX
HOHENSEE, W.  3 APHORISMEN.  CL,EHN,CBSN,TPT                        ISR
HOLZBAUER, I.-JANETZKY.  DIVERTIMENTO.  2BSN,2HN                    FRH
```

HOVHANESS, A. DIVERTIMENTO, OP 61/5 OB(CL),CL,HN(CL),BSN(BCL)	PET
JADIN, L. NOCTURNE #3. FL,CL,BSN,HN	EK
KAMMEL, A. SERENATA IN G MA. OB,BSN,2HN	M&M
KARKOFF, M. DIVERTIMENTO, OP 29 (1957). FL,OB,BSN,HN	STI
KAUDER, H. QUARTET (1948). OB,CL,BSN,HN	TP
KAY, N. MINIATURE QUARTET. FL,CL,BSN,HN	OX
KORDA, V. QUARTETTINO. FL,CL,HN,TPT	LDO
KREJCI, M. DIVERTIMENTO (1925). FL,CL,BSN,TPT	ART
KUNZ, A. EMANATION #2 (1964). FL,CL,BSN,HN	CAN
KUUSISTO, I. CASSAZIONE (1961). 2CL,2HN	MT
LOCKE, M. MUSIC FOR HIS MAJESTY'S SACKBUTS & CORNETS 2CL,BSN,HN	OX
MAJO, E. SUITE PER 4. 2CL,HN,BSN	FS
MENGAL, J. 3 WOODWIND QUARTETS. FL,CL,HN,BSN	CAM
MOLTER, J. CONCERTO A 4, #S 1,2,3; PUB SEPARATELY 2OB,BSN,TPT	MR
MOZART, W. ADAGIO, KV580A. EHN,BSN,2HN	EK
MOZART, W. CASSAZIONE. OB(FL),CL,HN,BSN	SO
MOZART, W.-JENSEN. DIVERTIMENTO. FL,OB,BSN,HN	CRE
MOZART, W.-SCHNEIDER. KEGEL-DIVERTIMENTO. OB,CL,HN,BSN	OHN
MOZART, W. KONZERTANTES QUARTETTE, K 19. OB,CL,BSN,HN	CF
PADOVANO, A. RONDO. OB(FL),CL,HN,BSN	GZ
PEARSON, W. HUNT, THE. FL,OB,CL,HN(BSN)	CA
PETYREK, F. GUTE NACHT, O WELT. OB,CL,HN,BSN	LDO
PLACHETA, H. QUARTET, OP 10. OB,CL,BSN,HN	LDO
PURCELL, H. FANTASIA #1. 2CL,HN,BSN	WI
REGNER, H. SERENADE. OB,CL,BSN,HN	OHN
RIISAGER, K. DIVERTIMENTO. FL,OB,BSN,HN	PET
ROSSINI, G. ANDANTE E VARIAZIONI. FL,CL,HN,BSN	HEU
ROSSINI, G.-OUBRADOUS. QUARTET #1. FL,CL,BSN,HN	EMT
ROSSINI, G.-ZACHERT. QUARTETTE, 2 VOLS. FL,CL,BSN,HN	SCH
RYAN, P. HAYDN MOVEMENT, A (SONATA #5). FL,OB,CL,HN(BSN,BCL)	CA
SABATINI, G. QUARTET. OB,CL,BSN,HN	COR
SCHAFFNER, N. 2 WOODWIND QUARTETS. FL,CL,HN,BSN	CAM
SCHNEIDER, W. KLEINES QUARTETT. FL,OB,CL,HN	MV
SCHNEIDER, W. VARIATIONEN UBER EIN SOMMERLIED. OB,CL,HN,BSN	MV
SCHUBERT, F.-BUSTO. WALTZ IN A MI. FL,CL,BSN,HN	CF
SCHURTZ, F. DIVERTIMENTO. OB,CL,HN,BSN	MV
SCHURTZ, F. KLEINE MUSIK. OB,CL,HN,BSN	MV
SCHUSTER, G. INTERMEZZI. EHN,2TPT,TRB	IMP
SCHWEGLER, J. QUARTET IN E FL MA. 2FL,2HN	WI
STAMITZ, C.-WEIGELT. QUARTET IN E FL MA, OP 8/2 OB,CL,BSN,HN	LEU
STAMITZ, C.-SCHULLER. QUARTET, OP 8/2. OB,CL,BSN,HN	M&M
STAMITZ, C. QUARTET, OP 8/2. OB,CL,BSN,HN	MAR
STRINGFIELD, L. OLD BRIDGE, AN. OB,CL,BSN,HN	MC
SUTERMEISTER, H. SERENADE. 2CL,BSN,TPT	SCH
SWIFT, R. FOLK SONG SUITE. FL,CL,BCL,HN	KN
TCHAIKOVSKY, P.-AARON. HUMORESQUE, OP 10. OB,CL,HN,BSN(BCL)	GS
TCHAIKOVSKY, P.-VON KREISLER. SARABANDE. 2CL,BSN,HN	SO
TENAGLIA, A.-CHEYETTE. ARIA 2CL,HN(ACL,ASAX,EHN,BSN),BSN(BAR SAX)	GA
TYLNAK, I. DIVERTIMENTO (1961). FL,2CL,HN	CHF
VELLERE, L. PRELUDE. OB,CL,HN,BSN	MAU
WALKER, R. CAPRICE. 2CL,BSN,HN	TM
WOOD, J. FUGUE IN C MI. OB,EHN,HN,BSN	MAN

4 PARTS: WOODWIND-STRING-433

ABEL, C.   QUARTET IN A MA.   FL,VN,VA,VC   GS
ABEL, C.   QUARTET IN A MA, OP 12/2.   FL(OB),VN,VA,VC   MR
ABEL, C.-HUNT.   QUARTET IN G MA.   FL,VN,VA,VC   S&C
AITKEN, H.   QUARTET.   CL,VN,VA,VC   AMC
ALMENRAEDER, K.   VARIATIONS ON AN ANCIENT MELODY   SPR
   BSN,VN,VA,VC
AMES, W.   QUARTET.   OB,VN,VA,VC   ACA
ANDREAE, V.-PAULER.   QUARTET, OP 43.   FL,VN,VA,VC   EUL
ANDRIESSEN, H.   CONCERT SPIRITUEL (1967).   FL,OB,VN,VC   SD
ANDRIESSEN, J.   QUARTETTO BUFFO (1974).   CL,VN,VA,VC   SD
ARNOLD, M.   OBOE QUARTET, OP 61 (1957).   OB,VN,VA,VC   FB
BABBITT, M.   COMPOSITION FOR 4 INSTRUMENTS (1947-48)   TP
   FL,CL,VN,VC
BACH, J.C.   QUARTET IN A MA.   FL,VN,VA,VC   MR
BACH, J.C.-BEYER.   QUARTET IN B FL MA.   OB,VN,VA,VC   EUL
BACH, J.C.   QUARTET IN C MA.   FL,VN,VA,VC   MR
BACH, J.C.-ERBRECHT.   QUARTET IN C MA,.   2FL,VA,VC   KIS
BACH, J.C.-DAMECK.   QUARTET IN C MA, OP 8/1.   FL(OB),VN,VA,VC   B&B
BACH, J.C.-ERBRECHT.   QUARTET IN D MA.   2FL,VA,VC   KIS
BACH, J.C.   QUARTET IN D MA.   FL,VN,VA,VC   MR
BACH, J.C.-ERMELER.   QUARTET IN D MA, OP 20/2.   2FL,VA,VC   B&N
BACH, J.C.-HILLEMANN.   QUARTET IN F MA, OP 8/4.   FL,VN,VA,VC   NV
BACH, J.C.-ERBRECHT.   QUARTET IN G MA.   2FL,VA,VC   KIS
BACH, J.C.-NAGEL.   QUARTET, OP 8/2.   FL,VN,VA,VC   MV
BACH, J.C.   QUARTET, OP 8/2.   FL,VN,VA,VC   MR
BACH, J.C.-NAGEL.   QUARTET, OP 8/5.   FL,VN,VA,VC   MV
BACH, J.C.   2 QUARTETS, OP 19/1,3.   FL,FL(VN),VA,VC   MR
BACH, J.C.-KOLBEL.   6 QUARTETS.   FL,VN,VA,VC   WZ
BACH, J.C.   3 QUARTETTES, OP 8/1,3,5.   FL(OB,CL),VN,VA,VC   CF
BACH, J.S.-DAVIS.   PRELUDE & FUGUE IN G MI.   OB,CL,VA,VC   WI
BACH, J.S.-NAGEL.   QUARTET IN E FL MA, OP 8/6.   FL,VN,VA,DB   SCH
BACH, J.S.   SONATE #4.   FL,VN,VA,VC   HAM
BAEKERS, S.   QUARTETTO (1977).   OB,VN,VA,VC   SD
BALLOU, E.   FANTASIA BREVIS.   OB,VN,VA,VC   ACA
BARKIN, E.   PRIM CYCLES (1973).   FL,CL,VN,VC   B-B
BEN-HAIM, P.   SERENADE.   FL,VN,VA,VC   IMP
BENJAMIN, T.   5 STUDIES.   CL,VN,VA,VC   SS
BENNETT, R.   QUARTET.   OB,VN,VA,VC   NO
BENTZON, J.   RACCONTO #1, OP 25.   FL,BSN,SAX,DB   WII
BERKELEY, L.   OBOE QUARTET (1967).   OB,VN,VA,VC   CHE
BERTOUILLE, G.   QUARTET #4 (1948).   FL,VN,VA,VC   CBD
BOATWRIGHT, H.   QUARTET.   CL,VN,VA,VC   OX
BOCCHERINI, L.-RAMPAL.   QUARTET.   FL,VN,VA,VC   INT
BOIS, R. DU.   KWARTET (1965).   OB,VN,VA,VC   SD
BOIS, R. DU.   SYMPOSION (1969).   OB,VN,VA,VC   SD
BOND, V.   RECITATIVE.   EHN,VN,VA,VC   SS
BOOREN, J. VAN DEN.   COLLECTION OF PIECES (1978).   FL,VN,VA,VC   SD
BOOREN, J. VANDEN.   ESTREMI (1967).   OB,VN,VA,VC   SD
BORRIS, S.   OBOE QUARTET, OP 17/1.   OB,VN,VA,VC   S-V
BOZAY, A.   IMPROVISATIONS, OP 27.   FL,VN,VA,VC   EMB
BRAEIN, E.   GLADE MUSIKANTER, DE- SERENADE.   CL,VN,VA,VC   NOR
BRITTEN, B.   PHANTASY QUARTET.   OB,VN,VA,VC   BH
BUCZYNSKI, W.   DIVERTIMENTO, OP 15 (1957).   CL,BSN,VN,VC   CAN
CABUS, P.   QUARTET.   FL,VN,VA,VC   MAU
CADOW, P.   VARIATIONS UBER EIN NORWEG. VOLKSLIED   ETB
   FL(OB),VN,VA,VC

161

```
CANNABICH, C.-STEINBECK.  QUARTET IN B FL MA.  OB,VN,VA,VC        LDO
CANNABICH, C.-WALTHER.  QUARTET IN G MA.  FL,VN,VA,VC             HEI
CARLSTEDT, J.  DIVERTIMENTO, OP 17 (1962).  OB,VN,VA,VC           ESU
CHEVREUILLE, R.  MUSIQUE DE SALON, OP 49 (1951).  FL,VN,VA,VC     CBD
CHILDS, B.  INTERBALANCES I.  OB,EHN,BCL/ASAX,DB                  ACA
CIMAROSA, D.-LENSKI.  QUARTET #1 IN D MA.  FL,VN,VA,VC            MR
CIMAROSA, D.-LENSKI.  QUARTET #2 IN F MA.  FL,VN,VA,VC            MR
CIMAROSA, D.-LENSKI.  QUARTET #3 IN A MI.  FL,VN,VA,VC            MR
COKER, W.  CONCERTINO.  BSN,VN,VA,VC                              TP
COLACO OSORIO-SWAAB, R.  KWARTET #1 (1952).  FL,VN,VA,VC          SD
COOKE, A.  QUARTET.  OB,VN,VA,VC                                  NO
COPLAND, A.  THRENODIES I & II.  FL/AFL,VN,VA,VC                  BH
COWELL.  QUARTET ROMANTIC (2 RHYTHM-HARMONY QUARTETS)             PET
   2FL,VN,VA
CRUFT, A.  FANTASY.  OB,VN,VA,VC                                  GAL
CRUSELL, B.-KNEUSSLIN.  QUARTET IN D MA, OP  8.  FL,VN,VA,VC      EK
CRUSELL, B.  QUARTET, OP  4.  CL,VN,VA,VC                         EK
CRUSELL, B.  QUARTET, OP  7.  CL,VN,VA,VC                         EK
DANZI, F.  QUARTET IN B FL MA, OP 40/2.  BSN,VN,VA,VC             MR
DANZI, F.  QUARTET IN B FL MA, OP 40/3.  BSN,VN,VA,VC             MR
DANZI, F.  QUARTET IN D MA, OP 56/1.  FL,VN,VA,VC                 MR
DANZI, F.-SONNTAG.  QUARTET IN D MI, OP 56/2.  FL,VN,VA,VC        HEI
DANZI, F.  QUARTET, OP 40/1.  BSN, VN,VA,VC                       MR
DANZI, F.  3 QUARTETS, OP 40.  BSN,VN,VA,VC                       EDK
DAVID, T.  FLUTE QUARTET, OP 11 (1959).  FL,VN,VA,VC             EMO
DEASON, D.  QUARTET.  FL,BSN,VN,VC                                SS
DELDEN, L.VAN.  QUARTETTO, OP 58 (1957).  FL,VN,VA,VC            SD
DELNOOZ, H.  QUARTET (1970).  FL,OB,VN,VC                         SD
DELVAUX, A.  CASSAZIONE (1966).  OB,CL,VN,VC                      CBD
DEVIENNE, F.  QUARTET IN G MA, OP  2/1.  FL,VN,VA,VC              B&V
DEVIENNE, F.  QUARTET IN G MA, OP 11/1.  FL,VN,VA,VC              GS
DEVIENNE, F.  QUARTET IN G MI, OP 73/3.  BSN,VN,VA,VC             MR
DEVIENNE, F.  QUARTET, OP 11/1.  FL,VN,VA,VC                      PET
DEVIENNE, F.  QUARTET, OP 73/1 IN C MA.  BSN,VN,VA,VC             MR
DEVIENNE, F.-VOXMAN.  QUARTET, OP 73/2 IN F MA.  BSN,VN,VA,VC     MR
DI DOMENICA, R.  QUARTET.  FL,VN,VA,VC                            EM
DONATO, A.  DRAG & RUN.  CL,2VN,VC                                OP
DONOVAN, R.  SERENADE.  OB,VN,VA,VC                               TP
DORAN, M.  QUARTET.  OB,CL,VA,BSN                                 WI
DOTZAUER, J.  QUARTET, OP 36.  BSN,VN,VA,VC                       EDK
DRUSCHETZKY, G.-VECSEY.  QUARTET IN E FL MA.  OB,VN,VA,VC         EMB
DRUSCHETZKY, G.-VECSEY.  QUARTET IN F MA.  OB,VN,VA,VC            EMB
DRUSCHETZKY, G.-VECSEY.  QUARTET IN G MI.  OB,VN,VA,VC            EMB
EDER, H.  QUARTET (1955).  CL,VN,VA,VC                            BRH
EISMA, W.  DIAPHONIA (1962).  OB,VN,VA,VC                         SD
EISMA, W.  WORLD WITHIN WORLD.  OB,VN,VA,VC                       PET
ETLER, A.  QUARTET.  OB,CL,BSN,VA                                 NVM
FARBER, O.  QUARTET, OP 15.  CL,VN,VA,VC                          ETB
FERNSTROM, J.  LITEN SERENAD, OP 73.  FL,CL,BSN,VC                EMF
FIALA, J.  2 QUARTETS.  OB,VN,VA,VC                               ES
FLOTHIUS, M.  CONCERTINO (1967).  OB,VN,VA,VC                     SD
FODI, J.  CALIGO (1972; REV 1973).  OB,BSN,VA,VC                  CAN
FODI, J.  POLYPHONY, OP 15 (1967).  FL,CL,VN,VC                   CAN
FOSTER, S.  VILLAGE FESTIVAL, A.  FL,2VN,DB                       EDM
FRANCAIX, J.  QUARTET.  EHN,VN,VA,VC                              SCH
FUCHS, F., JR.  LITTLE SUITE.  FL,2VN,VA                          AMP
GASSMANN, F.-KLEMENT.  3 DIVERTIMENTI.  OB,2VA,VC                 B&N
GASSMANN, F.-SCHROEDER.  QUARTET IN B FL MA.  OB,VA,2VC           MRL
GATTI, L.-RAINER.  QUARTET IN F MA.  OB,VN,VA,VC                  SIM
GEBAUER, F.  QUARTET #1.  OB,VN,VA,VC                             M&M
GEBAUER, F.  3 QUARTETS.  CL,VN,VA,VC                             M&M
GIORDANI, T.  QUARTET, OP  2/5.  FL,VN,VA,VC                      PET
```

```
GIORDANI, T.-STEINBECK.  QUARTET, OP 25/3.  OB,VN,VA,VC        BRH
GLASER, W.  QUARTET (1950).  ASAX,VN,VA,VC                     STI
GRIESBACH, K.  MUSIK.  FL,VN,VA,VC                             BRH
GROSSKOPF, E.  SONATA #3 (1967).  FL,VN,VA,VC                  B&B
GURSCHING, A.  QUARTET (1962).  OB,VN,VA,VC                    EMO
GYRING, E.  FUGUE # 1.  CL,VN,VA,VC                            ACA
GYRING, E.  FUGUE # 2.  CL,VN,VA,VC                            ACA
GYRING, E.  FUGUE # 3.  CL,VN,VA,VC                            ACA
GYRING, E.  FUGUE # 4.  CL,VN,VA,VC                            ACA
GYRING, E.  FUGUE # 5.  CL,VN,VA,VC                            ACA
GYRING, E.  FUGUE # 6.  CL,VN,VA,VC                            ACA
GYRING, E.  FUGUE # 7.  CL,VN,VA,VC                            ACA
GYRING, E.  FUGUE # 9.  CL,VN,VA,VC                            ACA
GYRING, E.  FUGUE #10.  CL,VN,VA,VC                            ACA
GYRING, E.  FUGUE #11.  CL,VN,VA,VC                            ACA
GYRING, E.  FUGUE #12.  CL,VN,VA,VC                            ACA
GYRING, E.  FUGUE #13.  CL,VN,VA,VC                            ACA
GYRING, E.  FUGUE #14.  CL,VN,VA,VC                            ACA
GYRING, E.  FUGUE #15.  CL,VN,VA,VC                            ACA
GYRING, E.  FUGUE #16.  CL,VN,VA,VC                            ACA
GYROWETZ, A.  DRITTE NACHTMUSIK, OP 26.  FL,VN,VA,VC           WZ
GYROWETZ, A.-HOLLANDERS.  QUARTET IN G MI, OP 19/2             B&V
   FL,VN,VA,VC
HALL, J.  QUARTET.  FL,VN,VA,VC                                CA
HANSCHKE, H.  VARIATIONS ON A CHILDREN'S SONG                  SCH
   FL,VN,VA(VN),VC
HAYDN, F.  HUSBAND & WIFE OR THE BIRTHDAY.  FL,VN,VA,VC        PET
HAYDN, F.  QUARTET (MAN & WIFE).  FL,VN,VA,VC                  TON
HAYDN, F.-KOELBEL.  QUARTET IN C MA.  FL,VN,VA,VC              PET
HAYDN, F.-SONNTAG.  QUARTET IN D MA.  FL,VN,VA,VC              MRL
HAYDN, F.  QUARTET IN D MA, OP  5/1.  FL,VN,VA,VC              GS
HAYDN, F.  QUARTET IN G MA, OP  5/2.  FL,VN,VA,VC              GS
HAYDN, F.  QUARTET, HOB II:B4.  OB,VN,VA,VC                    JB
HAYDN, F.-RAMPAL.  6 QUARTETS, 2 VOLS.  FL,VN,VA,VC            INT
HAYDN, J.-VOXMAN.  QUARTET, OP 50/5.  OB,VN,VA(EHN),VC         NOM
HAYDN, M.-RAINER.  QUARTET IN C MA.  EHN,VN,VC,DB              LDO
HAYDN, M.-RAINER.  QUARTET IN F MA.  FL,VN,VA,VC               LDO
HEIDEN, B.  SERENADE (1955).  BSN, STR TRIO                    AMP
HEKSTER, W.  FRESCO (1970).  CL,VN,VA,VC                       SD
HELM, E.  QUARTET.  FL,VN,VA,VC                                AMC
HEMEL, O. VAN.  ABOUT COMMEDIA DELL'ARTE (1967).  OB,VN,VA,VC  SD
HENNESSY, S.  4 CELTIC PIECES, OP 59.  EHN,STR TRIO            EES
HENNESSY, S.  VARIATIONS ON A SIX-NOTE THEME, OP 58            EES
   FL,STR TRIO
HEPPENER, R.  QUARTETTO (1967).  AFL,VN,VA,VC                  SD
HERMANS, N.  SERENADE, OP  3 (1948).  OB,VN,VA,VC              SD
HERMANSON, A.  IN SONO.  FL,OB,VN,VC                           NOR
HINDEMITH, P.  ABENDKONZERT #2.  FL,2VN,VC                     SCH
HINDEMITH, P.  ABENDKONZERT #4.  CL,VN,VA,VC                   SCH
HOCKNER, W.(ARR)-MLYNARCZYK.  DAS FLOTENQUARTETT.  FL,VN,VA,VC SIM
HODKINSON, S.  DRAWINGS, SET #6.  VN,2CL,BCL                   TP
HOFFER, P.  SERENADE "INNSBRUCK, ICH MUSS DICH LASSEN"         PET
   OB,VN,VA,VC
HOFFMEISTER, F.-ERMELER.  QUARTET IN C MI, OP 16/2            HEI
   FL,VN,VA,VC
HOFFMEISTER, F.-SONNTAG.  QUARTET IN G MA.  FL,VN,VA,VC        HSM
HOFFMEISTER, F.-HOCKNER.  2 QUARTETS.  CL,VN,VA,VC             SIM
HOLMBOE, V.  QUARTETTO, OP 90 (1972).  FL,VN,VA,VC             NOR
HONEGGER, A.  CANON SUR BASSO OBSTINEE A 4 VOIX               CHE
   FL,OB(EH),VN,VC
HOROWITZ.  QUARTET.  OB,VN,VA,VC                               BE
HUGGLER, J.  QUARTET, OP 27.  FL,VN,VA,VC                      ACA
```

4 PARTS: WOODWIND-STRING-433

```
HUGGLER, J.   QUARTET, OP 47.  BSN,VN,VA,VC                          ACA
HUMMEL, J.N.   QUARTET IN E FL MA.  CL,VN,VA,VC                      MR
HUMMEL, J.N.   QUARTET.  CL,VN,VA,VC                                 GS
HYE-KNUDSEN, J.   QUARTET.  FL,OB/EH,VN,VC                           CHE
JACOB, G.   4 FANCIES.  FL,VN,VA,VC                                  JE
JACOB, G.   QUARTET.  OB,VN,VA,VC                                    NO
JAMES, T.   QUARTET (1972).  FL,CL,VN,VC                             B-B
JIRASEK, I.   3 STUCKE (1971).  FL,VN,VA,VC                          CHF
JIRKO, I.   SERENATA (1969).  OB,VN,VA,VC                            CHF
KAHN, E.   7 CHANSONS POPULAIRES DE LA BRETAGNE.  FL,CL,BSN,VN       TP
KARLINS, M.   VARIATIONS (1963).  CL,VN,VA,VC                        ACA
KASBERGEN, M.   3 EPISODES.  FL,VN,VA,VC                             SD
KAUFMANN, A.   QUARTET, OP 17.  FL,VN,VA,VC                          LDO
KERSTERS, W.   QUARTET, OP 55 (1971).  CL,VN,VA,VC                   CBD
KEULEN, G. VAN.   SOUVENIR NOSTALGIUQE (1973).  FL,VN,VA,VC          SD
KINGMA, P.   SERENATA GEMINI.  FL,OB,VN,VC                           HU
KLUSAK, J.   CONCERTINO (1955).  FL,VN,VA,VC                         CHF
KNUSSEN, O.   QUARTET, OP 15 (1977).  OB,VN,VA,VC                    FB
KOEHLER, H.   3 QUARTETS, OP149.  FL,VN,VA,VC                        M&M
KOKAI, R.   QUARTETTINO.  CL,VN,VA,VC                                EMB
KREUTZER, C.-PAULER.   QUARTET IN E FL MA.  CL,VN,VA,VC              EUL
KREUTZER, C.-KNEUSSLIN.   QUATUOR IN E FL MA.  CL,VN,VA,VC           EK
KREUTZER, J.   QUARTET.  FL,VN,VA,VC                                 M&M
KROL, B.   QUARTET, OP 9.  OB,VN,VA,VC                               SIM
KROMMER-KRAMAR, F.-RACEK¬POHANKA.  CONCERTO IN F MA                  ES
   OB,VN,VA,VC
KROMMER-KRAMAR, F.   QUARTET.  OB,VN,VA,VC                           ES
KROMMER-KRAMAR, F.   2 QUARTETS.  OB,VN,VA,VC                        B&N
KROMMER, F.   QUARTET #2.  OB,VN,VA,VC                               ES
KROMMER, F.   QUARTET IN B FL MA, OP 46/1.  BSN,VN(VA),VA,VC         MR
KROMMER, F.-DOBREE.   QUARTET IN B FL MA, OP 83.  CL,VN,VA,VC        MR
KROMMER, F.   QUARTET IN C.  OB,VN,VA,VC                             NOM
KROMMER, F.-DOBREE.   QUARTET IN D MA, OP 82.  CL,VN,VA,VC           MR
KROMMER, F.-MICHAELS.   QUARTET IN D MA, OP 82.  CL,VN,VA,VC         HSM
KROMMER, F.-VOXMAN.   QUARTET IN E FL MA, OP 69.  CL,VN,VA,VC        MR
KROMMER, F.   QUARTET IN F.  OB,VN,VA,VC                             NOM
KRULL, D.   KVARTETT.  CL,2VN,VC                                     EMF
KRUYF, T. DE.   MOSAICO, OP 24 (1969).  OB,VN,VA,VC                  SD
KUBIN, R.   HUMORESKEN.  CL,VN,VA,VC                                 CHF
KUCERA, V.   SCENARIO, ZYKLUS (1969).  FL,VN,VA,VC                   CHF
LANG, I.   CONSTELLATIONS.  OB,VN,VA,VC                              EMB
LARSSON, L.   AUBADE, OP 63.  OB,VN,VA,VC                            CGM
LE FANU, N.   OBOE QUARTET.  OB,VN,VA,VC                             NO
LEFEVRE, X.   3 QUARTETS.  CL,VN,VA,VC                               M&M
LESSEL, F.-TAUROS.   QUARTET.  FL,VN,VA,VC                           AP
LIDHOLM, I.   CONCERTINO.  FL,OB,EHN,VC                              EMF
LOMBARDO, R.   IN MEMORIAM MICHELE LOMBARDO.  BSN,VN,VA,VC           ACA
LOTHAR, M.   MITSCHULDIGEN, DIE, OP 72.  FL,CL,BSN,VN                SIM
LOWMAN, K.   LOS ANGELES SKETCHES.  OB,CL,VA,BSN                     WI
MACONCHY, E.   QUARTET.  OB,VN,VA,VC                                 CA
MALIPIERO, G.   EPODI E GAMBI.  OB,BSN,VN,VA                         CHE
MARCO, T.   ROSA-ROSAE (1969).  FL,CL,VN,VC                          EDS
MARTINO, D.   QUARTET.  CL,VN,VA,VC                                  ECS
MARTINU, B.   MAZURKA-NOCTURNE (1949), OP. POSTH..  OB,2VN,VC        EES
MASSEUS, J.   SERENADE, OP 31 (1958).  OB,BSN,VN,VA                  SD
MASSONNEAU, L.-PAULER.   3 QUARTETS.  OB,VN,VA,VC                    EUL
MASTALIR, J.   QUARTET.  FL,VN,VA,VC                                 CHF
MC AFEE, D.   QUARTET.  FL,CL,VN,VC                                  AMC
MC CABE, J.   QUARTET (1968).  OB,VN,VA,VC                           NO
MECHEM, K.   DIVERTIMENTO, OP 12.  FL,VN,VA,VC                       ECS
METRAL, P.   DIAPARATES IMPRESSIONS SONORES (1961)                  EDT
   OB,VN,VC,DB
```

```
MICA, J.A.-STEINBECK.  QUARTET IN C MA.  OB,VN,VA,VC            LDO
MILLER, R.  LIVELY MOOD.  CL,2VN,VC                             BE
MILLER, R.  MARTIAL SPIRIT.  CL,2VL,VC                          BE
MILNER, A.  QUARTET.  OB,VN,VA,VC                               NO
MOERAN, E.  FANTASY QUARTET.  OB,VN,VA,VC                       CHE
MOESCHINGER, A.  IMAGES.  FL,ASAX,VN,VC                         BIL
MOJSISOVICS, R. VON.  SERENADE, OP 70.  FL,VN,VA,VC             LK
MORTARI, V.  3 DANZE ANTICHE.  FL,OB,VA,VC                      CAR
MORYL, R.  IMPROVISATIONS.  FL,CL,VN,VC                         BOW
MOST, A.  MINIATURE SUITE (1966).  OB,CL,BSN,VA                 CP
MOZART, W.-STOCKMEIER.  ADAGIO IN C MA, K580A.  EHN,2VN,VC      MV
MOZART, W.-RENZ.  ADAGIO, K580A.  EHN,2VN,VC                    PET
MOZART, W.-ROTHWELL.  OBOE QUARTET, KV370.  OB,VN,VA,VC         CHE
MOZART, W.  OBOE QUARTET, K370.  OB,VN,VA,VC                    BH
MOZART, W.  QUARTET IN A MA.  FL,VN,VA,VC                       CF
MOZART, W.  QUARTET IN A MA, K298.  FL,VN,VA,VC                 BRH
MOZART, W.  QUARTET IN C MA.  FL,VN,VA,VC                       CF
MOZART, W.  QUARTET IN D MA.  FL,VN,VA,VC                       CF
MOZART, W.  QUARTET IN D MA, K285.  FL,VN,VA,VC                 BRH
MOZART, W.-CRAXTON.  QUARTET IN F MA, K 370.  OB,VN,VA,VC       NOM
MOZART, W.-POHANKA.  QUARTET IN F MA, K370.  OB,VN,VA,VC        B&N
MOZART, W.  QUARTET IN F MA, K370.  OB,VN,VA,VC                 BRH
MOZART, W.  QUARTET IN F MA, K370.  OB,VN,VA,VC                 PET
MOZART, W.-EINSTEIN.  QUARTET IN G MA, K285A.  FL,VN,VA,VC      PET
MOZART, W.  QUARTET, K370.  OB,VN,VA,VC                         INT
MOZART, W.-SCHWEDLER.  3, K285,285B,298 QUARTET.  FL,VN,VA,VC   PET
MOZART, W.-POHANKA.  QUARTETS, KV285,285A,285B,298              B&N
   FL,VN,VA,VC
MOZART, W.  3 QUARTETS, K285,298,370.  FL(OB),VN,VA,VC          EDK
MOZART, W.  4 QUARTETS.  FL,VN,VA,VC                            INT
MULLER, I.  QUATUOR #2.  CL,VN,VA,VC                            M&M
MULLER, L.  12 VERANDERUNGEN.  FL,VN,VA,VC                      BRH
MULLER, S.  KAMMERMUSIK IN A MA, OP  1.  CL,VN,VA,VC            BRH
MYERS, R.  QUARTET.  FL,ASAX,BSN,VC                             SS
NELHYBEL, V.  ORATIO II.  OB,VN,VA,VC                           JER
NOWAK, L.  QUARTET.  OB,VN,VA,VC                                ACA
OSIECK, H.  SONATINE (1961).  OB(CL),VN,VA,VC                   SD
PADEREWSKI, I.  MINUET.  FL,2CL,DB                              PWM
PAISIELLO, G.-PAEULER.  6 DIVERTIMENTI.  FL,VN,VA,VC            EUL
PAISIELLO, G.-DELIUS.  QUARTET IN G MA.  FL,VN,VA,VC            EUL
PARK, S.  PASTORALE.  FL,2VN,VC                                 OP
PETRIC, I.  CONCERT IMPROVISATIONS.  OB,VN,VA,VC                EDD
PINKHAM, D.  PRELUDE.  FL,VN,VA,VC                              ACA
PLEYEL, I.-ALBRECHT.  QUARTET IN B FL MA, OP 20/2              KIS
   FL,VN,VA,VC
PLEYEL, I.-ALBRECHT.  QUARTET IN C MA, OP 20/3.  FL,VN,VA,VC    KIS
PLEYEL, I.-ALBRECHT.  QUARTET IN G MA, OP 20/1.  FL,VN,VA,VC    KIS
PLEYEL, I.  QUARTET, OP 17/2.  FL,VN,VA,VC                      MR
PLEYEL, I.-RAMPAL.  3 QUARTETS, OP 41.  FL,VN,VA,VC             INT
POWELL.  NOCTURNE.  FL,VN,VA,VC                                 SO
PRAAG, H. VAN.  3 MOVEMENTS (1958).  OB,VN,VA,BSN(VC)           SD
PREVOST, A.  MOBILES (1959).  FL,VN,VA,VC                       CAN
RAASTED, N.  SERENADE, OP 40.  FL,OB,VA,VC                      SPD
RAINIER, P.  QUANTA.  OB,VN,VA,VC                               S&C
RAMEAU, J.-URBAN.  TAMBOURIN.  OB,VN,VA,VC                      BE
RANDOLPH, D.  PRELUDE & VARIATIONS.  CL,VN,VA,VC                AMC
RAUTAVAARA, E.  QUARTET (1965).  OB,VN,VA,VC                    MT
RAWSTHORNE, A.  QUARTET.  CL,VN,VA,VC                           OX
RECHBERGER, H.  YLISTYSLAULU HOYRYVETURILL.  PIC,CL,VA,VC       FIN
REGT, H. DE.  MUSIC, OP 33 (1974).  FL,VN,VA,VC                 SD
REGT, H. DE.  MUSICA.  OB,VN,VA,VC                              SD
REGT, H. DE.  MUSICA, OP 13 (1971).  AFL,VN,VA,VC              SD
```

REICHA, A.-RACEK/JANETZKY. 3, OP 98/1-3 QUARTETS   ES
    FL,VN,VA,VC
REINER, K. SENTENCE. FL,VN,VA,VC   CHF
REUTER, F. SPIELMUSIK IN F MA, OP 30. FL,2VN,VC(VA)   FRH
RIETI, V. VARIATIONS. FL,CL,VN,VC   GEN
RIETZ, J. QUARTET. FL,VN,VA,VC   EDT
RIISAGER, K. SONATA. FL,CL,VN,VC   CHE
ROETSCHER, K. DIVERTIMENTO, OP 22. FL,CL,VN,VC   B&B
ROHWER, J. QUARTET. FL,VN,VA,VC   MV
ROSSINI, G.-FORSTER. QUARTET #2 IN A MA. FL,VN,VA,VC   EUL
ROSSINI, G.-FORSTER. QUARTET #3 IN B FL MA. FL,VN,VA,VC   EUL
ROSSINI, G.-FORSTER. QUARTET #4 IN D MA. FL,VN,VA,VC   EUL
ROXBURGH, E. ECLISSI. OB,VN,VA,VC   UMP
SALMENHAARA, E. QUARTET. FL,VN,VA,VC   FIN
SAMMARTINI, G.-RHAU. NOTTURNO A QUATRO. FL,2VN,VC   BRH
SARAI, T. QUARTET (1961-62). FL,VN,VA,VC   EMB
SCHIBLER, A. EPITAPH, FURIOSO UND EPILOG, OP 65. FL,VN,VA,VC A&S
SCHROEDER, H. QUARTET, OP 38. OB,VN,VA,VC   SCH
SCHUBERT, F.-URBAN. CRADLE SONG. FL,VN,VA,VC   BE
SCHULLER, G. 2 MOVEMENTS (1952). FL,VN,VA,VC   MAR
SCHUMACHER, S. SYMMETRIES. FL,SOP SAX(CL),BCL(BSN),DB   MEP
SCHWINDL, F. QUARTET IN G MA. FL,VN,VA,VC   PET
SEARLE, H. QUARTET, OP 12. CL,BSN,VN,VA   PET
SEHLBACH, E. INTRADA. FL,VN,VA,VC   MV
SEIBER, M. PASTORALE. FL,VN,VA,VC   SCH
SEMIATIN, L. ENCORE. CL,VN,VA,VC   AMC
SERMILA, J. PERCEPTION (1973). 2FL,2VC   ER
SHERMAN, N. REUNION, THE (1971). FL/PIC,VN,VA,VC   CAN
SHIELD, W. QUARTET IN F MA, OP 3/2. OB,VN,VA,VC   S&C
SIMONS, N. QUARTET. FL,VN,VA,VC   ACA
SIMS, E. FLOURISH. OB,VN,VA,VC   ACA
SIMS, E. FROM AN OBOE QUARTET. OB,VN,VA,VC   ACA
SIMS, E. II (VARIATIONS) (1973). OB,VN,VA,VC   ACA
SORENSON, T. LITEN MUSIK (1971/72). OB,2VN,VA   STI
SPERGER, J.-MALARIC. QUARTET IN D MA. FL,VA,VC,DB   LDO
SPERGER, J. QUARTET IN D MA. DB SOLO,FL,VA,VC   FRH
STAMITZ, C.-DRUNER. QUARTET #6. FL(CL),2VN,VC   LEU
STAMITZ, C.-OTT. QUARTET IN A MA, OP 4/6   LEU
    CL(FL,OB),VN,VA,VC
STAMITZ, C.-MONKMEYER. QUARTET IN C MA. FL,2VN,VC   SCH
STAMITZ, C.-UPMEYER. QUARTET IN D MA, OP 8/1   B&N
    FL(OB),VN,HN(VA),VC
STAMITZ, C.-HOCKNER. QUARTET IN E FL MA. CL,VN,VA,VC   HEI
STAMITZ, C. QUARTET IN E FL MA. CL(OB),VN,VA,VC   CF
STAMITZ, C. QUARTET IN E FL MA, OP 8/4. CL(OB),VN,VA,VC   INT
STAMITZ, C. QUARTET IN E FL MA, OP 19/3. CL,VN,VA,VC   MR
STAMITZ, C.-STEINS. QUARTET IN E FL MA, OP 8/4   B&B
    CL(OB),VN,VA,VC
STAMITZ, C.-MONKMEYER. QUARTET IN F MA. FL,2VN,VC   SCH
STAMITZ, C. QUARTET IN F MA, OP 8/3. OB(CL),VN,VA(HN),VC   MR
STAMITZ, C. QUARTET, OP 19/2. CL,VN,VA,VC   MR
STAMITZ, C. 2 QUARTETS, OP 19/5, 6. BSN,VN,VA,VC   EUL
STAMITZ, C. 2 QUARTETS,. OB,VN,VA,VC   M&M
STAMITZ, C.-MARX. 2 QUARTETS. CL,VN,VA,VC   M&M
STAMITZ, K. QUARTET, OP 8/4. CL(OB),VN,VA,VC   EDK
STRAESSER, J. INTERSECTIONS IV (1972). OB,VN,VA,VC   SD
STRAESSER, J. MUZIEK (1962). OB,VN,VA,VC   SD
STRATEGIER, H. QUARTET (1968). FL,VN,VA,VC   SD
SUTHERLAND, M. QUARTET. EHN,VN,VA,VC   AU
SYDEMAN, W. QUARTET (1962). OB,VN,VA,VC   SS
TAMAS, J. QUARTET IN B FL MA. CL,VN,VA,VC   PET
TATE, P. RAINBOW, THE & THE CUCKOO. OB,VN,VA,VC   OX

4 PARTS: WOODWIND-STRING-433

```
TAUB, B.   QUARTET.  FL,BSN,VN,VC                                ACA
TOCH, E.   QUARTET.  OB,CL,BSN,VA                                BE
TREMBLAY, G.   5 PIECES (1966).  OB,CL,BSN,VA                    CP
TROWBRIDGE, L.  PENSIVELY.  CL,VN,VA,VC                          OP
ULLMAN, B.  KVARTETT (1956).  FL,CL,VA,VC                        EMF
VERHAAR, A.  DIVERTIMENTO, OP 12 (1937).  FL,VN,VA,VC            SD
VIECENZ, H.  QUARTET.  FL,VN,VA,VC                               PET
VIOTTI, G.  QUARTET IN B FL MA, OP 22/1.  FL,VN,VA,VC            MR
VIVALDI, A.  CONCERTO IN G MI, F XII/20.  FL,OB,VN,BSN           RC
VOGEL, J.  QUARTET, OP  5/1.  BSN,VN,VA,VC                       MR
VOGEL, W.  "INSPIRE PAR JEAN ARP".  FL,CL,VN,VC                  HEI
VOGEL, W.  12 (1942) VARIETUDES.  FL,CL,VN,VC                    ESZ
VOGLER, G.-ZOLLER.  QUARTET IN B FL MA.  FL,VN,VA,VC             HSM
WAGNER, J.  THEME & VARIATIONS.  FL,CL,VN,VC                     SN
WAILLY, P. DE.  SERENADE.  FL,VN,VA,VC                           EDS
WANHAL, J.-SCHROEDER.  NOTTURNO IN C MA.  FL,2VN,VC              MRL
WANHAL, J.-BALASSA/WILHEIM.  QUARTET.  CL,VN,VA,VC               EMB
WANHAL, J.  QUARTET IN F MA.  CL,VN,VA,VC                        MR
WANHAL, J.  QUARTET, OP  7/1 & QUARTET, OP  7/2.  OB,VN,VA,VC    MR
WANHAL, J.  QUARTET, OP  7/4 IN E FL MA.  OB,VN,VA,VC            MR
WANHAL, J.  QUARTET, OP  7/5 IN A MA.  OB,VN,VA,VC               MR
WANHAL, J.  QUARTET, OP  7/6 IN C MA.  OB,VN,VA,VC               MR
WENDLING, J.-BOPP.  QUARTET IN G MA, OP 10/4.  FL,VN,VA,VC       B&N
WHETTAM, G.  OBOE QUARTET.  OB,VN,VA,VC                          GS
WILDBERGER, J.  QUARTETTO (1952).  FL,CL,VN,VC                   EMO
WILSON, D.  DOUBLES.  CL,BSN,VA,DB                               PET
WINTER, P. VON.  QUARTET IN E FL MA.  CL,VN,VA,VC                MR
WIREN, D.  KVARTETT, OP 31.  FL,OB,CL,VC                         CGM
WOLF, E.-HOCKNER-TISCHER.  QUARTET IN G MA.  FL,OB,BSN,VC        HEI
WOOLLEN, R.  QUARTET.  FL,VN,VA,VC                               ACA
WORDSWORTH, W.  OBOE QUARTET, OP 44.  OB,VN,VA,VC                LEN
WUORINEN, C.  BEARBEITUNGEN UBER DAS GLOGAUER LIEDERBUCH         PET
   FL/PIC,CL/BCL,VC,DB
YUN, T.  IMAGES (1968).  FL,OB,VN,VC                             B&B
ZIELCHE, H.-HOCKNER/MLYNARCZYK.  QUARTET IN G MA.  FL,2VN,VC     HEI
ZONN, P.  CONCERT PIECE.  BSN,VN,VA,VC                           ACA
ZONN, P.  MICRODITTIES.  OB,VN,VA,VC                             ACA
```

4 PARTS: WOODWIND-BRASS-STRING-434

```
ANGERER, P.  KONZERTANTES QUARTETT (1951).  OB,HN,VA,VC          LDO
ANGERER, P.  SERENATA (1951).  VN,VA,HN,BSN                      LDO
BOATWRIGHT, H.  SERENADE.  CL,HN,VN,VC                           OX
DOBROWOLSKI, A.  8 (1959) STUDIES.  OB,BSN,TPT,DB                AP
GABURO, K.  LINE STUDIES.  FL,CL,VA,TRB                          AMC
HALTENBERGER(MUNSTER).  DIVERTIMENTO.  FL,HN,VN,VA               EUL
HAWORTH, F.  GLORY & THE DREAM, THE (1957).  CL,HN(VA),VN,VC     CAN
HEDGES, A.  RONDO CONCERTANTE, OP 21.  CL,HN,VN,VC               CA
KOMOROUS, R.  UNTITLED 5.  FL,HN,VA,DB                           CAN
KRUYF, T. DE.  QUARTETTO.  FL,BSN,TPT,VN                         SD
KUBIZEK, A.  VERGNUGLICHE MINIATUREN, OP 28A.  CL,BSN,VN,TRB     LDO
MARCO, I.  KITICA.  FL,CL,VN,TRB                                 EDS
MICHALEK, S.  DIVERTIMENTO (1964).  CL,BSN,HN,VC                 PWM
MOZART, W.-MOYSE.  3 QUARTETS.  FL,VN,VA,VC                      GS
PAYNE, F.  QUARTET.  ASAX,TPT,VA,DB                              SS
POLLOCK, R.  STUDY (1970).  CL,HN,VN,VC                          B-B
RATTENBACH, A.  SERENATA.  FL,CL,TPT,VC                          SN
STAMITZ, K.-UPMEYER.  QUARTET IN D MA, OP  8/1.  FL,VN,HN,VC     B&N
```

4 PARTS: WOODWIND-BRASS-STRING-434

```
STEARNS, P.   CHAMBER SET #2.   ASAX,TPT,VN,DB             ACA
SYDEMAN, W.   QUARTET (1955).   CL,VN,DB,TPT                SS
TANENBAUM, E.   MUSIC FOR 3 CHAMBER GROUPS                 ACA
    FL/AFL,FL/PIC,VC,TRB(DB)
WYNER, Y.   PASSOVER OFFERING.   FL,CL,TRB,VC              AMP
```

4 PARTS: WOODWIND-BRASS-KEYBOARD-435

```
BALADA, L.   CUATRIS.   FL,CL,TRB,PF                       GEN
BEETHOVEN, L. VAN-PHILLIPS.   RONDINO IN E FL MA            OX
    OB(CL),CL,HN(CL),PF
BERWALD, F.-BENGTSSON/HAMMAR.   KLAVIERQUARTETT, OP  1     B&N
    CL,BSN,HN,PF
BERWALD, F.   QUARTET IN E FL MA.   CL,HN,BSN,PF           CGM
BISCOGLI.   CONCERTO IN D MA.   OB,BSN,TPT,PF               MR
CRUSELL, B.-WEELINK.   CONCERTANTE, OP  3.   CL,BSN,HN,PF  KAW
DEVIENNE, F.-PETIT.   QUARTET.   FL,HN,BSN,PF             KAW
DOHL, F.   TOCCATA (1962-63).   FL,TPT,CEMB,PF             HG
FORSTER, K.-BLOCK.   SONATA A 7.   2TPT,BSN,PF             MR
HUBEAU, J.   SONATINE HUMORESQUE.   FL,CL,HN,PF           BIL
MANICKE, D.   QUARTET IN D MI.   CL,BSN,HN,PF             SIM
PERUTI, C.   AUTUMN MUSIC.   FL,CL,TRB,PF                 MAN
PERUTI, C.   LEFTOVERS.   CL,BCL,TRB,PF                   MAN
PFEIFFER, G.-LAUSCHMANN.   SONATA.   FL,HN,BSN,PF         FRH
ROLAND-MANUEL, A.   SUITE DANS LE GOUT ESPAGNOL.   OB,BSN,TPT,PF  DUR
SCHULLER, G.   CURTAIN RAISER (1960).   FL,CL,HN,PF       MAR
SKALKOTTAS, N.   QUARTET.   OB,BSN,TPT,PF                 UE
STARER, R.   CONCERTO A TRE.   CL,TPT,TRB,PF               MC
WILBRANDT, J.   QUARTET.   CL,ASAX,TPT,PF                 ISR
```

4 PARTS: WOODWIND-STRING-KEYBOARD-436

```
AGER, K.   METABOLES (1976).   CL,VN,VC,PF                EMO
ANDRIESSEN, J.   SUITE DE NOEL (1944).   FL,VN,VA,PF       SD
ANTONIOU, T.   QUARTETTO GIOCOSO, OP 26 (1965).   OB,VN,VC,PF  B&N
BACH, C.P.E.-SCHMID.   QUARTET #1 IN A MI, WQ 93.   FL,VA,VC,PF  B&N
BACH, C.P.E.-SCHMID.   QUARTET #2 IN D MA, WQ 94.   FL,VA,VC,PF  B&N
BACH, C.P.E.-SCHMID.   QUARTET #3 IN G MA, WQ 95.   FL,VA,VC,PF  B&N
BACH, J.C.-RUF.   QUARTET IN C MA.   FL,VN,VA,BC          HEI
BACH, J.C.-NAGEL.   QUARTET, OP  8/6.   FL,VN,VA,BC        SCH
BACH, J.C.F.-KOLBEL.   QUARTET #2.   FL,VN,VA,BC           WZ
BACH, J.C.F.-RUF.   SONATA IN D MA.   FL,VN,VA,BC         B&N
BACH, J.S.-SONNLEITNER.   10 CANONS, BWV1080.   FL,VN,VC,HPCD  LDO
BACH, J.S.-GOUNOD.   MEDITATION (AVE MARIA)               PET
    FL(OB,CL),VN,VC,PF
BACH, J.S.   SONATA A 3.   FL,VN,VC,PF                     GS
BACH, J.S.-BELAUBRE.   SONATE EN TRIO.   2FL,VC,HPCD      BIL
BAERVOETS, R.   MUSICA NOTTURNA (1969).   FL,VN,VC,HPCD   CBD
BAERVOETS, R.   QUATUOR (1974).   FL,CL,VN,PF             CBD
BARATI, G.   QUARTET.   FL/AFL,OB/EHN,DB(VC),HPCD         PET
BARNES, M.   THREE-SIDED ROOM (1972).   CL,VN,VC,PF       CAN
BECK, J.   QUARTET.   FL,VN,VC,PF                          MV
BENKER, H.-HOHNER.   2 TANZE.   FL,VN,VC,ACC             HOH
BENTZON, N.   MOSAIQUE MUSICALE, OP 54.   FL,VN,VC,PF     CHE
```

168

```
BERKELEY, L.   CONCERTINO, OP 49.   FL,VN,VC,HPCD (PF)          CHE
BERTALI, A.   SONATA I IN D MI.   BSN,2VN,BC                    MR
BERTALI, A.   SONATA II IN D MI.   BSN,2VN,BC                   MR
BERTALI, A.   SONATA III IN A MI.   BSN,2VN,BC                  MR
BEVERSDORF, T.   DIVERTIMENTO DA CAMARA.   FL/PIC,OB/EHN,DB,HPCD   GS
BIZET, G.   ADAGIETTO.   FL,VN,VA(VC),PF                        EDM
BODINUS, S.-SCHULTZ/HAUSER.   CONCERTO #3 IN E MI.   FL,2VN,BC  LEU
BOGUSLAWSKI, E.   MUSICA PER ENSEMBLE MW-2 (1970).   FL,VC,2PF  PWM
BOONE, C.   QUARTET.   CL,VN,VC,PF                              EDS
BOTTJE, W.   DESIGNS.   2FL,VC,PF                               ACA
BOUVARD, J.   3 IMAGES.   FL,ASAX(CL),VN,PF                     BIL
BOZIC, D.   GLASBENA SLIKANICA.   FL,VN,VC,PF                   EDD
BRAUNLICH, H.   QUARTET.   FL,BSN,VA,PF                         MAN
BRESGEN, C.   QUARTET "UMREM, UMREM".   CL,VN,VC,PF             LDO
BRITTEN, B.   GEMINI VARIATIONS, OP 73 (1965)                  FB
    FL,VN,PF (2 PLAYERS)
BRUZDOWICZ, J.   ESQUISSES (1969).   FL,VA,VC,PF               PWM
BUCZYNSKI, W.   QUARTET/74 (1974).   FL,VC,HPCD,PF             CAN
BULL, E.   AD USUM AMICORUM.   FL,VN,VC,PF                      BIL
BURKHARD, W.   LYRISCHE MUSIK, OP 88.   FL,VA,VC,PF            B&N
CARTER, E.   SONATA (1952).   FL,OB,VC,HPCD                    AMP
CASTERA, R. DE.   CONCERT.   FL,CL,VC,PF                       EDS
COOPER, P.   CONCERT FOR 4 (1965).   FL,OB,DB,HPCD             CHE
CORELLI, A.   GAVOTTE & GIGUE.   FL,VN,VA(VC),PF               EDM
CORRETTE, M.-RUF.   CONCERTO IN E MI, OP  4/6.   FL,2VN,BC     SCH
CORRETTE, M.   SONATA EN TRIO, #5.   FL,VN,VC,PF               EMT
COUPERIN, F.   APOTHEOSE, L' DE CORELLI.   2FL,VA DA GAMBA,BC  MR
COUPERIN, F.   APOTHEOSE, L' DE LULLY.   2FL,VA DA GAMBA,BC    MR
COUPERIN, F.-HIGGINBOTTOM.   FRANCOISE, LA (LES NATIONS)       MR
    2FL,DB,BC
COUPERIN, F.-HIGGINBOTTOM.   IMPERIALE, L' (LES NATIONS)       MR
    2FL,DB,BC
COUPERIN, F.-HIGGINBOTTOM.   PIEMONTOISE, LA (LES NATIONS)     MR
    2FL,DB,BC
CRUMB, G.   11 ECHOES OF AUTUMN, 1965.   AFL,CL,VN,PF          PET
DELLA PERUTI, C.   WINTER MUSIC.   FL,CL,VC,PF                 MAN
DESHEVOV, V.   EXOTIC SUITE, OP 13.   OB,VN,VC,PF              MKE
ESCOBAR, A.   MOVEMENTOS (1970).   CL,VN,VC,PF                 EDT
FASCH, J.-RUF.   CONCERTO IN C MA.   FL,VN,BSN,BC              HEI
FASCH, J.-HECHLER.   CONCERTO IN G MA.   OB,2VN,BC             HEI
FASCH, J.-WOJCIECHOWSKI.   SONATA IN D MA.   FL,VN,BSN,BC      HSM
FASCH, J.   SONATA IN D MA.   FL,VN,BSN,BC                     B&V
FASCH, J.-WOEHL.   SONATE IN B FL MA.   FL,OB,VN,BC            B&N
FASCH, J.-GERLACH.   SONATE IN D MA.   FL,VN,BSN(VC),BC        B&N
FELDMAN, M.   DURATIONS #1 (1960).   AFL,VN,VC,PF              PET
FENIGSTEIN, V.   7 MINIATURE.   FL,OB(CL),VC,PF                EUL
FINGER, G.-HOLMAN.   SONATA IN C MA, OP 5/13.   VN,BSN,BC      NOM
FINKBEINER, R.   QUARTET (1966).   CL,VN,VC,PF                 BRH
FINNEY, R.   DIVERTISSEMENT.   CL,VN,VC,PF                     BOW
FONTYN, J.   MUSICA A QUATRO.   CL,VN,VC,PF                    ECH
FORTNER, W.   NEW-DELHI-MUSIK.   FL,VN,VC,PF                   SCH
FOSTER, S.   VILLAGE FESTIVAL, A.   FL,VN,VC,PF                EDM
FRANKEN, W.   DIVERTIMENTO (1948).   FL,VA,VC,PF               SD
FUX, J.-HILLEMANN.   SONATA A TRE IN D MI.   OB,VN,VC,BC       HEI
FUX, J.-HILLEMANN.   SONATA A TRE IN D MI.   FL,VN,VC,PF       PET
GASSMANN, F.-TOTTCHER/HARTIG.   QUARTET IN B FL MA            HSM
    OB,VA,VC,BC
GERBER, S.   TRAUMWERK.   FL,VA,VC,PF                          ACA
GIORDANI, T.   EIGHTEENTH CENTURY AIR, AN.   FL,VN,VC,PF       EDM
GIORDANI, T.-RUF.   QUARTET IN G MA.   FL,VN,VC,PF             SCH
GIRON, A.   QUARTET.   FL,CL,VA,PF                             CF
GODRON, H.(948).   SONATINE (.   FL,VN,VA,PF                   SD
```

```
GOLDMAN, R.  CHAMBER MUSIC SUITE.  2OB,VC(BSN),PF                    TP
GOOSSEN, J.  QUARTET.  CL,VN,VA,PF                                   AMC
GOW, D.  QUARTET, OP 28.  FL,OB,VC,HPCD                              MR
GRAUN, J.-BRINCKMANN/MOHR.  CONCERTO IN E MI.  FL,2VN,BC             B&N
GRAUN, J.-SCHROEDER.  CONCERTO IN F MA.  FL,2VN,BC                   HMO
GREEN, R.  HOLIDAY FOR FOUR-CHAMBER QUARTET.  CL,BSN,VA,PF           AME
GREENBERG, L.  QUARTET (1964).  AFL,BSN,VN,PF                        CAN
GUILLEMAIN, L.-KLENGEL.  CONVERSATION GALANTE ET AMUSANTE            BRH
    FL,VN,VC,PF
GUILLEMAIN, L.-POLNAUER.  QUARTET IN A MA, OP 12/4                   HSM
    FL,VN,VC,BC
GUILLEMAIN, L.-POLNAUER.  QUARTET IN B MI, OP 12/2                   HSM
    FL,VN,VA DA GAMBA,BC
GUILLEMAIN, L.-WINSCHERMANN.  QUARTET IN C MA, OP 12/6               HSM
    FL(OB),VN,VA,BC
GUILLEMAIN, L.-PETIT.  SONATE #3.  FL,VN,VC,BC                       EMT
GUILLOU, J.  COLLOQUES #1.  FL,OB,VN,PF                              ALE
GUYONNET, J.  POLYPHONIE #3.  AFL,VA,2PF                             UE
HAGERUP-BULL, E.  AD USUM AMICORUM.  FL,VN,VC,PF                     BIL
HANDEL, G.  CHAMBER TRIO #24 IN F MA.  OB,BSN,DB,HPCD                B&N
HANDEL, G.-ZOBELEY.  CONCERTO #1 IN D MI.  FL,VN,VC,BC               SCH
HANDEL, G.-MONKEMEYER.  8 PSALMOUVERTUREN, 2 VOLS.  OB,2VN,BC        PEL
HASSE, J.-MOHR.  CONCERTO IN A MA.  FL,2VN,BC                        B&N
HASSE, J.-SONNTAG.  CONCERTO IN D MA.  FL,2VN,BC                     SCH
HAUBIEL, C.  IN PRAISE OF DANCE.  OB,VN,VC,PF                        HE
HAUBIEL, C.  MASKS.  OB,VN,VC,PF                                     OP
HAUBIEL, C.  PARTITA.  OB,VN,VC,PF                                   OP
HAYDN, F.-UPMEYER.  QUARTET IN G MA, OP  5/4.  FL,VN,VA,BC           B&N
HEINICHEN, J.-JANETZKY.  CONCERTO IN G MA.  FL(OB),2VN,BC            FRH
HEINICHEN, J.  CONCERTO IN G MA.  FL(OB),2VN,BC                      CFV
HEISS, J.  QUARTET (1971).  FL,CL,VC,PF                              BOW
HEUSSENSTAMM, G.  TEXTURE VARIATIONS.  FL,VN,VC,HPCD                 SS
HILL, J.  SERENADE.  FL,VN,VC,PF                                     SS
HINDEMITH, P.  QUARTET (1938).  CL,VN,VC,PF                          SCH
HOSMER, J.  7/4 SERENADE (1966).  FL,OB,DB,HPCD                      M&M
HOVHANESS, A.  QUARTET #1, OP 97.  FL,OB,VC,HPCD                     PET
HOVHANESS, A.  QUARTET #2, OP112.  FL,OB,VC,PF                       PET
HUBER, N.  CHRONOGRAMM (1966).  CL,VN,VC,PF                          GBV
HURNIK, I.  SONATA DA CAMERA (1953).  FL,OB(CL),VC,PF                ART
IVES, C.-SINGLETON.  REMEMBRANCE                                     PI
    FL(TPT,HN,V),FL(VN),VN(FL),PF
JANITSCH, J.-WOLFF.  CHAMBER SONATA, OP  8, "ECHO"                   BRH
    FL,OB(FL),VA,BC
JANITSCH, J.  QUADRO "O HAUPT VOLL BLUT UND WUNDEN"                  H-V
    OB,VN,VA,BC
JANITSCH, J.-WINSCHERMANN.  QUARTET IN C MI.  OB,VN,VA,BC            HSM
JANITSCH, J.  SONATA IN C MA, OP  4.  FL,OB,VN,BC                    MR
JOHANSON(ARR).  GREENSLEEVES.  FL,VN,VC,PF                           WIL
JOHNSON, T.  ACTION MUSIC II.  FL,VC,PF,DANCER                       AMP
KAPR, J.  5 TESTIMONIES.  CL,VN,VC,PF                                ES
KARKOFF, M.  QUARTETTO PICCOLO, OP 53.  FL,VN,VC,PF                  EMF
KEMPFF, W.  QUARTET, OP 15.  FL,VN,VC,PF                             SIM
KING, H.  A FLEUR D'EAU (1964).  FL,VN,PF,VC                         SD
KING, H.  CONCERTINO AVIUM (1965).  FL,VN,VA D'GAMBA,HPCD            SD
KOECHLIN, C.  SUITE EN QUATUOR.  FL,VN,VA,PF                         EES
KOLMAN, P.  DUE CASTI, OP  2.  FL,CL,VN,PF                           SHF
KROMMER, F.-SPINDLER.  CONCERTANTE.  FL,OB,VN,PF                     FRH
KUPFERMAN, M.  INFINITIES 13.  FL,CL,VN,PF                           BOW
LEE, N.  VARIATIONS.  FL,OB,VC,PF                                    AMC
LEVINE, J.  HARPSICHORD QUARTET.  FL,CL,VN,HPCD                      ESZ
LINICKE, J.-SCHROEDER.  CONCERTO IN G MA.  FL,VN,VA,BC               PET
LOEILLET, J.-RUF.  CONCERTO IN D MA.  FL,2VN,BC                      B&N
```

```
LUDEWIG, W.  APOKALYPTISCHE VISION (1971/72).  CL,VN,VC,PF        B&B
MAASZ, G.  CONCERTINO.  FL,VN,VC,PF                               B&N
MAASZ, G.  HAMBURGISCHE TAFELMUSIK.  FL,VN,VC,PF                  R&E
MAGANINI, Q.  TRIO ALBUM.  FL,VN(VA),VC,PF                        EDM
MAGI, E.  DIALOGUES.  FL,CL,VC,PF                                 MKE
MARTINU, B.  QUARTET (1947).  OB,VN,VC,PF                         EES
MATHE, O.  LYRISCHE SUITE.  FL,OB,VA,HPCD                         ROB
MC CLELLAN, R.  MAZE.  FL,CL,VC,PF                                SS
MESSIAEN, O.  QUATUOR POUR LA FIN DU TEMPS.  CL,VN,VC,PF          DUR
MICHAEL, E.  PETITE SUITE ANTIQUE.  FL,VN,VC,PF                   PET
MOLTER, J.  CONCERTINO A 4 IN A MI.  FL,VN,BASS GAMBA,BC          HMP
MOLTER, J.-DOUGLAS.  SONATA A QUATRO IN F MA.  OB,VN,VA,BC        NOM
MORTENSEN, O.  QUATUOR CONCERTANT.  FL,VN,VC,PF                   CHE
MOSCHELES, I.-VOXMAN.  FANTASY, VARIATIONS, & FINALE, OP 46       MR
    CL,VN,VC,PF
MOSS, L.  PATTERNS.  FL,CL,VA,PF                                  SS
MUNTZIG, A.  KVARTETT.  CL,VA,VC,PF                               EMF
MUNTZIG, A.  SOMMARMUSIK.  CL,2VC,PF                              EMF
NAUDOT, J.-RUF.  CONCERTO IN G MA, OP 17/5.  FL(OB),2VN,BC        B&N
NAUMANN, J.-BORMANN.  QUARTET IN E FL MA, OP  1/5                 HSM
    FL,VN,VC,PF
ORREGO-SALAS, J.  SONATA A QUATTRO.  FL,OB,DB,HPCD                SN
PASQUOTTI, C.  LUTETIA.  FL/AFL,OB/EHN,VC,HPCD                    GZ
PERGOLESI, G.-KOLBEL.  CONCERTO IN D MA.  FL,2VN,BC               HEI
PERGOLESI, G.  SICILIAN AIR.  FL,VN,VC,PF                         EDM
PINCHARD, M.  TOMBEAU DE MARIN MARAIS.  FL,VN,VC,PF               EMT
POUSSEUR, H.  MADRIGAL #2.  FL,VN,VA DA GAMBA,HPCD                UE
RABL, W.  QUARTET, OP  1.  CL,VN,VC,PF                            SIM
RACHMANINOFF, S.  VOCALISE.  FL,VN,VA(VC),PF                      EDM
RANDS, B.  SCHERZI.  CL,VN,VC,PF                                  UE
ROCHBERG, G.  CONTRA MORTEM ET TEMPUS (1965).  FL,CL,VN,PF        TP
SALIERI, A.-WOJCIECHOWSKI.  TRIPLE CONCERTO IN D MA               HSM
    OB,VN,VC,PF
SALLINEN, A.  4 PER QUATTRO.  OB,VN,VC,HPCD                       FIN
SAMMARTINI, G.-MONKEMEYER.  SONATA IN D MA.  FL,2VN,BC            HEI
SAMONOV, A.  GREEK RHAPSODY.  CL,VN,VC,PF                         MKE
SCARLATTI, A.-WOEHL.  QUARTET IN F MA.  FL,2VN,PF,VC AD LIB       PET
SCHICKHARD, J.-PETER.  SONATE.  FL,OB,VC,PF                       MRL
SCHILLING, H.  CONCERTO PICCOLO.  FL,EHN,VA,PF                    BRH
SCHMELZER, J.  SONATA AD TABULAM.  FL,VN,VC,ORG                   ES
SCHMITT, F.  POUR PRESQUE TOUS LES TEMPS, OP134.  FL,VN,VC,PF     DUR
SCHRODER, H.  MUSIC.  FL,VN,VC,HPCD                               ROB
SCHUMANN, R.(FISCHER).  TRAUMEREI.  FL,CL,VC,PF                   FOR
SCHWARTZ, E.  SOLILOQUIES.  FL,CL,VN,PF                           BOW
SHAKARIAN, R.  ABSTRACTS (CHAMBER BALLET) (1976).  CL,VN,VC,PF    AMC
SKOLD, Y.  KVARTETT.  2FL,VC,PF                                   EMF
SMITH, W.  QUARTET.  CL,VN,VC,PF                                  MJ
SMOLANOFF, M.  SONATA DA CAMERA.  FL,OB,VC,HPCD                   SS
SOPRONI, J.  MUSICA DA CAMERA #2 (CAPRICORN MUSIC)               EMB
    CL,VN,VC,PF
STAMITZ, C.  TRIOSONATE, OP 14/5.  FL,VN,VC,PF                    BRH
STIEBLER, E.  STUDIE (1958).  FL,VA,VC,PF                         EMO
STUCKY, S.  QUARTET.  CL,VA,VC,PF                                 ACA
SUCOFF, H.  QUARTET.  FL,OB,VC,HPCD                               SS
SYDEMAN, W.  HAUS MUSIC.  FL,VN,VC,PF                             SS
SYDEMAN, W.  QUARTET (1963).  FL,CL,VN,PF                         SS
SYDEMAN, W.  QUARTET.  CL,VN,VC,PF                                SS
SYVERUD, S.  DEPARTURES.  OB,CL,VC,PF                             SS
TAKAHASHI, Y.  FOR YOU I SING THIS SONG.  CL,VN,VC,PF             Z-O
TAKEMITSY, T.  QUATRAIN II (1976).  CL,VN,VC,PF                   EDS
TELEMANN, G.-FRIEDRICH.  CONCERTO DI CAMERA.  FL,2VN,BC           SCH
TELEMANN, G.-RAMPAL.  CONCERTO IN A MI.  FL,OB,VN,PF              INT
```

```
TELEMANN, G.-VEYRON/LACROIX/RAMPAL.  CONCERTO IN A MI              JB
   FL,OB,VN,BC
TELEMANN, G.  CONCERTO IN B FL MA.  2FL,VC,PF                      EMT
TELEMANN, G.-RICHTER.  CONCERTO IN D MA.  FL,VN,VC,PF              SCH
TELEMANN, G.  CONCERTO IN E MA.  FL,OB D'AMORE,VA D'AMORE,PF       PET
TELEMANN, G.-TESKE.  CONCERTO IN G.  FL,2VN,BC                     EUL
TELEMANN, G.-UPMEYER.  CONCERTO IN G MA.  FL,2VN,BC,               B&N
TELEMANN, G.-BERGMANN.  CONCERTO PRIMO IN G MA.  FL,VN,VC,BC       B&N
TELEMANN, G.-BERGMANN.  CONCERTO SECONDO IN D MA.  FL,VN,VC,BC     B&N
TELEMANN, G.-DOHRN.  QUARTET IN B MI.  FL,VN,VC,BC                 B&N
TELEMANN, G.  QUARTET IN D MA.  FL,VN,VC,PF                        WZ
TELEMANN, G.-RAMPAL.  QUARTET IN D MI.  FL,VN,VC,PF                INT
TELEMANN, G.-DOHRN.  QUARTET IN E MI.  FL,VN,VC,BC                 B&N
TELEMANN, G.-RAMPAL.  QUARTET IN E MI.  FL,VN,VC,PF                INT
TELEMANN, G.-SEIFFERT.  QUARTET IN E MI.  FL,VN,VC,PF              BRH
TELEMANN, G.-BERGMANN.  QUARTET IN F MA                           SCH
   FL,OB,VN,PF,VC AD LIB
TELEMANN, G.-TOTTCHER/GREBE.  QUARTET IN G MA (TAFELMUSIK #1)      HSM
   FL,OB,VN,BC
TELEMANN, G.-HINNENTHAL.  QUARTET IN G MA.  FL,OB,VN,BC            B&N
TELEMANN, G.-WINSCHERMANN/BUCK.  QUARTET IN G MI                   HSM
   OB(FL),VN,VA,BC
TELEMANN, G.  QUARTET IN G MI.  FL,VN,VC,PF                        WZ
TELEMANN, G.  QUARTET IN G.  FL,OB,VC,BC                           EDK
TELEMANN, G.  QUATUOR.  FL,VN,VA,BC                                HUG
TELEMANN, G.-KOLBEL.  SONATA (QUARTET) IN G MA                     HSM
   FL,2VA DA GAMBA,BC
TELEMANN, G.-CRUSSARD.  SONATA.  FL,VN,VA,BC                       ECS
TELEMANN, G.-RICHTER.  SONATA IN A MI.  FL,VN,VA,BC                SCH
TELEMANN, G.-BERGMANN.  SONATA PRIMA IN A MA.  FL,VN,VC,BC         B&N
TELEMANN, G.-BRAUN.  SUITE.  FL,VN(OB),VC,PF,VA AD LIB             PET
TELEMANN, G.  SUITE IN B MI.  FL,VN,VC,BC                          H-V
TELEMANN, G.-ERMELER.  SUITE IN E MI.  FL,VN,VC,BC                 B&N
TELEMANN,G .-SCHNEIDER.  3 SCHERZI E 3 TRIETTI METHODICI           BRH
   2FL,VC,PF
TENAGLIA, A.  ARIA ANTICA.  CL,VN,VC,PF                            EDM
THILMAN, J.  DAS KLEINE REQUIEM, OP 27 (1945).  EHN,ASAX,VA,PF     B&N
VISE, S.  DIALOGUES.  FL,OB,VC,PF                                  CAN
VIVALDI, A.-SCHROEDER.  CONCERTO.  FL,2VN,BC                       HMO
VIVALDI, A.-RUF.  CONCERTO IN A MI.  FL(OB),2VN,BC                 SCH
VIVALDI, A.  CONCERTO IN A MI, F XII/11.  FL,2VN,HPCD              RC
VIVALDI, A.  CONCERTO IN D MA, F XII/27.  FL,VN,BSN,HPCD           RC
VIVALDI, A.  CONCERTO IN D MI, F XII/42.  FL,VN,BSN,BC             RC
VIVALDI, A.  CONCERTO IN F MA, F XII/21.  FL,VN,BSN,BC             RC
VIVALDI, A.  CONCERTO IN G MI.  FL,VN,BSN(VC),BC                   ART
VIVALDI, A.  CONCERTO IN G MI, F XII/8.  FL,VN,BSN,HPCD            RC
VIVALDI, A.  CONCERTO IN G MI, P404.  FL,VN,BSN,BC                 MR
VIVALDI, A.-FECHNER.  TRIO IN D MI.  FL,VN,BSN,PF                  PET
WARZECHA, P.  3 PIECES.  FL,CL,VA,PF                               PWM
WERNER, G.-MODER.  CONCERTO A QUATTRO IN A MA.  FL,2VN,BC          LDO
WILDER, A.  SUITE FOR BAROQUE QUARTET.  FL,OB,VC,HPCD              MAR
WILSON, T.  COMPLEMENTI.  CL/BCL,VN,VC,PF                          CA
WUORINEN, C.  TASHI.  CL,VN,VC,PF                                  PET
YAVELOW, C.  PHI-LINGS.  CL,VN,VC,PF                               ACA
YOUNG (ARR).  KING JAMES' PLEASURE.  2OB,DB,PF                     PET
YOUNG (ARR).  17TH-CENTURY SUITE.  2OB,DB,PF                       PET
YOUNG, W.  19 TANZSATZE.  2FL(2OB),VC,BC                           UE
ZELENKA, J.-SCHOENBAUM.  TRIOSONATE #1 IN F MA                     B&N
   2OB,BSN(VC),BC
```

4 PARTS: WOODWIND-BRASS-STRING-KEYBOARD-437

```
BANCQUART, A.   ECORCES 2.   VN,CL,HN,PF                                    JOB
BOIS, R. DU.   MUSIQUE D'ATELIER (1968).   CL,TRB,VC,PF                     SD
CASELLA, A.   SINFONIA (1932), OP 54.   CL,TPT,VC,PF                        B&N
CZERNY, C.   SERENADE IN E FL MA.   CL,HN,VC,PF                             MR
DELANNOY, M.   RHAPSODIE.   ASAX,TPT,VC,PF                                  HEU
DENISOV, E.   D-S-C-H.   CL,TRB,VC,PF                                       UE
DEVIENNE, F.-PETIT.   QUARTET.   FL,HN,VC,PF                                KAW
DI DOMENICA, R.   QUARTET.   FL,HN,VN,PF                                    MJ
DOBROWOLSKI, A.   KRABOGAPA (1969).   CL,TRB,VC,PF                          PWM
DOPPLER, F.-RAMPAL.   NOCTURNE, OP 19.   FL,VN,HN(VC),PF                    INT
ENRIQUEZ, M.   TZICURI (1977).   CL,VC,TRB,PF                               EMO
FASCH, J.-TOTTCHER & SPANNAGEL.   SONATA A 4.   OB,HN,VN,BC                 HSM
FERRITTO, J.   QUARTETTO, OP 13.   FL,HN,VA,PF                              ACA
FINGER, G.-MINTER.   SONATA.   OB,VN,TPT,BC                                 MR
GORECKI, H.   MUSIQUETTE #4, LA, OP 28 (1970).   CL,TRB,VC,PF               PWM
HESPOS, H.   POINT (1971).   BCL,VC,TRB,PF                                  EMO
KILAR, W.   TRAINING 68 (1968).   CL,TRB,VC,PF                              PWM
KOTONSKI, W.   POUR QUATRE.   CL,TRB,VC,PF                                  PWM
KRAUZE, Z.   POLYCHROMY (1968).   CL,VC,TRB,PF                              PWM
LORENTZEN, B.   SYNCRETISM.   CL,VC,TRB,PF                                  WH
MEALE, R.   LAS ALBORADAS.   FL,VN,HN,PF                                    JB
MILLER, M.   INTERACTION, A DIVERTIMENTO (1972)                            CAN
   EHN,HN,VC,PF(HPCD)
MIZELLE, J.   GREEN & RED.   BSN(SOP SAX),VN(VA),HN(PERC),HPCD             CPE
SCHAFFER, B.   QUARTET SG (1967).   CL,VC,TRB,PF                            EMO
SCHMELZER, J.   SONATA A 3.   VN,TRB,BSN,BC                                 MR
SEMEGEN, D.   JEUX DES QUATRES.   CL,TRB,VC,PF                              ACA
SEROCKI, K.   SWINGING MUSIC (1970).   CL,TRB,VC(DB),PF                     PWM
STIEBLER, E.   EXTENSION II (1972).   CL,VC,TRB,PF                          EMO
STOLZEL, G.   SONATA IN F MA.   OB,HN,VN,PF                                 BRH
SZALONEK, W.   IMPROVISATIONS SONORISTIQUES.   CL,TRB,VC,PF                 PWM
TOWNSEND, D.   EIGHT BY EIGHT, OP   3/1                                     PET
   FL,TPT(CL,OB),VC(BSN),PF
TUROK, P.   SARABANDE.   FL,HN,VC,PF                                        SS
WELIN, K.   MANZIT.   CL,VC,TRB,PF                                          A&S
WISZNIEWSKI, Z.   INSTRUMENTAL QUARTET.   FL,HN,DB,PF                       PWM
YAVELOW, C.   DIMENSION - L.   BSN,TRB,DB,PF                                ACA
```

4 PARTS INCLUDING HARP-438

```
AMY, G.   INVENTIONS I & II.   FL,PF,PERC,HP                               TP
ARNELL, R.   MUSIC FOR HARP.   FL,VN,VA,HP                                 SN
BIJL, T. VAN DER.   CONCERT IN F MA (1954).   FL,VN,VA,HP                  SD
CABUS, P.   SONATE.   3CL,HP                                               MAU
CHRISTOV, D.   QUARTET (1973).   FL,VA,HP,HPCD                             HG
EL-DABH, H.   LOOK AT LIGHTNING, A.   FL,OB,EHN,HP                         PET
FRID, G.   SONS ROUMAINS, OP 87 (1975).   FL/PIC,VA,HP,PERC                SD
GOLDBERG, T.   QUARTET (1962).   AFL,VA,VC,HP                              CAN
HAMBRAEUS, B.   MIKROGRAM.   AFL,VIB,VA,HP                                 EMF
HESPOS, H.   FROTTAGES (1967).   ASAX,VC,HP,MANDOLINE                      EMO
HOVHANESS, A.   FLOWERING PEACH, THE.   CL,ASAX,HP,CEL                     GS
```

```
HOVHANESS, A.  KOKE NO NUVA (MOSS GARDEN), OP181          PET
    EHN(CL),2PERC,HP
HOVHANESS, A.  ORBIT #1, OP 92/2.  FL,CEL,HP,DR            PET
HOVHANESS, A.  UPON ENCHANTED GROUND, OP 90/1.  FL,VC,HP,DR  PET
ISHII, M.  NUCLEUS (1973).  FL,HP,BIWA,SHAKUHACHI          HMO
JERSILD, J.  FANTASIA E CANTO AFFETTUOSO.  FL,CL,VC,HP     WH
JONES, C.  SERENADE.  FL,VN,VC,HP                          AMC
KARDOS, I.  NOTTURNO.  FL,EHN(VA),VN,HP                    GEN
KELLER, H.  REFRAINS.  FL,HP,CEL,PERC                      S-V
KLEBE, G.  AL ROVESCIO, OP 67.  FL,PF,HP,METALLIDIOPHONE   B&N
KLEBE, G.  7 BAGATELLEN, OP 35.  BASSET HN,TRB,HP,PERC     B&B
LOUEL, J.  SUITE (1967).  FL,VC,HP,VIB                     CBD
MACONCHY, E.  REFLECTIONS.  OB,CL,VA,HP                    OX
MATTHEWS, C.  SPECULA (1977).  FL,VA,HP,PERC               FB
MIGOT, G.  QUARTET.  FL,VN,CL,HP(PF)                       ALE
MULDER, E.  QUARTET (1946).  OB,BSN,VC,HP                  SD
NICHIFOR, S.  3 NOUVELLES IMPRESSIONS.  FL,VC,HP,PERC      EMO
NOBRE, M.  CANTICUM INSTRUMENTALE.  FL,HP,PF,TIMP          EDT
NUNES, E.  IMPROMPTU POUR UN VOYAGE.  FL,VA,TPT,HP         JOB
OTTEN, L.  PRELUDE EN KORAAL (1959).  FL,VA,VC,HP          SD
PEDERSEN, P.  SERIAL COMPOSITION (1965).  BSN,HN,VN,HP     CAN
PETRIC, I.  GAME FOR 3-GAME FOR 4.  FL,E FL CL,HP,PERC     EDD
PROSPERI, C.  4 INVENZIONI (1952/53).  CL,VN,VA,HP         ESZ
PYLKKANEN, T.  DIVERTIMENTO.  FL,OB,VC,HP                  FIN
REGT, H. DE.  MUSICA, OP 4 (1970).  OB,VC,HP,PERC          SD
RHODES, P.  QUARTET.  FL,VN,VC,HP                          PET
SCHULLER, G.  DENSITIES I.  CL,VIB,HP,DB                   MJ
SHEINKMAN.  DIVERTIMENTO.  CL,TPT,TRB,HP                   PET
SOURILAS, T.  SUITE.  OB,HN,VC,HP                          HLE
STAHL, E.  NOCTURNE, OP 66.  FL,VN,VC,HP                   WZ
STOJANOV, P.  QUARTET #3 (1973).  FL,VA,HP,PF              HG
STOUT, A.  RECITATIVE, CAPRICCIO, & ARIA (1967).  OB,HP,2PERC  AU
TAPKOV, D.  QUARTET (1973).  FL,VA,HP,HPCD                 HG
TON-THAT-TIET.  TUONG-NIEM.  FL,VA,2HP                     EMT
TRAFFORD, E.  WYNDE.  FL,OB,VC,HP(PF)                      SS
VELLONES, P.  RAPSODIE, OP 92.  ASAX,HP,CEL,PERC           HLE
WILDBERGER, J.  QUARTET (1967).  FL/AFL/BFL,OB/EHN,HP,PF   HG
```

4 PARTS INCLUDING GUITAR-439

```
ALMEIDA, L.  PUKA SHELLS.  FL,DB,GUIT,DR                   BRM
ALMEIDA, L. & M. ALLTON.  SEA & SAND.  AFL,DB,GUIT,DR      BRM
ALMEIDA, L. & S. MANNE.  CANON PER QUAD.  FL,DB,GUIT,DR    BRM
BARTOLOZZI, B.  REPITU (1975).  FL,VA,GUIT,PERC            ESZ
BEETHOVEN, L. VAN-SCHMIDT.  ADAGIO.  FL,VN,PF,GUIT         WZ
BOSKE, J. TEN.  SANGITA (1979).  FL,OB,2GUIT              SD
COLGRASS, M.  LIGHT SPIRIT.  FL,VA,GUIT,PERC               JB
DAVIES, P.  FROM STONE TO THORN.  CL,HPCD,GUIT,PERC        BH
DELDEN, L. VAN.  BALLET, OP 14 (1946).  FL,BSN,VA,GUIT     SD
DOMAZLICKY, F.  KAMMERMUSIK (1966).  CL,VN,VC,GUIT         CHF
ERDMANN, D.  NOTTURNO.  FL,3GUIT                           HG
ERDMANN, V.  4 BAGATELLEN (1972).  OB,VC,GUIT,ZITHER       EMO
FLOSMAN, O.  4 DON QUIJOT-SERENADEN (1965).  BCL,VN,VC,GUIT  CHF
HAYDN, F.-BROJER.  QUARTETTE, OP 5/4.  FL,VN,VA,GUIT       LDO
HESPOS, H.  FROTTAGES (1967).  ASAX,VC,HP,MANDOLINE        EMO
HLOUSCHEK, T.  QUARTET.  FL,MANDOLIN,GUIT,ACC              FRH
JOHNSON, J.  ROGERO.  FL,VC,GUIT,HPCD                      HEU
KOLB, B.  VERNISSAGE.  FL,VN,VA,GUIT                       BH
```

4 PARTS INCLUDING GUITAR-439

```
KOTONSKI, W.   SELECTION I.   CL,ASAX,TSAX,GUIT                    AP
KUBIZEK, A.   QUARTETTO DA CAMERA, OP 24 (1962)                   LDO
   ,OB,CL,BSN,GUIT
LAMPERSBERG, G.   QUARTETT.   FL,BCL,GUIT,VA                       UE
MONTEVERDI, C.   5 INSTRUMENTAL-CANZONETTEN                        GZ
   FL,VA DA BRACCIO,VA DA GAMBA,LUTE
PARSCH, A.   ESERCIZII (1970).   2FL,VC,GUIT                       CHF
REGT, H. DE.   MUSICA, OP 17.   FL,VA,VC,GUIT                      SD
SANTORSOLA, G.   QUARTET #2.   FL,VA,VC,GUIT                       SN
SCHUBERT, F.-KINSKY.   GUITAR QUARTET IN G MI.   FL,VA,VC,GUIT     PET
SCHUBERT, F.-BEHREND.   QUARTET (NOTTURNO, OP 21 BY MATIEGKA)      B&B
   FL,VA,VC,GUIT
SUR, D.   CATENA I (1961).   FL,MAR,BONGOS,MANDOLIN                B-B
SUR, D.   CATENA II (1962).   FL,VA,BONGOS,MANDOLIN                B-B
TELEMANN, G.-SCHALLER.   TRIO SONATA IN C MA.   AFL,VN,GUIT,VA     BRH
TELEMANN, G.-SCHALLER.   TRIO SONATA IN F MA.   2AFL,GUIT,VA       BRH
TILLIS, F.   3 PLUS 1.   CL,VN,GUIT,TAPE                           ACA
TRUHLAR, J.   QUARTET, OP 14 (1963).   FL,VN,VC,GUIT               ART
WERNICK, R.   STRETTI (1965).   CL,VN,VA,GUIT                      BE
WILDBERGER, J.   DOUBLE REFRAIN (1972)                            HG
   FL/BFL,OB/EHN,GUIT,TAPE
WOLFF, C.   ELECTRIC SPRING I.   HN,CBSN,DB,GUIT                   PET
```

4 PARTS INCLUDING PERCUSSION-440

```
ALBERT, T.   SOUND FRAMES.   OB,ASAX,TRB,VIB                       MEP
ALCALAY, L.   TRIO (1971).   FL,OB,CL,PERC                         EMO
ALMEIDA, L.   PUKA SHELLS.   FL,DB,GUIT,DR                         BRM
ALMEIDA, L. & M. ALLTON.   SEA & SAND.   AFL,DB,GUIT,DR            BRM
ALMEIDA, L. & S. MANNE.   CANON PER QUAD.   FL,DB,GUIT,DR          BRM
ALSINA, C.   RENDEZ-VOUS, OP 24 (1970).   CL,TRB,PF,PERC           ESZ
ANTONIOU, T.   SYNTHESIS (1971).   OB,PERC,DB,HAMMOND ORG          B&N
ATOR, J.   LIFE CYCLE.   OB,ASAX,VC,PERC                           SS
BACK, S.   FAVOLA.   CL,VC,PF,PERC                                 GS
BARTOLOZZI, B.   REPITU (1975).   FL,VA,GUIT,PERC                  ESZ
BAUER, R.   EXTREMITIES.   CL,EU,PF,PERC                           CAN
BERNAOLA, C.   ARGIA EZTA IKUSTEN.   CL,PF,VIB,PERC                EDA
BERNAOLA, C.   ASI.   CL,VN,PF,VIB                                 EEC
BERNAOLA, C.   SUPERFICIE #3.   FL,ASAX,XYL,PERC                   EDA
BIBALO, A.   AUTUNNALE.   FL,DB,PF,VIB                             WH
BOHAC, J.   SONETTI PER SONATORI.   FL,BCL,HPCD/PF,PERC            PAN
BOIS, R. DU.   ENIGMA (1969).   FL,BCL,PF,PERC                     SD
BOLLING, C.   SUITE.   FL,PF,DB,DR                                 HN
BOWLES, P.   MUSIC FOR A FARCE.   CL,TPT,PERC,PF                   HY
BROWN, J.   QUARTET.   CL,TRB,VIB/MAR,PF                           ACA
BUCZYNSKI, W.   TWO & A HALF SQUARES IN A CIRCLE (1967)            CAN
   FL,VN,VC,TIMP
CHIHARA, P.   CEREMONY II ("INCANTATIONS")                        PET
   AMPLIFIED FL,2 AMPLIFIED  VC,PERC
COLGRASS, M.   LIGHT SPIRIT.   FL,VA,GUIT,PERC                     JB
CONSTANTINIDES, D.   DEDICATIONS.   2FL,BSN,PERC                   SS
COPE, D.   KOOSHAREM.   CL,DB,PERC,PF                              SD
CORGHI, A.   STEREOFONIE X 4.   FL,VC,ORG,PERC                     RC
CRUZ DE CASTRO, C.   ESCORPION.   CL,VN,PF,PERC                    EEC
CUNNINGHAM, M.   NOETICAL ROUNDS.   OB,VN,DB,MAR                   SS
DAVIES, P.   FROM STONE TO THORN.   CL,HPCD,GUIT,PERC              BH
DIAS, J.   MEU BEM.   SAX,TPT,TRB,PERC                            PMP
DIEMENTE, E.   QUARTET (1966).   FL,CL,DB,VIB                      SS
```

4 PARTS INCLUDING PERCUSSION-440

```
DIEMENTE, E.  QUARTET (1967).  ASAX,TRB,DB,PERC                        SS
DREIFUS, G.  SEASONS, THE.  FL,VA,VIB,PERC                             SCH
DUBOIS, P.  LOU GASCARELET.  3OB,TAMBOURINE                            ALE
EHLE, R.  ESTRANGEON.  CL,VN,PF,PERC                                   CF
ENDO, R.  DESSEIN IMPROVISATION (1961).  FL,OB,PF,PERC                 ESZ
ERNST, D.  SUMMERTIME.  FL,VC,PF,PERC                                  MAN
FENIGSTEIN, V.  ICARES.  FL,VA,CEL,PERC                                EUL
FENNER, B.  STUDY.  BSN,VC,TRB,TIMP                                    SS
FISCHER, J.  7 BRIEFE (1971).  FL,CL,PF,PERC                           ART
FOSS, L.  ECHOI FOR 4 VIRTUOSI (1961/63).  CL,VC,PF,PERC               SCH
FRID, G.  SONS ROUMAINS, OP 87 (1975).  FL/PIC,VA,HP,PERC              SD
FRITSCH, J.  HOCHTONER (1974).  FL,VC,PERC,TAPE                        FEE
FURRER-MUNCH, F.  SOLENOID II (1972).  FL,CL,PERC,TAPE                 EMO
FURST, P.  BEAT THE BEAT.  CL,TRB,DB,PERC                              EMO
FUSSELL, C.  DANCE SUITE (1963).  FL,TPT,VA,PERC                       CAN
GIDEON, M.  FANTASY ON IRISH FOLK-MOTIVES.  OB,BSN,VA(VC),PERC         ACA
GOTTSCHALK, A.  SESSION, THE.  FL,ASAX,DB,VIB                          SS
GRAHN, U.  SOUNDSCAPE I (1973).  FL,EHN,BCL,PERC                       STI
HALIER, R.  COLOURED VEIL (1976).  FL,CL,VN,BELLS                      SD
HAMBRAEUS, B.  INTRODUZIONE-SEQUENZE-CODA (1958-59).  3FL,PERC         NOR
HAMBRAEUS, B.  MIKROGRAM.  AFL,VIB,VA,HP                               EMF
HARRIS, R.  SILENT THINGS.  CL,HN,PF,PERC                              SS
HAUFRECHT, H.  FANTASY FOR 4 ON HAITIAN THEMES.  CL,VA,PF,TIMP         ACA
HAZZARD, P.  VOYAGE.  FL,CL,DB,PERC                                    SS
HERMAN, V.  VARIANTE.  2CL,PF,PERC                                     EMU
HIBBARD, W.  GESTURES.  FL,DB,PERC,MAR                                 ACA
HODKINSON, S.  INTERPLAY (1967).  AFL/PIC,CL/ASAX,DB,PERC              CAN
HOVHANESS, A.  DANCE OF BLACK-HAIRED MOUNTAIN STORM.  FL,3PERC         PET
HOVHANESS, A.  ORBIT #1, OP 92/2.  FL,CEL,HP,DR                        PET
HOVHANESS, A.  UPON ENCHANTED GROUND, OP 90/1.  FL,VC,HP,DR            PET
JENNI, D.  CUCUMBER MUSIC (1969)                                       AMP
  PIC/AFL,VA/TOY PF,CEL/PF,PERC
JIRASEK, I.  SERENADEN (1967).  FL,BCL,2PERC                           CHF
JULIAN, J.  WAVE.  FL,DB,PERC,TAPE                                     SCH
KAPR, J.  CONCERTINO.  CL,VC,PF,PERC                                   SER
KATZ, E.  TOY CONCERTO.  PIC,FL,CEL,PERC                               SF
KAY, U.  AULOS.  FL SOLO,2HN,PERC                                      CF
KEE, C.  12 ORIGINAL TRIOS.  CL,HN,TPT,PERC                            HE
KELLER, H.  REFRAINS.  FL,HP,CEL,PERC                                  S-V
KLEBE, G.  7 BAGATELLEN, OP 35.  BASSET HN,TRB,HP,PERC                 B&B
KLEBE, G.  GRATULATIONS-TANGO, OP 40A.  ASAX,TPT,PF,PERC               B&B
KLEIN, L.  TRIO SONATA.  CL,VC,PF,DR                                   CAN
LATEEF, Y.  PSYCHICEMOTUS.  FL,PF,DB,DR                                EAM
LAWSON, P.  VALENTIA EXTRAMATERIAL.  FL,PF,2PERC                       PET
LOMBARDO, R.  YES!.  CL,TPT,VC,PERC                                    ACA
LOUEL, J.  SUITE (1967).  FL,VC,VIB,HP                                 CBD
LOVE, R.  QUARTET #2.  CL,TPT,PF,PERC                                  SS
LU, Y.  QUARTET.  CL,TU,2PERC                                          SS
LUNDEN, L.  SVART LEK (1957).  2FL,BCL,PERC                            STI
LUNETTA, S.  QUARTET 1965.  FL,VN,DB,VIB                               CPE
MARTINU, B.  QUARTET (1924).  CL,VC,HN,DR                              ES
MATOUSEK, L.  7 TUDSUNDEN DES HIERONYMUS BUSCH (1971)                  CHF
  FL,BCL,PF,PERC
MATTHEWS, C.  SPECULA (1977).  FL,VA,HP,PERC                           FB
MIROGLIO, R.  REFRACTIONS.  FL,VN,PF,PERC                              UE
MYERS, R.  DIVERTMENTS.  FL,OB,CEL,BELLS                               SS
NICHIFOR, S.  3 NOUVELLES IMPRESSIONS.  FL,VC,HP,PERC                  EMO
NOBRE, M.  CANTICUM INSTRUMENTALE.  FL,HP,PF,TIMP                      EDT
NOBRE, M.  TROPICALE.  PIC,E FL CL,PF,PERC                             EDT
NORDGREN, E.  6 MOVEMENTS (1966), OP 64.  FL,BSN,HN,DR                 STI
OLAN, D.  4 STUDIES.  CL,VN,PF,PERC                                    ACA
OLIVER, A.  VERSOS A CUATRO (1976).  CL,VN,PF,PERC                     EEC
```

4 PARTS INCLUDING PERCUSSION-440

```
PABLO, L. DE.  MASQUE (1973).  FL,CL,PF,PERC                      EDS
PAPORISZ, Y.  ARROGANCES (1969).  FL,VN,VC,PERC                   HMO
PAUK, A.  WHEREVER THERE IS DISTANCE.  FL,OB/EHN,VA,PERC          CAN
PETRIC, I.  GAME FOR THREE-GAME FOR FOUR.  FL,E FL CL,HP,PERC     EDD
PIER, G.  3 ETUDEN.  CL,TPT,PF,DR                                 LDO
PINKHAM, D.  ECLOGUE.  FL,HPCD,2PERC                              ECS
PINOS-SIMANDEL, A.  KONFLIKTE (1964).  BCL,VN,PF,PERC             PAN
PLESKOW, R.  3 BAGATELLES (1967).  FL,CL,DB,VIB(PF)              SS
REASER, R.  LIBERARE SONARE.  ASAX,PERC,3 TIMP,CHIMES             PI
REGT, H. DE.  MUSICA, OP 4 (1970).  OB,VC,HP,PERC                SD
REIF, P.  INTERPOLATIONS.  FL,CL,BSN,PERC                         GEN
ROREM, N.  LOVERS.  OB,VC,HPCD,PERC                               BH
ROUSE, C.  PHOENIX, THE.  FL/PIC,PF,2PERC                         ACA
ROWLAND, D.  TETRAD 1970).  FL,PF,PERC,TAPE                       SD
RUITER, W. DE.  QUARTET.  FL,BCL,PF,VIB                           SD
RZEWSKI, F.  SONG & DANCE.  FL,BCL,DB,VIB                         EMO
SCHAT, P.  2 (1959) STUKKEN.  FL,VN,TPT,PERC                      SD
SCHNEIDER, U.  KREUZE (1964/67).  FL,PF,XYL,HARMONIUM             HMO
SCHNITTKE, A.  HYMNUS III.  BSN,VC,HPCD,TIMP                      HSM
SCHOONENBEEK, K.  SUITE (1979).  OB,PERC,DB,PF                    SD
SCHUDEL, T.  4 MOVEMENTS.  FL/AFL,BSN,2PERC                       CAN
SCHUYT, N.  QUATUOR DE BALLET (1962).  CL,TPT,PF,PERC             SD
SHIMOYAMA, H.  STRUCTURE (1961).  BCL,VN,TPT,PERC                 ESZ
SIGURBJORNSSON, T.  FOR RENEE.  FL,VC,PF,PERC                     BH
SIMEONE, H.  CREOLE CLARINET.  CL,DB,PF,PERC                      SH
SMITH, S.  FINE OLD TRADITION, A.  ASAX,PF,ELECTRIC PF,PERC       MEP
STIBILJ, M.  MONDO.  CL,BCL,VN,PERC                               EDD
STOCKHAUSEN, K.  KREUZSPIEL (1951).  OB,BCL,PF,PERC               UE
STOUT, A.  RECITATIVE, CAPRICCIO, & ARIA (1967).  OB,HP,2PERC     AU
STRAESSER, J.  EMERGENCY CASE (1970; REV 1979)                   SD
   FL/AFL,PF,2PERC
STROE, A.  FRAGMENT D'UN PROCESSUS SONORE.  FL,2PF,PERC           EDS
SUBOTNICK, M.  SERENADE II.  CL,HN,PERC,PF                        M&M
SUR, D.  CATENA I (1961).  FL,MAR,BONGOS,MANDOLIN                 B-B
SUR, D.  CATENA II (1962).  FL,VA,BONGOS,MANDOLIN                 B-B
TAURIELLO, A.  ILINX.  CL,DB,PF,PERC                              BAR
TAVENER, J.  IN MEMORIAM IGOR STRAVINSKY.  2AFL,ORG,BELLS         CHE
THEOBALD, J.  PLANE-5.  ASAX,VA,PF,PERC                           SS
TIPPETT, M.  "CROWN OF THE YEAR": #8-PRELUDE.  OB,CL,DR,PF        S&C
ULLMAN, B.  RACCONTO II.  CL,VC,PF,PERC                           EMF
VILLA ROJO, J.  NOSOTROS (1976).  CL,VN,PF,VIB                    EEC
WAGNER-REGENY, R.  DIVERTIMENTO.  FL,CL,BSN,PERC                  BRH
WESTERGAARD, P.  QUARTET (1960).  CL,VN,VC,VIB                    SCH
WINKLER, D.  CHAMBER CONCERTO (1974).  FL,PF,2PERC               B-B
WOLPE, S.  QUARTET #1 (1950).  TSAX,TPT,PERC,PF                   M&M
WOLPE, S.  QUARTET.  OB,VC,PF,PERC                                M&M
WOLSCHING, R.  5 CAPRICHOS.  WWQUARTET,PERC                       DEU
YUASA, J.  INTER-POSI-PLAY-TION.  FL,PF,2PERC                     SCH
ZENDER, H.  QUARTET (1964-65).  FL,VC,PF,PERC                     B&B
ZONN, P.  TURNAROUND.  OB,E FL CL/BCL,VIB,TAPE                    ACA
```

4 PARTS INCLUDING RECORDER-442

```
FASCH, J.-MOECK.  SONATA IN G MA.  FL,2REC,BC                     HMO
JANITSCH, J.-HOFMANN.  QUADRO IN F MA, OP 6                       EAM
   REC(FL),OB,VN,BC
JOHNSON, T.  GAVOTTE.  REC,OB,CL,PF                               BOS
JOHNSON, T.  GIGUE.  REC,OB,CL,PF                                 BOS
```

4 PARTS INCLUDING RECORDER-442

```
LOEILLET, J.-POULTEAU.  SONATE EN TRIO IN G MI.  REC,OB,VC,PF    ALE
POGLIETTI, A.  SONATA A TRE IN C MA.  REC,OB,BSN,PF             PET
ROHWER, J.  2 QUARTETTSATZE.  REC,FL,VN,VC                       MV
SCHICKHARDT, J.  SONATA IN B FL MA.  REC,OB,VC,PF,VC AD LIB     PET
SCHICKHARDT, J.  6 SONATAS, OP 22.  OB,2REC,BC                   MR
TELEMANN, G.-TOTTCHER & GREBE.  CONCERTO IN A MI                HSM
   REC,OB,VN,BC
TELEMANN, G.-HINNENTHAL.  QUARTET IN D MI.  REC,2FL,BC          B&N
THYBO, L.  QUARTET "NON SI LEVAVA ANCOR".  REC,EHN,HN,BSN       CHE
VIVALDI, A.  CONCERTO IN G MI, P402.  REC,OB,BSN,BC             MR
```

4 PARTS INCLUDING TAPE-443

```
BAUER, R.  S.S.E./7,3,7.  FL,CL,TRB,TAPE                        CAN
COSTINESCO, G.  "...ET LES MEMES AUTRES" III (1969)            EDS
   SAX,DB,PF,ONDES  MARTENOT
FRITSCH, J.  HOCHTONER (1974).  FL,VC,PERC,TAPE                FEE
FURRER-MUNCH, F.  SOLENOID II (1972).  FL,CL,PERC,TAPE         EMO
GROSSKOPF, E.  DIALECTICS (1969).  FL,CL,TRB,TAPE             HMO
JULIAN, J.  WAVE.  FL,DB,PERC,TAPE                             SS
KLEBE, G.  AL ROVESCIO, OP 67.  FL,PF,HP,METALLIDIOPHONE       B&N
PERT, M.  AKHENATEN, OP 15.  3CL,TAPE                          JOW
REYNOLDS, R.  TRACES.  FL,VC,PF,TAPE                           PET
ROWLAND, D.  TETRAD (1970).  FL,PF,PERC,TAPE                   SD
TILLIS, F.  3 PLUS 1.  CL,VN,GUIT,TAPE                         ACA
WILDBERGER, J.  DOUBLE REFRAIN (1972)                          HG
   FL/BFL,OB/EHN,GUIT,TAPE
ZONN, P.  TURNAROUND.  OB,E FL CL/BCL,VIB,TAPE                 ACA
```

5 FLUTES-500

BOER, J. DEN. CIRRUS (1973)	SD
BOISMORTIER, J. DE-PAUBON. CONCERTO #1 IN G MA	BIL
BOISMORTIER, J. DE-PAUBON. CONCERTO #2 IN A MI	BIL
BOISMORTIER, J. DE-PAUBON. CONCERTO #3 IN D MA	BIL
BOISMORTIER, J. DE. CONCERTO #4	BIL
BOISMORTIER, J. DE. CONCERTO #5	BIL
BOISMORTIER, J. DE. CONCERTO #6	BIL
BOISMORTIER, J. DE(SPINDLER). CONCERTOS 4, 5, 6	EDK
BOISMORTIER, J.B. DE-GLASENAPP. 6, #S 1-3 CONCERTI	FRH
BOISMORTIER, J.B. DE-SPINDLER. 6, #S 4-6 CONCERTI	FRH
BOOREN, J. VAN DEN. BIRDS (1975)	SD
BOOREN, J. VAN DEN. FUR ELISE, AFTER L. VAN BEETHOVEN (1976)	SD
BOTTJE, W. QUINTET	ACA
BROWN, R. 3 FUGUES. 3FL,2AFL	WI
CUNNINGHAM, M. GLORIFICATION	AMC
CUNNINGHAM, M. PASTEL DESIGNS. 3FL,AFL,BFL	SS
EYNDEN, F. VAN DEN. MYCROPHONY (1971)	SD
EYSER, E. POLYMORPHY 1 (1968)	STI
FRANK, M. INTRODUCTION & SCHERZO	SF
GILTAY, B. ELEGIE (1969)	SD
HAYS, D. SCHEVENINGEN BEACH	SS
HUTCHISON, W. CHRYSALIS	SS
LORENZO, L. DE. SINFONIETTA, OP 75	PET
PRAAG, H. VAN. SONATA	SD
RUITER, W. & J. BANK. QUINTET (1976)	SD
RUITER, W. DE. QUINTET II (1978)	SD
VRIES, K. DE. 5-PART FANTASY	SD

5 OBOES-502

BOIS, R. DU. CHANSONS POUR APPATER LES CHEIROPTERES (1975) OB,2OB D 'AMORE,2EHN	SD
BOISMORTIER, J. DE. 3 CONCERTOS	FRH
GLOBOKAR, V. DISCOURS #3	PET

5 CLARINETS-504

BACH, J.C.-VOXMAN. ALLEGRO (SINFONIA #2). 3CL,ACL,BCL	RU
BACH, J.S.-JOHNSON. CELEBRATED AIR (SUITE #3). 3CL,ACL,BCL	RU
BACH, J.S.-GORDON. PRELUDE #4. 3CL,ACL,BCL	KN
BACH, J.S.-DANSBY. TERZETTO (CANTATA #38). 4CL,BCL(CL)	KN
BARGIEL, W.-HARRIS. MEDITATION CL(FL),CL(OB),CL,ACL(CL,HN),BCL(BSN)	CF
BEETHOVEN, L. VAN-JOHNSON. ADAGIO CANTABILE (SONATA #8) 3CL,ACL,BCL	RU
BEETHOVEN, L. VAN-JOHNSON. SCHERZO (OCTET, OP103) 3CL,ACL,BCL	RU

5 CLARINETS-504

BEETHOVEN, L. VAN-SCOTT. SONATA #19, OP 49/1. 5CL(5SAX)	WAT
BIZET, G.-FREEDMAN. 5 PIECES FROM "CARMEN". 3CL,ACL,BCL	MC
BOEHM, T.-DISHINGER. PRESTO	SP
BOTTJE, W. FLUCTUATUATIONS (1965)	CO
CORELLI, A.(MORSCH). PRELUDE	RD
DAVIS, V. SPINNING WHEEL, THE	SH
DVORAK, A.-JOHNSON. MENUETTO (SERENADE, OP 44). 3CL,ACL,BCL	RU
FOURCHOTTE. PIECE BREVE	BIL
FOX. PAVANNE. 4CL,BCL	SF
GLASER, W. MUSIK (1964). E FL CL,3CL,BCL	STI
GRIEG, E.-VOXMAN. LYRIC PIECE #2. 3CL,ACL,BCL	RU
HANDEL, G.-VOXMAN. SARABANDE & ALLEGRO (CONCERTO GROSSO #3)	RU
3CL,ACL,BCL	
HARMON. SUITE #1	WI
HAYDN, F.-JOHNSON. MOVEMENT #2 (SYMPHONY #100). 3CL,ACL,BCL	RU
HAYDN, F.-JOHNSON. MOVEMENT #3 (SYMPHONY # 94). 3CL,ACL,BCL	RU
JOHNSON, C. SCHERZO CAPRICCIO. 3CL,ACL,BCL	RU
KUHNAU, J.-DISHINGER. GIGUE	SP
MAGÁNINI, Q.-HARRIS. REVERIE	CF
MARIE, G.-HARRIS. BERCEUSE	CF
MC BRIDE. MELODY BY CHOPIN. 4CL,BCL	SF
MC BRIDE. MELODY BY GRIEG. 4CL,BCL	SF
MOFFITT, D. FRISKY	CF
MORSCH, J.(ED). 3 INTERLUDES	RD
MOZART, W. ADAGIO IN B FL MA, K411. 3CL,ACL,BCL:BSN)	TP
MOZART, W.-VOXMAN. ADAGIO, K411. 3CL,ACL,BCL	RU
MOZART, W.-JOHNSON. MENUETTO (EINE KLEINE NACHTMUSIK)	RU
3CL,ACL,BCL	
MOZART, W.-VOXMAN. MENUETTO (SERENADE #1). 3CL,ACL,BCL	RU
MUSSORGSKY, M. BALLET OF THE CHICKS IN THEIR SHELLS	EDM
NESTICO, S. STUDY IN CONTRASTS, A. 3CL,ACL(CL),BCL	KN
ROUSSAKIS, N. MARCH, SONG & DANCE	MC
SCHUBERT, F.-JOHNSON. MENUET & TRIO (SONATA, OP 78)	RU
3CL,ACL,BCL	
SCHUMANN, R.-MILANO. FUGA. 4CL,BCL	SF
SCHWARZ, I. CAPRICCIO. 3CL,ACL,BCL	RU
SEMLER-COLLERY, J. PIECE RECREATIVE	EES
SIMEONOV, B. BAROQUE CEREMONIAL, INTERMEZZO (1971)	CAN
E FL CL,2CL,ACL ,BCL	
TCHAIKOVSKY, P.-JOHNSON. ANDANTE CANTABILE (QUARTET, OP 11)	RU
3CL,ACL,BCL	
VERRALL, J. SERENADE. 3CL,ACL(CL),BCL(BSN)	TP
WEBER, C.M. VON. MINUET (QUINTET, OP 34)	CF
3CL,ACL(ASAX),BCL(BSN)	

5 SAXOPHONES-508

BROTONS, S. SAX-QUINTET-VENT	EEC
CAZDEN, N. FORMATION #4 (6 DISCUSSIONS)	SPR
DEBUSSY, C.-SIBBING. GIRL WITH THE FLAXEN HAIR, THE	DOR
SOP SAX,2ASAX,TSAX,BAR SAX	
DUHAMEL, A. HOMMAGE A MINGUS	EFM
EYSER, E. BAROQUE (LE SAXOPHONE BIEN TEMPERE) (1976)	STI
GAYFER, J. QUINTET CONCERTANTE (1973)	CAN
SOP SAX,2ASAX,TSAX,BAR SAX	
GLASER, W. QUINTET (1964/77)	STI
GRANDERT, J. QUINTET (1975)	STI
HARGER, E. BEGUINE FOR 5. 2ASAX,2TSAX,BAR SAX	BE

5 SAXOPHONES-508

```
HAYDN, F.-JOHNSON.  MOVEMENT #3 (SYMPHONY #100)            RU
LAKE, M.  ANDANTINO.  2ASAX,2TSAX,BAR SAX                  LU
LAKE, M.  CLEVELAND MARCH.  2ASAX,2TSAX,BAR SAX            LU
LAKE, M.  IRON MOUNTAIN.  2ASAX,2TSAX,BAR SAX              LU
LAKE, M.  LONG, LONG AGO.  2ASAX,2TSAX,BAR SAX             LU
LAKE, M.  LOUISIANA.  2ASAX,2TSAX,BAR SAX                  LU
LAKEY, C.  SAXET #4-5.  SOP SAX,2ASAX,TSAX,BAR SAX         SO
MORATIN.  QUINTETTE                                        EDR
MOZART, W.-SIBBING.  QUINTET, K406                         DOR
   SOP SAX,2ASAX,TSAX,BAR SAX
MOZART, W.-SIBBING.  QUINTET, K593                         DOR
   SOP SAX,2ASAX,TSAX,BAR SAX
MUSSORGSKY, M.  BALLET OF THE CHICKS IN THEIR SHELLS       EDM
   3ASAX,TSAX,BAR SAX
SARY, L.  INCANTO                                          EMB
SCHMALTZ, E.  STRICTLY FOR SAXES.  2ASAX,2TSAX,BAR SAX     BD
TOSELLI, E.-HARGER.  SERENADE.  2ASAX,2TSAX,BAR SAX        BE
WAELE DE.  QUINTETTE                                       EDR
```

5 PARTS: WOODWINDS
(FL,OB,CL,HN,BSN)-523

```
ABSIL, J.  DANSES BULGARES, OP103                         HLE
ABSIL, J.  QUINTETTE, OP 16 (1934)                        CBD
ADASKIN, M.  QUINTET (1974)                               CAN
ADLER, S.  INTRADA                                        OX
AGAY, D.  5 EASY DANCES                                   TP
AGER, K.  HOSHI (1974/75)                                 EMU
AGUSTSSON, H.  QUINTET (1968)                             B&B
AHLBERG, G.  IMPULSER (1972/73)                           STI
AHNELL, E.  WIND QUINTET #1                               MAN
AITKEN, H.  8 STUDIES                                     EV
ALSINA, C.  LETTER, A                                     ESZ
ALTMANN, E.  KLEINE TANZSUITE                             FRH
AMBROSI, D. D'.  INTRODUZIONE E ALLEGRO                   EDI
AMELLER, A.  A LA FRANCAISE                               EMT
AMES, W.  MOVEMENT                                        ACA
AMES, W.  WOODWIND QUINTET                                ACA
AMRAM, D.  QUINTET                                        PET
ANDERSEN, J.  QUINTET (1939)                              SPD
ANDERSON, T., JR.  5 ETUDES & A FANCY                     ACA
ANDRIESSEN, H.  QUINTET (1951)                            SD
ANDRIESSEN, J.  SCIARADA SPAGNULOA (1962)                 SD
ANGERER, P.  QUINTET                                      LDO
ANTONINI, A.  20TH CENTURY DOLL                           CA
ANTONIOU, T.  DO QUINTET, THE                             B&N
ARMA, P.  7 TRANSPARENCIES                                HLE
ARNE, T.-COLLINS.  SUITE OF DANCES                        SHB
ARNELL, R.  CASSATION, OP 45                              HI
ARNOLD, M.  3 SHANTIES                                    PAT
ARRIEU, C.  QUINTETTE IN C MA                             BIL
AUSTIN, J.  DIVERTIMENTO                                  ACA
AVNI, T.  QUINTET                                         BE
AXMAN, E.  QUINTET (1938)                                 CHF
BAAREN, K. VAN.  QUINTETTO A FIATI (1963)                 SD
BACEWICZ, G.  QUINTET (1933)                              AP
BACH, J.C.-MAROS.  QUINTET #3                             EMB
BACH, J.C.-JONES.  SINFONIA, #1                           TP
BACH, J.S.-CATELINET.  2 BACH FUGUES                      HI
```

BACH, J.S.-OREM. BOUREE (OVERTURE #3)	TP
BACH, J.S. CHORALE PRELUDE	CST
BACH, J.S.-WALN. CLASSICAL QUINTET	KJ
BACH, J.S.-DE ANGELIS. FUGUE III	EDK
BACH, J.S.-HIRSH. FUGUE IN C MI	TP
BACH, J.S.-DE ANGELIS. FUGUE V	EDK
BACH, J.S.-DE ANGELIS. FUGUE XXII	EDK
BACH, J.S.-STEVENS. LITTLE FUGUE IN G MI	WI
BACH, J.S.-RECHTMAN. ORGAN WORKS	BE
BACH, J.S.-CANTRELL. PRELUDE & FUGUE IN D MA	WI
BACH, J.S.-ROSENTHAL. PRELUDE & FUGUE IN E MI	WI
BACH, J.S.-ROSENTHAL. PRELUDE & FUGUE IN G MA	WI
BACH, J.S.-ROSENTHAL. PRELUDE & FUGUE IN G MI	WI
BACH, J.S. PRELUDE & FUGUE XXI	AMP
BACH, J.S.-NAKAGAWA. PRELUDE & FUGUE XXII	AMP
BACH, J.S.-POPKIN. PRELUDE #22	EV
BACH, J.S.-DE ANGELIS. PRELUDE AND FUGUE IN F MI	EDK
BACH, J.S.-GORDON. PRELUDE TO CANTATA #106	SO
BACH, J.S.-KESSLER. PRELUDE XXII, VOL #1	RU
BACH, J.S.-MICKENS. SARABANDE (FRENCH SUITE #1)	BH
BACH, J.S.-GORDON. SARABANDE & GAVOTTE	CF
BACH, J.S.-FOTE. SINFONIA #9	KN
BACH, J.S.-BRAHMS-CANTRELL. 4 TRANSCRIPTIONS	WI
BADINGS, H. QUINTET #2 (1929)	SD
BADINGS, H. QUINTET #4 (1948)	SD
BADINSKI, N. MOSKAUER BLASERQUINTETT (1969)	DEU
BAEKERS, S. QUINTET (1975)	SD
BAEYENS, A. QUINTETTE (1950)	CBD
BAGIN, P. AKVARELY	SHF
BAHK, J. ECH	PET
BAINBRIDGE, S. QUINTET	UMP
BAKER, M. INTERLUDE & DIVERTIMENTO (1965)	CAN
BAKER, M. QUINTET	CAN
BALASSA, S. QUINTET, OP 9	EMB
BALAY, G. L'AURORE SUR LA FORET	ALE
BALAY, G. LITTLE MINIATURE SUITE IN 18TH CENTURY STYLE	ALE
BALAY, G.-WALN. MENUET & RONDO (LITTLE MINIATURE SUITE)	KJ
BALAZS, A. SERENATA	EMB
BALFE, M. KVINTETT, OP 2 (1954)	STI
BALLARD. RITMO INDIO	BO
BAMERT, W. WOODWIND QUINTET	GS
BARATI, G. WOODWIND QUINTET	ACA
BARBER, S. SUMMER MUSIC, OP 31	GS
BARBOTEU, G. CARICATURES	ECH
BARBOTEU, G. PRELUDE ET DIVERTISSEMENT	ECH
BARRAINE, E. OUVRAGE DE DAME	CHM
BARROWS, J. MARCH	GS
BARTA, L. WOODWIND QUINTET #2 (1969)	CHF
BARTHE, A.-ANDRAUD. PASSACAILLE	SO
BARTHE, A.-VOXMAN. PASSACAILLE	RU
BARTHE, A.-WALN. PASSACAILLE	KJ
BARTHE, A. PASSACAILLE	ALE
BARTOS, F. DER BURGER ALS EDELMANN (1934)	ART
BARTOS, J. CASSATION (1961)	CHF
BARTOS, J. STUDENTEN-SERENADE, OP 29 (1950)	CHF
BARTOS, J. UNTER ZVICINA, OP 32 (1952)	CHF
BARTOW. DIVERTIMENTO	SH
BARTSCH, C. 3 MOUVEMENTS	MAU
BASSETT, L. WOODWIND QUINTET	ACA
BAUER, M. QUINTET, OP 48	ACA
BAUER, R. ONCE IN 4	CAN
BAUMANN, M. KLEINE KAMMERMUSIK, OP 11	S-V

5 PARTS: WOODWINDS (FL,OB,CL,HN,BSN)-523

BAUR, J.   QUINTETTO SERENO (1958)   BRH
BAUR, J.   SKETCHES (1974)   BRH
BAVICCI, J.   PRELUDE, FUGUE AND CODA   SS
BEACH, H.   PASTORALE   OP
BECK, J.   QUINTET (1966)   MV
BECK, J.   QUINTET #2   MV
BECKER, G.   SERPENTINATA (1968)   HG
BEDFORD, D.   PENTOMINO (1968)   UE
BEEKHUIS, H.   ELEGIE EN HUMORESKE (1939)   SD
BEERMAN, B.   ENSEMBLE I   ACA
BEETHOVEN, L. VAN-VESTER.   ADAGIO & ALLEGRO   UE
BEETHOVEN, L. VAN-HOLMES.   ALLEGRO (SYMPHONY #6)   BA
BEETHOVEN, L. VAN-DE BUERIS.   COUNTRY DANCE #1   CF
BEETHOVEN, L. VAN-MERSSON.   DIVERTIMENTO IN G MA   BOS
BEETHOVEN, L. VAN-DE BUERIS.   GAVOTTE IN F MA   CF
BEETHOVEN, L. VAN-HILFIGER.   MENUETTO   KN
BEETHOVEN, L. VAN-SKOWRANEK.   5 PIECES FOR MECHANICAL ORGAN   OX
BEETHOVEN, L. VAN-PHIL. WW QUINTET.   QUINTET, OP 71 IN E FL MA   TP
BEETHOVEN, L. VAN-TAYLOR.   RONDO IN F MA (PIANO SONATA, OP 10/2)   CF
BEETHOVEN, L. VAN-RYKER.   SONATA, OP 7   BER
BEETHOVEN, L. VAN-FILAS.   6 VARIATIONS ON A THEME BY PAISIELLO   PMP
BELL, R.   ML-MOODS OF LIFE   SS
BENES, J.   CANZONA   SHF
BENGUEREL, X.   SUCCESSIONS (1960)   EMO
BENNETT, D.   RHAPSODETTE   CF
BENNETT, R.R.   QUINTET (1967/68)   UE
BENSON, W.   MARCHE   SH
BENTZON, J.   RACCONTO #5, OP 46   WH
BEREZOWSKY, N.   SUITE #2   BE
BERGE, S.   YANG-GUAN (1967)   NOR
BERGER, A.   PARTITA   BE
BERGER, J.   6 SHORT PIECES   WZ
BERGMANN, W.   MUSIK FUR BLASERQUINTETT (1961)   LDO
BERGSMA, W.   CONCERTO   GA
BERKOWITZ, L.   QUINTET (1966)   MUC
BERKOWITZ, S.   SUITE FOR WINDS   TP
BERTHOLD.   QUINTETTINO   PET
BERTOUILLE, G.   QUINTET (1969)   CBD
BEYER, F.   QUINTET (1972)   B&B
BEYER, J.   MOVEMENT   AMC
BEZANSON, P.   WOODWIND QUINTET, HOMAGE TO GREAT AMERICANS   ACA
BIBALO, A.   SONATINA 2A, ASTRALE   WH
BIGGS, J.   SCHERZO   CPR
BIGGS, J.   STUDIES IN TEXTURE   CPR
BIRTWISTLE, H.   REFRAINS & CHORUSES (1957)   UE
BITSCH, M.   SONATINE   ALE
BIZET, G.(CHRISTENSEN).   HABANERA (CARMEN)   KN
BIZET, G.-HOLMES.   MINUETTO (L'ARLESIENNE SUITE)   BA
BIZET, G.-ELKAN.   QUINTET (CARMEN)   HE
BJELIK, M.   AUTOGRAMM   LDO
BJELIK, M.   MOBILE   LDO
BLAHA, I.   JARNI HRY (1964)   CHF
BLANK, A.   QUINTET   SS
BLANQUER PONSODA, A.   DIVERTIMENTO GIOCOSO   EAM
BLATNY, P.   DREITEILIGER SATZ (1958)   CHF
BLOCH, W.   SERENADE (1966)   LDO
BLUMENFELD, H.   EXPANSIONS   MC
BLUMER, T.   QUINTET, OP 52   WZ
BLUMER, T.   TANZ-SUITE, OP 53   SIM
BOBESCU, C.   PARAFRAZA PE MOTIVUL "HOREI STACCATO"   EMU
BOEDIJN, G.   KWINTET CONCERTANTE, OP150 (1957)   SD

BOIS, R. DU. CHANTS ET CONTREPOINTS (1962)	SD
BOIS, R. DU. REFLEXIONS SUR LE JOUR	SD
BOISDEFFRE, R. DE. SCHERZO (SEPTET, OP 49)	CF
BON, W. QUINTET #1, OP 13	SD
BON, W. QUINTET #2, OP 26 (1969)	SD
BONSEL, A. KWINTET #1 (1949)	SD
BOOREN, J. SPECTRA (1967)	SD
BORKOVEC, P. WOODWIND QUINTET (1932)	ES
BORRIS, S. WOODWIND QUINTET, OP 25/2	S-V
BOSMANS, A. DIABELLIANA	HE
BOTTJE, W. QUINTET	CO
BOURGUIGNON, F. 2, OP 71 (1941) PIECES	CBD
BOZAY, A. QUINTET (1962), OP 8	EMB
BOZZA, E. PENTAPHONIE	ALE
BOZZA, E. SCHERZO, OP 48	ALE
BOZZA, E. VARIATIONS SUR UN THEME LIBRE, OP 42	ALE
BRAHMS, J.-ROSENTHAL. CAPRICCIO	WI
BRANA, H. CINCO ENTRADAS	GEN
BRANA, H. ESTRIBILLO	GEN
BRANA, H. FILIGRANA	GEN
BRANA, H. LUNES AZUL	GEN
BRANA, H. METAMORPHOSIS	GEN
BRANA, H. TEMA	GEN
BRANDON, S. RONDO (1971)	MAN
BRANT, H. PREVAILING WINDS	CF
BRAUNLICH, H. QUINTET	MAN
BRAVNICAR, M. 4 PIECES	EDD
BRAZINSKAS, A. QUINTET	MKE
BREDOW, E. QUINTETTINO	SIM
BREDOW, E. SERENADE OF FRANCONIA	ABE
BREHM, A. DIVERTIMENTO	EM
BRENTA, G. SOLDAT FANFARON, LE	CBD
BRESGEN, C. SALZBURGER DIVERTIMENTO	LDO
BRETTINGHAM SMITH, J. GYRE FOR A WIND QUINTET, A	ROB
BRICKMAN, J. SUITE	STM
BRIGHT, H. 3 SHORT DANCES	SH
BRINGS, A. SUITE	SS
BRITAIN, R. 4 SARABANDES	SS
BROD, H.-SCHULLER. QUINTET, OP 2/1	M&M
BROD, H.-SCHULLER. QUINTET, OP 2/2	M&M
BRONS, C. BALLETTO (1961)	SD
BRONS, C. MUTAZIONE (1964)	SD
BROOKS, R. QUINTET	ACA
BROPHY, W.(ARR). HAPPY BIRTHDAY TO YOU	SH
BROTONS, S. ENFASIS	EEC
BROWN, C. DIVERTIMENTO	GP
BROWN, C. QUINTET	ECH
BROWN, N. QUINTET	SS
BROWN, R.(ARR). SHENANDOAH	BA
BRUBECK, H. 6 PIECES	SH
BRUGK, H. SERENADE, OP 22	HSM
BRUNS, V. BLASERQUINTETT, OP 16	FRH
BUCHANAN, G. SWEETS	GA
BUCHT, G. QUINTETTO AMICHEVOLE (1976)	STI
BUCK, O. SIGNES (1967)	WH
BUCZYNSKI, W. 2 PIECES (1975)	CAN
BUCZYNSKI, W. SUITE, OP 13 (1955)	CAN
BUICLIU, N. QUINTET	EMU
BULL-BYRD-GIBBONS-CANTRELL. 4 ELIZABETHAN PIECES	WI
BULL, J.-MOORTEL. PRELUDIO E CANZONE	EBR
BURIAN, E. QUINTET (1933)	ART
BUSH, G. QUINTET	GA

5 PARTS: WOODWINDS (FL,OB,CL,HN,BSN)-523

```
BUTTING, M.   4 SATZE                                          ISR
BUTTING, M.   SPIEL, EIN, OP 30                                ISR
CABUS, P.   QUINTET                                            MAU
CACAVAS, J.   WINDETTE                                         SF
CAGE, J.   MUSIC FOR WIND INSTRUMENTS (1937)                  PET
CAILLIET, L.   CONCERTINO                                      HE
CALABRO, L.   DIVERTIMENTO                                     EV
CALLHOFF, H.   BLASERQUINTETT (1967-69)                        HG
CALLHOFF, H.   BLASERQUINTETT (1972)                           HG
CAMBINI, G.   QUINTET #1                                       M&M
CAMBINI, G.-SIRKER.   QUINTET #2 IN D MI                       LEU
CAMBINI, G.   QUINTET #2 IN D MI                               M&M
CAMBINI, G.   QUINTET #3                                       M&M
CAMMAROTA.   INTRODUCTION, CHROMATIC FUGUE,                    EDB
CAMPO, F.   5 PIECES, OP 18                                    WI
CANO, F.   DIFERENCIAS AGOGICAS (1969)                         EEC
CARION, F.   FANTAISIE CONCERTANTE                             EBR
CARLSTEDT, J.   KVINTETT, OP 19 (1962)                         STI
CARLSTEDT, J.   PENTASTOMOS, OP 27 (1972-73)                   STI
CARLSTEDT, J.   SINFONIETTA (1959)                             STI
CARRENO, I.   QUINTETO                                         PI
CARTER, E.   WOODWIND QUINTET (1948)                           AMP
CASTEREDE, J.   QUINTET                                        ALE
CASTRO, C. DE.   PENTE (1970)                                  EEC
CAZDEN, N.   3 CONSTRUCTIONS, OP 38                            SPR
CELLIER, A.   IMAGES MEDIEVALES                                EMT
CEREMUGA, J.   ROZMARNA SUITA (1965)                           CHF
CEREMUGA, J.   WOODWIND QUINTET #2 (1967)                      CHF
CERVELLO, J.   CAPRICCIO (1971)                                EEC
CHAGRIN, F.   DIVERTIMENTO                                     GA
CHAILLEY, J.   BARCAROLLE                                      ALE
CHATTELUN, M.   SUITE INCHOATIVE                               JB
CHAVEZ, C.   SOLI #2                                           BE
CHAYNES, C.   SERENADE                                         ALE
CHEETHAM, J.   QUINTET                                         SH
CHEMIN-PETIT, H.   QUINTET (1948)                              MRL
CHERNEY, B.   INTERLUDE (1965)                                 CAN
CHERNEY, B.   QUINTET (1965)                                   CAN
CHEVREUILLE, R.   DIVERTISSEMENT, OP 21 (1942)               CBD
CHEVREUILLE, R.   SERENADE, OP 65 (1956)                      CBD
CHILDS, B.   WIND QUINTET #1 (1962)                           ACA
CHILDS, B.   WIND QUINTET #2                                  ACA
CHILDS, B.   WIND QUINTET #3                                  ACA
CHILDS, B.   WIND QUINTET #4                                  ACA
CHILDS, B.   WIND QUINTET #5                                  MEP
CHILDS, B.   WIND QUINTET                                     AMC
CHRISTENSEN, J.   FIVE FOR THE FUN OF IT                      KN
     FL,OB(CL),CL,HN(TSAX),BSN(BCL)
CHRISTENSEN, J.   ROMANCE IN B FL MA                          KN
CHRISTENSEN, J.(ARR).   SONGS OF AMERICA                      KN
CIPCI, K.   MINIATURE                                         EDD
CLAPP, P.   PRELUDE, VARIATION AND FUGUE                      EBM
CLARKE, H.   CONCATENATA; QUODLIBET                           ACA
CLARKE, H.   SARABAND FOR THE GOLDEN GOOSE                    ACA
CLARKE, M.   SOLO SUITE                                       KN
CLEEMPUT, W. VAN.   5 BAGATELLEN                              MAU
COHEN, S.   FOREST LULLABY (SUITE).   FL,OB,CL,HN,BSN(BCL)    ACA
COHEN, S.   MARCH-MILITAIRE (SUITE).   FL,OB,CL,HN,BSN(BCL)   CF
COHEN, S.   MARCH-MINIATURE                                   CF
COHEN, S.   MINUET-FANTASY (SUITE).   FL,OB,CL,HN,BSN(BCL)    CF
COKER, W.   QUINTET IN 3 MOVEMENTS                            TP
COLACO OSORIO-SWAAB, R.   SUITE (1948)                        SD
COLGRASS, M.   WOODWIND QUINTET                               MC
```

5 PARTS: WOODWINDS (FL,OB,CL,HN,BSN)-523

```
COMES, L.  DIVERTISMENT (1970)                               EMU
CONLEY, L.  DIVERSION #2                                     SP
CONSTANTINIDES, D.  DEDICATIONS                              SS
COOPER, P.  CONCERT FOR 5 (1966)                             CHE
CORDELL, F.  INTERPLAY                                       JE
CORDERO, R.  VARIATIONS & THEME FOR 5                        SN
CORELLI, A.  COURANTE                                        CST
CORTES, R.  3 MOVEMENTS                                      EV
COURSEY, R. DE.  FUGUE A LA RUMBA (1958)                     BER
COWELL, H.  BALLAD (1956)                                    AMP
COWELL, H.  SUITE                                            TP
COX, H.  QUINTETTE DU PRINTEMPS                              MAU
COYNER, L.  RICORSO                                          ACA
CRAWFORD-SEEGER, R.  SUITE                                   AB
CROLEY, R.  MICROESPRESSIONI I (1969)                        JB
CRUFT, A.  STRATFORD MUSIC, OP 57                            CA
CRUFT, A. (ARR).  2 ENGLISH KEYBOARD PIECES                  GA
CUI, C.  ORIENTALE                                           CF
CUNNINGHAM, M.  A LINEAR CEREMONY                            SS
CUSTER, A.  2 MOVEMENTS                                      GEN
CZYZEWSKI, H.  QUINTET                                       PWM
DAHL, I.  ALLEGRO & ARIOSO (1942)                            M&M
DALLINGER, F.  QUINTET                                       LDO
DALLINGER, F.  SUITE #1                                      LDO
DAMASE, J.  17 VARIATIONS, OP 22                             ALE
DANZI, F.-WALN.  ALLEGRETTO (OP 56/2)                        KJ
DANZI, F.-KNEUSSLIN.  BLASERQUINTETT IN F MA, OP 56/3        LEU
DANZI, F.-ROTTLER.  BLASERQUINTETT IN G MA, OP 67/1          LEU
DANZI, F.-MAGANINI.  GYPSY DANCE                             CF
DANZI, F.-WALN.  QUINTET IN B FL MA, OP 56                   KJ
DANZI, F.-WEIGELT.  QUINTET IN B FL MA, OP 56/1              LEU
DANZI, F.-VESTER.  QUINTET IN D MI, OP 68/3                  MR
DANZI, F.-BURMEISTER.  QUINTET IN E MI, OP 67/2              PET
DANZI, F.-BURMEISTER.  QUINTET IN F MA, OP 56/3              PET
DANZI, F.-WEIGELT.  QUINTET IN G MI, OP 56/2                 LEU
DANZI, F.-KNEUSSLIN.  QUINTET, OP 67/2, IN E MI              EK
DANZI, F.-RAMPAL.  QUINTET, OP 67/2, IN E MI                 INT
DANZI, F.-KNEUSSLIN.  QUINTET, OP 67/3, IN E FL MA           EK
DANZI, F.-KNEUSSLIN.  QUINTET, OP 68/1, IN A MA              EK
DANZI, F.  QUINTET, OP 68/2                                  EK
DAVID, G.  QUINTET #1 (1949)                                 EMB
DAVID, G.  QUINTET #3 (1964)                                 EMB
DAVID, G.  QUINTET #4                                        EMB
DAVID, G.  SERENADE                                          BE
DAVID, T.  BLASERQUINTETT (1966)                             LDO
DAVIS, W.  QUINTET                                           SO
DEAK, C.  KVINTETT (1965)                                    STI
DEAK, C.  UNGERSKA DANSER (1977)                             STI
DEBUSSY, C.-ELKAN.  ARABESQUE #1                             HE
DEBUSSY, C.-ELKAN.  ARABESQUE #2                             HE
DEBUSSY, C.-ROSENTHAL.  ARABESQUE #2                         WI
DEBUSSY, C.-DAVIES.  DEBUSSY SUITE #2                        JE
DEBUSSY, C.-DAVIES.  DEBUSSY SUITE #3                        JE
DEBUSSY, C.-HALLAM.  DEBUSSY SUITE, A                        JE
DEBUSSY, C.-BOZZA.  LITTLE NEGRO, THE                        ALE
DEBUSSY, C.-FRANK.  REVERIE                                  SF
DEDRICK, R.  GENTLE WINDS                                    KN
DEDRICK, R.  MY BABY'S SMILE.  FL,OB(CL),CL,HN,BSN(BCL)      KN
DELA, M.  PETITE SUITE MARITIME (1946)                      CAN
DELA, M.  SUITE (1963)                                       CAN
DELVAUX, A.  WALLISER SUITE (1966)                           CBD
DEMUTH, N.  PASTORALE & SCHERZO                              HI
```

5 PARTS: WOODWINDS (FL,OB,CL,HN,BSN)-523

DENHOFF, M.   QUASI UNA SERENATA (1978)   HG
DENISOV, E.   QUINTET   TP
DERUNGS, G.   DIVERTIMENTO, OP 69 (1976)   S-V
DESPIC, D.   VIGNETTE, OP 43B   HG
DESSERRE, G.   SUITE DANS LE STYLE ANCIEN   SEM
DIAMOND, D.   QUINTET (1957)   SN
DIEMENTE, E.   VARIATIONS   SS
DIERCKS, J.   WIND QUINTET (1955)   TP
DIMOV, B.   COMPOSITION III (1968)   EMO
DJAMBAZIAN, A.   QUINTET #2, OP 13   LDO
DOBIAS, V.   QUINTETTO PASTORALE (1953)   PAN
DOBIAS, V.   WOODWIND QUINTET (1934)   PAN
DOBRY.   ALLEGRO GIOCOSO   SH
DODGSON, S.   SUITE   CA
DOHL, F.   KLANGFIGUREN (1962)   HG
DOMAZLICKY, F.   BLASERQUINTETT I (1956)   CHF
DOMAZLICKY, F.   WOODWIND QUINTET #2 (1967)   CHF
DOMENICO, O. DI.   QUINTETTO   ALE
DONATO, A.   QUINTET   CAM
DONIZETTI, G.-WILSON.   FURTIVA LAGRIMA, UNA   AB
DOPPELBAUER, J.   BLASERQUINTETT (1970)   LDO
DOUGLAS, R.   DANCE CARICATURES (1939)   HI
DOWNEY, J.   AGORT   EFM
DRAGAN, R.   AUS DER JUGEND   IMP
DREJSL, R.   BLASERQUINTETT (1948)   CHF
DRESSLER, R.   MINIATUREN (1966)   BRH
DUBOIS, P.   FANTASIA   ALE
DUBOIS, T.   SUITE #1   HEU
DUPONT, P.   3 PIECES BREVES   BIL
DUREY, L.   SOIREES DE VALFERE, LES   BIL
DUROKO, Z.   IMPROVISATION   EMB
DUTTON, B.   DECEMBER SET   SS
DVORACEK, J.   WOODWIND QUINTET   CHF
EBEN, P.   BLASERQUINTETT (1965)   ES
EBERHARD, D.   PARAPHRASES   MEP
ECKHARDT-GRAMATTE, S.   WOODWIND QUINTET (1962-63)   CAN
EDER DE LASTRA, E.   WIND QUINTET   LDO
EDER, H.   QUINTET, OP 25   LDO
EDER, H.   SEPTUAGESIMA INSTRUMENTALIS, OP 51   LDO
EGGE, K.   QUINTET, OP 13   HLY
EGK, W.   5 STUCKE   SCH
EINEM, G. VON.   QUINTET, OP 46   BH
EISMAN, W.   FONTAMARA (1966)   SD
EKLUND, HANS.   IMPROVISATA (1958)   STI
EKLUND, HANS.   SOMMARPARAFRAS (1968)   STI
ELIASSON, A.   PICKNICK (1972)   STI
EPSTEIN, A.   QUINTET   SS
ERDLEN, H.   KLEINE VARIATIONEN, OP 27/1   WZ
ERICSSON, J.   QUINTET   STI
ERNST, D.   SHAPES   MAN
ERRANTE, B.   SCHIZZO MODERNO   PO
   FL,OB(FL,CL),CL,HN(ACL),BSN(BCL)
ERVIN, K.   TRACKS   SS
ESCHER, R.   QUINTET (1967)   SD
ESSEX, K.   WIND QUINTET (1941)   HI
ETLER, A.   QUINTET #1 (1955)   AMP
ETLER, A.   QUINTET #2 (1957)   AMP
EVANS, R.   PRELUDE & FUGUE   BER
FARBERMAN, H.   QUINTESSENCE   GEN
FARKAS, F.   ANTICHE DANZE UNGHERESI (1953)   EMB
FARKAS, F.   DIVERTISSEMENT (1967)   EMB
FARKAS, F.   SERENADE (1951)   EMB

FAVRE, G. METOPE	DUR
FELCIANO, R. CONTRACTIONS (MOBILE FOR WIND QUINTET)	ECS
FELD, J. QUINTET #1 (1949)	CHF
FELD, J. QUINTET #2 (1968)	CHF
FELDMAN, H. WIND QUINTET #1	M&M
FELDMAN, J. WOODWIND QUINTET (1966)	MAN
FELIX, V. QUINTET	PAN
FENNELLY, B. WIND QUINTET (1967)	ACA
FENNER, B. QUINTET	SS
FERNSTROM, J. KVINTETT, OP 59 (1943)	STI
FERRARI, D. PASTORALE	COR
FERRARI, G. MUSICA A 5	GZ
FIALA, G. MUSIQUE DE CHAMBRE (1948)	CAN
FIBICH, Z. IDYLISCHE SUITE	CHF
FINE, I. PARTITA	BH
FINE, I. ROMANZA	BE
FINKE, F. QUINTET	BRH
FISCHER, J. QUINTET	ART
FLOSMAN, O. QUINTET #2	PAN
FODI, J. VARIATIONS II, OP 42 (1975) FL/PIC,OB/EHN,E FL CL/CL/BCL, HN,BSN	CAN
FOERSTER, J. WOODWIND QUINTET, OP 95 (1909)	CHF
FOLPRECHT, Z. WIND QUINTET, OP 17 (1938)	CHF
FORD, C. ALLIANCES FOR WINDS (1975) FL,OB/EHN,E FL CL/CL,HN,BSN/CBSN	CAN
FORSBERG, R. VARIATIONER OVER ETT EGET TEMA I FOLKTON (1965)	STI
FORSTER, E.-REYNOLDS. QUINTET	SO
FORTNER, W. 5 BAGATELLEN (1960)	SCH
FOSS, L. CAVE OF THE WINDS, THE (1972)	EDS
FOUGSTEDT, N. DIVERTIMENTO	FIN
FRACKENPOHL, A. FRENCH SUITE	SH
FRACKENPOHL, A. SUITE	EV
FRANCAIX, J. QUINTETTE	SCH
FRANCIS, A. CONTEXTURE IN PARALAX II	JOW
FRANCK, C. SCHERZO (STRING QUARTET IN D MA)	JE
FRANCL, J. QUINTETTO	CHF
FRANCO, J. CANTICLE (1958)	ACA
FRANCO, J. 7 EPIGRAMS	ACA
FRANZEN, O. H-MUSIK (1975-76)	STI
FRANZEN, O. SPEL (1969)	STI
FREED, I. QUINTET	AMC
FREEDMAN, H. QUINTET (1962)	ECK
FREISTADT, M. WOODWIND QUINTET #1	AMC
FREISTADT, M. WOODWIND QUINTET #2	AMC
FREYER, J. DIVERTIMENTO	BRH
FRICKER, P.R. QUINTET, OP 5 (1947)	S&C
FRITCHIE, W. 2 PIECES	SS
FRUMERIE, G. DE. SUITE, OP 71	CGM
FURER, A. BLASERQUINTETT, OP 21	PEL
FURST, P. APROPOS BLASERQUINTETT, OP 49	LDO
FURST, P. KONZERTANTE MUSIK, OP 25	LDO
FURST, P. QUINTET #3, OP 29	LDO
FUTTERER, C. QUINTET IN B FL MA (1922)	EK
FUX, J. LARGO #1	CST
FUX, J. LARGO #2	CST
GAAL, J. BLASERQUINTETT	EK
GAAL, J. QUINTET #2	EMB
GABAYE, P. QUINTET (1959)	ALE
GADE, N.-ELKAN. MERRY-GO-ROUND	HE
GARDONYI, Z. DIVERTIMENTO	WZ
GARRIDO-LECCA, C. DIVERTIMENTO	SN
GAYFER, J. SUITE (1947)	BH

GEBAUER, F.-SIRKER. BLASERQUINTETT, #2, IN E FL MA		LEU
GEBAUER, F.-SIRKER. BLASERQUINTETT, #3, IN C MI		LEU
GEBAUER, F. QUINTET IN E FL MA		UE
GEE, H. (ARR). BRANSLE		BD
GEISSLER, F. FRUHLINGSQUINTETT		DEU
GEISSLER, F. HEITERE SUITE		BRH
GENTILUCCI, A. CILE (1973)		RC
GENTILUCCI, A. DIARIO II (1971)		RC
GENZMER, H. BLASER-QUINTETT (1956-57)		LIT
GERAEDTS, J. KLEINE WATERMUZIEK (1951)		SD
GERHARD, R. QUINTET (1928)		BE
GERSHWIN, G.-HARRIS. PROMENADE		CA
GERSTER, O. HEITERE MUSIK		SCH
GIBSON, D. LIGATURES		SS
GILLIS, D. BR'ER RABBIT DREAMS		BE
GILLIS, D. FIVE PIECE COMBO		BE
GILLIS, D. FROLIC IN B-BOP MA		BE
GILLIS, D. MR. TORTOISE WINS THE RACE, AND		BE
GILLIS, D. SERMONETTE (SOUTHERN STYLE)		BE
GILLIS, D. THEY'RE OFF		BE
GILTAY, B. QUINTETTO (1956)		SD
GIPPS, R. SEASCAPE		SF
GIULIANI, V. HAPPY DAWN		EDI
GLASER, W. MARSCH I SKRATTSPEGEL (1976)		STI
GLASER, W. QUINTET #1 (1942)		STI
GLASER, W. QUINTET #2 (1961-70)		STI
GLUCK, C.-JOSEP. GAVOTTE (PARIS & HELENA)		CF
GOEB, R. PRAIRIE SONGS		SN
GOLDMANN, F. ZUSAMMENSTELLUNG (1976)		PET
FL/AFL/PIC,OB/EHN,CL,HN,BSN/CBSN		
GOLEMINOV, M. QUINTET #2 (1947)		HG
GONZALEZ-ZULETA, F. QUINTETO 1960		SN
GOODE, D. SYMPHONIA, WOODWIND QUINTET #2		AMC
GOODENOUGH, F. WOODWIND QUINTET		ACA
GOODMAN, J. WOODWIND QUINTET (1954)		AB
GOTTLIEB, J. TWILIGHT CRANE		GS
GRABOCZ, M. ALTE UNGARISCHE TANZE DES 18 JAHRHUNDERTS		B&N
GRAHN, U. OPUS III (1964)		STI
GRAINGER, P. LISBON		S&C
GRAINGER, P. WALKING TUNE		S&C
GRANADOS, E.-ELKAN. ORIENTAL, OP 5		HE
GRANDERT, J. POUR PHILIPPE (1970)		STI
GRANT, W. SOLILOQUY & JUBILATION, OP 40		ACA
GREAVES, T. BEETHOVEN'S 5TH BOSSA NOVA		JE
GREEN, G. QUINTET		SS
GRETRY, A.-SABATINI. TAMBOURINE		COR
GRIEG, E.-LANG. ANITRA'S DANCE.		LN
GRIEG, E.-TRINKHAUS. EROTIKON, OP 43/4		HY
GRIEG, E.-TRINKAUS. MORNING MOOD (OP 46/1)		WB
GRIEG, E.-TRINKHAUS. RIGAUDON		HY
GROOT, H. DE. BURLA RITMICA		B&V
GROOT, H. DE. VARIATIESUITE (1944)		B&V
GRUBER, H. BOSSA NOVA, OP 21 IN E MI		LDO
GUDMUNDSEN-HOLMGREEN, P. TERRACE		WH
GUENTHER, R. RONDO		CF
GUENTZEL, G. SCHERZO		BA
GUENTZEL, G. TARANTELLA		BA
GUILMANT, A.-TAYLOR. CANZONETTA		WB
GUINFOAN, J. TRIPTICO (1965)		EEC
GUION, D.-WALN. HARMONICA PLAYER, THE (ALLEY TUNES)		KJ
GYRING, E. QUINTET		ACA
HAAS, P. QUINTET, OP 10 (1929)		M&M

```
HADDAD, D.   BLUES AU VENT.   FL,OB,CL,BSN,HN,PERC OPT          SH
HADDAD, D.   ENCORE "1812"                                      SH
HADDRILL, P.   RECITATION                                       PO
HADSHIEV, P.   3 STUCKE (1942)                                  HG
HAHNEL, H.   QUINTET                                            HEI
HAIDMAYER, K.   QUINTET #3                                      FS
HAIDMAYER, K.   SYMBIOSE II                                     FS
HALACZINSKY, R.   EPITAPH                                       HEI
HALL, P.   QUINTET (1944)                                       HLY
HALLNAS, H.   HOSTBALLADER (1976)                               STI
HAMBRAEUS, B.   JEU DE 5                                        CAN
HAMERIK, E.   QUINTET (1942)                                    SPD
HANDEL, G.-CHRISTENSEN.   HORNPIPE                              KN
HANDEL, G.-BAUER.   6 LITTLE FUGUES                             AMP
HANSEN, T.   CONTRASTS                                          SS
HANUS, J.   SUITA DOMESTICA, OP 57 (1964)                       ART
HARDISTY, D.   PISCES OF THE ZODIAC                             SH
HARTLEY, G.   DIVERTISSEMENT                                    AMP
HARTLEY, W.   2 PIECES                                          CRE
HARTZELL, E.   COMPANION PIECES TO A WIND QUINTET               LDO
HARTZELL, E.   PROJECTIONS (1970)                               LDO
HASHAGEN, K.   COLLOQUIUM                                       PET
HASSE, J.   CHAMBER MUSIC                                       ABE
HAUBIEL, C.   5 PIECES                                          OP
HAUFRECHT, H.   FROM THE HILLS                                  ACA
HAUFRECHT, H.   WOODLAND SERENADE, A                            RON
HAUGLAND, A.   LITTLE SUITE                                     CO
HAWKINS.   QUINTET                                              CAN
HAWORTH, F.   GLENROSE SUITE (1960)                             FH
HAYDN, F.-HOLMES.   ALLEGRETTO (SYMPHONY #11)                   BA
HAYDN, F.-PERRY.   DIVERTIMENTO IN B FL MA                      BH
HAYDN, F.-PHILA. QUINTET.   DIVERTIMENTO IN B FL MA             TP
HAYDN, F.-HAUFRECHT.   DIVERTIMENTO IN C MA                     ACA
HAYDN, F.-LONG.   DIVERTIMENTO IN C MA                          GS
HAYDN, F.-MC CATHREN.   FINALE (SONATA IN C MA)                 KN
HAYDN, F.-CUTLER.   7 GERMAN DANCES                             COR
HAYDN, F.-MEEK.   LARGO (OP 76/5)                               TP
HAYDN, F.-HOLMES.   MINUETTO (SYMPHONY #2)                      BA
HAYDN, F.-SKOWRONEK.   MUSICAL CLOCK PIECES                     M&M
HAYDN, F.-EMERSON.   OP 55, #3, IN B FL MA                      JE
HAYDN, F.-VESTER.   7 PIECES FOR THE MUSICAL CLOCK              UE
HAYDN, F.-KESZTLER.   QUINTET                                   EMB
HAYDN, F.-LONG.   QUINTET #1                                    SO
HAYDN, F.-LONG.   QUINTET #4                                    SO
HAYDN, F.   QUINTET                                             COR
HEIDEN, B.   SINFONIA (1949)                                    AMP
HEIDEN, B.   WOODWIND QUINTET (1965)                            AB
HEINIO, M.   QUINTET, OP 12                                     FIN
HEINSCH, W.   QUINTET (1977)                                    EMO
HEISS, H.   KONZERTMUSIK I & II                                 WMS
HEKSTER, W.   PENTAGRAM                                         SD
HEKSTER, W.   PULSATIONS (1967)                                 SD
HEKSTER, W.   WINDSONG #3 (1977).   FL/AFL,OB,CL/BCL,BSN,HN     SD
HELM, E.   WOODWIND QUINTET                                     SCH
HEMEL, O. VAN.   WIND QUINTET (1972)                            SD
HEMPEL, R.   MOVIMENTO (1966)                                   GBV
HENKEMANS, H.   QUINTET #2 (1962)                               SD
HENNING, E.   BADINAGE                                          TP
HENZE, H.   AUTUNNO, L'                                         SCH
     FL/PIC/AFL,OB/OB D'AMORE,CL/E FL CL/BCL,HN/T U,BSN/CBSN
HENZE, H.   QUINTET (1952)                                      SCH
HERRMANN, H.   PASTORALE PHANTASIETTEN, OP 51                   SIM
```

5 PARTS: WOODWINDS (FL,OB,CL,HN,BSN)-523

HESPOS, H. PROFILE (1972)   EMO
HESS, W. DIVERTIMENTO, OP 51   HI
HETU, J. QUINTET, OP 13 (1967)   CAN
HEUSSENSTAMM, G. CALLICHOREO, OP 23   SS
HEUSSENSTAMM, G. INSTABILITIES, OP 21   SS
HIDAS, F. QUINTET #2   GEN
HILFIGER, J. MIRAGE   KN
HINDEMITH, P. KLEINE KAMMERMUSIK, OP 24/2   SCH
HIRNER, T. WIND QUINTET (1960)   SHF
HIRSCH, H. QUINTETTO SERENO   PET
HLAVAC, M. WOODWIND QUINTET (1970)   CHF
HLOBIL, E. WIND QUINTET, OP 20 (1940)   CHF
HOCHEL, S. QUINTET   SHF
HOFFDING, F. QUINTET, OP 35   WH
HOFFER, P. BLASERQUINTETT (1947)   MIT
HOFMANN, W. BLASERQUINTETT IN D MA   BRH
HOFMANN, W. SERENADE   S-V
HOHENSEE, W. QUINTET IN D MA   BRH
HOLLER, K. SERENADE, OP 42A   WMS
HOLLIGER, H. H (1968)   BE
HOLM, M. SONATA, OP 25   WH
HOLM, P. 2 PIECES   WH
HOLMES, G. CASTILLIA (BOLERO)   BA
HOUNSELL(ARR). 3 PIECES   TM
HOVHANESS, A. WIND QUINTET, OP159   PET
HOVLAND, E. QUINTETT   NOR
HOYER, K. SERENADE, OP 29   SIM
HRISANIDE, A. DIRECTIONS (1970)   HG
HRUSKA, J. WOODWIND QUINTET (1949)   CHF
HUBER, K. 3 (1958-59) SATZE IN 2 TEILEN   B&N
HUBNER, W. FACETTEN II   BRH
HULA, Z. 4 MARCHEN--STIMMUNGEN, NACH K. J. ERBEN   CHF
HUMMEL, B. QUINTET   ABE
HUNTER, E. DANCE HUMORESQUE, OP 1/3   CF
HURNIK, I. DIE VIER JAHRESZEITEN (1952)   CHF
HURNIK, I. ROZMARNA HUDBA   CHF
HUSE, P. RECURRENCES (1966)   CAN
HUYBRECHTS, A. QUINTETTE (1936)   CBD
HYAMS, A. QUINTET   SO
IBERT, J. 3 PIECES BREVES   ALE
IKONOMOV, B. SUITE (1951)   HG
ILIEV, I. QUINTET #2, OP 62 (1968)   HG
ILIEV, I. QUINTET #6, OP101 (1974)   HG
IOANNIDIS, Y. ACTINIA (1969)   HG
IVEY, J. ANDROCLES & THE LION   AMC
JACKSON, J. 9 MINIATURES   SS
JACOB, G. QUINTET # 2   MR
JACOB, G. SWANSEA TOWN   JE
JACOBI, F. SCHERZO   CF
JACOBY, H. QUINTET (1946)   IMP
JAMES, P. SUITE IN 4 MOVEMENTS   CF
JANSONS, A. OLD LETTISH DANCES   SO
JARDANYI, P. PHANTASY & VARIATIONS (1955)   EMB
JERSILD, J. MUSIC-MAKING IN THE FOREST   WH
JETTEL, R. QUINTET #3   EUL
JETTEL, R. QUINTET   JOW
JIRA, M. QUINTET #3   CHF
JIRKO, I. SUITE (1956)   PAN
JIRKOVA, O. VARIATIONEN (1967)   CHF
JOACHIM, O. DIVERTIMENTO (1962)   CAN
JOHANSON, S. KVINTETT (1964)   STI
JOHANSSON, B. CONCERTINO (1963)   STI

5 PARTS: WOODWINDS (FL,OB,CL,HN,BSN)-523

JOHNSON, H. QUINTET IN C MA	CF
JOLIVET, A. SERENADE	BIL
JONES, K. QUINTET (1968)	PET
JONES, W. QUINTET	AMC
JONG, M. DE. APHORISTISCH TRIPTIEK, OP 82 BIS (1953)	CBD
JONG, M. DE. QUINTET #3, OP157 (1971)	CBD
JONGEN, J. CONCERTO, OP124	SO
JONGEN, J. 2 PIECES (PREAMBULE ET DANSES)	SO
JOPLIN, S.-IANNACCONE. EASY WINNERS, THE	SH
JOPLIN, S.-SACCI. ENTERTAINER, THE	KN
JOPLIN, S.(FRACKENPOHL). 2 JOPLIN RAGS	SH
JOPLIN, S.-MABRY. RAGTIME DANCE	SH
JUNGK, K. CHACONNE	HSM
KADOSA, P. QUINTET, OP 49A (1954)	EMB
KALABIS, V. DIVERTIMENTO (1952)	CHF
KALABIS, V. KLEINE KAMMERMUSIK, OP 27 (1967)	ART
KALLSTENIUS, E. DIVERTIMENTO, OP 29 (1943)	STI
KANTOR, J. WOODWIND QUINTET #1	WI
KARDOS, D. CONCERTO, OP 47	SHF
KARKOFF, M. KVINTETT, OP 24 (1956-57)	STI
KARKOFF, M. SERENATA PICCOLA, OP 34C	EMF
KARKOSCHKA, E. ANTINOMIE (1968)	EDT
KARLINS, M. WOODWIND QUINTET 1970	ACA
KASANDSHIEV, V. QUINTET (1971)	HG
KASEMETS, U. QUINTET, OP 48 (1957)	CAN
KAUDER, H. VARIATIONS ON A DANCE	SS
KAUFFMANN, L. QUINTET	UE
KAUFMANN, W. PARTITA	SH
KAYN, R. INERZIALI	HMO
KEETBAAS, D. QUINTET (1961)	CAN
KELDORFER, R. MUSIK (1968)	LDO
KELEMEN, M. ENTRANCES	PET
KELEMEN, M. ETUDES CONTRAPUNTIQUES	SCH
KELLER, H. QUINTET	S-V
KELLY, B. QUINTET	NOM
KELLY, R. PASSACAGLIA & FUGUE	ACA
KELTERBORN, R. 7 BAGATELLEN	EMO
KELTERBORN, R. KAMMERMUSIK (1974)	B&N
KERN, F. 4 STUCKE, OP 25	ETB
KERN, J.-HARRIS. WALTZ IN SWING TIME	HA
KERSTERS, W. QUINTET	MAU
KETTING, O. QUINTET "A SET OF PIECES"	SD
KIBBE, M. QUINTET #1	SH
KIESEWETTER, P. LE TOMBEAU DE LULLY, OP 6B	HG
KIEVMAN, C. SIROCCO (1975)	AMP
KING, H. KWINTET (1949)	SD
KINGMAN, D. QUINTET	WI
KJELLBERG, J. KVINTETT	STI
KLEIN, L. QUINTET (1952)	CAN
KLEIN, R. FANTASIE	MV
KLUGHARDT, A. QUINTET, OP 79	EDK
KLUGHARDT, A. QUINTET, OP 79	M&M
KLUGHARDT, A. QUINTET, OP 79	WZ
KLUSAK, J. 5 INVENTION "SCHACHSPIEL" (1965)	CHF
KNAB, A. SERENADE	PET
KOCH, F. SCHERZO FOR 5 WINDS	GEN
KOCSAR, M. QUINTET #1	EMB
KOCSAR, M. VARIAZIONI (1968)	EMB
KODALY, Z.-ELKAN. ZONGORA MUSZIKA #2	HE
KOETSIER, J. DIVERTIMENTO #2, OP 35/1 (1947)	SD
KOETSIER, J. DIVERTIMENTO, OP 16/1 (1937)	SD
KOHN, K. LITTLE SUITE	CF

5 PARTS: WOODWINDS (FL,OB,CL,HN,BSN)-523

KOHOUT, J.	6 MINIATUREN	FRH
KOHOUT, J.	MINIATURES	EDK
KOHOUT, J.	VARIATIONEN AUF EIN TSCHECHISCHES VOLKSLIED	CHF
KOHOUTEK, C.	SUITE (1959)	ART
KOHS, E.	WOODWIND QUINTET	AMC
KOKKONEN, J.	WOODWIND QUINTET (1972/73)	GS
KOLBERG, K.	A WIND QUINTET	NM
KONT, P.	QUINTET IN MEMORIAM FR. DANZI	LDO
KOPELENT, M.	TRISTE E CONSOLANTE (1976/77)	HG
KOPP, F.	CONVERSATIONS	SS
KOPP, F.	3 MOVEMENTS	SS
KOPP, F.	PASSACAGLIA IN THE OLDEN STYLE	SS
KORDA, V.	DIVERTIMENTO	LDO
KORINGER, F.	APHORISMEN	FS
KORN, P.	QUINTET FOR WINDS, OP 40	PET
KORTE, K.	DIABLERIE	AU
KOTONSKI, W.	MUSICAL GAMES	HMO
KOTONSKI, W.	QUINTET (1964)	AP
KOTSCHAU, J.	BLASERQUINTETT, OP 14	WZ
KOUNADIS, A.	"WER OHREN HAT ZU HOREN, DER HORE" (1970)	B&B
KOVAR, V.	SONATA	SHF
KOWALSKI, J.	5 INVENTIONS	SHF
KRAFT, L.	PARTITA #3	GEN
KRASKO, J.	SIT DOWN SUN	SHF
KRATZSCHMAR, W.	ANAKREONTISCHE PHANTASIE	DEU
KRAUSE-GRAUMNITZ.	CADENZA QUINTET #1	EDK
KRAUSE-GRAUMNITZ, H.	BLASERQUINTETT #1	BRH
KREJCI, I.	DECHOVY KVINTET (1964)	ART
KREK, U.	EPISODI CONCERTANTI	EDD
KRENEK, E.	ALPBACH-QUINTETT	UE
KRENEK, E.	PENTAGRAM (1952/57)	B&N
KROLL, G.	INVOCAZIONI	SCH
KROPFREITER, A.	QUINTET (1968)	LDO
KUBIZEK, A.	KAMMERQUINTETT, OP 15	LDO
KUHMSTEDT, P.	QUINTET	MV
KUHN, M.	SERENATA NOTTURNA	EUL
KUHNAU, J.-DISHINGER.	GIGUE	SP
KUHNEL, E.	QUINTET (SUITE), OP 29	ETB
KUNAD, R.	MUSIK FUR BLASER (1965)	DEU
KUNERT, K.	DIVERTIMENTO #2, OP 18	FRH
KUNERT, K.	QUINTET #4	BRH
KUNERT, K.	QUINTET, OP 14	ETB
KUNERT, K.	ZWEITES BLASERQUINTETT, OP 17	FRH
KUNZ, A.	QUINTET (1964)	CAN
KURI-ALDANA, M.	CANDELARIA	MR
KURTAG, G.	QUINTET (1959)	EMB
KURTAG, G.	QUINTET, OP 2	EMB
KVANDAL, J.	3 HYMN TUNES	NM
KVANDAL, J.	QUINTET, OP 34	NM
LACERDA, O.	VARIATIONS & FUGUE	SN
LADMIRAULT, P.	CHORAL ET VARIATIONS	EV
LAMPE, G.	PERMUTAZIONI	DEU
LANDRE, G.	KWINTET (1960)	SD
LANDRE, G.	QUINTETTO (1930)	SD
LANG, I.	QUINTET #1 (1964)	EMB
LANG, I.	QUINTET #2 (1965)	EMB
LANG, I.	QUINTET #3	EMB
LANG, R.	4 PIECES	LN
LANTZ, J.	5 MINIATURES	SH
LARSSON, L.	4, OP 55 (1968) TEMPI	CGM
LAUDENSLAGER, H.	WOODWIND QUINTET	COR
LAURISCHKUS, M.	AUS LITAUEN, OP 23	SIM

LAYZER, A. WOODWIND QUINTET	ACA
LAZAROF, H. CONCERTINO DA CAMERA	IMP
LECLAIR, J.-MUELLER. MINUET & HUNTING SCENE	SO
LEDUC, J. QUINTETT A VENT	MAU
LEES, B. 2 MINIATURES	BH
LEFEBVRE, C. CANON (SUITE, OP 57)	PO
LEFEBVRE, C.-WALN. PRELUDE FOR QUINTET (SUITE #2)	KJ
LEFEBVRE, C. SUITE, OP 57	CF
LEFEBVRE, C. SUITE, OP 57	EV
LEFEBVRE, C. SUITE, OP 57	HAM
LEFEBVRE, C. SUITE, OP 57	INT
LEGLEY, V. QUINTETTE, OP 58 (1961)	CBD
LEHMANN, D. WOODWIND QUINTET	AMC
LEHMANN, H. EPISODEN (1963/64)	SCH
LEHMANN, H. GEGEN-(BEI-)SPIELE	HUG
LEIBOWITZ, R. QUINTET, OP 11 (1944)	B-B
LEICHTLING, A. QUINTET #2, OP 24	AMC
LEICHTLING, A. QUINTET #3	SS
LEICHTLING, A. QUINTET, OP 33	AMC
LEITERMEYER, F. DIVERTIMENTO, OP 38	LDO
LEMARE, E.-TRINKHAUS. ANDANTINO	HY
LEMELAND, A. MUSIQUE NOCTURNE, OP 18	BIL
LENNON/MC CARTNEY-BUCKLEY. YESTERDAY; MAXWELL'S HAMMER	OP
LESSARD, J. PARTITA	GEN
LEUKAUF, R. BLASERQUINTETT, OP 25	LDO
LEVINE, B. QUINTET	MAN
LEVITT, R. WOODMEN OF THE WORLD	AMP
LIADOV, A. 8 RUSSIAN FOLKSONGS	WI
LIADOW, A. 8 RUSSIAN FOLK DANCES, OP 58	EDK
LICKL, J.-KNEUSSLIN. QUINTETTO CONCERTANTE IN F MA	EK
LIEDBECK, S. IMPROMPTU	STI
LIGETI, G. 6 BAGATELLES	SCH
LIGETI, G. 10 STUCKE	SCH
LILGE, H. VARIATIONEN UND FUGE UBER EIN EIGENES THEMA, OP 67	KIS
LILIEN, I. VOYAGE AU PRINTEMPS (1952)	SD
LINDGREN, O. SVIT IN G MI, OP 1 (1958)	STI
LINDGREN, P. ODYPASSE (1976)	STI
LINKE, N. BLASERQUINTETT IN EINEM SATZ	HG
LINN, R. QUINTET	WI
LISZT, F.-ANDRAUD. 3 CONCERT PIECES	SO
LISZT, F.-HAMILTON. PASTORALE (LES PRELUDES)	GA
LISZT, F.-SEAY. WEIHNACHTSLIED	SPR
LOCKWOOD, N. FUN PIECES	ACA
LOHSE, D. QUINTET	PET
LONDON, E. QUINTET	MJ
LONQUICH, H. MISSA (1971)	HG
LORA, A. 6, OLD & NEW DANCES	ACA
LORENTZEN, B. DANISH WIND	WH
LOTHAR, M. SPITZWEG-IMPRESSIONEN, OP 82	B&B
LOUEL, J. QUINTETTE (1958)	CBD
LOVEC, V. PARTITA	EDD
LUCKY, S. WOODWIND QUINTET (1946)	ES
LUDEWIG, W. MOSAIK (1973/74)	B&B
LUIGINI, A.-HOLMES. BALLET EGYPTIAN	BA
LUKAS, Z. WOODWIND QUINTET WITH TRIANGLE (1969)	CHF
LUNDE, I. 3 BAGATELLES	SH
LUNDE, I. SERENADE	SH
LUNDE, I. JR. PETITE SUITE, UNE	SH
LUNDEN, L. VARIATIONER ON "BYSSAN LULL"	NOR
LUNDKVIST, P. EN LITEN MORGONMUSIK (1961/1977)	STI
LUNDKVIST, P. KVINTETT	STI
LUNDQUIST, T. TEAMWORK (1967)	EHR

```
LUTOSLAWSKI, W.  KUKULCAN (1969/72)                      HMO
LUTYENS, E.  WIND QUINTET                                BE
LYBBERT, D.  VARIANTS                                    ACA
MAC DOWELL, E.-TRINKAUS.  IDYL, OP 28/2                  WB
MADDEN, J.  QUINTET # 3                                  NOM
MAGANINI, Q.-HARRIS.  REVERIE.  FL,OB,CL,HN,BSN(BCL)     CF
MAGANINI, Q.  SIMPLE AVEU.  FL,OB,CL,HN,BSN(BCL)         CF
MAGI, E.  OSTINATO                                       MKE
MALIGE, F.  QUINTET #2                                   BRH
MALIPIERO, G.  DIALOGUE IV                               RC
MALIPIERO, R.  MUSICA DA CAMERA (1959)                   ESZ
MALOVEC, J.  PRELUDIUM A BURLESKA                        SHF
MAMLOK, U.  FESTIVE SOUNDS                               PET
MAMLOK, U.  QUINTET                                      ACA
MANIET, R.  QUINTETTE A VENT #1                          MAU
MANN, L.  4 STUDIES IN THE BLUES IDIOM, OP 23 (1969)     CAN
MANNEKE, D.  WALKING IN FOGPATCHES (1971)                SD
MANNINO, F.  MINI QUINTETT                               EDI
MARCKHL, E.  SONATE                                      LDO
MARCO, T.  KUKULCAN                                      HMO
MARCONI, L.  INTRODUZIONE E FUGA                         EDI
MARECHAL, H.  AIR DU GUET                                HEU
MAREZ OYENS, T. DE.  2 (1963) SKETCHES                   SD
MARIATTI, F.  OUVERTURE BREVE                            EDI
MARIE, G.-HARRIS.  BERCEUSE.  FL,OB,CL,HN,BSN(BCL)       CF
MAROS, M.  QUINTET #1 (1961-62)                          STI
MAROS, R.  CONSORT (1970)                                SN
MAROS, R.  MUSICA LEGGIERA (1956)                        EMB
MARTIN-PIZZUTO.  HOMMAGE A BARTOK                        KN
MARTINO, D.  CONCERTO                                    ECS
MARTINON, J.  DOMENON                                    BIL
MASSIS, A.  THEME ET VARIATIONS                          BIL
MATHER, B.  EINE KLEINE BLASERMUSIK (1975)               CAN
MATHIAS, W.  WIND QUINTET, OP 22                         OX
MATYS, J.  KINDERBALLETTE (1959)                         CHF
MATYS, J.  MUSIC FOR WOODWIND QUINTET (1970)             CHF
MATYS, J.  3 SATZE (1969)                                CHF
MATZ, R.  5 MOVEMENTS                                    DSS
MC BRIDE, R.  CUATRO MILPAS                              ACA
MC BRIDE, R.  FANFARE FOR YOUNG PEOPLE                   ACA
MC BRIDE, R.  HOME ON THE RANGE                          ACA
MC BRIDE, R.  JAM SESSION                                OP
MC BRIDE, R.  MEXICAN DANCE                              ACA
MC BRIDE, R.  PAJARILLO BARRENQUENO                      ACA
MC BRIDE, R.  ROCK 'EM COWBOY                            ACA
MC BRIDE, R.  SERENADE TO COUNTRY MUSIC                  ACA
MC BRIDE, R.  5 WINDS BLOWING                            ACA
MC CALL, H.  2 TUNES FROM MOTHER GOOSE                   SO
MC DANIEL, W.  WOODWIND QUINTET #1                       CPS
MC INTYRE, P.  FANTASY ON AN ESKIMO SONG (1962)          CAN
MC KAY, D.  BAGATELLES FOR GEN WASHINGTON                SH
MC KAY, D.  COLONIAL BAND MUSIC                          SH
MC KAY, F.  BAINBRIDGE ISLAND SKETCHES                   BA
MC KAY, G.  JOYFUL DANCE                                 TP
MC KAY, G.  3 NAUTICAL CHARACTERS                        BA
MC KAY, G.  3 SEA SKETCHES                               BA
MC LEAN, H.  RONDO                                       CO
MC PEEK, B.  WOODWIND QUINTET (1961)                     CAN
MEALE, R.  PLATEAU                                       UE
MEALE, R.  QUINTET (1969)                                UE
MEDEK, T.  QUINTET #1                                    PET
MEDERACKE, K.  BOHMISCHE SUITE, OP 43                    FRH
```

5 PARTS: WOODWINDS (FL,OB,CL,HN,BSN)-523

MEESTER, L. DE. DIVERTIMENTO (1946)	CBD
MENDELSSOHN, F. FIGURATE HYMN	CF
MENDELSSOHN, F.-BOYD. INTERMEZZO (MIDSUMMER NIGHT'S DREAM)	CF
MENDELSSOHN, F.-SEAY. SCHERZETTO, OP102/3	SPR
MENDELSSOHN, F.-JOSPE. SCHERZO, OP110	CF
MENDELSSOHN, F.-CAFARELLA. SONG WITHOUT WORDS, OP 62/4	VO
MENGELBERG, M. OMRENT EEN COMPONISTEN-ACTIE	SD
MERSSON, B. MUSIK, OP 20	BRH
METRAL, P. VARIATIONS	EDT
MEULEMANS, A. QUINTET #1 (1931)	CBD
MEULEMANS, A. QUINTET #2 (1932)	CBD
MEULEMANS, A. QUINTET #3 (1958)	CBD
MEYER-TORMIN, W. KLEINES QUINTETT (1951)	B&B
MICHAEL, F. SERENATA PICCOLA (1966/67)	BRH
MICHEL, P. HOMMAGE A RABELAIS (1960)	CBD
MICHEL, W. BLASMUSIK (1972)	EMO
MIGOT, G. QUINTETTE	ALE
MIHELCIC, P. TEAM	EDD
MIKODA, B. WOODWIND QUINTET, OP 28	CHF
MILHAUD, D. CHEMINEE DU ROI RENE, LA (1939)	SO
MILHAUD, D. DIVERTISSEMENT IN 3 PARTS	HEU
MILHAUD, D. QUINTET	EES
MILHAUD, D. 2 SKETCHES	TP
MILLER, K. ODE TO SPRING	BD
MILLER, L. SONATINA (1962)	CAN
MILLS, C. SONATA FANTASIA	ACA
MIROGLIO, F. MASQUES	UE
MONACO, R. 3 MINIATURES	SH
MONTEVERDI, C.-TOWNSEND. SINFONIA	RC
MOORE, C. QUINTET (1964)	BE
MOORE, D. QUINTET	AMC
MORITZ, E. QUINTET, OP 41	WZ
MORITZ, E. QUINTET, OP169	WZ
MOROSS, J. SONATINA	EAM
MORTENSEN, F. QUINTET, OP 4	WH
MORTENSEN, F. SUITE, OP 36	NM
MORTENSEN, O. QUINTET	WH
MORTHENSON, J. SOLI	ER
MOULAERT, P. PASSEPIED EN RONDO (1940)	CBD
MOUSSORGSKY, M.-KESSLER. BALLET OF THE CHICKENS	RU
MOYSE, L. QUINTET	M&M
MOYZES, A. WIND QUINTET, OP 17	SIM
MOZART, F.-PILLNEY. 2 POLONAISEN, OP 2	WZ
MOZART, W. ADAGIO IN B FL MA	TP
MOZART, W.-WEIGELT. ADAGIO IN B FL MA, K411	LEU
MOZART, W. ADAGIO, K411	CF
MOZART, W.-VESTER. ANDANTE FUR EINE ORGELWALZE, K616	RC
MOZART, W.-MEYER. ANDANTE, K616	HSM
MOZART, W.-MAROS. DIVERTIMENTO	EMB
MOZART, W.-WEIGELT. DIVERTIMENTO # 9 IN B FL MA, KV240	LEU
MOZART, W.-ROTTLER. DIVERTIMENTO #12 IN E FL MA, KV252	LEU
MOZART, W.-BRYANT. DIVERTIMENTO #12, K252	GAL
MOZART, W.-WEIGELT. DIVERTIMENTO #13 IN F MA, KV253	LEU
MOZART, W.-WEIGELT. DIVERTIMENTO #14 IN B FL MA, KV270	LEU
MOZART, W.-MOORTEL. DIVERTIMENTO #14, KV270	EBR
MOZART, W.-BAINES. DIVERTIMENTO #14, K270	OX
MOZART, W.-ROTTLER. DIVERTIMENTO #16 IN E FL MA, KV289	LEU
MOZART, W.-WEIGELT. DIVERTIMENTO #8 IN F MA, KV213	LEU
MOZART, W.-MAROS. DIVERTIMENTO IN B FL MA, KV270	EMB
MOZART, W.-JENSEN. DIVERTIMENTO IN E FL MA, K252	CRE
MOZART, W.-VESTER. FANTASIE FUR EINE ORGELWALZE, K608	RC
MOZART, W.-PILLNEY. FANTASIE IN F MI, K594	BRH

5 PARTS: WOODWINDS (FL,OB,CL,HN,BSN)-523

MOZART, W.-MEYER. FANTASY IN F MI, K594	HSM
MOZART, W.-MEYER. FANTASY IN F MI, K608	HSM
MOZART, W.-EMERSON. K458 (HUNT QUARTET)	JE
MOZART, W.-POPKIN. MINUET #6, K355	TP
MOZART, W.-EMERSON. QUARTETS K465, K387, K575	JE
MOZART, W.-ROTTLER. QUINTET IN C MI, KV406	LEU
MOZART, W.-SNIECKOWSKI. QUINTET IN D MI (K422)	PWM
MOZART, W.-CAILLIET. QUINTET IN F MA, KV370	EV
MOZART, W.-NAKAGAWA. SONATA IN B FL MA, K358	AMP
MOZART, W.-POPKIN. 12 VARIATIONS, K265	TP
MUCZYNSKI, R. MOVEMENTS, OP 16	SH
MUELLER, F. 5 PIECES	COR
MUELLER, F. 3 TRANSCRIPTIONS	COR
MUELLER, P. QUINTET #1 IN E FL MA	MR
MUELLER, P. QUINTET #2 IN E FL MA	MR
MUELLER, P. QUINTET #3 IN A MA	MR
MULDER, H. KWINTET, OP119 (1961)	SD
MULDER, H. QUINTET, OP141 (1966)	SD
MULLER-MEDEK, W. LEINEWEBER, DIE	ETB
MULLER-MEDEK, W. WOODWIND QUINTET #1	PET
MULLER-SIEMENS, D. SANGLOTS LONGS, LES	SCH
NECKE, H.-TAYLOR. MILL OF SANS SOUCI	BE
NELHYBEL, V. QUINTET #3	GEN
NELHYBEL, V. WOODWIND QUINTET #2	GEN
NERO, P. MONSOON. FL,OB,CL,HN,BSN(BCL)	CF
NEUBERT, G. MUSIK (1968/69)	DEU
NEVIN, E.-GORDON. GONDOLIERI	TP
NIELSEN, C. QUINTET, OP 43	WH
NILSSON, B. DEJA CONNU, DEJA ENTENDU	NOR
NOBIS, H. 5 BAGATELLEN (1972)	B&N
NOBRE, M. QUINTET, OP 29	EDT
NORDGREN, P. 3 ENTICEMENTS	FIN
NORDGREN, P. QUINTET #2	FIN
NOVAK, J. CONCERTINO	CHF
NOWKA, D. QUINTET, OP 35	ISR
OLDFIELD, A. SOLOS FOR WOODWIND QUINTET	CO
OLIVER, A. INTERPOLACIONES (1970)	EDA
OLIVER, H. QUINTET	CF
OLSEN, S. QUINTET, OP 35	HLY
OLSSON, S. QUINTET (1975)	STI
ONSLOW, G.-REDEL. QUINTET IN F MA, OP 81/3	LEU
ONSLOW, G. QUINTET	M&M
ORGAD, B. LANDSCAPES (NOFIM) (1969)	ISR
OSTENDORF, J. BLASERQUINTETT	HSM
OSTERC, S. BLASERQUINTETT (1932)	HG
OTT, J. CYBERNETIC STRUCTURE #1	CU
OTT, J. SUITE	CU
OTTEN, L. BLAASKWINTET #2 (1954)	SD
OTTEN, L. MOVEMENTS FOR WIND QUINTET	SD
OTTOSON, D. SVIT	STI
OUBRADOUS, F. FANTAISIE DIALOGUEE	EDL
PACIORKIEWICZ, T. QUINTET (1951)	AP
PALKOVSKY, O. WOODWIND QUINTET #2 (1958)	CHF
PAPINEAU-COUTURE, J. FANTAISIE (1963)	BER
PARCHMAN, G. SONATA	SS
PARRIS, H. WOODWIND MINIATURES	HE
PARRIS, R. SONATINA FOR WINDS	ACA
PARSCH, A. TRANSPOSIZIONI I	CHF
PARTOS, O. NEBULAE (1966)	ISR
PATACHICH, I. BALKAN	FS
PATTERSON, P. COMEDY	JOW
PATTERSON, P. QUINTET (1967)	JOW

5 PARTS: WOODWINDS (FL,OB,CL,HN,BSN)-523

PAUER, J. BLASERQUINTETT (1960)	ART
PAYNE, A. SONATAS & RICERCARS (1970)	CHE
PEDERSEN, P. WIND QUINTET (1959)	CAN
PELEMANS, W. QUINTET #1	MAU
PELEMANS, W. QUINTET #2	EME
PERGAMENT, M. LITEN SVIT (1970)	STI
PERLE, G. QUINTET #1	TP
PERLE, G. QUINTET #2, OP 4 (1960)	B-B
PERLE, G. QUINTET #3 (1967)	B-B
PERSICHETTI, V. PASTORAL, OP 21 (1943)	GS
PERT, M. CERNUNNOS, OP 24	JOW
PESSARD, E. AUBADE, OP 6	CF
PETERSMA, W. WIND QUINTET (1976)	SD
PETERSON, W. METAMORPHOSES	SS
PETRIC, I. WOODWIND QUINTET #1	EDD
PETRIC, I. WOODWIND QUINTET #2	EDD
PETRIC, I. WOODWIND QUINTET #3	EDD
PETROVICS, E. WIND QUINTET (1964)	EMB
PETRUSHKA, S. V'SAMACHTA BEHAGECHA (AND REJOICE) (1974)	ISR
PFISTER, H. OTTOBEUREN QUINTET	EUL
PHILLIPS, B. MUSIC FOR THIS TIME OF YEAR	EV
PHILLIPS, D. LULLABIC DIGRESSIONS	COA
PHILLIPS, P. LITTLE PRELUDE & BLUES	MJ
PICHA, F. WOODWIND QUINTET, OP 31 (1944)	CHF
PIERCE, E. ROMANCE	PO
PIERNE, G.-ANDRAUD. MARCH OF THE LITTLE TIN SOLDIERS, OP 14/6	ALE
PIERNE, G. PASTORALE, OP 14/1	ALE
PIERNE, G. PASTORALE, OP 14/1	CF
PIERNE, P. SUITE PITTORESQUE	ALE
PIETSCH, E.-MC CATHREN. MINIATURE SUITE	S&
PIJPER, W. QUINTET (1929)	SD
PILSS, K. SERENADE	LDO
PISK, P. WOODWIND QUINTET, OP 96	ACA
PISTON, W. QUINTET (1956)	AMP
PLACHETA, H. DIVERTIMENTO, OP 8	LDO
POLDINI, E.-ELKAN. GENERAL BOOM-BOOM	HE
POLDOWSKI, D.-BARRERE. SUITE MINIATURE	GA
POLLET(ARR). 2 WOODWIND QUINTETS	KN
POLLOCK, R. QUINTET (1975)	B-B
PONSE, L. KWINTET, OP 32 (1961)	SD
PONSE, L. 2 PIECES (1943)	SD
POOT, M. CONCERTINO	ALE
PORCELIJN, D. PULVERIZATIONS	SD
PORCELIJN, D. 12 NOVEMBER 1819 (1976)	SD
PORSCH, G. SUITE MODIQUE	WB
PORTER, Q. DIVERTIMENTO (1960)	PET
POSPISIL, J. GLOSY, OP 20/2	SHF
POUSSEUR-MONK. TROISIEME VUE SUR LES JARDINS INTERDITS	ESZ
POWELL, M. DIVERTIMENTO	AMC
PRAAG, H. VAN. QUINTET #1 (1938)	SD
PRAAG, H. VAN. QUINTET #2 (1948)	SD
PRAAG, H. VAN. SONATA (1963)	SD
PRESSER, W. MINUET, SARABANDE & GAVOTTE	TP
PRESSER, W. QUINTET	TP
PRIETO, C. JUEGO DE LA MUSICA, EL (1971)	EDA
PROCACCINI, T. CLOWN MUSIC	GZ
PUHAKKA, J. EPITAPHE I, OP 11	FIN
PURDIE, H. CANON APERTUS	PO
PUSZTAI, T. QUINTET (1974)	MAR
PUTSCHE', T. WIND QUINTET (1964)	SS
QUINET, M. 8 PETITES PIECES (1946)	CBD
QUINET, M. QUINTET (1949)	CBD

RADULESCU, M. BLASERQUINTETT	LDO
RAE, A. IMPRESSIONS (1971)	CAN
RAGWITZ, E. MUSIC, OP 32	BRH
RAINIER, P. 6 PIECES	S&C
RAITIO, P. QUINTET	FIN
RAJTER, L. WIND QUINTET (1946)	SHF
RAKUJAS, B. SUMOM DRAGANOM	DSS
RAMEAU-NAKAGAWA. SUITE IN G MI	ONG
RAMEAU, J-DESORMIERE. BALLET MUSIC (ASCANTE & CEPHISE)	ALE
RAMEAU, J.(NAKAGAWA). GAVOTTE WITH 6 DOUBLES	GS
RAMEAU, J.-NAKAGAWA. L'AGACANTE & L'INDISCRETE	AMP
RAMEAU, J.-OUBRADOUS. SYMPHONIES & DANCES	ALE
RAMOVS, P. ANSWERS	EDD
RAMOVS, P. WOODWIND QUINTET	EDD
RAMSEY, G. MIRROR & BAGATELLE	ACA
RANKI, G. PENTAEROPHONIA (1958)	EMB
RAPF, K. 6 PIECES (1963)	LDO
RAVEL, M.-KESSLER. PIECE EN FORME DE HABANERA	ALE
RAVEL, M.-JONES. TOMBEAU DE COUPERIN	DUR
READ, G. SCHERZINO, OP 24 (1935)	SN
REDDING, J. QUINTET	COR
REED, H. SYMPHONIC DANCE	BE
REGT, H. DE. MUSICA, OP 3 (1969)	SD
REICHA, A.-WALN. ANDANTE & MENUETTO ALLEGRO (OP 91)	KJ
REICHA, A. 2 ANDANTES & ADAGIO	B&V
REICHA, A.-SMITH. INTRODUCTION & ALLEGRO (OP 88/4)	TP
REICHA, A.-SEYDEL. QUINTET IN B FL MA, OP 88/5	LEU
REICHA, A.-KNEUSSLIN. QUINTET IN C MI, OP 91/6	EK
REICHA, A.-KNEUSSLIN. QUINTET IN D MI, OP 88/4	EK
REICHA, A. QUINTET IN D MI, OP 91/4	EDK
REICHA, A.-WEIGELT. QUINTET IN E FL MA, OP 88/2	LEU
REICHA, A. QUINTET IN E MI, OP 88/1	EK
REICHA, A. QUINTET IN G MI, OP 91/4	BIL
REICHA, A.-WISE. QUINTET, OP 88/2	WI
REICHA, A. QUINTET, OP 88/6	EK
REICHA, A.-KNEUSSLIN. QUINTET, OP 91/1 IN C MA	EK
REICHA, A. QUINTET, OP 91/2 IN A MI	EK
REICHA, A. QUINTET, OP 91/3 IN D MA	EK
REICHA, A.-KNEUSSLIN. QUINTET, OP 91/5 IN A MA	EK
REICHA, A.-VESTER. QUINTET, OP 99/2	MR
REICHA, A. QUINTET, OP100/4 IN E MI	EK
REICHA, A.-HERTL/SMETACEK. 3 QUINTETS, OP 88/3, OP 91/9,11	ES
REIF, P. WIND SPECTRUM (1966)	SS
REINER, K. DODICI SUITA (1963)	ART
REINHOLD, O. BLASERQUINTETT (1962)	LIT
REITER, A. MUSIK	LDO
REULAND, J. PARTITA (1967)	SD
REYNOLDS, R. GATHERING	PET
REYNOLDS, V. WOODWIND QUINTET	MC
RHODES, P. ENSEMBLE ETUDES	ACA
RICE, T. FANTASY	SS
RIEGGER, W. BLASERQUINTETT, OP 51	SCH
RIETI, V. QUINTET (1957)	AMP
RIETI, V. SILOGRAFIE (WOODCUTS)	GEN
RIMSKY-KORSAKOV, N.-ATKINS. FLIGHT OF THE BUMBLE BEE	WI
RIMSKY-KORSAKOV, N.-TUSTIN. FLIGHT OF THE BUMBLE BEE	SPR
RINCK, J. WOODWIND QUINTET	COR
RIVIER, J. CAPRICCIO	BIL
ROE. AUTUMN IN RETROSPECT	KN
ROETSCHER, K. QUINTET, OP 41	B&B
ROGERS, J. ROTATIONAL ARRAYS	BOW
ROLLIN, R. SUITE	SS

ROOS, R. DE. INCONTRI	SD
ROPARTZ, J. 2 PIECES	DUR
RORICH, C. QUINTET, OP 58	WZ
ROSEMAN, R. SUITE OF RENAISSANCE PIECES	ECS
ROSENBERG, H. KVINTETT (1959)	STI
ROSENGREN, F. QUINTET (1949)	STI
ROSENTHAL, L. COMMEDIA	CA
ROSETTI, F.-KNEUSSLIN. QUINTET IN E FL MA	EK
ROSETTI, F.-PHIL WW QUINTET. QUINTET IN E FL MA	TP
ROSETTI, F. QUINTET IN E FL MA	UE
ROSS, W. DIVERTIMENTO	BH
ROSSEAU, N. QUINTET, OP 54 (1955)	CBD
ROSSUM, F. PYROGRAVURES, OP 19 BIS (1968)	CBD
ROTA, N. PETITE OFFRANDE MUSICALE	ALE
ROTA, N. QUINTET	RC
ROUSSEAU, J.-HAUFRECHT. AIRS POUR JOUES A LA PROUPE MARCHANT	ACA
ROWLAND, D. MONOLOGUES (1977)	SD
RUBIN, M. SERENADE	LDO
RUGGIERI. ALLEGRO	CST
RUSSELL, R. WOODWIND QUINTET	GEN
RUYNEMAN, D. NIGHTENGALE QUINTET (1949)	SD
RUYNEMAN, D. REFLEXIONS #4 (1961)	SD
RYCHLIK, J. QUINTET	ES
SABATINI, W. MUSIC FOR KORRI	CAM
SACHSSE, H. BLASERSUITE, OP 32	ABS
SAGVIK, S. 8 MEDITATIONER, OP 61 (1976)	STI
SAGVIK, S. QUIN-TAT, OP 62 (1976)	STI
SAINT-MARCOUX, M. GENESIS (1975)	CAN
SALONEN, S. QUINTET, OP 25	FIN
SANDNER, P. QUINTET #2	EUL
SANTA CRUZ, D. QUINTET	SN
SANTIAGO, R. DE. CONCORDANCIAS I (1976)	EEC
SANTIAGO, R. DE. TERSURA MUSICAL SI BECUADRO (1970)	EEC
SATIE, E.-WILSON. 3 GYMNOPEDIES	AB
SAVELIEV, B. SUITE	MC
SAXTON, R. ECHOES OF THE GLASS BEAD GAME (1975)	CHE
SCARLATTI-SIEKMANN. SONATA #79	KN
SCARLATTI, D.-HERDER. SONATA	AMP
SCARLATTI, D. SUITE IN F MA	CAM
SCARMOLIN, A. BY THE SLEEPING NILE	AMC
SCHAEFERS, A. QUINTET	EDT
SCHAT, P. IMPROVISATIONS & SYMPHONIES (1960)	SD
SCHERCHEN-HSIAO, T. ZIGUIDOR (1977)	BH
SCHIBLER, A. KALEIDOSKOP (1954), OP 41	A&S
SCHIDLOWSKY, L. QUINTET (1968)	ISR
SCHIERBECK, P. CAPRICCIO, OP 53	WH
SCHIFFMAN, H. ALLEGRO CON SPIRITO DI SAN NICCOLO	B&B
SCHILLING, H. QUINTET, OP 67	BRH
SCHILLING, H. ZEACIS HAFIS QUINTET 76	BRH
SCHISKE, K. QUINTET, OP 24 (1945)	LDO
SCHLEMM, G. BLASER-QUINTETT	ETB
SCHMID, H. QUINTET, OP 28	SCH
SCHMIDEK, K. SONATINE, OP 31	LDO
SCHMITT, F. CHANTS ALIZES, OP125	DUR
SCHMITT, F. TELEMANN MINUETS	DUR
SCHMUTZ, A. SCHERZO POETIQUE	CF
SCHNEIDER, W. QUINTET	MV
SCHOENBERG, A. QUINTET, OP 26	UE
SCHOLLUM, R. 5 STUCKE, OP 82	LDO
SCHONBERG, S. LITET STYCKE, OP 8/3 (1957)	STI
SCHOUWMAN, H. NEDERLANDSE SUITE, OP 40B (1953)	SD
SCHRAMM, H. WOODWIND QUINTET	AMC

```
SCHRODER, H.  DIVERTIMENTO                                          PET
SCHUBERT, F.-HOLMES.  ALLEGRETTO                                    BA
SCHUBERT, F.-GOLDSTEIN.  INTRO, VARIATIONS & FINALE, OP 82/2        GS
SCHUBERT, F.-TAYLOR.  MARCHE HONGROISE                              BE
SCHUBERT, F.-SCHOENBACH.  SHEPHERD MELODY #6 (ROSAMUNDE)            TP
SCHUBERT, F.-ELKAN.  VALSE SENTIMENTALE                             HE
SCHUBERT, M.  MOMENTS MUSICAUX (1967)                               DEU
SCHULLER, G.  SUITE                                                 M&M
SCHULLER, G.  WOODWIND QUINTET (1958)                               AMP
SCHUMANN, R.-GEE.  KNIGHT, THE                                      PO
SCHUMANN, R.-FILAS.  5 PIECES                                       PMP
SCHUMANN, R.-STACEY.  7 PIECES                                      AU
SCHUSTER, G.  3 ARABESKEN                                           IMP
SCHWAEN, K.  MAHRISCHES HOLZBLASERQUINTETT                          PET
SCHWEINITZ, W. VON.  QUINTET, OP 9                                  HSM
SCHWERTSIK, K.  QUERSCHNITT DURCH EINE OPERETTE                     LDO
SEHLBACH, E.  BLASERQUINTETT, OP113 (1968)                          MV
SEHLBACH, E.  KORTUM-SERENADE, OP 30                                MV
SEIBER, M.  PERMUTAZIONI A CINQUE (1958)                            S&C
SENAILLE, J.-TAYLOR.  RONDO SERIOSO                                 BE
SEREBRIER, J.  LITTLE SUITE                                         SN
SESTAK, Z.  DIVERTIMENTO                                            CHF
SHERMAN, R.  QUINTET                                                ACA
SHOSTAKOVICH, D.-SMITH.  POLKA (GOLDEN AGE)                         KN
SIBELIUS, J.-LANGENUS.  PASTORALE (PELLEAS & MELISANDE)             CF
SIEGL, O.  QUINTET (1972)                                           LDO
SIEKMANN, F.  DESCRIPTIVE PIECE                                     SS
SIENNICKI, E.  DIVERSION                                            LMP
SILVERMAN, F.  WINDSCAPE                                            SS
SIMEK, M.  QUINTET                                                  CHF
SIMEONOV, B.  FAREWELL, PASTORALES!                                 CAN
SIMEONOV, B.  PASTORALE, INTERMEZZO & SCHERZINO (1971)              CAN
SIPILA, E.  PARTITA                                                 FIN
SIRULNIKOFF, J.  DOCTOR IN SPITE OF HIMSELF, THE (1961)             CAN
SJOBLOM, H.  MUSIKANTISK SVIT (1976)                                STI
SKOGLUND, E.  LITEN FUGA (1954/1975)                                STI
SKOLNIK, W.  PASTORALE                                              TRI
SKORZENY, F.  EINE NACHTMUSIK (1963)                                LDO
SLONIMSKI, S.  DIALOGE                                              HSM
SLOWINSKI, W.  QUINTET (1958)                                       AP
SMITH, L.  WIND QUINTET                                             ACA
SMUTNY, J.  3 SATZE (1969)                                          CHF
SOBECK, J.  ALLEGRETTO GIOJOSO (OP 11)                              BE
SOBECK, J.  ALLEGRO MOSSO (OP 14)                                   BE
SOBECK, J.  ANDANTE SOSTENUTO (OP 11)                               BE
SOBECK, J.  LARGHETTO                                               BE
SOBECK, J.  TARANTELLA                                              BE
SOKOLOFF, N.  QUINTET                                               AMC
SOMIS, G.-HENRIED.  ADAGIO & ALLEGRO                                CF
SOMMERFELDT, O.  4 NORWEGIAN RELIGIOUS FOLK TUNES, OP 23B           NM
SONNINEN, A.  DIVERTIMENTO (1970)                                   MT
SORENSON, T.  MUSIC ON "VENI REDEMPTOR GENTIUM" (1965)              STI
SORRENTINO, C.  BENEATH THE COVERED BRIDGE                          BE
SOUKUP, V.  WOODWIND QUINTET (1967)                                 CHF
SOURIS, A.  RENGAINES (1937)                                        ALE
SOWERBY, L.  POP GOES THE WEASEL                                    FZ
SPIES, L.  SONATA #2 (1963)                                         ISR
SPIREA, A.  QUINTET                                                 IMP
SPISAK, M.  QUINTET (1949)                                          AP
SPRONGL, N.  BLASERQUINTETT, OP 90                                  LDO
STANDFORD, P.  SUITE FRANCAISE                                      NO
STEARNS, P.  QUINTET                                                ACA
```

5 PARTS: WOODWINDS (FL,OB,CL,HN,BSN)-523

STEDRON, M. MUSICA FICTA (1969)	CHF
STEIN, H. SOUR SUITE	WI
STEIN, L. QUINTETTE	ACA
STEIN, L. SUITE	ACA
STEWART, R. 2 MOVEMENTS	ACA
STEWART, R. 3 PIECES	ACA
STEWART, R. 5 VISIONS	ACA
STOCKHAUSEN, K. ADIEU	UE
STOKER, R.-BRAIN. QUINTET	HI
STORP, S. KAMMERMUSIK	MV
STRADELLA, A. SONATA IN G MA	COR
STRINGFIELD, L. MOONSHINER LAUGHS, A	BF
STROBL, O. SUITE	LDO
SUCHON, E. SERENADE, OP 5	SHF
SUCHY, F. KONZERTQUINTETT, OP 34 (1947)	PAN
SULYOK, I. MUSICA ARCAICA	SCH
SUMERA, L. QUINTET	MKE
SUND, R. PER SPELMAN	CGM
SURDIN, M. PIECE (1969)	CAN
SUTER, R. 4 ETUDES (1962)	HEN
SVARA, D. QUINTET, OP 92	EDD
SWACK, I. WOODWIND QUINTET	AMC
SWEELINCK, J.-LUBIN. VARIATIONS ON A FOLKSONG	BH
SYDEMAN, W. QUINTET #1	SS
SYDEMAN, W. QUINTET #2	M&M
SYDEMAN, W. QUINTET	AMC
SYDEMAN, W. TEXTURE STUDIES (1966)	SS
SYLVAN, S. QUINTET, OP 5 (1949)	STI
SZALONEK, W. AARHUS MUSIC	SS
SZALOWSKI, A. WIND QUINTET	SF
SZEKELY, E. QUINTET #1	BE
SZEKELY, E. QUINTET #3	EMB
SZELIGOWSKI, T. QUINTET (1950)	AP
SZERVANSKY, E. QUINTET #1 (1953)	EMB
SZERVANSKY, E. QUINTET #2 (1957)	EMB
TAFFANEL, P. QUINTET	ALE
TAFFANEL, P. QUINTET	EDK
TAFFANEL, P. QUINTET	INT
TAKACS, J. EINE KLEINE TAFELMUSIK, OP 74	LDO
TAKACS, J. SERENADE NACH ALTGRAZER KONTRATANZEN, OP 83A	LDO
TAL, J. QUINTET (1966)	ISR
TANENBAUM, E. SONATINA	ACA
TANENBAUM, E. WOODWIND QUINTET #2	ACA
TARANOV, G. QUINTET	CHM
TARTINI, G.-TRINKHAUS. ARIOSO IN E MI	HY
TARTINI, G.-TRINKHAUS. EVENING SONG	HY
TAUSINGER, J. 2 APOSTROPHEN	CHF
TAUTENHAHN, G. QUINTET	SS
TAYLOR, C. QUINTET #2	ACA
TAYLOR, C. QUINTET, OP 7	ACA
TAYLOR, P. WOODWIND QUINTET (1973)	MR
TCHAIKOVSKY, P.-TRINKAUS. ANDANTE CANTABILE	CF
TCHAIKOVSKY, P.-TRINKHAUS. APRIL, OP 37/4	HY
TCHAIKOVSKY, P.-SEAY. CHANT SANS PAROLES, OP 40/6	SPR
TCHAIKOVSKY, P.-TRINKHAUS. JUNE, OP 37/6	HY
TCHAIKOVSKY, P.-LYCHENHEIM. MELODIE, OP 42/3	CF
FL,OB,CL,HN,BSN(BCL)	
TCHAIKOVSKY, P.-WILSON. NUTCRACKER SUITE	AB
TCHAIKOVSKY, P.-NAKAGAWA. 3 TANZE, OP 39/8, 10, 14	SCH
TCHEREPNIN, A. QUINTET	PET
TELCS, A. KVINTETT	REU
TELEMANN, G.-WEIGELT. OUVERTUREN-SUITE	LEU

5 PARTS: WOODWINDS (FL,OB,CL,HN,BSN)-523

TEMPLETON-STRONG, G. 5 (1933) AQUARELLES	HEN
TEMPLETON, A.-RHOADS. PASSEPIED	TP
TEUBER, F. INTRODUCTION PIECE	SH
THILMAN, J. APHORISMEN	BRH
THILMAN, J. QUINTET, OP 44A	MIT
THOMAS, A.-TRINKHAUS. GAVOTTE (MIGNON)	HY
THOMSEN-MUCHOVA, G. SERENATA (1964)	ART
TIESSEN, H. KLEINE SUITE, OP 51	KIS
TISNE, A. DISPARATES	BIL
TOEBOSCH, L. SARABANDE EN ALLEGRO, OP 71 (1959)	SD
TOMAN, J. WOODWIND QUINTET (1967)	CHF
TOMASI, H. 5 DANSES PROFANES ET SACREES	ALE
TOMASI, H. QUINTETTE	HLE
TOMASI, H. VARIATIONS SUR UN THEME CORSE	ALE
TREDE, Y. CHANT DES OISEAUX, LE	PET
TREMBLAY, G. WIND QUINTET	ACA
TREXLER, G. SPITZWEG-SUITE (1956)	BRH
TROJAN, V. QUINTET, OP 8 (1937)	ART
TSOUYOPOULOS, G. MUSIK	HG
TULL, F. SUITE	SH
TURNER, R. SERENADE (1960)	CAN
TUROK, P. DUO CONCERTANTE, OP 27A	SS
TUROK, P. PICTURE #99, OP 34/2	SS
TUROK, P. WIND QUINTET, OP 17	SS
TUTHILL, B. SAILOR'S HORNPIPE, OP 14/1 (1935)	CF
TYLNAK, I. WOODWIND QUINTET #2 (1962)	CHF
UDOW, M. PATTERNS	ACA
UNDERWOOD, T. SUITE	CO
URAY, E. HOMMAGE A JOHANN STRAUSS	LDO
URAY, E. MUSIK FUR BLASERQUINTETT	LDO
URAY, E. SCHLADMINGER TANZE	LDO
URBANEC, B. QUINTET	SHF
URBANNER, E. ETUDE FUR BLASER (1965)	LDO
VACHEY, H. QUINTETTEA VENT	ALE
VALEN. SERENADE, OP 42 (1947)	HLY
VAN HULSE, C. QUINTET, OP 3	SH
VAN ROSSUM, F. PYROGRAVURES, OP 19	HE
VAN VACTOR, D. MUSIC FOR WOODWINDS, 2 VOLS	RR
VAN VACTOR, D. SUITE (1959)	RR
VANDOR, I. WINDS 845 (1969)	ESZ
VASZY, V. QUINTET	EMB
VAZZANA, A. QUINTET	AMC
VEERHOFF, C. BLASER-QUINTETT	B&B
VEERHOFF, C. QUINTET #2 (1971)	ESZ
VELDEN, R. VAN DER. CONCERT #1	MAU
VELDEN, R. VAN DER. CONCERTO #2	EME
VERRALL, J. SERENADE (1944)	TP
VERRALL, J. SERENADE #2	TRI
VILEC, M. WIND QUINTET	SHF
VINCZE, I. DIVERTIMENTO (1962)	EMB
VIVALDI, A. GAVOTTA	CST
VLACH-VRUTICKY, J. CASSAZIONE (1966)	CHF
VLIET, H. PRELUDIO E FUGA (1973)	SD
VLIJMEN, J. QUINTETTO (1960)	SD
VLIJMEN, J. VAN. QUINTET #2 (1972)	SD
VON KREISLER, A. ANDANTE & ALLEGRO	SO
VON KREISLER, A. PASTORALE (MUSIC FOR WOODWIND QUINTET)	SO
VON KREISLER, A. 2 PORTRAITS	SO
VOSS, F. CAPRICCIOSO (1965)	BRH
VREDENBURG, M. AU PAYS DES VENDAGES (1951)	SD
VRIES, K. DE. 3 PIECES (1968)	SD
WAGEMANS, P. WIND QUINTET, OP 6	SD

5 PARTS: WOODWINDS (FL,OB,CL,HN,BSN)-523

WAGNER, R.-BOYD. ALBUM LEAF, AN	CF
WALKER, R. IN JOYOUS MOOD	BA
WALKER, R. RIGAUDON	KN
WALZEL, L. QUINTETTO IMPETUOSO, OP 42	LDO
WARD-STEINMAN, D. MONTAGE	MJ
WARD, W. LITTLE DANCE SUITE	BE
WASHBURN, R. QUINTET	OX
WASHBURN, R. SUITE (1960)	TP
WATSON, W. 3 SHORT PIECES	CO
WEBER, A. QUINTETTE	ALE
WEBER, B. CONSORT OF WINDS, OP 66 (1974)	B-B
FL/PIC/AFL,OB,CL/BCL,HN,BSN	
WEBER, L. QUINTET	MV
WEIGEL, E. SHORT, SLOW & FAST	AMC
WEIGL, V. MOOD SKETCHES	ACA
WEINGERL, A. ECLOGUE	EDD
WEINZWEIG, J. WOODWIND QUINTET (1963-64)	CAN
WEIS, F. SERENADE	WH
WEISGALL, H. HOLIDAY DANCE #1 (HANUKKAH)	TP
WELIN, K. ETWAS FUR...(1966)	STI
WELLEJUS, A. BLASERKVINTET	SPD
WELLESZ, E. SUITE, OP 73	HSM
WERNER, S. JUBILUS (1968)	CHE
WESTERGAARD, S. QUINTETTO #2, OP 15	WH
WESTON, P. ARBEAU SUITE	GAL
WHEAR, P. QUINTET (1956)	SO
WHITE, D. CONCERTINO	LU
WHITE, D. THREE FOR FIVE	SH
WHITTENBERG, C. FANTASY	ACA
WHITTENBERG, C. GAMES OF 5	SER
WIJDEVELD, W. QUINTET (1934)	SD
WILDER, A. CHILDREN'S SUITE	MAR
WILDER, A. QUINTET # 1	MAR
WILDER, A. QUINTET # 3	GS
WILDER, A. QUINTET # 4	MAR
WILDER, A. QUINTET # 5	MAR
WILDER, A. QUINTET # 6	MAR
WILDER, A. QUINTET # 7	MAR
WILDER, A. QUINTET # 8	MAR
WILDER, A. QUINTET # 9 (SUITE)	MAR
WILDER, A. QUINTET #10	MAR
WILDER, A. QUINTET #12	MAR
WILDER, A. QUINTET #13	KN
WINKEL HOLM, M. SONATE, OP 25	WH
WINKEL, H. 3 BURLESKEN	HSM
WIREN, D. QUINTET, OP 42	CGM
WIRKANDER, B. KRISTALLEN DEN FINA (1970)	STI
WIRTH, H. KLEINE CLEMENTIADE	HSM
WISSE, J. LIMITAZIONI #2 (1962)	SD
WISSE, J. RITORNELLO	SD
WITTINGER, R. TENSIONI, OP 15 (1970)	BRH
WOOD, J. RONDO CAPRICE	MAN
WOOLLEN, R. WOODWIND QUINTET	ACA
WUENSCH, G. QUINTET #2, OP 34	CAN
WUORINEN, C. MOVEMENT	TP
WUORINEN, C. WIND QUINTET	PET
WURDINGER, E. QUINTET, OP 8	LDO
YODER, P. RELAX!	KJ
YODER, P. (ARR). DRY BONES	KJ
YORK, W. NEO GOTHICS	RH
ZAFRED, M. QUINTET	RC
ZAGWIJN, H. QUINTETTO (1948)	SD

5 PARTS: WOODWINDS (FL,OB,CL,HN,BSN)-523

ZAHRADNIK, Z. WOODWIND QUINTET	CHF
ZAMECNIK, J. ALLEGRO GIUBILOSO	SF
ZAMECNIK, J. GONDOLIERA, LA	SF
ZANDER, H. QUINTET	MV
ZANINELLI, L. DANCE VARIATIONS	SH
ZANINELLI, L. MUSICA DRAMMATICA	SH
ZEMLINSKY, A. HUMORESKE	UE
ZENDER, H. QUINTET (1950), OP 3	B&B
ZILCHER, H. QUINTET, OP 91	B&N
ZILLIG, W. LUSTSPIELSUITE (1934)	B&N
ZIMMER, J. WIND QUINTET, OP 61	SHF
ZIPP, F. SERENADE	MV
ZONN, P. LIBERATA III	ACA
ZOUHAR, Z. 151- MUSIC FOR WOODWIND QUINTET	CHF
ZUCKERT, L. LITTLE PRINCE IN MONTREAL (1968)	CAN
ZUR, M. CONCERTINO	SS
ZWEDBERG, T. CARE OF (1976)	STI

5 PARTS: WOODWIND QUINTET (COLLECTIONS)-524

ANDRAUD, A. (COMP). 3 LITTLE PIECES	SO
ANDRAUD, A. (COMP). 22 WOODWIND QUINTETS	SO
BARNES, C. (ARR). ROBBINS COLLECTION OF CLASSICS	B3
GORDON, P. (ARR). ELKAN-VOGEL WOODWIND ENSEMBLE FOLIO	EV
HERMANN, F. ZUR UBUNG IM ZUSAMMENSPIEL, BK #2	BRH
TAYLOR, R. (ARR). 18 WOODWIND QUINTETS	SO
ULRICH, H. (ARR). ENSEMBLE MUSIC FOR 5 INSTRUMENTS	BT
FL(OB,CL),FL(OB,CL),CL,CL(HN),BCL(BSN)	
VOXMAN, H. & HERVIG, R. (ARR). ENSEMBLE REPERTOIRE	RU

5 PARTS: WOODWINDS (W/O FL,OB,CL,HN,BSN)-525

ASCHENBRENNER, J. QUINTET. FL,OB,BCL,BSN,HN	EMO
ASCOUGH, R. QUINTET. FL,OB,CL,SOP SAX,BSN	EXM
ASPELMAYR, F.-PULKERT. PARTITA IN D MA. 2OB,2HN,BSN	LEU
ASPELMAYR, F.-PULKERT. PARTITA IN F MA. 2OB,2HN,BSN	LEU
BACH, J.C.-STEIN. BLASER-SINFONIEN, 2 VOLS. 2CL,2HN,BSN	FRH
BACH, J.C.-WOJCIECHOWSKI. 3 MARCHES. 2OB(2FL),2HN,BSN	HSM
BACH, J.C. 4 QUINTETS, 2 VOLS. 2CL,2HN,BSN	BH
BACH, J.S.-BANQUER. BADINERIE (SUITE #2). FL,3CL,BCL	MC
BACON, E. OLD AIRS FROM MANY COUNTRIES	GS
FL,OB,2CL,BSN,PERC OPT	
BEETHOVEN, L. VAN-GREIST. MENUETTO (OP 18/5). FL,3CL,BCL	MC
BEETHOVEN, L. VAN-HESS/ZELLNER. QUINTET. OB,BSN,3HN	SCH
BEETHOVEN, L. VAN-DRAPER. SCHERZO (VLN SONATA, OP 24)	OX
4CL,BSN	
BESOZZI, C.-NIMETZ. PARTHIA IN D MA. OB(FL),OB,HN(CL),HN,BSN	LEU
BESOZZI, C.-NIMETZ. SONATA #13. OB(FL),OB,HN(CL),HN,BSN	LEU
BESOZZI, C.-NIMETZ. SONATA #20. OB(FL),OB,HN(CL),HN,BSN	LEU
BISSELL, K. FOLK-SONG SUITE, A (1960). 2FL,2CL,BCL(BSN)	BH
BISSELL, K. SERENADE FOR 5 WINDS (1972). 2OB,2HN,BSN	CAN
BJORKLUND, S. PASTORAL (1970). FL,EHN,CL,BSN,HN	STI
BOELLMANN, L. MENUET GOTHIQUE. OB,EHN,CL,BSN,HN	DUR
CHATTELUN, M. SUITE INCHOATIVE. FL,EHN,CL,HN,BSN	EMT

5 PARTS: WOODWINDS (W/O, FL, OB, CL, HN, BSN)-52

```
CHILDS, B.   TAKE 5.   ANY 5 INSTRUMENTS                          TP
CONE, E.   STANZAS.  FL,EHN,CL,BSN,HN                             EM
CUNNINGHAM, M.   PASTEL DESIGNS.  3FL,2CL                         SS
DESORMIERE, R.   6 DU XVI SIECLE DANSERIES.  FL,CL,EHN,HN,BSN     ALE
DITTERS, K.-RHAU.  3 PARTIEN (FMA,AMA,DMA).  2OB,2HN,BSN          BRH
DITTERSDORF, K.-WOJCIECHOWSKI.  DIVERTIMENTO.  2OB,2CL,BSN        HSM
DOPPLER, F.   BIRD OF THE FOREST, THE, OP 21.  FL,4HN            M&M
DRUSCHETZKY, G.   PARTITA # 9 IN F MA.  2OB,2HN,BSN               BRH
DRUSCHETZKY, G.   PARTITA #10 IN F MA.  2OB,2HN,BSN               BRH
DRUSCHETZKY, G.   PARTITA #13 IN B FL MA.  2OB,2HN,BSN            BRH
DRUSCHETZKY, G.   PARTITA #21 IN G MA.  2OB,2HN,BSN               BRH
DUSSEK, F.   PARTHIA.  2OB,BSN,2HN                               M&M
EYSER, E.   QUINTETT 70 (1970).  FL,OB,BCL,CBSN,HN               STI
FIALA, J.-JANETZKY.  QUINTETS (EFLMA,BFLMA,EFLMA)                FRH
   2EHN,2HN,BSN
FIALA, J.   3 QUINTETS.  2EHN,2HN,BSN                            EDK
FITELBERG, J.   CAPRICCIO.  FL,OB,CL,BCL,BSN(TRB)                 SF
FLOTHUIS, M.   QUINTET, OP 13 (1942).  FL,OB,CL,BCL,BSN          SD
FRID, G.   SERENADE, OP 4 (1928).  FL,2CL,BSN,HN                 SD
GASTYNE, S. DE.   PARTITA (1956).  2FL,2CL,BSN                   FER
GEHOT, J.   24 MILITARY PIECES.  2CL,2HN,BSN                     SPR
GERVAISE, C.(BULLARD).  4 DANCES.  2FL,2CL,HN                    OX
GOLABEK, J.-OCHLEWSKI.  PARTITA.  2CL,BSN,2HN                    AP
GRIEG, E.-SKINDER.  GNOMES' PARADE, OP 54.  FL,OB,2CL,BSN        PWM
GRIEG, E.-RALSTON.  7 NORWEGIAN MINIATURES.  FL,OB,2CL,BSN       BH
HANDEL, G.   2 ARIAS.  2OB,2HN,BSN                               MR
HANNIKEN, J.   4 INVENTIONS.  FL,3CL,BCL                         HE
HANSEN, T.   TOCCATA.  2FL,OB,CL,BSN                             SS
HAYDN, F.-BANQUER.  RONDO (OP 33/3).  FL,3CL,BCL                 MC
HAZZARD, P.   SUITE.  EHN,3CL,BCL                                SS
HOLBORNE, A.   SUITE FOR BRASS.  2CL(2OB),HN,2BSN                OX
HORVIT, M.   CONCERT MUSIC.  FL,3CL,BCL                          AMC
HUGHES, L.   ALLEGRO SCHERZOSO, OP 92.  2FL,OB,CL,BSN            BT
HUGUES, L.-CAVALLY.  ALLEGRO SCHERZOSO.  2FL,OB,CL,BSN           SO
KIM, Y.   3 MOVEMENTS.  FL,OB,EHN,BSN,HN                         SS
KNAB, A.   SERENADE.  FL,OB,2CL,BSN                              LIT
LE FLEMING, C.   HOMAGE TO BEATRIX POTTER.  FL,OB,2CL,BSN        CHE
LE JEUNE, C.-BANQUER.  REVECY VENIR DU PRINTANS.  FL,3CL,BCL     MC
LEE, E.   COMPOSITION.  FL,OB,EHN,CL,BSN                         B-B
LOCKE, M.   MUSIC FOR HIS MAJESTY'S SACKBUTS & CORNETS           OX
   3CL,2BSN
LUNDEN, L.   RONDINO.  FL,OB,2CL,BSN                             NO
LUNDEN, L.   3 SWEDISH TUNES.  FL,OB,2CL,BSN                     CHE
LUNDEN, L.   WHEATEAR, THE.  FL,OB,2CL,BSN                       CHE
MAGANINI, Q.-HARRIS.  REVERIE                                    CF
   FL(CL),OB(CL),CL,ACL(ASAX,CL),BCL(BSN)
MANN, L.   WIND QUINTET, OP 19 (1961).  FL,EHN,CL,BSN,HN         CAN
MARIE, G.-HARRIS.  BERCEUSE                                      CF
   FL(CL),OB(CL),CL,ACL(ASAX,CL),BCL(BSN)
MEULEMANS, A.   RAPSODIE (1961).  3CL,BCL,ASAX                   CBD
MONTEVERDI, C.   OH, LET ME DIE.  OB,OB(CL),2CL,BCL(BSN)         JER
MORITZ, C.   HEITERE SUITE, OP 12.  FL,OB,2CL,BSN                R&E
MORRICONE, E.   IMMOBILE (1978).  4CL,HN                         EDS
MOZART, W.   ADAGIO & ALLEGRO, K594.  2CL,2OB(2FL),BSN           OX
MOZART, W.   ADAGIO IN B FL MA, K411.  2CL,3BASSET HN            BRH
MOZART, W.-LANG.  ADAGIO, K411.  2OB,2EHN,BSN                    LN
MOZART, W.   ADAGIO, K411.  2CL,2CL(2OB),BSN                     OX
MOZART, W.-SPIES.  ANDANTE (FUR EINE ORGELWALZE), K616           PET
   2FL,FL(OB,CL) ,2CL
MOZART, W.-BANQUER.  ANDANTE CANTABILE (K330).  FL,3CL,BCL       MC
MOZART, W.-CAPUTO.  MINUET.  OB,2CL,BSN,HN                       VO
MOZART, W.-DRAPER.  4 MOVEMENT (LES PETIT RIENS).  4CL,BSN       OX
```

5 PARTS: WOODWINDS (W/O FL,OB,CL,HN,BSN)-525

NORDENSTROM, G. QUINTET (1977). PIC,OB,CL,HN,BSN		B&N
PROWO, P.-KOCH. CONCERTO A 5, #1 IN F MA. 3OB,2BSN		MV
PUSZTAI, T. CANTICLES (1971). 3CL,2HN		MAR
REGNER, H. EINE KLEINE WALDMUSIK. OB,CL,2HN,BSN		MV
REICHA, A.-VESTER. 2 ANDANTES & ADAGIO. FL,EHN,CL,HN,BSN		UE
RIETI, V. VALSETTE. 2FL,2CL,BSN		GEN
ROUSSAKIS, N. MARCH, SONG & DANCE. FL,OB,BSN,2CL		BE
SALIERI, A.-ANGERMULLER. PICCOLA SERENATA IN B FL MA 2OB,2HN,BSN		LDO
SALIERI, A.-SPADA. SERENATA IN E FL MA "PICCOLA SERENATA" 2OB,2HN,BSN		ESZ
SCHULLER, G. PERPETUUM MOBILE (1948). BSN,4HN		MAR
SCHUMANN, R.-BANQUER. 2 PIECES (ALBUM FOR THE YOUNG) FL,3CL,BCL		MC
SCHWERTSIK, K. EICHENDORFF-QUINTET. PIC,OB,CL,HN,BSN		UE
SETER, M. DIPTYQUE (1955). FL,EHN,CL,BSN,HN		ISR
STAMITZ, K.-LEBERMANN. 12 SERENADES. 2FL,2HN,BSN		HSM
STOCKHAUSEN, K. ZEITMASSE (1955/56). OB,EHN,CL,BSN,HN		UE
SULPIZI, F. PUNTEGGIATURA, OP 20. FL,2CL,HN,BSN		EBE
SULPIZI, F. QUINTETTO. FL,2CL,BSN,HN		EBE
TARLOW, K. MUSIC FOR WIND QUINTET. FL,OB,CL,HN,SAX		SS
TARLOW, K. MUSIC. FL,EHN,CL,HN,BSN(ASAX)		SS
TELEMANN, G.-HINNENTHAL. OVERTURE-SUITE IN D MA. 2OB,2HN,BSN		LEU
VILLA-LOBOS, H. QUINTETTE EN FORME DE CHOROS (1928) FL,OB,EHN,BSN		EES
VIVALDI, A.-BANQUER. ALLEGRO (CONCERTO IN D MA). FL,3CL,BCL		MC
VOGEL, W. TICINELLA (1941). FL,OB,CL,ASAX,BSN		ESZ
WANHAL, J. DIVERTIMENTO. 2OB,BSN,2HN		PET
ZELENKA, I. CHRONOLOGIE (1965). FL,OB,BCL,BSN,HN		LDO

5 PARTS: WOODWIND-KEYBOARD (INCL HORN)-528

BANK, J. FIVE (1977). OB,CL,BSN,HN,PF		SD
BARNBY, J.-HOLMES. SWEET & LOW. 2ASAX,TSAX,BAR SAX,PF		RU
BARRAUD, H. CONCERTINO. FL,CL,BSN,HN,PF		SEM
BEETHOVEN, L. VAN-KROSS. QUINTET IN E FL MA, OP 16 OB,CL,HN,BSN,PF		JB
BEETHOVEN, L. VAN. QUINTET IN E FL MA, OP 16 OB,CL,BSN,HN,PF		BRH
BEETHOVEN, L. VAN. QUINTET IN E FL MA, OP 16 OB,CL,BSN,HN,PF		INT
BEETHOVEN, L. VAN. QUINTET IN E FL MA, OP 16 OB,CL,BSN,HN,PF		MR
BEETHOVEN, L. VAN. QUINTET, OP 16. OB,CL,BSN,HN,PF		EDK
BEETHOVEN, L. VAN. QUINTET, OP 16. OB,CL,BSN,HN,PF		PET
BERKELEY, L. QUINTET (1975). OB,CL,BSN,HN,PF		CHE
BONNEAU, P. DIVERTISSEMENT. 4FL,PF		ALE
BROWN, R. QUINTET. SOP SAX,ASAX,TSAX,BAR SAX,ORG		WI
BROWN, T. FRECKLES & FLOWERS. 4FL,PF		KN
CARAVAN, R. LAMENT FOR AN UNKNOWN INFANT (1979) SOP SAX,ASAX,TSAX,BAR SAX,PF		ETH
CARLE-WHEELER. ENCHANTMENT. 4SAX,PF		VO
CARLE-WHEELER. ENCHANTMENT,. 4BSN,PF		VO
CORELLI, A. GAVOTTE & GIGUE. 2FL,2CL,PF		EDM
CORRETTE, M. CONCERTO. 4BSN,HPCD		CP
DAHM, P. PARADE OF THE SCOUTS. 4CL,PF		VO
DANZI, F. QUINTET IN D MI, OP 41. OB,CL,BSN,HN,PF		B&V
DANZI, F. QUINTET IN D MI, OP 41. OB,CL,HN,BSN,PF		GS

```
DANZI, F.   QUINTET IN D MI, OP 41.   OB,CL,BSN,HN,PF             MR
DANZI, F.   QUINTET, OP 41.   OB,CL,BSN,HN,PF                     PET
DANZI, F.-MEERWEIN.   QUINTET, OP 53/1 IN F MA                    MR
  FL,OB,CL,BSN,PF
DANZI, F.-MEERWEIN.   QUINTET, OP 54/2 IN D MA                    MR
  FL,OB,CL,BSN,PF
DANZI, F.-BLOCK.   SINFONIA CONCERTANTE IN E FL MA               MR
  FL,OB,HN,BSN,PF
DARNLEY, C. (ARR).   8 EASY PIECES.   FL,OB,CL,BSN,PF             CHE
DELIBES, L.-GROFF.   PIZZICATO POLKA.   4FL,PF                    GS
DENZA, L.-HARRIS.   FUNICULI-FUNICULA.   4CL,PF                   CF
DVORAK, A.-HOLMES.   LARGO (NEW WORLD SYMPHONY)                   RU
  2ASAX,TSAX,BAR SAX,PF
EKLUND, H.   ZODINAI (1966).   FL,2CL,BSN,PF                      STI
ELGAR, E.-HOLMES.   SALUT D'AMOUR.   2ASAX,TSAX,BAR SAX,PF        RU
ESCUDIE, L.   ANDANTE.   4SAX,PF                                  EDR
FISCHER, J.C.F.   SUITEN.   4WW,BC                                B&N
FOTEK, J.   TRIMORPHIE (1966).   3FL,HPCD,PF                      PWM
FRITSCH, J.   SEPTEMBER 70, GRAND QUATUOR.   4FL,PF               FEE
GHEDINI, G.   CONCERTO A CINQUE.   FL,OB,CL,BSN,PF                RC
GIESEKING, W.   QUINTET.   OB,CL,HN,BSN,PF                        M&M
GLUCK, C.-FISCHER.   LARGO.   FL,CL,OB,HN(BSN),PF                 FOR
GRIEG, E.   WATCHMAN'S SONG, OP 12/3.   4CL,PF                    CEN
HANDEL, G.-JOOSEN.   MENUET.   4WW,PF                             HU
HANUS, J.   SHORT STORY, OP 29/5.   FL,OB,CL,BSN,PF              GEN
HEKSTER, W.   DIVERSITIES.   FL,CL,BSN,HN,PF                      SD
HERZOGENBERG, H.   QUINTET, OP 43.   OB,CL,BSN,HN,PF             MR
HUYBRECHTS, A.   SUITE (1929).   FL,OB,CL,BSN,PF                  CBD
ILJINSKY, A.   BERCEUSE.   4CL,PF                                 CEN
JONGEN, L.   QUINTUOR (1958).   FL,CL,BSN,HN,PF                   CBD
JOOSEN, B.   SPIRITUAL QUARTET I.   4WW,PF                        HU
JOOSEN, B.   WELSH DANCES.   4WW,PF                               HU
JOSTEN, W.   CANZONA SERIA.   FL,OB,CL,BSN,PF                     HE.
KALMAN, E.   COIN SOUS LES TOITS, UN. TANGO.   2CL,ACL,BCL,PF     EES
KELLER, G.-TILMOUTH.   QUINTET IN D MI.   2FL,2OB,BC              SCH
LAUBE, P.   ALSATIAN DANCE.   FL,OB,CL(ASAX),BSN(HN),PF           CF
LEE, N.   QUINTET.   FL,OB,CL,BSN,PF                              AMC
LONGO, A.   SCENETTA PASTORALE.   FL,OB,CL,BSN,PF                 EDI
LUNDQUIST, T.   4 RONDEAUX (1969).   FL,OB,CL,BSN,PF             STI
MAGNARD, A.   QUINTET.   FL,OB,CL,BSN,PF                          EDS
MANCINI, H.-REISMAN.   FLUTERS' BALL.   4FL,PF,OPT RHYTHM         KN
MAREZ OYENS, T. DE.   MOSAIC (1979).   OB,CL,HN,BSN,PF            SD
MAROS, M.   DISCUSSION (1969).   FL,OB,CL,BSN,PF                  STI
MASSENET, J.-HOLMES.   ANGELUS (SCENES PITTORESQUES)             RU
  2ASAX,TSAX,BAR SAX,PF
MATEJ, J.   MUSIK.   4WW,PF                                       ART
MAW, N.   CHAMBER MUSIC.   OB,CL,BSN,HN,PF                        CHE
MC CALL, H.   ANNIE LAURIE.   2ASAX,TSAX,BAR SAX,PF              LU
MC CALL, H.   2 SPIRITUALS.   2ASAX,TSAX,BAR SAX,PF              LU
MENDELSSOHN, F.   SONG WITHOUT WORDS #48.   4CL,PF                CEN
MEYERBEER, G.-HOLMES.   CORONATION MARCH (THE PROPHET)           RU
  2ASAX,TSAX,BAR SAX,PF
MOFFITT, D.   IN THE SPOTLIGHT.   2CL,ACL,BCL,PF                  CF
MOLLOY, J.-HARRIS.   KERRY DANCE.   4CL,PF                        CF
MOLLOY, J.-SEARS.   KERRY DANCE.   4CL,PF                         PO
MOLTER, J.-GUTHMANN.   3 CONCERTI.   4FL,BC                       UE
MOLTER, J.-DOUGLAS.   CONCERTO IN A MA.   4FL,BC                  NOM
MONGER (ARR).   ENSEMBLE ALBUM #1.   4FL(4CL),PF                  TP
MOZART, W.-PILLNEY.   ANDANTE IN RONDO FORM IN F MA, K616         BRH
  FL,OB,CL,BSN,HPCD
MOZART, W.-STARK.   KONZERTANTES QUARTETT IN E FL MA             BRII
  OB,CL,BSN,HN,PF
```

```
MOZART, W.-EMERSON.  K478 IN G MI.  OB,CL,HN,BSN,PF                JE
MOZART, W.  MINUET & TRIO (SYMPHONY IN E FL MA).  4CL,PF          CEN
MOZART, W.-FEDERHOFER.  QUINTET IN E FL MA, KV452                 B&N
    OB,CL,HN,BSN,PF
MOZART, W.  QUINTET IN E FL MA, K452.  OB,CL,HN,BSN,PF            BRH
MOZART, W.  QUINTET IN E FL MA, K452.  OB,CL,HN,BSN,PF            INT
MOZART, W.  QUINTET IN E FL MA, K452.  OB,CL,HN,BSN,PF            MR
MOZART, W.-LEECH.  QUINTET, K452.  OB,CL,BSN,HN,PF                HI
MOZART, W.  QUINTET, K452.  OB,CL,HN,BSN,PF                       SO
MOZART, W.  SINFONIA CONCERTANTE IN E FL MA.  OB,CL,HN,BSN,PF     BRH
MOZART, W.  SINFONIA CONCERTANTE IN E FL MA, K297B               MR
    OB,CL,HN,BSN,PF
MOZART, W.  SINFONIA CONCERTANTE, K297B.  OB,CL,BSN,HN,PF         INT
NATANSON, T.  TOCCATA.  2CL,2HN,PF                                PWM
OFFENBACH, J.-GUY.  ORPHEUS OVERTURE.  2ASAX,TSAX,BAR SAX,PF      RU
PALKOVSKY, O.  3 STUDIEN (1967).  OB,CL,BSN,HN,ACC               CHF
PAPINEAU-COUTURE, J.  SUITE (1947).  FL,CL,BSN,HN,PF             CAN
PASSANI, E.  QUINTET (1954).  FL,OB,CL,BSN,PF                    EMT
PAUER, E.  QUINTET, OP 44.  OB,CL,HN,BSN,PF                      M&M
PEPUSCH, J.  CONCERTO, OP  8/1.  2FL,2OB,BC                      MR
PEPUSCH, J.  CONCERTO, OP  8/2.  2FL,2OB,BC                      MR
PEPUSCH, J.  CONCERTO, OP  8/3.  2FL,2OB,BC                      MR
PEPUSCH, J.  CONCERTO, OP  8/4.  2FL,2OB,BC                      MR
PEPUSCH, J.  CONCERTO, OP  8/5.  2FL,2OB,BC                      MR
PEPUSCH, J.  CONCERTO, OP  8/6.  2FL,2OB,BC                      MR
PFEIFFER, G.-LAUSCHMANN.  SONATA.  FL,OB,HN,BSN,PF               FRH
PLEYEL, I.  QUINTET IN C MA.  OB,CL,HN,BSN,PF                    MR
PLEYEL, I.  SINFONIA CONCERTANTE.  FL,OB,BSN,HN,PF               MR
PLEYEL, I.  SYMPHONIE CONCERTANTE #5.  FL,OB(CL),BSN,HN,PF       EMT
QUINET, M.  CONCERTO GROSSO (1964).  4CL,PF                      CBD
RAWSTHORNE, A.  QUINTET.  CL,OB,BSN,HN,PF                        OX
RIETI, V.  SONATA A CINQUE.  FL,OB,CL,BSN,PF                     GEN
RIMSKY-KORSAKOV, N.  QUINTET IN B-FLAT.  FL,CL,BSN,HN,PF         EDK
RIMSKY-KORSAKOV, N.  QUINTET IN B FL MA.  FL,CL,BSN,HN,PF        BEL
RIMSKY-KORSAKOV, N.  QUINTET IN B FL MA.  FL,CL,BSN,HN,PF        INT
RIMSKY-KORSAKOV, N.-BARNBY/HOLMES.  SONG OF INDIA- SWEET & LOW   RU
    2ASAX,TSAX,BAR SAX,PF
ROBLES, D.-BOYER.  CONDOR PASA, EL.  4FL,PF                      EM
SCHINDELMEISSER, L.-VOXMAN.  CONCERTANTE, OP ?.  4CL,PF          MR
SCHMIDT, W.  CONCERTINO.  4SAX,PF                                WI
SCHMIDT, W.  SONATINA.  FL,OB,CL,BSN,PF                          WI
SCHUBERT, F.-HOLMES.  MARCHE MILITAIRE.  2ASAX,TSAX,BAR SAX,PF   RU
SHORT, J.  FLIRTY FLUTES.  4FL,PF                                KN
SINOPOLI, G.  NUMQUID (1972)                                     ESZ
    OB,EHN,OB D'AMORE,HECKELPHONE,PF/CEL/H PCD
SIXTA, J.  KVINTETO.  FL,OB,CL,BSN,PF                            SHF
SPOHR, L.-SCHMITZ.  QUINTET IN C MI, OP 52.  FL,CL,HN,BSN,PF     B&N
SPOHR, L.  QUINTET, OP 52.  FL,CL,BSN,HN,PF                      AB
SPOHR, L.  QUINTET, OP 52.  FL,CL,BSN,HN,PF                      EDK
SPOHR, L.  QUINTET, OP 52.  FL,CL,BSN,HN,PF                      MR
TAYLOR, L.  CLARINET CALYPSO.  4CL,PF                            HL
TENAGLIA, A.-FISCHER.  ARIA.  FL,OB,CL,BSN,PF                    FOR
TOLL, R. (ARR).  6 LITTLE GEMS FROM THE MASTERS.  4CL,PF         CF
TON-THAT TIET.  TU DAI CA'NH.  FL,OB,CL,BSN,PF                   EMT
TOWER, J.  PRELUDE FOR 5 PLAYERS.  FL,OB,CL,BSN,PF              ACA
TURNER, R.  LAMENT (1951).  FL,OB,CL,BSN,PF                      CAN
UGGEN, E. (ARR).  PLAYWELL TRIO & QUARTET FOLIO                  S&
    4FL(4CL,4SAX),PF
VERDI, G.-HARRIS.  QUARTET (RIGOLETTO).  4CL,PF                  CF
VERETTI, A.  DIVERTIMENTO.  FL,OB,CL,BSN,PF                      RC
VERHEY, T.  QUINTET, OP 20.  OB,CL,BSN,HN,PF                     BRH
VERHEY, T.  QUINTET, OP 20.  OB,CL,HN,BSN,PF                     M&M
```

5 PARTS: WOODWIND-KEYBOARD (INCLUDING HORN)-528

```
VOLBACH, F.  QUINTET, OP 24.   OB,CL,BSN,HN,PF              BRH
VOORN, J.  QUINTET (PRELUDE & FUGUE) (1975-76)             SD
   OB,CL,HN,BSN,PF
WEBER, C.M. VON-HOLMES.  FREISCHUTZ SELECTION, DER         RU
   2ASAX,TSAX,BAR SAX,PF
WEST, C.  CAPRICIOUS WINDS.  4CL,PF                        SP
WILLIAMSON, M.  PAS DE 4.  FL,OB,CL,BSN,PF                 JOW
```

5 PARTS: WOODWIND-BRASS-532

```
BARCE, R.  PARABOLA.  FL,OB,CL,BSN,TPT                     EDA
BROWN, N.  PASTORALE.  FL,CL,SAX,TPT,TRB                   SS
CORAL, G.  DIALOGHI (1968).  FL,OB,CL,HN,TPT              ESZ
DIJK, J. VAN.  CHORALES.  FL,CL,BSN,HN,TPT                SD
EDER, H.  LITZLBERG-SERENADE, OP 67.  2CL,HN,BSN,TPT      LDO
HANDEL, G.  MARCHES.  2CL(2OB),2TPT,BASS INSTR            TP
HARTLEY, W.  SONATA DA CAMERA.  TRB,OB,2CL,BSN            CRE
HARTLEY, W.  SUITE FOR 5 WINDS.  FL,OB,CL,ASAX,TRB        CRE
HARTMANN, K.  TANZSUITE.  CL,HN,BSN,TPT,TRB               SCH
HERTEL, J.-SALLAGAR.  CONCERTO A CINQUE.  TPT,2OB,2BSN    OHN
KIM, Y.  QUINTET.  FL,OB,CL,BCL,TRB                       SS
KOWALSKI, J.  GRIMACES.  FL,CL,HN,TRB,TU                  SHF
LABURDA, J.  KASACE #1.  FL,CL,HN,TPT,TRB                 SS
MACERO, T.  CANZONA #1.  2ASAX,TSAX,BAR SAX,TPT           TP
MILLER, J.  SETTIGNANO (1968).  AFL,OB,CL,BSN,TPT         SS
NOON, D.  INTRODUCTION, DIRGE & FROLIC, OP 18             CF
   FL/PIC,CL,BSN,TPT,TRB
POWELL, M.  DIVERTIMENTO.  FL,OB,CL,BSN,TPT               CF
PRAETORIUS, M.-HAZELGROVE.  DANCES FROM TERPSICHORE, 2 VOLS  RC
   2TPT,HN,2BSN
PREMRU, R.  CONCERTINO (1954).  FL,OB,CL,BSN,TRB          MR
REVUELTAS, S.  LITTLE SERIOUS PIECE #1.  PIC,OB,CL,BAR SAX,TPT  SN
REVUELTAS, S.  LITTLE SERIOUS PIECE #2.  PIC,OB,CL,BAR SAX,TPT  SN
SEEGER, P.  KLEINE JAGDGESCHICHTE.  4WINDS,TPT            PG
WECKMAN, M.-BINKERD.  NOW DANCE & SING.  OB,EHN,BSN,2TRB  AMP
```

5 PARTS: WOODWIND-STRING-533

```
ADASKIN, M.  QUINTET.  BSN,2VN,VA,VC                      CAN
ADOLPHUS, M.  ELEGY, OP 81.  CL,HN,VN,VA,VC               ACA
AHO, K.  QUINTET.  FL,OB,VN,VA,VC                         FIN
AITKEN, H.  QUINTET.  OB,2VN,VA,VC                        AMC
ALBERT, K.  QUINTETTE.  FL,OB,VN,VA,VC                    EME
AMES, W.  QUINTET.  CL,2VN,VA,VC                          ACA
ANDRIESSEN, H.  DIVERTIMENTO A 5.  FL,OB,VN,VA,VC         SD
ANDRIESSEN, J.  HOMMAGE A MILHAUD (1948).  FL,2VN,VA,VC   SD
ARNOLD, M.  QUINTET.  FL,BSN,HN,VN,VA                     CF
BACH, J.S.-NELHYBEL.  BIST DU BEI MIR.  OB,2VN,VA,VC      JER
BACH, J.S.  PASTORALE.  OB,2VN,VA,DB                      COR
BALLOU, E.  FANTASIA BREVIS II.  OB,2VN,VA,VC             ACA
BALORRE, C.  QUINTETTE.  CL,2VN,VA,VC                     HAM
BARATI, G.  QUINTET.  OB,2VN,VA,VC                        ACA
BAX, A.  QUINTET.  OB,2VN,VA,VC                           CA
BEECKE, I.-GOTTRON.  QUINTETTO IN G MA.  FL,OB,VN,VA,VC   B&N
```

```
BEN-HAIM, P.  QUINTET.  CL,2VN,VA,VC                             IMP
BENTZON, J.  VARIAZIONI INTERROTTI.  CL,BSN,VN,VA,VC             CHE
BERLIN, D.  QUINTET.  BSN,2VN,VA,VC                              MAN
BIGGS, J.  PASTORALE.  CL,2VN,VA,VC                              CPR
BLACHER, B.  QUINTET (1973/74).  FL,OB,VN,VA,VC                  B&B
BLACKWOOD, E.  CONCERTINO, OP 5.  FL,OB,VN,VA,VC                 GS
BLISS, A.  CONVERSATIONS.  FL,OB,VN,VA,VC                        FB
BLISS, A.  QUINTET.  CL,2VN,VA,VC                                NO
BLISS, A.  QUINTET.  OB,2VN,VA,VC                                OX
BOCCHERINI, L.  QUINTET IN D MA, OP 21/1.  FL,2VN,VA,VC          MR
BOCCHERINI, L.  QUINTET IN E FL MA, OP 21/6.  FL,2VN,VA,VC       INT
BOCCHERINI, L.-LEBERMANN.  QUINTETS, OP 45/1-3.  OB,2VN,VA,VC    PET
BOCCHERINI, L.-GEIGLING.  3 QUINTETS, OP 45/4-6                  HSM
   OB(FL),2VN,VA,VC
BOCCHERINI, L.  QUINTETTO IN C MA.  FL,OB,VN,VA,VC               MR
BOCCHERINI, L.  QUINTETTO, OP 21/6.  FL,2VN,VA,VC                ESA
BOGUSLAWSKI, E.  METAMORPHOSEN, (1967).  OB,CL,VN,VA,VC          HMO
BOIS, R. DU.  MELODY (1974).  BCL,2VN,VA,VC                      SD
BON, W.  SANS PAROLES (1970).  CL,BCL,VN,VA,VC                   SD
BOTTENBERG, W.  FA SO LA TI DO RE (1972).  SOP SAX,2VN,VA,VC     CAN
BOTTJE, W.  CONCERTINO.  EHN(ASAX),2VN,VA,VC                     CO
BOTTJE, W.  QUINTET.  FL,2VN,VA,VC                               ACA
BOURGAULT-DUCOUDRAY.  ABERGAVENNY.  FL,2VN,VA,VC                 HLE
BOURGUIGNON, F. DE.  QUINTET, OP100 (1952).  OB,2VN,VA,VC        CBD
BRAHMS, J.  QUINTET IN B MI.  CL,2VN,VA,VC                       RC
BRAHMS, J.  QUINTET IN B MI, OP115.  CL,2VN,VA,VC                BRH
BRAHMS, J.  QUINTET IN B MI, OP115.  CL,2VN,VA,VC                INT
BRAHMS, J.  QUINTET IN B MI, OP115.  CL,2VN,VA,VC                MR
BRAHMS, J.  QUINTET.  CL,2VN,VA,VC                               CF
BRAHMS, J.  QUINTET, OP115.  CL,2VN,VA,VC                        EDK
BRAHMS, J.  QUINTET, OP115.  CL,2VN,VA,VC                        PET
BRAUN, R.  SUITE.  CL,2VN,VA,VC                                  YM
BRAUTIGAM, H.  FROHLICHE MUSIK.  FL,OB,3VN                       BRH
BRAUTIGAM, H.-WAGNER.  TANZERISCHE SPIELMUSIK.  2FL,2VN,VC(DB)   SCH
BRINGS, A.  SUITE.  FL,OB,CL,HN,DB                               AMC
BRUNETTI, G.  QUINTET #4.  BSN,2VN,VA,VC                         MR
BUCKMANN, R.  5 KLEINE STUCKE.  OB(CL),2VN,VA,VC                 ETB
CADOW, P.  VARIATIONS UBER EINE SCHWED. VOLKSLIED                ETB
   OB,2VN,VA,VC
CAMBINI, G.-PARDINI.  6 QUINTETTI, OP  8, 9.  FL,OB,VN,VA,DB     GZ
CEELY, R.  SPECULATION.  FL,OB,CL,BCL,VC                         ACA
CEREMUGA, J.  QUINTET.  FL,OB,VN,VA,VC                           PAN
CHAGRIN, F.  4 LYRIC INTERLUDES.  FL(OB),2VN,VA,VC               NO
CHERNEY, B.  QUINTET (1962).  ASAX,2VN,VA,VC                     CAN
COLERIDGE-TAYLOR, S.  QUINTET.  CL,2VN,VA,VC                     M&M
COLERIDGE-TAYLOR, S.  QUINTET.  CL,2VN,VA,VC                     MR
COOKE, A.R.  QUINTET.  CL,2VN,VA,VC                              OX
CRUSELL, B.  DIVERTIMENTO IN C MA.  OB,2VN,VA,VC                 MT
CRUSELL, B.-MICHAELS.  DIVERTIMENTO, OP  9.  OB,2VN,VA,VC        HSM
CRUSELL, B.  QUINTET #1 IN E FL MA.  CL,2VN,VA,VC                MT
CRUSELL, B.  QUINTET #2 IN C MA.  CL,2VN,VA,VC                   MT
CRUSELL, B.  QUINTET #3 IN D MA.  CL,2VN,VA,VC                   MT
CRUSELL, B.  QUINTET, OP  2/1 IN E FL MA.  CL,2VN,VA,VC          EK
CRUSELL, B.  QUINTET, OP  4 IN C MI.  CL,2VN,VA,VC               EK
CRUSELL, B.  QUINTET, OP  7 IN D MA.  CL,2VN,VA,VC               EK
DAVID, T.  QUINTET.  CL,VN,VA,VC,DB                              LDO
DI DOMENICA, R.  QUINTET.  CL,2VN,VA,VC                          MAR
DIAMOND, D.  QUINTET.  CL,2VA,2VC                                SN
DONOVAN, R.  RICERCARE.  OB,2VN,VA,VC                            AMC
DUPUY, E. & K. BRAUN-HENNIGE.  QUINTET.  BSN,2VN,VA,VC           HSM
DUSHKIN.  QUINTET IN A MA.  FL,2VN,VA,VC                         MR
DUSHKIN, D.  QUINTET FOR AMANDA.  CL(FL,OB),2VN,VA,VC            NVM
```

```
EDWARDS, G.  KREUZ UND QUER (1971).  FL,CL,VN,VA,VC              B-B
EISMA, W.  SONATA (1959).  CL,HN,VN,VA,VC                         SD
ELLIOT, W.  POEM.  BSN,2VN,VA,VC                                  COR
EYSER, E.  QUINTET (1968).  EHN,VN,VA,VC,DB                       STI
EYSER, E.  SERENATA SPAGNOLA (1959).  EHN,2VN,VA,VC               STI
FINCH, R.  QUINTET.  OB,2VN,VA,VC                                 JE
FRANCAIX, J.  QUINTET.  CL,2VN,VA,VC                              SCH
FRANCO, J.  DIVERTIMENTO.  FL,2VN,VA,VC                           ACA
FRANKEL, B.  QUINTET.  CL,2VN,VA,VC                               CHE
FROMM-MICHAELS, I.  MUSICA LARGA.  CL,2VN,VA,VC                   HSM
FUCHS, R.  QUINTET, OP102.  CL,2VN,VA,VC                          JB
GAL, H.  CONCERTINO, OP 82.  FL,2VN,VA,VC                         UE
GAL, H.  QUINTET, OP107.  CL,2VN,VA,VC                            RS
GASSMANN, F.  3 DIVERTIMENTI.  OB,3VA,VC                          ART
GASTYNE, G. DE.  SUITE RHETAISE, OP 26.  ASAX,2VN,VA,VC           FER
GELLMAN, S.  MYTHOS II (1968).  FL,2VN,VA,VC                      CAN
GINASTERA, A.  IMPRESSIONS OF PUNA.  FL,2VN,VA,VC                 SN
GIUFFRE, J.  CLARINET QUINTET #1.  CL,2VN,VA,VC                   MJ
GLAZUNOV, A.  ORIENTAL REVERIE.  CL,2VN,VA,VC                     COR
GOLDBERG, T.  QUINTET, OP 7 (1952).  CL,2VN,VA,VC                 B&B
GOLZ, W.  FOR FLUTE & MUTED STRING QUARTET.  FL,2VN,VA,VC         OP
HA, J.  SONATA.  CL,2VN,VA,VC                                     MAN
HARRIS, R.  FOUR MINUTES & TWENTY SECONDS.  FL,2VN,VA,VC          BE
HARTIG, H.  COMPOSITION, OP 50.  FL,OB,VN,VA,VC                   B&B
HARTLEY, W.  QUINTET MOVEMENT.  CL,2VN,VA,VC                      CRE
HARTMANN, R.  VARIATIONEN UBER EIN THEMA VON PAGANINI, OP  1      B&B
     FL,OB,VN,VA,VC
HAUTA-AHO, T.  SONATINA.  CL,BSN,HN,VC,DB                         FIN
HAYDN, M.-HOCKNER.  DIVERTIMENTO A 5 IN G MA.  FL,VN,VA,HN,BSN    SIM
HAYDN, M.-STRASSL.  DIVERTIMENTO IN B FL MA.  OB,BSN,VN,VA,DB     LDO
HAYDN, M.-STRASSL.  DIVERTIMENTO IN G MA.  FL,HN,VN,VA,DB         LDO
HAYDN, M.-BALASSA.  QUINTETTO.  CL,BSN,HN,VN,VA                   EMB
HAZZARD, P.  SUITE.  EHN,2VN,VA,VC                                SS
HEMEL, O. VAN.  CLARINET QUINTET (1958).  CL,2VN,VA,VC            SD
HENNING, E.  QUINTET.  FL,HN,VN,VA,VC                             AMC
HESS, W.  QUINTET, OP 63.  CBSN(BSN),2VN,VA,VC                    EUL
HEUSSENSTAMM, G.  MINI-VARIATIONS, OP 25.  FL,OB,VN,VA,VC         SS
HINDEMITH, P.  QUINTET, OP 30.  CL,2VN,VA,VC                      SCH
HOESSLIN, F. VON.  QUINTET IN C SH MI.  CL,2VN,VA,VC              SIM
HOLLER, K.  CLARINET QUINTET, OP 46.  CL,2VN,VA,VC               B&N
JACOB, G.  SUITE.  BSN,2VN,VA,VC                                  MR
JOHANSEN, D.  QUINTET.  FL,2VN,VA,VC                              NOR
KALLSTENIUS, E.  KLARINETTKVINTETT.  CL,2VN,VA,VC                 EMF
KARLINS, M.  QUINTET.  ASAX,2VN,VA,VC                             SS
KELLY, R.  QUINTET.  CL,2VN,VA,VC                                 ACA
KEURIS, T.  CONCERTINO (1976-77).  BCL,2VN,VA,VC                  SD
KNEZEK, V.-KLEMENT.  12 PARTITEN.  2CL,2VN,VC                     B&N
KOERPPEN, A.  SERENADE (1952).  FL,2VN,VA,VC                      BRH
KOETSIER, J.  QUINTET (1968).  CL,2VN,VA,VC                       SD
KOETSIER, J.  QUINTET, OP 3 (1932; REV. 1964)                     SD
     FL,OB,VN,VA,VC
KOETSIER, J.  QUINTET, OP 43 (1955).  EHN,2VN,VA,VC               SD
KONT, P.  CONCERTO LIRICO, OP 61/2.  FL,CL,VN,VA,VC               LDO
KOPP, F.  OCTOBER '55.  CL,2VN,VA,VC                              SS
KORNAUTH, E.  CLARINET QUINTET, OP 33.  CL,2VN,VA,VC              LDO
KORTE, K.  QUINTET (1959).  OB,2VN,VA,VC                          CAN
KRAUS, J.-LEBERMANN.  QUINTET IN D MA (1783).  FL,2VN,VA,VC       BRH
KRAUS, J.-HOFFMAN.  WIENER FLOTENQUINTETT IN D MA                 MV
     FL,2VN,VA,VC
KRIEGER, J.-SEIFFERT.  PARTIE IN F MA.  2OB,EHN,VA,BSN            KIS
KROMMER, F.  QUINTET IN B FL MA, OP 95.  CL,VN,2VA,VC             EK
KROMMER, F.  QUINTET IN B FL MA, OP 95.  CL,VN,VA(VN),VA,VC       MR
```

```
KUHLAU, F.-WINKEL.  QUINTET, OP 51/1 (1823).  FL,2VN,VA,VC      SPD
KUHLAU, F.  QUINTET, OP 51/3.  FL,2VN,VA,VC                     MR
LADERMAN, E.  CELESTIAL BODIES.  FL,2VN,VA,VC                   OX
LADERMAN, E.  SINGLE VOICE.  OB,2VN,VA,VC                       OX
LEDERER, J.  QUINTET, OP 45.  CL,2VN,VA,VC                      ETB
LEMELAND, A.  MOUVEMENT CONCERTANT.  FL,OB,VN,VA,VC             BIL
LEUKAUF, R.  QUINTET, OP 32A.  FL,OB,VN,VA,VC                   LDO
LEVY, F.  QUINTET.  FL,2VN,VA,VC                                COR
LIPSCOMB, H.  DESIGN.  CL,2VN,VA,VC                             TP
LOCKWOOD, N.  CLARINET QUINTET.  CL,2VN,VA,VC                   ACA
LOURIE, A.  PASTORALE DE LA VOLGA.  OB,BSN,2VA,VC               EES
MAASZ, G.  DIVERTIMENTO.  FL(OB),2VN,VA,VC                      HSM
MACERO, T.  ELECTRIQUE.  ASAX,2VN,VA,VC                         AMC
MACONCHY, E.  QUINTET.  CL,2VN,VA,VC                            OX
MALIPIERO, R.  WINTERQUINTET (1976).  CL,2VN,VA,VC              ESZ
MANASSEN, A.  MEI (1974).  FL,2VN,VA,VC                         SD
MARKOVIC, Z.  NOCTURNO & SCHERZO.  FL,2VN,VA,VC                 DSS
MARTINU, B.  SERENADE.  2CL,VN,VA,VC                            EES
MC BRIDE, R.  COMFORTABLE FLIGHT.  EHN,2VN,VA,VC                ACA
MC BRIDE, R.  QUINTET.  OB,2VN,VA,VC                            GS
MEYER, E.  CLARINET QUINTET.  CL,2VN,VA,VC                      PET
MEYER, E.  KLEINE EROFFNUNGSMUSIK.  CL,2VN,VA,VC                BRH
MEYER, K.  INTERLUDIO STATICO, OP 11 (1963-64).  CL,4VC         PWM
MEYERS, E.  SUITE.  CL,2VN,VA,VC                                AMC
MEZO, I.  QUINTET.  2FL,CL,BSN,DB                               EMB
MILHAUD, D.  REVES DE JACOB, LES.  OB,VN,VA,VC,DB               HEU
MIMAROGLU, I.  MUSIC.  4BSN,VC                                  SS
MOORE, D.  QUINTET.  CL,2VN,VA,VC                               CF
MOURANT, W.  BURLETTA.  CL,2VN,VA,VC                            ACA
MOZART, W.-LEVIN.  ALLEGRO IN B FL MA.  CL,2VN,VA,VC            B&N
MOZART, W.  CLARINET QUINTET.  CL,2VN,VA,VC                     BH
MOZART, W.  CLARINET QUINTET, K581.  CL,2VN,VA,VC               EDK
MOZART, W.  QUINTET #6.  CL,2VN,VA,VC                           CF
MOZART, W.-SCHMID.  QUINTET IN A MA, KV581.  CL,2VN,VA,VC       B&N
MOZART, W.  QUINTET IN A MA, K581.  CL,2VN,VA,VC                BRH
MOZART, W.  QUINTET IN A MA, K581.  CL(VA),2VN,VA,VC            INT
MOZART, W.  QUINTET.  CL,2VN,VA,VC                              BIL
MOZART, W.-CHRISTMANN.  QUINTET, K581.  CL,2VN,VA,VC            GS
MOZART, W.  QUINTET, K581.  CL,2VN,VA,VC                        DEU
MOZART, W.  QUINTET, K581.  CL,2VN,VA,VC                        PET
MOZART, W.  QUINTET, K581.  CL,2VN,VA,VC                        RC
MUL, J.  KWINTET (1957).  CL,BSN,VN,VA,VC                       SD
NEUKOMM, S. VON.  QUINTET, OP 8.  CL,2VN,VA,VC                  SIM
NIELSEN, C.  SERENATA INVANO.  CL,BSN,HN,VC,DB                  WH
NIEWIADOMSKI, S.  FLIBBERTIBIGGET.  2CL,2HN,DB                  PWM
NOVAK, M.  MUSIC.  FL,2VN,VA,VC                                 SIIF
PARK, S.  PASTORALE.  FL,2VN,VA,VC                              SO
PARRIS, R.  QUINTET.  FL,OB,BSN,VN,VA                           ACA
PARTOS, O.  MAQAMAT.  FL,2VN,VA,VC                              IMP
PEDERSEN, P.  CHORALE PRELUDE #2 (1958).  FL(OB,CL),2VN,VA,VC   CAN
PELEMANS, W.  CONCERTINO #3.  FL,CL,VN,VA,VC                    MAU
PEPIN, C.  SEQUENCES (1972).  FL,OB/EHN,VN,VA,VC                CAN
PERGAMENT, M.  ADAGIO (1973).  AFL,2VN,VA,VC                    STI
PERGAMENT, M.  FANTASIA (1973).  BFL,2VN,VA,VC                  STI
PERGAMENT, M.  INTERMEZZO (1973).  FL,2VN,VA,VC                 STI
PERGAMENT, M.  PEZZO (1972).  FL,2VN,VA,VC                      STI
PERGAMENT, M.  SCHERZO (1973).  PIC,2VN,VA,VC                   STI
PETRIC, I.  3 ESQUISSES.  FL,2VN,VA,VC                          EDD
PISTON, W.  QUINTET.  FL,2VN,VA,VC                              AMP
PLEYEL, I.-STEINBECK.  QUINTET IN E FL MA, OP 10/3             LDO
    FL,OB,VN,VA,VC
PONSE, L.  KWINTET, OP 25 (1956).  FL,OB,VN,VA,VC               SD
```

```
PORTER, Q.  QUINTET.  FL,2VN,VA,VC                              ACA
PORTER, Q.  QUINTET.  CL,2VN,VA,VC                              GA
POSPISIL, J.  WIDERSPRUCHE.  CL,2VN,VA,VC                       SHF
PRESSER, W.  PASSACAGLIA.  CL,VN,VA,VC,HN                       OP
PRINZ, A.  QUINTET.  FL,2VN,VA,VC                               LDO
PROKOFIEV, S.  QUINTET IN G MI, OP 39.  OB,CL,VN,VA,DB          INT
PROKOFIEV, S.  QUINTET.  OB,CL,VN,VA,DB                         EDK
PROKOFIEV, S.  QUINTET, OP 39.  OB,CL,VN,VA,DB                  BH
RANDOLPH, D.  PRELUDE & VARIATIONS.  CL,2VN,VA,VC               AMC
RAPHAEL, G.  QUINTET, OP 4.  CL,2VN,VA,VC                       SIM
RATHAUS, K.  ALLEGRO CONCERTANTE.  OB(CL),2VN,VA,VC             IMP
RATHBURN, E.  PASTORELLA (1949).  OB,2VN,VA,VC                  CAN
REGER, M.  QUINTET, OP146.  CL,2VN,VA,VC                        PET
REICHA, A.  QUINTET IN B FL MA.  CL,2VN,VA,VC                   MR
REICHA, A.  QUINTET IN B FL MA.  CL,2VN,VA,VC                   PET
REICHA, A.  QUINTET IN F MA.  OB,2VN,VA,VC                      MR
REICHA, A.-MERKA.  QUINTET IN F MA, OP107.  CL,2VN,VA,VC        GZ
REICHA, A.  QUINTET.  CL,2VN,VA,VC                              B&V
REICHA, A.  QUINTETTO, OP107.  OB,2VN,VA,VC                     M&M
REIZENSTEIN, F.  THEME, VARIATIONS & FUGUE.  CL,2VN,VA,VC       LEN
REULAND, J.  CONCERTINO (1959).  FL,2VN,VA,VC                   SD
RHODES, P.  MUSEUM PIECES.  CL,2VN,VA,VC                        PET
RIBARI, A.  CHAMBER MUSIC (1970).  FL,CL,VN,VA,VC               GEN
RIDKY, J.  QUINTET (1926).  CL,2VN,VA,VC                        CHF
RIETZ, J.  MYSTERIUM.  OB,2VN,VA,VC                             EDT
RINGGER, R.  FUR P. (1976).  FL,2VN,VA,VC                       S-V
ROCHE, G.  BALLADE.  OB,2VN,VA,VC                               E&C
ROMBERG, A.  QUINTET, OP 57.  CL,VN,2VA,VC                      M&M
ROSEN, J.  QUINTET (1974).  ASAX,2VN,VA,VC                      ACA
ROSEN, J.  QUINTET.  CL,2VN,VA,VC                               ACA
RUBBRA, E.  SUITE: THE BUDDHA.  FL,OB,VN,VA,VC                  LEN
RUDZINSKI, W.  QUINTET (1954).  FL,2VN,VA,VC                    AP
SALIERI, G.-WOJCIECHOWSKI.  ADAGIO CON VARIAZIONI              HSM
    CL,2VN,VA,VC
SCARMOLIN, L.  QUINTET.  CL,HN,VN,VA,VC                         AMC
SCHAFER, G.  QUINTET.  CL,2VN,VA,VC                             SIM
SCHWANTNER, J.  CONSORTIUM.  FL,CL,VN,VA,VC                     PET
SCHWARTZ, E.  MINICONCERTO.  FL,OB,VN,VA,VC                     CF
SERMILA, J.  CRISIS.  CL,2VN,VA,VC                              ER
SIEGEL, A.  COUNTRY CHURCHYARD.  FL,2VN,VA,VC                   AMC
SIEGL, O.  QUINTET-SERENADE.  CL,BSN,VN,VA,VC                   LDO
SIMONS, N.  QUINTET (1953).  FL,OB,CL,BSN,DB                    ACA
SIMPSON, R.  CLARINET QUINTET.  CL,2VN,VA,VC                    ALL
SIMS, E.  QUINTET.  FL,CL,VN,VA,VC                              ACA
SLIMACEK, M.  QUINTET (1970).  CL,2VN,VA,VC                     CHF
SMITH, J.  QUINTET.  OB(CL),2VN,VA,VC                           CF
SMITH, L.  QUINTET.  BSN,2VN,VA,VC                              ACA
SNYDER, R.  QUINTET.  ASAX,2VN,VA,VC                            DOR
SOKORSKI, J.  LITTLE QUINTET (1963).  CL,2VN,VA,VC             AP
SPOHR, L.  FANTAISIE & VAR ON A THEME BY DANZI, OP 81          MR
    CL,2VN,VA,VC
STAEPS, H.  CHORIC QUINTET.  FL(OB),CL,BSN,VN,VA               UE
STALLAERT, A.  QUINTET.  ASAX,2VN,VA,VC                         BIL
STAMITZ, K.-HOCKNER.  QUINTET.  OB,HN,2VA,VC                    SIM
STAMITZ, K.-WINSCHERMANN/BUCK.  QUINTETS, OP 11/1, 2           HSM
    OB,HN,2VA,VC
STEIN, L.  QUINTET,.  ASAX,2VN,VA,VC                            COR
STERANS, P.  NOCTURNE, DANCE & AUBADE.  CL,BCL,VN,VA,VC         AMC
STILL, R.  CLARINET QUINTET.  CL,2VN,VA,VC                      LEN
STOCK, D.  QUINTET, OP 12.  CL,2VN,VA,VC                        ACA
STOCK, D.  SERENADE FOR 5 INSTRUMENTS.  FL,CL,HN,VA,VC          ACA
STOJANOVIC, J.  SUMMER QUARTET, A VISIT TO THE PUPPET SHOW      DSS
    OB,2VN,V A,VC
```

5 PARTS: WOODWIND-STRING-533

```
STRAESSER, E.  CLARINET QUINTET, OP 34.  CL,2VN,VA,VC        SIM
STRATEGIER, H.  3 STUKKEN (1937).  OB,2VN,VA,VC              SD
STRAUSS, R.-HASENOEHRL.  TILL EULENSPIEGEL EINMAL ANDERS!    PET
   CL,BSN,HN,VN,DB
STRAVINSKY, I.  PASTORALE.  VN,OB,EHN,CL,BSN                 SCH
SUSSMAYER, F.-STEINBECK.  QUINTET.  FL,OB,VN,VA,VC           LDO
TALMA, L.  SUMMER SOUNDS.  CL,2VN,VA,VC                      CF
TARP, S.  SERENADE (1930).  FL,CL,VN,VA,VC                   SPD
TAYLOR, S.  QUINTET.  CL,2VN,VA,VC                           M&M
THILMAN, J.  CLARINET QUINTET, OP 73.  CL,2VN,VA,VC          PET
TIENSUU, J.  CONCERTO DA CAMERA.  FL,EHN,CL,BSN,VC           FIN
TREDE, Y.  QUINTETT IN EINEM SATZ.  CL,2VN,VA,VC             PET
TUTHILL, B.  NOCTURNE.  FL,2VN,VA,VC                         AB
VAN VACTOR, D.  QUINTET (1932).  FL,2VN,VA,VC                TP
WEBER, C. VON.  QUINTET IN B FL MA.  CL,2VN,VA,VC            EDK
WEBER, C.M. VON.  GRAND QUINTET, OP 34.  CL,2VN,VA,VC        MRL
WEBER, C.M. VON-KOHL.  INTRODUKTION, THEMA UND VARIATIONEN   B&B
   CL,2VN,VA,VC
WEBER, C.M. VON.  QUINTET IN B FL MA, OP 34.  CL,2VN,VA,VC   INT
WEBER, C.M. VON.  QUINTET IN B FL MA, OP 34.  CL,2VN,VA,VC   MR
WEBER, C.M. VON.  QUINTET, OP 34.  CL,2VN,VA,VC              BRH
WEBER, C.M. VON.  QUINTET, OP 34.  CL,2VN,VA,VC              CF
WELLESZ, E.  QUINTET, OP 81.  CL,2VN,VA,VC                   HEI
WERDIN, E.  CONCERTINO.  2FL,2VN,VC                          SCH
WESTERGAARD, S.  TEMA CON VARIAZIONI E FUGA, OP 11           WH
   CL,2VN,VA,VC
WHITNEY, M.  ADAGIO & FUGUE.  FL,CL,VN,VA,VC                 OP
WILSON, D.  QUINTET.  CL,2VN,VA,VC                           GA
WOESTIJNE, D.  MUSIC (1953).  FL,OB,VN,VA,VC                 CBD
WORDSWORTH, W.  QUINTET, OP 50.  CL,2VN,VA,VC                LEN
ZELEZNY, L.  QUINTET (1960).  CL,2VN,VA,VC                   CHF
ZIEMS, H.  QUINTET (1965).  CL,2VN,VA,VC                     B&B
ZIPP, F.  ARIA E FANTASIA (1970).  CL,2VN,VA,VC             WMS
ZIPP, F.  AU CLAIR DE LA LUNE (1963).  FL(OB),2VN,VA,VC     WMS
```

5 PARTS: WOODWIND-BRASS-STRING-534

```
CASELLA, A.  SERENATA.  CL,BSN,TPT,VN,VC                     UE
COHEN, E.  MADRIGAL (1967).  FL/PIC,BCL,TPT,VA,DB            B-B
FULKERSON, J.  CO-ORDINATIVE SYSTEMS #3 (1973).  CL,TRB,VC,2DB  EMO
HAIEFF, A.  DANCE SUITE.  FL,BSN,TPT,VN,VC                   BEL
HESPOS, H.  EN-KIN (DAS FERN-NAHE) (1970)                    EMO
   BCL,BSN,SSAX,FLUEGEL HN,D B
SMITH, L.  INTRODUCTION & DIVERTIMENTO.  CL,TPT,VN,VA,VC     ACA
THOMSON, V.  SONATA DA CHIESA.  E FL CL,TPT,HN,TRB,VA        BH
TISNE, A.  STRATES COLOREES.  OB,EHN,VA,TPT,TRB             EMT
WHITTENBERG, C.  STRUCTURES WITH CHORALE.  CL,BSN,TRB,VA,VC  ACA
```

5 PARTS: WOODWIND-BRASS-KEYBOARD-535

```
CARCASIO.  SONATA.  2OB,2TPT,BC                              H-V
COTEK, P.  DECHOVA HUDBA (1970).  PIC,TPT,BASS TPT,TRB,PF    ART
GRABS, M.  QUINTET (1965).  CL,BSN,TPT,TRB,PF               ISR
PERUTI, C.  3 SUNDAY PIECES.  CL,BCL,TPT,TRB,PF             MAN
```

```
ADASKIN, M.  CASSENTI CONCERTANTE (1963).  OB,CL,BSN,VN,PF      CAN
ALBRIGHT, W.  DANSE MACABRE.  FL,CL,VN,VC,PF                    BOW
BABBITT, M.  ARIE DA CAPO.  FL,CL,VN,VC,PF                      PET
BACH, J.C.  QUINTET IN A MA, OP 11/5.  FL,OB,VN,VA,BC           MR
BACH, J.C.  QUINTET IN C MA, OP 11/1.  FL,OB,VN,VA,BC           MR
BACH, J.C.-ERMELER.  QUINTET IN D MA.  FL,OB,VN,VC,PF           B&N
BACH, J.C.-ERHART.  QUINTET IN D MA.  OB,VN,VA,VC,PF            SCH
BACH, J.C.  QUINTET IN F MA, OP 11/3.  FL,OB,VN,VA,BC           MR
BACH, J.C.  QUINTET IN G MA, OP 11/2.  FL,OB,VN,VA,BC           MR
BACH, J.C.-STEGLICH.  QUINTET, OP 11/1 IN C MA                 B&N
   FL,OB,VN,VA,BC
BACH, J.C.-STEGLICH.  QUINTET, OP 11/2 IN G MA                 B&N
   FL,OB,VN,VA,BC
BACH, J.C.-STEGLICH.  QUINTET, OP 11/3 IN F MA                 B&N
   FL,OB,VN,VA,BC
BACH, J.C.-STEGLICH.  QUINTET, OP 11/4 IN E FL MA              B&N
   FL,OB,VN,VA,BC
BACH, J.C.-STEGLICH.  QUINTET, OP 11/5 IN A MA                 B&N
   FL,OB,VN,VA,BC
BACH, J.C.-STEGLICH.  QUINTET, OP 11/6 IN D MA                 B&N
   FL,OB,VN,VA,BC
BADINGS, H.  FUGA (1938).  FL,OB,VN,VA,ORG                      SD
BARKIN, E.  MIXED MODES (1975).  CL/BCL,VN,VA,VC,PF            B-B
BEHR, S.  5 PIECES (1968).  FL,VN,VA,VC,PF                      PWM
BENNETT, W.  HYPERBOLEX.  FL,CL,BSN,VC,PF                       SS
BEYER, F.  CONCERTO (1968).  FL,CL,VN,VC,PF                     B&B
BIRTWISTLE, H.  3 LESSONS IN A FRAME (1967).  FL,CL,VN,VC,PF    UE
BOISMORTIER, J.-RUF.  CONCERTO IN E MI.  FL,OB,BSN,VN,BC        RC
BOLCOM, W.  DUETS FOR QUINTET.  FL,CL,VN,VC,PF                  BOW
BOLCOM, W.  WHISPER MOON.  AFL,CL,VN,VC,PF                      BOW
BURGE, D.  AEOLIAN MUSIC.  FL,CL,VN,VC,PF                       BOW
COOKE, G.  QUINTET.  CL,VN,VA D'AMORE,VC,PF                     VA
CORDERO, R.  QUINTETO.  FL,CL,VN,VC,PF                          SN
CORELLI, A.  GAVOTTE & GIGUE.  FL,2VN,VA,PF                     EDM
COUPERIN, F.-DESORMIERE.  QUATRIEME CONCERT ROYAL              EDL
   FL,OB,BSN,VN,HPCD
COUPERIN, F.-BOULAY.  SULTANE, LA                              EMT
   FL(OB),VN(FL),2VA DA GAMBA (VC),PF
DIAMOND, D.  QUINTET.  FL,VN,VA,VC,PF                           SN
DONATONI, F.  ETWAS RUHIGER IM AUSDRUCK (1967)                 ESZ
   FL,CL,VN,VC,PF
DUBOIS, F.  QUINTET.  OB,VN,VA,VC,PF                            HEU
DUBOIS, T.  QUINTET.  OB,VN,VA,VC,                             EDK
DUCKWORTH, W.  7 SHADES OF BLUE.  FL,CL,VN,VC,PF               BOW
EDWARDS, G.  EXCHANGE-MISERE (1974)                            B-B
   FL/PIC/AFL,CL/BCL,VN/VA,VC,PF
FASCH, J.-SALLAGAR.  CONCERTO.  BSN,2VN,VA,BC                  HEI
FELDMAN, M.  3 CLARINETS, CELLO & PIANO (1971.  3CL,VC,PF      UE
FIBICH, Z.  QUINTET, OP 42.  CL,VN,VC,HN,PF                     JB
FOSTER, S.  VILLAGE FESTIVAL, A.  FL,2VN,DB,PF                  EDM
GABLER, W.  QUINTET FOR YOUNG PLAYERS, OP 56.  FL,2VN,VC,PF     PM
GANDINI, G.  MUSICA NOCTURNA.  FL,VN,VA,VC,PF                   SN
GILBERT, A.  9 OR 10 OSANNAS, OP 10.  CL,HN,VN,VC,PF           S&C
GLICK, S.  SUITE HEBRAIQUE #2 (1969).  CL,VN,VA,VC,PF          CAN
GRAUPNER, C.-ANGERHOFER.  CONCERTO.  BSN,2VN,VA,PF(HPCD)       FRH
```

5 PARTS: WOODWIND-STRING-KEYBOARD-536

```
HALLNAS, H.   KVINTETT.  FL,OB,VA,VC,PF                          EMF
HAMBRAEUS, B.   DIPTYCHON (TABU-MANU), OP 30                     EMF
    FL,OB,VA,CEL,HPCD
HANDEL, G.   EINLEITUNGEN ZU 3 ANTHEMS.  OB,2VN,VC,BC           MV
HARBISON, J.   KURZE, DIE.  FL,CL,VN,VC,PF                      ACA
HARRIS, D.   LUDUS II.  FL,CL,VN,VC,PF                          JOB
HARRIS, R.   DANCE GROUP, OP 13.  CL,BSN,VN,2PF                 ACA
HASSE, J.A.-KOLBEL.  SINFONIA A 5 IN G MA.  2FL,2VN,BC          B&N
HAUFRECHT, H.   FROM THE GROUND UP.  FL,CL,VN,VC,PF             ACA
HAYDN, F.   DIVERTISSEMENT.  OB,VN,VA DA GAMBA,DB,PF            OX
HAYDN, F.-SITT.   SINFONIE CONCERTANTE.  OB,BSN,VN,VC,PF        INT
HAYDN, F.-SITT.   SINFONIE CONCERTANTE, OP 84.  OB,BSN,VN,VC,PF BRH
HAYDN, F.   SYMPHONY CONCERTANTE, OP 84.  OB,BSN,VN,VC,PF       EDK
HEDWALL, L.   KVINTETT (1965).  FL,OB,VN,VC,HPCD               STI
HEINICHEN, J.   CONCERTO IN G MA.  FL,2VN,VC,PF                PET
HELPS, R.   QUINTET (1975).  FL,CL,VN,VC,PF                    ACA
HOCH, F.   C'E KARL E KARL (1972).  FL,CL,VN,VC,PF            ESZ
HOLLER, K.   DIVERTIMENTO, OP 11.  FL,VN,VA,VC,PF             B&N
HOLZBAUER, I.-SCHROEDER.   QUINTET IN G MA.  FL,VN,VA,VC,PF   BRH
HRISANIDE, A.   M.P. 5 (1967).  TSAX(CL),VN,VA,VC,PF         EDS
IVES, C.   ADAGIO SOSTENUTO.  EHN(FL),3VN,VC AD LIB,PF(HP)    SN
JANITSCH, J.-WOLFF.   KAMMERSONATE "ECHO", OP 8              BRH
    FL,OB(FL),VA,VC,PF
JOUBERT, J.   SONATA A 5, OP 43.  FL,VN,VA,VC,HPCD            NO
JURISALU, H.   QUINTET #2.  FL,CL,VN,VC,PF                    MKE
KARKOSCHKA, E.   AUS DREIEN (1969).  FL,CL,VN,VC,PF          HG
KENINS, T.   CONCERTINO A CINQUE (1968).  FL,OB,VA,VC,PF     CAN
KOPELENT, M.   MUSIK FUR FUNF.  OB,CL,BSN,VA,PF              HG
KRAFT, L.   PARTITA 4 (1975).  FL/PIC,CL/BCL,VN,DB,PF        AMC
KREUTZER, C.-BLOCK.   QUINTET.  FL,CL,VN,VC,PF               MR
LABOR, J.   QUINTET, OP 11.  CL,VN,VA,VC,PF                  M&M
LANG, I.   RHYMES.  FL,CL,VA,VC,PF                           EMB
LECLAIR, J.-CRUSSARD.   CONCERTO IN C MA.  FL,2VN,VA,BC      HUG
LENOT, J.   CLAMEURS.  AFL,EHN,VA,VC,PF                      APH
LEVIN, G.   LOVE'S BLOOM.  FL,CL,VN,VC,PF                    BOW
LUIGINI, A.   SERENADE ROMANTIQUE.  FL,VN,VC,PF,ORG          HLE
LUTI, V.   MIXED QUINTET.  FL,CL,VN,VC,PF                    BOW
LUTYENS, E.   CONCERTANTE, OP 22.  FL/PIC,CL/BCL,VN/VA,VC,PF BE
MAKSYMIUK, J.   IMPROMPTU #2 (1969).  FL,VN,VA,VC,PF         PWM
MALIPIERO, G.   SONATA A CINQUE.  FL,VN,VA,VC,PF             RC
MARCO, T.   ALBOR (1970).  FL,CL,VN,VC,PF                    EEC
MARX, K.   DIVERTIMENTO, OP 21A.  FL,VN,VA,VC,PF             B&N
MASSEUS, J.   TANGO.  3FL,VC(BSN),PF                         HU
MC CLELLAN, R.   GEESE OVER THE WATER.  FL,CL,VN,VA,PF       SS
MIEG, P.   QUINTUOR (1969).  FL,2VN,VC,PF                    EUL
MIEREANU, C.   SURSUM CORDA I (1967).  CL,VN,VA,VC,PF        SCH
MIROGLIO, F.   PHASES.  FL,VN,VA,VC,PF                       UE
MOZART, W.   ADAGIO & RONDO IN C MI, K617.  FL,OB,VA,VC,PF   INT
MOZART, W.-BIGGS.   ADAGIO & RONDO, K617.  FL,OB,VA,VC,ORG   TP
MOZART, W.   ADAGIO AND RONDO, K617.  FL,OB,VA,VC,PF         EDK
MOZART, W.-PILLNEY.   ANDANTE IN RONDO FORM IN F MA, K616    BRH
    FL,2VN,VA,HPCD
MUSGRAVE, T.   CHAMBER CONCERTO #2                           CHE
    FL/PIC/AFL,CL/BCL,VN/VA,VC,PF
OLIVEROS, P.   AEOLIAN PARTITIONS.  FL,CL,VN,VC,PF           BOW
PALMER, R.   QUINTET.  CL,VN,VA,VC,PF                        SN
PLESKOW, R.   3 MOVEMENTS.  FL,CL,VN,VC,PF                   BOW
POLIN, C.   MAKIMONO I.  FL,CL,VN,VC,PF                      SS
POPOVICI, D.   QUINTETTE (1967).  CL,VN,VA,VC,PF             EDS
POUSSEUR, H.   QUINTETTE A LA MEMOIRE D'ANTON WEBERN (1955)  ESZ
    CL,BCL,VN,VC,PF
RAMOVS, P.   PIANISSIMO.  FL,HN,VN,DB,PF                     EDD
```

```
RATIU, A.  CONCERTO PER LA "MUSICA NOVA".  CL,VN,VA,VC,PF      EMU
RAWSTHORNE, A.  QUINTET.  CL,HN,VN,VC,PF                       OX
REGAMEY, K.  QUINTET (1944).  CL,BSN,VN,VC,PF                  AP
ROSSEAU, N.  PENTAPHONIUM, OP164 (1964).  FL,OB,VA,VC,PF       CBD
RUYNEMAN, D.  DIVERTIMENTO (1927).  FL,CL,HN,VA,PF             CHE
RUYNEMAN, D.-DU BOIS.  DIVERTIMENTO (1927/1974)               SD
   FL,CL,HN,VA,PF
RUYNEMAN, D.  REFLEXIONS #3 (1960-61).  FL,VN,VA,VC,PF         SD
SAMUEL-ROUSSEAU.  BERGERS ET MAGES.  OB,BSN,VN,VC,PF           HEU
SAUGUET, H.  PRES DU BAL.  FL,CL,BSN,VN,PF                     EDS
SCARLATTI, A.-ROY.  SONATA IN A MA.  2FL,2VN,BC                HMO
SCHICKHARDT, J.  SONATA, OP 5/2.  FL,2OB,VC,BC                 OX
SCHICKHARDT, T.-PETER.  3 SONATAS.  FL,2OB,VC,PF              MR
SCHMIDT, F.  QUINTET IN A MA.  CL,VN,VA,VC,PF                  JOW
SCHMIDT, F.  QUINTET IN B FL MA.  CL,VN,VA,VC,PF               JOW
SCHOENBERG, A.-WEBERN.  KAMMERSYMPHONIE, OP  9                UE
   FL,CL,VN,VC,PF
SCHWEIZER, K.  KAMMERMUSIK (1971).  FL,EHN,VN,VC,HPCD          B&N
SHIFRIN, L.  SERENADE.  OB,CL,HN,VA,PF                         PET
SHIFRIN, S.  IN EIUS MEMORIAM.  FL,CL,VN,VC,PF                 PET
SOLLBERGER, H.  RIDING THE WIND I.  FL,CL,VN,VC,PF            ACA
SOLLBERGER, H.  SOLOS.  FL,CL,VN,HN,PF                         M&M
SPITZMULLER, A.  DIVERTIMENTO, OP  6.  2VN,VA,BSN,PF          UE
STEVENS, H.  QUINTET.  FL,VN,VA,VC,PF                          AMC
TAUB, B.  EXTREMITIES (QUINTET III).  FL/PIC,CL/BCL,VN,VC,PF   ACA
TELEMANN, G.-SEIFFERT.  QUARTET IN D MI.  BSN,2FL,VC,PF        BRH
TROMBLY, P.  WINDMILLS OF PARIS, THE (1976).  FL,CL,VN,VC,PF   ACA
VAILLANT, R.  DE-CI, DE-LA.  FL,VN,VA,VC,PF                    EMT
VAUCLAIN, C.  SUITE FOR YOUTH.  FL,CL,VN,VC,PF                 PI
VERRALL, J.  INTRODUCTION, VARIATIONS & ADAGIO (1974)         ACA
   FL,OB,VN,VC,P F
VIERU, A.  CRIBLE D'ERATOSTHENE (1969).  CL,VN,VA,VC,PF        EDS
VIVALDI, A.  CONCERTO IN C MA, F. XII/24.  FL,OB,VN,BSN,HPCD   RC
VIVALDI, A.  CONCERTO IN C MA, F. XII/30.  FL,OB,2VN,HPCD      RC
VIVALDI, A.  CONCERTO IN C MA, P 81.  FL,OB,2VN,BC            MR
VIVALDI, A.-RAMPAL.  CONCERTO IN C MA, P 82.  FL,OB,VN,BSN,PF  INT
VIVALDI, A.  CONCERTO IN C MA, P 82.  FL,OB,VN,BSN,BC         MR
VIVALDI, A.  CONCERTO IN D MA, F. XII/25.  FL,OB,VN,BSN,HPCD   RC
VIVALDI, A.  CONCERTO IN D MA, F. XII/29 (LA PASTORELLA)       RC
   FL,OB,VN,B SN,HPCD
VIVALDI, A.  CONCERTO IN D MA, F. XII/9 (DEL GARDELLINO)       RC
   FL,OB,VN,B SN,HPCD
VIVALDI, A.  CONCERTO IN D MA, P155.  FL,OB,BSN,VN,BC         MR
VIVALDI, A.  CONCERTO IN F MA, F. XII/26.  FL,OB,VN,BSN,HPCD   RC
VIVALDI, A.-RAMPAL.  CONCERTO IN F MA, P323.  FL,OB,VN,BSN,PF  INT
VIVALDI, A.  CONCERTO IN F MA, P323.  FL,OB,BSN,VN,BC         MR
VIVALDI, A.  CONCERTO IN G MA, F. XII/13.  FL,OB,VN,BSN,BC     RC
VIVALDI, A.  CONCERTO IN G MA, P105.  FL,OB,VN,BSN,BC         MR
VIVALDI, A.-GHEDINI.  CONCERTO IN G MI                        INT
   FL,OB,BSN,VN,PF,VC & DB AD LI B
VIVALDI, A.  CONCERTO IN G MI, F. XII/6.  FL,OB,VN,BSN,HPCD    RC
VIVALDI, A.  CONCERTO IN G MI, P342.  FL,BSN,2VN,BC          MR
VIVALDI, A.  CONCERTO IN G MI, P360.  FL,OB,BSN,VN,BC         MR
VIVALDI, A.-LASOCKI.  CONCERTO IN G MI, P403.  FL,OB,VN,BSN,BC MR
VIVALDI, A.-RAMPAL.  CONCERTO IN G MI, P403.  FL,OB,VN,BSN,PF  INT
VIVALDI, A.-GHEDINI.  SONATA IN D MA.  FL,VN,BSN,VC (DB),PF    INT
WEIGEL, E.  QUINTET.  CL,VN,VA,VC,PF                           AMC
WEIGL, V.  NEW ENGLAND SUITE.  FL(VN),CL,VC,HN,PF             ACA
WENDEL, E.  INTERFERENZE.  CL,VN,VA,VC,PF                      HG
WERNER, G.-MODER.  CONCERTO A 4.  FL,2VN,VC,HPCD             LDO
WIDDOES, L.  FROM A TIME OF SNOW (1970).  FL,CL,VN,VC,PF       BOW
WIDOR, C.  SERENADE, OP 10.  FL,PF,VN,VC,HARMONIUM           HAM
```

5 PARTS: WOODWIND-STRING-KEYBOARD-536

```
WILLIAMSON, M.   SERENADE.  FL,VN,VA,VC,PF                    JOW
WILSON, T.   CONCERTO DA CAMERA.  FL,OB,VN,VC,PF             CA
WOOD, H.   QUINTET, OP 9 (1967).  CL,VN,VC,HN,PF            CHE
WUORINEN, C.   CONCERTANTE III.  OB,VN,VA,VC,HPCD           M&M
ZELJENKA, I.   KLAVIRNE KVINTETO (1956).  CL,VN,VA,VC,PF    SHF
```

5 PARTS: WOODWIND-BRASS-STRING-KEYBOARD-537

```
BRANDON, S.   PIECE FOR 5 (1976).  2CL,VC,TRB,PF                    MAN
FELDMAN, M.   PROJECTION II (1951).  FL,VN,VC,TPT,PF               PET
GLICK, S.   DANCE CONCERTANTE #2 (1964).  FL,CL,TPT,VC,PF          CAN
HENDERSON.   CAPRICCIO (1966).  ASAX,VN,2TRB,PF                    WI
HINDEMITH, P.   3 STUCKE (1925).  CL,TPT,VN,DB,PF                  SCH
KLAMI, U.   RAGTIME.  CL,TPT,2VN,PF                                FIN
KRAUZE, Y.   MUSICIANS, THE & THE DRUMMER (1973)                   HMO
   OB/EHN,CL/ASAX/BASS ET HN,TPT,VC,PF
LINIKE, J.-MINTER.   SONATA "MORATORIUM" A 5.  FL,OB,VN,TPT,BC     MR
PERUTI, C.   ENDGAME.  2CL,VC,TRB,PF                               MAN
STEWART, R.   5 MOVEMENTS.  BSN,FL,FLUGELHORN,DB,PF                ACA
WECKMANN, M.   SONATA A 4.  OB,VN,TRB,BSN,BC                       MR
```

5 PARTS INCLUDING HARP-538

```
ABSIL, J.   CONCERT A CINQ, OP 38 (1939).  FL,VN,VA,VC,HP          CBD
ANDERBERG, C.   HOSTENS HOKAR.  CL,BSN,VN,VC,HP                    EMF
ANDERSON, T.   SET IV.  FL,OB,CL,TRB,HP                            ACA
BADINGS, H.   CAPRICCIO.  FL,VN,VA,VC,HP                           SD
BOEHNLEIN, F.   ETHEREAT.  FL,VN,VC,HP,PF                          MAN
BREDOW, E.   5 APHORISMEN.  FL,OB,CL,BSN,HP                        SIM
BROWN, R.   PARTITA "WICKED POLLY".  FL,OB,CL,BSN,HP               WI
CRAS, J.   QUINTETTE.  FL,VN,VA,VC,HP                              EDS
DAMASE, J.   QUINTET.  FL,VN,VA,VC,HP                              HLE
DANDELOT, G.   QUINTETTE.  FL,VN,VA,VC,HP                          EFM
DEMARQUEZ, S.   SONATINA.  FL,VN,VA,VC,HP                          EMT
DENISOV, E.   ROMANTISCHE MUSIK.  OB,VN,VA,VC,HP                   UE
DINERSTEIN, N.   SERENADE (1963).  OB,CL,VN,VC,HP                  CAN
FAITH, R.   QUINTET.  FL,CL,VN,VC,HP                               MAN
FARINAS, C.   IN RERUM NATURA.  CL,VN,VC,HP,PERC                   EDT
FRANCAIX, J.   QUINTET.  FL,VN,VA,VC,HP                            SCH
HOVHANESS, A.   WORLD BENEATH THE SEA(II), THE, OP133/2            PET
   CL,DB,HP,2PE RC
HOVHANESS, A.   WORLD BENEATH THE SEA, THE, OP133/1               PET
   SAX,VIB,HP,2PERC
HUGON, G.   PRELUDE A 4 EGLOGUES DE VIRGIL.  FL,CL,HN,HP,PF        EFM
INDY, V. D'.   SUITE EN PARTIES.  FL,VN,VA,VC,HP                   HEU
JOLIVET, A.   CHANT DE LINOS.  FL,VN,VA,VC,HP(PF)                  ALE
JONGEN, J.   CONCERT FOR 5, OP 71.  FL,VN,VA,VC,HP                 HE
KALMAR, L.   TRIANGOLI.  CL,VN,VC,HN,HP                            EMB
KELEMEN, M.   RADIANT.  FL,VA,PF,HP,PERC                           PET
KOHN, K.   CAPRICCIOS.  FL,CL,VC,PF,HP                             CF
KUEGERL, H.   QUINTET.  FL,VN,VA,VC,HP                             LK
LAJTHA, L.   MARIONNETTES.  FL,VN,VA,VC,HP                         EDS
LAJTHA, L.   QUINTET #2, OP 46.  FL,VN,VA,VC,HP                    ALE
LAZAROF, H.   TEMPI CONCERTATI.  FL,PF,HPCD,HP,CEL                 GS
```

5 PARTS INCLUDING HARP-538

LESUR, D. SUITE MEDIEVALE. FL,VN,VA,VC,HP   DUR
LIEDBECK, S. FANTASI. OB,FL,VN,VC,HP   EMF
LOUCHEUR, R. 4 PIECES EN QUINTETTE. FL,VN,VA,VC,HP   EFM
MAKLAKIEWICZ, T. QUINTET. FL,2CL,BSN,HP   PWM
MALEC, I. MINIATURES POUR LEWIS CARROLL (1964)   HG
   FL/PIC,VN,HP,2PERC
MALIPIERO, G. SONATA A CINQUE. FL,VN,VA,VC,HP   RC
MANEN, C. QUINTET. FL,VN,VA,VC,HP   HLE
MARTTINEN, T. ILMATAR, ILMAN IMPI. PIC,BSN,HP,VIB,PERC   FIN
MONNIKENDAM, M. SUITE IN C MA (1960). FL,OB,CL,BSN,HP   SD
MUSGRAVE, T. SERENADE. FL,CL,VA,VC,HP   CHE
PETRIC, I. NUANCES EN COULEUR. FL/PIC,BSN,VC,PF,HP   EDD
PIERNE, G. VARIATIONS AU CLAIR DE LUNE. FL,VN,VA,VC,HP   HLE
PIERNE, G. VARIATIONS LIBRE ET FINAL. FL,VN,VA,VC,HP   EDS
PIERNE, G. VOYAGE AU PAYS DU TENDRE. FL,VN,VA,VC,HP   ALE
PILLOIS, J. 5 HAI-KAI. FL,VN,VA,VC,HP   DUR
RIETI, V. CONCERTO. FL,VA,VC,HP,HPCD   EMO
ROCCA. STORIELLA. BSN,2TPT,PF,HP   RC
ROPARTZ, J. PRELUDE, MARINE ET CHANSONS. FL,VN,VA,VC,HP   DUR
ROSLAVETZ, N. NOCTURNE. OB,2VA,VC,HP   M&M
ROTA, N. QUINTET. FL,OB,VA,VC,HP   RC
ROUSSEL, A. SERENADE, OP 30. FL,VN,VA,VC,HP   DUR
SCARLATTI, D.-FRANCAIX. 5 SONATAS. FL,VN,VA,VC,HP   EMT
SCHMITT, F. SUITE EN ROCAILLE, OP 84. FL,VN,VA,VC,HP   DUR
SCHUBERT, F.-FRANCAIX. 6 IMPROMPTUS ET MOMENTS MUSICALS   EMT
   FL,VN,VA,VC,HP
SMIT, L. QUINTET (1928). FL,VN,VA,VC,HP   SD
STALVEY, D. POINTS, LINES, CIRCLES (1968-69)   EDS
   CL,DB,GUIT,HP,PERC
TAKEMITSU, T. BRYCE (1976). FL,2HP,MAR,PERC   EDS
THILMAN, J. OSTINATI. FL,VA,VC,HP,PERC   PET
THORARINSSON, L. KADENSAR. OB,CL,BCL,BSN,HP   M&M
TOCCHI, G. ARLECCHINO. FL,CL,VN,VA,HP   CAR
TOURNIER, M. SUITE. FL,VN,VA,VC,HP   HLE
VILLA-LOBOS, H. QUINTET. FL,VN,VA,VC,HP   EME
ZAGWIJN, H. NOCTURNE (1918). FL,EHN,CL,BSN,HP   SD
ZAGWIJN, H. QUINTET (1954). FL,VN,VA,VC,HP   SD

5 PARTS INCLUDING GUITAR-539

AGER, K. METABOLES II (1977). CL,ASAX,VN,PF,GUIT   EMO
BARTOLOZZI, B. CONCERTAZIONI (1965). OB,VA,DB,GUIT,PERC   ESZ
BUHE, K. EUROPAISCHE VOLKS-UND TANZWEISEN   SCH
   FL,ACC,GUIT,DB,PERC
BUHE, K. VOLKS-UND TANZWEISEN AUS AMERIKA   SCH
   FL,ACC,GUIT,DB,PERC
FARINAS, C. TIENTO I. BCL,PF,GUIT,2PERC   EDT
FELD, J. CAPRICCIO (1964). FL,OB,CL,BSN,GUIT   PAN
FERRITTO, J. DIFFUSIONE (1964). BCL,VN,DB,GUIT,PERC   ACA
FINNISSY, M. LOST LANDS (1977). E FL CL,SSAX,VN,PF,GUIT   EMO
HASELBACH, J. OUT-SIDE (1976). FL,CL,VA,VC,GUIT   S-V
HAYDN, F. ZINGARESE #1, #6, #8. CL,2VN,DB,GUIT   BOS
HESPOS, H. EINANDER - BEDINGENDES   GBV
   FL/PIC,CL/E FL CL,GUIT,TSAX,VA
HESPOS, H. FROTTAGES. ASAX,VC,HP,PERC,MANDOLINE   EMC
KRAFT, K. MUSIK UNTERM FENSTER, OP 14. 2VN,CL,DB,LUTE   ABS
MARSHALL, N. SUITE. FL,CL,VN,VC,GUIT   S&C
REGT, H. DE. MUSICA, OP 11. FL,VA,VC,GUIT,PERC   SD

5 PARTS INCLUDING GUITAR-539

```
SILVERMAN, S.  CREPUSCULE.  CL,VN,DB,2GUIT              BE
SINGER, L.  MEMORY, A (1966).  OB,VA,VC,GUIT,PERC       ESZ
SPINNER, L.  QUINTET, OP 14.  CL,HN,BSN,DB,GUIT         BH
STALVEY, D.  POINTS, LINES, CIRCLES (1968-69)          EDS
   CL,DB,GUIT,HP,PERC
STERNBERG (ARR).  VARIATIONS ON GERMAN FOLK SONGS, 2 VOLS    DEU
   CL(SAX),DB ,GUIT,PF,PERC
SUSSMAYR, F.-RAGOSSNIG/MEIER.  GUITAR QUINTET IN C MA   SCH
   OB,VN,VA,VC,GUIT
SYDEMAN, W.  MUSIC.  FL,VA,GUIT,2PERC                   PET
WELIN, K.  RENOVATIONES (1960).  FL,VN,VC,PERC,MANDOLINE    EDT
```

5 PARTS INCLUDING PERCUSSION-540

```
ADAMIS, M.  ANAKYKLESIS (1964).  FL,OB,VA,VC,CEL        EMO
AGER, K.  I REMEMBER A BIRD (1976).  CL,TRB,PF,PERC,TAPE    EMO
AMRAM, D.  DISCUSSIONS.  FL,VC,2PERC,PF                 PET
ASTOLI, B. D'.  IMAGENES.  FL,TRB,PF,VC,PERC            BAR
BARNES, M.  MASQUE OF RED DEATH, THE.  OB,VA,VC,HPCD,PERC   CAN
BARTOLOZZI, B.  CONCERTAZIONI (1965).  OB,VA,DB,GUIT,PERC   ESZ
BECKER, G.  ANKLANGE/REMINISCENCES.  FL,VN,VC,PF,PERC   HG
BENGUEREL, K.  ARGUMENTS (1966).  FL,CL,VN,PF,VIB       SS
BLICKHAN, T.  QUINTET.  AFL,VA,TRB,PF,PERC              SS
BLOCK, S.  PUTTIN' IT TOGETHER.  2SAX,2DB,DRUM SET      ACA
BLOMDAHL, K.  DANS-SVIT NR 1.  FL,VN,VA,VC,PERC         EMF
BOLCOM, W.  SESSION III.  E FL CL,VN,VC,PF,PERC         TP
BUHE, K.  EUROPAISCHE VOLKS-UND TANZWEISEN              SCH
   FL,ACC,GUIT,DB,PERC
CABUS, P.  TREDECIM.  4CL,PERC                          MAU
CARMEL, D.  FRACTIONS.  FL,TPT,VC,PF,VIB                IMP
CHIHARA, P.  CEREMONY I.  OB,2VC,DB,PERC                PET
CHIHARA, P.  WILLOW, WILLOW.  FL,TU,3PERC               PET
CHRISTLIEB, D. (ARR).  4 PIECES.  2OB,EHN,BSN,SDR       CP
COPE, D.  VORTEX.  FL,TRB,PF,CEL,PERC                   AB
COWELL, H.  26 SIMULTANEOUS MOSAICS.  CL,VN,VC,PF,PERC  PET
DE YOUNG, L.  CHAMBER MUSIC.  OB,BSN,SAX,VIB,PF         SS
DENISOV, E.  CONCERTO.  FL,OB,PF,TIMP,PERC              UE
DESPORTES.  SONATE POUR UN BAPTEME.  FL,ASAX,EHN,PF,PERC    BIL
EHLE, R.  5 PIECES FOR INSTRUMENTS WITH PREPARED ELECTRONICS    CF
   CL,VN, PF,PERC,TAPE
FARINAS, C.  IN RERUM NATURA.  CL,VN,VC,HP,PERC         EDT
FARINAS, C.  TIENTO I.  BCL,PF,GUIT,2PERC               EDT
FELDMAN, M.  INSTRUMENTS I.  AFL,OB,TRB,CEL,PERC        UE
FERRITTO, J.  CONCERTINO, OP 15.  OB,ASAX,DB,2PERC      ACA
FERRITTO, J.  DIFFUSIONE.  BCL,VN,DB,GUIT,PERC          ACA
FISCHER, A.  TIME PRISMS.  SOP SAX,TSAX,BAR SAX,PF,VIB  SS
FLEMING, R.  INDIAN LEGEND (1967).  FL,OB,BSN,PF,PERC   CAN
FODI, J.  SIGNALS, OP 22 (1969).  SOP SAX,TSAX,TRB,PF,PERC   CAN
FORTNER, J.  FLOW CHART I - APRES JONAS 5:5            EV
   CL,BSN,TPT,TRB,PERC
FOX, F.  VARIABLES 6.  FL,CL,VN,VC,PERC                 SS
GEHLHAAR, R.  HELIX (1967).  SAX,TRB,DB,PF,PERC         FEE
GIRON, A.  VIAS.  FL,CL,VC,PF,PERC                      CF
GRAHN, U.  THIS REMINDS ME OF... (1972).  FL,CL,HN,TRB,PERC  STI
HANSEN, T.  COLLAGE.  2FL,OB,CL,VIB                     SS
HARRISON, L.  PRAISE FOR THE BEAUTY OF HUMMINGBIRDS     SN
   FL,2VN,CEL,PERC
HARTWELL, H.  MATINEE D'IVRESSE (1966).  CL,VN,VC,PF,PERC    CAN
```

```
HEIDEN, B.  4 MOVEMENTS (1976).  SOP SAX,ASAX,              S EQM
HEININEN, P.  QUINTETTO (1961).  FL,SAX,PF,VIB,PERC           MT
HENZE, H.  AMICIZIA.  CL,TRB,VC,PF,PERC                       SCH
HEUSSENSTAMM, G.  TETRALOGUE, OP 36.  E FL CL,CL,ACL,BCL,PERC  WI
HOBSON, B.  QUINTET (1970).  FL,VN,HN,VC,MAR                  B-B
HOLEWA, H.  KVINTETT (1962).  CL,VC,TRB,PF,PERC               EMF
HOLM, M.  PHILEMON & BAUCIS, OP 16.  PIC,FL,TPT,CEL,PERC      WH
HOLT, S. TEN.  DIFFERENTIES (1969).  3CL,PF,VIB              SD
HOVHANESS, A.  BURNING HOUSE OVERTURE, THE, OP185A.  FL,4PERC  PET
HOVHANESS, A.  WORLD BENEATH THE SEA (II), THE, OP133/2      PET
   CL,DB,HP,2P ERC
HOVHANESS, A.  WORLD BENEATH THE SEA, THE, OP133/1          PET
   SAX,VIB,HP,2PERC
IVES, C.  SEER, THE.  E FL CL,TPT,BAR,PF,PERC                AMP
KAUFMANN, A.  4 PIECES, OP 77.  CL,VN,VC,DB,PERC             LDO
KELEMEN, M.  RADIANT.  FL,VA,PF,HP,PERC                      PET
KORTE, K.  SYMMETRICS.  SAX,4PERC                            SS
KUCERA, V.  DIPTYCHON (1966).  FL,BCL,PF,2PERC               ES
LANZA, A.  ACUFENOS I (1966-III)                             BH
   TRB SOLO,FL/PIC,CL/E FL CL,VIB,PF
LAZAROF, H.  TEMPI CONCERTATI.  FL,PF,HPCD,HP,CEL            GS
LINDA, B.  MUSICA PER SYLVANUM.  FL,BSN,VN,HN,XYL            EMF
MALEC, I.  MINIATURES POUR LEWIS CARROLL (1964)             HG
   FL/PIC,VN,HP,2PERC
MAMANGAKIS, N.  KONSTRUKTIONEN (1958).  2FL,3PERC            EMO
MARTTINEN, T.  ILMATAR, ILMAN IMPI.  PIC,BSN,HP,VIB,PERC     FIN
MAYER, W.  MESSAGES.  FL,VN,VA,VC,PERC                       TP
MERCURE, P.  TETRACHROMIE (1963)                            CAN
   CL,ASAX,BCL,PERC,ELECTRONICS
MIEREANU, C.  PLANETARIUM I (1975).  2FL,TRB,PF,VIB          EDS
MILLNAS, A.  PER CASO.  ASAX,TRB,VN,DB,PERC                  EDT
MILLS, C.  PAUL BUNYAN JUMP.  ASAX,TPT,PF,DB,DR              ACA
MIROGLIO, F.  PHASES.  FL,PF,3PERC                           UE
NODA, T.  QUINTETTO (MATTINATA).  3FL,DB,MAR                 TP
OLAVIDE, G. DE.  COMPOSICION (1963).  FL,CL,VN,VC,VIB        EEC
PAUL, B.  SERENADE.  FL,CL,VA,VC,VIB                         HSM
PENNISI, F.  QUINTETTO IN 4 PARTI (1965).  FL,TPT,TRB,PF,PERC  ESZ
PETRASSI, G.  SERENATA (1958).  FL,VA,DB,HPCD,PERC           ESZ
POLOLANIK, Z.  MUSICA CONCISA (1963).  FL,BCL,PERC,HPCD,PF   ART
PUSZTAI, T.  EPISODES (1975).  3FL/AFL/PIC,2PERC             MAR
RABE, F.  IMPROMPTU 1962.  BCL,TRB,VC,PF,PERC               EMF
RABE, F.  IMPROMPTU.  CL/BCL,TRB,VC,PF,PERC                 NOR
REGT, H. DE.  MUSICA, OP 11.  FL,VA,VC,GUIT,PERC            SD
REIF, P.  QUINTET.  CL,VA,PF,PERC,TAPE                      AB
ROUSSAKIS, N.  CONCERTINO.  FL,OB,CL,BSN,PERC               AB
RYTTERKVIST, H.  TRE SATIRER.  CL/BCL,VIB,XYL,PF,VC         EMF
SCHNITTKE, A.  SERENADE.  CL,VN,DB,PERC,PF                  UE
SCHRODER, H.  MUSIK IN 7 SATZEN.  OB,3VN,DR                 MRL
SCHUDEL, T.  DIVERTIMENTO #1.  FL,OB,VN,VC,PERC             CAN
SEMERAK, O.  KAMMERMUSIK (1966).  FL,BCL,VN,TRB,PERC        CHF
SHEPPARD, J.  BITTER ICE.  SAX,TPT,PF,DB,PERC               SS
SIMONIS, J.  SUGGESTIONS, OP 20/2 (1970).  FL,4PERC         CBD
SINGER, L.  MEMORY, A (1966).  OB,VA,VC,GUIT,PERC           ESZ
STALVEY, D.  POINTS, LINES, CIRCLES (1968-69)              EDS
   CL,DB,GUIT,HP,PERC
STEDRON, M.  VIA CRUCIS (STAZIONI DI VARSAVIA 1944)        PAN
   FL,BCL,PF,HPCD, PERC
STERNBERG (ARR).  VARIATIONS ON GERMAN FOLK SONGS, 2 VOLS   DEU
   CL(SAX),DB ,GUIT,PF,PERC
STOUT, A.  SUITE, OP 73/1.  FL/AFL,4PERC                    PET
STROUD, R.  QUINTET.  CL,4PERC                              SS
SYDEMAN, W.  MUSIC.  FL,VA,GUIT,2PERC                       PET
```

5 PARTS INCLUDING PERCUSSION-540

```
SYDEMAN, W.  QUINTET.  HN(TRB),PF,PERC,DB                          CL
TAIRA, Y.  PENTALPHA.  AFL,CL,DB,MAR,PERC                          ERR
TAKEMITSU, T.  BRYCE (1976).  FL,2HP,MAR,PERC                      EDS
TAKEMITSU, T.  WAVES (1976).  CL,HN,2TRB,DR                        EDS
TANENBAUM, E.  CHAMBER PIECE #1.  FL,CL,VC,PF,PERC                 ACA
TANENBAUM, E.  WORDS OR BLUES FOR US.  ASAX,DB,VIB,PERC,TAPE       ACA
TAUSINGER, J.  DE REBUS MUSICALIBUS (1967)                        CHF
    FL,BCL,PF,VIB,PERC
THILMAN, J.  OSTINATI.  FL,VA,VC,HP,PERC                           PET
THOMAS, C.  ILLUMINATIONS (1976).  CL,VN,VA,VC,PERC               AMC
TILLIS, F.  QUINTET (1962).  FL,OB,CL,BSN,PERC                     SN
WASHBURN, G.  PASSACAGLIA.  OB(CL),TPT,VC,PF,PERC                  SS
WASHBURN, G.  QUINTETT II.  2BAR SAX,2PERC,TAPE                    SS
WELIN, K.  RENOVATIONES (1960).  FL,VN,VC,PERC,MANDOLINE           EDT
WIDMER, E.  COCO 1961 (DIVERTIMENTO #3).  FL,CL,HN,PF,PERC         HEI
WILKINSON, M.  VARIANTS OF GLASS.  PIC,FL,OB,2PERC                 UE
ZONN, P.  ONE SLOW TURN OF THE WORLD                              ACA
    FL/PIC,OB,CL/BCL,DB,PERC
```

5 PARTS INCLUDING RECORDER-542

```
FINGER, G.-HOLMAN.  2 SONATAS, # 3 IN G MI & # 4 IN F MA           NOM
    2OB,2REC,BC
KELLER, G.  SONATA IN C.  2OB,2REC,BC                             NOM
KELLER, G.-LASOCKI/MADDEN.  SONATA IN G MA.  2REC,2OB,BC          NOM
LOEILLET, J.-ERMELER.  QUINTET IN B MI.  2FL,2REC,BC             B&N
MILLS, C.  PIECE.  FL,REC,VN,VA,VC                                ACA
SCHICKHARDT, J.  SONATAS.  REC,2OB(2FL),VC,PF,VC AD LIB          PET
VIVALDI, A.  CONCERTO IN D MA, P201.  REC,OB,VN,BSN,BC           MR
VIVALDI, A.  CONCERTO IN D MA, P204.  REC,OB,VN,BSN,VC           MR
VIVALDI, A.-LASOCKI.  CONCERTO IN G MA.  AREC,OB,VN,BSN,BC       HMP
```

5 PARTS INCLUDING TAPE-543

```
AGER, K.  I REMEMBER A BIRD (1976).  CL,TRB,PF,PERC,TAPE          EMO
BERLIN, D.  3 MIXTURES.  4BSN,TAPE                                MAN
BOTTJE, W.  MODALITIES.  4SAX,TAPE                                ACA
BOTTJE, W.  SYMBIOSIS.  FL,AFL,CL,VC,TAPE                         ACA
BRANDON, S.  TRIO DA CAMERA.  OB,CL,TSAX,PF,TAPE                 MAN
CLAFLIN, A.  PASTORAL- THE ORIOLE.  2FL,2CL,TAPE                  ACA
DAVIDOVSKY, M.  SYNCHRONISMS #2 (1964).  FL,CL,VN,VC,TAPE        M&M
EHLE, R.  5 PIECES FOR INSTRUMENTS WITH PREPARED ELECTRONICS      CF
    CL,VN, PF,PERC,TAPE
FENNELLY, B.  EVANESCENCES.  AFL,CL,VN,VC,TAPE                    ACA
HELLERMANN, W.  COLUMBUS CIRLE.  3WW,PF,ELECTRONICS               ACA
MERCURE, P.  TETRACHROMIE (1963)                                 CAN
    CL,ASAX,BCL,PERC,ELECTRONICS
OTT, J.  AEOLIAN HARP.  FL,CL,VN,VC,TAPE                          CBP
REIF, P.  QUINTET.  CL,VA,PF,PERC,TAPE                            AB
SCHWARTZ, E.  ECHO MUSIC II (1974).  FL,OB,CL,BSN,TAPE           AMC
SUBOTNICK, M.  SERENADE #3.  FL,CL,VN,PF,TAPE                    BOW
TANENBAUM, E.  WORDS OR BLUES FOR US.  ASAX,DB,VIB,PERC,TAPE     ACA
WASHBURN, G.  QUINTET II.  2BAR SAX,2PERC,TAPE                   SS
```

6 CLARINETS-604

LETELLIER, R. PIECE RECREATIVE   EDR

6 SAXOPHONES-608

BACH, J.C.-AXWORTHY. SYMPHONY #2   DOR
  SOP SAX,2ASAX,TSAX,BAR SAX,BASS SAX(BAR SAX)
DALLIN, L. AUBADE IN BLUE   BE
DVORAK, A.-JOHNSON. MOVEMENT #1 (SERENADE, OP 44)   RU
GOMEZ, A.-JOHNSON. IL GUARANY   RU
GUILMANT, A.-TAYLOR. CANTILENE PASTORALE   BE
  3ASAX,2TSAX,BAR SAX
HAYDN, F.-JOHNSON. MOVEMENT #3 (SYMPHONY #100)   RU
JOHNSON, W. CONCERT OVERTURE   BE
KRAMER, M. LAWD   MC
MASSENET, J.-JOHNSON. PHEDRE OVERTURE   RU
NASH, R. IMPRESSIONS   SF
OSTRANSKY, L. 3 PIECES   RU
OSTRANSKY, L. POEM & DANCE   RU
PUTSCHE', T. THEME SONG & VARIATIONS. 6SAX   SS
SWEELINCK, J.-AXWORTHY. ANGELUS AD PASTORES AIT   DOR
  2SOP SAX,ASAX,TSAX,BAR SAX,BASS SAX
TCHAIKOVSKY-TALLMADGE, I. SAXOPHONE SEXTET #1 (SWAN LAKE)   BE
WALTERS, H. MOONRISE   RU

6 PARTS: WOODWINDS
INCLUDING HORN-621

ACKER, D. ATTITUDEN (1968/71). 2CL,2HN,2BSN   HG
ADLER, S. 7 EPIGRAMS. 2FL,OB,CL,BCL,BSN   OX
ALLERS, H. ELEGIE UND CAPRICCIO. 2CL,2HN,2BSN   MV
ALLERS, H. SUITE. FL,OB,CL,2HN,BSN   MV
ALTMANN, E. KLEINE TANZSUITE. FL,OB,CL,2HN,BSN   FRH
AMY, G. ALPHA-BETH. FL,OB,CL,BCL,BSN,HN   HEU
BASSETT, L. WIND MUSIC. FL,OB,CL,ASAX,HN,BSN   EV
BEERMAN, B. FRAME. 6FL   SO
BEETHOVEN, L. VAN-LELOIR. MARCHE DES GRENADIERS   BIL
  2CL,2HN,2BSN
BEETHOVEN, L. VAN. MARSCH IN B FL MA. 2CL,2HN,2BSN   BRH
BEETHOVEN, L. VAN-KAHN. MINUET & MARCH. 2CL,2BSN,2HN   EM
BEETHOVEN, L. VAN. SEXTET IN E FL MA, OP 71. 2CL,2BSN,2HN   BRH
BEETHOVEN, L. VAN. SEXTET IN E FL MA, OP 71. 2CL,2BSN,2HN   INT
BEETHOVEN, L. VAN. SEXTET, OP 71. 2CL,2BSN,2HN   EDK
BEETHOVEN, L. VAN. SEXTET, OP 71. 2CL,2BSN,2HN   HI
BENES, J. INTERMEZZO. 6FL   SHF
BOER, J. DE. ELEMENTS (1978-79). 6FL   SD
BOZZA, E. LUCIOLES. E FL CL,2CL,BASSET HN,BCL,CBCL   ALE
BRAUN, R. AIR FROM ERIN, AN. FL,CL,CL(ASAX),CL,CL(TSAX),CL   YM
BRAUN, R. ANGEVIN CAROL. FL,CL,CL(ASAX),CL,CL(TSAX),CL   YM

6 PARTS: WOODWINDS INCLUDING HORN-621

```
BRIXI, F.   INTERMEZZO.   2HN,2BSN,2EHN                              CHF
CADOW, P.   PASTORALE IM ALTEN STIL.   2OB,EHN,2BSN,HN               PGM
CARMICHAEL, H.-KLICKMANN.   STAR DUST.   FL,OB,2CL,HN,BSN            BE
CASTIL-BLAZE, F.   SEXTET #1 IN E FL MA.   2CL,2BSN,2HN              MR
CHAGRIN, F.   7 PETITES PIECES.   PIC,FL,OB,CL,HN,BSN                NO
CHILDS, B.   INTERBALANCES V.   FL,OB,CL,ASAX,BSN,HN                 ACA
DANZI, F.-WOJCIECHOWSKI.   SEXTET IN E FL MA.   2CL,2BSN,2HN         HSM
DAVIES, P.   ALMA REDEMPTORIS MATER.   FL,OB,2CL,BSN,HN              S&C
DRUSCHETZKY, G.   PARTITA IN E FL MA.   2CL,2BSN,2HN                 EK
DRUSCHETZKY, G.   SESTETTO.   2CL,2BSN,2HN                           SCH
DUBOIS, P.   SINFONIA DA CAMERA.   FL,OB,CL,ASAX(CL),BSN,HN          ALE
FROSCHAUER, H.   SEXTET.   FL,OB,2CL,BSN,HN                          LDO
GAN, N.   SUITE (CHILDREN'S PICTURES).   FL,OB,2CL,BSN,HN            MKE
GENZMER, H.   SEXTET.   2CL,2BSN,2HN                                 LIT
GIEFER, W.   DISKONTINUUM (1974).   2CL,2BSN,2HN                     HG
GOSSEC, F.   CHASSE DE CHANTILLY, LA.   2CL,2HN,2BSN                 HEU
HARTLEY, W.   CHAMBER MUSIC (1959-60).   ASAX,FL,OB,CL,BSN,HN        CRE
HAYDN, F.-LANDON.   DIVERTIMENTO #1, HOB II: 15.   2OB,2BSN,2HN      LDO
HAYDN, F.-LANDON.   DIVERTIMENTO #2, HOB II: 23.   2OB,2BSN,2HN      LDO
HAYDN, F.-LANDON.   DIVERTIMENTO #3, HOB II: 7.   2OB,2BSN,2HN       LDO
HAYDN, F.-LANDON.   DIVERTIMENTO #5 IN D MA, HOB II: 18             LDO
   2OB,2BSN,2HN
HAYDN, F.-LANDON.   DIVERTIMENTO #6, HOB II:   3.   2OB,2BSN,2HN     LDO
HAYDN, F.-LANDON.   DIVERTIMENTO #7 IN G MA.   2OB,2BSN,2HN          LDO
HAYDN, F.-LANDON.   DIVERTIMENTO #8 IN D MA.   2OB,2BSN,2HN          LDO
HAYDN, F.-SPIEGEL.   DIVERTIMENTO IN F MA                           OX
   2FL(2OB),2HN(2CL),CL(BSN),B SN
HAYDN, F.-WASTALL.   FELD-PARTHIE IN C MA.   2OB,2HN,2BSN            BH
HAYDN, F.-WASTALL.   FELD-PARTHIE IN F MA.   2OB,2HN,2BSN            BH
HAYDN, F.   MARCHE REGIMENTO DE MARSHALL.   2OB,2HN,2BSN             EAM
HAYDN, F.   PARTHIA IN F MA.   2OB,2HN,2BSN                          GS
HAYDN, M.-RAINER.   DIVERTIMENTO IN D MA.   2OB,2HN,2BSN             LDO
HAZZARD, P.   MUSIC IN COUNTERPOINT.   2FL,2CL,BCL,HN                SS
HEIDEN, B.   INTRADA.   FL,OB,CL,BSN,HN,ASAX                         SO
HENNING, E.   FUGUE.   FL,OB,CL,2BSN,HN                              AMC
HEUSSENSTAMM, G.   SET FOR DOUBLE REEDS.   2OB,2EHN,2BSN             WI
HUMMEL, B.   5 BAGATELLEN.   6CL                                     SIM
JANACEK, L.   MLADI (YOUTH) (1924).   FL,OB,CL,BCL,BSN,HN            ART
JANACEK, L.   MLADI.   FL,OB,CL,BCL,BSN,HN                           INT
JANSSEN, G.   MUSIC (1972).   FL,OB,3CL,BSN                          SD
KABELAC, M.   SEXTETT, OP 8 (1940).   FL,EHN,2CL,BSN,HN              ART
KELTERBORN, R.   MEDITATIONEN.   2CL,2BSN,2HN                        OHN
KLEINSINGER, G.   DESIGN FOR WOODWINDS.   FL,OB,2CL,HN,BSN           AMP
KREJCI, M.   SEXTET.   2CL,BSN,3BASSET HN                            CHF
KROMMER, F.-GUTTE.   PARTITA IN C MI.   2CL,2HN,2BSN                 FRH
KROMMER, F.-MYSLIK.   PARTITA IN C MI.   2CL,2HN,2BSN                ES
KURZBACH, P.   BLASERSEXTETT.   FL,OB,2CL,HN,BSN                     ISR
LAGRENZE, G.   LA BUSCHA.   4OB,2BSN                                 CP
LANCEN, S.   CONCERT A 6.   6CL                                      CHP
LEIBOWITZ, R.   PETITE SUITE, OP 90.   6CL                           B-B
LOCKE, M.   3 WORKS.   2OB,EHN,3BSN                                  CP
LOUCHEUR, R.   EN FAMILLE.   6CL                                     BIL
LULLY, J.   5 WORKS.   2OB,2EHN,2BSN                                 CP
LUNDEN-WELDEN, G.   4 SMABITAR (1976).   2FL,OB,2CL,BSN              STI
LUNDEN, L.   QUADRILLE.   2FL,2CL,BCL(SAX),BSN                       CHE
LUNDEN, L.   QUEEN CHRISTINA'S SONG.   2FL,2CL,BCL(SAX),BSN          CHE
LYONS, G.   PASTORALE.   2FL,4CL                                     EMI
MAC KINNON, R.   SUITE.   2FL,2CL,BCL,BSN                            UNI
MANICKE, D.   SEXTET.   2CL,2HN,2BSN                                 SIM
MARCO, T.   CAR EN EFFET (1971).   3CL,3SAX                          EDS
MELNIK.   CLARINET HOLIDAY.   6CL                                    SF
MILHAUD, D.-STEWART.   SCARAMOUCHE.   ASAX,FL,OB,CL,BSN,HN           EDS
```

```
MISSAL, J.  RONDO CAPRICE.  6FL                                        SO
MOZART, W.-WASTALL.  ADAGIO (SERENADE #11, K375)                       BH
   2CL,2HN,2BSN
MOZART, W.-BREARLEY.  ADAGIO, K516.  FL,OB,2CL,HN,BSN                  HI
MOZART, W.-THILDE.  ANDANTE.  6CL                                      BIL
MOZART, W.-KAHN.  CONTRADANCE IN RONDO FORM.  2OB,2BSN,2HN             EM
MOZART, W.  DIVERTIMENTO # 8 IN F MA, K213.  2OB,2HN,2BSN              BRH
MOZART, W.  DIVERTIMENTO # 9 IN B FL MA, K240.  2OB,2HN,2BSN           BRH
MOZART, W.  DIVERTIMENTO #12 IN E FL MA, K252.  2OB,2HN,2BSN           BRH
MOZART, W.  DIVERTIMENTO #12, K252.  2OB,2BSN,2HN                      EDK
MOZART, W.  DIVERTIMENTO #13 IN F MA, K253.  2OB,2HN,2BSN              BRH
MOZART, W.  DIVERTIMENTO #13, K253.  2OB,2BSN,2HN                      EDK
MOZART, W.  DIVERTIMENTO #14 IN B FL MA, K270.  2OB,2HN,2BSN           BRH
MOZART, W.  DIVERTIMENTO #14, K270.  2OB,2BSN,2HN                      EDK
MOZART, W.  DIVERTIMENTO #16 IN E FL MA, K289.  2OB,2HN,2BSN           BRH
MOZART, W.  DIVERTIMENTO #16, K289.  2OB,2BSN,2HN                      EDK
MOZART, W.-SPIEGEL.  DIVERTIMENTO IN B FL MA, KV196                    SCH
   2CL,2HN,2BSN,2OB AD LIB
MOZART, W.  DIVERTIMENTO, K213.  2OB,2BSN,2HN                          EDK
MOZART, W.  DIVERTIMENTO, K240.  2OB,2BSN,2HN                          EDK
MOZART, W.-BREARLEY.  MENUETTO & TRIO, K516.  FL,OB,2CL,HN,BSN         HI
MOZART, W.-DE SMET.  ROMANZE, MENUETTO & TRIO.  2OB,2CL,2BSN           HI
MOZART, W.-HAAS.  SERENADE IN E FL MA, K375.  2CL,2BSN,2HN             MR
MOZART, W.-HELLYER.  SERENADE, K375.  2CL,2HN,2BSN                     OX
MOZART, W.-DRUSCHETZKY.  VARIATIONS ON A THEME BY GLUCK, K455          EK
   2CL,2BSN,2HN
NELHYBEL, V.  IMPROMPTUS FOR 6 WOODWINDS.  2FL,OB,2CL,BSN             BT
NORDENSTROM, G.  PALM SPRINGS SEXTET.  FL/PIC,OB,CL,BCL,HN,BSN        B&N
OLIVER, R.  LORD RANDALL.  6CL                                        EDM
PARCHMAN, G.  SEXTET (1966).  FL,OB,CL,2BSN,HN                        SS
PIERNE, G.  PRELUDIO & FUGHETTA, OP 40/1.  2FL,OB,2BSN,CL             EDK
PLEYEL, I.-VOXMAN.  SEXTET IN E FL MA.  2CL,2BSN,2HN                  MR
PROWO, P.  CONCERTO IN D.  2FL,2OB,2BSN                               EDK
PUTSCHE', T.  THEME AND VARIATIONS.  6CL                              SS
RAE, A.  FUN & GAMES (1968).  2FL,OB,2CL,BSN                          CAN
RINGBOM, N.  WIND SEXTET (1959).  OB,EHN,CL,BCL,BSN,HN                MT
ROSETTI, F.  PARTHIA IN B FL MA.  OB,2CL,BSN,2HN                      B&B
ROSETTI, F.  PARTHIA IN D MA.  OB,2CL,BSN,2HN                         B&B
ROSETTI, F.-PAEULER.  PARTITA IN B FL MA.  OB,2CL,2HN,BSN             EUL
ROSSLER-ROSETTI, F.  PARTITA.  2CL,2BSN,2HN                           GZ
SCHAPER, H.  AUFZUG UND FROHLICHER TANZ.  FL,OB,CL,2HN,BSN            MV
SCHROEDER, H.  SEXTET, OP 49 (1975).  2CL,2HN,2BSN                    HG
SCHUBERT, F.  HIRTENMELODIEN (ROSAMUNDE).  2CL,2HN,2BSN               BRH
SCHUBERT, F.-SCHOENBACH.  SHEPHERD MELODY #6 (ROSAMUNDE)              TP
   2OB,2BSN,2H N
SEIBER, M.  SERENADE.  2CL,2BSN,2HN                                   WH
SOCOR, M.  3 SALVIRI.  6WW                                           EMU
STEIN, L.  SEXTET.  ASAX,FL,OB,CL,BSN,HN                              COR
STRAVINSKY, I.-STONE.  NAPOLITANA.  FL,OB,2CL,HN,BSN                  DG
SVENSSON, SVEN.  SEXTET.  FL,OB,CL,BCL,BSN,HN                         EMF
TCHAIKOVSKY, P.-SKINDER.  AUTUMN SONG, OP 37.  OB,3CL,2BSN            PWM
TEMPLETON, A.-RHOADS.  PASSEPIED.  FL,OB,EHN,CL,BCL,BSN               TP
THOMSON, V.  BARCAROLLE.  FL,OB,EHN,CL,BCL,BSN                        GS
TOMASI, H.  PRINTEMPS.  FL,OB,CL,BSN,ASAX,HN                          ALE
TREMBLAY, G.  SEXTET.  FL,OB,CL,BCL,TSAX,BSN                          ACA
TROJAHN, M.  COULEURS DE LA PLUIE, LES.  5FL,AFL                      HSM
VOORN, J.  SUCEVITA CHORALS (1974).  2OB,2CL,BCL,BSN                  SD
VOORTMAN, R.  HEXAPHONIE (1976).  6CL                                 SD
VRANICKY, A.  MARSCHE.  2CL,2HN,2BSN                                  ES
WANHAL, J.  DIVERTIMENTO IN C MA.  2OB,2HN,2BSN                       JB
WATERS, C.  SOLEMN MINUET.  FL,OB,2CL,2BSN                            HI
WEBER, C.M. VON-DOBREE.  ADAGIO & RONDO.  2CL,2HN,2BSN                MR
```

```
WEBER, C.M. VON-SANDNER.  ADAGIO & RONDO.  2CL,2HN,2BSN          SCH
ZAHRADNIK, Z.  STELE.  OB,EHN,CL,BCL,BSN,CBSN                    CHF
ZEHM, F.  MUSICA PASTORALE.  2FL,OB,EHN,2BSN                     SIM
ZETTLER, R.  ALLGAUER SKIZZEN.  2CL,ASAX(CL),ASAX(HN),TSAX,BSN   MV
```

6 PARTS: WOODWIND QUINTET-KEYBOARD-626

```
ANDRIESSEN, J.  INCONTRO DI CESARE E CLEOPATRA, L' (1956)        SD
ARRIEU, C.  CONCERTO                                            RC
BADINGS, H.  SEXTET (1952)                                      SD
BEALE, J.  SEXTET, OP 39                                        ACA
BENTZON, N.  SEXTET, OP278                                      WH
BEZANSON, P.  SEXTET                                            ACA
BIZET, G.-WILSON.  QUINTET (CARMEN).  FL,OB,CL,HN,BSN(BCL),PF   CF
BLUMER, T.  SEXTET, OP 45                                       SIM
BLUMER, T.  SEXTET, OP 92                                       R&E
BOCCHERINI, L.  MENUET.  FL,OB,CL,HN,BSN(BCL),PF                CF
BROWN, R.  DIVERTIMENTO                                         WI
BULLERIAN, H.  SEXTET, OP 38                                    SIM
CASADESUS, R.  SEXTUOR, OP 58                                   DUR
CHERNEY, B.  NOTTURNO (1974).  FL,AFL,OB/EHN,CL/BCL,BSN,HN,PF   CAN
COULTHARD, J.  DIVERTIMENTO (1968)                              CAN
COYNER, L.  WOODENLY BOOMING ALONG LIKE A CARVED BEE            ACA
CRESTON, P.  CONCERTINO, OP 99                                  ECK
CRUFT, A.  DANCE MOVEMENT                                       GAL
DAVID, J. BOHLE.  KUME, KUMGESELLE MIN, OP 24, DIVERTIMENTO     BRH
DEKKER, D.  ZERO DYNAMIQUE (1972)                               SD
DI DOMENICA, R.  SEXTET                                         EM
DIONISI, R.  DIVERTIMENTO                                       GZ
DRESDEN, S.  KLEINE SUITE IN C MA (1913)                        SD
DRESDEN, S.  SUITE #3 (1920)                                    SD
DRESDEN, S.  SUITE NAAR RAMEAU (1916)                           SD
DVORAK, A.-HARRIS.  HUMORESKE.  FL,OB,CL,HN,BSN(BCL),PF         CF
FLOSMAN, O.  SONATA (1970)                                      ART
FRANCAIX, J.  HEURE DU BERGER, L'                               SCH
FRENSEL-WEGENER, E.  SEXTET (1927)                              SD
FRID, G.  SEXTET                                                SD
GODRON, H.  SERENADE (1947)                                     SD
GORNER, H.  KAMMERKONZERT, OP 29                                PET
GREENBERG, L.  SEXTET (1963)                                    CAN
HEMEL, O. VAN.  SEXTET (1962)                                   SD
HILL, E.  SEXTET, OP 39                                         TP
HUSA, K.  SERENADE.  FL,OB,CL,BSN,HN,PF(HP)                     ALE
HUSA, K.  SERENADE                                              B&N
IBARRONDO, F.  LUEGO EL SILENCIO                                EEC
INDY, V. D'.  SARABANDE & MINUET, OP 24 BIS                     INT
JACOB, G.  SEXTET                                               MR
JENTSCH, W.  KLEINE KAMMERMUSIK, OP 5                           R&E
JONGEN, J.  RHAPSODIE, OP 70 (1922)                             CBD
JUON, P.  DIVERTIMENTO, OP 51                                   MRL
KAHOWEZ, G.  STRUCTURES                                         LDO
KEFALIDI, I.  SEXTET                                            MKE
KOETSIER, J.  INTRODUCTION ET FOLATRERIE AVEC UN THEME (1961)   SD
KOHN, K.  SERENADE.  FL/PIC,OB,CL,HN,BSN,PF                     CF
KOX, H.  SEXTET #3 (1959)                                       SD
KOX, H.  SEXTET #4 (1960)                                       SD
LADMIRAULT, P.  CHORAL ET VARIATIONS                           HLE
LAKNER, Y.  SEXTET (1951)                                       ISR
```

```
MARGOLA, F.   SONATINA A SEI                                        EDB
MARTINU, B.   SEXTET (1929)                                         PAN
MC CABE, J.   CONCERTO                                              NO
MC CLELLAN, R.   PARAMETERS.  WW5,HPCD                              SS
MENDELSSOHN, F.   INTERMEZZO (MIDSUMMER NIGHT'S DREAM)              CF
    FL,OB,CL,HN,BSN(BCL),PF
MENDELSSOHN, F.-JOSPE.   SCHERZO, OP110                             CF
    FL,OB,CL,HN,BSN(BCL),PF
MEULEMANS, A.   AUBADE (1934)                                       CBD
MILLER, R.   3 AMERICAN DANCES, OP 25.  FL,OB,CL,HN,BSN(BCL),PF     CF
MOZART, W.-SABATINI.   SEXTET                                       CAM
MOZART, W.   SEXTET                                                 COR
MOZART, W.-PIJPER.   SEXTET, K608                                   SD
MULDER, E.   SEXTET (1946)                                          SD
MYERS, R.   SEXTET                                                  SS
NORDGREN, E.   SERENAD, OP 64 (1965)                                STI
ONSLOW, G.   SEXTUOR, OP 77                                         HEU
OSIECK, H.   DIVERTIMENTO (1950)                                    SD
PALKOVSKY, O.   3 STUCKE (1965)                                     CHF
PIJPER, W.   SEXTET (1923)                                          SD
PILLIN, B.   SERENADE                                               WI
POULENC, F.   SEXTET (1932/39)                                      WH
POUWELS, J.   SEXTET (1958)                                         SD
REED, A.   SYMPHONIC DANCE                                          BE
REUCHSEL, A.   SEXTUOR                                              HLE
REYNOLDS, V.   CONCERTARE III                                       CF
RIEGGER, W.   CONCERTO, OP 53                                       AMP
ROLDAN, A.   RITMICA #1                                             SN
ROOS, R. DE.   SEXTUOR (1935)                                       SD
ROUSSEL, A.   DIVERTISSEMENT, OP  6                                 EDK
ROUSSEL, A.   DIVERTISSEMENT, OP  6                                 EDS
SCHROEDER, H.   SEXTET, OP 36                                       SCH
SCHUBERT, F.   ROSAMUNDE.  FL,OB,CL,HN,BSN(BCL),PF                  CF
SMIT, L.   SEXTUOR (1933)                                           SD
SMITH, H.   VARIATIONS FOR 6 PLAYERS                                EM
STRATEGIER, H.   SEXTET (1951)                                      SD
SUGAR, R.   FRAMMENTI MUSICALI (1958)                              EMB
TANSMAN, A.   DANCE OF THE SORCERESS                                EES
THUILLE, L.   GAVOTTE (SEXTET, OP  6).  FL,OB,CL,HN,BSN(BCL),PF    CF
THUILLE, L.   SEXTET IN B FL MA, OP  6                              BRH
THUILLE, L.   SEXTET IN B FL MA, OP  6                              INT
TUTHILL, B.   VARIATIONS ON "WHEN JOHNNY COMES MARCHING HOME"       GA
ULTAN, L.   SEXTET                                                  SS
VAN DER VELDEN, R.   SEXTET                                         EES
VARCARCEL, E.   CHECAN I                                            EDT
WAGNER, R.-BOYD.   ALBUM LEAF, AN.  FL,OB,CL,HN,BSN(BCL),PF         CF
WEIGL, K.   4 BAGATELLES                                            ACA
ZAGWIJN, H.   SCHERZO (1946)                                        SD
ZAGWIJN, H.   SUITE (1912)                                          SD
```

6 PARTS: WOODWIND-KEYBOARD-627

```
BOCCHERINI, L.   MENUET,                                            CF
    FL(CL),OB(CL),CL,ACL(ASAX,CL),BCL(BSN),PF
CASTRO, C. DE.   PAN (1974).  5FL,PF                                EDA
DENZA, L.-HARRIS.   FUNICULI-FUNICULA.  5CL,PF                      CF
DVORAK, A.-HARRIS.   HUMORESKE,.  5CL,PF                            CF
HARVEY, J.   TRYPTICH.  FL,OB,2CL,BSN,PF                            SCH
```

6 PARTS: WOODWIND-KEYBOARD-627

```
LOEVENDIE, T.  3 STUKKEN (1964).  2FL,OB,2CL,PF              SD
PLEYEL, I.-HARRIS.  RONDO.  5CL,PF                           CF
SCHUBERT, F.  ROSAMUNDE BALLET MUSIC.  5CL,PF                CF
SCHUBERT, F.  ROSAMUNDE                                      CF
   FL(CL),OB(CL),CL,ACL(ASAX,CL),BCL(BSN),PF
SEIDEL, F.  SEXTET.  FL,OB,BSN,2HN,HPCD(PF)                  M&M
VUURSTEEN, F.  INTEGRATIE (1978)                            SD
   FL/PIC,FL/AFL,OB/EHN,CL/BCL,BSN/CBSN,ACC
WAGNER, R.-BOYD.  ALBUM LEAF, AN.  FL,2CL,HN,BSN,PF          CF
```

6 PARTS: WOODWIND-KEYBOARD (INCL HORN)-628

```
TELEMANN, G.-HOFFMANN.  CHASSE, LA.  2OB,2HN,BSN,BC         MV
TELEMANN, G.-HOFFMANN.  2 OUVERTURENSUITEN.  2OB,2HN,BSN,BC  MV
```

6 PARTS: WOODWIND-BRASS-632

```
ACHRON, J.  SEXTET.  FL,OB,CL,BSN,HN,TPT                     TP
ALBAM, M.  ESCAPADE.  TRB SOLO, FL,OB,CL,BSN,HN              KN
BACH, J.S.-SIBBING.  SINFONIA (CANTATA #209)                DOR
   SOP SAX,2TPT,HN,TRB,TU
BARCE, R.  OBERTURA FONETICA (1968).  FL,OB,CL,SAX,TPT,TRB  EEC
BECKERATH, A. VON.  VOLKSWEISEN AUS BOHMEN.  2CL,4BR INSTR   PGM
BEREAU, J.  SEXTUOR.  FL,OB,CL,BSN,HN,TPT                   ECH
BOTYAROV, E.  3 PIECES.  FL,OB,CL,BSN,HN,TPT                MKE
CROSSE, G.  CANTO, OP 4.  FL,OB,CL,BSN,HN,TRB               OX
GABRIELI, G.-SHUMAN.  CANZONI A 6.  CL,2TPT,2TRB,TU         SN
GIRON, A.  SEXTET.  FL,OB,CL,BSN,HN,TPT                     CF
GWINNER, V.  6 NIEDERDEUTSCHE VOLKSTANZE.  2CL,TPT,2HN,TRB  MV
HERMANSON, A.  ARS LINEAE, OP 17 (1976).  FL,OB,CL,BSN,HN,TRB  STI
HUTH, G.  MUSIK DER NACHTE AN DER ISER.  2CL,2TPT,BAR,TU    CHF
KARJALAINEN, A.  SEXTET.  OB,CL,BSN,HN,TPT,TRB             FIN
MOLTER, J.  SINFONIA CONCERTANTE #1 IN D MA.  2OB,2HN,BSN,TPT  MR
MOLTER, J.  SINFONIA CONCERTANTE #2 IN D MA.  2OB,2HN,BSN,TPT  MR
MUSSORGSKY, M.  BALLET OF THE CHICKS IN THEIR SHELLS       EDM
   FL,OB,2CL,BSN, TPT
PATZIG, G.(ED).  MILITARMARSCHE DES 18, JAHRHUNDERTS, VOL #3  B&N
   OB,2CL, 2BSN,TPT
READ, G.  NINE BY SIX.  FL/PIC,OB/EHN,CL/BCL,BSN,HN,TPT    PET
SCHMIDT, W.  CONCERTINO.  FL,OB,CL,BSN,HN,TU               WI
SCHWERTSIK, K.  PROVIANT.  FL,OB,CL,BSN,HN,TPT             LDO
SHEPPARD, J.  SEXTET.  PIC,FL,CL,HN,BSN,TPT                SS
SUTERMEISTER, H.  SERENADE #2.  FL,OB,CL,BSN,HN,TPT        SCH
WEISGALL, H.  HOLIDAY DANCE #2.  FL,OB,CL,BSN,HN,TPT       TP
WEISLING, R.  POON LIM--A NIGHT UPON THE WAVES            MEP
   2FL,BCL,BSN,HN,TRB
ZETTLER, R.  ALLGAUER SKIZZEN.  CL,TPT,2HN,BAR,TRB        MV
```

```
AMES, W.   SEXTET.   OB,2VN,2VA,VC                                     ACA
ANDERSON, R.   PRELUDE & RONDO.   FL,STR QUINTET                       AMC
BACH, J.S.-REED.   NUN KOMM, DER HEIDEN HEILAND.   OB,4VC,DB           EDK
BACH, J.S.-JANETZKY.   SEXTET IN E-FLAT.   CL,2HN,VN,VA,VC             EDK
BACH, J.S.-REED.   WENN WIR IN HOCHSTEN NOTHEN SEIN                    EDK
   EHN,4VC,DB
BACH, W.F.E.-JANETZKY.   SEXTET IN E FL MA.   CL,2HN,VN,VA,VC          PET
BALORRE, C.   ALLEGRO APPASSIONATO.   OB,CL,2VN,VA,VC                  HAM
BAUER, M.   CONCERTINO.   OB,CL,2VN,VA,VC                              BH
BEN-YOHANAN, A.   CHAMBER MUSIC FOR 6.   FL,CL,HN,VN,VA,DB             ISR
BERKELEY, L.   SEXTET.   CL,HN,2VN,VA,VC                               CHE
BETJEMAN, P.   SLOW BURN (1976).   CL,2VN,VA,VC,DB                     ACA
BOCCHERINI, L.-BORMANN.   SEXTET IN E FL MA, OP 42/2                   HSM
   OB(FL),HN,BSN,VN ,VA,DB
BOGUSLAWSKI, E.   METAMORPHOSES (1967).   OB,CL,2VN,VA,VC              AP
BUTTING, M.   FESTSCHRIFT FOR BACH, OP 77.   FL,EHN,BSN,VN,VA,VC       PET
ENCINAR, J.   SAMADHI (1972).   FL,CL,BSN,VN,VA,VC                     ESZ
ENGEL, J.   SUITE I.   CL,2VN,VA,VC,DB                                 UE
ERLANGER, G.   SEXTET, OP 41.   CL,BSN,HN,VN,VA,VC                     KIS
ETLER, A.   SEXTET (1959).   OB,CL,BSN,VN,VA,VC                        AMP
FLOTHUIS, M.   DIVERTIMENTO, OP 46 (1952).   CL,BSN,HN,VN,VA,DB        SD
GERHARDT, C.   SEXTET IN G MA.   FL,EHN,BSN,VN,VA,VC                   MRL
GHISI, F.   MUSICHE CONCERTATE.   OB,DB,2VN,VA,BSN                     EDI
GIULIANI, V.   DIVERTIMENTO.   FL,OB,CL,VN,VA,VC                       EDI
GLUCK, C.   MARCHE RELIGIEUSE (ALCESTE).   FL,STR QUINTET              DUR
HANDEL, G.-GEVAERT.   ANDANTE.   OB,STR QUINTET                        DUR
HARBISON, J.   SERENADE.   FL,CL,BCL,VN,VA,VC                          AMP
HARTLEY, W.   DIVERTIMENTO.   VC,FL,OB,CL,BSN,HN                       CRE
HARTLEY, W.   SERENADE.   FL,OB,CL,BSN,HN,DB                           CRE
HAYDN, F.-LANDON.   DIVERTIMENTO IN C MA, HOB II. 11                   LDO
   FL,OB,2VN,VC,DB
HAYDN, M.-RAINER.   DIVERTIMENTO IN G MA.   OB,2HN,BSN,VA,VN           LDO
HEALEY, D.   MOVEMENTS.   FL,OB,CL,VN,VA,VC                            CAN
HEILLER, A.   SEXTET.   OB,CL,BSN,VN,VA,VC                             UE
HODDINOTT, A.   SEXTET.   FL,CL,BSN,VN,VA,VC                           OX
HOFFMEISTER, F.-HOCKNER.   SERENATA IN F MA, OP  9                     HEI
   FL,VN,VA,VC,2HN
IRELAND, J.   SEXTET.   CL,HN,2VN,VA,VC                                GAL
LADERMAN, E.   DOUBLE HELIX.   FL,OB,2VN,VA,VC                         OX
LANDRE, G.   SEXTET (1959).   FL,CL,2VN,VA,VC                          SD
LEEUW, T. DE.   5 SCHETSEN (1952).   OB,CL,BSN,VN,VA,VC                SD
LEVY, F.   SEXTET.   FL,CL,BSN,VN,VA,VC                                COR
LUENING, O.   LYRIC SCENE.   FL,2VN,VA,VC,DB                           PET
MARTINU, B.   SERENADE #1 (1932).   CL,HN,3VN,VC                       ART
MC KINLEY, W.   PAINTINGS #2 (1974-75).   FL,OB,CL,VN,VA,VC            MAR
MULDER, E.   FUGA #3 (1940).   OB,CL,BSN,VN,VA,VC                      SD
MULLER, L.   TANZERISCHE IMPRESSIONEN.   FL,OB,CL,HN,BSN,DB            BRH
PABLO, L. DE.   CESURAS (1963).   FL,OB,CL,VN,VA,VC                    EDT
PAPINEAU-COUTURE, J.   SEXTUOR (1967).   OB,CL,BSN,VN,VA,VC            CAN
PECK, R.   SIX PAK.   FL,CL,HN,VN,VC,DB                                CF
PERUTI, C.   4 MOVEMENTS.   2FL,OB,CL,BSN,DB                           MAN
PISK, P.   ENVOY, OP104.   OB,CL,BSN,VN,VA,VC                          ACA
POSER, H.   KLEINE SPIELMUSIK.   FL(OB),2VN,VA,VC,DB                   HSM
PRAAG, H. VAN.   4 REFLEXIONS (1950).   FL,OB,CL,BSN,HN,VN             SD
QUINET, M.   BALLADE (1962).   VN,FL,OB,CL,HN,BSN                      CBD
```

6 PARTS: WOODWIND-STRINGS-633

```
RATHAUS, K.  ALLEGRO CONCERTANTE.  CL(OB),2VN,VA,VC,DB          HEI
REZNICEK, P.  MUSICA DA CONCERTO (1968).  FL,OB,CL,BSN,HN,DB    ES
ROSETTI, F.-BELSKY-RACEK.  NOTTURNO IN D MA.  FL,2HN,VN,VA,VC   ES
SCARMOLIN, L.  SUITE.  CL,HN,VN,VA,VC,DB                        AMC
SCHAUB, H.  SPIELMUSIK.  FL,OB,CL,BSN,VN,VA                     SIM
SEIBER, M.  FANTASIA (1945).  FL,HN,2VN,VA,VC                   ESZ
SORGE, E.  KOMM, DER VOLKER HEILAND.  OB,5STR                   S-V
SPERGER, J.-MALARIC.  CASSATION IN D MA.  FL,2HN,VN,VA,DB       LDO
SPERGER, J.-MALARIC.  RONDO.  FL,2HN,VN,VA,DB                   LDO
STEARNS, P.  SEXTET.  FL,CL,HN,VN,VA,DB                         ACA
TELEMANN, G.-SABATINI.  CONCERTO.  VN,FL,OB,CL,BSN,HN           CAM
THILMAN, J.  SEXTET, OP 74.  OB,CL,BSN,VN,VA,DB                 ISR
TROMBLY, P.  IN MEMORIAM: I. STRAVINSKY (1972)                  ACA
    FL/PIC/AFL,OB/EHN,CL /BCL,BSN,VA,DB
WAGNER-REGENY, R.  KLEINE GEMEINSCHAFTSMUSIK                    PET
    OB,CL,BSN,VN,VA,VC
WACNER, R. (H. BAERMANN).  ADAGIO.  CL,2VN,VA,VC,DB             BRH
WELIN, K.  VISOKA 12 (1965).  2FL,2VN,2VC                       STI
WHITTENBERG, C.  SEXTET.  FL/PIC,CL,BSN,VN,VC,DB                ACA
WRIGHT, M.  CHAMBER SYMPHONY (1974).  2FL,2HN,2VC              AMP
WUORINEN, C.  BEARBEITUNGEN UBER DAS GLOGAUER LIEDERBUCH        PET
    FL,PIC,CL, BCL,VN,DB
```

6 PARTS: WOODWIND-BRASS-STRINGS-634

```
ARDEVOL, J.  MUSICA DE CAMERA.  FL,CL,BSN,TPT,VN,VC            SN
BOGUSLAWSKI, E.  VERSIONS (1968).  FL,BSN,TPT,TRB,VN,DB        PWM
BOLCOM, W.  SESSION I.  FL/PIC/AFL,OB/EHN,BSN,VA,VC,TRB        TP
FELDMAN, M.  2 PIECES (1961).  FL,AFL,HN,TPT,VN,VC            PET
HAIEFF, A.  DANCE SUITE.  FL,BSN,TPT,PF,VN,VC                  BEL
HAUBENSTOCK-RAMATI, R.  MULTIPLE III (1970).  2WW,2BR,2STR    UE
KELTERBORN, R.  VARIANTI.  FL,CL/BCL,TPT,VN,VA,VC             OHN
LEWIN, F.  DUNLAP'S CREEK.  FL,EHN,CL,VC(BSN),OB,TPT          ACA
MACERO, T.  CANZONA #1.  SAX,2VN,VA,VC,TPT                     TP
MUSGRAVE, T.  CHAMBER CONCERTO #1.  OB,CL,BSN,TPT,TRB,VN      CHE
REIF, P.  SEXTET.  3CL,BCL,TPT,VC                              SS
ROJO, J.  PLANIFICACIONES.  CL,BSN,TPT,TRB,VN,VC              EDA
SANNER, L.  SEXTETT.  OB,TPT,2VN,VA,VC                         EMF
STIEBLER, E.  CONTINUO (1974).  CL,BSN,HN,TRB,VA,VC           EMO
TAKAHASHI, Y.  NIKITE.  OB,CL,TPT,TRB,VC,DB                   PET
VILLA ROJO, J.  PLANIFICACIONES (1972).  CL,BSN,TPT,TRB,VN,VC  EDA
XENAKIS, I.  EPEI (1976).  EHN,CL,TPT,2TRB,DB                  EDS
YANNAY, Y.  MUTATIS MUTANDIS.  OB,CL,HN,TPT,VN,DB             ACA
```

6 PARTS: WOODWIND-BRASS-KEYBOARD-635

```
ALBINONI, T.-WOJCIECHOWSKI.  CONCERTO IN C MA.  TPT,3OB,BSN,BC  HSM
BRANDON, S.  CHACONNE & VARIATIONS (1969).  OB,ASAX,2HN,TRB,PF  MAN
GERSCHEFSKI, E.  AMERICA VARIATIONS FOR WINDS, OP 44/14A       ACA
    FL,CL,ASAX ,BSN,TPT,PF
SEYFRIT, M.  CONTINUUM, VACUUM, RESIDUUM                        ACA
    CL,EHN,TRB,PF(3 PLAYERS)
```

```
ABBOTT, A.  MOUVEMENTS.  FL,OB,CL,VA,VC,PF                           EFM
ACHRON, J.  CHILDREN¬S SUITE, OP 57.  CL,2VN,VA,VC,PF               UE
BACH, J.C.  SEXTET IN C MA.  OB,VN,VC,2HN,HPCD                       MR
BACH, J.S.-FISCHER.  MEDITATION AVE MARIA                           FOR
    FL(OB),VN,VC(BSN),CL,HN,PF
BAKER, M.  MUSIC FOR 6 PLAYERS (1973).  FL,OB,VN,VA,VC,HPCD         CAN
BARNES, M.  CONCERTO GROSSO (1973).  FL,CL,VN,VC,2PF                CAN
BROZAK, D.  REINE DE JOIE (1978).  2FL,VA,VC,DB,HPCD               SD
BURGON, G.  GLORIA (1973).  PIC,OB,CL,HN,VC,PF                      CHE
CANO, F.  MUSICA A SEIS (1976).  FL,CL,VN,VA,VC,PF                 EDA
CHAJES, J.  HEBREW SUITE.  CL,2VN,VA,VC,PF                          AB
COPLAND, A.  SEXTET.  CL,2VN,VA,VC,PF                               BH
DELDEN, L. VAN.  INTRODUZIONE E DANZA, OP 26 (1950)                SD
    FL,CL,VN,VA,VC,P F
DIJK, J. VAN.  PASTORALE (1938).  FL,2VN,VA,VC,PF                  SD
DOHNANYI, E.  SEXTET IN C MA, OP 37.  CL,HN,VN,VA,VC,PF            LEN
DURKO, Z.  FIRE MUSIC.  FL,CL,VN,VA,VC,PF                          EMB
EBERL, A.  SEXTET.  CL,HN,VN,VA,VC,PF                               MR
EISLER, H.  14 ARTEN DEN REGEN ZU BESCHREIBEN                      PET
    FL,CL,VN,VA,VC,PF
ENCINAR, J.  MUSICA PER A UN AMIC (1976).  FL,CL,VN,VA,VC,PF       ESZ
ESCHER, R.  TOMBEAU DE RAVEL, LE (1952).  FL,OB,VN,VA,VC,HPCD      SD
FALLA, M. DE.  CONCERTO (1926).  HPCD(PF),FL,OB,CL,VN,VC           EES
FAUCONIER, C.  SEXTUOR FACILE.  FL,2VN,VC,DB,PF                    SCF
FESCH, W. DE-RUF.  CONCERTO IN B FL MA, OP  3/2                    RC
    2OB(2FL),BSN,2VN,BC
FORSTER.  CONCERTO IN E MI.  OB,2VN,VA,VC,BC                       FOR
GALUPPI, B.-SCHROEDER.  CONCERTO IN E MI.  2FL,2VN,VA,BC           HEI
HAMBRAEUS, B.  KAMMARMUSIK.  FL,OB,CL,ASAX,VA,HPCD                 EMF
HARRIS, R.  CONCERTO, OP  2.  CL,2VN,VA,VC,PF                      AMP
HASSE, J.-ENGLANDER.  CONCERTO IN G MA.  FL,2VN,VA,VC,PF           NV
HASSE, J.  KONZERT IN B MI.  FL,2VN,VA,VC,PF                       BRH
HEKSTER, W.  TROPOS N1974-75).  FL,OB,VN,VA,VC,PF                  SD
HERTEL, J.  SINFONIA A 6.  2FL,2VN,VA,BC                           MV
HIER, E.  SUITE FOR CHAMBER ENSEMBLE.  FL,OB,VN,VA,VC,PF           AMC
IVES, C.  ADAGIO SOSTENUTO.  EHN,3VN,VC,PF                         JB
IVES, C.  ALLEGRETTO SOMBREOSO.  FL,EHN,3VN,PF                     SN
JANACEK, L.  CONCERTINO (1925).  CL,BSN,HN,2VN,PF                  ES
KINGMA, P.  SEXTET (1973).  FL,OB,VN,VA,VC,PF                      SD
KOX, H.  SEXTET (1957).  FL,OB,VN,VA,VC,HPCD                       SD
KRAFT, L.  SEXTET.  CL,2VN,VA,VC,PF                                AMC
KRESKY, J.  MUSIC AT NIGHT (1976).  FL,CL,BSN,VN,VC,PF             AMC
LEHMANN, H.  FACES (1972).  FL,OB,BCL,VN,VC,HPCD(PF)               HG
LESUR, D.  SEXTUOR.  FL,OB,VN,VA,VC,PF                             APH
LEWIS, P.  SEPTET.  FL,CL,BSN,VN,VA,PF                             AMC
LYNCH, T.  ANDROMEDA.  FL,CL,HN,VN,VC,PF                           MAN
MAMLOK, U.  SEXTET.  FL/PIC,E FL CL,BCL,VN,DB,PF                   PET
MC CAULEY, W.  KALEIDOSCOPE QUEBECOIS (1974).  FL,CL,VN,VC,2PF     CAN
MEIJERING, C.  UTAH (1978).  FL,2VN,VA,VC,PF                       SD
ONSLOW, G.  GRAND SEXTUOR, OP 77 BIS.  FL,CL,BSN,HN,DB,PF          HEU
ORREGO-SALAS, J.  SEXTET.  CL,2VN,VA,VC,PF                         SN
PONSE, L.  SEXTET, OP 27 (1958).  FL,OB,VN,VA,VC,HPCD              SD
PRADO, A.  PORTRAIT OF LILI BOULANGER.  FL,2VN,VA,VC,PF            EDT
PRIETO, C.  ARAMBOL (1976).  FL,CL,PF,VN,VA,VC                     EEC
PROKOFIEV, S.  OVERTURE ON HEBREW THEMES.  CL,2VN,VA,VC,PF         EDK
```

6 PARTS: WOODWIND-STRING-KEYBOARD-636

```
PROKOFIEV, S.  OVERTURE ON HEBREW THEMES, OP 34              INT
   CL,2VN,VA,VC,PF
PROKOFIEV, S.  OVERTURE ON JEWISH THEMES.  CL,2VN,VA,VC,PF   BH
RAXACH, E.  SCATTERTIME (1917).  FL,CL,VN,VC,PF,ELEC ORG     SD
SARRI, D.-MEYLAN.  SONATA IN A MI.  FL,2VN,VA,VC,PF          LEU
SCHWANTNER, J.  ELIXIR.  FL,CL,VN,VA,VC,PF                   PET
SOLLBERGER, H.  SOLOS FOR VIOLIN & 5 INSTRUMENTS             M&M
   VN,FL,CL,HN,DB,PF
STAMITZ, J.-KOLBEL.  CONCERTO IN C MA.  FL,2VN,VA,VC,BC      B&N
STRANG, G.  CONCERTO FOR CELLO.  FL,OB,CL,BSN,VC,PF          ACA
STRATEGIER, H.  SONATA DA CAMERA (1978)                      SD
   FL,OB/EHN,VN,VA,VC,PF
SZEKELY, E.  SESTETTO.  CL,2VN,VA,VC,PF                      EMB
TANSMAN, A.  MUSIQUE A 6.  CL,2VN,VA,VC,PF                   EES
TARTINI, G.-NAGEL/RADEKE.  CONCERTO A 5 IN G MA, #2          HSM
   FL,2VN,VA,VC,BC
ULRICH, J.  IN COOL AUGUST.  FL,2VN,VA,VC,PF                 WH
URBANNER, E.  SEXTET (1973).  FL,OB,BSN,VN,VC,HPCD           LDO
VALCARCEL, E.  MONTAJE 59 PARA LUDWIG.  CL,2VN,VA,VC,PF      EDT
VALEK, J.  SYMPHONIE #6.  FL,OB,VN,VA,VC,HPCD                CHF
WEBER, B.  SERENADE, OP 39.  FL,OB,VN,VA,VC,HPCD(PF)         ACA
WILSON, T.  CANTI NOTTURNI.  FL/AFL,CL,VN,VA,VC,PF           CA
ZAGWIJN, H.  ENTRATA E FUGA (1950).  FL,OB,VN,VA,VC,HPCD     SD
```

6 PARTS: WOODWIND-BRASS-STRING-KEYBOARD-637

```
AITKEN, H.  PARTITA.  OB,CL,TPT,VA,VC,PF                     AMC
ANDERBERG, C.  HEXAFONI.  CL,TPT,TRB,VN,DB,PF                ESU
DONOVAN, R.  MUSIC FOR 6.  OB,CL,TPT,VN,VC,PF                PET
ERB, D.  HEXAGON (1963).  FL,ASAX,TPT,TRB,VC,PF             CAN
IVES, C.  ALL THE WAY AROUND & BACK.  CL(FL),VN,TPT,HN,2PF   PI
IVES, C.-SINCLAIR.  HOLIDAY QUICKSTEP.  PIC,2VN,2TPT,PF      TP
MARTINU, B.  REVUE DE CUISINE, LA.  VN,VC,CL,BSN,TPT,PF      ALE
OLIVEROS, P.  VARIATIONS FOR SEXTET.  FL,CL,HN,TPT,PF,VC     SMI
PERUTI, C.  HALLOWEEN MUSIC.  BSN,TPT,TRB,TU,DB,PF           MAN
SCHMELZER, J.  SONATA A 5.  BSN,2VN,TPT,VA DA GAMBA,BC       MR
STOCKMEIER, W.  REAKTIONEN.  FL,OB,VN,VC,TPT,PF              MV
WEBER, B.  BALLET, OP 26, THE POOL OF DARKNESS               ACA
   FL,BSN,TPT,VN,VC,PF
WRIGHT, M.  NOISE DID RISE LIKE THUNDER, A (1975)            B-B
   TRB SOLO,AFL,EHN, FLUEGEL HN,PF,DB
```

6 PARTS INCLUDING HARP-638

```
ADAMS, J.  WINDFLOWERS (1974).  FL,HP,VA,VC,ELEC PF,PERC     AMC
ADDISON, J.  SERENADE.  FL,OB,CL,BSN,HN,HP                   OX
AHLBERG, G.  EXERCITIO III (1964).  FL,VN,VA,VC,HP,VIB       STI
BALAI, L.  DIVERTISSEMENT.  FL,OB,CL,BSN,HN,HP               MKE
BANCQUART, A.  EXPLOSANTE FIXE.  FL,OB,CL,BSN,HN,HP          JOB
BEECROFT, N.  CONTRASTS FOR 6 PERFORMERS (1962)             CAN
   OB,VA,HP,3PERC
BEERMAN, B.  COLORS.  CL,VN,DB,PF,HP,PERC                    ACA
BOUTRY, R.  2 PIECES EN SEXTUOR.  FL,OB,CL,BSN,HN,HP(PF)     ALE
BROWN, E.  TIMES FIVE (1963).  FL,TRB,VN,VC,HP,TAPE          UE
```

6 PARTS INCLUDING HARP-638

CASANOVA, A. DUE CANZONI, OP 49 (1973)   B-B
  ASAX,CL,TPT,PERC,GUIT,ELEC ORG
CHOU, WEN-CHUNG. SUITE. FL,OB,CL,BSN,HN,HP   PET
CHRISTOV, D. CONCERTO. FL,2VN,HP,PF,PERC   EMO
DRUCKMAN, J. DIVERTIMENTO (1950). CL,HN,HP,STR TRIO   MC
GOEHR, A. SUITE, OP 11. VN/VA,VC,FL,CL,HN,HP   S&C
HAYDN, F.-TOCCHI. CAPRICCIO. FL,CL,VN,VA,VC,HP   ESA
HOLEWA, H. CONCERTINO (1960). CL,VA,HN,PF,HP,PERC   EMF
HOVHANESS, A. FLOWERING PEACH, THE (1954)   AMP
  CL,ASAX,TIMP,PERC,HP,CEL
KNUSSEN, O. PUZZLE MUSIC. FL/AFL,CL,HP,2PERC,GUIT/MANDOLIN   GS
LACHENMANN, H. INTROVERSION II (1964). CL,TPT,DB,HP,ORG,PERC   EDT
LANJEAN, M. SOULEIBRADO, PETITE SUITE PROVENCALE   EMT
  FL,OB,2CL,VC,HP
LAZAROF, H. TEMPI CONCERTATI. FL,HP,PF,CEL,HPCD,XYL   AMP
MARTINU, B. MUSIQUE DE CHAMBRE #1. CL,VN,VA,VC,PF,HP   EES
MARTINU, B. REVUE DE CUISINE, LA. CL,BSN,VN,VC,TPT,HP   ALE
MASON, D. 3 PIECES. FL,2VN,VA,VC,HP   TP
MORAN, R. 4 VISIONS. FL,2VN,VA,VC,HP   UE
MOULAERT, R. CONCERT (1950). FL,OB,CL,HN,BSN,HP   CBD
PACIORKIEWICZ, T. MUSIC (1963). FL,OB,CL,HN,BSN,HP   PWM
PERRAULT, M. SEXTUOR (1955). CL,HP,2VN,VA,VC   CAN
PETRIC, I. MOSAICS. CL,TRB,VC,HP,2PERC   EDD
PETRIC, I. 5 PIECES. OB,2VN,VA,VC,HP   EDD
RANDS, B. ACTIONS FOR 6 (1962/63). FL,VA,VC,HP,2PERC   UE
REDEL, M. RELIEFS (1970). OB/EHN,VC,HN,HP,2PERC   B&B
RUDZINSKI, W. PRELUDES (1967). CL,VA,HP,VIB,MAR,PERC   PWM
SHINOHARA, M. CONSONANCE (1967). FL,HN,VC,HP,VIB,MAR   HMO
SOLER, J. QUETZALCOATL (1966). FL,CL,VN,VC,PF,HP   SS
SOLER, J. SONATINA (1964). FL,CL,VN,VC,PF,HP   SS
SURINACH, C. 3 BERBER SONGS. FL,OB,CL,VA,VC,HP   SN
THOMSON. ONDINE. FL,VC,DB,HP,CEL,PERC,OPT STR QUARTET   BE
TOGNI, C. AUBADE (1965). FL,CL,VIB,VC,HP,HPCD   ESZ
VANDOR, I. SERENATA (1964). FL,BCL,HN,VA,VC,HP   ESZ
VILLA-LOBOS, H. SEXTUOR MYSTIQUE (1917)   EES
  FL,OB,ASAX,GUIT,HP,CEL
WIRTEL, T. 5 PIECES. FL,OB,DB,HP,2PERC   ACA
WOLPE, S. SEXTET. CL,TPT,VN,VC,HP,PF   M&M

6 PARTS INCLUDING GUITAR-639

CANINO, B. CADENZE (1962). CL,TPT,DB,GUIT,HPCD,PERC   ESZ
DAVIES, P. ALL SONS OF ADAM. FL,CL,VA,VC,MAR,GUIT   BH
DAVIES, P. RENAISSANCE SCOTTISH DANCES   BH
  FL,CL,VN,VC,GUIT,PERC
FACKLER, H. INTRODUCTION & RONDO GIOCOSO   OHN
  OB,DB,GUIT,3 MANDOLINES
GERHARD, R. LIBRA. FL,CL,VN,PF,GUIT,PERC   OX
GIUFFRE, G. SONETTO PER UNGERETTI. 2FL,ORG,GIUT,2PERC   SS
GLICK, S. DIVERTISSEMENT (1968). CL,VIB,GUIT,MANDOLINE,VC,DB   CAN
HUPFER, K. MUSIK FUR TRIAL & ERROR (1971)   HG
  OB/EHN,CL/BCL,HN,GUIT,VN ,VC
KILLMAYER, W. WOODS SO WILDE, THE. FL,VA,GUIT,3PERC   SCH
KNUSSEN, O. PUZZLE MUSIC. FL/AFL,CL,HP,2PERC,GUIT/MANDOLIN   GS
MIEREANU, C. SOURCE DE JUIN (1972)   EDS
  FL,CL,TPT,TRB,PERC,ELEC GUIT
RICHTER, N. SERENADE (1934). FL,OB,VN,VA,VC,GUIT   SD
SLONIMSKY, N. EXOTIC SUITE. SAX,2VN,2ELEC GUIT,PERC   MKE

6 PARTS INCLUDING GUITAR-639

```
SUBOTNICK, M.   SERENADE #1.   FL,CL,VC,VIB,PF,MANDOLINE          M&M
TAKEMITSU, T.   VALERIA (1965).   2PIC,VN,VC,GUIT,ELEC ORG        UE
TOMASI, H.   RECUERDOS DE LAS BALEAUS.   OB,3GUIT,PF,PERC         EV
VILLA-LOBOS, H.   SEXTUOR MYSTIQUE (1917)                         EES
   FL,OB,ASAX,GUIT,HP,CEL
WUORINEN, C.   ARABIA FELIX.   FL,BSN,VN,PF,VIB,GUIT              PET
ZELENKA, I.   FRUH-STUCK.   AFL,BCL,HN,TRB,VA,GUIT                EMO
```

6 PARTS INCLUDING PERCUSSION-640

```
ADAMS, J.   WINDFLOWERS (1974).   FL,HP,VA,VC,ELEC PF,PERC        AMC
AHLBERG, G.   AFORISMER (1965).   FL,AFL,E FL CL,BCL,PF,PERC      STI
AHLBERG, G.   EXERCITIO III (1964).   FL,VN,VA,VC,HP,VIB          STI
AMES, W.   HENRY IV. INCIDENTAL MUSIC.   OB,5PERC                 ACA
AMZALLAG, A.   MUSIK (1970).   FL,5PERC                           ISR
BACH, J.S.-DAVIES.   2 PRELUDES & FUGUES.   FL,CL,VA,VC,MAR,HPCD  BH
BACK, S.   FAVOLA.   CL,PF,4PERC                                  WH
BALADA, L.   GEOMETRIAS (1966).   FL,OB,CL/BCL,TPT,BSN,PERC       GEN
BARBE, H.   MINIATUREN ZU EINEM LUSTPIEL (1959)                   GBV
   CL,TPT,TRB,DB,PERC,P F
BARKIN, E.   REFRAINS.   FL,CL,VN,VA,VC,CEL                       ACA
BECKER, G.   EPIKLESIS ALPHA (1970).   FL,CL,VA,VC,PERC,TAPE      HG
BEDFORD, D.   SWORD OF ORION, THE (1970).   FL,CL,2PERC,VN,VC     UE
BEECROFT, N.   CONTRASTS FOR 6 PERFORMERS (1962)                  CAN
   OB,VA,HP,3PERC
BEERMAN, B.   COLORS.   CL,VN,DB,PF,HP,PERC                       ACA
BENNETT, R.   COMMEDIA I.   FL,BCL,ASAX,TPT,VC,PERC               JB
BENTZON, N.   SINFONIA CONCERTANTE, OP100                         WH
   CL,VN,VA,VC,BRASS INSTR, P ERC
BISSELL, K.   SUITE.   BSN,2VN,VA,VC,PERC                         CAN
BOZAY, A.   MUHLE, DIE, OP 23.   FL,OB,EHN,CL,PERC,REGAL          EMB
BROWN, E.   HODOGRAPH I (1959).   FL,PF,CEL,VIB,MAR,GLOCKENSPIEL  AMP
BUCZYNSKI, W.   SEXTET/74 (1974).   FL,VN,VC,PF,2PERC             CAN
CAMPO, F.   VIAGGI, OP 56.   FL,OB,CL,HN,BSN,PERC                 MUC
CANINO, B.   CADENZE (1962).   CL,TPT,DB,GUIT,HPCD,PERC           ESZ
CASANOVA, A.   DUE CANZONI, OP 49 (1973)                         B-B
   ASAX,CL,TPT,PERC,GUIT,ELEC  ORG
CASTIGLIONI, N.   TROPI.   FL,CL,VN,VC,PF,PERC                    ESZ
CHRISTLIEB, D. (ARR).   3 PIECES.   2OB,EHN,BSN,2SDR             CP
CHRISTOV, D.   CONCERTO.   FL,2VC,HP,PF,PERC                      EMO
COLE, B.   CAESURA.   FL,CL,VN,VC,PF,PERC                         BH
CUOMO, J.   FOR ZEBULON PIKE & HENRY.   3OB,BSN,MAR,PERC          MEP
DAVIES, P.   ALL SONS OF ADAM.   FL,CL,VA,VC,MAR,GUIT             BH
DAVIES, P.   AVE MARIS STELLA.   FL,CL,VC,PF,MAR                  BH
DAVIES, P.   RENAISSANCE SCOTTISH DANCES                         BH
   FL,CL,VN,VC,GUIT,PERC
DAVIES, P.   SI QUIS DILIGIT ME.   AFL,CL,VA,VC,CEL,CROTALES      BH
DONATONI, F.   LUMEN (1975).   PIC,CL,VA,VC,VIB,CEL               ESZ
DONOVAN, R.   SOUNDINGS.   TPT,BSN,4PERC                          ACA
DUCKWORTH, W.   AN UNSEEN ACTION.   FL,PF,4PERC                   SS
DZIEWULSKA, M.   STRAVAGANZA (1966).   CL,VN,VA,2VC,PERC          PWM
EDWARDS, R.   SHADOW D-ZONE (1977).   FL,CL,VN,VC,PF,PERC         FB
ERB, D.   MIRAGE.   FL,BSN,TPT,TRB,PF,PERC                        TP
FELDMAN, M.   VIOLA IN MY LIFE I, THE (1970)                      UE
   FL,PERC,PF,VN,VA,VC
FINE, V.   DIVERTIMENTO.   3WW,TPT,PF,PERC                        AMC
FINK, S.   SERENADE IN PERCUSSIONE.   CL,ASAX,DB,3PERC            SIM
FINNISSY, M.   AFAR (1966/67).   FL,EHN,3TPT,PERC                 ESZ
```

```
FODI, J.  PARTIMENTO.  FL,OB,VC,2PF,PERC                            CAN
FODI, J.  VARIATIONS, OP 37 (1972).  FL,CL,VN,VA,DB,PERC            CAN
GAAL, J.  SEXTETT.  FL,VN,VA,VC,CEL,PERC                            EMB
GERHARD, R.  LIBRA.  FL,CL,VN,PF,GUIT,PERC                          OX
GERVAISE, C.-BULLARD.  4 DANCES                                     OX
  FL,OB(FL),OB(CL),BSN(CL),BSN,DR
GILBERT, A.  INTROIT, GRADUAL & 2 CHORALS                           SCH
  CL,HN,TPT,TRB,VC,PERC
GIUFFRE, G.  SONETTO PER UNGARETTI.  2FL,ORG,GUIT,2PERC             SS
GLASER, W.  TALE (1977).  BAR SAX,5PERC                             STI
GLICK, S.  DIVERTISSEMENT (1968).  CL,VIB,GUIT,MANDOLIN,VC,DB       CAN
GLODEANU, G.  INVENTIUNI (1967).  FL,OB,CL,BSN,HN,PERC              EMU
GRANDIS, R. DE.  CANTI SULLE PAUSE (1961)                           EDT
  TSAX,VN,TRB,VIB,CEL,PERC
HALFFTER, C.  ODA (1969).  FL,BCL,PF/CEL,VA,VC,PERC                 UE
HARTWELL, H.  SOUL-PIECE (1967).  ASAX,TSAX,TPT,DB,PF,PERC          BER
HEININEN, P.  MUSIQUE D'ETE (1963).  FL,CL,VN,VC,HPCD,PERC          MT
HEKSTER, W.  REFLECTIONS (1964).  CL,HN,VC,VIB,CEL,PERC             SD
HERVIG, R.  CHAMBER MUSIC.  FL,CL,VN,DB,PF,PERC                     ACA
HESPOS, H.  EN-KIN.  SOP SAX/TSAX,TPT,VN,VC,DB,PERC                 EMO
HOLEWA, H.  CONCERTINO (1960).  CL,VA,HN,PF,HP,PERC                 EMF
JOHNSON, R.  TRIPTYCH.  FL,CL,VN,VC,PF,PERC                         OX
KANTUSER, B.  2 IMAGES.  FL,CL,VC,2PERC,PF                          EDD
KAUFMANN, A.  4 PIECES, OP 77.  CL,2VN,VC,DB,PERC                   LDO
KILLMAYER, W.  WOODS SO WILDE, THE.  FL,VA,GUIT,3PERC               SCH
KNUSSEN, O.  PUZZLE MUSIC.  FL/AFL,CL,HP,2PERC,GUIT/MANDOLIN        GS
KOMADINA, V.  MICROSONATES.  FL,CL,BCL,VC,PF,PERC                   DSS
LACHENMANN, H.  INTROVERSION II (1964).  CL,TPT,DB,HP,ORG,PERC      EDT
LAMPERSBERG, G.  CONCERTINO.  CL,TPT,4PERC                          UE
LAZAROF, H.  TEMPI CONCERTATI.  FL,HP,PF,CEL,HPCD,XYL               AMP
LE SIEGE, A.  PHIDIAN.  2FL,AFL,BCL,PF,VIB                          SS
LONGTIN, M.  IMMORTELS D'AGAPIA, LES (1972)                         CAN
  FL,CL,PF,2PERC,RUBAN
MACHAUT, G. DE-BIRTWISTLE.  HOQUETUS DAVID                          UE
  FL/PIC,E FL CL,2PERC,VN,VC
MARCO, T.  NUBA (1973).  FL,OB,CL,VN,VC,PERC                        HMO
MEALE, R.  INCREDIBLE FLORIDAS (1971)                               UE
  FL,CL/BCL,PERC,PF,VN/VA,VC
MELLNAS, A.  CEREMUS (1973).  FL,CL,TPT,TRB,DB,PERC                 STI
MELLNAS, A.  PER CASO (1963).  ASAX,TRB,VN,DB,2PERC                 EDT
METRAL, P.  VARIANTI.  FL,5PERC                                     EDT
MIEREANU, C.  SOURCE DE JUIN (1972)                                 EDS
  FL,CL,TPT,TRB,PERC,ELEC GUIT
MIZELLE, J.  STRAIGHT AHEAD.  FL,VN,TPT,TRB,PERC,TÁPE               CPE
MOFFITT.  WHAM DOODLE.  5CL,DR                                      CF
MORYL, R.  ATLANTIS.  EHN,PF,2PERC,TAPE,MIME                        SER
NATANSON, T.  6 PIECES.  CL,BSN,VN,VC,TIMP,PERC                     PWM
OCKEGHEM, J.-BIRTWISTLE.  UT HEREMITA SOLUS                         UE
  FL/PIC/AFL,CL/BCL,VA,VC,PF,PERC
PABLO, L. DE.  PROSODIA (1962).  FL,CL,VIB,3PERC                    EDT
PABLO, L. DE.  RECIPROCO, OP 16 (1963).  4FL,PERC,PF               EMO
PAICH, M.  TOCCATA IN F MA.  SOP SAX,ASAX,TSAX,BAR SAX,DB,DR        EQM
PARRIS, R.  BOOK OF IMAGINARY BEINGS, THE                          ACA
  FL/PIC,VN,VC,PF,2PERC
PATTERSON, P.  FLOATING MUSIC.  FL,CL,VN,VC,PERC,PF/CEL             JOW
PEHKONEN, E.  CONCERTO.  OB,CL,TRB,PF,PERC,ELEC ORG                 CHE
PERT, M.  ANCIENT PATTERN, OP 34.  CL,VC,TPT,PF,PERC,TAPE           JOW
PETRIC, I.  MOSAICS.  CL,TRB,VC,HP,2PERC                            EDD
PICKER, T.  SEXTET #2 "HALLE'S RAVINE".  OB,CL,VN,VC,VIB,PF         ACA
PINCHARD, M.  INTERLUDES POUR L'ODYSSEE                             HEU
  FL,2CL,VN,VC(BSN),PERC
PLAIN, G.  SCENARIO.  FL,BSN,VN,VC,PF,MAR                           AMC
```

6 PARTS INCLUDING PERCUSSION-640

```
POUSSEUR, H.  MADRIGAL III (1962).  CL,VN,VC,PF,2PERC            UE
RAE, A.  RAINBOW SKETCHES (1976).  FL/AFL,OB/EHN,VN,PF,2PERC     CAN
RANDS, B.  ACTIONS FOR 6 (1962/63).  FL,VA,VC,HP,2pERC          UE
RAXACH, E.  ESTROFAS (1962).  FL,BCL,VN,VC,DB,PERC              EDT
REA, J.  JEUX DE SCENE.  FL,OB,VC,PF,2PERC                      CAN
REA, J.  RECEPTION & OFFERING MUSIC (ANAPHORA IV) (1975)        CAN
   FL,OB,CL,H N,BSN,PERC
REA, J.  SESTINA (1968).  AFL,CL,TPT,VC,HPCD,PERC               CAN
REDEL, M.  RELIEFS (1970).  OB/EHN,VC,HN,HP,2PERC               B&B
RODGERS, R.-MAY.  DANCING ON THE CEILING.  4SAX,DB,DR           SH
RUDZINSKI, W.  PRELUDES (1967).  CL,VA,HP,VIB,MAR,PERC          PWM
SARDA, A.  ISORRITME.  OB,CL,VA,VC,PF,CEL                       SN
SCHERCHEN, T.  SUN (1968).  OB/EHN,TPT,TRB,PERC,2VC             UE
SCHIDLOWSKY, L.  CONCERTO.  CL,BCL,TPT,XYL,TIMP,PF              SN
SCHWANTNER, J.  CONSORTIUM II.  FL,CL,VN,VC,PF,PERC             ACA
SEIBER, M.  JAZZOLETTES.  2SAX,TPT,TRB,DR,PF                    AU
SEREBRIER, J.  6 FOR TELEVISION.  FL,OB,CL,BSN,HN,PERC          SN
SEYFRIT, M.  LATENT IMAGES.  CL,BSN,VN,VC,PF,MAR                ACA
SHINOHARA, M.  CONSONANCE (1967).  FL,HN,VC,HP,VIB,MAR          HMO
SIVIC, P.  DIPTYCH.  FL,2VN,VA,VC,PERC                          EDD
SLONIMSKY, N.  EXOTIC SUITE.  SAX,2VN,2 ELEC GUIT,PERC          MKE
SMITH, L.  PELDIMXY #1.  2SAX,TPT,PF,DB,PERC                    ACA
SUBOTNICK, M.  SERENADE #1.  FL,CL,VC,VIB,PF,MANDOLIN           M&M
SUR, D.  CATENA III (1976).  FL,BCL,VN,VC,MAR,BONGOS            B-B
TANENBAUM, E.  JAZZ SET.  TSAX,TPT,DB,PF,DR,TAPE                ACA
TARANU, C.  DIALOGUES (1966).  FL,CL,TPT,PF,VIB,PERC            EDS
THILMAN, J.  EPIGRAMME.  FL,VN,VA,DB,PF,PERC                    BRH
THOMSON.  ONDINE.  FL,VC,DB,HP,CEL,PERC,OPT STR QUARTET         BE
TIPPETT, M.  PRELUDE-SUMMER.  2FL,TPT,VN,DR,PF                  S&C
TOGNI, C.  AUBADE.  FL/PIC,CL,VC,HPCD,VIB,HP                    ESZ
TOMASI, H.  RECUERDOS DE LAS BALEAUS.  OB,3GUIT,PF,PERC         EV
TOWER, J.  BREAKFAST RHYTHMS I & II                            ACA
   CL SOLO,FL/PIC,VN,VC,PF,PERC
TREMBLAY, G.  SOLSTICES (1971).  FL,CL,HN,DB,2PERC              CAN
VILLA-LOBOS, H.  SEXTUOR MYSTIQUE (1917)                        EES
   FL,OB,ASAX,GUIT,HP,CEL
WELIN, K.  WARUM NICHT? (1964).  FL,VN,VC,VIB,2PERC             STI
WESTERGAARD, P.  VARIATIONS FOR 6 PLAYERS                       AB
   FL/PIC,CL/BCL,VN,VC,PF,PE RC
WILDER, A.  SEXTET.  FL,OB,CL,HN,BSN,MAR                        MAR
WILLIS, R.  COLLOQUY.  FL,OB,CL,HN,BSN,PERC                     MUC
WIRTEL, T.  5 PIECES.  FL,OB,DB,HP,2PERC                        ACA
WITTINGER, R.  MONTAGGIO, OP 21 (1971/72)                       BRH
   FL,OB,VA,VC,PF/HPCD/CEL,P ERC
WUORINEN, C.  ARABIA FELIX.  FL,BSN,VN,PF,VIB,GUIT              PET
WUORINEN, C.  SPECULUM SPECULI.  FL,OB,BCL,DB,PF,PERC           PET
ZONN, P.  DIVERTIMENTO #2.  CL,3PERC,DB,TAPE                    ACA
```

6 PARTS INCLUDING RECORDER-642

```
HUBER, K.  CONCERTO PER LA CAMERATA.  REC,FL,OB,VN,VC,PF        HEI
PROWO, P.-OCHS.  CONCERTO A 6 IN C MA.  2REC,2OB,2VC,PF AD LIB  HMO
PROWO, P.-HAUSSWALD.  CONCERTO IN D MI.  2REC,2OB,2BSN          FRH
TELEMANN, G.-HECHLER.  CONCERTO A 6.  REC,BSN,2VN,VA,BC         OHN
```

6 PARTS INCLUDING TAPE-643

```
BANK, J.  FLUTE QUINTET (1976).  5FL,TAPE                        SD
BECKER, G.  EPIKLESIS ALPHA (1976).  FL,CL,VA,VC,PERC,TAPE      HG
BERIO, L.  DIFFERENCES (1958-59).  FL,CL,VA,VC,HP,TAPE          UE
BOTTJE, W.  3 ETUDES.  FL,OB,CL,HN,BSN,TAPE                     ACA
BRANDON, S.  FABRICATION (1976).  FL,OB,CL,HN,BSN,TAPE          MAN
BROWN, E.  TIMES FIVE (1963).  FL,TRB,VN,VC,HP,TAPE             UE
BRUYNEL, T.  MECANIQUE (1967).  FL,OB,CL,BSN,HN,TAPE            SD
BRUYNEL, T.  SIGNS (1969).  FL,OB,CL,HN,BSN,TAPE                SD
DRUCKMAN, J.  DELIZIE CONTENTE CHE L'ALME BEATE                 BH
     FL,OB,CL,HN,BSN,TAP E
HASELBACH, J.  TONUNGEN (1976).  FL,OB,CL,BSN,HN,TAPE           S-V
LEEUW, T. DE.  ANTIPHONIE (1960).  FL,OB,CL,BSN,HN,TAPE         SD
MAIGUASHCA, M.  OELDORF 8 (1974).  CL,VN,VC,TAPE,2 ELEC ORG     FEE
MIEREANU, C.  SEGUNDAFEIRA (1974).  PIC,FL,AFL,2BFL,TAPE        EDS
MIZELLE, J.  STRAIGHT AHEAD.  FL,VN,TPT,TRB,PERC,TAPE           CPE
MORYL, R.  ATLANTIS.  EHN,PF,2PERC,TAPE,MIME                    SER
MOSS, L.  AUDITIONS.  FL,OB,CL,HN,BSN,TAPE                      CF
OTT, J.  11:11:73.  FL,OB,CL,BSN,HN,TAPE                        CU
PERT, M.  ANCIENT PATTERN, OP 34.  CL,VC,TPT,PF,PERC,TAPE       JOW
SCHWARTZ, E.  INTERRUPTIONS (1965).  FL,OB,CL,BSN,HN,TAPE       CF
SONSTEVOLD, K.  SELECTED (1975).  FL,OB,CL,BSN,HN,TAPE          STI
SONSTEVOLD, K.  WINDSTOCK (1976).  FL,OB,CL,BSN,HN,TAPE         STI
TANENBAUM, E.  JAZZ SET.  TSAX,TPT,DB,PF,DR,TAPE                ACA
VEYVODA, G.  INTO THE ARTIFICE OF ETERNITY                      SS
     FL,OB,CL,BSN,HN,TAPE
ZONN, P.  DIVERTIMENTO #2.  CL,3PERC,DB,TAPE                    ACA
```

7 PARTS: WOODWINDS
INCLUDING HORN-721

```
BACH, C.P.E.-SIMON.  6 MARCHES.   2OB,2CL,BSN,2HN,PERC AD LIB      EM
BACH, C.P.E.  6 SONATAS.  2FL,2CL,2HN,BSN                         MR
BACH, J.C.-RAPHAEL.  SEPTETT.  OB,2CL,2BSN,2HN                    BRH
BACH, J.S.-KENNAWAY.  SARABANDE.  2FL,OB,3CL,BSN                  JE
BACH, J.S.-EMERSON.  3 SARABANDES.  2FL,OB,3CL,BSN                JE
BOLZONI, G.-CONN.  MINUETTO.  FL,OB,2CL,ACL,BSN,BCL               CF
BUSCH, C.  OZARK REVERIE, AN.  FL,OB,2CL,BSN,2HN                  FZ
CAVALLY, R.  8 MADRIGALS.  7FL                                    SO
DOPPELBAUER, J.  DIVERTIMENTO (1967).  FL,OB,EHN,CL,BCL,BSN,HN    LDO
DRIESSLER, J.  APHORISMEN, OP 7A (1948)                           B&N
     FL,OB,EHN,CL,BCL,HN,BSN
FROMMEL, G.  BLASER-SUITE, OP 18.  FL,OB,2CL,CBSN,2HN             B&N
HANMER, R.  SUITE FOR 7.  2FL,OB,3CL,BSN                          JE
INDY, V. D'.  CHANSON ET DANSES, OP 50.  FL,OB,2CL,2BSN,HN        DUR
KESZTLER-KOVACS (ARR).  BAROQUE MUSIC FOR WOODWINDS               EMB
     2FL,OB(FL),2CL,B SN,HN
KOECHLIN, C.  SEPTUOR.  FL,OB,CL,HN,ASAX,EHN,BSN                  EDL
MAURY.  CHANGES.  7FL                                             WI
MICHAEL, D.  PARTHIA II.  FL,2CL,2HN,2BSN                         BH
MOUQUET, J.  SUITE.  FL,OB,2CL,2BSN,HN                            HLE
NELHYBEL, V.  IMPROMPTUS.  2FL,PIC,OB,2CL,BSN                     GEN
NESTICO, S.(ARR)-HIGGINS.  CHRISTMAS: THE JOY & SPIRIT            KN
     4ASAX,2TSAX,BAR SAX
PAISIELLO, G.  DIVERTISSEMENT.  2FL,2CL,2HN,BSN                   MKE
PIERNE, G.  PRELUDIO & FUGHETTA, OP 40/1.  2FL,OB,CL,2BSN,HN      INT
PIERNE, G.  PRELUDIO ET FUGHETTA, OP 40.  2FL,OB,CL,2BSN,HN       HAM
PILLIN, B.  3 PIECES FOR DOUBLE-REED SEPTET                       WI
     2OB,2EHN,2BSN,CBSN
PRAAG, H. VAN.  3 SCHETSEN (1960).  FL,2OB,2CL,2BSN               SD
RHENE-BATON.  AUBADE, OP 53.  FL,OB,2CL,2BSN,HN                   DUR
ROBERTS, W.  SUITE.  FL,OB,EHN,CL,BCL,BSN,HN                      COR
ROSETTI, A.  PARTHIA IN B FL MA.  2OB,2CL,BSN,2HN                 B&B
ROSETTI, A.  PARTHIA IN F MA                                      B&B
     OB SOLO,2OB,EHN,BSN,2HN,DB AD LIB
ROSETTI, F.-KNEUSSLIN.  PARTHIA #3 IN D MA.  2OB,2CL,2HN,BSN      EK
ROSETTI, F.-JANETZKY.  PARTIA IN B FL MA.  OB,2HN,2HN,2BSN        PET
SCHUBERT, F.-EMERSON.  SCHERZO & TRIO IN G MI.  2FL,OB,3CL,BSN    JE
SCHUBERT, F.-EMERSON.  SCHERZO & TRIO, OP147.  2FL,OB,3CL,BSN     JE
SEARLE, H.  DIVERTIMENTO OP 54.  7CL                              FB
SEROCKI, K.  KRASNOLUDKI (DIE ZWERGE)                            HMO
     FL,OB,EHN,CL,BSN,HN,TPT
STRANG, G.  LOST & WANDERING.  2FL,2EHN,CL,BSN,HN                 ACA
WILDER, A.  MOVEMENT FOR FLUTE ENSEMBLE.  PIC,2FL,2AFL,BFL        SF
WILDER, A.  SUITE.  FL,OB,CL,BSN,2HN,BAR SAX                      MAR
```

7 PARTS: WOODWIND-KEYBOARD-727

```
REGT, H. DE.  MUSICA, OP 26 (1973).  6WW,HPCD                     SD
WILLIAMSON, M.  CONCERTO.  FL,OB,CL,BSN,HN,2PF                    JOW
```

7 PARTS: WOODWIND-BRASS-732

```
ALCALAY, L.  GLIEDERUNGEN (1970).  FL,OB,CL,BSN,HN,TPT,TRB          EMO
BEZANSON, P.  PETITE SUITE.  FL,OB,CL,BSN,HN,TPT,TRB                 ACA
BOZZA, E.  4 MOUVEMENTS.  FL,OB,CL,BSN,HN,TPT,TRB                    ALE
BRUGK, H.  DIVERTIMENTO, OP 29.  FL,OB,CL,TPT,2HN,BSN                SIM
EDER, H.  SEPTET, OP 55.  FL,OB,CL,BSN,2HN,TPT                       LDO
GABRIELI, A.-SHUMAN.  RICERCARE #2.  CL,3TPT,2TRB,TU                 SN
HINDEMITH, P.  SEPTET (1948).  FL,OB,CL,BCL,BSN,HN,TPT               SO
LOUCHEUR, R.  CONCERTINO.  TPT SOLO,E FL CL,2CL,ACL,BCL,CBCL         EDS
MOCKL, F.  IPHIGENIE IN DELPHI.  FL,OB,CL,BSN,HN,TPT,TRB             HEI
PABLO, L. DE.  CORAL, OP 2 (1953).  FL,OB,CL,BSN,HN,TPT,TRB          EMO
PATZIG, G. (ED).  MILITARMARSCHE DES 18. JAHRHUNDERTS, VOL #1        B&N
    2OB,2CL,2BSN,TPT
PAZ, J.  CONCRECION.  FL,CL,BSN,HN,TPT,TRB,TU                        EDT
PIERNE, G.  PASTORALE VARIEE, OP 30.  FL,OB,CL,2BSN,HN,TPT           DUR
PLUISTER, S.  DIVERTIMENTO (1937).  2FL,OB,CL,BSN,TPT,TRB            SD
```

7 PARTS: WOODWIND-STRING-733

```
AMES, W.  WALTZ IN 6 PARTS.  FL,CL,BSN,VN,VA,VC,DB                   ACA
BAAREN, K. VAN.  SETTETTO (1952).  FL,OB,CL,BSN,HN,VN,DB             SD
BEETHOVEN, L. VAN.  SEPTET IN E FL MA, OP 20                         BRH
    CL,BSN,HN,VN,VA,VC,DB
BEETHOVEN, L. VAN.  SEPTET IN E FL MA, OP 20                         INT
    CL,BSN,VN,VA,VC,HN,DB
BEETHOVEN, L. VAN.  SEPTET IN E FL MA, OP 20                         RC
    OB,CL,HN,BSN,VN,VA,VC
BEETHOVEN, L. VAN.  SEPTET, OP 20.  CL,BSN,HN,VN,VA,VC,DB            EDK
BEETHOVEN, L. VAN.  SEPTET, OP 20.  CL,BSN,HN,VN,VA,VC,DB            PET
BEETHOVEN, L. VAN-LAMPE.  WIENER TANZE.  2CL,2HN,2VN,DB              FRH
BERWALD, F.  STOR SEPTETT.  CL,BSN,HN,VN,VA,VC,DB                    CGM
BORRIS, S.  KLEINE SUITE, OP 31/3.  FL,OB,CL,BSN,VN,VA,VC            S-V
BRUNSWICK, M.  SEPTET IN 7 MOVEMENTS.  FL,OB,CL,BSN,HN,VA,VC         ACA
CORY, E.  SEPTET.  FL,OB,BSN,HN,VN,VA,VC                             ACA
CROSSE, G.  VILLANELLES, OP 2.  FL,OB,CL,BSN,HN,VN,VC                OX
EISLER, H.  SEPTET #2 (1947).  FL/PIC,CL,BSN,2VN,VA,VC               VNM
EISLER, H.  SUITE FOR SEPTET #1, OP 92A                              VNM
    FL/PIC,CL,BSN,2VN,VA,VC
FISCHER, I.  DIVERTIMENTO IN D MA.  FL,CL,BSN,HN,VN,VC,DB            ACA
GLUCK, C.  GAVOTTE (IPHIGENIE EN AULIDE).  2OB,STR QUINTET           DUR
HANDEL, G.-GEVAERT.  FRAGMENT DU 5TH CONCERTO                        DUR
    2OB,STR QUINTET
HARTWELL, H.  SEPTET (1969).  CL,CL/E FL CL,BCL,HN,VN,VA,VC          CAN
HAUTA-AHO, T.  SEPTETTO.  CL,BSN,HN,VN,VA,VC,DB                      FIN
HAYDN, F.-JANETZKY.  CASSATION IN F MA                               PET
    OB,BSN,2HN,VN,VA,VC(DB)
HAYDN, F.-JANETZKY.  DIVERTIMENTO IN D MA.  2FL,2HN,2VN,VC           PM
HAYDN, F.-LANDON.  NOTTURNO #1 IN CMA, HOB II: 25                    LDO
    FL,OB,2CL,2VN,VC
HEPPENER, R.  SEPTET (1958).  FL,CL,BSN,2VN,VA,VC                    SD
HESPOS, H.  DRUCKSPUREN-GESCHATTET (1970)                            EMO
    BCL/E FL CL,ASAX,BSN,2TPT ,TRB,DB
```

7 PARTS: WOODWIND-STRING-733

```
KENINS, T.  SEPTUOR (1949).  CL,BSN,HN,VN,VA,VC,DB          CAN
KLEIN, R.  FANTASIE.  FL,CL,HN,BSN,VN,VA,VC                 MV
KOETSIER, J.  SEPTETT, OP 4 (1932).  CL,BSN,HN,VN,VA,VC,DB  SD
KONT, P.  SEPTET, OP 61/3.  FL,CL,BSN,VN,VA,VC,DB           LDO
KREUTZER, C.  GRAND SEPTUOR, OP 62.  CL,BSN,HN,VN,VA,VC,DB  M&M
KREUTZER, C.-REDTENBACHER.  SEPTET, OP 62                   LDO
   CL,BSN,HN,VN,VA,VC,DB
KREUTZER, C.  SEPTET, OP 62.  CL,BSN,HN,VN,VA,VC,DB         MR
LACOMBE, P.  SERENADE.  FL,OB,HN,2VN,VA,VC                  HAM
MARTINU, B.  SERENATA III (1932).  4VN,VC,OB,CL             ART
MILHAUD, D.  PASTORALE.  FL,EHN,BSN,VN,VA,VC,DB             UE
MILHAUD, D.  SERENADE.  FL,CL,BSN,VN,VA,VC,DB               UE
MOZART, W.  IDOMENEE, MARCHE.  2OB,STR QUINTET              DUR
PALKOVSKY, O.  CONCERTINO (1966).  FL,CL,BSN,HN,VN,VA,VC    CHF
PERRY, J.  PASTORAL.  FL,2VN,2VA,2VC                        SN
PHILIPPOT, M.  OCTUOR (1974).  CL,HN,2VN,VA,VC,DB           EDS
RIDOUT, G.  INTRODUCTION & ALLEGRO (1968)                   CAN
   FL,OB,CL,BSN,HN,VN,VC
ROSETTI, A.-PAEULER.  PARTITA IN F MA.  3OB,BSN,2HN,DB      PET
ROSSINI, G.  SERENADE FOR SMALL ENSEMBLE.  FL,OB,EHN,2VN,VA,VC  EDK
ROSSINI, G.  SERENATA PER PICCOLO COMPLESSO                 M&M
   FL,OB,EHN,2VN,VA,VC
SAGVIK, S.  SEPTET, OP 37 (1974-76).  CL,6STR              STI
SAGVIK, S.  SUITE DANSANT, OP 32 (1972/76).  OB,6STR       STI
SALIERI, A.-BALLOLA.  SERENATA IN B FL MA.  2CL,2BSN,2HN,VC  ESZ
SCHUBERT, M.  SEPTET IN 2 SATZEN.  CL,BSN,HN,VN,VA,VC,DB    DEU
STEARNS, P.  SEPTET.  CL,TSAX,HN,VN,VA,VC,DB                ACA
STEVENS, H.  SEPTET.  CL,BSN,HN,2VA,2VC                     ACA
STRANG, G.  CONCERTO GROSSO.  FL/PIC,CL,BSN,HN,VN,VA,VC     ACA
TIESSEN, H.  SEPTET IN G MA, OP 20.  FL,CL,HN,2VN,VA,VC     R&E
VERRALL, J.  PASTORAL ELEGY.  2FL,2VA,3VC                   ACA
VILLA-LOBOS, H.  CHOROS #7.  FL,OB,CL,ASAX,BSN,VN,VC        SCH
WEBER, B.  CONCERTINO, OP 45 (1956).  FL,OB,CL,2VN,VA,VC    B-B
YUN, I.  MUSIK (1959).  FL,OB,CL,BSN,HN,VN,VC               B&B
```

7 PARTS: WOODWIND-BRASS-STRING-734

```
ALCALAY, L.  3 (1964) STATISCHE GEBILDE                     EMO
   FL,CL,HN,TRB,VN,VA,VC
CAGE, J.  6 (1933) SHORT INVENTIONS.  AFL,CL,TRB,VN,2VA,VC  PET
HAINES, E.  CONCERTINO.  FL,CL,HN,TPT,VN,VA,VC              CF
HAUBENSTOCK-RAMATI, R.  MULTIPLE II (1970).  2WW,2BR,3STR   UE
INDY, V. D'.  SUITE EN RE.  2FL,TPT,2VN,VA,VC               HAM
INDY, V. D'.  SUITE IN OLDEN STYLE, OP 24.  2FL,TPT,2VN,VA VC  EDK
INDY, V. D'.  SUITE IN OLDEN STYLE, OP 24.  2FL,TPT,2VN,VA,VC  INT
JACOB, W.  KOMPOSITION 5/7.  FL,BCL,TPT,TRB,VN,VA,DB        BRH
JONES, C.  SEPTET.  FL,CL,BSN,TPT,TRB,VN,DB                 AMC
KOMOROUS, R.  UNTITLED 4.  4OB,2TPT,VN                      CAN
NEUKOMM, S. VON.  SEPTET.  FL,OB,CL,BSN,HN,TPT,DB           M&M
SCHONBACH, D.  CANZONA DA SONAR IV (1966)                   HMO
   2 LOTOSFLOTEN,CL,TPT,TRB, VN,DB
TIKKA, K.  3 FANTASIESTUCKE.  FL,CL,BSN,HN,TPT,VA,VC        FIN
```

7 PARTS: WOODWIND-BRASS-KEYBOARD-735

```
HASHAGEN, K.   SEPTALIE (1966).   FL,OB,CL,TPT,BSN,TRB,PF        GBV
MIROUZE, M.   PIECE EN SEPTUOR.   FL,OB,CL,BSN,HN,TPT,PF         ALE
```

7 PARTS: WOODWIND-STRING-KEYBOARD-736

```
AMES, W.   SEPTET.   FL,OB,2VN,VA,VC,PF                          ACA
BACH, C.P.E.-LAUSCHMANN.   CONCERTO #1 IN B FL MA                FOR
   OB,2VN,VA,VC,DB,BC
BACH, C.P.E.-DAMECK.   SONATINE IN C MA.   PF,2FL,2VN,VA,VC      B&B
BACH, J.C.F.-SCHUNEMANN.   SEPTET IN C MA.   OB,2HN,VN,VA,VC,PF  KIS
BACH, J.S.-PILLNEY.   MUSIKALISCHES OPFER, BWV 1079             BRH
   FL,2VN,VA,2VC,PF
BERGER, A.   SEPTET.   FL,CL,BSN,VN,VA,VC,PF                     PET
BIBER, C.-SHERMAN.   SONATA.   2OB(2EHN),2VN,ORG,BSN,DB          UE
CERHA, F.   FANTASIEN NACH CARDEW'S HERBST 60 (1960)            EMO
   CL,BCL,TSAX,VN, VA,VC,PF
DIETHELM, C.   SEPTET, OP110.   FL,2VN,VA,VC,DB,HPCD             S-V
EDER, H.   MUSICA SEMPLICE, OP 23/1.   FL,2VN,VA,VC,DB,HPCD      BRH
FAHRES, M.   IMITATION, VERSION 211/STRUKTUR 3                   SD
   FL,BSN,2VN,VA,VC,PF
GAGNON, A.   SEPTUOR.   FL,OB,VN,VA,DB,PF,HPCD                   CAN
GLUCK, C.-BARGE.   MELODIE (DANCE OF THE BLESSED SPIRITS)        CF
   FL,2VN,VA,VC,DB,PF
HABA, K.   SEPTET (1929).   CL,BSN,HN,VN,VA,VC,PF                CHF
HALFFTER, C.   ANTIPHONISMOI.   FL,OB/EHN,CL,VN,VA,VC,PF         UE
HAYDN, F.-LANDON.   DIVERTIMENTO IN C MA, "MANN UND WEIB"        LDO
   FL,OB,2VN,VC,DB,HPCD
HEINICHEN, J.-BACHMAIR.   WEIHNACHTS-PASTORALE                  BRH
   2OB(FL),2VN(OB),VA,VC( BSN),PF
HIDALGO, J.   CAURGA (1957).   PIC/FL,EHN,CL,BSN,VN,VC,PF        EEC
HUMMEL, J.N.   SEPTET, OP 74.   FL,OB,HN,VA,VC,DB,PF             PET
IMBRIE, A.   DANDELION WINE.   OB,CL,2VN,VA,VC,PF                SH
JANACEK, L.   CONCERTINO (1925).   PF,CL,BSN,HN,2VN,VA           ART
JANACEK, L.   CONCERTINO.   CL,BSN,HN,2VN,VA,PF                  INT
KASANDSHIEV, V.   VARIATIONS FOR 7 INSTRUMENTS (1954)            HG
   FL,CL,BSN,VN,V A,VC,PF
LEWIS, P.   SEPTET.   FL,CL,BSN,VN,VA,VC,PF                      TP
MARX, K.   KAMMERMUSIK, OP 56.   FL,OB,VA DA GAMBA,PF,VN,VA,VC   B&N
MIEG, P.   MUSIK (1954).   FL,OB,VN,VA,VC,DB,HPCD               B&B
MOORE, T.   RHONDALLET.   FL,OB,CL,2VN,VC,PF                     AMC
MOTTE, D. DE LA.   CONCERTO (1973).   3FL,CL,BCL,VC,PF           B&N
NATRA, S.   MUSIC (1964).   FL,CL,2VA,VC,DB,HPCD                ISR
NEIKRUG, M.   CONCERTINO (1976).   FL,OB,CL,VN,VA,VC,PF          AMC
PIJPER, W.   SEPTET (1920).   FL/PIC,OB/EHN,CL,BSN,HN,DB,PF      SD
PLESKOW, R.   BAGATELLES (1975).   FL,CL,BCL(BSN),VN,VC,DB,PF    ACA
POULENC, F.   RHAPSODIE NEGRE.   FL,CL,2VN,VA,VC,PF,VOICE AD LIB CHE
REA, J.   ANAPHORA (1970).   FL,CL,BSN,VN,VA,VC,PF               CAN
RIETI, V.   PARTITA.   FL,OB,2VN,VA,VC,HPCD                      BR
SCHOENBERG, A.   SUITE, OP 29.   E FL CL,CL,BCL,VN,VA,VC,PF      UE
SCHUBERT, M.   MUSIK.   FL,CL,BSN,VN,VA,VC,PF                    ISR
SIVIC, P.   RELATIONS.   FL,PF,2VN,VA,VC,DB                      EDD
```

7 PARTS: WOODWIND-STRING-KEYBOARD-736

```
SPOHR, L.  SEPTET, OP147.  FL,CL,BSN,HN,VN,VC,PF              MR
STRAVINSKY, I.  SEPTET.  CL,BSN,HN,VN,VA,VC,PF                BH
TELEMANN, G.-HECHLER.  CONCERTO IN A MI.  2FL,2OB,2VN,BC      SCH
TELEMANN, G.-TOTTCHER.  CONCERTO IN B FL MA.  3OB,3VN,BC      HSM
TELEMANN, G.-KOLBEL.  CONCERTO IN D MA.  2FL,2VN,VA,BSN,BC    HEI
TELEMANN, G.-KEHR.  OUVERTURE A 7 IN C MA.  3OB,2VN,VA,BC     SCH
TROJAHN, M.  KAMMERKONZERT.  2FL,2CL,VN,VC,HPCD/PF            HSM
VIVALDI, A.  CONCERTO IN F MA, F. XII/32                      RC
   2OB,BSN,VA D'AMORE,2HN,HPC D
VOSTRAK, Z.  AFEKTY (1963).  FL,CL,BSN,VN,VA,VC,PF            ART
WEBER, B.  CONCERTO, OP 32.  PF SOLO,VC,FL,OB,CL,BSN,HN       ACA
WILSON, T.  SINFONIA.  CL,BSN,HN,VN,VA,VC,PF                  CA
```

7 PARTS: WOODWIND-BRASS-STRING-KEYBOARD-737

```
ANGERER, P.  CONCERTO.  HPCD,VA,OB,EHN,2BSN,TPT              UE
BETTS, L.  MUSIC FOR THEATRE (1950).  OB,2CL,HN,TPT,DB,PF    CAN
HUMMEL, J.N.  MILITARY SEPTET, OP114.  FL,CL,TPT,VN,VC,DB,PF MR
HUMMEL, J.N.  SEPTETT MILITAIRE, OP114.  FL,CL,TPT,VN,VC,DB,PF MRL
JEZ, J.  WINTER TALE.  2FL,CL,TPT,VN,VC,PF                   EDD
LAUFER, E.  VARIATIONS.  FL,CL,BSN,TPT,VN,VC,PF              NVM
MACERO, T.  ONE-THREE QUARTERS.  PIC(FL),VN,VC,TRB,TU,2PF    PET
MARTINU, B.  RONDI (1930).  OB,CL,BSN,TPT,2VN,PF             ART
MASELLI, G.  DIVERTIMENTO (1964).  FL,OB,TPT,TRB,VN,DB,HPCD  ESZ
OLIVEIRA, J.  ITERACOES.  FL,CL,HN,TPT,VC,DB,PF              EDT
SZATHMARY, Z.  ALPHA (1968).  FL,CL,TPT,PF,VN,VA,VC          HMO
WRIGHT, M.  CHAMBER SYMPHONY (1973)                          B-B
   FL/PIC,CL/BCL,TPT,TRB,VN,VC,PF
WYNER, Y.  SERENADE.  FL,HN,TPT,TRB,VA,VC,PF                 ACA
```

7 PARTS INCLUDING HARP-738

```
ANGULO, M.  SIGLAS.  FL,OB,CL,HP,PF,VC,PERC                  EDA
BALLIF, C.  IMAGINAIRE I.  FL,CL,TPT,TRB,VN,VC,HP            EFM
BEECROFT, N.  RAGAS (1968).  FL,VN,VA,VC,PERC,HP,PF          CAN
DAVIES, P.  CANON IN MEMORY OF IGOR STRAVINSKY               BH
   FL,CL,2VN,VA,VC,HP
FELDMAN, M.  STRAITS OF MAGELLAN, THE                        PET
   FL,HN,TPT,GUIT,HP,PF,DB
FRID, G.  NOCTURNES, OP 24 (1925).  FL,STR QUINTET,HP        SD
GENZMER, H.  SEPTET.  FL,CL,HN,VN,VA,VC,HP                   SCH
HEALEY, D.  LAUDES, OP 26 (1967).  FL,HN,2VN,VC,HP,PERC      CAN
HODDINOTT, A.  VARIATIONS.  FL,CL,HP,2VN,VA,VC               OX
KLEBE, G.  TENNEN NO BI, OP 62 (1972).  FL,OB,CL,HP,PF,VC,DB B&N
KROL, B.  HARFEN-SEPTETT, OP 7.  CL,BSN,HN,HP,VN,VA,VC       PM
KRUYF, T. DE.  SERENATA, OP 21 (1968).  FL,CL,2VN,VA,VC,HP   SD
LORD, D.  SEPTET.  FL,CL,HP,2VN,VA,VC                        UE
LUNDBORG, E.  COMBONE.  OB,BCL,VC,DB,PF,HP,PERC              ACA
MENGELBERG, K.  BALLADE.  FL,CL,2VN,VA,VC,HP                 SD
PETRIC, I.  7 COMPOSITIONS.  OB,CL,HN,TPT,VN,VC,HP           EDD
PETRIC, I.  CROQUIS SONORES.  HP SOLO,OB,BCL,HN,PF,DB,PERC   EDD
RAVEL, M.  INTRODUCTION & ALLEGRO.  FL,CL,2VN,VA,VC,HP       DUR
RAVEL, M.  INTRODUCTION & ALLEGRO.  FL,CL,2VN,VA,VC,HP       INT
READ, G.  SONORIC FANTASIA (1968).  5FL,HP,PERC              SS
```

```
SUTER, R.   SERENATA.  FL,OB D'AMORE,BCL,HP,VN,VA,VC          HEI
ZAGWIJN, H.  NOCTURNE.  FL,EHN,CL,BSN,HN,HP,CEL               PET
ZENDER, H.  KAMMERKONZERT.  FL,2VN,VA,VC,HP,HPCD              SCH
```

7 PARTS INCLUDING GUITAR-739

```
BEDFORD, D.  HORSE, A, HIS NAME WAS HUNRY FENCEWAVER WALKINS  UE
   FL,CL, VN,VC,DB,PF,GUIT
DAVIES, P.  PSALM 124.  FL,AFL,BCL,VN,VC,PERC,GUIT           BH
DELAS, J.  DENKBILD- KURZE SCHATTEN (1977)                   HG
   FL,CL/BCL,BSN,PERC,VA,VC ,GUIT
FELDMAN, M.  STRAITS OF MAGELLAN, THE (1961)                 PET
   FL,HN,TPT,GUIT,HP,PF,D B
GELLMAN, S.  SONATE (1975).  FL/PIC,CL,VC,PF/CEL,GUIT,2PERC  CAN
GLICK, S.  DIVERTISSEMENT (1968)                             CAN
   CL,VIB,GUIT,VC,DB,PERC,MANDOLIN
HEKSTER, W.  EPICYCLE I & II (1975)                          SD
   FL,BCL,DB,TPT,GUIT,PERC,ACC
KOMOROUS, R.  YORK.  FL,OB(TPT)                              UE
PAPINEAU-COUTURE, J.  NOCTURNES (1969; REV 1976)            CAN
   FL,CL,VN,VC,HPCD,G UIT,PERC
RECK, D.  NUMBER 2.  ACTRESS,FL/PIC,BCL,VN,DB,GUIT,PERC      PET
SCHONBERG, A.  SERENADE, OP 24                               CHE
   CL,BCL,MANDOLIN,GUIT,VN,VA,VC,VOICE   AD LIB
SCHULLER, G.(ARR).  COUNTRY DANCE MUSIC                      MAR
   FL,VN,DB,GUIT,ACC,PF,DR
TANENBAUM, E.  CONSORT.  FL,ASAX,HN,VC,DB,GUIT,VIB           ACA
```

7 PARTS INCLUDING PERCUSSION-740

```
AITKEN, R.  KEBYAR (1971).  FL,CL,TRB,2DB,PERC,TAPE         EDS
ALCALAY, L.  3 SERENADES (1973).  FL,OB,CL,HN,VN,VA,PERC    EMO
AMRAM, D.  SUMMERNIGHT'S DREAM.  OB,BSN,VN,VC,TPT,HPCD,PERC  PET
ANZAGHI, D.  REMOTA (1977).  PIC/AFL,CL,PF,VA,VC,DB,PERC     ESZ
AVIDON, M.  ENIGMA (1962).  FL,OB,CL,BSN,HN,PF,PERC          ISR
BABBITT, M.  ALL SET.  ASAX/TSAX,TPT,TRB,PF,DB,DR,VIB        AMP
BAINBRIDGE, S.  SPIROGYRA.  FL/PIC,HN,VN,VA,VC,CEL/MAR,VIB   UMP
BAKER, M.  LETTER, THE (1974).  FL/PIC,CL,VN,VA,VC,CEL,PERC  CAN
BARATI, G.  HAWAIIAN FORESTS.  FL,CL,HN,VN,VA,VC,PERC        ACA
BARBE, H.  MINIATUREN ZU "2 HERREN AUS VERONA" (1959)        GBV
   CL,TPT,TRB,DB ,PF,2PERC
BEECROFT, N.  RAGAS (1968).  FL,VN,VA,VC,PERC,HP,PF          CAN
BEERMAN, B.  POINTS.  FL,CL,HN,VN,VA,DB,PERC                 ACA
BENGUEREL, X.  JOC.  FL,OB,CL,VN,VA,VC,PERC                  HMO
BERGSMA, W.  CHANGES FOR 7.  FL,OB,CL,BSN,HN,PF,PERC         GA
BERRY, W.  DIVERTIMENTO.  FL,OB,CL,BSN,HN,PF,PERC            EV
BIELER, H.  QUICK FINGERS.  FL,PF,5PERC                      MV
BIRTWISTLE, H.  MEDUSA (1969/70)                             UE
   FL/PIC,CL/SOP SAX,PERC,PF/CEL,VN/V A,VC,TAPE
BLANK, A.  AMERICAN MEDLEY.  FL,2TPT,HN,TRB,TU,PERC          AMP
BOEHNLEIN, F.  MEDITATIONS.  CL,BSN,TPT,VN,VC,2PERC          MAN
BOONE, C.  STARFISH (1966).  FL,CL,2VN,2PERC,PF             EDS
BOYD, A.  METAMORPHOSES OF THE FEMALE PHOENIX, THE (1971)    FB
   FL,OB,CL, BSN,HN,PF,PERC
```

7 PARTS INCLUDING PERCUSSION-740

```
BRAUN, R.   BASSOON BUG.   FL,OB,CL,2BSN,HN,PERC                      YM
BRETTINGHAM SMITH, J.   O RISE, OP  6 (1973)                          B&B
   PIC/FL/AFL/BFL,TRB,VC,P F,HPCD,2PERC
BROSH, T.   MUSIC.   FL,OB,CL,BSN,HN,DR,TAPE                          MAN
BROTT, A.   MINI-MINUS (1968).   CL,BSN,VN,TPT,TRB,DB,PERC            CAN
BUDD, H.   III FOR DOUBLE ENSEMBLE.   FL,CL,VC,VIB,TPT,DB,DR          CPE
CARMICHAEL, H.-KLICKMAN.   STAR DUST.   2FL,OB(FL),2CL,BELLS          BE
CASAGRANDE, A.   FRASI.   FL,CL,BSN,VN,VA,VC,PERC                     CAR
CASTRO, C. DE.   TUCUMBALAM (1973).   FL,OB,CL,VN,VC,TRB,PERC         EDA
CEELY, R.   MODULES.   FL,ASAX,VN,VA,DB,PF,PERC                       ACA
CORDERO, R.   PERMUTACIONES 7.   CL,VN,VA,DB,TPT,PF,PERC              SN
DAVIES, P.   ANTECHRIST.   PIC,BCL,VN,VC,3PERC                        JB
DAVIES, P.   AVE MARIS STELLA.   FL,AFL,CL,VA,VC,PF,MAR               BH
DAVIES, P.   PSALM 124.   FL,AFL,BCL,VN,VC,PERC,GUIT                  BH
DE YOUNG, L.   HOMAGE TO DIXIELAND.   CL,TPT,TRB,4PERC                SS
DELAS, J.   DENKBILD- KURZE SCHATTEN (1977)                          HG
   FL,CL/BCL,BSN,PERC,VA,VC ,GUIT
DONATONI, F.   FOR GRILLY (1960).   FL,CL,BCL,VN,VA,VC,PERC           ESZ
EATON, J.   LION, THE, & ANDROCLES.   FL,OB,BCL,BSN,2PF,PERC          SH
FELDMAN, M.   VIOLA IN MY LIFE II, THE (1970)                        UE
   FL,CL,PERC,PF,VN,VA,VC
GELLMAN, S.   SONATE (1975).   FL/PIC,CL,VC,PF/CEL,GUIT,2PERC         CAN
GERSCHEFSKI, E.   AMERICA VARIATIONS FOR WINDS, OP 45/10             ACA
   FL,OB,CL,BSN,TPT,TRB,PERC
GLICK, S.   DIVERTISSEMENT (1968)                                    CAN
   CL,VIB,GUIT,VC,DB,PERC,MANDOLIN
GREEN, R.   3 PIECES FOR Δ CONCERT.   2CL,2TPT,TRB,PF,PERC            AMF.
HARTWELL, H.   ACITORE (1968)                                        CAN
   FL/SOP SAX/ASAX,CL/AFL/TSAX,BCL/BAR SA X,TU,PF,2PERC
HEALEY, D.   LAUDES, OP 26 (1967).   FL,HN,2VN,VC,HP,PERC             CAN
HEDWALL, L.   METAMORFOSI.   FL,CL,EHN,VN,VC,XYL,PERC                 EMF
HEIDER, W.   PASSATEMPO.   CL,BSN,TPT,TRB,VN,VC,PERC                  PET
HEKSTER, W.   EPICYCLE I & II (1975)                                 SD
   FL,BCL,DB,TPT,GUIT,PERC,ACC
HELFRITZ, H.   TANZSUITE.   2FL,3VN,VC,PERC                          PEL
HOLLOWAY, R.   RIVERS OF HELL, OP 34, THE                            BH
   FL/PIC/AFL,OB/EHN,CL/E FL CL/BCL,VA,VC,PF,PERC
JOHANSON, S.   BRONSALDERSSVIT (1954)                                STI
   OB,CL,BSN,TPT,TRB,TIMP,XYL
KASILAG, L.   TOCCATA.   CL,IIN,TPT,TRB,TIMP,PERC,PF                  PI
KERSTERS, W.   SEPTET, OP 37 (1966).   4CL,PERC,TIMP,PF              CBD
KIRCHNER, V.   NACHTMUSIK (1971).   FL,CL,VN,VC,DB,2PERC             EMO
KOMOROUS, R.   YORK.   FL,OB(TPT),BSN,PF,DB,TR,MANDOLINE             UE
KONT, P.   TRAURIGEN JAGER (1958).   FL,2HN,2VN,DB,PERC              EMO
KORTE, K.   MATRIX 7.   FL,OB,CL,HN,BSN,PERC,PF                      ECS
KUPKOVIC, L.   PRAPARIERTER TEXT 2.   FL,TPT,VN,VC,DB,TIMP,TAPE      UE
LAYTON, B.   DIVERTIMENTO, OP  6.   CL,BSN,VN,VC,TRB,HPCD,PERC        GS
LINDE, H.   CAPRICCIO (1963).   3FL,VN,VA,VC,DR                      AMP
LUDWIG, J.   STENOGRAMME.   FL,TSAX,TRB,DB,PERC,VIB,HPCD             EMO
LUNDBORG, E.   COMBONE.   OB,BCL,VC,DB,PF,HP,PERC                     ACA
MAMLOK, U.   FOR 7.   CL,BCL,TPT,VN,VC,DB,PERC                        ACA
MANZONI, G.   MUSICA NOTTURNA (1966).   FL,2CL,BSN,HN,PF,PERC        ESZ
MARCELLI, N.   MUSIC BOX MINUET.   PIC,2FL,OB(FL),2CL,BELLS           BE
MARTIN, V.   CHAMBER SYMPHONY.   FL,OB,CL,TRB,DB,PF,TIMP             AMC
MASSEUS, J.   HABANANGO.   4CL,DB,PF,PERC                            HU
MIEREANU, C.   MUSIQUE ELEMENTAIRE DE CONCERT (1978)                EDS
   FL,OB,CL,VC,PF, HPCD,PERC
MITREA-CELARIANU, M.   SETH (1969).   FL,CL,TPT,TRB,DB,PF,PERC        EDS
MOSS, L.   EXCHANGES (1968).   2FL,OB,2TPT,TB,PERC                   FER
MOTTE, D. DE LA.   SEPTET (1965).   CL,BSN,TPT,TRB,VN,DB,PERC        B&N
MOZART, W.-KAHN.   DIVERTIMENTO #5.   2CL,3TPT,TRB,TIMP               EM
MOZART, W.-KAHN.   DIVERTIMENTO #6.   2CL,3TPT,TRB,TIMP               EM
```

7 PARTS INCLUDING PERCUSSION-740

NESSLER, R. MOTIONEN (1964). CL,BSN,TPT,VN,VC,PF,PERC   EMO
NONO, L. POLIFONICA-MONODIA-RITMICA   S&C
    FL,CL,BCL,ASAX,HN,PF,PERC
OHANA, M. SIGNES. FL,PF,CITHARE,4PERC   APH
PAPINEAU-COUTURE, J. NOCTURNES (1969; REV 1976)   CAN
    FL,CL,VN,VC,HPCD,G UIT,PERC
PARRIS, R. DIRGE FOR THE NEW SUNRISE. FL,VN,VC,TIMP,3PERC   ACA
PENNISI, F. CHORALIS CUM FIGURIS (1968)   ESZ
    FL,OB,CL,BSN,VN,DB,PERC
PERSICHETTI, V. KING LEAR, OP 35. FL,OB,CL,HN,BSN,PF,TIMP   EV
PERSSON, B. OM SOMMAREN SKONA II (1965)   STI
    FL,CL,TRB,VC,VIB,PERC,TAPE
PERT, M. OMEGA CENTAURI, OP 11. FL,OB,CL,VN,PF,PERC,TAPE   JOW
PETRIC, I. CROQUIS SONORES. HP SOLO,OB,BCL,HN,PF,DB,PERC   EDD
PICKER, T. SEPTET. FL/AFL/PIC,TPT,TRB,BSN/CBSN,VN,PF,VIB   ACA
QUINTANAR, H. ILLAPSO. CL,BSN,TPT,TRB,VN,DB,PERC   EDT
RAZZI, F. 4 INVENZIONI (1961). FL,CL,TRB,VN,VA,VC,VIB   ESZ
READ, G. SONORIC FANTASIA (1968). 5FL,HP,PERC   SS
RECK, D. NUMBER 2. ACTRESS,FL/PIC,BCL,VN,DB,GUIT,PERC   PET
ROVICS, H. TRANSACTIONS. FL,CL,VN,VC,DB,PF,DR   ACA
SCHAT, P. SEPTET. FL,OB,BCL,HN,VC,PF,PERC   SD
SCHULLER, G.(ARR). COUNTRY DANCE MUSIC   MAR
    FL,VN,DB,GUIT,ACC,PF,DR
SCULTHORPE, P. TABUH TABUHAN (1968). FL,OB,CL,BSN,HN,2PERC   FB
SOMER, A. CONCERTINO. FL,CL,BSN,VA,VC,PF,PERC   AMC
SREBOTNJAK, A. MACEDONIAN DANCES. 2OB,2CL,2BSN,PERC   GS
STOUT, A. TOCCATA. ASAX,6PERC   AM
STRAESSER, J. ENCOUNTERS (1973; REV 1975). BCL,6PERC   SD
STRAVINSKY, I. HISTORY OF A SOLDIER, THE   WH
    CL,BSN,TPT,TRB,VN,DB,PERC
SURINACH, C. HOLLYWOOD CARNIVAL (1954)   RON
    FL/PIC,CL,TPT,2PERC,TIMP,DB
TAKAHASHI, Y. CHROMAMORPHE I. FL,VN,DB,HN,TPT,TRB,VIB   PET
TANENBAUM, E. CONSORT. FL,ASAX,HN,VC,DB,GUIT,VIB   ACA
TIPPETT, M. PRELUDE-AUTUMN. OB,2VN,VA,VC,PERC,PF   S&C
TOCH, E. CANZONETTA, CAPRICE, NIGHT SONG   BE
    FL,OB,CL,BAN,2HN,DR
TOCH, E. CAVALCADE. FL,OB,CL,BSN,2HN,DR   BE
TOCH, E. ROUNDELAY. FL,OB,CL,BSN,2HN,DR   BE
TOWER, J. BLACK TOPAZ. FL,CL/BCL,TPT,TRB,PF,2PERC   ACA
VLIET, H. VAN DER. CONCERTINO (1968). FL,CL,TRB,VN,VC,XYL,PF   SS
WOLPE, S. PIECE FOR 2 INSTRUMENTAL UNITS   M&M
    FL,OB,VN,VC,DB,PF,PERC

7 PARTS INCLUDING TAPE-743

AITKEN, R. KEBYAR (1971). FL,CL,TRB,2DB,PERC,TAPE   EDS
ANGULO, M. SIGLAS. FL,OB,CL,HP,PF,VC,PERC   EDA
BIRTWISTLE, H. MEDUSA (1969/70)   UE
    FL/PIC,CL/SOP SAX,PERC,PF/CEL,VN,/ VA,VC,TAPE
BROSH, T. MUSIC. FL,OB,CL,BSN,HN,DR,TAPE   MAN
KUPKOVIC, L. PRAPARIERTER TEXT 2. FL,TPT,VN,VC,DB,TIMP,TAPE   UE
OLAN, D. SATZ. FL,CL,VN,VA,VC,PF,TAPE   ACA
PERSSON, B. OM SOMMAREN SKONA II (1965)   STI
    FL,CL,TRB,VC,VIB,PERC,TAPE
PERT, M. OMEGA CENTAURI, OP 11. FL,OB,CL,VN,PF,PERC,TAPE   JOW
SUBOTNIK, M. PLAY!. FL,OB,CL,BSN,HN,PF,TAPE   AMC
WARD-STEINMAN, D. PUTNEY 3. FL,OB,CL,BSN,HN,PF,TAPE   EM

8 PARTS: WOODWINDS
INCLUDING HORN-821

```
ALPAERTS, F.  MUSIQUE DU SOIR.  2FL,2OB,2CL,2BSN                    EES
ALPAERTS, F.  SERENADE.  2FL,2OB,2CL,2BSN                           HE
ANDRIESSEN, J.  OCTUOR (1948).  FL,2OB,2CL,BCL,2BSN                 SD
ANDRIESSEN, J.  SINFONIA DELL'ARTE (1972).  2FL,2OB,2CL,2BSN        SD
BAKSA, R.  OCTET IN E FL MA.  2FL,2OB,2CL,2BSN                      AB
BEETHOVEN, L. VAN.  OCTET IN E FL MA, OP103.  2OB,2CL,2BSN,2HN      BR
BEETHOVEN, L. VAN.  OCTET, OP103.  2OB,2CL,2BSN,2HN                 EDK
BEETHOVEN, L. VAN.  OCTET, OP103.  2OB,2CL,2BSN,2HN                 MR
BEETHOVEN, L. VAN.  OKTETT IN E FL MA, OP103                        BRH
   2OB,2CL,2BSN,2HN
BEETHOVEN, L. VAN.  RONDINO IN E-FLAT.  2OB,2CL,2HN,2BSN            EDK
BEETHOVEN, L. VAN-MAY.  RONDINO.  2OB,2CL,2BSN,2HN                  SCH
BEETHOVEN, L. VAN.  RONDINO IN E FL MA.  2OB,2CL,2HN,2BSN           B&N
BEETHOVEN, L. VAN.  RONDINO IN E FL MA.  2OB,2CL,2BSN,2HN           BRH
BEETHOVEN, L. VAN.  RONDINO IN E FL MA.  2OB,2CL,2BSN,2HN           INT
BEETHOVEN, L. VAN.  RONDINO IN E FL MA.  2OB,2CL,2BSN,2HN           RC
BEETHOVEN, L. VAN.  RONDINO IN E FL MA                              TP
   2OB(FL,OB),2CL,2BSN(BSN,BCL),2HN
BERGER, A.  CANZON OCTAVI MODI.  4OB,2EHN,2BSN                      CP
BETTINELLI, B.  OTTETTO (1975).  2FL,OB,2CL,2BSN,HN                 CAR
BIALAS, G.  ROMANZA E DANZA.  OKTETT (J. MEYERBEER)                 B&N
   2OB,2CL,2HN,2BSN
BONSEL, A.  OCTET (1975).  FL/PIC,2OB,2CL,2BSN,HN                   SD
BOZZA, E.  OCTANPHONIE.  2OB,2CL,2HN,2BSN                           ALE
BRADLEY, W.  DEEP QUARRY, THE.  8CL                                 TP
BRADLEY, W.  HONEYSUCKLE & CLOVER.  5CL,2BCL,BASSET HN              AMC
BRUN, G.  PASSACAILLE.  2FL,OB2CL,BSN,2HN                           HLE
CALLHOFF, H.  MOVIMENTI (1973).  FL,2OB,2CL,HN,2BSN                 HG
DI LASSO, O.-YATES.  ECHO SONG.  4CL,2ACL,2BCL                      KN
DRUSCHETZKY, G.-WEINMANN.  PARTITAS I-VI.  2OB,2CL,2BSN,2HN         LDO
DUBOIS, T.  SUITE #1.  2FL,OB,2CL,2BSN,HN                           EDK
DUBOIS, T.  SUITE #2.  2FL,OB,2CL,2BSN,HN                           ALE
DUBOIS, T.  SUITE #2.  2FL,OB,2CL,2BSN,HN                           EDK
DURAND, P.  LET US TAKE A WALK IN THE WOODS                         BE
   2FL,2OB,2CL,BCL,BSN
DVORAK, A.-CLEMENTS.  SLAVONIC DANCE, OP 46/8                       BH
   2OB,2CL,2HN,2BSN, OPT DB(CBSN)
DVORAK, A. CLEMENTS.  SLAVONIC DANCE, OP 72/1                       BH
   2OB,2CL,2HN,2BSN, OPT DB(CBSN)
DVORAK, A.-CLEMENTS.  SLAVONIC DANCE, OP 72/7                       BH
   2OB,2CL,2HN,2BSN, OPT DB(CBSN)
EK, G.  OKTETT (1970).  2FL,2OB,2CL,2BSN                            STI
ERDMANN, C.  RAUMKOMPOSITION.  8FL                                  JB
FAURE, G.  NOCTURNE.  FL,2OB,2CL,2HN,BSN                            HAM
GABRIELI, A.-EPHROSS.  SONATA PIAN'E FORTE.  8FL                    TP
GARLICK, A.  PIECE.  8CL                                            SS
GRIEG, E.-AUSLENDER.  WEDDING DAY AT TROLDHAUGEN                    WI
   2PIC,2FL,2CL,2BCL
HANDEL, G.(FINDLAY).  ANDANTE-LARGHETTO                             CF
   FL,OB,3CL,ACL,BCL,BSN
HANDEL, G.-HINDSLEY.  SARABANDA.  8FL                               SO
HANDEL, G.(CAMPBELL).  SINFONIA (SOLOMON).  2OB,2CL,2BSN,2HN        JE
HAWES, J.  PIECES OF 8.  2FL,2OB,2CL,2BSN                           JE
HAYDN, F.-KAHN.  ALLEGRO (OCTET).  2OB,2CL,2BSN,2HN                 EM
HAYDN, F.-BOUDREAU.  DIVERTIMENTO #1.  2OB,2HN,3BSN,CBSN(DB)        PET
```

```
HAYDN, F.-GEIRINGER.  DIVERTIMENTO IN E FL MA              UE
   2OB,2CL,2BSN,2HN
HAYDN, F.-MAY.  FELDPARTIE.  2OB,2CL,2BSN,2HN             SCH
HAYDN, F.-WOLLHEIM.  MUSIK IN F MA.  2FL(2OB),2CL,2BSN,2HN B&B
HAYDN, F.  OCTET IN F MA.  2OB,2CL,2BSN,2HN               INT
HAYDN, F.  OCTET.  2OB,2CL,2HN,2BSN                       EDK
HAYDN, F.-TRIEBENSEE.  OXFORD SYMPHONY.  2OB,2CL,2HN,2BSN  JE
HENNEBERG, R.  SERENAD. OCTET.  FL,OB,2CL,2BSN,2HN        STI
HLOBIL, E.  OCTET (1956).  2OB,2CL,2BSN,2HN              CHF
HORVATH, J.  REDUNDANZ #1 (1966).  2OB,2CL,2HN,2BSN       LDO
HUMMEL, J.N.  OCTET-PARTITA IN E FL MA                    MR
   2OB,2CL,2HN,2BSN,CBSN AD LIB
HUMPERDINCK, E.-FINDLAY.  HANSEL & GRETEL MELODIES         CF
   FL,OB,3CL,ACL,BCL,BSN
JACOB, G.  DIVERTIMENTO IN E FL MA.  2OB,2CL,2BSN,2HN     MR
KETTING, O.  MARCH (1979).  4CL,4SAX                      SD
KOETSIER, J.  OCTET (1968).  2OB,2CL,2BSN,2HN             SD
KOSCHINSKY, F.  VARIATIONS UBER DAS MANTELLIED            HEI
   2OB,2CL,2HN,2BSN
KRAMAR-KROMMER, F.  OCTET, OP 79.  2OB,2CL,2BSN,2HN       MR
KROL, B.  LINZER HARMONIEMUSIK, OP 67.  2OB,2CL,2HN,2BSN  B&B
KROMMER, F.  OCTET-PARTITA, OP 57                         MR
   2OB,2CL,2HN,2BSN,CBSN AD LIB
KROMMER, F.  OCTET-PARTITA, OP 67                         MR
   2OB,2CL,2HN,2BSN,CBSN AD LIB
KROMMER, F.  OCTET-PARTITA, OP 69                         MR
   2OB,2CL,2HN,2BSN,CBSN AD LIB
LACHNER, F.  OCTET, OP156.  FL,OB,2CL,2HN,2BSN            MR
LADERMAN, E.  OCTET IN 1 MOVEMENT.  2OB,2CL,2HN,2BSN      OX
LANDOWSKI, L.  WIND OCTET (1973).  2OB,2CL,2HN,2BSN       PWM
LOWE, T.  SUITE OF DANCES.  2FL,OB,3CL,BSN,HN             JE
MOURANT, W.  EVENING SONG.  8CL                           ACA
MOZART-WENDT/VOXMAN.  COSI FAN TUTTE.  2OB,2CL,2BSN,2HN   MR
MOZART, TRIEBENSEE/VOXMAN.  CLEMENZA DI TITO, LA          MR
   2OB,2CL,2BSN,2HN
MOZART, W.-VOXMAN.  ABDUCTION FROM THE SERAGLIO, THE, 2 VOLS  MR
   2OB,2CL,2BSN,2HN
MOZART, W.  DIVERTIMENTO IN D MA, 166.  2OB,2EHN,2CL,2BSN  BRH
MOZART, W.-EINSTEIN.  DIVERTIMENTO IN E FL MA, KV182      PET
   2OB,2CL,2BSN,2H N
MOZART, W.-EINSTEIN.  DIVERTIMENTO IN E FL MA, KV226      PET
   2OB,2CL,2BSN,2H N
MOZART, W.-EINSTEIN.  DIVERTIMENTO IN E FL MA, KV227      PET
   2OB,2CL,2BSN,2H N
MOZART, W.-VOXMAN.  DON GIOVANNI.  2OB,2CL,2HN,2BSN       MR
MOZART, W.  DON GIOVANNI HARMONIEMUSIK.  2OB,2CL,2HN,2BSN SCH
MOZART, W.-GIEGLING.  ENTFUHRUNG AUS DEM SERAIL, DIE      B&N
   2OB,2EHN,2BSN,2 HN
MOZART, W.-VOXMAN.  MAGIC FLUTE, THE.  2OB,2CL,2BSN,2HN   MR
MOZART, W.-BLOCK/VOXMAN.  MARRIAGE OF FIGARO, THE, 2 VOLS MR
   2OB,2CL,2BSN,2HN
MOZART, W.  OCTET, K196E.  2OB,2CL,2BSN,2HN              M&M
MOZART, W.-TOPILOW.  SELECTIONS FROM COSI FAN TUTTE      CST
   2OB(2FL),2CL,2HN,2BSN
MOZART, W.  SERENADE #10, K361.  2OB,2CL,2HN,2BSN        EDK
MOZART, W.  SERENADE #11 IN E FL MA, K375.  2OB,2CL,2BSN,2HN  BR
MOZART, W.  SERENADE #11 IN E FL MA, K375.  2OB,2CL,2HN,2BSN  MR
MOZART, W.  SERENADE #11, K375.  2OB,2CL,2HN,2BSN        EDK
MOZART, W.  SERENADE #12 IN C MI, K388.  2OB,2CL,2BSN,2HN  BR
MOZART, W.  SERENADE #12, K388.  2OB,2CL,2BSN,2HN        EDK
MOZART, W.  SERENADE #12, K388.  2OB,2CL,2HN,2BSN        MR
MOZART, W.  SERENADE IN B FL MA, KV196F.  2OB,2CL,2BSN,2IIN  SCH
```

8 PARTS: WOODWINDS INCLUDING HORN-821

```
MOZART, W.   SERENADE IN C MI, K388.  2OB,2CL,2BSN,2HN          BRH
MOZART, W.   SERENADE IN E FL MA, K375.  2OB,2CL,2BSN,2HN       BRH
MOZART, W.   SERENADE, K182.  2OB,2CL,2BSN,2HN                  M&M
MOZART, W.-WENDT.  12 STUCKE (DON GIOVANNI)                     B&N
    2OB,2EHN,2CL,2HN,2BSN
MYSLIVECEK, J.-RACEK/SCHOENBAUM.  3 OCTETS.  2OB,2CL,2HN,2BSN   ES
NILSSON, B.  FREQUENZEN.  FL,PIC,OB,EHN,CL,BCL,TSAX,BSN         UE
NILSSON, B.  ZEITEN IM UMLAUF.  PIC,FL,OB,EHN,CL,BCL,TSAX,BSN   UE
NOVACEK, R.  SINFONIETTA, OP 48.  FL,OB,2CL,2HN,2BSN            BRH
NOVACEK, R.  SINFONIETTA, OP 48.  FL,OB,2CL,2BSN,2HN            M&M
PETYREK, F.  DIVERTIMENTO.  2FL,OB,CL,2BSN,2HN                  UE
POOT, M.  MOSAIQUE.  2FL,2OB,2CL,2BSN                           UE
RAUTAVAARA, E.  WIND OCTET (1964).  8WW                         MT
REINECKE, C.  OCTET, OP216.  FL,OB,2CL,2HN,2BSN                 H-V
RYCHLIK, J.  SERENADE (ERINNERUNGEN).  2OB,2CL,2BSN,2HN         CHF
SAINT-SAENS, C.-TAFFANEL.  FEUILLET D'ALBUM, OP 81             DUR
    FL,OB,2CL,2BSN,2H N
SALIERI, A.-BALLOLA.  ARMONIA PER UN TEMPLO DELLA NOTTE         ESZ
    2OB,2CL,2BSN,2HN
SCHICKELE, P.  MONOCHROME I.  8FL                               EV
SCHNEIDER, G.-WOLLHEIM.  HARMONIE-MUSIK IN F MA                 B&B
    2FL,2CL,2BSN,2HN
SCHUBERT, F.  MENUETT & FINALE (OCTET IN F MA)                  BRH
    2OB,2CL,2BSN,2HN
SCHUBERT, F.  MENUETT & FINALE.  2OB,2CL,2BSN,2HN               M&M
SCHUBERT, F.-LANDON.  7 MENUETTE, VOL #2(4-6)                   B&N
    FL,OB,2CL,2HN,2BSN
SCHUBERT, F.-BROWN.  MINUET & FINALE IN F MA                    NOM
    2OB,2CL,2HN,2BSN
SCHUBERT, F.-KAHN.  MINUET.  2OB,2CL,2BSN,2HN                   EM
SHEWAN, D.  WIND OCTET.  2FL,2OB,2CL,HN,BSN                     JB
SIXTA, J.  OCTET.  2FL,2OB,2CL,2BSN                             SHF
STADLMAIR.  OCTET.  2OB,2CL,2BSN,2HN                            PET
STEARNS, P.  OCTET.  PIC,FL,OB,EHN,CL,BCL,BSN,CBSN              ACA
TANSMAN, A.  4 IMPRESSIONS.  2OB,2CL,2BSN,2HN                   MC
TRIEBENSEE, J.-BROWN.  MENUETTO CON VARIAZIONI (DON GIOVANNI)   NOM
    2OB,2CL,2BSN,2HN
TULL, F.  SCHERZINO.  PIC,3FL,3CL,BCL                           BH
UHL, A.  EINE VERGNUGLICHE MUSIK (OKTET).  2OB,2CL,2BSN,2HN     UE
VENT, J.  PARTHIA #17.  2FL,2CL,2BSN,2HN                        CHF
VRANA, F.  SERENADE.  2OB,2CL,2BSN,2HN                          CHF
WAGENSEIL, G.-JANETZKY.  PARTHIA IN C.  2OB(FL),2EHN,2HN,2BSN   EUL
WHITLOCK, P.-EMERSON.  FOLK TUNE.  2FL,OB,3CL,BSN,HN            JE
```

8 PARTS: WOODWIND-KEYBOARD (INCL HORN)-828

```
NILSSON, T.  KAMMARKONSERT (1963).  2FL,3OB,2BSN,ORG           STI
```

8 PARTS: WOODWIND-BRASS-832

```
ANGERER, P.  QUINTA TOLEN.  FL,OB,CL,BSN,HN,2TPT,TRB           UE
BLOCK, H.  OCTET.  2FL,OB,CL,BSN,HN,TPT,TRB                    LDO
BORRIS, S.  BLASER-OKTETT, OP 55.  FL,OB,CL,BCL,BSN,2HN,TPT    S-V
BOTTENBERG, W.  OCTET (1972).  FL/PIC,OB,CL,BSN,TPT,2HN,TRB    CAN
```

8 PARTS: WOODWIND-BRASS-832

```
BRUSSELMANS, M.  PRELUDE & FUGUE.  FL,2OB,2CL,BSN,HN,TPT          EDS
COUPERIN, F.-PETIT.  STEINKERQUE, LA                              BIL
    FL,OB,CL,BSN,HN,2TPT,TRB
FELLEGARA, V.  OTETTO (1953).  FL,OB,CL,BSN,HN,2TPT,TRB           ESZ
FRANCIS, A.  CONTEXTURE IN PARALAX I.  FL,CL,2BSN,2TPT,2TRB       JOW
GABRIELI, G.-SHUMAN.  CANZON SEPTIMI TONI.  CL,3TPT,3TRB,TU       SN
GAL, H.  DIVERTIMENTO, OP 22.  FL,OB,2CL,BSN,2HN,TPT              LEU
HAYDN, F.-LANDON.  MARSCHE.  2CL,2BSN,2HN,TPT,TU                  LDO
HERMANS, N.  BAGATELLEN (1964).  2FL,2OB,2CL,BSN,TPT             SD
HOMS, J.  OCTET DE VENT (1968).  FL,OB,CL,BCL,HN,TPT,TRB,TU       SS
LAZAROF, H.  OKTETT.  FL,OB,CL,BCL,BSN,HN,TPT,TRB                B&B
LESSARD, J.  OCTET.  FL,CL,BSN,2HN,2TPT,TRB                       GEN
MAREZ OYENS, T. DE.  OCTET.  2FL,OB,CL,BSN,HN,TPT,TRB             SD
PASCAL, C.  OCTUOR.  2FL,OB,CL,2BSN,HN,TPT                        DUR
PENTLAND, B.  OCTET FOR WINDS (1948)                              CAN
    FL,OB,CL,BSN,TPT,2HN,TRB
RATHBURN, E.  MINIATURE (1949).  PIC,OB,CL,BSN,2TPT,HN,TRB        CAN
RAUTAVAARA, E.  OCTET, OP 21.  FL,OB,CL,BSN,2HN,TPT,TRB           JOW
SAGVIK, S.  GUENILLES DES JONGLEURS, OP 74 (1977)                STI
    FL/PIC/AFL,OB/EHN ,E FL CL,2CL,ASAX,BSN,CT
SALLINEN, A.  SERENADE (1963).  FL,OB,CL,BSN,HN,TPT,TRB,TU        FIN
SCHAT, P.  OCTET.  FL,OB,CL,BSN,HN,2TPT,TRB                       SD
SCHUBERT, F.-PETIT.  MENUET & ALLEGRO                             BIL
    FL,OB,CL,BSN,HN,2TPT,TRB
SCHUBERT, F.-BROWN.  MINUET & FINALE IN F MA (O72)               NOM
    2OB,2CL,2BSN,2HN
SJOBLOM, H.  LITEN SVIT I SPELMANSTON (1976)                      STI
    FL,OB,3CL,BSN,HN,TPT
STRAVINSKY, I.  OCTET.  FL,CL,2TPT,2TRB,2BSN                      BH
VARESE, E.  OCTANDRE.  FL,OB,CL,BSN,HN,TPT,TRB,DB                ECK
WILDER, A.-MC GLOHON.  AIR.  ASAX,3HN,3TRB,TU                     KN
WILLIAMS, E.  FANT'SY I (1973).  2FL,OB,EHN,BSN,TPT,TRB,TU        B-B
```

8 PARTS: WOODWIND-STRING-833

```
ALTMANN, E.  TANZ-SUITE.  FL,OB,2CL,BSN,2HN,DB                    FRH
ARBATSKY, Y.  SINFONIA SACRA UTICANA.  OB,CL,BSN,3VN,2DB          M&M
BADINGS, H.  OCTET (1952).  CL,BSN,HN,2VN,VA,VC,DB                SD
BADINSKI, N.  OCTET (DIE RUINEN UNTER SOFIA)                      DEU
    CL,BSN,HN,2VN,VA,VC,DB
BANCQUART, A.  MADE IN U.S.A..  CL,HN,BSN,2VN,VA,VC,DB            JOB
BARTOLINI, ET AL.  3 CANZONAS.  4WW,4STR                          PET
BEETHOVEN, L. VAN.  6 KONTRATANZE.  FL,CL,2HN,2VN,VA,DB           BOS
BENARY, P.  OCTET.  CL,HN,BSN,2VN,VA,VC,DB                        MV
BJELIK, M.  KONTUREN.  CL,BSN,HN,2VN,VA,VC,DB                     LDO
BLACHER, B.  OCTET (1965).  CL,BSN,HN,2VN,VA,VC,DB               B&B
BORRIS, S.  OKTETT, OP 99/4.  CL,BSN,HN,2VN,VA,VC,DB             S-V
BOURLAND, R.  7 POLLOCK PAINTINGS (1978)                          MAR
    FL,CL,SOP SAX,BCL,VN,VA,VC ,DB
CHAVEZ, C.  SUITE FOR DOUBLE QUARTET.  FL,OB,CL,BSN,2VN,VA,VC     BE
DOHL, F.  OKTETT (VARIANTI) (1961).  FL,OB,CL,BSN,2VN,VA,VC       HG
EDER, H.  OTTETTO BREVE, OP 33.  FL,OB,CL,BSN,2VN,VA,VC           LDO
ENCINAR, J.  OP 15 (1977).  FL,OB,CL,BCL,2VN,VA,VC               ESZ
FERGUSON, H.  OCTET.  CL,BSN,HN,STR                               BH
FRESCOBALDI-GUAMI/MOENKEMEYER.  2 CANZONAS.  4WW,4STR            PET
FRESCOBALDI, G.(STEVENS).  RICERCAR #10; CANZON #5               NO
    2OB,2BSN,2VN,VA,V C
FRICKER, P.  OCTET, OP 30.  FL,CL,BSN,HN,VN,VA,VC,DB             S&C
```

```
GABRIELI, G.  CANZONA #2 (1597).  4WINDS,4STR                    PET
GABRIELI, G.  SONATA #13 (1615).  4WINDS,4STR                    PET
GANICK, P.  OCTET.  4CL,2VN,VA,VC                                SS
GRAINGER, P.  MY ROBIN IS TO THE GREENWOOD GONE                  S&C
   FL,EHN,VN,2VA,2VC,D B
GRILLO, G.  CANZONA #1.  4WINDS,4STR                             PET
GRILLO, G.-WINTER.  CANZONE #2.  4WINDS,4STR                     PET
GUSSAGO.  PORCELLAGA, LA (SONATA).  4WINDS,4STR                  PET
HAUER, J.  ZWOLFTONSPIEL (1957).  FL,OB,BCL,BSN,2VN,VA,VC        LDO
HAYDN, F.  DIVERTIMENTO.  FL,2HN,2VN,VA,VC,DB                    EMB
HAYDN, F.  KATHARINEN-TANZE #4,6,8,12.  FL,CL,2HN,2VN,VA,DB      BOS
HENZE, H.  4 FANTASIE (ADAGIO; KAMMERMUSIK)                      SCH
   CL,BSN,HN,STR QUINTET
HIDALGO, J.  JA-U-LA (1964).  FL,CL,2VN,2VA,VC,TUMBA             EEC
HINDEMITH, P.  OCTET (1957/58).  CL,BSN,HN,VN,2VA,VC,DB          SCH
HODDINOTT, A.  DIVERTIMENTI FOR 8 INSTRUMENTS                    OX
   FL,CL,BSN,HN,VN,VA,VC ,DB
JOSEPHS, W.  OCTET, OP 43.  CL,HN,BSN,2VN,VA,VC,DB               CA
JOUBERT, J.  OCTET, OP 33.  CL,BSN,HN,2VN,VA,VC,DB               NO
KELTERBORN, R.  OKTETT (1969).  CL,BSN,HN,2VN,VA,VC,DB           B&B
KOHN, K.  INTRODUCTIONS & PARODIES.  CL,BSN,HN,PF,2VN,VA,VC      CF
KONARSKI, J.  MUSIC (1962).  FL,OB,CL,BSN,2VN,VA,VC              SD
LADERMAN, E.  THEME, VARIATIONS, & FINALE                        OX
   FL,CL,HN,BSN,VN,VA,VC,DB
LANNER, J.  BRUDER HALT, OP 16.  FL,CL,2HN,2VN,VA,DB             BOS
LANNER, J.  HANSJORGEL-POLKA, OP194.  FL,CL,2HN,2VN,VA,DB        BOS
LANNER, J.  JAGERS LUST, OP 82.  FL,CL,2HN,2VN,VA,DB             BOS
LANNER, J.  MALAPOU-GALOPP, OP148.  FL,CL,2HN,2VN,VA,DB          BOS
LANNER, J.  2 MAZURKAS.  FL,CL,2HN,2VN,VA,DB                     BOS
LANNER, J.  PESTHER WALZER, OP 93.  FL,CL,2HN,2VN,VA,DB          BOS
LAPPI, P.-WINTER.  NEGRONA, LA.  4WINDS,4STR                     PET
MACUDZINSKI, R.  MEDITATION & DANCE, OP 40A                      SHF
   VN SOLO,FL,OB,CL,BSN,HN ,VC,DB
MASSAINO, T.-WINTER.  CANZONE.  4WINDS,4STR                      PET
MATTHUS, S.  OCTET (1970).  CL,BSN,HN,2VN,VA,VC,DB               DEU
MOZART, W.  4 DEUTSCHE TANZE.  FL,CL,2HN,2VN,VA,DB               BOS
MOZART, W.  3 KONTRATANZE, K462.  FL,CL,2HN,2VN,VA,DB            BOS
MUSGRAVE, T.  CHAMBER CONCERTO #3 (1966)                         CHE
   CL,BSN,HN,2VN,VA,VC,DB
PACINI, G.-BALLOLA.  OTTETTO IN F MA.  OB,BSN,HN,3VN,VC,DB       ESZ
PALKOVSKY, O.  KAMMERMUSIK (1964).  OB,CL,BSN,HN,2VN,VA,VC       CHF
PILSS, K.  OCTET IN C MI.  CL,BSN,HN,2VN,VA,VC,DB                LDO
POOT, M.  OCTUOR (1948).  CL,BSN,HN,STR QUINTET                  CBD
REICHA, A.-JANETZKY.  OCTET, OP 96.  OB,CL,BSN,HN,2VN,VA,VC      MR
REINER, H.  EICHENENDORFF-OCTET (1955)                          EUL
   OB,FL,CL,BSN,VN,VA,VC,DB
ROJO, J.  UNOS RESULTADOS.  CL,3VN,3VC,DB                        EDA
SCHOLLUM, R.  OCTET, OP 63.  FL,OB,CL,BSN,VN,VA,VC,DB            LDO
SCHUBERT, F.  OCTET IN F MA, OP166.  CL,HN,BSN,2VN,VA,VC,DB      EDK
SCHUBERT, F.  OCTET IN F MA, OP166.  CL,BSN,HN,2VN,VA,VC,DB      INT
SCHUBERT, F.  OCTET IN F MA, OP166.  CL,BSN,HN,2VN,VA,VC,DB      PET
SCHUBERT, F.  OCTET, OP166.  OB,CL,BSN,HN,2VN,VA,VC              RC
SCHUBERT, F.  OKTETT IN F MA, OP166.  CL,BSN,HN,2VN,VA,VC,DB     BRH
SCHUBERT, M.  NACHTSTUCK & PASSACAGLIA                           DEU
   CL,BSN,HN,2VN,VA,VC,DB
SKALKOTTAS, N.  OCTET.  FL,OB,CL,BSN,2VN,VA,VC                   UE
SPOHR, L.-UHLENDORFF.  OCTET IN E MA, OP 32                      B&N
   CL,2HN,VN,2VA,VC,DB
SPOHR, L.  OCTET IN E MA, OP 32.  CL,2HN,VN,2VA,VC,DB            M&M
SPOHR, L.  OCTET IN E MA, OP 32.  CL,2HN,VN,2VA,VC,DB            MR
SPOHR, L.  OCTET IN E MA, OP 32.  CL,2HN,VN,2VA,VC,DB            MRL
STRAUSS, E.-REHFELD.  MIT CHIC, OP221.  FL,CL,2HN,2VN,VA,DB      ECM
```

8 PARTS: WOODWIND-STRING-833

STRAUSS, E.-REHFELD. WO MAN LACHT UND LEBT,OP108   ECM
    FL,CL,2HN,2VN,VA,DB
STRAUSS, J.-REHFELD. DIPLOMATEN-POLKA, OP448   ECM
    FL,CL,2HN,2VN,VA,DB
STRAUSS, J.-REHFELD. LOB DER FRAUEN, OP315   ECM
    FL,CL,2HN,2VN,VA,DB
STRAUSS, J.-REHFELD. LUST'GER RAT, OP350   ECM
    FL,CL,2HN,2VN,VA,DB
STRAUSS, J.-REHFELD. TAUBEN VON SAN MARCO, DIE, OP414   ECM
    FL,CL,2HN,2VN,VA,DB
STRAUSS, J.-REHFELD. TELEGRAMME, OP318. FL,CL,2HN,2VN,VA,DB ECM
STRAUSS, J.-REHFELD. WILHELMINEN-WALZER, OP 39   ECM
    FL,CL,2HN,2VN,VA,DB
STRAUSS, J. JR. EISELE U. BEISELE SPRUNGE, OP202   BOS
    FL,CL,2HN,2VN,VA,DB
STRAUSS, J. JR.-REHFELD. FRISCH DURCHS LEBEN, OP 27   ECM
    FL,CL,2HN,2VN,VA,DB
STRAUSS, J. JR. SCHERZ-POLKA, OP 72. FL,CL,2HN,2VN,VA,DB BOS
STRAUSS, J. SR. ANNEN-POLKA, OP137. FL,CL,2HN,2VN,VA,DB   BOS
STRAUSS, J. SR. JUGENDFEUER-GALOPP, OP 90   BOS
    FL,CL,2HN,2VN,VA,DB
STRAUSS, J. SR. SEUFZER-GALOPP, OP 9. FL,CL,2HN,2VN,VA,DB BOS
STRAUSS, JOS.-REHFELD. DITHYRAMBE, OP236   ECM
    FL,CL,2HN,2VN,VA,DB
STRAUSS, JOS.-REHFELD. EINGESENDET, OP240   ECM
    FL,CL,2HN,2VN,VA,DB
STRAUSS, JOS. MARIENKLANGE, OP214. FL,CL,2HN,2VN,VA,DB BOS
STRAUSS, JOS.-REHFELD. SCHLARAFFEN-POLKA, OP179   ECM
    FL,CL,2HN,2VN,VA,DB
SYDEMAN, W. DIVERTIMENTO (1957). FL,CL,BSN,STR QUINTET SS
TAEGGIO, G.-WINTER. PORTA, LA. 4WINDS,4STR   PET
TAKACS, J. OCTET, OP 96. FL,OB,CL,HN,BSN,VN,VC,DB   LDO
THARICHEN, W. OCTET, OP 40. CL,BSN,HN,2VN,VA,VC,DB   B&B
VILLA ROJO, J. UNOS RESULTADOS (1970). CL,3VA,3VC,DB   EDA
VOGEL, E. OCTET (1970). CL,BSN,HN,2VN,VA,VC,DB   LDO
WELLESZ, E. OCTET, OP 67. CL,BSN,HN,2VN,VA,VC,DB   LDO
XENAKIS, I. ANAKTORIA (1969). CL,BSN,HN,2VN,VA,VC,DB   EDS
YUN, I. OCTET (1977). CL,BSN,HN,2VN,VA,VC,DB   B&B

8 PARTS: WOODWIND-BRASS-STRING-834

DAVIES, P. RICERCAR & DOUBLES. FL,OB,CL,BSN,HN,VA,VC,HPCD   S&C
JANSSEN, G. OCTET (1978). CL,BSN,HN,TPT,TRB,VN,VC,DB   SD
TERZAKIS, D. HOMMAGE A MORSE (1970). FL,OB,CL,TRB,2VN,VA,VC HG
WITTINGER, R. COMPENSAZIONI, OP 9 (1966/67)   BRH
    FL,OB,CL,HN,TPT,TRB,V N,VC
WOLPE, S. PIECE FOR TRUMPET. TPT,CL,BSN,HN,VN,VA,VC,DB   PET

8 PARTS: WOODWIND-BRASS-KEYBOARD-835

BASHMAKOV, L. OCTETTO. FL,OB,CL,BSN,HN,TPT,TRB,PF   FIN
BOEHMER, K. ZEITLAUFTE (1962). EHN,CL,BCL,BSN,2PF,2BRASS   EDT
EINFELDT, D. STATIONEN (1973). FL,OB,CL,BSN,HN,TPT,TRB,PF EMO
JANACEK, L. CAPRICCIO (1926). FL/PIC,2TPT,3TRB,TU,PF   ART

8 PARTS: WOODWIND-
STRING-KEYBOARD-836

```
BALAKIREV, M.  OCTET, OP  3.  FL,OB,HN,VN,VA,VC,DB,PF        EDK
BARATI, G.  OCTET.  FL,OB,2VN,VA,VC,DB,HPCD                  SN
CIORTEA, T.  DIN "ISPRAVILE LUI PACALA"                      EMU
   FL,OB/EHN,CL,BSN,HN,VA,VC,PF
DITTRICH, P.  CONCERT AVEC PLUSIEURS INSTRUMENTS #1 (1976)   HG
   HPCD SOL O,FL,OB,HN,VN,VA,VC,DB
DONATONI, F.  ASH (1976).  FL,OB,CL,VN,VA,VC,PF,HPCD         ESZ
DUPONT, J.  OCTUOR.  CL,BSN,HN,2VN,VA,VC,PF                  HAM
EICHNER, E.  CONCERTO.  FL,2HN,2VN,VA,DB,PF                  FRH
ELLIOTT, W.  SENECIO HERREIANUS (1975)                      AMC
   FL/PIC,OB,CL,BSN,VN,VA,VC,PF
FLEMING, R.  DIVERTIMENTO (1970).  2OB,2VN,VA,VC,DB,ORG      CAN
HALLER, H.  OCTET, OP 51 (1976).  OB,CL,BSN,2VN,VA,VC,PF     PET
HAYDN, F.-LANDON.  SCHERZANDO #1 IN F MA.  2OB,2HN,2VN,VC,HPCD  LDO
HAYDN, F.-LANDON.  SCHERZANDO #2 IN C MA.  2OB,2HN,2VN,VC,HPCD  LDO
HAYDN, F.-LANDON.  SCHERZANDO #3 IN D MA.  2OB,2HN,2VN,VC,HPCD  LDO
HAYDN, F.-LANDON.  SCHERZANDO #4 IN G MA.  2OB,2HN,2VN,VC,HPCD  LDO
HAYDN, F.-LANDON.  SCHERZANDO #5 IN E MA.  2OB,2HN,2VN,VC,HPCD  LDO
HAYDN, F.-LANDON.  SCHERZANDO #6 IN A MA.  2OB,2HN,2VN,VC,HPCD  LDO
JUON, P.  OCTET, OP 27A.  OB,CL,BSN,HN,VN,VA,VC,PF           MRL
KAPR, J.  BARVY TICHA (FARBEN DER STILLE) (1973)            B&N
   FL,OB,BSN,VN,VA,VC ,DB,HPCD
KLUSAK, J.  CONTRAPPUNTO FIORITO (1966)                      CHF
   FL,EHN,CL,BSN,VN,VA,VC,PF
METZLER, F.  ES IST EIN ROS ENTSPRUNGEN.  2FL,2VN,VA,VC,DB,ORG  H-V
PETRIC, I.  GEMINICONCERTINO.  OB,BSN,HN,VN,VA,VC,DB,PF      EDD
RAMOVS, P.  FLUCTUATIONS.  FL,OB,CL,VN,VA,VC,DB,PF           EDD
RIES, F.  OCTET, OP128.  CL,BSN,HN,VN,VA,VC,DB,PF            MR
TIPPETT, M.  PRELUDE- SPRING.  2FL,CL,2VN,VA,VC,PF           S&C
```

8 PARTS: WOODWIND-
BRASS-STRING-KEYBOARD-837

```
BLACHER, B.  TRIGA EINER CHROMATISCHEN LEITER. WESTEN (1970)  B&B
   FL,CL, 2VN,VA,VC,PF,TPT
BROWN, E.  NOVARA.  FL,BCL,TPT,PF,2VN,VA,VC                  UE
HAIEFF, A.  DANCE SUITE.  FL,BSN,TPT,2VN,2VC,PF              BEL
KROL, B.  CAPRICCIO DA CAMERA, OP 35                         SIM
   TRB SOLO,FL,BCL,BSN,HN,TPT,PF, DB
LEE, E.  COMPOSITION FOR 8 INSTRUMENTS (1975)               B-B
   FL,CL,2TPT,VN,VA,VC,P F
SCHAFFRATH, C.-KASTNER.  DUET IN F MI.  BSN,2OB,2VN,2TPT,BC  HEI
VIOLA, A.-KASTNER.  CONCERTO IN F MA.  BSN,2OB,2TPT,2VN,BC   HEI
VODAK, J.  OCTET.  OB,CL,BSN,TPT,2VN,DB,PF                   CHF
WUORINEN, C.  OCTET.  OB,CL,HN,TRB,VN,VC,DB,PF               M&M
```

8 PARTS INCLUDING HARP-838

AITKEN, R. SHADOWS (PART II) "LALITA" (1973)   CAN
   FL,3VC,2HP,2PERC
BEYER, F. CONCERTO (1966; 1969)   B&B
   ORG SOLO,FL,OB,VA,VC,DB,HP,TPT
BROWN, E. SYNTAGM III (1970). FL,BCL,HP,PF/CEL,VN,VC,VIB,MAR   UE
DELAS, J. DE. EILANDEN. CL,GUIT,2VN,VA,HP,PF,PERC   HG
DONATONI, F. QUARTO ESTRATTO   ESZ
   PIC,FL,VN,CEL,HP,PF,HPCD,MANDOLIN
EICHENWALD, P. ASPEKTE. FL,BCL,VN,VC,HP,PF,2PERC   EMO
FELCIANO, R. CRASIS. FL,CL,VN,VC,HP,PF,PERC,TAPE   ECS
GRANDIS, R. DE. INSTRUMENTALMUSIK ("IL CIECO DI HYUGA")   EDT
   FL,DB,HP,CE L,HPCD,3PERC
HARTWELL, H. KAME'A (1971). AFL/PIC,HN,TPT,TRB,HP,DB,2PERC   CAN
ISHII, M. LA-SEN (SPIRALE), 1969). FL,OB,PF,HP,3PERC,TAPE   HMO
KOELLREUTER, H. CONSTRUCTIO AD SYNESIN (1962)   EMO
   PIC,EHN,BCL,CBSN,VN, HP,PF,PERC
KUNERT, K. OCTET, OP 19. FL,EHN,BCL,VN,VA,VC,DB,HP   BRH
LAZAROF, H. CONCERTAZIONI. TPT SOLO,FL,CL,HN,VC,PERC,HP,TAPE TP
LEBIC, L. KONS IN A MI. FL,CL,HN,PF,HP,VN,VA,VC   EDD
LENOT, J. SOLACIUM. FL,OB/EHN,CL/BCL,VN,VA,VC,PF,HP   APH
LIEBERSON, P. ACCORDANCE (1975-76)   EDS
   FL,OB,BCL,VA,DB,PF,VIB,HP
LONGTIN, M. THRENE POUR RACHEL ET DIMITRI (1975)   CAN
   2FL/2PIC,2VC,HP,P F,2PERC
MADERNA, B. SERENATA PER UN SATELLITE   RC
   FL/PIC,OB/OB D'AMORE/MUSETTE ,CL,VN,MAR,HP,GUIT,MANDOLINE
PARRIS, R. RITE OF PASSAGE (1978)   ACA
   CL,VC,DB,PF,CEL,HP,PERC,ELEC GUI T
RAMOVS, P. OSCILLATION. FL,2VN,VA,VC,DB,HP,PERC   EDD
RAMOVS, P. PORTRAIT. HP SOLO,FL,CL,HN,VN,VA,VC,PERC   EDD
SCHNABEL, A. DUODECIMET. FL/PIC,OB,2CL,BSN,HN,PERC,HP   BH
SIBELIUS, J.-STRAVINSKY. CANZONETTA, OP 62A   BRH
   CL,BCL,4HN,HP,DB
SMITH, H. INTRODUCTION, CADENZAS & INTERLUDES   EM
   FL,OB,CL,VN,VA,VC,PF ,HP
STRAESSER, J. ALLIAGES #2 (1964). FL,CL,HN,TPT,VA,VC,HP,PERC SD
TAKEMITSU, T. WATERWAY (1978). CL,VN,VC,PF,2HP,2VIB   EDS
WEBER, B. CHAMBER FANTASIE, OP 51. SOLO VN,2CL,BCL,HP,2VC,DB ACA
WINKLER, D. DOUBLE CONCERTO (1973)   ACA
   FL,BCL,VN,VA,VC,PF,HP,PERC
ZELENKA, I. FRUH-STUCK (HORS D'OEUVRE) (1962)   EMO
   AFL,BCL,HN,TRB,VA,DB ,HP,GUIT

8 PARTS INCLUDING GUITAR-839

ANDRIESSEN, J. ARS ANTIQUA MUSICAE   SD
   FL,OB,2HN,TPT,GUIT,PERC,VA
AVSHALOMOV, J. CUES FROM THE LITTLE CLAY CART   ACA
   FL/PIC,CL,VA,VC,GUIT ,3PERC
CORY, E. OCTAGONS (1976). FL,CL,BSN,VN,VC,PF,VIB,GUIT   ACA
DELAS, J. DE. EILANDEN. CL,GUIT,2VN,VA,HP,PF,PERC   HG

8 PARTS INCLUDING GUITAR-839

```
DONATONI, F.  QUARTO ESTRATTO                                    ESZ
    PIC,FL,VN,CEL,HP,PF,HPCD,MANDOLIN
FRACKENPOHL, A.  FLUTES 4.  4FL,DB,GUIT,PF,DR                    SH
GERHARD, R.  CONCERT FOR 8.  FL,CL,GUIT,PERC,DB,PF,MANDOLIN      OX
GRANDERT, J.  KAMMARMUSIK (1961).  FL,CL,2VN,VA,VC,GUIT,PERC     STI
HALACZINSKY, R.  VARODIE (1972)                                 HG
    OB/EHN,CL,HN,PF,GUIT,VN,VC,TRB
JYRKIAINEN, R.  CONTRADICTIONS.  FL,CL,2VN,VA,VC,PF,GUIT         MT
KARKOFF, M.  KLEINE SUITE.  REC,CL,TPT,GUIT,PF,VN,VC,HPCD        WH
LUNDBORG, E.  BUTTE CHORD.  FL,CL,BSN,VN,VC,PF,GUIT,PERC         ACA
MADERNA, B.  SERENATA PER UN SATELLITE                          RC
    FL/PIC,OB//B D'AMORE/MUSETTE ,CL,VN,MAR,HP,GUIT,MANDOLINE
PAISIELLO, G.-BALLOLA.  SERENATA IN C MA                        ESZ
    2OB,CL,2BSN,2HN,GUIT
PARRIS, R.  RITE OF PASSAGE (1978)                              ACA
    CL,VC,DB,PF,CEL,HP,PERC,ELEC GUI T
ZELENKA, I.  FRUH-STUCK (HORS D'OEUVRE) (1962)                  EMO
    AFL,BCL,HN,TRB,VA,DB ,HP,GUIT
```

8 PARTS INCLUDING PERCUSSION-840

```
AITKEN, R.  SHADOWS (PART II) "LALITA" (1973)                   CAN
    FL,3VC,2HP,2PERC
ALBRIGHT, W.  CAROMS.  FL/AFL,BCL,TPT,DB,PF,CEL,2PERC           JOB
ALEXANDER, J.  3 PIECES FOR 8.  FL,CL,TPT,VN,VC,DB,PF,PERC      GEN
AMES, W.  PREAMBLE.  FL,IIN,6PERC                               ACA
AMRAM, D.  INCIDENTAL MUSIC TO "AFTER THE FALL"                 PET
    FL,TSAX,HN,VN,VA,DB ,PF,DR
AMY, G.  INVENTION I & II.  FL,PF,HP,VIB,4PERC                  HEU
ANDERSON, T.  INTERVALS: SET II.  FL,OB,CL,BCL,TRB,TU,2PERC     ACA
ANDRIESSEN, J.  ARS ANTIQUA MUSICAE                            SD
    FL,OB,2HN,TPT,GUIT,PERC,VA
ANTONIOU, T.  EVENTS III (1969).  FL,OB,CL,BSN,PF,TAPE,2PERC    B&N
AVSHALOMOV, J.  CUES FROM THE LITTLE CLAY CART                  ACA
    FL/PIC,CL,VA,VC,GUIT ,3PERC
BERGMAN, E.  CONCERTINO DA CAMERA, OP 53                        EDF
    FL,CL,BCL,VN,VA,VC,PF,PERC
BERLIN, D.  OCTET.  FL,CL,HN,TPT,TRB,VN,DB,PERC                 MAN
BJELIK, M.  OKTETT.  FL,CL,BCL,VN,VA,VC,2PERC                   LDO
BOZIC, D.  AUDIOGEM V.  FL,OB,CL,HN,VA,VC,DB,PERC               EDD
BROWN, E.  SYNTAGM III (1970).  FL,BCL,HP,PF/CEL,VN,VC,VIB,MAR  UE
CAGE, J.  16 DANCES (1951).  FL,TPT,VN,VC,4PERC                 PET
CARLUCCIO, F.  MON MANDARIN (1973-74)                           ESZ
    FL,CL,VN,VA,PF,CEL,VIB,MAR
CERHA, F.  ENJAMBEMENTS.  FL/PIC,TPT,TRB,VN,DB,3PERC            UE
CERQUEIRA, F.  QUANTA                                           EDT
    PIC/FL,OB/EHN,E FL CL/BCL,VN/VA,VC,PF,HPCD,PE RC
CHIARAMELLO, G.  CONCERTO DA CAMERA (1962)                      ESZ
    VC SOLO,FL,CL,BSN,VN,VA, DB,PERC
CLEMENTI, A.  CONCERTO (1970)                                   ESZ
    PF SOLO,BSN,HN,TPT,3VA,HARMONIUM
CORY, E.  OCTAGONS (1976).  FL,CL,BSN,VN,VC,PF,VIB,GUIT         ACA
DAO NGUYEN THIEN.  TUYEN LUA (1968)                             EDS
    FL,2VN,VA,VC,PF,PERC,TAPE
DAVIES, P.  STEDMAN CATERS                                      BH
    FL,CL,VA,VC,HPCD,PERC,TIMP,DULCIMER
DAVIES, P.  VESALII ICONES.  VC SOLO,FL,AFL,CL,BCL,VN,PF,PERC   BH
DELAS, J. DE.  EILANDEN.  CL,2VN,VA,PF,HP,PERC,GUIT             HG
```

255

```
DONATONI, F.  QUARTO ESTRATTO                                      ESZ
    PIC,FL,VN,CEL,HP,PF,HPCD,MANDOLIN
EICHENWALD, P.  ASPEKTE (1958).  FL,BCL,VN,VC,HP,PF,2PERC          EMO
EL-DABH, H.  THUMANIYA.  FL,OB,CL,2TPT,HN,2PERC                    PET
FELCIANO, R.  CRASIS.  FL,CL,VN,VC,HP,PF,PERC,TAPE                 ECS
FELLEGARA, V.  SERENATA (1960)                                    ESZ
    FL,CL,BCL(BSN),VN,VA,VC,PF,PERC
FIRAT, E.  UYGAR CIGLIKLARLA.  EHN,CL,BSN,TPT,TRB,PF,DB,PERC       SS
FRACKENPOHL, A.  FLUTES 4.  4FL,DB,GUIT,PF,DR                      SH
GERHARD, R.  CONCERT FOR 8                                        OX
    FL,CL,GUIT,PERC,DB,PF,MANDOLIN,ACC
GIBSON, J.  MELODY, PARTS B, I-III (1975)                         AMC
    ASAX,TRB,ORG,VN,VA,VC,DB, VIB
GRANDERT, J.  KAMMARMUSIK (1961).  FL,CL,2VN,VA,VC,GUIT,PERC       STI
GRANDIS, R. DE.  INSTRUMENTALMUSIK ("IL CIECO DI HYUGA")          EDT
    FL,CL,2VN,V A,VC,GUIT,PERC
GREEN, R.  3 PIECES FOR A CONCERT.  FL,2CL,2TPT,TRB,PF,PERC        CF
HARTWELL, H.  KAME'A (1971).  AFL/PIC,HN,TPT,TRB,HP,DB,2PERC       CAN
HODEIR, A.  FLAUTANDO.  3FL,2AFL,DB,PF,PERC                        MJ
HOFFMANN, R.  DECADANSE.  CL,BCL,TPT,TRB,VN,DB,2PERC               B-B
HOUNSELL.  SHOWCASE FOR SAXES.  5SAX,PF,DB,PERC                    TM
HUINJOAN, J.  VARIORUM (1975).  FL,CL,TPT,TRB,VN,VC,PF,PERC        EMT
ISHII, M.  LA-SEN (SPIRALE, 1969).  FL,OB,PF,HP,3PERC,TAPE        HMO
JOHNS, D.  CONCERTO PICCOLO.  FL,CL,2VN,VA,VC,DB,TIMP              LDO
KOELLREUTER, H.  CONSTRUCTIO AD SYNESIN (1962)                    EMO
    PIC,EHN,BCL,CBSN,VN, HP,PF,PERC
KORTE, K.  MATRIX.  FL,OB,CL,HN,BSN,ASAX,PF,PERC                  ECS
KUNST, J.  NO TIME XXI:4 (1974).  3CL,BCL,PF,3PERC                SD
LAZAROF, H.  CONCERTAZIONI.  TPT SOLO,FL,CL,HN,VC,PERC,HP,TAPE    TP
LEWIS, P.  MANESTAR.  FL,TRB,VN,VA,VC,PF,PERC,TAPE                ACA
LIEBERSON, P.  ACCORDANCE.  AFL,BCL,OB,VA,DB,PF,HP,PERC           EDS
LONGTIN, M.  THRENE POUR RACHEL ET DIMITRI (1975)                CAN
    2FL/2PIC,2VC,HP,P F,2PERC
LULLY, J.  CARROUSEL DU ROY, LE, 1ERE PARTIE                     HEU
    2OB,EHN,BSN,3TPT,TIMP
LULLY, J.  CARROUSEL DU ROY, LE, 2EME PARTIE                     HEU
    2OB,EHN,BSN,3TPT,TIMP
LUNDBORG, E.  BUTTE CHORD.  FL,CL,BSN,VN,VC,PF,GUIT,PERC          ACA
LUNDBORG, E.  SOUNDSOUP.  FL,CL,BSN,CBCL,TPT,TU,PF,PERC           ACA
MADERNA, B.  SERENATA PER UN SATELLITE                           RC
    FL/PIC,OB/OB D'AMORE/MUSETTE ,CL,VN,MAR,HP,GUIT,MANDOLINE
MARTINO, D.  NOTTURNO.  FL/PIC/AFL,CL/BCL,VN/VA,VC,PF,3PERC       ECS
MARTIRANO, S.  OCTET (1963)                                      CAN
    FL,CL,CONTRA ALTO CL,MAR,CEL,VN,VC,DB
MATSUSHITA, S.  COMPOSIZIONE DA CAMERA                           TP
    FL,CL,TPT,TRB,VN,VC,PF,PERC
MOSS, L.  REMEMBRANCES.  FL,CL,HN,TPT,VN,VC,VIB,PERC              AMC
MOZART, W.  DIVERTIMENTO #5 IN C MA, K187.  2FL,5TPT,TIMP         BRH
MOZART, W.  DIVERTIMENTO #6 IN C MA, K188.  2FL,5TPT,TIMP         BRH
NATANSON, T.  3 PICTURES (1960)                                  AP
    OB,BSN,ASAX,TPT,TRB,VC,PF,PERC
NELHYBEL, V.  AURIEL VARIATIONS.  FL,OB,EHN,2CL,BCL,BSN,VIB       JER
NILSSON, B.  SCENE I.  2FL,2TPT,VIB,HP,PF,PERC                   UE
ORFF, C.  KLEINES KONZERT NACH LAUTENSATZEN                      SCH
    FL,OB,BSN,TPT,TRB,HPCD, 2PERC
OSTERC, S.  SUITE.  FL,EHN,CL,BSN,HN,TPT,TU,PERC                 EDD
PARRIS, R.  RITE OF PASSAGE (1978)                              ACA
    CL,VC,DB,PF,CEL,HP,PERC,ELEC GUI T
PATTERSON, P.  INTERSECTIONS.  FL,CL,HN,TRB,VN,VC,PF,PERC         JOW
PERT, M.  EARTH DANCES, OP 31.  CL,HN,VN,VA,VC,PF,PERC,TAPE       JOW
RAMOVS, P.  OSCILLATIONS.  FL,2VN,VA,VC,DB,HP,PERC               EDD
RAMOVS, P.  PORTRAIT.  HP SOLO,FL,CL,HN,VN,VA,VC,PERC            EDD
```

8 PARTS INCLUDING PERCUSSION-840

RAMOVS, P.   THEME DONNE.   TRB SOLO,FL,CL,BSN,VN,VA,VC,PERC   EDD
RANDS, B.   FORMANTS II- LABYRINTHE (1969/70)   UE
   CL,TRB,2PERC,CEL,PF,VA ,VC
RANDS, B.   TABLEAU.   FL,AFL,CL,BCL,VA,VC,PF/CEL,PERC   UE
RATHBURN, E.   PARADE (1949).   FL,OB,CL,BSN,TPT,HN,TRB,PERC   CAN
REDEL, M.   DISPERSION (1972).   FL/PIC,OB,CL,PF,VN,VA,VC,PERC   B&B
REDEL, M.   INTERPLAY (1975).   FL,CL,VN,VA,VC,DB,PF,VIB/XYL   B&B
REVUELTAS, S.   TOCCATA (WITHOUT A FUGUE)   SN
   PIC,3CL,HN,TPT,VN,TIMP
REYNOLDS, V.   CONCERTARE V.   FL,OB,CL,BSN,HN,TPT,TRB,PERC   CF
RILEY, D.   CONCERTANTE MUSIC II.   FL,CL,TRB,VN,VA,VC,2PERC   PET
RUITER, W. DE.   2 QUARTETS TOGETHER.   FL,BCL,VIB,PF,2VA,2VC   SD
SCHNABEL, A.   DUODECIMET.   FL/PIC,OB,2CL,BSN,HN,PERC,HP   BH
SCHNITTKE, A.   DIALOG.   VC SOLO,FL,OB,CL,HN,TPT,PF,PERC   UE
SMITH, W.   ELEGY FOR ERIC   MJ
   FL/ASAX,CL/BAR SAX,TPT,TRB,VIB,DB,VN,PERC
STEFFEN, W.   MUSIC, OP 44.   FL/PIC/BFL,CL,VN,VA,VC,DB,PF,PERC   B&B
STERNFELD, R.   RETURN TO ISRAEL.   CL,HN,TPT,TRB,DB,3PERC   SS
STERNFELD, R.   THOUGHTS OF C & C.   FL,CL,BCL,TRB,4PERC   SS
STRASSER, J.   ALLIAGES #2 (1964).   FL,CL,HN,TPT,VA,VA,HP,PERC   SD
SURINACH, C.   RITMO JONDO.   CL,TPT,3PERC,3 HAND CLAPPERS   AMP
SUTER, R.   ESTAMPIDA.   FL,CL,TSAX,HN,TPT,TRB,DB,PERC   EMO
TAILLEFERRE, G.   IMAGE.   FL,CL,PF,2VN,VA,VC,CEL   WH
TAKEMITSU, T.   WATERWAY (1978).   CL,VN,VC,PF,2HP,2VIB   EDS
TANENBAUM, E.   REMEMBRANCE.   FL,ASAX,VN,VC,DB,2PERC,TAPE   ACA
VILLA-LOBOS, H.   CHOROS #7 (1924)   EES
   FL,OB,CL,BSN,SAX,VN,VC,PERC
VIS, L.   ESSAY I.   FL,CL,BCL,VN,VA,VC,XYL,MAR   SD
WASHBURN, G.   HEXAD PLUS ONE.   6FL,PF,CEL   SS
WEISS, M.   OCTET.   FL,CL,BSN,VN,VA,VC,PF,PERC   ISR
WILDER, A.   3 VIGNETTES.   FL,OB,CL,BSN,HN,TRB,PF,MAR   KN
WINKLER, D.   DOUBLE CONCERTO (1973)   ACA
   FL,BCL,VN,VA,VC,PF,HP,PERC
WISZNIEWSKI, Z.   TRISTIA.   FL,CL,TPT,TRB,VA,DB,PF,PERC   EMO
YUN, I.   PIECE CONCERTANTE (1976)   B&B
   FL/AFL,CL/BCL,VN,VA,VC,DB,PF,PERC
ZIMMERMANN, W.   EINER IST KEINER (1972)   HMO
   CL,SAX,TRB,2VN,VA,VC,TAPE

8 PARTS INCLUDING RECORDER-842

KARKOFF, M.   KLEINE SUITE.   REC,CL,TPT,GUIT,PF,VN,VC,HPCD   WH
TELEMANN, G.-BRUGGEN.   CONCERTO A 7.   2REC,2OB,2VN,VC,PF   SCH
WERDIN, E.   KONZERTANTE MUSIK.   REC,FL,OB,EH,2VN,VA,VC   PET

8 PARTS INCLUDNG TAPE-843

ANTONIOU, T.   EVENTS III (1969).   FL,OB,CL,BSN,PF,TAPE,2PERC   B&N
DAO NGUYEN THIEN.   TUYEN LUA (1968)   EDS
   FL,2VN,VA,VC,PF,PERC,TAPE
FELCIANO, R.   CRASIS.   FL,CL,VN,VC,HP,PF,PERC,TAPE   ECS
GILTAY, B.   POLYCHROMY II.   PIC,FL,AFL,4FL,TAPE   SD
ISHII, M.   LA-SEN (SPIRALE, 1969).   FL,OB,PF,HP,3PERC,TAPE   HMO
LAZAROF, H.   CONCERTAZIONI.   TPT SOLO,FL,CL,HN,VC,PERC,HP,TAPE   TP

8 PARTS INCLUDING TAPE-843

```
LEWIS, P.  MANESTAR.  FL,TRB,VN,VA,VC,PF,PERC,TAPE          ACA
PERT, M.  EARTH DANCES, OP 31.  CL,HN,VN,VA,VC,PF,PERC,TAPE  JOW
TANENBAUM, E.  REMEMBRANCE.  FL,ASAX,VN,VC,DB,2PERC,TAPE     ACA
```

9 PARTS: WOODWINDS
INCLUDING HORN-921

```
ALLGEN, C.   ADAGIO OCH FUGA                                        STI
    FL/PIC,AFL,OB,EHN,CL,BCL,ASAX/BAR SAX,B SN/CBSN,HN
BARTOS, J.   DIVERTIMENTO I, OP 79.   FL,2OB,2CL,2HN,2BSN           PAN
BEETHOVEN, L. VAN-HESS.   ADAGIO IN F MA (1799)                     BRH
    FL,2OB,2CL,2HN,2BSN
BEETHOVEN, L. VAN-SEDLAK.   FIDELIO.   2OB,2CL,2HN,2BSN,CBSN        MR
BRAUTIGAM, H.   KLEINE JAGDMUSIK, OP 11.   FL,2OB,2CL,2HN,2BSN      BRH
CHAUN, F.   DIVERTIMENTO (1961).   FL,2OB,2BCL,2BSN,2HN             CHF
CHERUBINI, L.-BALLOLA.   MARCIA IN F MA.   2OB,2CL,3BSN,2HN         ESZ
COLE, H.   SERENADE.   FL,OB,OB/FL,2CL,CL/BSN,HN/CL/ASAX,2BSN       NO
DONIZETTI, G.-PAULER.   SINFONIA.   FL,2OB,2CL,2HN,2BSN             EUL
DONIZETTI, G.-TOWNSEND.   SINFONIA FOR WINDS                        AB
    FL,2OB,2CL,2BSN,2HN
DUBOIS, P.   HUIT-UN.   FL,2OB,2CL,2HN,2BSN                         BIL
GOUNOD, C.   PETITE SYMPHONIE.   FL,2OB,2CL,2HN,2BSN                BIL
GOUNOD, C.   PETITE SYMPHONIE.   FL,2OB,2CL,2HN,2BSN                INT
HAYDN, F.-SKINDER.   12 SHORT PIECES.   2FL,2OB,3CL,2BSN            PWM
HEKSTER, W.   RELIEF #III (1968).   FL,2OB,2CL,2BSN,2HN             SD
HEMON, S.   CONCERTO (1970).   OB SOLO,FL,EHN,2CL,BSN,CBSN,2HN      SD
HOFFMEISTER, F.-HESS.   SERENADE IN E FL MA                         EK
    2OB(2FL),2CL,2HN,2BSN,CBS N(DB)
HOLLOWAY, R.   DIVERTIMENTO (1972).   FL/PIC,2OB,2CL,2HN,2BSN       BH
MOZART, W.-PILLNEY.   FANTASIE IN F MI, K608                        BRH
    FL,2OB,2CL,2HN,2BSN
OTTEN, L.   DIVERTIMENTO #3 (1964).   FL,2OB,2CL,2BSN,2HN           SD
PARRY, C.   NONET IN B FL MA, OP 70.   FL,OB,EHN,2CL,2HN,2BSN       JE
PRAAG, H. VAN.   FANTASIE (1962).   2FL,2OB,2CL,2HN,BSN             SD
REINER, K.   KLEINE SUITE (1960).   FL,2OB,2CL,2BSN,2HN             CHF
SCHICKELE, P.   MONOCHROME III.   9CL                               EV
SCHILDKNECHT, B.   FUGERAT FORSPEL (1946).   2FL,2OB,2CL,BSN,2HN    STI
SCHRECK, G.   NONETT, OP 40.   2FL,OB,2CL,2BSN,2HN                  BRH
SIEBERT, F.   SCHERZETTO.   HN,2FL,2OB,2CL,2BSN                     EUL
STANNARD, D.   MINIATURE SUITE CANADIENNE (1961)                    CAN
    FL,OB,E FL CL,2CL,B CL,BSN,2HN
TCHEREPNINE, I.   WHEELWINDS                                        SCH
    2FL,AFL,OB,EHN,E FL CL,CL,BCL,BSN
VOGEL, R.   DIVERTIMENTO.   9SAX                                    SS
VOMACKA, B.   NONETT (1957).   FL,2OB,2CL,2BSN,2HN                  CHF
WEAIT, C.   2 CANADIAN FOLKSONGS (1971; REV 1974)                   CAN
    2OB,2CL,2BSN,2HN,C BSN
WERNER, V.   DIVERTIMENTO.   2FL,2OB,2CL,BSN,2HN                    CHF
```

9 PARTS INCLUDING HARP-938

```
ARRIGO, G.   FLUXUS, OP 7 (1961).   FL,2CL,BSN,TPT,VA,VC,DB,HP      BRU
BALASSA, S.   XENIA-NONET, OP 20                                    EMB
    FL,CL,BSN,VN,VA,VC,PF,HP,PERC
BENES, J.   PREFERENCE.   FL,CL,VN,VC,DB,HN,TPT,HP,GUIT             SHF
BOLCOM, W.   SESSION IV.   CL,2VA,VC,TRB,PF,HP,2PERC                TP
BROWN, E.   PENTATHIS.   FL,CL,TPT,TRB,HP,PF,VN,VA,VC               EDS
BUDD, H.   BISMILLAHI 'RRAHMANI 'RRAHIM (1975)                      AMC
    ASAX,VN,HP,4PERC,ELEC PF,CEL
```

```
CERHA, F.   EXERCISES FOR 9, #1                                         UE
   BCL,BAR SAX,BSN,TPT,TRB,TU,VC,DB,HP
DAVIES, P.   ERAM QUASI AGNUS.  FL,OB,BSN,CBSN,HN,2TRB,HP,PERC          BH
DELDEN, L. VAN.  FANTASIA, OP 87 (1965).   2OB,2CL,2BSN,2HN,HP          SD
EDWARDS, G.   UROBOROS.  FL,2VA,VC,CEL,HPCD,HP,GUIT,MANDOLINE           ACA
FLEMING, R.   MARITIME SUITE (1962).   FL,OB,CL,BSN,HP,2VN,VA,VC        CAN
KAHN, E.   PETITE SUITE BRETONNE                                       ACA
   FL,OB,CL,BSN,HN,VN,VA,VC,HP(PF)
LEBIC, L.   KONS (A).   FL,CL,HN,PF,HP,VN,VA,VC,PERC                    EDD
LEBIC, L.   KONS (B).   3BCL,2VN,VA,VC,HP,PERC                         EDD
MAGDIC, J.   APEIRON.  HP SOLO,FL,CL,2VN,VA,VC,DB,PERC                  EDD
MILHAUD, D.   PRINTEMPS, LE.  PIC,FL,OB,CL,2VN,VA,VC,HP                 UE
NUNES, E.   OMENS.  FL,CL,TPT,TRB,VA,VC,HP,VIB,CEL                     JOB
PACCAGNINI, A.   MUSICA DA CAMERA                                      UE
   PIC,FL,BCL,HN,VN,VC,DB,HP,VIB
PETRIC, I.   CAPRICCIO.  VC SOLO,OB,BSN,HN,VN,VA,DB,PF,HP              EDD
PETRIC, I.   PETIT CONCERTO DE CHAMBRE                                 EDD
   OB,CL,BCL,HN,VN,VA,VC,DB,HP
PINOS-SIMANDEL, A.   GENISIS (1970)                                    CHF
   SOP SAX,TRB,VN,VC,PERC,HP,HPCD,F ILM,IONIKA
RAMOVS, P.   APEL.  FL,CL,HN,2VN,VA,VC,DB,HP                           EDD
RAMOVS, P.   ENNEAPHONIA.  FL,CL,BSN,VN,VA,VC,PF,HP,PERC               EDD
STRIETMAN, W.   LIGEIA (1973).  FL,ORG,HP,6PERC                        SD
VRIEND, J.   PAROESIE.  FL,BSN,HN,TPT,VN,DB,HP,PF,PERC                 SD
ZONN, P.   CANZONNI, OVERO SONATE CONCERTARE CON-SERERE               ACA
   FL,OB,TPT,FLUEGEL HN,TRB,DB,PF,HP,VIB
```

9 PARTS INCLUDING GUITAR-939

```
BARTOLOZZI, B.   CONCERTAZIONI (1973)                                  ESZ
   CL SOLO,HN,TPT,TRB,GUIT,PERC,VA,VC,DB
BECKER, G.   GAME FOR 9 (1962)                                        HG
   FL,CL,BCL,PERC,VIB,GUIT,VN,VA,VC
BENES, J.   PREFERENCE.  FL,CL,VN,VC,DB,HN,TPT,HP,GUIT                 SHF
BUTTING, M.   HAUSMUSIK, OP119                                        DEU
   FL,CL,2VN,VC,TPT,GUIT,TAMB,HARMONICA
EDWARDS, G.   UROBOROS.  FL,2VA,VC,CEL,HPCD,HP,GUIT,MANDOLINE          ACA
EMMER, H.   CAMERA EYE (1978-79).   2SAX,VC,2PF,2GUIT,2PERC           SD
GORECKI, H.   CONCERTO (1957), OP 11                                  AP
   FL,CL,TPT,XYL,MANDOLINE,2VN,VA, VC
NILSSON, B.   FREQUENZEN.  PIC,FL,2PERC,VIB,XYL,ORG,GUIT,DB           UE
POLLOCK, R.   REVOLUTION (1976)                                       B-B
   FL,CL,BSN,HN,VN,DB,GUIT,MAR,PERC
SCHULLER, G.   ABSTRACTION.  ASAX,GUIT,PERC,2VN,VA,VC,2DB             MJ
SCHULLER, G.   TEAR DROP (1967)                                      MAR
   FL,CL/ASAX/BAR SAX,HN,TPT,TRB,TU,DB, DR,GUIT
SILVERMAN, S.   PLANH.  FL,CL,VN,VA,VC,PERC,GUIT,MAR,MANDOLIN         BE
```

9 PARTS INCLUDING PERCUSSION-940

```
ALSINA, C.   AUFTRAG (1967).  FL,CL,BSN,HN,VN,VA,VC,DB,PERC           ESZ
ALSINA, C.   FUNKTIONEN, OP 14 (1965)                                 ESZ
   FL,CL,BSN,TPT,PF,2PERC,VN,VC
BALASSA, S.   XENIA-NONET.  FL,CL,BSN,VN,VA,VC,PF,HP,PERC             EMB
```

9 PARTS INCLUDING PERCUSSION-940

BARCE, R. CONCIERTO DE LIZARA II (1967)   EDA
 PERC SOLO,FL,OB,CL,BSN,HN, 2TPT,TRB
BARTOLOZZI, B. CONCERTAZIONI (1973)   ESZ
 CL SOLO,HN,TPT,TRB,GUIT,PERC,V A,VC,DB
BECKER, G. GAME FOR 9 (1962)   HG
 FL,CL,BCL,PERC,VIB,GUIT,VN,VA,VC
BENTZON, N. CHAMBER CONCERTO, OP 52. CL,2BSN,TPT,DB,PERC,3PF CHE
BOLCOM, W. SESSION IV. CL,2VA,VC,TRB,PF,HP,2PERC TP
BORTZ, D. KAMMARMUSIK (1964). FL,CL/BCL,TPT,TRB,VN,VC,3PERC STI
BOZAY, A. SERIE, OP 19. FL,OB,CL,VN,VA,VC,DB,PF,PERC EMB
BOZAY, A. SOROZAT. FL,OB,CL,VN,VA,VC,DB,PF/HPCD,PERC EMB
BRESGEN, C. KAMMERKONZERT, OP 6   WMS
 FL,CL,HN,VN,VA,VC,DB,PF,TIMP
BUCHTGER, F. CONCERTINO II. FL,2VN,VA,VC,DB,VIB,PERC,PF GBV
BUDD, H. BISMILLAHI 'RRAHMANI 'RRAHIM (1975)   AMC
 ASAX,VN,HP,4PERC,ELEC PF,CEL
BUSONI, F.-SCHONBERG. BERCEUSE ELEGIAQUE   BRH
 FL,CL,2VN,VA,VC,DB,PF,HARMONIUM
BUTTING, M. HAUSMUSIK, OP119   DEU
 2VN,VC,FL,CL,TPT,GUIT,TAMB,HARMONICA
CHEMIN-PETIT, H. SUITE "DR. JOHANNES FAUST"   MRL
 OB,CL,BSN,2VN,VA,VC,DB ,PERC
CHOU WEN-CHUNG. YU KO. AFL,EHN,BCL,VN,2TRB,2PERC,PF PET
CHOU, WEN-CHUNG. YUN. FL,CL,BSN,HN,TPT,TRB,PF,2PERC PET
CIUCIURA, L MUSICA (1976)   PWM
 FL SOLO,PIC,EHN,VA,VC,BSN,TPT,CEL,PF
DAVIES, P. ERAM QUASI AGNUS. FL,OB,BSN,CBSN,HN,2TRB,HP,PERC BH
DODGE, C. FOLIA (1964). FL,EHN,BCL,TU,VN,VA,PF,2PERC B-B
DONOVAN, R. FANTASIA. SOLO BSN,BSN,VN,VA,VC,DB,CEL,TIMP,PERC ACA
EDWARDS, G. UROBOROS. FL,2VA,VC,CEL,HPCD,HP,GUIT,MANDOLINE ACA
EISLER, H. NONETT 2 (1939). FL/PIC,CL,BSN,TPT,3VN,DB,PERC VNM
EMMER, H. CAMERA EYE (1978-79). 2SAX,VC,2PF,2GUIT,2PERC SD
FELDMAN, M. NUMBERS (1964)   PET
 FL,VN,VC,DB,HN,TRB,TU,PERC,PF/CEL
FELLAGARA, V. SERENATA. FL,CL,BCL(BSN),2VN,VA,VC,PF,PERC ESZ
FREEDMAN, H. TSOLUM SUMMER. FL,3VN,2VA,VC,DB,PERC CAN
GERHARD, R. NONET. FL,OB,CL,BSN,HN,TPT,TRB,TU,ACC BE
GIBSON, J. MELODY IV (1975). ASAX,TRB,2ORG,VN,VA,VC,DB,VIB AMC
GORECKI, H. CONCERTO (1957), OP 11   AP
 FL,CL,TPT,2VN,VA,VC,XYL,MANDOLI NE
GRANDERT, J. 86 T. FL,EHN,BCL,BAR SAX,CBSN,2TPT,PERC,PF STI
HAMBRAEUS, B. GIUCO DEL CAMBIO. FL,EHN,PF,HPCD,VIB,4PERC NOR
HAMBRAEUS, B. INTRODUZIONE-SEQUENZE-CODA. 3FL,6PERC CHE
HECHTEL, H. TRIAL (1973). FL,CL,TRB,VN,VA,VC,PF,2PERC HG
HIBBARD, W. 4 PIECES. FL,CL,HN,TRB,VN,DB,PF,VIB,PERC ACA
HIBBARD, W. SENSUOUS EXTRACTIONS   AMC
 FL,CL,HN,TRB,VN,DB,PF,MAR,PERC
HODDINOTT, A. RITORNELLI, OP 85   OX
 TRB SOLO,FL/PIC,OB,CL,BCL,BSN,HN,T PT,PERC
HRUSOVSKY, I. COMBINAZIONI SONORICHE (1963)   SHF
 FL,OB,BCL,TPT,PF,VN,VA ,VC,VIB
HUSE, P. OBJECTS (1962). FL,OB,CL,BSN,TPT,HN,TRB,PF,PERC CAN
KNUSSEN,O. OPHELIA DANCES I,OP 13A (1975)   FB
 FL,OB,CL,HN,VN,VA,VC,PF, CEL
LEBIC, L. KONS (B). 2CL,BCL,2VN,VA,VC,HP,PERC EDD
LEGRAND, M. PORCELAINE DE SAXE   BE
 E FL SOP SAX,SOP SAX,ASAX,TSAX,BAR SAX,BASS SAX,DB,TRB,DR
LEIBOWITZ, R. CHAMBER CONCERTO, OP 10 (1944)   B-B
 FL,OB,CL,HN,BSN,VN,VA,VC,DB
LOMBARDI, L. GESPRACH UBER BAUME (1976)   HMO
 FL,CL,VN,VA,VC,TRB,PF,2PER C
LONGTIN, M. 2 RUBANS NOIRS III. OB,CL,3VC,4PERC CAN

9 PARTS INCLUDING PERCUSSION-940

MACHI, T.   3 VIRTUOSO STUDIES (1959)   AP
  2FL,OB,CL,BSN,HN,TPT,DB,TIMP
MAGDIC, J.   APEIRON.   HP SOLO,FL,CL,2VN,VA,VC,DB,PERC   EDD
MATTHEWS, C.   CERES (1973).   3FL,2VC,DB,VIB,GUIT,BELLS   FB
NAUMANN, S.   CADENZE (1964).   CL,VN,VC,2TPT,HN,TRB,FL,PERC   STI
NILSSON, B.   FREQUENZEN.   PIC,FL,2PERC,VIB,XYL,ORG,GUIT,DB   UE
NONO, L.   POLIFONICA-MONODIA, RITMICA (1951)   SCH
  FL,CL,BCL,ASAX,PF,4PER C
NUNES, E.   OMENS.   FL,CL,TPT,TRB,VA,VC,HP,VIB,CEL   JOB
OLAN, D.   GATHERING (1972)   ACA
  FL/PIC,CL/BCL,TPT,TRB,VN,VC,PF,2PERC
OLIVER, A.   GRUPOS DE CAMARA (1975)   EDA
  OB,CL,BSN,TPT,VN,VC,DB,PF,PERC
PACCAGNINI, A.   MUSICA DA CAMERA   UE
  PIC,FL,BCL,HN,VN,VC,DB,HP,VIB
PADROS, D.   STYX (1971).   FL,OB,CL,VA,VC,DB,PF,2PERC   HG
PARRIS, R.   ST. WINEFRED'S WELL.   FL,2VC,PF,PERC,4TIMP   ACA
PETERSON, W.   ENCOUNTERS (1976)   AMC
  FL/PIC,CL/BCL,HN,TPT,VN,VC,PF,2PERC
PINOS-SIMANDEL, A.   GENESIS (1970)   CHF
  SOP SAX,TRB,VN,VC,PERC,HP,HPCD,FILM,IONIKA
PLESKOW, R.   MOVEMENT FOR 9 PLAYERS (1967)   M&M
  FL,CL,VN,VC,TPT,DB,PF,PE RC,CEL
POLLOCK, R.   REVOLUTION (1976)   B-B
  FL,CL,BSN,HN,VN,DB,GUIT,MAR,PERC
POSPISIL, J.   NONET #2.   FL,OB,BCL,TPT,HN,VN,VA,VC,PF,TIMP   SHF
POSPISIL, J.   TROJVERSIA, OP 22   SHF
  FL,BCL,HN,TPT,TRB,VIB,VN,VA,VC
RAE, A.   MAIDEN OF DECEPTION PASS, THE (1972)   CAN
  FL/PIC,OB,CL,BSN,HN,2 PERC,2SYNTHESIZERS
RAMOVS, P.   ENNEAPHONIA.   FL,CL,BSN,VN,VA,VC,PF,HP,PERC   EDD
REYNOLDS, R.   WEDGE.   2FL/PIC,2TPT,2TRB,DB,PF,PERC   PET
SCHULLER, G.   ABSTRACTION.   ASAX,GUIT,PERC,2VN,VA,VC,2DB   MJ
SCHULLER, G.   TEAR DROP (1967)   MAR
  FL,CL/ASAX,BAR SAX,HN,TPT,TRB,TU,DB, DR,GUIT
SILVERMAN, S.   PLANH.   FL,CL,VN,VA,VC,PERC,GUIT,MAR,MANDOLIN   BE
STRIETMAN, W.   LIGEIA (1973).   FL,ORG,HP,6PERC   SD
SZABELSKI, B.   APHORISMS "9" (1962)   AP
  FL,OB,CL,TPT,TRB,VN,VA,VC,PERC
TANENBAUM, E.   NOVE   ACA
  PIC/FL/AFL,CL/ASAX,BSN,TPT,TRB,VN,DB,PF,PERC
TREMBLOT DE LA CROIX.   DIVERTIMENTO.   8WW,PERC   ALE
VRIEND, J.   PAROESIE.   FL,BSN,HN,TPT,VN,DB,HP,PF,PERC   SD
WINKLER, D.   CONCERTO   ACA
  PF SOLO,FL,CL,BCL,BSN,CBSN,TPT,TRB,PERC
WOLFF, C.   NINE.   FL,CL,HN,TPT,TRB,2VC,PF,CEL   PET
XENAKIS, I.   ATREES (1960).   FL,CL,BCL,HN,TPT,TRB,PERC,VN,VC   EDS
YTTREHUS, R.   MUSIC FOR WINDS, PERCUSSION & VIOLA   ACA
  FL/PIC,BCL,HN,TPT ,TRB,VA,PF,TIMP,PERC
ZONN, P.   CANZONNI, OVERO SONATE CONCERTARE CON-SERERE   ACA
  FL,OB,TPT,FLUEGELHORN,TRB,DB,PF,HP,VIB

9 PARTS W/O HARP, GUITAR, OR PERCUSSION-941

ADASKIN, M.   RONDINO (1961).   FL,OB,CL,BSN,HN,2VN,VA,VC   CAN
ANDRIESSEN, L.   DE VOLHARDING (1972).   3SAX,3TPT,3TRB   SD
ANGERER, P.   COGITATIO.   FL,OB,CL,BSN,HN,VN,VA,VC,DB   LDO
ARBAN, J.   VARIATIONS ON NORMA.   CT SOLO,FL,2CL,2HN,VN,VC,DB   MAR

```
BABUSEK, F.  NONETO.  FL,OB,CL,BSN,HN,VN,VA,VC,DB              SHF
BAKSA, R.  NONET.  FL,OB,CL,BSN,2VN,VA,VC,DB                   AB
BASSETT, L.  NONET.  FL,OB,CL,BSN,HN,TPT,TRB,TU,PF             PET
BAUR, J.  NONETT.  FL,OB,CL,HN,BSN,2VN,VA,VC                   B&N
BIALAS, G.  PASTORALE UND RONDO (NONETT) (1969)               B&N
    OB,CL,HN,BSN,2VN,VA ,VC,DB
BLUM, R.  MUSIK.  FL,CL,HN,BSN,2VN,VA,VC,DB                    S-V
BOEHNLEIN, F.  IDEALOGIES.  PIC,FL,OB,BCL,BSN,2VN,VA,VC        MAN
BOGUSLAWSKI, E.  INTONAZIONI I (1962)                         PWM
    FL,CL,TPT,TRB,2VN,VA,VC,PF
BORKOVEC, P.  NONETTO (1940).  FL,OB,CL,BSN,HN,VN,VA,VC,DB     ES
BOTTJE, W.  SERENADE.  FL,OB,CL,BSN,HN,2VN,VA,VC               ACA
BROWN, R.  PASSACAGLIA WITH FUGUES                            WI
    FL,AFL,OB,EHN,CL,BCL,BSN,CBSN,PF
BUBAK, J.  NONETTO, OP 17.  FL,OB,CL,BSN,HN,VN,VA,VC,DB        CHF
CAZDEN, N.  6 DEFINITIONS.  CL,EHN,HN,TPT,2VN,VA,VC,DB         AMC
CHARPENTIER, M.-HITCHCOCK.  NOELS.  2FL,2VN,VA,ORG,VC,BSN,DB   UE
CHAVEZ, C.  ENERGIA.  PIC,FL,BSN,TPT,HN,TRB,VA,VC,DB           BE
CLEMENTI, A.  CONCERTINO IN FORMA DI VARIAZIONI (1956)        ESZ
    FL,OB,BSN,CB SN,HN,VN,VC,DB,PF
CLEMENTI, M.-SPADA.  NONETTO IN E FL MA                       ESZ
    FL,OB,CL,BSN,HN,VN,VA,VC,DB
DAVID, T.  KONZERT (1961).  FL,OB,CL,BSN,HN,VN,VA,VC,DB        LDO
DAVIDOVSKY, M.  NONETO.  FL,OB,CL,BSN,2VN,VA,VC,DB             EM
DELDEN, L. VAN.  NONET, OP101 (1975)                         SD
    CL,BSN,HN,2VN,VA,VC,DB,PF
DEPELSENAIRE, J.  DIVERTISSEMENT NOCTURNE                     HLE
    2FL,2VN,VA,VC,DB,TPT,PF
DOBIAS, V.  O RODNE ZEMI (1952).  FL,OB,CL,BSN,HN,VN,VA,VC,DB  ES
DONATONI, F.  TERZO ESTRATTO (1975)                          ESZ
    PF SOLO,2OB,2BSN,2TPT,2TRB
DROGOZ, P.  TRIPTYQUE.  3FL,3CL,3VN                           HEU
DUBOIS, T.  NONETTO.  FL,OB,CL,BSN,2VN,VA,VC,DB               HEU
ECKHARDT-GRAMATTE, S.  NONET (1966)                          CAN
    FL,OB,CL,BSN,HN,VN,VA,VC,DB
EGK, W.  POLONAISE, ADAGIO & FINALE                          SCH
    OB,CL,HN,BSN,2VN,VA,VC,DB
EISLER, H.  NONETT #1.  FL,CL,BSN,HN,2VN,VA,VC,DB             PET
ERBSE, H.  NONETT, OP 28.  OB,CL,BSN,HN,2VN,VA,VC,DB          HG
FELD, J.  KAMMERSUITE (1961).  FL,OB,CL,BSN,HN,VN,VA,VC,DB     ALE
FELDMAN, M.  PROJECTION 5 (1951).  3FL,3VC,TPT,2PF           PET
FISHER, S.  MUSIC FOR 9 INSTRUMENTS                          MJ
    CL,BSN,HN,TPT,TRB,TU,VN,VC,DB
FLOSMAN, O.  NONETTO II (SUITE).  FL,OB,CL,BSN,HN,VN,VA,VC,DB  CHF
FOERSTER, J.  NONET, OP147.  FL,OB,CL,BSN,HN,VN,VA,VC,DB       M&M
FOERSTER, J.  NONETT, OP147 (1931)                          ART
    FL,OB,CL,BSN,HN,VN,VA,VC,DB
FOLPRECHT, Z.  CONCERTINO, OP 21 (1940)                      ART
    FL,OB,CL,BSN,HN,VN,VA,VC,DB
FRANCAIX, J.  HEURE DU BERGER, L'.  FL,OB,2CL,2BSN,HN,TRB,PF   EAM
FROHLICH, T.-SCHERCHEN.  WALZER.  FL,OB,2CL,2BSN,2HN,TRB       SCH
GEISSLER, F.  NONETT.  FL,OB,CL,BSN,HN,VN,VA,VC,DB            DEU
GEISSLER, F.  ODE AN EINE NACHTIGALL (1967/68)              DEU
    FL,OB,CL,BSN,HN,2VN, VA,VC
GENZMER, H.  NONETT (CAPRICCIO).  OB,CL,BSN,HN,2VN,VA,VC,DB    PET
GILSE, J. VAN.  NONET (1916).  OB,CL,BSN,HN,2VN,VA,VC,DB       SD
GIURANNA, B.  ADAGIO E ALLEGRO DA CONCERTO                    RC
    FL,OB,CL,HN,BSN,VN,VA,VC ,DB
GOOSSENS, E.  FANTASY.  FL,OB,2CL,2BSN,2HN,TPT               ALE
GRANDERT, J.  NONETT (1964).  FL,OB,CL,BSN,HN,TPT,TRB,BAR,VC   STI
HABA, A.  ERSTES NONETT (1931), OP 40                       HG
    FL,OB,CL,BSN,HN,VN,VA,VC,DB
```

```
HABA, A.   NONETT 3, OP 82 (1953).  FL,OB,CL,HN,BSN,VN,VA,VC,DB    ART
HAUER, J.   DANCE SUITE #1, OP 70.  FL,OB,CL,BSN,2VN,VA,VC,PF      UE
HAUER, J.   DANCE SUITE #2, OP 71.  FL,OB,BCL,BSN,2VN,VA,VC,PF     UE
HAUER, J.   ZWOLFTONSPIEL (1951).  FL,CL,BCL,BSN,2VN,VA,VC,PF      LDO
HAYDN, F.-LANDON.  CONCERTO #1 IN C MA, HOB VIIH: 1               LDO
   FL,OB,2HN,2VN,2VA,VC
HAYDN, F.-LANDON.  CONCERTO #2 IN G MA, HOB VIIH: 2               LDO
   FL,OB,2HN,2VN,2VA,VC
HAYDN, F.-LANDON.  CONCERTO #3 IN G MA, HOB VIIH: 3               LDO
   FL,OB,2HN,2VN,2VA,VC
HAYDN, F.-LANDON.  CONCERTO #4 IN F MA, HOB VIIH: 4               LDO
   FL,OB,2HN,2VN,2VA,VC
HAYDN, F.-LANDON.  CONCERTO #5 IN F MA, HOB VIIH: 5               LDO
   FL,OB,2HN,2VN,2VA,VC
HAYDN, F.-STEPPAN.  DIVERTIMENTO IN C MA, HOB II:17               LDO
   2CL,2HN,2VN,2VA, VC
HAYDN, F.-LANDON.  DIVERTIMENTO IN F MA, HOB II:20                LDO
   2OB,2HN,2VN,2VA,D B
HENKEMANS, H.  PRIMAVERA (1944).  FL,OB,3VN,2VA,VC,DB             SD
HLOBIL, E.  NONETTO, OP 27 (1946/47)                             ART
   FL,OB,CL,HN,BSN,VN,VA,VC,DB
HOVHANESS, A.  TOWER MUSIC, OP129                                BR
   FL,OB,CL,BSN,2HN,TPT,TRB,TU
JANACEK, K.  MALA SUITA.  FL,OB,CL,BSN,HN,VN,VA,VC,DB             CHF
JAROCH, J.  KINDERSUITE.  NONETT (1952)                          AiT
   FL,OB,CL,BSN,HN,VN,VA,VC,DB
JAROCH, J.  NONETTO II (1965).  FL,OB,CL,BSN,HN,VN,VA,VC,DB       PAN
KALABIS, V.  KLASICKY NONET (1956)                               CHF
   FL,OB,CL,BSN,HN,VN,VA,VC,DB
KALACH, J.  KAMMERMUSIK.  FL,OB,CL,BSN,HN,VN,VA,VC,DB             CHF
KAREL, R.  NONETTO (1945).  FL,OB,CL,BSN,HN,VN,VA,VC,DB           CHF
KELTERBORN, R.  MUSIK.  FL,OB,2CL,BSN,HN,TPT,TRB,PF              S-V
KEURIS, T.  MUSICA CONCERTANTE (1972-73)                         SD
   CL,HN,BSN,PF,2VN,VA,VC,DB
KLUSAK, J.  VI. INVENTION (1969).  FL,OB,CL,BSN,HN,VN,VA,VC,DB    CHF
KNUSSEN, O.  PANTOMINE.  FL,OB,CL,BSN,HN,2VN,VA,VC                GS
KOETSIER, J.  NONETT (1967).  FL,OB,CL,HN,BSN,2VN,VA,VC           SD
KOETSIER, J.  RONDO SERENO (1976).  CL,BSN,HN,2VN,VA,VC.DB,PF    SD
KOHN, K.  IMPROMPTUS.  2FL,CL,2BSN,2TPT,2TRB                      CF
KORNAUTH, E.  KAMMERMUSIK, OP 31.  FL,OB,CL,HN,2VN,VA,VC,DB       LDO
KOX, H.  CYCLOPHONY VIII.  FL,OB,CL,BSN,HN,VN,VA,VC,DB            SD
KRENEK, E.  SINFONISCHE MUSIK, OP 11                             UE
   FL,OB,CL,BSN,2VN,VA,VC,DB
KROL, B.  KONZERTANTE MUSIK, OP 6.  VA,2OB,2CL,2BSN,2HN          BRH
KUBIN, R.  NONETTO.  FL,OB,CL,BSN,HN,VN,VA,VC,DB                  CHF
KUBIZEK, A.  SINFONIA DA CAMERA, OP 26B                          LDO
   FL,OB,CL,BSN,HN,VN,VA,VC,DB
KUCERA, V.  DRAMATA (1961).  PIC,OB,CL,BSN,HN,VN,VA,VC,DB         ES
KWIATKOWSKI, R.  BALTIC SONNETS.  FL,OB,CL,BSN,HN,VN,VA,VC,PF     PWM
LADERMAN, E.  NONETTE.  FL,CL,BSN,TPT,HN,TRB,VN,VC,PF            OX
LEIBOWITZ, R.  SUITE, OP 81.  FL,OB,CL,BSN,HN,VN,VA,VC,DB         JOB
LEVINAS, M.  STRETTES TOURNANTES- MIGRATIONS (1978)              EDS
   FL,BCL,BSN,2HN, TPT,VA,VC,DB
LINKE, N.  PROFIT TOUT CLAIR (1967)                              HG
   OB,CL,BSN,HN,2VN,VA,VC,DB
LINN, R.  CONCERTINO.  VN,2FL,2OB,2CL,2BSN                        WI
LULLY, J.-SCHILLING.  CHACONNE.  2OB(2FL),BSN,STR QUINTET,PF      BRH
LUTOSLAWSKI, W.  DANCE PRELUDES VERSION #3, 1959)                CHE
   FL,OB,CL,BSN,HN,V N,VA,VC,DB
MARTINU, B.  NONETTO (1959).  FL,OB,CL,BSN,HN,VN,VA,VC,DB         ART
MARTINU, B.  NONETTO- FRAGMENT (1927)                            PAN
   FL,OB,CL,BSN,HN,2VN,VC,PF
```

```
MARTINU, B.   PASTORALS (1951).   5REC,CL,2VN,VC                    B&N
MARTTINEN, T.   NONET.   FL,OB,CL,BSN,HN,VN,VA,VC,DB                FIN
MASTALIR, J.   NONETTO (1935).   FL,OB,CL,BSN,HN,VN,VA,VC,DB        CHF
MC PHEE, C.   CONCERTO.   PF SOLO,2FL,OB,CL,BSN,HN,TPT,TRB          AMP
MERIKANTO, A.   CONCERTO.   CL,VN,HN,STR SEXTET                     MT
MERIKANTO, A.   NONETTO.   FL,EHN,CL,PF,STR QUINTET                 MT
MIKODA, B.   NONETTO, OP 30 (1948)                                 CHF
     FL,OB,CL,BSN,HN,VN,VA,VC,DB
MILHAUD, D.   ASPEN SERENADE.   FL,OB,CL,BSN,TPT,VN,VA,VC,DB        HEU
MILHAUD, D.   MUSIQUE POUR GRAZ.   FL,OB,CL,BSN,HN,VN,VA,VC,DB      UE
MIRK, V.   NONET.   FL,OB,CL,BSN,HN,VN,VA,VC,DB                     EDD
MIROGLIO, F.   ESPACES V.   FL,OB,CL,BSN,2VN,VA,VC,DB               ESZ
MULDER, E.   FUGA #4 (1940).   FL,OB,CL,HN,2VN,VA,VC,DB             SD
MUSGRAVE, T.   CHAMBER CONCERTO.   OB,CL,BSN,HN,TPT,TRB,VN,VA,VC    CHE
NOVAK, J.   BALETTI A 9 (1955).   FL,OB,CL,BSN,HN,VN,VA,VC,DB       ART
ODSTRCIL, K.   SILHOUETTEN (1959).   FL,OB,CL,BSN,HN,VN,VA,VC,DB    CHF
ONSLOW, G.   NONETTO, OP 77.   FL,OB,CL,HN,BSN,VN,VA,VC,DB          M&M
PATZIG, G. (ED).   MILITARMARSCHE DES 18. JAHRHUNDERTS, VOL #2      B&N
     2OB,2C L,2BSN,2HN,TPT
PISTON, W.   DIVERTIMENTO.   FL,OB,CL,BSN,2VN,VA,VC,DB              AMP
POULENC, F.   MOUVEMENTS PERPETUELS                                CHE
     FL,OB/EHN,CL,BSN,HN,VN,VA,VC,DB
RAMOVS, P.   SIGNALS.   PF SOLO,FL,OB,CL,BSN,HN,VN,VA,VC,           EDD
RHEINBERGER, J.   NONET, OP139.   FL,OB,CL,BSN,HN,VN,VA,VC,DB       MR
RUDZINSKI, W.   NONET (1947).   FL,OB,CL,BSN,HN,VN,VA,VC,DB         AP
RYCHLIK, J.   AFRICKY CYKLUS (1961)   FL,OB,CL,BSN,2HN,2TRB,PF      ES
SCHAFER, R.   CONCERTO FOR HARPSICHORD (1954)                      CAN
     HPCD,2FL,OB,2CL,2BSN,H N
SCHMIDT, F.   TULLNERBACHER BLASMUSIK.   2OB,3HN,2TPT,TU,DR         LDO
SCHUBERT, F.   EINE KLEINE TRAUERMUSIK.   2CL,2BSN,CBSN,2HN,2TRB    EP
SCHUBERT, F.   EINE KLEINE TRAUERMUSIK.   2CL,2BSN,CBSN,2HN,2TRB    M&M
SCHUBERT, F.-LANDON.   6, 2 VOLS MENUETTE                          B&N
     2OB,2CL,2HN,2BSN,TPT
SCHWANTNER, J.   DIAPHONIA INTERVALLUM                             PET
     ASAX,FL,PF,2VN,VA,2VC,DB
SEARLE, H.   SINFONIETTA, OP 49 (1969)                            FB
     FL/PIC,OB,CL,BSN,HN,VN,VA,VC, DB
SIXTA, J.   NONETO.   FL,OB,CL,HN,BSN,2VN,VA,VC                     SHF
SKVOR, F.   NONET II. "PRAZSKY" (1961)                             CHF
     FL,OB,CL,BSN,HN,VN,VA,VC,DB
SKVOR, F.   NONETTO IN B MI (1955)                                 CHF
     FL,OB,CL,BSN,HN,VN,VA,VC,DB
SMALLEY, R.   MISSA PARODIA II (1967)                              FB
     FL/PIC,OB,CL,HN,TPT,TRB,VN,VA, PF
SPOHR, L.   NONET, OP 31.   FL,OB,CL,BSN,HN,VN,VA,VC,DB             M&M
SPOHR, L.   NONET, OP 31.   FL,OB,CL,BSN,HN,VN,VA,VC,DB             PET
SPOHR, L.   NONETT, OP 31.   FL,OB,CL,BSN,HN,VN,VA,VC,DB            MRL
SROM, K.   ETUDY (1959).   FL,OB,CL,BSN,HN,VN,VA,VC,DB              CHF
SROM, K.   MARCHEN (1952).   FL,OB,CL,BSN,HN,VN,VA,VC,DB            ES
STEWART, R.   NONET.   FL,CL,BSN,HN,TPT,VN,VA,VC,PF                 ACA
STEWART, R.   2 RICERCARE.   FL,OB,CL,BSN,HN,2VN,VA,VC              ACA
STRANBERG, N.   VERSES FOR 5.   PIC,FL,AFL,CL,BCL,VN,VA,VC,PF       MAN
TAKAHASHI, Y.   BRIDGES II.   2OB,2CL,2TPT,3VA                     PET
THOMSEN-MUCHOVA, G.   NONETT.   FL,OB,CL,BSN,HN,VN,VA,VC,DB         CHF
TRIMBLE, L.   CONCERTO.   FL,OB,CL,BSN,2VN,VA,VC,DB                 PET
VERRALL, J.   NONETTE.   FL,OB,CL,BSN,HN,2VN,VA,VC                  ACA
WEBERN, A.   CONCERTO, OP 24.   FL,OB,CL,HN,TPT,TRB,VN,VA,PF        UE
WELIN, K.   NR 3.   FL,OB,CL,BCL,HN,TPT,TRB,VN,DB                   SIM
WETTSTEIN, P.   TONUNGEN. NONETT (1976)                            S-V
     FL,CL,BSN,HN,2VN,VA,VC,DB
WHITTENBERG, C.   VARIATIONS FOR 9                                 PET
     FL,OB,CL,BSN,HN,TPT,TRB,VN,DB
```

```
WOZNIAK, F.  PRELUDE INTERROMPUE.  FL,OB,CL,BSN,HN,VN,VA,VC,DB
WUORINEN, C.  WINDS, THE.  FL,OB,CL,BCL,BSN,TPT,TRB,TU,PF
ZELINKA, J.  KURZWEILIGE STUCKE (1943).  2CL,2HN,2TPT,2TRB,TU
ZICH, O.  NONETTO.  FL,OB,CL,BSN,HN,VN,VA,VC,DB
ZILLIG, W.  SERENADE II (1929).  2CL,BCL,CT,TPT,TRB,VN,VA,VC
```

10 PARTS: WOODWINDS INCLUDING HORN-1021

```
ANDRIESSEN, J.  CONCERTINO (1962).  2FL,2OB,2CL,2BSN,2HN        SD
ANDRIESSEN, J.  RESPIRATION-SUITE (1962)                        SD
   2FL,2OB,2CL,2BSN,2HN
BALLOU, E.  SUITE FOR WINDS.  2FL,2OB,2CL,2BSN,2HN              ACA
BERNARD, E.  DIVERTISSEMENT, OP 36.  2FL,2OB,2CL,2BSN,2HN       DUR
BERNARD, E.  DIVERTISSEMENT, OP 36.  2FL,2OB,2CL,2HN,2BSN       M&M
BLANK, A.  PAGANINI CAPRICE #24.  2FL,2OB,2CL,2BSN,2HN          ACA
BOEHM, Y.  DIVERTIMENTO (1957).  2FL,2OB,2CL,2HN,2BSN           IMP
CLEMENTI, A.  INTERMEZZO.  2FL,2OB,2CL,2HN,2BSN                 ESZ
CORGHI, A.  ACTUS I (1975).  2FL,2OB,2CL,2HN,2BSN               ESZ
COSSART, L.  SUITE.  2FL,2OB,2CL,2BSN,2HN                       HEI
ENESCO, G.  DIXTUOR.  2FL,2OB,2CL,2HN,2BSN                      EDS
ENESCO, G.  DIXTUOR.  2FL,2OB,2CL,2BSN,2HN                      M&M
EROD, I.  CAPRICCIO (1976/77).  2FL,2OB,2CL,2HN,2BSN            LDO
FRANCAIX, J.  7 DANSES D'APRES "LES MALHEURS DE SOPHIE"         SCH
   2FL,2OB,2CL ,2HN,2BSN
FRANCAIX, J.  9 PIECES CARACTERISTIQUES.  2FL,2OB,2CL,2HN,2BSN  SCH
GORLI, S.  SERENATA SECONDA.  2FL,2OB,2CL,2BSN,2HN              ESZ
JACOB, G.  OLD WINE IN NEW BOTTLES                              OX
   2FL,2OB,2CL,2BSN,CBSN AD LIB,2IIN ,2TPT AD LIB
JAEGER, D.  DOUBLE WOODWIND QUINTET.  2FL,2OB,2CL,2HN,2BSN      CAN
LENOT, J.  COMME AU LOIN (1977).  2FL,2OB,2CL,2HN,2BSN          ESZ
LILIEN, I.  SONATINE APOLLINIQUE (1939).  2FL,2OB,2CL,2BSN,2HN  SD
LUTYENS, E.  MUSIC FOR WIND.  2FL,2OB,2CL,2HN,2BSN              S&C
MENGELBERG, M.  HELLO WINDY BOYS.  2FL,2OB,2CL,2BSN,2HN         SD
MILHAUD, D.  PETITE SYMPHONIE #5 (DIXTUOR)                      UE
   PIC,FL,OB,EHN,CL,BCL,2BS N,2HN
MOZART, W.  DIVERTIMENTO #3 IN E FL MA, K166                    BRH
   2OB,2CL,2EHN,2HN,2BSN
MOZART, W.  DIVERTIMENTO #4 IN B FL MA, K186                    BRH
   2OB,2EHN,2CL,2HN,2BSN
NILSSON, B.  ZEITPUNKTE                                         UE
   FL,AFL,OB,EHN,CL,BCL,ASAX,TSAX,BSN,CBSN
PABLO, L. DE.  CREDO (1976).  2FL,2OB,2CL,2HN,2BSN              ESZ
RAFF, J.-STEINBECK.  SINFONIETTA, OP188.  2FL,2OB,2CL,2BSN,2HN  EUL
ROPARTZ, G.  LAMENTO.  OB SOLO,2FL,OB,2CL,2HN,2BSN              EDS
SCHIBLER, A.  PROLOGUE.  2FL,2OB,2CL,BCL,2BSN,CBSN              A&S
SCHIBLER, A.  SIGNAL, BESCHWORUNG.  2FL,2OB,EHN,2CL,BCL,2BSN    A&S
SCHMITT, F.  LIED ET SCHERZO, OP 54                            DUR
   2FL,2OB,2CL,2BSN,SOLO HN,HN
SPINO, P.  PRELUDE FOR WOODWINDS                                STM
   2FL,OPT OB,3CL,BCL,OPT BSN,2ASAX,T SAX,BAR SAX
SUTERMEISTER, H.  MODESTE MIGNON NACH EINEM WALZER              SCH
   2FL,2OB,E FL CL, CL,2HN,2BSN
TANEYEV, A.  ANDANTE.  2FL,2OB,2CL,2HN,2BSN                     M&M
ZIMMER, L.  YANKEE CAKEWALK.  2FL,OB,2CL,BCL,2ASAX,TSAX,BSN     JB
```

10 PARTS INCLUDING HARP-1038

```
BEALE, J.  5 STILL LIFES, OP 32                                 ACA
   2FL/PIC,2CL,BCL,BSN,VC,VIB,2HP
```

267

10 PARTS INCLUDING HARP-1038

```
BERIO, L.  CHEMINS II ON SEQUENZA VI (1967)                    UE
    VA SOLO,FL,CL,TRB,VA,VC ,HP,2PERC,ELEC ORG
CEELY, R.  MUSIC FOR 10 INSTRUMENTS                            ACA
    PIC,CL,CBSN,HN,TPT,TRB,VN,VC,DB ,HP
CHOU, WEN-CHUNG.  2 MINIATURES FROM T'ANG                      ACA
    2FL,CL,HN,VN,VA,VC,HP,PF,P ERC
DELAS, J. DE.  IMAGO (1965)                                    HG
    FL,AFL,CL,BCL,PF,HP,PERC,VN,VA,VC
DZIERLATKA, A.  MELODIES.  FL,CL,HN,TPT,PF,HP,VC,3PERC         ESZ
FRANKEL, B.  BAGATELLES (5 PEZZI NOTTURNI)                     NO
    FL,OB,CL,BSN,2VN,VA,VC,D B,HP
HEIDER, W.  SONATINA.  FL,CL,TSAX,HN,TRB,HP,VIB,PF,DB,PERC     MJ
HOVHANESS, A.  MOUNTAINS & RIVERS WITHOUT END                  PET
    FL,OB,CL,TPT,TRB,TU,3 PERC,HP
IBERT, J.  CAPRICCIO.  FL,OB,CL,BSN,TPT,HP,2VN,VA,VC           ALE
KOHN, K.  PROPHET BIRD, THE: CONCERT MUSIC II (1976)           AMC
    FL/PIC,CL,BSN, HN,TRB,VN,VA,VC,HP,PERC
MASSON, G.  OUEST I (1967).  FL,TPT,TRB,CL,BCL,BSN,VN,VC,HP,PF EDS
MIROGLIO, F.  RESEAUX.  FL,CL,BSN,TRB,2VN,VA,VC,HP,PERC        UE
RYDMAN, K.  KHOROS #1 (1964).  3FL,OB,VN,VA,VC,DB,HP,PERC      MT
SCHAFFER, B.  PERMUTATIONEN                                    A&S
    FL,OB,CL,SAX,TPT,TRB,VA,PERC,HP,PF
SCHULLER, G.  AUTOMATION (1962)                               MAR
    FL,CL,BSN,HN,VN,DB,PF,HP,2PERC
SCHULLER, G.  TWELVE BY ELEVEN                                 MJ
    FL,CL,TSAX,HN,TRB,VIB,PF,HP,DB,PERC
STOCKHAUSEN, K.  KONTRA-PUNKTE #1 (1952/53)                    UE
    FL,CL,BCL,BSN,TPT,TRB,V N,VC,PF,HP
URBANNER, E.  LYRICA.  FL,CL,HN,TRB,HP,CEL,VN,DB,PF,PERC       LDO
XENAKIS, I.  ST/10-1,080262.  CL,BCL,2HN,2VN,VA,VC,HP,PERC     BH
```

10 PARTS INCLUDING GUITAR-1039

```
LEWIS, J.  MILANESE STORY, THE                                MJ
    FL,TSAX,GUIT,PF,DB,PERC,2VN,VA,VC
RUYNEMAN, D.  HIEROGLYPHS.  3FL,HP,PF,2MANDOLINE,2GUIT,PERC    WH
SCHWERTSIK, K.  SALOTTO ROMANO, OP 5                          EMO
    BCL,BAR SAX,BSN,HN,TRB,TU,PER C,DB,VC,GUIT
```

10 PARTS INCLUDING PERCUSSION-1040

```
ACILU, A.  CONTRACTURAS (1966)                                EEC
    PIC,FL,CL,BCL,HN,TPT,VA,VC,VIB,XYL
ANDERSON, T.  SET III.  EHN,2BSN,CBSN,3VC,2VC,CEL             ACA
ANDRIESSEN, J.  ANTIFONA E FUSIONE (1966)                     SD
    FL,OB,CL,BSN,2HN,2TPT,TRB,TIMP
BEALE, J.  5 STILL LIFES, OP 32                               ACA
    2FL/PIC,2CL,BCL,BSN,VC,VIB,2HP
BENVENUTI, A.  STUDI (1960-61)                                BRU
    FL,CL,BSN,HN,TPT,TRB,VA,VC,PF,XYL
BERIO, L.  CHEMINS II ON SEQUENZA VI (1967)                   UE
    VA SOLO,FL,CL,TRB,VA,VC ,HP,2PERC,ELEC ORG
BRANT, H.  CONCERTO.  SAX,FL,4CL,ACL,BCL,TU,PERC              CF
CAGAN, S.  DIVERTISSEMENT- SUITE FOR THE DANCE                PI
    FL,OB,CL,BSN,TPT,TRB ,VC,DB,2PERC
```

10 PARTS INCLUDING PERCUSSION-1040

```
CATURLA, A.  BEMBE.  FL,OB,CL,BSN,2HN,TPT,TRB,PF,PERC           EDS
CHAVEZ, C.  XOCHIPILLI.  PIC,FL,E FL CL,TRB,6PERC               BE
CHILDS, B.  JACK'S NEW BAG.  FL,TPT,TRB,VA,VC,DB,2PF,2PERC      SMI
CHOU, WEN-CHUNG.  2 MINIATURES FROM T'ANG                       ACA
     2FL,CL,HN,VN,VA,VC,HP,PF,P ERC
DELAS, J. DE.  CINCO SELLOS (1972)                             HG
     FL,CL,BCL,TPT,PF,VN,VC,DB,PERC,TA PE
DELAS, J. DE.  IMAGO (1965)                                     HG
     FL,AFL,BCL,CL,PF,HP,PERC,VN,VA,VC
DZIERLATKA, A.  MELODIES.  FL,CL,HN,TPT,PF,HP,VC,3PERC          ESZ
EBENHOH, H.  4 SCENES FOR 10, OP 21/1                           LDO
     FL,OB,CL,BSN,2VN,VA,VC,DB,PER C
FERRARI, L.  INTERRUPTEUR (1967)                               HMO
     EHN,CL,BCL,HN,TPT,VN,VA,VC,2PERC,3 MAGNETO-PHONE AD LIB
FRANCO, J.  PILGRIM'S PROGRESS, THE                            ACA
     FL/PIC,OB/EHN,CL,BSN,3TPT,TRB,P F,PERC
FRIBEC, K.  DANZA DI GIOJA.  OB,TPT,TRB,2VC,DB,PF,VIB,2PERC    EMO
FRIBEC, K.  PANTA RHEI.  PIC,FL,EHN,BCL,VA,DB,PF,XYL,VIB,PERC  EMO
GERHARD, R.  HYMNODY.  FL,OB,CL,HN,TPT,TRB,TU,2PF,PERC         OX
GERHARD, R.  LEO.  FL/PIC,CL,HN,TPT,VN,VC,PF,CEL,2PERC         OX
GIEFER, W.  PRO-KONTRA (1970)                                  HG
     FL,OB,CL,BSN,HN,VN,VA,VC,DB,PERC
GROSSKOPF, E.  CONCERTO: FLECKTREUE RARITATENKUNST P (1969)    B&B
     CL SOLO ,FL,OB,HN,VN,VA,DB,PF,2PERC
GUDMUNDSEN-HOLMGREEN, P.  2 (1961) IMPROVISATIONS              SPD
     FL,CL,HN,TPT,TRB, DB,VIB,PF,2PERC
GUINJOAN, J.  IMPROVISACION I (1973)                           EDA
     PIC/FL,OB,CL,PF,VN,VA,VC,DB,2P ERC
HANDEL, G.-KAHN.  FIREWORK MUSIC II.  2OB,BSN,3TPT,3HN,TIMP    EM
HEIDER, W.  SONATINA  FL,CL,TSAX,HN,TRB,HP,VIB,PF,DB,PERC      MJ
HESPOS, H.  PASSAGEN (1969)                                    EMO
     E FL CL/CL,ASAX,TPT,TRB,VA,DB,4PERC
HOCH, F.  TRASPARENZA PER NUOVI ELEMENTI (1976)               ESZ
     FL,OB,CL,BCL,VN,VA, VC,DB,PF,PERC
HOLMBOE, V.  CHAMBER CONCERTO #2, OP 20                        SPD
     FL,3VN,VA,VC,DB,TIMP,DR,CEL
HOVHANESS, A.  MOUNTAINS & RIVERS WITHOUT END                 PET
     FL,OB,CL,TPT,TRB,TU,3 PERC,HP
HUGGLER, J.  MUSIC, OP 63.  FL,2CL,2TPT,TIMP,PF,VN,DB,PERC    PET
IVES, C.-COWELL.  CALCIUM LIGHT NIGHT                          TP
     PIC,OB,CL,BSN,TPT,TRB,2PF,2PER C
IVES, C.  SCHERZO (OVER THE PAVEMENTS)                         PI
     PIC,CL,BSN,TPT,3TRB,2PERC,PF
KAI, S.  TRIGA EINER CHROMATISCHEN LEITER. OSTEN              B&B
     FL,CL,BSN,TPT,TRB, MAR,DR,VN,VA,VC
KOHN, K.  PROPHET BIRD, THE: CONCERT MUSIC II (1976)         AMC
     FL/PIC,CL,BSN, HN,TRB,VN,VA,VC,HP,PERC
LEWIS, J.  MILANESE STORY, THE                                MJ
     FL,TSAX,GUIT,PF,DB,PERC,2VN,VA,VC
LIGETI, G.  FRAGMENT.  CBSN,TRB,TU,PERC,HP,HPCD,PF,3DB       UE
MALIPIERO, G.  SERENATA MATTUTINA.  FL,OB,CL,2BSN,2HN,2VA,CEL UE
MANZONI, G.  PARAFRASI CON FINALE (1969)                      ESZ
     FL,CL,BSN,HN,TPT,TRB,HPCD, ORG,DB,PERC
MATSUDAIRA, Y.  SERENATA (1963).  FL,OB,CL,6VN,PERC          ESZ
MERILAINEN, U.  IMPRESSION (1965)                             B&B
     FL,OB,CL,BSN,HN,VA,VC,DB,PF,PERC
MIROGLIO, F.  RESEAUX.  FL,CL,BSN,TRB,2VN,VA,VC,HP,PERC      UE
OLIVER, A.  OMICRON 73 (1973)                                 EDA
     FL,CL,TPT,TRB,VN,VA,VC,PF,VIB,PERC
PAUMGARTNER, B.  DIVERTIMENTO                                 UE
     PIC,EHN,ASAX,BSN,HN,TPT,PF,VA,VC,PERC
REVUELTAS, S.  OCHO POR RADIO.  CL,BSN,TPT,2VN,VC,DB,3PERC   PI
```

```
REVUELTAS, S.  3 SONNETS.   2CL,2TPT,HN,PERC,BCL,BSN,TU,PF         SN
ROVICS, H.   EVENTS II.   OB,2CL/BCL,TPT,VN,VC,DB,PF,2PERC         ACA
ROWLAND, D.  TROPISMS (1979)                                      SD
   FL,OB,CL,BCL,BSN,HN,TPT,TRB,PERC,PF
RUYNEMAN, D.  HIEROGLYPHS (1918)                                  WH
   3FL,CEL,CUPBELLS,PF,2MANDOLINS,2GU IT
RYDMAN, K.  KHOROS #1 (1964).   3FL,OB,VN,VA,VC,DB,HP,PERC         MT
SCHAFFER, B.  PERMUTATIONEN                                       A&S
   FL,OB,CL,SAX,TPT,TRB,VA,PERC,HP,PF
SCHULLER, G.  AUTOMATION (1962)                                   MAR
   FL,CL,BSN,HN,VN,DB,PF,HP,2PERC
SCHULLER, G.  MUSIC FROM YESTERDAY IN FACT (1963)                 MAR
   FL,BCL,ASAX,HN,VN ,VC,DB,TPT,PF,DR
SCHULLER, G.  TWELVE BY ELEVEN                                    MJ
   FL,CL,TSAX,HN,TRB,VIB,PF,HP,DB,PERC
SCHWARTZ, E.  CONCERT PIECE.  FL,OB,CL,BSN,HN,VA,VC,DB,2PERC       AB
URBANNER, E.  IMPROVISATION III (1969)                            LDO
   FL,OB,CL,BSN,2VN,VA,VC,DB,PE RC
URBANNER, E.  LYRICA.  FL,CL,HN,TRB,HP,CEL,VN,DB,PF,PERC           LDO
VARESE, E.  HYPERPRISM.  FL,CL,3HN,2TPT,2TRB,PERC                  ECK
VILLA ROJO, J.  VOSOTROS Y...                                     EEC
   CL SOLO,FL,OB,CL,HN,TRB,VN,VA,VC,VIB
WILDER, A.  DEBUTANTE'S DIARY, A                                  KN
   FL,OB,2CL,BCL,EHN(ASAX),BSN,PF,DB, DR
WILDER, A.  SHE'LL BE 7 IN MAY                                    KN
   FL,OB,2CL,BCL,EHN(ASAX),BSN,PF,DB,DR
WILDER, A.  SUCH A TENDER NIGHT                                   KN
   FL,OB,2CL,BCL,EHN(ASAX),BSN,PF,DB,D R
WILDER, A.  WALKING HOME IN SPRING                                KN
   FL,OB,2CL,BCL,EHN(ASAX),BSN,PF,D B,DR
XENAKIS, I.  ST/10-1,080262.  CL,BCL,2HN,2VN,VA,VC,HP,PERC         BH
```

10 PARTS W/O HARP, GUITAR, OR PERCUSSION-1041

```
AITKEN, H.  SERENADE.  FL,OB,CL,BSN,HN,STR QUINTET                AMC
AMES, W.  COMPOSITION.  FL,OB,CL,BSN,HN,2VN,VA,VC,DB              ACA
ANDERSON, T.  TRANSITIONS.  FL,CL,BSN,HN,TPT,TRB,VN,VA,VC,PF      ACA
ANDRIESSEN, J.  HOMMAGE A MILHAUD                                 SD
   FL,OB,CL,ASAX,BSN,TPT,TRB,VN,VA,V C
ARRIEU, C.  DIXTUOR.  2FL,OB,2CL,2BSN,HN,TPT,TRB                  BIL
BIALAS, G.  PARTITA (1969).  FL,2OB,2CL,2BSN,2HN,DB               B&N
BOTTENBERG, W.  VARIABLES (1969)                                 CAN
   REC,FL,OB,CL,BSN,STR QUINTET
CERVELLO, J.  CATALISIS (1975).  FL,OB,CL,BSN,EHN,2VN,VA,VC,DB    EEC
CIGLIC, Z.  ABSURDI.  FL/PIC,OB,BSN,TPT,TRB,2VN,VA,VC,DB          EDD
CUNNINGHAM, M.  SPRING SONNET.  FL,2CL,2SAX,BCL,3HN,DB            SS
DUBOIS, T.  DIXTUOR.  FL,OB,CL,HN,BSN,2VN,VA,VC,DB                HEU
DVORAK, A.  MARCH (SERENADE).  2OB,2CL,2BSN,CBSN AD LIB,3HN,VC    E M
DVORAK, A.  SERENADE, OP 44.  2OB,2CL,2BSN,2HN,VC,DB              EDK
EGK, W.  DIVERTISSEMENT                                           SCH
   FL/PIC,2OB,CL,CL/BCL,2HN,BSN,BSN/CBSN,TPT
EISLER, H.  OUVERTURE ZU EINEM LUSTSPIEL                          PET
   FL,CL,BSN,PF,2VN,VA,VC,DB
EISMA, W.  IF... (1970).  FL,OB,CL,HN,BSN,2VN,VA,VC,DB            SD
ESCHER, R.  SINFONIA (1976).  FL,OB,CL,HN,BSN,2VN,VA,VC,DB        SD
FELDMAN, M.  IXION.  3FL,CL,HN,TPT,TRB,VC,DB,PF                   PET
FONTYN, J.  COLLOQUE.  FL,OB,CL,BSN,HN,5STR                       SS
FRANCAIX, J.  GAY PARIS, LE.  TPT SOLO,FL,2OB,2CL, BSN,2HN        EAM
```

```
FRID, G.  12, OP 54A METAMORPHOSES.  2FL,2OB,2CL,2BSN,HN,PF      SD
FRIEDLANDER, E.  RHAPSODY FOR BASSOON (1964)                     CAN
   BSN SOLO,OB,CL,BSN,HN, 2VN,VA,VC,DB
GABRIELI, G.  CANZONA # 7 (1597).  5WW,5STR                      PET
GABRIELI, G.-WINTER.  CANZONE #10.  5WW,5STR                     PET
GUACCERO, D.  ...ITER SEGNATO, UN (1960)                         BRU
   OB,CL,BSN,TPT,TRB,2VN,VA,V C,DB
HARRIS, D.  LUDUS.  FL,OB,CL,HN,BSN,2VN,VA,VC,DB                 JOB
HARTLEY, W.  DOUBLE CONCERTO                                     ARM
   ASAX,TU,FL,OB,CL,BSN,HN,2TPT,TRB
HASQUENOPH, P.  DIVERTISSEMENT.  FL,OB,CL,BSN,HN,2VN,VA,VC,DB    LDO
HAUER, J.  ZWOLFTONSPIEL (1957)                                 LDO
   FL,OB,BCL,BSN,2VN,VA,VC,PF(2 PLAYER S)
HAYDN, F.-LANDON.  CASSATIO IN G MA, HOB II: G 1                LDO
   2OB,2HN,2VN,2VA,VC, DB
HETU, J.  CYCLE, OP 16 (1969).  FL,CL,BCL,BSN,HN,2TPT,2TRB,PF   CAN
HOVHANESS, A.  TOWER MUSIC.  FL,OB,CL,BSN,2TPT,2HN,TRB,TU       RON
HOVLAND, E.  MUSIC, OP 28.  FL,OB,CL,BSN,HN,2VN,VA,VC,DB        IILY
KAHN, E.  ACTUS TRAGICUS.  FL,OB,CL,BSN,HN,2VN,VA,VC,DB         ACA
LAZAROF, H.  ESPACES.  2FL,CL,BCL,2VA,2VC,2PF                    AMP
LUTYENS, E.  6 TEMPI.  FL,OB,CL,BSN,HN,TPT,VN,VA,VC,PF           BE
MAKSYMIUK, J.  DECET.  FL,OB,CL,BSN,HN,PF,2VN,VA,VC             PWM
MALIPIERO, R.  MOSAICO (1961).  FL,OB,CL,BSN,HN,2VN,VA,VC,DB    ESZ
MARTINU, B.  SERENADE #4 (DIVERTIMENTO).  2OB,3VN,2VA,VC,DB,PF  ART
MC CAULEY, W.  5 (1968) MINIATURES                              CAN
   FL,OB,CL,BSN,2HN,2TPT,TRB,TU
MILHAUD, D.  CONCERTINO D'AUTOMNE.  FL,OB,3HN,2VA,VC,2PF        HEU
MILHAUD, D.  CONCERTINO D'ETE                                   UE
   FL,OB,CL,BSN,HN,TPT,VA SOLO,2VC,DB
MILLS, C.  CHAMBER CONCERTO.  FL,OB,CL,BSN,2HN,2VN,VA,VC        ACA
MIROGLIO, F.  ESPACES IV.  FL,OB,BSN,HN,2VN,VA,VC,DB,TAPE       ESZ
MOOR, E.  SUITE, OP103.  FL,OB,CL,HN,BSN,2VN,VA,VC,DB           EDS
MOZART, W.-EINSTEIN.  GALIMATHIAS MUSICUM (QUODLIBET), KV 32    PET
   2OB,2HN ,BSN,2VN,VA,VC,PF
NAGEL, R.  DIVERTIMENTO.  FL,OB,CL,BSN,2TPT,2HN,TRB,TU          MEN
PEDLEY, D. (ARR).  3 ENGLISH TUNES                              CA
   2FL,2OB,3CL,2TPT(2HN),TRB(BSN)
PERSICHETTI, V.  SERENADE #1.  FL,OB,CL,BSN,2TPT,2HN,TRB,TU     EV
POST, J.  NEXT CALL (1978-79), THE                             SD
   FL,OB,CL,BSN,2HN,TPT,TRB,2DB
PRAAG, H. VAN.  DIXTUOR (1949).  FL,OB,CL,BSN,HN,2VN,VA,VC,DB   SD
RAWSTHORNE, A.  CONCERTO FOR 10 INSTRUMENTS                     OX
   FL,OB,CL,BSN,HN,2VN,VA, VC,DB
RAZZI, F.  MUSICA (1968).  3OB,CL,2BSN,2TPT,2TRB               ESZ
REED, A.  DOUBLE WIND QUINTET.  FL,OB,CL,HN,BSN,2TPT,HN,TRB,TU  EM
SCHISKE, K.  DIVERTIMENTO, OP 49                                LDO
   CL,BSN,HN,TPT,TRB,2VN,VA,VC,DB
SCHUDEL, T.  SET #2 (1967).  FL,OB,CL,BSN,HN,2TPT,HN,TRB,TU     CAN
SCHULLER, G.  DOUBLE QUINTET.  FL,OB,CL,BSN,2HN,2TPT,TRB,TU     AMP
SCHWERTSIK, K.  MUSIK VOM MUTTERLAND MU.                        LDO
   FL,OB,CL,BCL,HN,TRB,VN,VA, VC,DB
SEARLE, H.  VARIATIONS & FINALE, OP 34                          S&C
   FL,OB,CL,BSN,HN,2VN,VA,VC,DB
TARABA, B.  3 MEDITATIONS (1922).  FL,OB,CL,2BSN,HN,2VN,VA,VC   CHF
TURNER, R.  VARIATIONS & TOCCATA (1959)                        CAN
   FL,OB,CL,BSN,HN,STR QUINTET
VRANICKY, P.  JAGERMARSCHE.  2OB,2CL,2BSN,CBSN,2HN,TPT          ART
VRIES, K. DE.  MOEILIJKHEDEN (1977).  FL,2SAX,HN,2TPT,3TRB,PF   SD
WASHBURN, R.  CONCERTINO.  FL,OB,CL,BSN,2HN,2TPT,TRB,TU         OX
WISZNIEWSKI, Z.  CHAMBER MUSIC #4                               PWM
   FL,OB,CL,BSN,HN,VN,VA,VC,DB,PF
```

11 PARTS: WOODWINDS INCLUDING HORN-1121

```
ARNOLD, M.  TREVELYAN SUITE, OP 96 (1967)                        FB
   3FL,2OB,2CL,2HN,2BSN(VC)
BRAHMS, J.  HERZLICH TUT MICH VERLANGEN, OP122/10               CP
   FL,AFL,OB,EHN,BAR  OB,2CL,BCL,2BSN,CBSN
BRANT, H.  ANGELS & DEVILS.  3PIC,6FL,2AFL                      PET
DELDEN, L. VAN.  SINFINIA #7, OP 83 (1964)                     SD
   2FL,2OB,2CL,BCL,2HN,2BSN
ELLIS, D.  GOLDEN APPLES OF THE SUN                            UMP
   FL SOLO,2FL,2OB,2CL,2HN,2BSN
GOULD (ARR).  IT CAME UPON THE MIDNIGHT CLEAR                  CA
   2FL,OB,5CL,ACL,BCL,BSN
LEWIS, P.  SESTINA.  2FL,2OB,2CL,BCL,2BSN,2HN                  ACA
PONSE, L.  EUTERPE, OP 37 (1964).  2FL,2OB,3CL,2BSN,2HN        SD
PRAAG, H.  MUSIC (1965).  2FL,2OB,3CL,2BSN,2HN                 SD
TUULSE, T.  MENUETT (1976).  2FL,2OB,3CL,2HN,2BSN             STI
```

11 PARTS INCLUDING HARP-1138

```
BIRTWISTLE, H.  TRAGOEDIA                                       UE
   FL,OB,CL,HN,BSN,2VN,VA,VC,HP,CLAVES
BLANK, A.  COMPOSITION FOR 11 PLAYERS, SECTION #1             ACA
   FL,CL,BCL,HN,TPT, TRB,VN,VC,DB,PF,HP
BOESMANS, P.  EXPLOSIVES.  FL,CL,2VN,VA,VC,DB,PF,HP,2PERC      JOB
CASANOVA, A.  SERENATA.  FL,CL,BSN,TPT,TRB,XYL,HP,2VN,VA,VC    BIL
CHERNEY, B.  CHAMBER CONCERTO (1975)                          CAN
   VA SOLO,FL/PIC,CL/BCL,HN,TPT,T RB,VN,VC,DB,PERC,HP
CORDERO, R.  PAZ-PAIZ-PEACE                                    PI
   FL,AFL,EHN,CL,BCL,BSN,VN,VA,VC,DB,HP
DELAS, J. DE.  EILANDEN (1967)                                HG
   CL,2VN,VA,HPCD,HP,PERC,CEL,HARMONIUM, GUIT,TAPE
DUFOURT, H.  MURA DELLA CITTA DI DITE                         JOB
   FL,OB,CL,BCL,HN,TPT,TRB,HP,CE L,2PERC
GERSCHEFSKI, E.  PRELUDE, OP  6/5                             ACA
   PIC,FL,OB,EHN,CL,BCL,HN,HP,3PERC
HODEIR, A.  AMBIQUITE I                                        MJ
   FL,E FL CL,CL,BSN,HN,TRB,HP,VIB,PF,DB,PERC
LENDVAI, E.  KAMMERSUITE, OP 32                               SIM
   FL,OB,CL,HN,BSN,2VN,VA,VC,DB,HP
LIEBERSON, P.  CONCERTO FOR 4 GROUPS OF INSTRUMENTS           EDS
   FL,OB,CL,BSN,HP ,PF,2VN,VA,VC,DB
MADERNA, B.  SERENATA #2 (1957)                              ESZ
   FL,CL,BCL,HN,TPT,VN,VA,DB,PF,PERC,H P
MAROS, R.  MUSICA DA CAMERA.  FL,2CL,2VN,VA,VC,DB,HPCD,PERC,HP SN
ROREM, N.  11 STUDIES FOR 11 PLAYERS                          JB
   FL,OB,CL,VN,VA,VC,TPT,HP,2PERC ,PF
STUHEC, I.  CTION.  FL,CL,HN,TPT,TRB,VN,VC,DB,PF,HP,PERC      EDD
TOMASI, H.  JEUX DE GEISHAS                                   EES
   FL,OB,CL,BSN,HN,2VN,VA,VC,HP,PERC
WUORINEN, C.  CHAMBER CONCERTO.  OB,TU,HP,PF,DB,6PERC         PET
```

11 PARTS INCLUDING GUITAR-1139

CERVETTI, S. 6 SEQUENCES FOR DANCE (1966)   HMO
   FL,HN,CEL,PF,VC,5PERC,EL EC GUIT
DELAMONT, G. CENTUM (1966)   KN
   ASAX/CL,BAR SAX/BCL,3TPT,3TRB,GUIT,DB,D R
DELAS, J. DE. EILANDEN (1967)   HG
   CL,2VN,VA,HPCD,HP,PERC,CEL,HARMONIUM, GUIT,TAPE
KILLMAYER, W. KINDERTAGE   SCH
   FL,VA,PF,GUIT,ELEC ORG,ACC,5PERC,ZITHER
RUYNEMAN, D. HIEROGLYPHS (1918)   SD
   3FL,CEL,PF,2GUIT,2MANDOLINES,HP,CUPBELLS
SCHULLER, G. PROGRESSION IN TEMPO   MJ
   FL,CL,2VN,VA,VC,DB,PF,GUIT,VIB,P ERC
TRIMBLE, L. PANELS I   PET
   PIC,BAR SAX,VN,VA,VC,DB,2PERC,ELEC GUIT,ELEC   ORG,ELEC HPCD
WUORINEN, C. CHAMBER CONCERTO   PET
   FL,DB,PF,HP,GUIT,HPCD,CEL,4PERC

11 PARTS INCLUDING PERCUSSION-1140

ADLER, S. MUSIC FOR 11. 2FL,OB,CL,BCL,BSN,TIMP,XYL,3PERC   OX
ANDERSON, T. SET V. PIC,ASAX,TSAX,3TPT,TRB,PF,2DB,DRUM SET   ACA
ANTONIOU, T. CONCERTINO, OP 21 (1963)   B&N
   FL,OB,2CL,2BSN,2HN,TPT,PERC, PF
ANTUNES, J. INTERVERTIGE (1974)   ESZ
   FL,OB,CL,HN,BSN,2VN,VA,VC,2PERC
BENTZON, N. CHAMBER CONCERTO, OP 52   WH
   CL,BSN,2TPT,3PF,VIB,TIMP,PERC, DB
BENVENUTI, A. 3 (1960-61) STUDIES   AB
   FL,CL,BSN,HN,TPT,TRB,VN,VA,VC,PF ,XYL
BIRTWISTLE, H. TRAGOEDIA   UE
   FL,OB,CL,HN,BSN,2VN,VA,VC,HP,CLAVES
BLAKE, E.-SCHULLER. CHARLESTON RAG (1917)   MAR
   PIC,OB,TPT,TRB,TU,PF,VN,VA,VC,DB,PERC
BLICKHAN, T. VARIATIONS/PERMUTATIONS   SS
   FL,OB,CL,BSN,HN,TPT,TRB,PF,3P ERC
BOESMANS, P. EXPLOSIVES. FL,CL,2VN,VA,VC,DB,PF,HP,2PERC   JOB
BOIS, R. DU. CERCLE (1963). FL,OB,2CL,2BSN,2HN,TPT,PERC,PF   SD
BOIS, R.DU. ESPACES A REMPLIR 1963)   SD
   2CL,TSAX,TPT,TRB,TU,DB,PF,VIB,2PERC
BORTOLOTTI, M. STUDIO PER CUMMINGS #2 (1964)   ESZ
   OB,CL,E FL CL/SAX,BCL ,HN,VA,VC,DB,3PERC
BOZIC, D. CONCERTO GROSSO IN F MA   EDD
   CL,TSAX,TPT,TRB,DB,PF,5PERC
BROWN, J. FRAGMENTS. FL,OB,CL,TPT,TRB,2VN,VA,VC,PF,PERC   ACA
BRUN, H. GESTURES FOR 11   SMI
   FL/PIC,OB/EHN,CL/BCL,BSN/CBSN,HN,TPT,TRB, VN,VA,DB,PERC/PF
CASANOVA, A. SERENATA. FL,CL,BSN,TPT,TRB,XYL,HP,2VN,VA,VC   BIL
CASTRO, C. DE. 10 + 1 (1975)   EEC
   FL,OB,CL,HN,TPT,TRB,2VN,VA,VC,PERC
CERVETTI, S. 6 SEQUENCES FOR DANCE (1966)   HMO
   FL,HN,CEL,PF,VC,5PERC,EL EC GUIT

11 PARTS INCLUDING PERCUSSION-1140

CHERNEY, B.   CHAMBER CONCERTO (1975)   CAN
   VA SOLO,FL/PIC,CL/BCL,HN,TPT,T RB,VN,VC,DB,PERC,HP
COLE, B.   FENESTRAE SANCTAE   BH
   OB,CL,BSN,HN,TPT,TRB,2VN,VA,VC,PERC
CROLEY, R.   CONCERTO FOR FLUTE & METAL ORCHESTRA   JB
   FL,4TRB,TU,TIMP,PF ,3PERC
DAVIDOVSKY, M.   INFLEXIONS   EM
   2FL,CL,TPT,TRB,PERC,PF,VN,VA,VC,DB
DELAMONT, G.   CENTUM (1966)   KN
   ASAX/CL,BAR SAX/BCL,3TPT,3TRB,GUIT,DB,D R
DELAS, J. DE.   EILANDEN (1967)   HG
   CL,2VN,VA,HPCD,HP,PERC,CEL,HARMONIUM, GUIT,TAPE
DERUNGS, M.   VARIATIONS FOR 2 ENSEMBLES (1976/77)   S-V
   SAX,2TPT,TRB,PERC ,TAPE,5 RENAISSANCE INSTR
DUFOURT, H.   MURA DELLA CITTA DI DITE   JOB
   FL,OB,CL,BCL,HN,TPT,TRB,HP,CE L,2PERC
EDWARDS, G.   BITS.   FL,OB,CL,BSN,VN,VA,VC,DB,PF,2PERC   ACA
FELDMAN, M.   11 INSTRUMENTS (1953)   PET
   FL,AFL,HN,TPT,BASS TPT,VN,VC,TRB ,TU,VIB,PF
GENTILUCCI, A.   FANTASIA #2 (1968).   FL,4VN,2VA,2VC,DB,PERC   ESZ
GERSCHEFSKI, E.   PRELUDE, OP 6/5   ACA
   PIC,FL,OB,EHN,CL,BCL,HN,HP,3PERC
GILBERT, A.   BRIGHTON PIECE   SCH
   E FL CL,CL,BCL,HN,TPT,TRB,VC,VIB,3PERC
GUEZEC, J.   CONCERT EN 3 PARTIES (1961)   EDS
   FL,OB,CL,BSN,2VN,VA,VC,DB,P F,PERC
GUINJOAN, J.   FRAGMENT (1970)   EEC
   FL,OB,CL,BSN,TPT,PF,2VN,VA,VC,PERC
HARSANYI, T.   HISTOIRE DU PETIT TAILLEUR, L'   EES
   FL,CL,BSN,TPT,VN,VC,PF ,XYL,3PERC
HAYDN, F.   7 MARCHES.   2OB,2CL,2BSN,2HN,TPT,TU,PERC   LDO
HEISS, J.   FLUTE CONCERTO (1977)   AMC
   FL,OB,CL,BSN,HN,TPT,TRB,PERC,VN,VA ,VC
HODEIR, A.   AMBIQUITE I   MJ
   FL,E FL CL,CL,BSN,HN,TRB,HP,VIB,PF,DB,PERC
HOLLOWAY, R.   CONCERTINO #3   BH
   FL,CL,BSN,SAX,TPT,HN,TRB,2VN,2PERC
HOLM, M.   ST. ANNALAND, OP 24   WH
   3FL,3TPT,HPCD,VA DA GAMBA,CEL,PERC,SP INET
HOMS, J.   MUSICA PARA 11.   FL,OB,CL,TPT,TRB,PF,PERC,2VN,VA,VC   EDA
JOACHIM, O.   ILLUMINATION II (1969)   BER
   FL,CL,BSN,HN,VN,VA,VC,DB,PF,PER C,TAPE
KAHOWEZ, G.   BARDO-PULS.   FL,CL,HN,TPT,VN,VA,VC,DB,2PERC,PF   UE
KILLMAYER, W.   KINDERTAGE   SCH
   FL,VA,PF,GUIT,ELEC ORG,ACC,5PERC,ZITHER
MADERNA, B.   SERENATA #2 (1957)   ESZ
   FL,CL,BCL,HN,TPT,VN,VA,DB,PF,PERC,H P
MAROS, R.   MUSICA DA CAMERA.   FL,2CL,2VN,VA,VC,DB,HPCD,PERC,HP   SN
MATTHEWS, W.   LETTERS FROM HOME   ACA
   FL/PIC,CL,BSN,VA,DB,PF,HPCD,4PERC
MESTRAL, P.   ALLIAGES   JOB
   FL,CL,ASAX,2TRB,2PERC,PF,ORG,DB,TPT SOLO
NIKODEMOWICZ, A.   CHAMBER CONCERTO   PWM
   FL,CL,BSN,HN,VN,DB,PF,4PERC
PABLO, L. DE.   MODULOS I (1964-65).   3CL,2VN,VA,VC,2PF,2PERC   EDT
PABLO, L. DE.   POLAR (1961).   BCL,SOP SAX,VN,8PERC   EDT
PARRIS, R.   GOLDEN NET, THE   ACA
   FL,OB,CL,BSN,HN,TPT,VN,VA,VC,TIMP,PERC
PRIETO, C.   IMPROVISACION (1966).   FL,BCL,VA,VC,TRB,VIB,5PERC   EDA
REYNOLDS, R.   PROMISES OF DARKNESS, THE   PET
   FL,CL,VN,BSN,TRB,HN,TPT,VC, DB,PF,PERC
ROREM, N.   11 STUDIES FOR 11 PLAYERS   JB
   FL,OB,CL,TPT,2PERC,HP,VN,VA,VC ,PF

11 PARTS INCLUDING PERCUSSION-1140

SCHWERTSIK, K. LIEBESTRAUME, OP 7 (1962)   EMO
    ASAX,DB,TRB,PF,VIB,MAR,5 PERC
STRAVINSKY, I. RAGTIME. FL,CL,HN,TPT,TRB,2VN,VA,DB,2PERC   CHE
STUHEC, I. CTION. FL,CL,HN,TPT,TRB,VN,VC,DB,PF,HP,PERC   EDD
TAUB, B. CHAMBER VARIATIONS 4   ACA
    FL,OB,CL,BSN,TRB,VN,VA,VC,DB,PF,TIMP
TEMPLE-SHAW, N. AUDACITY. FL,OB,4CL,BCL,ASAX,DB,VIB,PF   BE
TEMPLE-SHAW, N. DUPLICITY. FL,OB,4CL,BCL,ASAX,DB,VIB,PF   BE
TEMPLE-SHAW, N. FELICITY. FL,OB,4CL,BCL,ASAX,DB,VIB,PF   BE
TEMPLE-SHAW, N. PERPLEXITY. FL,OB,4CL,BCL,ASAX,DB,VIB,PF   BE
TISNE. CARACTERES. FL,OB,CL,HN,BSN,2VN,VA,VC,DB,PERC   BIL
TOMASI, H. JEUX DE GEISHAS   EES
    FL,OB,CL,BSN,HN,2VN,VA,VC,HP,PERC
TRIMBLE, L. PANELS I   PET
    PIC,BAR SAX,VN,VA,VC,DB,2PERC,ELEC GUIT,ELEC ORG,ELEC HPCD
WAHREN, K. REVERSIBEL (1969)   B&B
    FL,CL,VN,VA,VC,TRB,2PF,2PERC,TAPE
WUORINEN, C. CHAMBER CONCERTO   PET
    VC SOLO,FL,OB/EHN,CL/BCL,BSN,VN,VA,D B,PF,2PERC
WUORINEN, C. COMPOSITION. SOLO,2OB,BCL,2HN,2TRB,PF,DB,PERC   VN
ZEHM, F. SCHWIERIGKEITEN & UNFALLE MIT 1 CHORAL   SCH
    2FL,2OB,2CL,2HN,2BSN,PERC
ZONN, P. SONORUM I. FL,OB,CL,HN,TPT,TRB,VN,VA,DB,VIB,PERC   ACA
ZONN, P. VOYAGE OF COLUMBUS, THE (1975)   AMC
    TPT SOLO,AFL/PIC,OB,SOP SAX,FLUEGELHORN,TRB,2PERC,VN,DB,PF

11 PARTS W/O HARP, GUITAR, OR PERCUSSION-1141

ANDRIESSEN, L. ON JIMMY YANCEY (1973)   SD
    FL,2ASAX,TSAX,HN,TPT,3TRB,DB,PF
ARNELL, R. SERENADE, OP 57 (1949). 2FL,2OB,2CL,2HN,2BSN,DB   JE
BOIS, R. DU. SPRINGTIME (1978). PIC,3SAX,HN,2TPT,2TRB,TU,PF   SD
BORSTLAP, D. FANFARE II (1965)   SD
    FL/PIC,2ASAX,TSAX,HN,TPT,3TRB,DB,PF
BORSTLAP, D. OVER DE VERANDERING (1974)   SD
    FL,2ASAX,TSAX,HN,TPT,3TRB,DB,PF
BRANDON, S. FROM GOULIES & GHOSTIES (1974)   MAN
    CL,VN,VA,VC,2TPT,TRB,2P F,ORG,TAPE
CHERNEY, B. KONTAKION (1969)   CAN
    FL,OB,CL,HN,BSN,2VN,VA,VC,DB,PF
CHRISTIANSEN, C. TOY BOX, THE. 2FL,OB,2CL,2BSN,2HN,TPT,TRB   CGM
COOKE, A. SINFONIETTA. FL,OB,CL,BSN,HN,TPT,2VN,VA,VC,DB   BE
DONATONI, F. MOVIMENTO (1959). 3FL,2CL,BSN,2HN,TPT,HPCD,PF   ESZ
DVORAK, A. MARCH (SERENADE)   EM
    2OB,2CL,2BSN,CBSN AD LIB,3HN,VC,DB
EISMA, W. 10 FLUTES & TAPE (1973). 10FL,TAPE   SD
FINKE, F. SUITE #5 (1955). FL,OB,CL,BSN,2HN,2TPT,2TRB,TU   BRH
GODRON, H. AMABILE-SUITE (1943). CL,4VN,2VA,2VC,DB,PF   SD
HESS, W. SERENADE, OP 19 (1940). FL,OB,CL,2BSN,2HN,2VN,VA,VC   EUL
LYBBERT, D. SONORITIES. PIC,FL,2CL,2ASAX,HN,VN,VA,VC,PF   ACA
MALIPIERO, G. RICERCARI. FL,OB,CL,BSN,HN,4VA,VC,DB   UE
MALIPIERO, G. RITROVARI. FL,OB,CL,BSN,HN,4VA,VC,DB   UE
MENDELSSOHN, F. NOTTURNO. FL,2OB,EHN,2CL,2BSN,2HN,TPT   DEU
MENGELBERG, M. DRESSOIR (1977). FL,3SAX,HN,2TPT,2TRB,TU,PF   SD
PETRASSI, G. SONATA DA CAMERA (1948)   ESZ
    HPCD SOLO,FL,OB,CL,BSN,2VN,2V A,VC,DB
PORCELIJN, D. CONTINUATIONS (1968). 2FL,2OB,2CL,2BSN,2HN,TPT   SD
TARENSKEEN, B. MACHTELT SUITE (1978)   SD
    2ASAX,2TSAX,HN,2TPT,3TRB,DB

275

TAVENER, J. MUSICAL GAME "GRANDMA'S FOOTSTEPS", A   CHE
    OB,BSN,HN,4VN,2VA,2VC,5MUSIC BOXES
VERN, A. NOCTURNE EN HARMONIE. FL,2CL,2HN,2BSN,2OB,TPT,TRB   EDH
WIMBERGER, G. SHORT STORIES (1975). 2FL,2OB,2CL,2BSN,2HN,TPT   B&N
XENAKIS, I. PHLEGRA (1975)   EDS
    FL/PIC,OB,CL/BCL,BSN,HN,TPT,TRB,VN,VA,VC,DB

12 PARTS: WOODWINDS INCLUDING HORN-1221

GANZ, R. WOODY SCHERZO   BE
    PIC,2FL,2OB,EHN,E FL CL,2CL,2BSN,CBSN
GOULD (ARR). AWAY IN A MANGER; O LITTLE TOWN OF BETHLEHEM   CA
    2FL,2OB,2 CL,2BSN,4HN
KOHN, K. CONCERT MUSIC. 2FL,2OB,2CL,2BSN,EHN,BCL,2HN   CF
MICHALSKY, D. FANFARE AFTER 17TH CENTURY DANCES. 12 WINDS·   SH
MOZART, W.-HARRIS. BEI MANNERN (MAGIC FLUTE)   AB
    2FL,3OB,2CL,3BSN,2HN
MOZART, W.-HARRIS. MENUETTO (DON GIOVANNI)   AB
    2FL,3OB,2CL,3BSN,2HN
MOZART, W.-HARRIS. VIVAT BACCHUS, BACCHUS LEBE (SERAGLIO)   AB
    2FL,3OB,2CL,3BSN,2HN
STRAUSS, R. SUITE. 2FL,2OB,2CL,2BSN,4HN   M&M

12 PARTS INCLUDING HARP-1238

BABBITT, M. COMPOSITION FOR 12 INSTRUMENTS   AMP
    FL,OB,CL,BSN,HN,TPT,VN,VA,VC,DB,HP,CEL
BIRTWISTLE, H. WORLD IS DISCOVERED, THE   UE
    2FL,OB,EHN,CL,BASSET HN(BC L),2BSN,2HN,HP,GUIT
CURTIS-SMITH, C. ENSEMBLES/SOLOS (1977)   AMC
    CL,SAX,HN,TPT,VN,VA,VC,2PF ,VIB,GUIT,HP
DELAS, J. DE. CONJUNTOS (1975/76)   HG
    FL/AFL,OB,CL,HN,PERC,HP,PF,VN,VA,VC,OB,TAPE
DELAS, J. DE. IMAGO (1964)   HG
    FL,AFL,CL,BCL,HP,CEL,2PERC,VN,VA,VC,PF
HARRISON, L. SUITE   AMP
    VN & PF SOLO,2FL,OB,2VC,DB,HP,CEL,DR,TACK PF
KOLB, B. SOUNDINGS (1972)   PET
    FL,OB,CL,HN,BSN,2VN,VA,VC,PERC,HP,TAPE
KOPELENT, M. FEW MINUTES WITH AN OBOIST, A (1972)   HG
    OB,TPT,2GUIT,MAN DOLIN,BANJO,HP,PF,2PERC,VN,DB
LAMPERSBERG, G. SINFONIE   UE
    FL,CL,BSN,HN,TPT,TRB,HP,CEL,GUIT,VN,VA,VC
LEWIS, R. MUSIC FOR 12 PLAYERS   TP
    FL,CL,BSN,HN,TPT,TRB,VIB,HP,VN,VC,D B,PF
LIEBERSON, P. CONCERTO FOR VIOLONCELLO   EDS
    VC,FL,OB,BCL,TPT,HP,PF,TIMP ,2VN,DB,MANDOLIN
MILHAUD, D. STANFORD SERENADE   EES
    OB SOLO,FL,CL,BSN,TPT,2VN,VA,VC,DB,P ERC,HP
OVERTON, H. PULSATIONS   ACA
    FL,CL,BSN,HN,TPT,TRB,VN,VC,DB,PF,HP,PERC
PETRESCU, D. MUSIQUE (1969)   EDS
    FL,CL,TPT,VN,VA,VC,DB,PF,HP,ORG,HPCD,P ERC
SOUTHERS, L., JR. CONCERT PIECE (1965)   CAN
    FL,OB,CL,BSN,HN,2VN,VA,VC,D B,HP,PERC
TAUTENHAHN, G. BASSOON CONCERTO. BSN,HP,10 PERC   SS
TROMBLY, P. CHAMBER CONCERTO   ACA
    FL,OB,CL,HN,TPT,TRB,VN,VA,DB,PF,HP,PE RC
WUORINEN, C. CANZONA   PET
    FL,OB/EHN,CL/BCL,BSN,TPT,VN,VA,VC,DB,HP,VIB,P F

12 PARTS INCLUDING GUITAR-1239

```
BENNETT, R.  KONZERT FUR GITARRE                              UE
    GUIT,FL/PIC,OB/EHN,BCL,HN,TPT,2PER C,VN,VA,VC,CEL
BIRTWISTLE, H.  WORLD IS DISCOVERED, THE                      UE
    2FL,OB,EHN,CL,BASSET HN(BCL),2BSN,2HN,HP,GUIT
CURTIS-SMITH, C.  ENSEMBLES/SOLOS (1977)                      AMC
    CL,SAX,HN,TPT,VN,VA,VC,2PF ,VIB,GUIT,HP
DAVIES, P.  POINTS & DANCES FROM TAVENER                      BH
    AFL,CL,CBSN,TPT,TRB,VA,VC,HPCD,REGAL,POSITIVE ORG,TIMP,GUIT
KOPELENT, M.  FEW MINUTES WITH AN OBOIST, A (1972)            HG
    OB,TPT,2GUIT,MANDOLIN,BANJO,HP,PF,2PERC,VN,DB
LAMPERSBERG, G.  SINFONIE                                     UE
    FL,CL,BSN,HN,TPT,TRB,HP,CEL,GUIT,VN,VA,VC
LIEBERSON, P.  CONCERTO FOR VIOLONCELLO                       EDS
    VC,FL,OB,BCL,TPT,HP,PF,TIMP ,2VN,DB,MANDOLIN
RECK, D.  NUMBER 1 FOR 12 PERFORMERS                          MJ
    FL,CL,TSAX,HN,VA,DB,GUIT,VIB,P F,3PERC
SCHUBERT, F.-CLEMENTI.  DEUTSCHER MIT ZWEI TRIOS              ESZ
    FL,OB,CL,BSN,HN,TPT,TRB,VN,VA,VC,GUIT,CEL
SCHULLER, G.  VARIANTS ON A THEME OF JOHN LEWIS (DJANGO)      MJ
    FL,ASAX/FL ,VIB,GUIT,PF,2VN,VA,VC,2DB,PERC
SCHWERTSIK, K.  SALOTTO ROMANO, OP  5 (1961)                  EMO
    BASSET HN,BCL,BSN,CBSN ,2HN,TRB,TU,VC,DB,GUIT,PERC
SYMONDS, N.  IIND PERSPECTIVE (1967)                          CAN
    ASAX,BAR SAX,3TPT,3TRB,GUIT,DB ,DR,TAPE
WILSON, G.  CONCATENATIONS                                   JOB
    FL,CL,BCL,HN,TPT,TRB,VN,VC,DB,PERC,ACC,ELEC GUIT
```

12 PARTS INCLUDING PERCUSSION-1240

```
ALBRIGHT, W.  MARGINAL WORLDS                                JOB
    FL,CL/ASAX,BSN/TSAX,TPT,TRB,PF,VN,VA, VC,DB,2PERC
BABBITT, M.  COMPOSITION FOR 12 INSTRUMENTS                  AMP
    FL,OB,CL,BSN,HN,TPT,VN, VA,VC,DB,HP,CEL
BACH, J.S.-SCHULLER.  PRELUDE #8                             MAR
    FL,OB,ASAX,TSAX,BAR SAX,HN,TPT,TRB,TU,PF,DR,DB
BENNETT, R.  KONZERT FUR GITARRE                             UE
    GUIT,FL/PIC,OB/EHN,BCL,HN,TPT,2PER C,VN,VA,VC,CEL
BLOCK, S.  CHEMICAL WEDDING.  5FL/PIC,HN,TPT,2TRB,3PERC      ACA
BURT, G.  EXIT MUSIC.  FL,CL,BCL,HN,TRB,BTRB,TU,2PERC,VN,VC,DB   JOB
CURTIS-SMITH, C.  ENSEMBLES/SOLOS (1977)                     AMC
    CL,SAX,HN,TPT,VN,VA,VC,2PF ,VIB,GUIT,HP
DAVIES, P.  POINTS & DANCES FROM TAVENER                     BH
    AFL,CL,CBSN,TPT,TRB,VA,VC,HPCD,REGAL,POSITIVE ORG,TIMP,GUIT
DELAS, J. DE.  CONJUNTOS (1975/76)                           HG
    FL/AFL,OB,CL,HN,PERC,HP,PF,VN,VA,VC,OB,TAPE
DELAS, J. DE.  IMAGO (1964)                                  HG
    FL,AFL,CL,BCL,HP,CEL,2PERC,VN,VA,VC,PF
DENISOV, E.  MUSIC.  FL,2OB,2CL,2BSN,2HN,TPT,TRB,TIMP        PET
EDLER, R.  REFLEXIONS (1963).  CL,VN,VA,VC,HN,TRB,PF,VIB,4PERC   EDT
ETLER, A.  CONCERTO.  CL,3TPT,3TRB,2DB,3PERC                 AMP
FELCIANO, R.  LAMENTATIONS FOR JANI CHRISTOU                 ECS
    FL,OB,HN,TPT,TRB,TU,2PERC,PF,VC,DB,TAPE
```

12 PARTS INCLUDING PERCUSSION-1240

FELDMAN, M.   MADAME PRESS DIED LAST WEEK AT NINETY (1970)   UE
  2FL,HN,TP T,TRB,TU(BCL),CEL,2VC,2DB,PERC

HANDEL, G.-KAHN.   FIREWORK MUSIC I.   3OB,2BSN,3TPT,3HN,TIMP   EM

HARRISON, L.   SUITE   AMP
  VN & PF SOLO,2FL,OB,2VC,DB,HP,CEL,DR,TACK PF

HARVEY, J.   SMILING IMMORTAL (1977)   FB
  FL,OB,CL,HN,TPT,2VN,VA,VC,PF,PERC,TAPE

HILLER, L.   DIVERTIMENTO   TP
  PIC,FL,OB,CL,BSN,HN,TPT,TRB,DB,GUIT,2PERC

KASZYCKI, J.   CHAMBER MINIATURES (1965).   FL,VC,2PF,8PERC   PWM

KOLB, B.   SOUNDINGS (1972)   PET
  FL,OB,CL,HN,BSN,2VN,VA,VC,PERC,HP,TAPE

KOPELENT, M.   FEW MINUTES WITH AN OBOIST, A (1972)   HG
  OB,TPT,2GUIT,MANDOLIN,BANGO,HP,PF,2PERC,VN,DB

KURTZ, E.   CONVERSATIONS   JOB
  FL,OB,CL,HN,TPT,PERC,PF,2VN,VA,VC,DB

LAMPERSBERG, G.   SINFONIE   UE
  FL,CL,BSN,HN,TPT,TRB,HP,CEL,GUIT,VN,VA,VC

LELEU, J.   SUITE SYMPHONIQUE   ALE
  2FL,2OB,CL,BSN,HN,2TPT,TRB,PERC,PF

LEWIS, R.   MUSIC FOR 12 PLAYERS   TP
  FL,CL,BSN,HN,TPT,TRB,VIB,HP,VN,VC,D B,PF

LIEBERSON, P.   CONCERTO FOR VIOLONCELLO   EDS
  VC,FL,OB,BCL,TPT,HP,PF,TIMP ,2VN,DB,MANDOLIN

MATUSZCZAK, B.   MUSICA DA CAMERA (1967).   3FL,4TIMP,5DR   HMO

MILHAUD, D.   STANFORD SERENADE   EES
  OB SOLO,FL,CL,BSN,TPT,2VN,VA,VC,DB,P ERC,HP

OVERTON, H.   PULSATIONS   ACA
  FL,CL,BSN,HN,TPT,TRB,VN,VC,DB,PF,HP,PERC

PETRESCU, D.   MUSIQUE (1969)   EDS
  FL,CL,TPT,VN,VA,VC,DB,PF,HP,ORG,HPCD,P ERC

PETRIC, I.   INLAID-WORK   EDD
  FL,CL,BSN,HN,TPT,TRB,2VN,VA,VC,DB,PERC

RECK, D.   NUMBER 1 FOR 12 PERFORMERS   MJ
  FL,CL,TSAX,HN,GUIT,VIB,PF,VA,D B,3PERC

SCHERCHEN-HSIAO, T.   BIEN   UE
  CL,BSN,TPT,TRB,2VN,VA,VC,DB,PF,2PERC

SCHUBERT, F.-CLEMENTI.   DEUTSCHER MIT ZWEI TRIOS   ESZ
  FL,OB,CL,BSN,HN,TPT,TRB,VN,VA,VC,GUIT,CEL

SCHULLER, G.   VARIANTS ON A THEME OF JOHN LEWIS (DJANGO)   MJ
  FL,ASAX/FL ,VIB,GUIT,PF,2VN,VA,VC,2DB,PERC

SCHWERTSIK, K.   SALOTTO ROMANO, OP 5 (1961)   EMO
  BASSET HN,BCL,BSN,CBSN ,2HN,TRB,TU,VC,DB,GUIT,PERC

SOEGIJO, P.   TO CATCH A FLY (1969)   B&B
  PIC,FL,CL,TPT,TRB,VN,VA,VC,PF,3P ERC

SOLLBERGER, H.   CHAMBER VARIATIONS   ACA
  2FL,OB,CL,BSN,VN,VA,VC,DB,PF,2PE RC

SOUTHERS, L., JR.   CONCERT PIECE (1965)   CAN
  FL,OB,CL,BSN,HN,2VN,VA,VC,D B,HP,PERC

SYMONDS, N.   IIND PERSPECTIVE (1967)   CAN
  ASAX,BAR SAX,3TPT,3TRB,GUIT,DB ,DR,TAPE

TAUTENHAHN, G.   BASSOON CONCERTO.   BSN,HP,10 PERC   SS

TERZAKIS, D.   ICHOCHRONOS II (1972/73)   HG
  LOTOS FLUTE,FL,CL,HN,TU,TIMP ,PERC,2VN,VA,VC,DB

TREMBLAY, G.   CHAMPS III (VERS) (1969)   CAN
  2FL,CL,TPT,HN,3VN,DB,3PERC

TREMBLAY, G.   SERENADE.   FL,CL,BSN,HN,TPT,2VN,VA,VC,DB,PF,PERC   ACA

TREMBLAY, G. .   CHAMPS II (SOUFFLES) (1968)   CAN
  2FL,OB,CL,HN,2TPT,2TRB,D B,PF,PERC

TROMBLY, P.   CHAMBER CONCERTO   ACA
  FL,OB,CL,HN,TPT,TRB,VN,VA,DB,PF,HP,PE RC

VARESE, E.   INTEGRALES.   2FL,OB,2CL,HN,2TPT,TRB,2TU,PERC   ECK

279

12 PARTS INCLUDING PERCUSSION-1240

VLAD, R. SERENATA (1959). FL,2OB,2CL,2BSN,2HN,2VA,CEL   ESZ
WANEK, F. 4 GROTESKEN. 2FL,2OB,2CL,2HN,2BSN,TPT,PERC   SCH
WIDMER, E. ECLOSAO   S-V
    FL,CL,TPT,TRB,TU,ELEC PF,2PERC,VN,VA,VC,DB
WILLIAMS, E. FANT'SY II (1974)   B-B
    FL,2OB,CL,BSN,TPT,TRB,2VN,VA,VC,PER C
WILLIAMS, E. FANT'SY III (1974)   B-B
    FL,2OB,CL,BSN,TPT,TRB,2VN,VA,VC,MA R
WILSON, G. CONCATENATIONS   JOB
    FL,CL,BCL,HN,TPT,TRB,VN,VC,DB,PERC,ACC,ELEC GUIT
WUORINEN, C. CANZONA   PET
    FL,OB/EHN,CL/BCL,BSN,TPT,VN,VA,VC,DB,HP,VIB,P F
YAVELOW, C. INTERCOSMOS   ACA
    FL,BSN,TPT,TRB,VN,VC,4TIMP,FILM,PERC

12 PARTS W/O HARP, GUITAR, OR PERCUSSION-1241

APOSTEL, H. FISCHERHAUS-SERENADE, OP 45   LDO
    FL,OB,CL,BSN,HN,TPT,TRB,2V N,VA,VC,DB
ARENSKY, A.-SKINDER. 6 CHILDREN'S SCENES   PWM
    FL,OB,3CL,2BSN,2HN,2TPT,TRB
BEDFORD, D. JACK OF SHADOWS. VA SOLO,4FL,2HN,TRB,TU,2VC,DB   UE
BEDFORD, D. TRONA FOR 12 (1967)   UE
    FL,OB,CL,BSN,2TPT,2TRB,2VN,VA,VC
BEDFORD, D. WITH 100 KAZOOS   UE
    FL,OB,CL,BCL,HN,TPT,TRB,2VN,VA,VC,DB
BENTZON, N. SONATA, OP257   WH
    FL,OB,CL,BSN,HN,TPT,TRB,PF,VN,VA,VC,DB
CERHA, F. CURRICULUM (1972). 2OB,2CL,2BSN,2HN,TPT,TRB,TU,BAR   UE
DVORAK, A. SERENADE IN D MI, OP 44   MR
    2OB,2CL,2BSN,CBSN,3HN,VC,DB
ꞋᴿAK, A. SERENADE, OP 44. 2OB,2CL,3BSN,3HN,VC,DB   INT
FINNISSY, M. PIANO CONCERTO #2 (1975/76)   EMO
    2AFL,3VN,2VA,2VC,2DB,PF
GWILT, D. SUITE. 2FL,OB,2CL,BSN(CL),2HN,2TPT,2TRB,OPT PERC   NO
HERMANS, N. BALLET DES PETITS PIEDS   SD
    2FL,2OB,2CL,2BSN,2HN,2TPT
HESS, W. SUITE, OP 53. 2FL,2OB,2CL,2BSN,2HN,TPT,TRB   BRH
HORVATH, J. REDUNDANZ 3 (1968). WIND OCTET,2VN,VA,VC   LDO
JADIN, L. SYMPHONIE FUR BLASINSTRUMENTE   FRH
    2FL,2CL,2BSN,SERPENT(BSN), 2HN,2TPT,TRB
JOSEPHS, W. CONCERTO A DODICI, OP 21   JOW
    PIC,FL,OB,EHN,CL,BCL,BSN,CBSN ,HN,TPT,TRB,TU
KLUSAK, J. SONATA (1963/65)   EMO
    SOLO VN,FL,2OB,2CL,2HN,2BSN,TPT,TRB
LEIBOWITZ, R. CHAMBER SYMPHONY, OP 16 (1948)   B-B
    FL,OB,CL,BCL,BSN,HN,TPT,TRB,VN,VA,VC,DB
LEITERMEYER, F. DIVERTIMENTO, OP 53   LDO
    PIC,FL,OB,EHN,CL,BCL,BSN,CBSN, 2HN,TPT,TRB
LESSARD, J. CONCERTO FOR WIND INSTRUMENTS   TP
    2FL,OB,2CL,2BSN,2HN,2TPT ,TRB
MACCHI, E. COMPOSIZIONE 3 (1960)   BRU
    FL,OB,CL,BSN,HN,TPT,TRB,VN,2VA,VC ,DB
PENDERECKI, K. CAPRICCIO. OB,6VN,2VA,2VC,DB   HMO
RAYKI, G. BURLESKE. FL,OB,2CL,2BSN,3HN,2TPT,TRB   UE
ROSETTI, A.-HELLYER. PARTITA IN F MA   OX
    2FL,2OB,2CL,3HN,2BSN,DB
SPIES, C. LXXXV. 4CL,BCL,3VN,3VA,VC   BH

STACHOWIAK, L.   3 (1963) IMPROVISATIONS   AP
     3FL,3CL,2HN,2VN,VA,VC
STRAVINSKY, I.   CONCERTINO   CHE
     FL,OB,EHN,CL,2BSN,2TPT,TRB,BASS TRB,VN,VC
WALKER, J.   SCHERZO (ENCORE FOR WINDS)   GS
     2FL,2BSN,2OB,2CL,2HN,2TPT
WEBER, C. VON.   MARCH.   FL,2OB,2CL,2BSN,2HN,2TPT,TRB   MR
WEBER, C. VON-MEERWEIN.   MARCIA IN C MA   DEU
     FL,2OB,2CL,2HN,2BSN,2TPT,TRB

13 PARTS: WOODWINDS INCLUDING
HORN-1321

```
ANDERSON, L.   SUITE OF CAROLS                                    BE
    PIC,2FL,2OB,EHN,2CL,ACL,BCL,2BSN,CBSN
BRAHMS, J.   O GOTT DU FROMMER GOTT, OP122/7                      CP
    FL,AFL,2OB,EHN,BAR OB,2 CL,BCL,3BSN,CBSN
MOZART, W.   SERENADE #10 IN B FL MA, K361                        BR
    2OB,2CL,2BASSET HN(2CL),2BSN,CBSN(DB),4HN
MOZART, W.   SERENADE #10 IN B FL MA, K361                        BRH
    2OB,2CL,2BASSET HN,2BSN,CBSN,4HN
MOZART, W.   SERENADE #10 IN B FL MA, K361                        MR
    2OB,2CL,2BASSET HN(2CL),2BSN,CBSN(DB),4HN
SPINO, P.   STATEMENT FOR HORN & WOODWINDS                       STM
    SOLO HN,2FL,OB,3CL,BCL,BS N,2ASAX,TSAX,BAR SAX
STRAUSS, R.   SERENADE IN E FL MA, OP  7                          UE
    2FL,2OB,2CL,2BSN,CBSN,4HN
STRAUSS, R.   SERENADE, OP 7.   2FL,2OB,2CL,2BSN,CBSN,4HN         EDK
STRAUSS, R.   SERENADE, OP 7.   2FL,2OB,2CL,2BSN,CBSN,4HN         INT
STRAUSS, R.   SUITE IN B FL MA, OP  4                             LEU
    2FL,2OB,2CL,2BSN,CBSN,4HN
```

13 PARTS INCLUDING HARP-1338

```
BERGER, A.   CHAMBER MUSIC                                       PET
    FL,OB,CL/BCL,BSN,HN,TPT,2VN,VA,VC,DB,CEL, HP
BOYKAN, M.   CONCERTO (1973)                                     B-B
    FL/PIC,OB,CL,BCL,BSN,HN,TPT,VN,VA,VC,DB ,PF,HP
CORY, E.   CONCERTINO II                                         ACA
    PF SOLO,OB,EHN,CL,BSN,HN,TRB,HP,4PERC,MANDOLINE
DONATONI, F.   LIED (1972).   2FL,2CL,2VN,2VA,PF,HP,VIB,CEL,HPCD  ESZ
MADERNA, B.   SERENATA #2                                        ESZ
    FL,CL,BCL,HN,TPT,VN,VA,DB,PF,HP,XYL,VIB,GLOCK
MINGUS, C.   REVELATIONS (1957)                                  MAR
    FL,ASAX,TSAX,HN,TPT,TRB,BSN,HP,PF,VI B,GUIT,DB,PERC
PETRIC, I.   DIVERTIMENTO FOR SLAVKO OSTERC                      EDD
    FL,OB,CL,BSN,HN,PF,HP,PE RC,2VN,VA,VC,DB
PETYREK, F.   ARABISCHE SUITE                                    UE
    2FL,OB,2CL,2BSN,2HN,TRB,HP,DB,PERC
SATIE, E.(CONSTANT).   MESSE DES PAUVRES                         EDS
    FL,CL,BCL,BSN,HN,TPT,TRB,PF, HP,VN,VC,2PERC
SAXTON, R.   REFLECTIONS OF NARZISS & GOLDMUND (1975)            CHE
    FL/AFL,OB,CL,A SAX,HN,TPT,TRB,2VA,VC,DB,HP,PF/CEL
```

13 PARTS INCLUDING GUITAR-1339

```
CORY, E.   CONCERTINO II                                         ACA
    PF SOLO,OB,EHN,CL,BSN,HN,TRB,HP,4PERC,MANDOLINE
HESPOS, H.   KEIME UND MALE                                      JOB
    PIC,FL,2CL,ASAX,HN,GUIT,VN,VA,DB,3PERC
```

13 PARTS INCLUDING GUITAR-1339

KOLB, B. TROBAR CLUS   BH
    FL,AFL,CL,BSN,VN,VA,2TPT,2TRB,HPCD,PERC,GUIT
MINGUS, C. REVELATIONS (1957)   MAR
    FL,ASAX,TSAX,HN,TPT,TRB,BSN,HP,PF,VI B,GUIT,DB,PERC
PARODI, R. CONCERTO. FL,4VN,2VA,2VC,2DB,HP,CEL   RC
SCHIFRIN, L. RITUAL OF SOUND   MJ
    FL,CL,BCL,HN,2TPT,TRB,TU,GUIT,VIB,2DB ,PERC

13 PARTS INCLUDING PERCUSSION-1340

BEETHOVEN, L. VAN. MARSCH IN C MA   BRH
    FL,2OB,2CL,3BSN,2HN,2TPT,PERC
BERGER, A. CHAMBER MUSIC   PET
    FL,OB,CL/BCL,BSN,HN,TPT,2VN,VA,VC,DB,CEL, HP
BIRTWISTLE, H. VERSES FOR ENSEMBLES (1969)   UE
    PIC/AFL,OB/EHN,E FL CL/ CL,CL/BCL,BSN/CBSN,HN,2TPT,2TRB,3PERC
CONSTANT, M. MUSIQUE DE CONCERT   ALE
    FL,OB,BSN,ASAX,HN,TPT,TRB,2PERC,PF ,VN,VC,DB
CORY, E. CONCERTINO II   ACA
    PF SOLO,OB,EHN,CL,BSN,HN,TRB,HP,4PERC,MANDOLINE
CROSSE, G. ARIADNE, OP 31   OX
    OB,FL/PIC,CL,CL/BCL,TPT,2TRB,PERC,PF/CEL ,VN,VA,VC,DB
DONATONI, F. LIED (1972). 2FL,2CL,2VN,2VA,PF,HP,VIB,CEL,HPCD ESZ
DRUCKMAN, J. INCENTERS   BE
    FL,OB,CL,BSN,HN,TPT,TRB,PF/ORG,VN,VA,VC,DB, PERC
FERRARI, L. FLASHES   EMT
    PIC,OB,CL,BSN,HN,TPT,TRB,2VN,VA,VC,DB,PERC
FIELDS, F. CHANT RITUAL #1. 12WW,TIMP   SN
FRITSCH, J. MODULATION II   FEE
    FL/PIC,EHN,BCL,TPT,2TRB,2PF,PERC,VN,VA,VC,DB
HESPOS, H. KEIME UND MALE   JOB
    PIC,FL,2CL,ASAX,HN,GUIT,VN,VA,DB,3PERC
KOLB, B. TROBAR CLUS   BH
    FL,AFL,CL,BSN,VN,VA,2TPT,2TRB,HPCD,PERC,GUIT
KUBIK, G. DIVERTIMENTO #1 (1959)   MC
    FL/PIC,OB/EHN,CL/BCL,BSN,HN,TPT,TRB,VN,VA,VC,DB,PERC,PF/HPCD
MADERNA, B. SERENATA #2   ESZ
    FL,CL,BCL,HN,TPT,VN,VA,DB,PF,HP,XYL,VIB,GLOCK
MILHAUD, D. ACTUALITES. 2CL,2TPT,TRB,PERC,2VN,2VA,2VC,DB   UE
MINGUS, C. REVELATIONS (1957)   MAR
    FL,ASAX,TSAX,HN,TPT,TRB,BSN,HP,PF,VI B,GUIT,DB,PERC
MITREA-CELARIANU, M. SIGNAUX (SUR L'OCEAN U) (1971)   EDS
    PIC,FL,CL,BCL, TPT,TRB,TU,PF,VN,VA,DB,2PERC
OLAH, T. PERSPECTIVES (1970)   EDS
    FL,OB/EHN,CL/BCL,HN,TPT,TRB,VN,VA,VC, DB,3PERC
OLAN, D. MUSIC (1966). FL,CL,BSN,HN,TPT,TRB,VN,VA,VC,4PERC   ACA
PARODI, R. CONCERTO. FL,4VN,2VA,2VC,2DB,HP,CEL   RC
PETRIC, I. DIVERTIMENTO FOR SLAVKO OSTERC   EDD
    FL,OB,CL,BSN,HN,PF,HP,PE RC,2VN,VA,VC,DB
PETYREK, F. ARABISCHE SUITE   UE
    2FL,OB,2CL,2BSN,2HN,TRB,HP,DB,PERC
REYNOLDS, R. QUICK ARE THE MOUTHS OF EARTH   PET
    3FL/PIC,OB,3VC,TPT,2PERC,PF
SAMUEL, G. COLD WHEN THE DRUM SOUNDS FOR DAWN (1975)   BE
    FL/PIC/AFL,2O B/EHN,2HN,BSN,2VN,VA,VC,DB,PERC,HPCD/CEL
SATIE, E.-CONSTANT. MESSE DES PAUVRES   EDS
    FL,CL,BCL,BSN,HN,TPT,TRB,PF,HP,VN,VC,2PERC
SCHIFFRIN, L. RITUAL OF SOUND   MJ
    FL,CL,BCL,HN,2TPT,TRB,TU,GUIT,VIB,2D B,PERC

13 PARTS INCLUDING PERCUSSION-1340

SCHULLER, G. ATONAL STUDY IN JAZZ (1948)   MAR
   FL,OB,ASAX,TSAX,BAR SAX,2 HN,TPT,TRB,TU,PF,DB,DR
SCHWANTNER, J. CANTICLE OF THE EVENING BELLS   PET
   FL SOLO,OB/EHN,CL,BSN ,HN,TPT,TRB,VN,VA,VC,DB,PF,PERC
TCHEREPNIN, N. SONATINE, OP 61   BEL
   2FL,2OB,CL,2BSN,HN,2TPT,TRB,TIMP,XY L
TREMBLAY, G. CHAMPS II (SOUFFLES) (1968)   CAN
   2FL,OB,CL,HN,2TPT,2TRB,PF ,DB,2PERC
WNUK, J. D.Z.W.M. (1973). FLEXAPHONE SOLO,PIC,FL,OB,9PERC   PWM

13 PARTS W/O HARP, GUITAR,
OR PERCUSSION-1341

ANGERER, P. MUSICA ARTICOLATA   LDO
   2FL,2OB,2CL,BCL,2BSN,2HN,TPT,TRB
BEYER, F. CONCERTINO A TRE (1974)   B&B
   2OB,TPT,TRB,PF,4VN,2VA,2VC
BON, W. PASSACAGLIA IN BLUE. 2FL,2OB,2CL,2BSN,2HN,TPT,TRB,DB   SD
BROWN, N. CHANT AND JUBILEE. FL,4HN,4TPT,2TRB,2TU   SS
COPLAND, A. APPALACHIAN SPRING: SUITE   BH
   FL,CL,BSN,4VN,2VA,2VC,DB,PF
DECSENYI, J. COLLOIDES. FL,12 INSTR   EMB
HEDWALL, L. PARTITA (1961). 2FL,2OB,2CL,2BSN,2HN,2TPT,TRB   STI
HOCH, F. OGGETTO DISINCANTATO, L'   ESZ
   FL,OB,CL,BSN,HN,TPT,TRB,PF,HPCD, VN,VA,VC,DB
HORVATH, J. SOTHIS I   LDO
   FL/PIC,OB/EHN,CL,BCL,BSN,HN,TPT,TRB,2VN,VA,VC ,DB
HUGGLER, J. MUSIC FOR 13 INSTRUMENTS, OP 75   PET
   2FL,OB,2CL,BCL,BSN,CBS N,2HN,TPT,TRB,VC
JACOB, G. MORE OLD WINE IN NEW BOTTLES   JE
   2FL,2OB,2CL,2BSN,CBSN,2HN,2 TPT
MOZART, W. SERENADE #10, K361   H-V
   2OB,2CL,2BASSET HN(2CL),4HN,2BSN,DB(CBSN)
NUNES, E. DAWN WO. 2FL,OB,EHN,3CL,BSN,CBSN,2HN,TPT,TRB   JOB
PAUER, J. MUSICA DA CONCERTO (1971)   ART
   2FL,2OB,2CL,2BSN,2HN,2TPT,TRB
PIECHOWSKA, A. IMAGINAIRE (1976). OB,7VN,2VA,2VC,DB   PWM
SCHWARTZ, E. TEXTURE FOR STRINGS, WINDS, & BRASS (1966)   BR
   13 PLAYERS
TAVENER, J. GRANDMA'S FOOTSTEPS. OB,BSN,HN,2VN,4VN,2VA,2VC   CHE
YAVELOW, C. SERMON. CL,3TPT,HN,TRB,3VN,3VA,SLIDES   ACA
ZIMMERMANN, B. RHEINISCHE KIRMESTANZE (1950/62)   SCH
   2FL,2OB,2CL,2HN,2BSN,TPT,TRB,TU

FLUTE CHOIR -1400

```
BACH, J.S.(CHRISTENSEN).  AIR                                    SO
BASHMAKOV, L.  FANTASIA                                          FIN
BERLIN, D.  FLUCTUATIONS                                         MAN
BIGGS, J.  WIND COLLAGE                                          CPR
BONSEL, A.  ANTHRISCUS SYLVESTRIS (1974)                         SD
CEELY, R.  RITUALS                                              ACA
ERDMANN, H.  RAUMKOMPOSITION                                    HSM
FAURE, G.-CHRISTENSEN.  PAVANE                                   ZA
GABRIELI, A.-EPHROSS.  SONATA PIAN' E FORTE                      SO
GRIMM, C.  DIVERTIMENTO                                          SO
GRIMM, C.  5 ETUDES                                             SO
JENNI, D.  CHERRY VALLEY                                        AMP
MOLS, R.-PELLERITE.  EXCURSION.                                  ZA
PAUK, A.  CUMULUM                                               CAN
PAYNE, F.  PAVANE AND OSTINATO                                   SS
PENN, W.  NIGHT MUSIC.  11 FL,PF                                 SS
PURCELL, H.-PELLERITE.  CHACONNE                                 ZA
REBIKOV, V.-CAVALLY.  MUSICAL SNUFFBOX                           SO
RODEN, R.  ELEGANCE                                             SO
STEWART, D.  FLUTISTE BONNE ANNIVERSAIRE, LE                    EDS
STRANGE, A.  HAIRBREATH RING SCREAMERS, THE.  FL CHOIR,TAPE      ZA
SUEYOSHI, Y.  REI                                              EDS
TCHAIKOVSKY, P.-EPHROSS.  MARCHE MINIATURE                       SO
TULL, F.  CYCLORAMA 1                                            BH
VLIEGER, H. DE.  MOBILE (1977)                                   OD
WALTERS, H.  SCENES FROM THE WEST                                RU
WILDER, A.  MOVEMENT                                            MAR
YATES.  AIR                                                     SO
ZANINELLI, L.  ARIA                                             ZA
ZANINELLI, L.  3 CHILDREN'S DANCES                              ZA
```

CLARINET CHOIR -1401

```
ANCHARES-BROWN.  VERSETS                                         WI
BACH, J.S.-SACCI.  AIR (SUITE #3 IN D MA)                        KN
BACH, J.S.-CAILLIET.  AWAKE,AWAKE,A VOICE IS CALLING             SO
BACH, J.S.-UNDERWOOD.  FANTASIA & FUGUE IN C MI                  KN
BACH, J.S.-LANG.  FUGA XVI                                       LN
BACH, J.S.-WARD.  GAVOTTE                                        PO
BACH, J.S.-GEE.  MINUETS                                         PO
BACH, J.S.-FOTE.  PRAELUDIUM XXII                                KN
BACH, J.S.-JENNINGS.  PRELUDE & FUGUE IN G MI                    KN
BACH, J.S.-YATES.  PRELUDE IN D MA                               KN
BACH, J.S.-SCHMIDT.  PRELUDE IN F MA                             WI
BACH, J.S.-HOWLAND.  SACRED HEAD                                CRE
BACH, J.S.-FOTE.  SARABANDE (FRENCH SUITE IN D MI)               KN
BACH, J.S.-KIRK.  SICILIANO & MINUET                             SO
BACH, J.S.-HOWLAND.  SINFONIA (CHRISTMAS ORATORIO)              CRE
BARAT, J.-ROACH.  PIECE IN G MINOR                               SO
BARBER, S.-CAILLIET.  ADAGIO FOR STRINGS                         GS
BARGIEL, W.  MEDITATION                                          CF
```

CLARINET CHOIR-1401

BARNES, C.(ARR). ROBBINS COLLECTION OF CLASSICS   B3
BARON. LAST TRYST   SO
BARTOK, B.-MORRIS. EVENING WALK (10 EASY PIECES)   PO
BARTOK, B.-ERICKSON. FOLK SONG SUITE   GS
BEETHOVEN, L.-SACCI. ADAGIO CANTABILE (SONATA PATHETIQUE)   KN
BIZET, G.-CAILLIET. ADAGIETTO (L'ARLESIENNE)   SO
BIZET, G.-FELDSHER. ALLEGRO & VIVACE (SYMPHONY)   TM
BLOCH, E.-O'REILLY. PRELUDE & PROCESSIONAL   GS
BOCCHERINI, L. MENUET   CF
BORODIN, A.-CABRAL. NOCTURNE (QUARTET #4)   KN
BRAHMS, J.-FOTE. CHORALE PRELUDE # 8   KN
BRAHMS, J.-FOTE. CHROALE PRELUDE #11   KN
BROWN, R. SYMPHONY FOR CLARINETS   WI
BULL, J.-UNDERWOOD. FANTASIA   KN
BUXTEHUDE, D.-BROWN. FUGUE   WI
CABLE, H. WIND SONG   CA
CACAVAS, J. BARCAROLLE   SHB
CACAVAS, J. 2 MINIATURES   EV
CAILLIET, L. CAPRICE SENTIMENTAL   SO
CAILLIET, L. CARNAVAL   SO
CAILLIET, L. CLARINET POEM   SO
CAILLIET, L. FANTAISIE   SO
CARDEW, P. WHIRLWIND POLKA   BH
CASTEEL & MC CATHREN(ARR). LONDONDERRY AIR   KN
CHOPIN, F.-UNDERWOOD. NOCTURNE, OP 15/3   KN
CLERISSE, R.-ROACH. VIELLE CHANSON   SO
CORELLI, A.-THORNTON. CHURCH SONATA, OP 1/2   SO
CORELLI, A.-MORRIS. FOLIES D'ESPAGNE   PO
COX, D. OCTET   SS
DEBUSSY, C.-HOWLAND. BALLET (PETITE SUITE)   CRE
DEBUSSY, C.-MC CATHREN. CLAIR DE LUNE   KN
DEBUSSY, C.-HOWLAND. CORTEGE (PETITE SUITE)   CRE
DEBUSSY, C.-HOWLAND. EN BATEAU (PETITE SUITE)   CRE
DEBUSSY, C.-HOWLAND. MINUET (PETITE SUITE)   CRE
DEBUSSY, C.-CONLEY. NUAGES   KN
DEBUSSY, C.-BARNES. SARABANDE   TM
DEBUSSY, C.-DAVIS. SARABANDE   WI
DEJESU, J. LARGO APPASSIONATA   HL
DEJESU, J. PRELUDE TO "TRAVIATA"   HL
DEJESU, J. TO A WILD ROSE   HL
DEL BORGO, E. DODECAPHONIC ESSAY   KN
DVORAK, A. HUMORESQUE   CF
ELLMENREICH, A.-WILLARD. SPINNING SONG   PO
ERBACH, C.-ANDERSON. CANZONA   GS
EYSER, E. OTTOLETTO (1975)   STI
FAURE, G.-LESTER. PAVANE, OP 50   WI
FINDLAY, F. FROM SWEDEN   CF
FRACKENPOHL, A. PRELUDE & ALLEGRO   SH
FRESCOBALDI, G.-FOTE. FUGUE   KN
FRESCOBALDI, G.-UNDERWOOD. RICERCARE   KN
GABRIELI, G.-AYRES. CANZONA PER SONARE #2   BA
GATES, E. SEASONAL SKETCHES   SO
GESUALDO, D.-ANDERSON. OCCHI DEL MIO COR VITA   SH
GESUALDO, D.-ANDERSON. SONATA IN G MA   GS
GORDON, P. CAPRICCIO   KN
GRIEG, E.-AUSLENDER. HOLBERG SUITE   WI
HANDEL, G.-FOTE. ARIOSO   KN
HANDEL, G.-WINKING. BOURREE (SONATA #3)   PO
HANDEL, G.-ANDERSON. CONCERTO IN F MI   SH
HANDEL, G.-SACCI. LARGHETTO   KN
HANDEL, G. LARGO (XERXES)   CF
HANDEL, G. LARGO & GIGUE   YM

CLARINET CHOIR-1401

HANDEL, G.-WILCOX. OVERTURE TO "JULIUS CAESAR"	SH
HANDEL, G.-WEBB. PASTORAL SYMPHONY (MESSIAH)	KN
HANDEL, G.-GORDON. PASTORAL SYMPHONY	KJ
HANDEL, G.-WEBB. SARABANDE & BOURREE	KN
HAYDN, F.-STOUFFER. ALLEGRO	PO
HAYDN, F.-HINDSLEY. DIVERTIMENTO #1	SO
HAYDN, F.-FELDSHER. MENUETTO & TRIO (SYMPHONY #88)	KN
HAYDN, F.-FELDSHER. MENUETTO & TRIO (SYMPHONY #94)	TM
HAYDN, F.-FELDSHER. PRESTO	PO
HAYDN, F.-TROXELL. RONDO (DIVERTIMENTO #1)	PO
HEIM, N. ELEGY	KN
HEIM, N. PRELUDIUM & CANZONA	KN
HUTCHISON, W. SUITE	KN
JACOB, G. INTRODUCTION & RONDO	BH
JOPLIN, S.-WILLARD. SWIPESY CAKEWALK	PO
KAREL, L. ELEGY & DANSE	SO
KARG-ELERT, S.-HEIM. NOW THANK WE ALL OUR GOD	KN
KHACHATURIAN, A.-ESTES. ARMENIAN SONG	KN
KLAUSS, N.-MC CATHREN. CLARINETICS	KN
KLAUSS, N. DOLCE (WITH A BEAT)	KN
KLAUSS, N. SONG FOR TWILIGHT	PO
KRENEK, E.-ERICKSON. 3, OP 83 SHORT PIECES	GS
LANG, R. GRENADILLA RHAPSODY	LN
LANG, R. OPUS IN EBONY	LN
LAUBE, P. ALSATIAN DANCE	CF
LOGAN, R. ANDANTE	HL
LOTTI, A. ARIETTA	EDM
LOUCHEUR, R. EN FAMILLE	B&V
LUNDE, I. NUANCES, OP 55	KN
MAGANINI, Q. SHENANDOAH	EDM
MAGNANI, A. REVERIE	CF
MARTINI, P. PLAISIR D'AMOUR	EDM
MASCAGNI, P.-MC CATHREN. INTERMEZZO (CAVALLERIA RUSTICANA)	KN
MASSENET, J.-CAILLIET. ANGELUS	SO
MC CATHREN, D.-REED. CLARINETTE VALSANTE	KN
MC CATHREN, D.-KLAUSS. ELECTRONIC BRAIN	KN
MENDELSSOHN, F.-FELDSHER. ALLEGRO VIVACE	PO
MENDELSSOHN, F.-SCHWARZ. CONCERT PIECE #1	SMO
MENDELSSOHN, F.-HOWLAND. SALTARELLO (SYMPHONY #4)	CRE
MENDELSSOHN, F.-WEBB. TARANTELLA, OP102/3	KN
MENDELSSOHN, F.-FOTE. VARIATION SERIEUSES, OP 54	KN
MOROSS, J. SONATINA	CA
MOZART, W.-SACCI. ADAGIO (QUINTET IN G MI)	KN
MOZART, W.-WASTALL. ADAGIO (SERENADE, K375)	BH
MOZART, W.-DANFELT. ALLEGRO & ALLEGRETTO (DIVERTIMENTO #2)	SH
MOZART, W.-SACCI. ALLEGRO MAESTOSO (K417)	KN
MOZART, W.-RIED. ANDANTE (DIVERTIMENTO #1, K136)	KN
MOZART, W.-SACCI. ANDANTE & RONDO (K417)	KN
MOZART, W.-JOHNSON. DIVERTIMENTO #6	RU
MOZART, W.-SACCI. EINE KLEINE NACHTMUSIK (MOVEMENT #1)	KN
MOZART, W.-SACCI. EINE KLEINE NACHTMUSIK (MOVEMENT #2)	KN
MOZART, W.-SACCI. EINE KLEINE NACHTMUSIK (MOVEMENT #3)	KN
MOZART, W.-SACCI. EINE KLEINE NACHTMUSIK (MOVEMENT #4)	KN
MOZART, W.-HOWLAND. IMPRESARIO OVERTURE	CRE
MOZART, W.-CAILLIET. MARRIAGE OF FIGARO OVERTURE	SO
MOZART, W.-SACCI. MENUETTO (QUINTET IN G MI)	KN
MOZART, W.-SACCI. MOZART HORN QUINTET (K407)	KN
MOZART, W.-CASTEEL/MC CATHREN. OVERTURE TO COSI FAN TUTTE	KN
MOZART, W.-PILLIN. RONDO	WI
MOZART, W.-HOWLAND. SCENE & DANCE (MARRIAGE OF FIGARO)	CRE
MOZART, W.-FRACKENPOHL. SINFONIETTA	SH
MOZART, W.-MORRIS. THEME (CONCERTO #21)	PO

MURRAY, L. CLARINET CAPRIOLE	WI
NELHYBEL, V. CHORALE & DANZA	SO
NELHYBEL, V. RICERCARE. CL & SAX CHOIRS	SO
NELHYBEL, V. SUITE #1	ECK
NESTICO, S. STUDY IN CONTRASTS, A	KN
OFFENBACH, J. BEGGARS'S CANON (THE BRIGANDS)	GS
OLIVER, R. LORD RANDALL	EDM
OWEN, H. FANTASIES ON MEXICAN TUNES. 3TPT,CL CHOIR	WI
PACHELBEL, J.-FOTE. FUGA	KN
PALESTRINA, G.-CONLEY. ADORAMUS TE	KN
PAYNE, F. MINIATURES	SS
PEZEL, J.-EARLE. 3 PIECES	KN
PLEYEL, I. RONDO	CF
PRESSER, W. CHORAL FANTASY	SO
RHEINBERGER, J.-BROWN. INTRODUCTION & PASSACAGLIA	WI
RIMSKY-KORSAKOV, N.-ROACH. DANSE DES BOUFFONS	SO
RIMSKY-KORSAKOV, N.-CAILLIET. FLIGHT OF THE BUMBLE BEE, THE ASAX,CL CHOIR	SO
RODEN, R. DIFFERENCE OF OPINION	SO
RODEN, R. WALTZ & BEGUINE	SO
RODEN, R. 2 WATER COLORS	SO
ROSSINI, G.-PALMER. ITALIAN IN ALGIERS	KN
SAINT-SAENS, C.-CAILLIET. ROMANCE IN F MA. ASAX,CL CHOIR	SO
SATIE, E.-ANZALONE. GYMNOPEDIE #1	KN
SCARLATTI, D.-MORRIS. SONATA IN D MI	PO
SCHAEFFER, D. CLARINET CHOIR, THE	PO
SCHEIDT, S.-ANDERSON. CANZON SUPER INTRADAM AECHIOPICAM	GS
SCHEIN, J. MUSICAL BANQUET, A	EDM
SCHMIDT, W. TURKISH LADY, THE. TPT SOLO,CL CHOIR	WI
SCHMIDT, W. VENDOR'S CALL. PF,CL CHOIR	WI
SCHUBERT, F. ROSAMUNDE	CF
SCHUBERT, F.-SACCI. SCHERZO, OP166	KN
SCHUMANN, R. ETUDE, OP 56/5	WI
SCHUMANN, R. ETUDE, OP 56/6	WI
SCHUMANN, R. FUGUE, OP 60/1	WI
SCHUMANN, R.-FOTE. OPUS 68, #30	KN
SCHUMANN, R. SKETCH, OP 58/4	WI
SCHUMANN, R.-FOTE. SPRING SONG	KN
SCHWARTZ-HITE. VIENNA BAROQUE	LU
SIMEONOV, B. 4 PIECES	ECK
SLACK. TOO MANY CLARINETS	SF
SNAVELY, J. MOTIF & VARIATIONS	KN
STEINBERG, P. EBONATA	KN
STOVER, F. ECOLOGUE	SS
STRAVINSKY, I.-LESTER. RONDE DES PRINCESSES	WI
STUCKY, S. DIVERTIMENTO. CL CHOIR,PF,2PERC	MAN
TAMIAMI, C. 4 EARLY AMERICAN SPIRITUALS	WI
TARTINI, G.-JACOB. CONCERTINO	BH
TCHAIKOVSKY, P.-SACCI. ANDANTE CANTABILE	KN
TCHAIKOVSKY, P.-CAILLIET. CANZONETTA (VIOLIN CONCERTO) ASAX,CL CHOI R	SO
TCHAIKOVSKY, P.-CASTEEL. CHANSON TRISTE	BA
TCHAIKOVSKY, P.-SEWARD. ELEGIE	WJ
TCHAIKOVSKY, P.-CAILLIET. FINALE (VIOLIN CONCERTO) CL,CL CHOIR	SO
TCHAIKOVSKY, P.-APPLEBAUM. PIZZICATO OSTINATO	EAM
TCHAIKOVSKY, P.-MORRIS. TREPAK	PO
TCHAIKOVSKY, P.-SACCI. WALTZ (SERENADE FOR STRINGS, OP 48)	KN
TELEMANN, G.-JOHNSON. LARGO & PRESTO (SUITE IN A MI)	RU
TELEMANN, G.-JOHNSON. POLONAISE & PASSEPIEDS	RU
UBER, D. ANDANTE & DANZA (OP109)	KN
UBER, D. INTERDIFFUSIONS & SCHERZANDO (OP109)	KN

CLARINET CHOIR-1401

```
UBER, D.  MASQUES (OP 68)                                         KN
UBER, D.  PARADE, OP 68                                          KN
VILLA-LOBOS, H.-KRANCE.  BACHIANAS BRASILEIRAS #5: ARIA          AMP
VIVALDI, A.-FECHNER.  ALL'NMBRA DI SOSPETTO.  S,FL,BC            DEU
VIVALDI, A.-YATES.  CONCERTO, OP 46/1.  2TPT,CL CHOIR            AMP
VOXMAN, H. (ARR).  CLARINET CHOIR REPERTOIRE                     RU
WILDER, A.  SUITE                                               MAR
YODER, P. (ARR).  BACH SUITE                                     SO
YOUNG, D.  KROYER VARIATIONS                                     KN
YOUNG, D.  NORTHERN LEGEND                                       KN
ZINGARELLI, N.-JOSEPH.  MOTET                                    KN
```

WOODWIND CHOIR-1402

```
CARTER, A.  SIX PIECES (1980)                                    OX
```

FLEXIBLE INSTRUMENTATION-1404

```
BANTAI, V. & I. KOVACS (ED).  LEICHTE KAMMERMUSIK               EUL
   1,2,OR 3FL,PF
PORCELIJN, D.  AMOEBE FOR X FLUTES                               SD
```

VOICE WITH INSTRUMENTS-1410

```
ABBADO, M.  CANTATA (1948).  V,FL,CL,VN,VA,VC,PF                ESZ
ABBADO, M.  CIAPO (1945).  V,FL,OB,2CL,BSN,PF,DB,2PERC          ESZ
ABBADO, M.  QUINDICI POESIE T'ANG (1959).  MS,FL,OB,VC,PF       ESZ
ACILU, A.  ASCHERMITTWOCH (1968)                                EDA
   V,PIC/FL,CL,BSN,TPT,PF,VN,VA,VC,PERC
ACILU, A.  SERIEGRAFONIA (1971).  S,BAR,FL,HN,VC                EDA
ADAM, A.-SCHMIDT.  BRAVOUR-VARIATIONEN.  V,FL,PF                R&E
ADAM, A.  BRAVOUR-VARIATIONEN.  S,FL,PF                         MRL
ADAM, A.-LIEBLING.  BRAVURA VARIATIONS.  V,FL,PF                GS
ADOLPHUS, M.  LILACS.  V,CL,PF                                  ACA
AHLBERG, G.  MOSAIK.  S,3SAX                                    STI
AHRENS, J.  7 REGNUM DEI. MEDITATIONS                           WMS
   BAR,FL,OB,EHN,CL,HN,BSN,DB
AHRENS, J.  TRILOGIA SACRA #2: REGNUM DEI                       WMS
   BAR,FL,OB,EHN,CL,BSN,HN,D B
AITKEN, H.  CANTATA #1.  T,OB,VN,VC                             OX
AITKEN, H.  CANTATA #2.  T,FL,OB,VC,DB                          OX
AITKEN, H.  CANTATA #3.  T,OB,VA                                OX
AITKEN, H.  CANTATA #4.  S,FL,OB,VC,DB                          OX
ALABIEFF, A.-DIES.  NIGHTINGALE, THE.  S,FL,PF                  GS
ALABIEFF, A.-LIEBLING.  RUSSIAN NIGHTINGALE, THE.  S,FL,PF      GS
ALAIN, J.  MESSE MODALE EN SEPTUOR.  S,A,FL,2VN,VA,VC(ORG)      LDO
ALBERT, S.  TO WAKE THE DEAD (1977)                            AMC
   S,FL/AFL,CL/BCL,VN/VA,VC,PF,HAR MONIUM
AMES, W.  AMONG THE GODS.  S,CL,2VN,VA,VC                       ACA
AMRAM, D.  3 SONGS FOR AMERICA                                  PET
   B,FL,OB,CL,HN,BSN,2VN,VA,VC,DB
```

AMY, G.   ...D'UN DESASTRE OBSCUR. MS,CL   UE
ANDERS, E. FLOTENLIEDER, OP109. S,FL,PF   WZ
ANDERSON, T. BEYOND SILENCE. T,CL,TRB,VA,VC,PF   ACA
ANDERSON, T. VARIATIONS ON A THEME BY M. B. TOLSON   ACA
   S,ASAX,VN,VC,TP T,TRB,PF
ANDRIESSEN, H. 3 ROMANTISCHE LIEDEREN (1969). MS,FL,OB,PF   SD
ANDRIESSEN, H. LA VIERGE A MIDI (1966)   SD
   MS,FL,OB,HN,2VN,VA,VC,DB
ANDRIESSEN, J. EPITAPH VOOR VAN TULDER (1973). S(T),CL,PF   SD
ANDRIESSEN, J. POLDERPASTICHES (1978). V,CL,VC   SD
ANDRIESSEN, J. TO WET A WIDOW'S EYE. A,T,CL,VA DA GAMBA,PERC   SD
ANDRIESSEN, J. 4 TUCHOLSKY LIEDEREN (1972). MS, ,FL,GUIT,VC   SD
ANHALT, I. CHANSONS D'AURORE (1955). S,FL,PF   CAN
ANONYMOUS (18TH CENT)-FLOTHUIS. MENUET EN AIR. S,FL,BC   B&V
ANTONIOU, T. EPILOG NACH HOMERS ODYSSEE (1963)   B&N
   MS,V,OB,HN,GUIT,PF, DB,PERC
APOSTEL, H.-FELDMAYR. 5 LIEDER, OP 22. V,FL,CL,BSN   UE
ARCHER, V. 2 SONGS (1958). S,CL   CAN
ARGENTO, D. 6 ELIZABETHAN SONGS. V,FL,OB,VN,VC,HPCD   BH
ARGENTO, D. TO BE SUNG UPON THE WATER (1973). V,CL/BCL,PF   BH
ARMBRUSTER, R. TANKA. S,FL,VN,VC   S-V
ARMBRUSTER, R. ZITATE. S,FL,PERC   S-V
ARNE, T.-SALKELD. MORNING, THE. S,FL,PF   S&C
ARNE, T.-BERGMANN. UNDER THE GREENWOOD TREE. S,FL,PF   S&C
ARNE, T.-WESTON. WHEN DAISIES PIED. S,CL,PF   JE
ARNE, T.-SALKELD. WOOD NYMPH, A. S,FL,PF   S&C
ATOR, J. HAIKANSONA. MS,OB,SAX,VC   SS
AVNI, T. COLLAGE (1967). V,FL,PERC,TAPE   ISR
AVSHALOMOV, J. LITTLE CLAY CART, THE   ACA
   V,FL/PIC,CL,BANJO/GUIT,VA,VC, PERC
AVSHALOMOV, J. 2 OLD BIRDS. S,CL,PF   ACA
BABBITT, M. 2 SONNETS. BAR,CL,VA,VC   AMP
BACH, J.S.-SEIBER. ACH LIEBEN CHRISTEN. T,FL,PF   BH
BACH, J.S.-MADDEN. COMPLETE ARIAS & SINFONIAS, VOLS #1-4   MR
   S,OB,BC
BACH, J.S.-MADDEN. COMPLETE ARIAS & SINFONIAS, VOLS #5-7   MR
   A,OB,BC
BACH, J.S.-MADDEN. COMPLETE ARIAS & SINFONIAS, VOLS #8-10   MR
   T,OB,BC
BACH, J.S.-HERVIG. COMPLETE ARIAS, VOLS #1-2. S,FL,BC   MR
BACH, J.S.-DURR. ENSURIENTES (MAGNIFICAT)   S&C
   A,2FL,PF,VC AD LIB
BACH, J.S.-CHAMPION. JESU PRAISE (CANTATA #152). MS,2FL,PF   S&C
BACH, J.S.-BARON. JESUS NIMMT DIE SUNDER AN (CANTATA #113)   OX
   T,FL,BC
BACH, J.S.-SEIBER. MEINE SEUFZER, MEINE TRANEN. B,FL,PF   BH
BACH, J.S.-KELLER. SEUFZER, TRANEN, KUMMER, NOT. S,OB,BC   B&N
BACH, J.S.-HUNT. SHEEP MAY SAFELY. S,2FL,PF   S&C
BACH, J.S.-HUNT. STONE ABOVE ALL OTHERS TREASURED   S&C
   S,FL,VN,PF
BACH, J.S. UNSCHULD, KLEINOD REINER SEELEN. S,FL,OB,VA,VN   EDK
BACH, J.S.-SCHUMANN. VERGNUGTE PLEISSEN-STADT   MRL
   S,A,FL,OB,VC,PF
BACH, J.S.-SEIBER. WAS GOTT THUT, DAS IST WOHLGETAN. T,FL,PF   BH
BACH, J.S.-CHAMPION. YET JESUS WILL THE RIGHTEOUS KEEP   S&C
   A,2FL,EHN
BADINGS, H. 3 GEESTELIJKE LIEDEREN (1950). A,OB,ORG   SD
BADINGS, H. 3 LIEDEREN UIT "LENTEMAAN" (1931)   SD
   A,FL,CL,VN,VA,VC
BADINGS, H. 3 OLD DUTCH SONGS (1967). V,FL,HP   SD
BAINBRIDGE, S. PEOPLE OF THE DAWN (1975)   UMP
   S,2CL,BCL,PERC,PF/CEL

```
BAIRD, T.   CHANSONS DES TROUVERES.  MS,2FL,VC                       AP
BALASSA, S.   ANTINOMIA, OP 14.  S,CL,VC                             EMB
BANCQUART, A.   EROTIQUE VOILEE                                      JOB
   MS,FL,CL,2VN,VA,VC,DB,PF,CYMBALUM
BARNES, M.   DYBBUK, THE: A MASQUE FOR DANCING                       CAN
   T,CL,VN,VC,TPT,PF,PER C
BARNES, M.   NOCTURNES (1961).  S,FL                                 CAN
BARNES, M.   POEMS FOR VOICE & FLUTE- #2 "THE NEW YEAR" (1964)       CAN
   V,FL
BARTOLOZZI, B.   3 RECUERDOS DEL CIELO (1967)                        ESZ
   V,FL,CL,BSN,EHN,VA,VC, DB,GUIT,TIMP,PERC
BASSETT, L.   TIME & BEYOND.  BAR,CL,VC,PF                           PET
BAUER, R.   SERENATA NERAK.  MS,SAX                                  CAN
BAUER, R.   TABITO: RETURNING TO HIS OLD HOME.  S,FL,CL,DB,PERC      CAN
BAUTISTA, J.   4 CANTOS CALEGOS.  A,FL,OB,CL,VA,VC,HP                PI
BAZLIK, M.   5 SONGS OF CHINESE POETRY (1960).  A,FL,VC,PF           SHF
BEALE, J.   LAMENTATIONS, OP 35.  S,FL,PF                            ACA
BEALE, J.   PROVERBS, OP 28.  BAR,EHN,VIB,PF/CEL                     ACA
BECKER, G.   MOIROLOGIE.  S,E FL CL,CL,BCL,HP                        WZ
BECKER, G.   RIGOLO (1967).  V,FL,CL,VN,VC,PF,TAPE                   HG
BECKWITH, J.   GREAT LAKES SUITE, THE (1949).  S,BAR,CL,VC,PF        CAN
BEDFORD, D.   MUSIC FOR ALBION MOONLIGHT                             UE
   S,FL,CL,VN,VC,PF,HARMONICA
BEDFORD, D.   THAT WHITE & RADIANT LEGEND (1966)                     UE
   S,NAR,FL,OB,CL,BSN, VN,VA,VC,DB
BEECROFT, N.   RAGAS II (1973).  A,FL,GUIT,PF,HP,2PERC,TAPE          CAN
BEECROFT, N.   RAGAS III (1974).  S,FL,TRB,PF,PERC,TAPE              CAN
BEECROFT, N.   TWO WENT TO SLEEP.  S,FL,PERC,TAPE                    CAN
BEEKHUIS, H.   DANS EN PASTORALE.  V,FL,VN,PF                        B&V
BEEKHUIS, H.   LES 2 FLUTES (1967).  S,2FL,PF                        SD
BEEKHUIS, H.   MIDDELEEUWS KERSTLIEDJE.  V,FL,3VN,VC                 B&V
BEEKHUIS, H.   OUD-HOLLANDSCHE MELODIE (1949).  V,FL,HP(PF)          SD
BEEKHUIS, H.   VERRASSING (1928).  MS,FL,PF                          SD
BEERMAN, B.   CONSORT & SONG.  S,CL,VC,PF,PERC                       ACA
BEERMAN, B.   MASS.  T,FL,PERC,TAPE,HP                               ACA
BEERMAN, B.   MIXTURES.  V,FL,CL,HN,VN,TAPE                          MEP
BELLINI, V.-LIEBLING.  IT WAS HERE IN ACCENTS TENDER.  S,FL,PF       GS
BENDER, J.   FROM HEAVEN HIGH, I COME TO EARTH                       CON
   SA(TB),VN,OB,VC,ORG
BENEDICT, SIR J.   WREN, THE.  S,FL,PF                               GS
BENHAMOU, M.   MIZMOR-CHIR                                           JOB
   S,FL,HN,TPT,TRB,VN,VA,VC,DB,VIB,MAR,PERC
BENNETT, R.   CRAZY JANE (1968/69).  S,CL,VC,PF                      UE
BENNETT, R.   JAZZ PASTORAL (1969)                                  UE
   V,ASAX,TSAX,BAR SAX,HN,2TPT,TRB,T U,PF,DB,DR
BENNETT, R.   SOLILOQUY (1966).  V,ASAX,TSAX,TPT,TRB,PF,DB,DR        UE
BENTON, D.   LOVE SONG.  V,FL,HP                                     SS
BENTON, D.   2 SHAKESPEARE SONGS.  S,FL,BCL,VN                       SS
BENTZON, J.   MICROPHONY, OP 44 (1939).  BAR,FL,VN,VC,PF             SPD
BENVENUTI, A.   CANTUS GEMELLUS (1961).  V,FL                        BRU
BERGER, A.   3 POEMS OF YEATS.  V,FL,CL,PF                           TP
BERGER, J.   5 SONGS.  V,FL,VA,VC                                    JB
BERGMANN, W.   PASTORALE.  A,FL                                      S&C
BERIO, L.   AGNUS (1971).  2V,3CL,ELECTRIC ORG                       UE
BERIO, L.   CHAMBER MUSIC (1953).  V,CL,VC,HP                        ESZ
BERIO, L.   EL MAR LA MAR (1951)                                     UE
   S,MS,FL/PIC,CL,CL/BCL,VC,DB,HP,ACC
BERIO, L.   FOLKSONGS (1964).  MS,FL/PIC,CL,VA,VC,HP,2PERC           UE
BERIO, L.   MELODRAMA (1969)                                        UE
   T,FL,CL,PERC,PF,VN,VC,DB,ELECTRIC ORG
BERIO, L.   O KING.  MS,FL,CL,VN,VC,PF                               UE
BERIO, L.   OPUS NUMBER ZOO(1950-51; REV1970) NAR,FL,OB,CL,HN,BSN UE
```

BERNHARD, C.-GRUSNICK. FURCHTET EUCH NICHT. S,2VN,BSN,BC   B&N
BETTINELLI, B. TERRA, LA. S,CL,PF   GZ
BETTS, L. PRELUDE FOR SPRING (1951). MS,BAR,FL,HP,2VN,VA,VC   CAN
BIALAS, G. GESANG VON DEN TIEREN. A,FL,CL,HPCD,XYL,DR   MV
BIALAS, G. 3 GESANGE NACH GEDICHTEN VON LOPE DE VEGA   B&N
   BAR,FL,GUIT
BIALAS, G. MENSCH, EIN UND EINE FLIEGE, HAIKU-FOLGE I. S,FL   B&N
BIALOSKY, M. 3 SONGS. S,CL   SS
BIJVANCK, H. 2 LIEDREN (1951). A,OB,ORG   SD
BILUCAGLIA, C. LIED (1974). S,FL,OB,TPT,PF,VN,VA,VC,DB,PERC   ESZ
BIRTWISTLE, H. CANTATA (1969)   UE
   S,FL/PIC,CL,PF/CEL,VN/VA,VC,PERC
BIRTWISTLE, H. ENTR'ACTES & SAPPHO FRAGMENTS   UE
   S,FL,OB,VN,VA,HN,PERC
BIRTWISTLE, H. MONODY FOR CORPUS CHRISTI. S,FL,VN,HN   UE
BIRTWISTLE, H. NENIA ON THE DEATH OF ORPHEUS   UE
   S,3BCL,PF,CROTALES
BIRTWISTLE, H. PROLOGUE (1970). T,BSN,HN,2TPT,TRB,VN,VC   UE
BIRTWISTLE, H. RING A DUMB CARILLON. S,CL,PERC   UE
BISHOP, SIR H.-DEIS. LO! HERE THE GENTLE LARK. S,FL,PF   GS
BISSELL, K. OVERHEARD ON A SALTMARSH. MS,FL,PF   ECK
BLACHER, B. JAZZ-KOLORATUREN (1929). S,ASAX,BSN   B&B
BLACHER, B. 5 NEGRO SPIRITUALS (1962). V,3CL,TRB,DB,PERC   B&B
BLACHER, B.-BEYER. 3 PSALMEN (1943). BAR,CL,BSN,VN,VA,VC,ORG   B&B
BLANK, A. BEING. S,CL   SMI
BLANK, A. COALITIONS. S,2CL,TRB,PF,2PERC   ACA
BLANK, A. DON'T LET THAT HORSE EAT THAT VIOLIN. MS,BSN,VN   SS
BLANK, A. 4 DREAM POEMS. S,CL,TPT,PF   ACA
BLANK, A. ESTHER'S MONOLOGUE. S,OB,VA,VC   ACA
BLANK, A. 2 HOLY SONNETS BY JOHN DONNE. A,OB/EHN,VA,HP   ACA
BLANK, A. PENNYCANDYSTORE BEYOND THE EL, THE. S,BSN   SS
BLANK, A. POEM. V,CL,VC,HP   AMP
BLANK, A. 4 POEMS BY EMILY DICKINSON. S,FL,CL   ACA
BLANK, A. 13 WAYS OF LOOKING AT A BLACKBIRD   AMP
   S,FL/PIC,CL/BCL,VN/VA, VC,PF
BLAZEK, V. PSALM 134-100-93-133, OP 40. A,2FL,HP   CHF
BLICKHAN, T. SPEAK SOFTLY. S,FL,VIB   SS
BLISS, A. MADAM NOY. S,FL,CL,BSN,VA,DB,HP   WH
BLISS, A. 2 NURSERY RHYMES. S,CL,PF   WH
BLOCH, A. SALMO GIOIOSO (1970). S,FL,OB,CL,BSN,HN   PWM
BOESMANS, P. UPON-LA-MI. V,FL,CL,HN,2VN,VA,VC,DB,PF,2PERC,HP   JOB
BOIS R. DU. EINE REDE (1974). S,CL,BASSET HN,BCL   SD
BOIS, R. DU. BECAUSE GOING NOWHERE (1967). MS,FL,PF,   SD
BOIS, R. DU. POUR FAIRE CHANTER (1965). S,FL,3PF   SD
BOIS, R.DU. HYMN TO MYSELF (1966). MS,FL,VC,PF   SD
BON, M. KRISTAL TEGEN SPIEGEL (1966). NAR,FL,CL,VC,PF   SD
BON, W. JADIS ET NAGUERE (1970). MS,CL,VN,PF   SD
BON, W. 3 POEMES DE VERLAINE (1967). MS,FL,VC,PF   SD
BON, W. SILENCE (1978). MS,FL,OB,CL,BSN,HN,PF   SD
BOND, V. CORNOGRAPHY. S,BSN,HN   SS
BOOGAARD, V. VAN. SYNTHETIC POEME. MS,ASAX,BCL,PF   SD
BOONE, C. LINEA MERIDIANA. V,FL,CL,VA,VC,PF,ORG,HP,PERC   EDS
BORTOLOTTI, M. CONTRE VOCALIZZO (1965). V,CL,VN,DB,TRB,PF   EDT
BOTTENBERG, W. 3 AMERINDIAN SONGS (1961; REV 1968)   CAN
   BAR(MS),FL,CL,H PCD
BOTTENBERG, W. MY FUNNY LITTLE CLOCK (1969). MS(BAR),CL,PF CAN
BOTTENBERG, W. THOSE PASSIONS...WHICH YET SURVIVE (1968)   CAN
   B,FL,CL,V N,VA,VC,PERC
BOTTJE, W. DIVERSIONS (1961). NAR,FL,OB,CL,HN,BSN,PF   ACA
BOTTJE, W. IN A WORD. S,OB,HN,PF,TAPE   ACA
BOUCOURECHLIEV, A. GRODEK. S,FL,3PERC   UE
BOULEZ, P. MARTEAU SANS MAITRE, LE. V,FL,VA,VIB,GUIT,2PERC UE

```
BOZAY, A.  SLIPS OF PAPER, OP  5 (1962).  S,CL,VC          EMB
BOZIC, D.  COLLAGE SONORE.  2NAR,ACL,TPT,2VN,VA,VC,DB      EDD
BRANDON, S.  2 SONGS OF EAST OREGON.  B,OB,TRB             MAN
BRANDON, S.  2 VISIONS (1970).  S,OB,PF                    MAN
BRAUN, G.  FRAGMENTE (1974).  MS,FL/AFL,VC,PF,PERC         HMO
BREIT & WARD.  BOY WHO WANTED A TUBA, THE.  NAR,FL,CL,TPT,TU  BD
BRESGEN, C.  4 GESANGE (1965).  BAR,CL,DB,PERC,PF         HG
BRETTINGHAM SMITH, J.  SONGS FOR A FOOL, OP  4             B&B
  A,FL/PIC/AFL,CL/BCL,  VN,VA,VC,PF,TRB,PERC
BREUER, H.  IN MEMORIAM HANS ARP (1968)                    B&N
  S,FL,TSAX,TPT,PF/CEL,DB,PER C
BRODER, T.  6 RUBAIYYAT OF KHAYYAM (1958).  S,FL,CL        ISR
BROOKS, R.  LAST NIGHT I WAS THE WIND.  BAR,FL,OB,CL,HN,BSN  ACA
BROQUA, A.  3 CANTOS URUGUAYOS.  V,FL,2GUIT               EES
BROTT, A.  SEPT FOR SEVEN (1954).  NAR,CL,ASAX,VN,VA,VC,PF  CAN
BROWN, A.  SOUNDSCAPES #1.  V,ASAX,BSN,TPT,PF,PERC,TAPE   SS
BROWN, N.  GLASER SET.  MS,CL,TPT,PF                       SS
BROWN, N.  SET OF THREE POEMS.  S,FL,HN                    SS
BRUGK, H.  LEUCHTENDE NACHT, OP 18.  V,FL,PF               SIM
BRUNO, C.  3 SONETTI DI RUSTICO DI FILIPPO                EDI
  V,FL,PIC,2CL,BSN,HN,VN,2 VC
BRUZDOWICZ, J.  SKETCHES FROM THE HARBOUR (1967).  MS,FL,PERC  PWM
BUCK, O.  JAN & MAJ (1968).  NAR,FL,VC,GUIT              WH
BUCZYNSKI, W.  2 FRENCH LOVE POEMS (1967).  S,FL,PF      CAN
BUCZYNSKI, W.  HOW SOME THINGS LOOK (1967).  S,FL,CL,VC,PF  CAN
BUCZYNSKI, W.  MILOSC (LOVE) (1967)  S,FL,PF             CAN
BUCZYNSKI, W.  TALES OF NANABOZHO, THE (1976)           CAN
  NAR,FL,OB,CL,BSN,HN
BUJARSKI, Z.  CHAMBER PIECE (1963).  V,FL,HP,PF,PERC     AP
BUNGE, S.  SPEELDOOS, DE (1971).  V,FL,PF               SD
BURGON, G.  CANTATA ON MEDIAEVAL LATIN TEXTS (1964)      CHE
  T,FL,OB,BSN
BURKHART, F.  3 ADVENTLIEDER.  V,OB,GUIT                 LDO
BURKHART, F.  VON GUTER ART.  V,OB,GUIT                  LDO
CALAFATO, S.  GUERRA A LA GUERRA POR LA GUERRA (1967)    ESZ
  BAR,2FL,PF,VA ,VC,PERC
CALDARA, A.  QUELL' USIGNUOLO.  S,FL,PF                  WZ
CANINO, B.  CANTATA #2.  MS,FL,VA,HP,PERC                RC
CANINO, B.  FORTIS.  MS,FL,VA,HP,PERC,HARMONIUM          RC
CANO, F.  PAJARO DE COBRE, EL (1969)                    EEC
  V,PIC,FL,AFL,OB,HN,TPT,TRB,VN, VC,XYL
CAPDEVIELLE, P.  AMOURS DE PIERRE DE RONSARD, LES        EFM
  S(T),FL,VN,VA,VC, HP
CAPDEVIELLE, P.  CHANT D'ALPHESIBEE, LE.  S,FL,VN,VA,VC,HP  EFM
CAPLET, A.  ECOUTE, MON COEUR!.  V,FL                    DUR
CAPLET, A.  VIENS! UNE FLUTE INVISIBLE SOUPIRE.  V,FL,PF  DUR
CARDY, P.  GOLDEN DAYS, SILVER NIGHTS                    CAN
  S,FL,OB,VC,PF,ELEC PF,PERC
CAROL-KLAUSE, G.  WAKE, NIGHTINGALE, AWAKE.  SAB,FL      CON
CARRILLO, J.  PRELUDIO A COLON.  S,FL,2VN,VA,VC,HP,GUIT  JOB
CASANOVA, A.  DIVERTIMENTO.  MS,FL,OB,CL,BSN,VN,VC,PF    JOB
CHAILLY, L.  LIRICHE DELLA RESISTENZA VIETNAMITZ (1974)  ESZ
  BAR,2FL,CL, BSN,HN,HP,VN,DB,3PERC
CHAMINADE, C.  PORTRAIT.  V,FL,PF                        E&C
CHAN, P.  JEUNE PARQUE, LA (1970).  S,FL,2VN,VA,VC,HP    B-B
CHANCE, N.  BATHSABE'S SONG.  V,SAX,TAPE                 SS
CHARPENTIER, M.  JESU CORONA VIRGINIUM.  S,FL,BC         B&V
CHERNEY, B.  ECLIPSE (1972)                             CAN
  S,FL/AFL/PIC,OB/EHN,CL/BCL,HN,VN,VA,VC, HP,PERC
CHERNEY, B.  MOBILE IV (1969)                          CAN
  S,FL/PIC/AFL,OB/EHN,CL/BCL,HN,VN,VA,V C,HP,PERC
CHILDS, B.  7 EPIGRAMS (1955).  V,CL                    TP
```

CHOWMAN, H.   EEN GOED LYEDEKEN (1953).   V,FL,ORG   SD
CIMAROSA, D.-WOJCIECHOWSKI.   GLORIA PATRI.   S,OB,2VN,BC   PET
CIMAROSA, D.-WOJCIECHOWSKI.   QUONIAM TU SOLUS SANCTUS   PET
     S,OB,TPT,2VN,B C
CLARKE, H.   LIFE IN GHANA.   V,FL,PF   ACA
CLARKE, H.   LORD IS MY SHEPHERD, THE.   V,FL,TIMP(DB)   ACA
CLARKE, H.   MERCY, PITY, PEACE, & LOVE.   S,A,FL,OB,PERC   ACA
CLARKE, H.   QUALITY OF MERCY, THE.   S,A,FL,OB,PERC   ACA
CLARKE, H.   RONDEAU REDOUBLE.   BAR(MS),CL,BSN,VC   ACA
CLARKE, H.   SONG TO A YOUNG PIANIST.   V,FL   ACA
CLARKE, H.   WOMAN OF VIRTUE, A.   V,REED INSTR,PERC   ACA
CLEMENTI, A.   SILBEN (1966).   V,CL,VN,2PF   ESZ
CLERAMBAULT, L.-TUNLEY.   ORPHEUS.   S,FL,VN,BC   FB
COLACO OSORIO-SWAAB, R.   WIJZANG,(1937).   S,Z,FL   SD
COLE, B.   PANTOMIMES.   S,MIME,FL,CL,GUIT,PERC,PF,VN,VC   BH
COLE, B.   SPRAY OF DEAD ARROWS.   S,CL,VN,PF   BH
CONSOLI, M.   3 CANZONI.   S,FL,VC   ACA
CONSOLI, M.   EQUINOX I.   MS,FL,VC,PF,PERC   ACA
CONSOLI, M.   EQUINOX II.   V,FL,CL,VN,VC,PF,PERC,VIB,CEL   ACA
CONSOLI, M.   ISONIC I.   S,FL,2PF,VIB,XYL,2PERC,CHIMES   ACA
CONSTANT, F.   TRIADE, OP 30 (1967).   V,ASAX,PF,PERC   CBD
CONTILLI, G.   IMMAGINI SONORE (1964)   ESZ
     S,FL,CL,VN,VA,DB,VIB,PF,GUIT,C EL,XYL
CONTILLI, G.   OFFERTA MUSICALE (1959).   S,CL,VN,VA,VC,PF   ESZ
COOKE, A.   3 SONGS OF INNOCENCE (1957).   S,CL,PF   OX
COOPER, P.   EPITAPHS (1969).   A,FL,HP,DB   CHE
COPLAND, A.   AS IT FELL UPON A DAY.   V,FL,CL   BH
CORGHI, A.   SYMBOLA.   V,FL,VC,PF,PERC,TAPE   ESZ
CORTESE, L.   2 CANTI PERSIANI (1932).   MS,FL,PF   ESZ
CORTESE, L.   SALMO VIII (1943).   V,FL,VC,PF   ESZ
CORY, E.   ARIA VIVA.   T,FL,OB,EHN,BSN,GUIT   ACA
CORY, E.   WAKING.   S,CL,TSAX,BSN,TPT,VN,VA,VC,DB,PF,PERC   ACA
COULTHARD, J.   4 PROPHETIC SONGS (1975).   A,FL,VC,PF   CAN
COUPERIN, F.   ADOLESCENTULUS SUM.   S,2FL,VN,ORG   EDL
COWELL, H.   SEPTET.   2S,A,T,B,CL,PF   PET
COWELL, H.   TOCCANTA.   S,FL,VC,PF   BH
COWELL, H.   VOCALISE.   V,FL,PF   PET
COWIE, E.   CHARM OF FINCHES, A (1973).   S,PIC/FL,FL,FL/AFL   CHE
COWIE, E.   SHINKOKINSHU (1968/72).   V,PIC/FL,CL/BCL,CEL,PERC   CHE
CRAWFORD, P.   FEERIE.   2S,CL,VA,PF,VIB   CAN
CRAWFORD, R.   3 SONGS.   A,OB,PF,PERC   TP
CROFT, W.-SPIEGL.   CELLADON.   S,OB,PF   S&C
CROSSE, G.   CORPUS CHRISTI CAROL, OP 5.   V,CL,HN,2VN,VA,VC   OX
CROSSE, G.   MEDIEVAL FRENCH SONGS, OP 14A.   V,CL,PF,PERC   OX
CRUMB, G.   ANCIENT VOICES OF CHILDREN (1970)   PET
     S,T,OB,HP,PERC,MANDOLI N,ELECTRIC PF
CRUMB, G.   LUX AETERNA FOR 5 MASKED MUSICIANS (1971)   PET
     S,BFL/REC,2PER C,SITAR
CRUMB, G.   MADRIGALS, BK II (1965).   S,AFL,PERC   PET
CRUMB, G.   MADRIGALS, BOOK IV (1969).   S,FL/PIC/AFL,HP,DB,PERC   PET
CRUMB, G.   NIGHT OF THE 4 MOONS (1969)   PET
     A,AFL/PIC,BANJO,ELEC VC,PERC
CRUSELL, B.-WESTON.   FROM GANGES' BEAUTEOUS STRANDS.   S,CL,PF   JE
CUMMING, R.   AS DEW IN APRIL.   V,OB(CL),PF   BH
CURRAN, A.   HOME-MADE.   S,FL,DB,PERC   CPE
DALLAPICCOLA, L.   6 CARMINA ALCAEI (1943)   ESZ
     S,FL,OB,CL,BSN,HN,TPT,PF, VN,VA,VC,HP
DALLAPICCOLA, L.   DIVERTIMENTO IN QUATTRO ESERCIZI   CAR
     S,FL/PIC,OB,CL,V A,VC
DALLAPICCOLA, L.   GOETHE LIEDER (1953).   V,3CL   ESZ
DALLAPICCOLA, L.   SICUT UMBRA   ESZ
     MS,PIC,FL,AFL,E FL CL,CL,BCL,VN,VA,VC,HP,CEL,VIB

```
DASHOW, J.  MAXIMUS, TO HIMSELF.  S,FL,PF                          SS
DAUS, A.  SONGS OF RACHEL.  V,FL,VA                                IMP
DAVID, F.  CHARMANT OISEAU.  S,FL,PF                               S&C
DAVID, G.  ROSE IS FLAMING, THE (1966).  S,FL,VA                   EMB
DAVID, J.  FROHLICH WIR NUN ALL FANGEN AN (1941).  V,OB,ORG        BRH
DAVIES, P.  BLIND FIDDLER, THE.  S,FL,OB,VN,VC,GUIT,TIMP,PERC      BH
DAVIES, P.  FIDDLERS AT THE WEDDING                               BH
   MS,AFL,GUIT,PERC,MANDOLIN
DAVIES, P.  HYMN TO SAINT MAGNUS                                  BH
   S,FL,BASSET CL,VA,VC,PF,HPCD,CEL,TIMP,PERC
DAVIES, P.  MISS DONNITHORNE'S MAGGOT                             BH
   MS,FL,AFL,CL,VN,VC,PF,PERC
DAVIES, P.  8 (1969) SONGS FOR A MAD KING                         BH
   V,FL,CL,VN,VC,PF,HPCD,PER C
DAVIES, P.  TENEBRAE SUPER GESUALDO                               BH
   MS,AFL,BCL,VA,VC,HPCD,CEL,GUIT,PERC,HARMONIUM
DAVIS, S.  3 POEMS OF WILLIAM BLAKE.  S,ACL,BCL,CBCL              WI
DAVIS, S.  THOUGH MEN CALL US FREE.  S,CL,PF                      WI
DAVIS, S.  WILDFLOWER SUITE.  S,FL,OB,VN,VC,PF                    WI
DE BERADINIS, J.  SONG CYCLE.  MS,AFL,GUIT                        SS
DE JONG, C.  HIST WIST.  V,FL,VA,PERC                             GS
DEBUSSY, C.-PECK.  BILITIS.  NAR,FL,PF                            BO
DEBUSSY, C,-LOUYS.  CHANSONS DE BILITIS, LES.  2FL,2HP,CEL,NAR    JOB
DEKKER, D.  LITTLE JOHN'S MORNING AFTER.  V,FL,VC,PF              SD
DEL TREDICI, D.  NIGHT CONJURE-VERSE                              BH
   S,MS,PIC/FL,FL,OB,CL,BCL/CL,BSN,HN,2VN,VA,VC
DELAGE, M.  ALOUETTE.  V,FL,PF                                    DUR
DELAGE, M.  7 HAI-KAI.  S,FL,OB,CL,2VN,VA,VC,PF                   JOB
DELAS, J., DE.  FRONS (1972).  S,FL,OB,CL,BSN,HN,PERC             HG
DELDEN, L. VAN.  L'AMOUR (1937).  S,FL,CL,VN,VA,VC                SD
DELIBES, L.  ROSSIGNOL, LE.  S,FL                                 WZ
DENISOV, E.  CHANSONS ITALIENNES.  S,FL,VN,HN,CIMBALS             UE
DERR, E.  I NEVER SAW ANOTHER BUTTERFLY (1977).  S,ASAX,PF        DOR
DESSAU, P.  BEGRUESSUNG (DIE FREUNDE).  V,FL,2VN,VA,VC            B&B
DEVRIES, I.  CHANSON DE FORTUNIO.  BAR,FL,BSN                     APH
DI DOMENICA, R.  SONATA AFTER ESSAYS (1977)                      MAR
   S,BAR,FL/AFL,PF,TAPE
DIAMOND, D.  MAD MAID'S SONG, THE.  V,FL,HPCD                     PI
DIEPENBROCK, A.  COME RAGGIO DI SOL (1917).  S,FL,OB,CL,HN,BSN    SD
DIEPENBROCK, A.  WENN ICH IHN NUR HABE (1915)                    SD
   S,FL,OB,CL,HN,BSN,DB
DIJK, J. VAN.  HET MASKER VAN DEN ROODEN DOOD                    SD
   NAR,2FL,2OB,HN,PF,VA,VC,DB
DIJK, J. VAN.  6 LIEDEREN (1952).  A,OB,ORG                      SD
DIJK, J. VAN.  5 LIEDEREN (1954).  BAR,FL,2VN,VA,VC              SD
DIJK, J. VAN.  SEPTET (1950).  S,FL,CL,HN,VN,VA,VC,DB            SD
DIMOV, B.  INCANTATIONES I (1963).  S,FL,TPT,VA,HP               EMO
DIMOV, B.  INCANTATIONES II (1967).  S,FL,TPT,2VA,HP,PERC        EMO
DIMOV, B.  RAUMSPIEL (1969/70)                                   HG
   S,FL,OB,CL,HN,BSN,2VN,VA,VC,PF
DIONISI, R.  2 CANTI SACRI.  V,CL,PF                             GZ
DIONISI, R.  2 PEZZI.  V,CL                                      GZ
DISPA, R.  ODE TO THE CHILD (1976).  B,FL,2VN, A,VC,DB,PERC      SD
DITTRICH, P.  KAMMERMUSIK III.  BAR,FL,OB,CL,BSN,HN              PET
DITTRICH, P.-HEINZ.  QUA-SIE (1971).  2NAR,CL,VC,PF,TAPE         HG
DODGSON, S.  CADILLY (REYNOLDS).  S,A,T,B,FL,OB,CL,HN,BSN        CA
DODGSON, S.  OLD CIGARETTE LIGHTER, THE.  NAR,FL,OB,PF           CA
DODGSON, S.  3 WINGET SONGS.  V,OB,PF                            CA
DOHL, F.  EPITAPH "TICH YUANG TUC" (1963)                        HG
   S,FL,OB,CL,HN,BSN,PF,PERC
DOHL, F.  FRAGMENT "SYBILLE" (1963).  BAR,FL,VA,VC,PF            HG
DOHL, F.  7 HAIKU (1963).  S,FL,PF                               HG
```

```
DOHL, F.   SZENE UBER EINEN KLEINEN TOD (1975).   V,FL,VC          HG
DONIZETTI, G.-LIEBLING.   MAD SCENE, THE (LUCIA DI LAMMERMOOR)     GS
   S,FL,P F
DOPPELBAUER, J.-GEORGE.   3 GESANGE (1949).   S,FL,VA,VC           LDO
DRESDEN, S.   4 VOCALISES (1935).   MS,FL,CL,BSN,VN,VA,PF,PERC     SD
DRUCKMAN, J.   LAUDE (1952).   BAR,AFL,VA,VC                       MC
DUNI, R.-FLOTHUIS.   ARIETTE (LE PEINTRE AMOUREUX).   S,FL,VN      B&V
DURKO, Z.   COLLOIDES (1969).   5A,PIC,FL,BSN,2VN,VA,VC            EMB
EBERHARD, D.   PARODY (1972)                                      MAR
   S,FL/PIC,CL/BCL,TRB,PF/CEL,VN,VC,3PERC
ECKERT, M.   SEA-CHANGES.   MS,2FL,2CL,HN,TPT,VN,VA,VC,PF/CEL      ACA
EDWARDS, G.   CAPTIVE, THE                                         ACA
   S,FL,OB,CL,BCL,2VN,2VA,VC,DB,HPCD,VIB
EHLBACH, E.   3 ALTE DEUTSCHE LIEBESLIEDER, OP 14.   S(T),OB,VA    MV
EHLE, R.   ALGORHYTHMS.   S,CL,DB,PF                               CF
EHRLICH, A.   WRITING OF HEZEKIAH, THE (1962).   S,VN,OB,BSN       ISR
EINFELDT, D.   SIZILIANISCHE IMPRESSIONEN.   S,FL,OB,CL,BSN,PF     GBV
EISLER, H.   CANTATA IN EXILE, OP 62.   A,2CL,VA,VC                UE
EISLER, H.   CANTATA ON THE DEATH OF A FRIEND, OP 64              UE
   A,2CL,VA,VC
EISLER, H.   KRIEGSKANTATA, OP 65.   A,2CL,VA,VC                   UE
EISLER, H.   OHNE KAPITALISTEN GEHT ES BESSER                     DEU
   V,CL,ASAX,TPT,TRB,GUIT ,PF,DB,PERC
EISLER, H.   PALMSTROM, OP  5.   V,FL/PIC,CL,VN/VA,VC              UE
EISLER, H.   ROMAN CANTATA, THE, OP 60.   A,2CL,VA,VC              UE
EISMA, W.   .CHEVAL MORT, LE (1976).   MS,BCL,PF,PERC,TAPE         SD
EISMA, W.   GIBET, LE (1971).   BAR,FL,OB,CL,VN,VC,PF,PERC         SD
EL-DABH, H.   TAHMEELA.   S,VN,FL,OB,CL,BSN,HN                     PET
ELKUS, J.   TRIPTYCH.   MS,4BSN                                    M&M
EMMANUEL, M.   3 ODELETTES ANACREONTIQUES.   V,FL,PF               DUR
ENCINAR, J.   HOMENAJE A J. CORTAZAR (1971)                       ESZ
   MS,PIC,FL,BSN,CBSN
ESCHER, P.   NAGA-UTA, OP 48 (1949).   S,FL                        EUL
EVETT, R.   BILLY IN THE DARBIES.   BAR,CL,2VN,VA,VC               ACA
FAITH, R.   SOLITARY REAPER, THE.   BAR,FL,PF                      MAN
FALLA, M. DE.   PSYCHE.   MS,FL,VN,VA,VC,HP                        CHE
FARKAS, F.   TIBICINIUM.   V,FL                                    EMB
FAURE, G.   PAVANE, OP 50.   V,FL,GUIT                             BRM
FELDMAN, M.   I MET HEINE ON THE RUE FURSTEMBERG                  UE
   V,FL,CL,PERC,PF,VN, VC
FELDMAN, M.   JOURNEY TO THE END OF THE NIGHT (1949)               PET
   S,FL,CL,BCL,BSN
FELDMAN, M.   RABBI AKIBA (1963)                                  PET
   S,FL,EHN,HN,TPT,TRB,TU,PERC,PF/CEL, VC,DB
FELDMAN, M.   VERTICAL THOUGHTS III (1963)                        PET
   S,FL,HN,TPT,TRB,TU,PF/CEL ,VN,VC,DB,2PERC
FELLEGARA, V.   EPITAPHE (1964).   2S,FL,PF/CEL,VIB,TIMP,PERC      ESZ
FENNELLY, B.   SONGS WITH IMPROVISATION.   V,CL,PF                 ACA
FERRITTO, J.   4 MADRIGALI.   BAR,FL,CL                            ACA
FERRITTO, J.   OGGI, OP  9.   S,CL,PF                              ACA
FERRO, P.   SUITE AGRESTE.   V,FL,EHN,CL,VA,HP                     RC
FINE, V.   GREAT WALL OF CHINA, THE.   V,FL,VC                     TP
FLANAGAN, W.   GOOD-BYE, MY FANCY.   S,FL,GUIT(PF)                 SN
FLANAGAN, W.   WEEPING PLEIADES, THE.   BAR,FL,CL,VN,VC,PF         PI
FLOTHIUS, M.   EEN AMSTERDAMSCH LIED (1951)                        SD
   S,BAR,FL,CL,2VN,VA,VC,DB,PF
FLOTHIUS, M.   4 MINIATURES RUMANTSCHAS (1966).   S,FL             SD
FLOTHIUS, M.   NEGRO LAMENT (1953).   A,ASAX(HN,BASSET HN,VA)PF    SD
FLOTHUIS, M.   LIEDEREN (1943; REV. 1969)                         SD
   MS,FL,OB D'AMORE,CL,HN,BSN,DB
FLOTHUIS, M.   LOVE & STRIFE, OP 34.   A,FL,OB D'AMORE(OB),VA,VC   SD
FORBES, S.   DEATH'S DOMINION.   T,FL,CL,VN,VA,VC,PF               CA
```

```
FORD, C.  THORYBOPOIOUMENOI (1972).  V,FL,VA,TAPE                    CAN
FORTNER, J.  SPRING.  V,FL,ASAX,BSN,VA,VC,DB,VIB,HP,PF              JOB
FOX, F.  TIME EXCURSIONS (1976)                                     AMC
   S,NAR,FL,CL,VN,VA,VC,PF,2PERC
FRAENKEL, W.  5 LIEDER NACH GEDICHTEN VON MORGENSTERN               UE
   A,OB D'AMORE, ASAX,TSAX,BSN,TPT,VN,VA,VC
FRANCO, J.  2 DUETS.  BAR(MS),FL                                    ACA
FRANCO, J.  LORD COMETH, THE!.  V,EHN,CL,BCL                        ACA
FRANCO, J.  SONG OF LIFE, THE.  S(T),EHN,CL,BCL                     ACA
FRANCO, J.  SONGS OF THE SPIRIT.  V,FL,OB,CL,BSN,HN                 ACA
FREEDMAN, H.  EXPLAINER, THE.  NAR,FL,OB,VC,PF                      CAN
FREEDMAN, H.  LOVE & AGE (1975)                                     CAN
   S,BAR,FL,OB,CL,HN,BSN,2TPT,HN,TRB,T U
FREEDMAN, H.  PAN (1972).  S,FL,PF                                  CAN
FREEDMAN, H.  TIKKI TIKKI TEMBO (1971).  NAR,FL,OB,CL,BSN,HN        CAN
FREEDMAN, H.  TOCCATA (1968).  S,FL                                 ECK
FREEDMAN, H.  2 VOCALISES (1954).  S,CL,PF                          CAN
FRID, G.  FRUHLINGSFEIER (1952).  S,A,FL,CL,BSN,HN,VN,VA,VC,PF      SD
FRID, G.  KLEINE SUITE (1975).  NAR,ASAX,PF                         SD
FRID, G.  3 POEMS (1976).  NAR,ASAX,GUIT                            SD
FRITSCH, J.  BESTANDTEILE DES VORUBER (1962)                        FEE
   S,BCL,BSN,HN,2TRB,TU,3 DB
FROIDEBISE, P.  AMERCOEUR.  S,FL,OB,EHN,CL,BSN,HN,PF                IIE
FUSSAN, W.  DIE CHINESISCHE FLOTE.  S,FL,2VN,VA,VC                  BRH
FUSSEL, K.  MIORITA.  S,FL/AFL,CL/BCL,VN/VA,PF                      UE
FUSSL, K.  DIALOGUE IN PRAISE OF THE OWL & THE CUCKOO               UE
   T,FL,CL,TRB,V N,DB,HP,GUIT
GABER, J.  VOCE II.  V,FL,PERC                                      ACA
GABURO, K.  TWO.  MS,AFL,DB                                         TP
GAGNON, A.  OIES SAUVAGES, LES (1973)                               CAN
   V,FL,OB,VN,VA,DB,PF,HPCD
GAL, H.  FANTASIEN, OP 5.  CONTRALTO,CL,HN,PF                       UE
GARANT, S.  ANERCA (1961; REV 1963)                                CAN
   S,FL,CL,BSN,VN,VA,VC,HP,PERC
GARBER, H.  VOCE II.  A,AFL,PERC                                    WLP
GASLINI, G.  MAGNIFICAT.  S,ASAX,PF,DB                              UE
GASTYNE, S. DE.  2 CHANSONS FRANCAISES.  S,FL,VIB                   FER
GASTYNE, S. DE.  IL BACIO, OP 45.  A,CL,PF                          FER
GAUBERT, P.  SOIR PAIEN.  V,FL,PF                                   E&C
GAVEAUX, P.-FLOTHUIS.  ARIA (LE TROMPEUR TROMPE).  S,CL,PF          B&V
GAYFER, J.  WHO ARE YOU, LITTLE I? (1963).  S,OB,CL,PF             CAN
GEISSLER, F.  LIEDER NACH TEXTEN VON J. RINGELNATZ                  DEU
   S,FL,OB,CL,BSN,H N
GERHARD, R.  7 HAIKU.  V,FL,OB,CL,BSN,PF                            BE
GERSTER, O.  DIE AMSEL.  S,OB                                       VNM
GHEZZO, D.  CANTOS NUEVOS.  MS,CL,VC,TAPE                           SS
GHEZZO, D.  PONTICA 2.  NAR,FL,SAX,2HN,2TPT,PF                      SS
GIDEON, M.  CONDEMNED PLAYGROUND, THE (1963)                       B-B
   S,T,FL,BSN,2VN,VA,VC
GIDEON, M.  HOUND OF HEAVEN, THE.  V,OB,STR TRIO                    GA
GIDEON, M.  NOCTURNES.  V,FL,OB,VN,VC,VIB                           ACA
GIDEON, M.  QUESTIONS ON NATURE (1964).  V,OB,PF,2PERC             B-B
GIDEON, M.  RHYMES FROM THE HILL (1968).  V,CL,VC,MAR              B-B
GIEFER, W.  EINES SCHATTENS TRAUM (1971/72).  MS,FL,VC             HG
GLASER, W.  6 BITTERMANDLAR.  V,CL,FL,VC,GUIT,2PERC                STI
GLOBOKAR, V.  ACCORD.  S,FL,TRB,VC,ORG,PERC                         PET
GLUCK, C.-FLOTHUIS.  ARIA (LA RENCONTRE IMPREVUE).  T,FL,PF         B&V
GLUCK, C.-BUCK.  O SAVIOUR, HEAR ME.  S,FL,PF                       GS
GOEYVAERTS, K.  GOATHEMALA.  MS,FL                                  HE
GOLDBERG, T.  SAMOGONSKI-TRIO, OP 8.  BAR,CL,VC,PF                 B&B
GOORHUIS, R.  NADER TOT U (NEAR YOU) (1977).  BAR,FL,PF,PERC        SD
GOUNOD, C.  TELL ME, BEAUTIFUL MAIDEN.  V,FL,PF                     GS
```

```
GRANDERT, J.  AIAKURA (1966).  S,BAR,FL,VA,DB                          STI
GRANDERT, J.  OKTETT (1966).  3V,FL,VA,DB,TRB                          STI
GRETRY, A.  RECITATIV ET AIR.  V,FL,PF                                 WZ
GRUNAUER, I.  BESICHTIGUNG, VERSTEIGERUNG UND BESEITIGUNG              SCH
   S,CL,PERC ,VA,PF
GRUNAUER, I.  FAMA E FOME.  T,FL,CL,VA,PF,PERC                         EMO
GUACCERO, D.  STUDIO PER UN QUARTETTO (1961)                           BRU
   S,T,E FL CL,TSAX
GUBITOSI, E.  FLAUTO NOTTURNO, IL.  S,FL,PF                            EDI
GUINJOAN, J.  ACTA EST FABULA (1975)                                  EDA
   V,FL,CL,TPT,TRB,VN,VC,DB,PF,PE RC,TAPE
GULKE(ARR).  ALTNIEDERLANDISCHE TRAUERMUSIK                            DEU
   A,FL,OB,EHN,BCL,BSN,2TPT ,2TRB,VA,VC,HP
GURSCHING, A'.  ANAKREONTIKA.  BAR,FL,BSN,VN,DB,HPCD,PERC              EMO
HALLNAS, H.  CANTATA.  S,FL,CL,VC,PF                                   ESU
HAMBRAEUS, B.  GACELAS Y CASIDAS DE FED. G. LORCA                      WH
   T,FL,EHN,BCL,CEL, VIB,PERC
HAMBRAEUS, B.  SPECTROGRAMM, OP 34.  S,FL,PERC                         WH
HAMMERSCHMIDT, A.  O BELOVED SHEPHERDS                                 CON
   SATB,FL(OB),CL(TPT),VC(TRB)
HANDEL, G.-GUNTHER.  ARIA (ALMIRA).  V,OB,PF                           B&B
HANDEL, G.  ARIA (BERENICE).  S,OB,BC                                  B&V
HANDEL, G.-GUNTHER.  CARA SPOSA (RINALDO).  V,OB,PF                    B&B
HANDEL, G.-SCHEIT.  2 GESANGE AUS DEN "DEUTSCHEN ARIEN"                LDO
   S,FL,GUIT,VC AD LIB
HANDEL, G.-HUNT.  HUSH YE PRETTY WARBLING QUIRE                        S&C
   S,FL,2VN,VC,PF
HANDEL, G.-GUNTHER.  LIEBLICHE WALDER (ALMIRA).  S,OB,PF               B&B
HANDEL, G.-SEYDEL.  NACHTIGALLENARIE.  S,FL,PF                         LEU
HANDEL, G.-BEHREND.  NELL DOLCE DELL'OBLIO.  S,FL,GUIT                 B&B
HANDEL, G.-BERGMANN.  NELL DOLCE DELL'OBLIO.  S,FL,PF                  S&C
HANDEL, G.-SCHEIT.  NELL DOLCE DELL'OBLIO.  S,FL(OB),GUIT              LDO
HANDEL, G.  NELL DOLCE DELL'OBLIO.  V,FL,PF                            WZ
HANDEL, G.-FLOTHUIS.  SUSSE STILLE.  S,FL,PF                           B&V
HANDEL, G.-WASNER.  SWEET FORGETTING.  S,FL,PF                         GS
HANDEL, G.-FLOTHUIS.  TRIUMPH OF TIME & TRUTH.  S,OB,PF                B&V
HANDEL, G.-ZENCK.  UM DIE FLAMME.  S,2FL,OB,BSN,2VN,VA,BC              B&N
HANNAY, R.  CABARET VOLTAIRE.  V,SOP SAX,PERC                          SS
HARRIS, R.  CALIBAN IN APT. 112.  T,ASAX,PF,2PERC                      SS
HARRISON, L.  AIR (RAPUNZEL).  V,FL,VN,VA,VC,HP,PF                     SN
HARTIG, H.  TRINKER UND DIE SPIEGEL, DER                               B&B
   BAR,FL,CL,TPT,VA,DB,PF,PER C
HARTLEY, W.  PSALM CYCLE.  MS,FL,PF                                    TP
HARTWELL, H.  HOW TO PLAY WINNING BRIDGE (1969).  A,FL,VA,PERC         CAN
HARTWELL, H.  RESTA DI DARMI NOIA....  S,FL,PF                         CAN
HATRIK, J.  DENNIK TANE SAVICOVEJ.  S,FL,OB,CL,BSN,HN                  SHF
HAUBENSTOCK-RAMATI, R.  BLESSINGS (SEGENSSPRUCHE)                      IMP
   V,FL,4VN,PF,CEL,P ERC,HP
HAUBENSTOCK-RAMATI, RC.  CREDENTIALS, OR "THINK, THINK, LUCKY"         UE
   V,CL,TRB,VN,PF,CEL,VIB,2PERC
HAUFRECHT, H.  LET'S PLAY MACCABEES.  V,OB,CL,HP,PERC                  ACA
HEAD, M.  BIRD-SONG.  V,FL,PF                                          BH
HEAD, M.  PIPER.  V,FL,PF                                              BH
HEAD, M.  WORLD IS MAD, THE.  V,CL,PF                                  JE
HEIDER, W.  PICASSO-MUSIK.  MS,CL,VN,PF                                PET
HEINICHEN, H.-JANETZKY.  NISI DOMINUS AEDIFICAVERIT DOMUM              DEU
   S(T),OB,BC
HEISS, H.  GALGENLIEDER NACH GEDICHTEN VON C. MORGENSTERN              WMS
   S,FL
HEISS, H.  LIEDER.  A,FL,PF                                            WMS
HEISS, H.-KASTNER.  ZUM NEUEN JAHR (1954).  S,CL,PF                    BRH
HEISS, J.  SONGS OF NATURE (1975).  MS,FL,CL,VN,VC,PF                  AMC
```

```
HEKSTER, W.   3 HAIKU SONGS (1977).   BAR,OB/EHN,GUIT            SD
HEKSTER, W.   SNOW MAN, THE (1969).   S,BCL,PERC                 SD
HEKSTER, W.   SONG OF PEACE, A (1979).   V,CL,ASAX,VC,PERC       SD
HELLERMANN, W.   POEM.  S,FL,BCL,VC,TRB                          ACA
HENNAGIN, M.   UNKNOWN, THE (1967).   SSA,FL,PF,PERC             CAN
HENNINGER, R.   3 SONGS OF WINTER (1972).   S,FL,PF,TAPE         CAN
HENZE, H.   CIMMARON, EL.   V,FL,GUIT,PERC                       BE
HENZE, H.   KAMMERMUSIK UBER DIE HYMNE "IN LIEBLICHER BLAUE"     SCH
   T,GUIT, CL,HN,BSN,2VN,VA,VC,DB
HERMANS, N.   FLUTE DE JADE,LA (1952).   A,FL,HP                 SD
HERMANS, N.   2 NOCTURNES (1952).   MS,FL,PF                     SD
HILLERT, R.   AND YOU, O BETHLEHEM.   SA(TB),FL,ORG              CON
HINDEMITH, P.   DIE SERENADEN, OP 35.   S,OB,VA,VC,PF            SCH
HINDEMITH, P.   JUNGE MAGD, DIE, OP 23/2.   A,FL,CL,2VN,VA,VC    SCH
HLOBIL, E.   EVOCATION.  S,2FL                                   CHF
HODKINSON, S.   ARC (1969).   S,FL,PIC,PF,PERC                   CAN
HOFFDING, F.   CHAMBER MUSIC (1927).   S,OB,PF                   SPD
HOFFMAN, A.   DUO.  SAX,NAR                                      DOR
HOLLOWAY, R.   3 POEMS.   MS,FL,CL,SAX,HPCD,DB,7PERC             OX
HOLM, M.   BECAUSE I AM LONELY, OP 31                            WH
   MS,OB,3TRB,HPCD,ELEC ORG, 2 EL EC GUIT
HOMBERG, J.   MENSAGEM.   S,CL,BSN,TPT,TRB,VN,DB                 HG
HONEGGER, A.   CHANSONS- SIRENES, POIRE; BERCEUSE- SIRENE        EDS
   V,FL,2VN,VA,VC
HONEGGER, A.   SONG (PIERRE DE RONSARD).   V,FL,2VN,VA,VC        EDS
HOOK, J.-BERGMANN.   3 SONGS.   S,CL,PF                          S&C
HOPKINS, D.   2 POMES.   S,BCL,TPT,VA,HP                         UE
HORST, A.   3. LIEDEREN, SERIE 2 OUD-NED.   V,FL,ORG(PF)         ALS
HORVARTH, J.   BLINDE, DIE.   A,2V,FL,TPT,VC,PF                  PET
HORVARTH, J.   4 SONGS.   S(T),FL,CL,VA,VC                       PET
HOSSEIN, A.   CHANT DE CHAMELIER.   V,FL,PF                      E&C
HOVHANESS, A.   SATURN, OP243.   S,CL,PF                         PET
HOVLAND, E.   MAGNIFICAT, OP 44.   A,AFL,HP                      NOR
HUBER, K.   ASKESE.   NAR,FL,TAPE                                B&N
HUBER, K.   AUF DIE RUHIGE NACHT-ZEIT.   S,FL,VA,VC              B&N
HUBER, K.   ENGELS ANREDUNG AN DIE SEELE, DES.   T,FL,CL,HN,HP   UE
HUBER, K.   PSALM OF CHRIST (1967).   BAR,CL,BCL,TPT,HN,VN,VA,VC SCH
HUE, G.   SOIR PAIEN.   V,FL,PF                                  EDS
HUFSCHMIDT, W.   3 ALTTESTAMENTLICHE SPRUCHE.   S,FL,VA          B&N
HUGGLER, J.   BITTERE NUESSE.   S,FL,CL/BCL,VN,VA,VC             PET
HUGGLER, J.   FOR COLORATURA, CLARINET, VIOLA, CELLO, OP 20      ACA
   S,CL,VA, VC
HUNDZIAK, A.   LYRICS (1963)                                    PWM
   S,FL,VN,VC,TPT,VIB,XYL,CEL,HP,PERC
HUNT, A.   4 SONGS.   V,FL,PF                                    CAN
HUTCHESON, J.   PASSING,PASSING.   S,CL,TRB,VC,PF                SS
HYDE.   FISHERMAN, THE & HIS WIFE                                WI
   S,NAR,FL,OB,CL,BSN,BCL,HP,PF,PERC
JACOB, G.   3 SONGS.   S,CL,PF                                   OX
JACOB, W.   MUSIK DER TRAUER.   NAR,FL,TAPE                      BRH
JAMA, A.   VOCATIO (1971).   MS,CL,PF                            SD
JAMES, T.   4 POEMS OF MICHAEL FRIED (1973)                     B-B
   S,FL,CL,BCL,VN,VA,VC
JANSSEN, G.   EEN BEETJE INSPRAAK (1972).   NAR,FL,PERC,TAPE     SD
JELINEK, H.   SELBSTBILDNIS DES MARC AUREL, OP 24 (1954)         EMO
   NAR,FL,BCL, VC,PF
JENKINS, J.   CZECH LULLABY CAROL (1959).   SSA,3CL,VC,DB        CAN
JENKINS, J.   PSALM #67 (1959).   SATB,FL,OB,HN,TPT,ORG          CAN
JENSCH, L.   NOTTURNO SCORDATO (1972).   V,FL,VC                 HG
JEPPESEN, K.   DOMINE REFUGIUM FACTUS ES NOBIS.   S,FL,VN        WH
JERGENSON, D.   TANKA PIECES.   S,FL,CL,                         SS
JEZ, J.   3 MURN'S POEMS.   V,FL,VA                              EDD
```

JEZ, J. PASTORAL SONGS. 2V,FL,CL,VN,PF	ED.
JEZ, J. POGLED NARAVE (BLICK DER NATUR) ((1974)	HG
2V,CL,HN,PERC	
JEZ, J. REFLECTIONS ON OMAR KHAYYAM'S POETRY	EDD
S,CL,BSN,TPT,VN,VA,VC ,HP	
JIRASEK, I. HUDBA (1967). S,FL,HP	ART
JIRASEK, I. WOMAN'S PORTRAIT. S,FL,BCL,PF,VIB	PAN
JIRKO, I. DALEKY HLAS (1969). S,FL,AFL	CHF
JOACHIM, O. ILLUMINATION I (1965)	BER
NAR,FL/AFL/BFL,GUIT,PF,2PERC	
JOHNSTON, B. 5 FRAGMENTS. V,OB,BSN,VC	SMI
JOHNSTON, B. SEA DIRGE, A. MS,FL,OB,VN	SMI
JOLIVET, A. MADRIGAL. 4V,FL,PIC,EHN,BSN	BH
JOLIVET, A. SUITE LITURGIQUE. V,EHN/OB,VC,HP	DUR
KADOSA, P. VOLKSLIEDERKANTATE, OP 30. V,CL,VN,VC	EMB
KAGEL, M. MARE NOSTRUM. BAR,T,FL,OB,GUIT,HP,VC,PERC	UE
KAHOWEZ, G. SOMMERPOESIE-WINTERPOESIE (1965)	EMO
S,OB,CL,TRB,VA,PF,PER C	
KAPR, J. DREAMBOOK, THE. V,FL,HP	ES
KAPR, J. UBUNGEN FUR GYDLI. S,FL,HP	ES
KARKOSCHKA, E. PSYLEX (1968). MS,FL,TAPE	GBV
KARLINS, M. SONG FOR SOPRANO. S,AFL,VC	ACA
KARLINS, M. 3 SONGS FROM 16TH & 17TH CENTURY POEMS	ACA
S,FL,VN/VA,VC	
KASEMETS, U. CANCIONES (1955-56). V,FL,GUIT	CAN
KAUDER, H. SONG. V,FL,HP	SS
KELEMEN, M. MUSIC FOR HEISSENBUTTEL. MS,CL,VN,VC,PF	PET
KELTERBORN, R. CONSORT-MUSIC (1975)	B&B
S,FL/PIC/AFL,CL/BCL,VN,VA,VC,D B,PERC	
KELTERBORN, R. DER TRAUM MEINES LEBENS VERDAMMERT	B&N
MS,FL,2CL(BCL),HP,2VN,VA,VC	
KELTERBORN, R. SESTINA (1957). S,FL,VN,GUIT,TPT,PF,PERC	B&N
KERN, M. CANTICUM EZECHIAE. V,FL,OB,EHN,BSN,TPT	MV
KERR, H. NOTATIONS ON A SENSITIZED PLATE. S,CL,2VN,VA,VC,PF	TP
KILLMAYER, W. BLASONS (1968). S,CL,VN,VC,PF	SCH
KILLMAYER, W. PETIT SAVOYARD, LE (1956)	EMO
S,FL,PIC,VN,VC,DB,HPCD,4PE RC	
KIM, E. DEAD CALM. S,PIC,OB,CL,2PERC,VN,VC	EM
KING, H. ETRE POETE (1954). S,FL,CL,PF	SD
KING, H. 3 FABELEN (1942). V,OB(CL,FL),PF	SD
KLERK, A. DE. MISSA MATER SANCTAE LAETITIAE. S,A,FL,EHN,BSN	SD
KLERK, A. DE. 5 NOELS FRANCAIS (1963)	SD
A(MS),2FL,2CL,2BSN,2HN	
KNUSSEN, O. OCEAN DE TERRE, OP 10 (1973)	FB
S,FL,CL,VN,VC,DB,PF,PERC	
KNUSSEN, O. ROSARY SONGS, OP 9 (1972). S,CL,VA,PF	FB
KNUSSEN, O. TRUMPETS (1975). S,3CL	FB
KOELLREUTTER, H. 8 HAIKAI DES PEDRO XISTO. B,FL,PF,GUIT,PERC	EMO
KOERPPEN, A. VAGANTENBALLADE, DIE (1949). B,FL,PF,PERC	BRH
KOETSIER, J. AMSTERDAM (1948). S(T),FL,CL,2VN,VA,VC,PF	SD
KOHLER, E. DIE WELLE, OP 83. V,FL,pF	WZ
KOLB, B. 3 PLACE SETTINGS. NAR,CL,VN,DB,PERC	CF
KOLINSKI, M. CONCERTINO (1974). S,CL,PF	CAN
KOLINSKI, M. 6 FRENCH FOLKSONGS. S,FL,PF	BER
KOLINSKI, M. LYRIC SEXTET (1929). S,FL,2VN,VA,VC	CAN
KOMMA, K. MAGNIFICAT 1965. S,FL,OB,VA,VC,DB,PERC	H-V
KOMTER, J. CHANSON D'AUTOMNE (1954). MS,FL	SD
KOSTECK, G. REFRAINS & CANONS (1965). SSAA,4CL	CAN
KOUNADIS. CHOREIA I. S,FL,VC,PF,CEL,GUIT	TON
KOUNADIS, A. 2 GEDICHTE DES KONSTANTINOS KAVAFIS	TON
S,FL,CEL,GUIT,VC, PF	
KOUNADIS, A. 3 NOCTURNES NACH SAPPHO (1960)	EMO
S,FL,VN,VA,VC,CEL,VIB	

```
KOUNADIS, A.   4 PEZZI.  S,FL,VC,PF                              TON
KOVAR, V.   WO DIE VOGLEIN LEBEN.  S,FL,CL,BSN,HN,PF,VN,DB       SHF
KRAFT, W.   HEINZELMANNCHEN-BALLADE.  S,FL,VN,VA,VC              B&N
KRAUZE, Z.   3 MALAY PANTUNS (1961).  MS,3FL                     AP
KRAUZE, Z.   WIR BESITZEN KEINERLEI FAHIGKEIT                    HMO
   MS,EHN,ASAX/CL,BSN,TPT ,TRB,VC,DB
KRCEK, J.   CONCERTO E GIOCO (1969).  S,CL,VA,HP                 CHF
KRENEK, E.   SESTINA (1957).  S,FL,VN,PF,GUIT,TPT,PERC           B&N
KRENEK, E.   THEY KNEW WHAT THEY WANTED, OP227 (1977)            AMC
   NAR,OB,PF,PERC ,TAPE
KRIEGER, J.-MARX-RIKKO.  SING, OH MY SPIRIT.  V,2FL,VA,VC,PF     M&M
KROLL, G.   MAGNIFICAT (1958).  S,OB,CL,ASAX,BCL,VC,DB           GBV
KROPFREITER, A.   ALTDORFER-PASSION                              LDO
   A,BAR,FL/PIC,OB/EHN,CL,HN,BSN,2V N,2VC,DB,ORG
KROPFREITER, A.F.-RILKE.  IN MEMORIAM (1963).  S,FL,VA,VC        LDO
KRUYF, T. DE.   EINST DEM GRAU (1964)                            SD
   MS,AFL,EHN,BASSET HN,TRB,VC,DB, HP,PERC
KUNAD, R.   MELODIE, DIE ICH VERLOREN HATTE (1968)               DEU
   S, FL,2VN,2VC
KUNZ, A.   LOVE, DEATH & FULLMOONNIGHTS (1964)                   CAN
   BAR,OB(FL,CL),PF
KUNZ, A.   SONG OF THE CLARINET, THE (1961)                     CAN
   NAR,FL,OB,CL,BSN,STR QUI NTET
KUPFERMAN, M.   CONCEPTUAL WHEEL, THE.  S,CL,PF                  SER
KUPKA, K.   3 CANZONAS.  B,CL,PF,VN                              CHF
KUPKA, K.   GESANG, LIED.  B,CL,PF,3PERC                         CHF
LA FORGE, F.   MENUET VARIE.  V,FL,PF                            GS
LA MOTTE, D. DE.   GESAMMELTE WERKE.  S,FL,PF                    B&N
LACHENMANN, H.   TEMA (1968).  V,FL,VC                           HG
LADERMAN, E.   FROM THE PSALMS.  S,FL,CL,VN,VC,PF                OX
LAMBERT, J.   FOR A WHILE.  S,FL/AFL,CL,VA,DB,PF,PERC            CA
LANERI, R.   ESORCISMI I.  V,CL,VA,TRB,PERC                      SS
LANG, I.   CHAMBER CANTATA (1962).  S,CL,VC,PF,PERC              EMB
LANG, I.   PEZZI (1964).  S,FL,CL,VA,2PERC                       EMB
LAUCK, T.   IM A ( )...S (1975).  S,ASAX,VN,PF                   EMO
LAUFER, E.   NOSTOS.  S,AFL,BCL,VC,PF                            CAN
LE FANU, N.   SAME DAY DAWNS, THE.  S,FL/AFL,CL/BCL,VN,VC,PERC   NO
LECHNER, K.   CANTICA I (1965).  MS,PF,BCL,GUIT,HN,VN,VC,PERC    HG
LECHNER, K.   CANTICA II (1971).  S,FL,VC,PERC,TAPE             HG
LECHNER, K.   REQUIEM.  A,2OD,EHN,VA,VC,DB,HPCD(ORG)             PET
LEEUW, T. DE.   DE TOVERFLUIT (1954).  S,FL,VC,PF                3D
LEGE, G.   UBI CARITAS (1967).  T,BAR,B,FL,4VN                   B&N
LEHMANN, H.   BRINGEN UM ZU KOMMEN (1972).  S,FL,CL,BCL,VN,VC    HG
LEHMANN, H.   TANTRIS (1976/77).  S,FL,VC                        HG
LEIBOWITZ, R.   CAPRICCIO, OP 41 (1956)                          B-B
   S,FL,BCL,VA,VC,HP,CEL,3PERC
LEIBOWITZ, R.   CHANSON DADA, OP 76B (1968).  V,CL,HN,VC,PF      B-B
LEIBOWITZ, R.   MOTIFS, OP 74 (1967).  NAR,FL,CL,VN,VA           B-B
LEIBOWITZ, R.   3 POEMS OF GEORGES LIMBOUR, OP 46 (1958)         B-B
   S,FL,CL,VN, VA,VC,PF
LEIBOWITZ, R.   SERENADE, OP 38 (1955)                           B-B
   BAR,FL,OB,CL,HN,VN,VA,VC,HP
LEIBOWITZ, R.   SONNET, OP 77 (1967).  S,FL,CL,HN,VN,VC          B-B
LEICHTLING, A.   CANTICLE #1, OP 51.  S,FL                       SS
LEICHTLING, A.   2 PROVERBS.  MS,3CL                             SS
LEICHTLING, A.   RUBAIYAT FRAGMENTS, OP 55.  BAR,CL,HN,PF        SS
LEICHTLING, A.   TRIAL & DEATH OF SOCRATES.  V,CL,FL,HP          SS
LERDAHL, F.   EROS (1975)                                        B-B
   MS,AFL,VA,HP,2PERC,2ELEC GUIT,ELEC PF
LESUR, D.   4 LIEDER.  V,FL,PF,HP                                DUR
LEVI, P.   TRUTH, THE.  S,VL,CL,BSN,2VN,VA,2VC,HPCD,PF           ACA
LEVINAS, M.   VOIX DANS UN VAISSEAU D'AIRAIN (1977)              EDS
   V,FL,HN,PF
```

LEWKOVITCH, B. CANTATA SACRA. T,FL,EHN,CL,BSN,TRB,VC   WH
LEWKOVITCH, B. 3 ORATIONES. T,OB,BSN   WH
LIDL, V. ABENDS AM WASSER. S,FL,HP   CHF
LIDL, V. PAMPELISKY (1966). S,FL,HP   CHF
LIER, B. VAN. 3 OUD-PERZISCHE KWATRIJNEN (1956)   SD
   S,AFL,OB D'AMORE,PF
LILDL, V. 3 MILOSTNE PISNE (1970). S,FL,HP   CHF
LINKE, N. BENN-EPITAPH. A,CL,VN,VC,PF   HG
LIPTAK, D. FEUILLET D'ALBUM. V,FL,TAPE   SS
LOEVENDIE, T. 6 TURKISH FOLKPOEMS (1977)   SD
   S,FL,CL,HP,PF,PERC,VN,VC
LOMBARDI, L. TUI-GESANGE (1977). S,FL,CL,VN,VC,PF   ESZ
LOMBARDO, R. EROGENOUS ZONES, OR NEGLECTED PARTS   ACA
   S,PIC/FL/AFL,PERC
LOMBARDO, R. FROSTED WINDOW. S,BSN,VA,PERC   ACA
LOMBARDO, R. 2 LYRIC POEMS (1962). SATB,CL   CAN
LORENZINI, D. TRE LIRICHE HAN (1970)   ESZ
   S,FL,2VN,VA,VC,VIB,CEL,HP,PER C
LOTHAR, M. 8 HAIKU, OP 85. S,FL,VA,PF,PERC   EUL
LOTHAR, M. OBOEN-LIEDER, OP 47. V,OB,PF   R&E
LU, Y. CONCERT PIECE I. V,FL,CL,VN,VC,PERC   SS
LUMSDAINE, D. ANNOTATIONS OF AUSCHWITZ (1964, REV 1970)   UE
   S,FL/BFL,T PT,HN,VN,VC,PF
LUMSDAINE, D. EASTER FRESCO (1966, REV 1971). S,FL,HN,HP,PF   UE
LUTOSLAWSKI, W. INVITATION AU VOYAGE, L' (1971)   HMO
   V,S,3CL,PF,PERC
LUTOSLAWSKI, W. STRAW CHAIN, A (1951). S,MS,FL,OB,2CL,BSN   AP
LYBBERT, D. LEOPARDO CANTI. S,FL,VA,BCL   ACA
LYBBERT, D. OCTAGON. S,FL,BCL,VN,VC,DB,PF,PERC   ACA
MACHA, O. MALY TRIPTYCH. S,FL,PERC   CHF
MAGANINI, Q. 3 LYRICS. S,FL,DR   EDM
MAKLAKIEWICZ, J. VIERGES AUX CREPUSCULES, LES (1927)   AP
   2MS,FL,VA,HP
MALIPIERO, G. 4 VECCHIE CANZONI (1940)   ESZ
   V,FL,OB,CL,BSN,HN,VA,DB
MALIPIERO, R. IN TIME OF DAFFODILS   ESZ
   S,BAR,FL,EHN,BCL,VA,DB,GUIT,PERC
MALIPIERO, R. SEI POESIE DI DYLAN THOMAS (1959)   ESZ
   S,FL,OB,BCL,2VN,VA ,VC,PERC
MAMANGAKIS, N. KASSANDRA (1963). S,FL,HN,TU,HP,PERC   EMO
MAMANGAKIS, N. MUSIK FUR VIER PROTAGONISTEN (1960)   EMO
   S,A,T,B,FL,CL,B SN,VC,PF,2PERC
MAMLOK, U. HAIKU SETTINGS. S,FL   ACA
MAMLOK, U. 5 SONGS FROM "STRAY BIRDS". S,FL,VC   ACA
MANASSEN, A. DEATH, AND (1974). V,FL,GUIT   SD
MANN, L. 3 SONGS TO POEMS OF SHAKESPEARE, OP 23A (1967)   CAN
   A,CL
MANZONI, A. PRELUDIO- GRAVE DI WARING CUNEY. V,CL,3STR   RC
MARCO, T. TEA-PARTY (1969). S,MS,T,B,CL,TRB,VC,VIB   EDS
MARCO, T. ULTRAMARINA (1975). S,CL,PF,PERC   HMO
MAREZ OYENS, T. DE. RYOANJI TEMPLE. A,OB,VN,VA,VC   SD
MARIETAN, P. RECIT SUIVE DE LEGENDE. V,FL,HN,EHN,CL,PF,HP,VA JOB
MAROS, M. DESCORT. S,FL,DB   NOR
MARTIN, F. 4 SONNETS. MS,FL,VA,VC   HUG
MARTIN, F. 3 WEIHNACHTSLIEDER. V,FL,PF   UE
MARTIRANO, S. O,O,O,O, THAT SHAKESPEHERIAN RAG (1960)   AMP
   SATB,CL,ASAX ,TPT,2TRB,DB,PF,PERC
MARX, K. CHRISTUS GEBOREN WAR, DA (1951). A,FL,VN,VC,HPCD   B&N
MARX, K. DIE UNENDLICHE WOGE, OP 14. T,CL,VC   B&B
MASSE, V. JEANNETTENS HOCHZEIT. S,FL,PF   MRL
MASSE, V.-LIEBLING. SONG OF THE NIGHTINGALE. S,FL,PF   GS
MATHER, B. MADRIGAL I (1967). S,A,FL,MANDOLIN,HP,VN,VC   CAN

```
MATHER, B.   MADRIGAL II.  S,A,FL,VN,VA,VC,HP                          JOB
MATHER, B.   MADRIGAL IV (1972).  S,FL,PF,TAPE                        CAN
MATHER, R.   MUSIQUE POUR CHAMPIGNY.  S,MS,A,CL,HN,HP,PF,PERC          CAN
MATHER, B.   VENICE (1957).  S,CL,VC,PF                                CAN
MATOUSEK, L.   II. KANTATE (1966).  S,CL,BSN,TRB                       CHF
MATSUDAIRA, Y.  KATSURA.  S,FL,GUIT,HPCD,HP,PERC                       TP
MATSUDAIRA, Y.  ROEI "JISEI" (1969)                                   ESZ
   V,FL,OB,4VN,PF,VIB,HP,MAR,WHIP
MATTHUS, S.  GALILEI.  V,FL,TRB,PF,MAR,VC,TAPE                         DEU
MATUSZCZAK, B.  CHAMBER DRAMA, A.  BAR,A,BCL,VC,DB,PERC,TAPE           JB
MAXWELL(ARR).  WATER OF TYNE, THE.  S,CL,PF                            S&C
MAYUZUMI, T.  SPHENOGRAMMES.  A,FL,ASAX,VN,VC,PF,MAR                   PET
MC BRIDE, R.  NONSENSE SYLLABLES.  S,FL                                ACA
MC BRIDE, R.  VOCALISE.  S,FL,PF                                       ACA
MC INTYRE, P.  OUT OF THE CRADLE ENDLESSLY ROCKING (1966)              CAN
   V,FL,VA,V C,HPCD
MC PEEK, B.  CRAZY JANE (1957).  V,CL,PERC,PF                          CAN
MEFANO, P.  MADRIGAL (1972).  3V,FL,HP,PERC,PF                         EDS
MEIMA, H.  2 CHANSONS (1976).  S,FL,PF                                 SD
MESRITZ-VAN VELTHUYSEN, A.  3 LIEDEREN (1945).  MS,FL,VC,PF            SD
MESRITZ-VAN VELTHUYSEN, A.  RIWAJAK KAMPONG (1946)                     SD
   T(A),OB,PF,2VN,VA,VC
MEYER, K.  5 CHAMBER PIECES, OP 18 (1967).  S,CL,VN,VA                 PWM
MEYERBEER, G.  HIRTENLIED (RELLSTAB).  S(T),CL,PF                      MRL
MEYERBEER, G.  HIRTENLIED.  V,CL,PF                                    INT
MEYERBEER, G.  HIRTENLIED.  S,CL,PF                                    M&M
MICHEELSEN, H.  SINGET DEM HERRN.  S,FL,ORG(HPCD)                      B&N
MICHEL, W.  STANDPUNKTE (1974).  S,FL,PF,2PERC                         EMO
MIHALY, A.  3 APOCRYPHA (1962).  3S,CL,PERC                            EMB
MIKODA, B.  SONATA (1934).  S,FL,PF                                    CHF
MILHAUD, D.  MACHINES AGRICOLES.  FL,CL,BSN,VN,VA,VC,DB,V              HEU
MILHAUD, D.  VI. SINFONIE.  S,A,T,B,OB,VC                              UE
MILLER, E.  MISTS & WATERS.  S,CL,VN,PF,PERC                           ACA
MIROGLIO, F.  MAGIES (1960)                                           ESZ
   S,FL,OB/EHN,SAX,VN,VA,VC,DB,HN,TRB,PERC
MOMMER, H.  HEILIGEN DREI KONIGE, DIE.  A,FL,2VN,VA,VC,DB              B&B
MONOD, J.  CHAMBER ARIA (1952).  S,FL,OB,CL,BSN,HN,TPT,PF              AMP
MONSIGNY, P.-FLOTHUIS.  ARIETTE (LE MAITRE EN DROIT).  S,OB,PF         B&V
MONTEVERDI, C.-FLOTHUIS.  ARIA CON SINFONIA.  S,VN(FL,OB),BC           B&V
MOORE, D.  BALLAD OF WILLIAM SYCAMORE, THE.  B,FL,TRB,PF               GA
MOORE, D.  SONGS.  MS,OB                                               ACA
MOORER, P.  AUTUMN'S EVEN (1977-78).  S,FL,PF,VIB,PERC                 SD
MORRICONE, E.  MOLTO LONTANO, DA.  S,FL,VIB,HP,PERC,VA                 EDS
MORTARI, V.  CANZONE.  S,FL                                           ESA
MORTARI, V.  2 LAUDE.  V,FL,VC,PF                                      CAR
MORTARI, V.  POESIE RUMENE.  V,FL,HPCD                                 EDI
MORTON, D.  TEARS.  S,OB,HP                                            JB
MORYL, R.  LIED, DAS.  V,OB,PF,DB,PERC                                 SER
MOSS, L.  NIGHTSCAPE, A THEATERPIECE (1978)                           AMC
   S,FL,CL/BCL,VN,PERC,DAN CER
MOSS, L.  UNSEEN LEAVES (1975).  S,OB,TAPE,SLIDES,LIGHTS               CF
MOTTE, D. DE LA.  NIEMANDSROSE, DIE                                    B&N
   BAR,FL,CL,BSN,VN,VA,VC,HP
MOZART, W.-FLOTHUIS.  ARIA (LA CLEMENZA DI TITO).  S,CL,PF             B&V
MOZART, W.  DUE PUPILLE, K439.  S,B,3BASSET HN(2CL,BCL)                M&M
MOZART, W.  ECCO QUEL FIERO ISTANTE, K436                             M&M
   2S,B,3BASSET HN(2CL,BCL)
MOZART, W.-DEIS.  FAITHFUL HEART ENRAPTURED.  S,FL,PF                  GS
MOZART, W.  LUCI CARE, LUCI BELLE, K346                               M&M
   2S,B,3BASSET HN(2CL,BCL)
MOZART, W.  MI LAGNERO TACENDO, K437.  2S,B,2CL,BASSET HN(BCL)         M&M
MOZART, W.  PARTO! MA TU BEN MIO! (TITUS, K621).  S,CL,PF              BRH
```

```
MOZART, W.  PARTO!.  S,CL,PF                                        INT
MOZART, W.-BERGMANN.  PARTO,PARTO.  S,CL,PF                         S&C
MOZART, W.  PIU NON SI TROVANO, K549                               M&M
   2S,B,3BASSET HN(2CL,BCL)
MOZART, W.  SE LONTAN, BEN MIO, TU SEI, K438                       M&M
   2S,B,2CL,BASSET HN(BCL )
MUL, J.  GALANT KWARTET (1952).  S,FL,VC,PF                         SD
MULDER, H.  3 LIEDEREN (1959).  V,FL,PF                             SD
MUSGRAVE, T.  PRIMAVERA.  S,FL                                      CHE
MYERS, G.  MINI-SONG CYCLE, A.  S,FL                                EMC
NAVARRO, J.  INTEMPERANCES 1962                                     SN
   V,FL,PIC,BCL,TPT,TRB,TIMP,PERC
NAYLOR, B.  DEJECTION (1973).  BAR,FL,CL,BSN,HN,2VN,VA,VC,PF        CAN
NAYLOR, B.  NYMPH COMPLAINING FOR THE DEATH OF HER FAUN, THE        CAN
   MS,FL, OB,CL,BSN,2VN,VA,VC
NELHYBEL, V.  TAKE TIME.  V,FL,PF                                   SER
NIEHAUS, M.  IT HAPPENS (1972).  S,A,2T,B,CL,HP,2VN,VA,VC           HG
NIELSEN, S.  DUET.  S,A,FL,VC,VIB,TIMP                              WH
NIELSEN, S.  PRISMA SUITE (1966).  A,FL,VA,PERC                     WH
NOBRE, M.  MODINHA.  V,FL,GUIT                                      EDT
NORGAARD, H.  SERENADE TO YOUNG MAN WITH A HORN (1959)              SPD
   V,CL,TPT,TRB ,VIB,DB
NOVAK, J.  MIMUS MAGICUS.  V,CL,PF                                  GZ
NOVAK, J.  PASSER CATULLI (1961).  B,FL,OB,BSN,HN,VN,VA,VC,DB       EMO
NOWAK, L.  SUMMER IS AWAY.  V,FL,CL,BSN,VC,PF                       ACA
OBOUSSIER, R.  3 ARIEN.  S,OB,HPCD                                  B&N
OLAH, T.  EQUINOXE.  V,CL,PF                                        EMU
OLIVE, J.  MAR-RI-IA-A (1975)                                       ACA
   S,FL/PIC,CL/BCL,HN,VN,VC,PERC,TAPE
OLKUSNIK, J.  CHAMBER MUSIC.  S,FL,VA,VC,VIB,PF                     PWM
OLTHUIS, K.  ALMANACH AUX IMAGES (1976)                            SD
   BAR,CL,BSN,HN,2VN,VA,VC,DB, PF
ORGAD, B.  LEAVE OUT MY NAME (1947).  MS,FL                        ISR
ORGAD, B.  OUT OF THE DUST (1956).  MS,FL,BSN,VA,VC                ISR
ORLAND, H.  LOVE & PITY.  S,CL,VA                                   SS
ORREGO-SALAS, J.  GARDEN SONGS, OP 47.  S,FL,VA,HP                  PI
ORTHEL, L.  4 SONGS, OP 64 (1972).  S(T),CL                        SD
OTTE, H.  TASSO=CONCETTI.  S,FL,PF,PERC                             UE
OTTEN, L.  DIVERTIMENTO (1957).  S,FL,EHN,VA,VC                    SD
OTTEN, L.  ENTERTAINING MUSIC (1967).  MS,FL,VC,PF                 SD
OTTEN, L.  QUADRO (1954).  S,FL,VA,PF                              SD
PABLO, L. DE.  BERCEUSE (1974).  S,3FL,ORG,2PERC,ACTOR             ESZ
PABLO, L. DE.  COMMENTARIOS (1958).  S,PIC,DB,VIB                  EMO
PABLO, L. DE.  WORT, EIN (1965).  V,CL,VN,PF                       EDT
PAER, F.  BEATUS VIR (ARIA IN E FL).  S,CL,PF                       NOM
PAISIELLO, G.-FLOTHUIS.  ARIA (IL BARBIERE DI SIVIGLIA)             B&V
   S,FL,PF
PAISIELLO, G.-HUNT.  RIEN NE PEUT CALMER MA PEINE.  S,FL,PF        S&C
PALLASZ, E.  FRAGMENTS TO SAPPHO'S TEXTS.  S,FL,HP,VA,PERC         PWM
PANNI, M.  4 MELODIE (1964).  S,OB,VC,MANDOLINE                    ESZ
PAPINEAU-COUTURE, J.  CHANSON DE RAHIT (1972).  V,CL,PF            CAN
PAPINEAU-COUTURE, J.  EGLOGUES (1942).  A,FL,PF                    CAN
PARIK, I.  2 LIEDER.  MS,A,CL,GUIT,PERC                            SHF
PARRIS, R.  DREAMS.  S,FL,OB,CL,VN,VC,DB,PF,CEL,PERC               ACA
PARTOS, O.  5 ISRAELI SONGS (1960).  MS,OB,VC,PF                   ISR
PASATIERI, T.  FAR FROM LOVE.  S,CL,VN,VC,PF                        BE
PAYNE, A.  WORLD'S WINTER, THE (1976)                              CHE
   S,FL,OB,CL,HN,HP,VN,VA,VC
PEACOCK, K.  SONGS OF THE CEDAR (1950).  MS,FL,VC,DB,PF            CAN
PECK, R.  AUTOMOBILE.  S,FL,DB,PERC                                 CF
PEDERSEN, P.  COME AWAY (1959).  S,BSN,PF                          CAN
PEDERSEN, P.  OLD SONG (1973), AN.  S,ELEC FL,PF                   CAN
```

```
PELEMANS, W.  AD MUSICAM.  MS,4CL                                    MAU
PENNISI, F.  FOSSILE (1966).  V,FL,CL,BCL,HN,VA,HPCD,CEL,2PERC       ESZ
PEPUSCH, J.-WATLES.  CORYDON.  S,FL,PF                               S&C
PERKOWSKI, P.  SAPPHO'S SONGS.  NAR,2FL,2CL                          PWM
PERT, M.  5 SONGS FROM THE JAPANESE, OP 14.  S,FL,PF                 JOW
PETRASSI, G.  DUE LIRICHE DI SAFFO (1941)                            ESZ
    V,FL,OB,CL,BSN,HN,TPT,2VN ,VA,VC,HP
PETRASSI, G.  PROPOS D'ALAIN                                         ESZ
    BAR,EHN,CL,TRB,2VA,2VC,MAR,XYL,TIMP,PERC
PETZOLD, J.  CHRISTMAS STORY, THE.  SAB,FL(OB),ORG                   CON
PEYTON, M.  SONGS FROM SHAKESPEARE (1960).  MS,2CL,VN,VA,VC          B-B
PEZ, J.-WINTER.  MENTRE FRA MILLE FIORI.  S,FL,BC                    HSM
PEZZATI, R.  CORRESPONDANCES (1972).  V,FL,CL,TRB,VN,VA,DB,PF        ESZ
PHILIDOR, F.-FLOTHUIS.  ARIA (LE MARECHAL FERRANT).  S,OB,BC         B&V
PHILIDOR, F.-FLOTHUIS.  ARIA (SANCHO PANCA).  S,OB,BC                B&V
PIECHOWSKA, A.  SONGS OF BILITIS.  S,FL,PF,HP,PERC                   PWM
PILLNEY, K.  IN DULCI JUBILO.  V,FL,VA,VC,PF                         BRH
PINKHAM, D.  2 MOTETS.  S(T),FL,GUIT                                 ECS
PISK, P. MEADOW SAFFRONS.  V,CL,BCL                                  TP
PLESKOW, R.  DUE BICINIA.  2S,FL,CL,VC                               ACA
PLESKOW, R.  FOR 5 PLAYERS & BARITONE.  BAR,FL,CL,VN,VC,PF           ACA
PLESKOW, R.  MOTET & MADRIGAL (1973).  T,S,FL,CL,VN,VC,PF            ACA
PLESKOW, R.  ON 2 ANCIENT TEXTS.  S,FL,VC,PF                         ACA
PLESKOW, R.  ON 3 OLD ENGLISH RHYMES.  V,FL,CL,VC,PF                 ACA
PLESKOW, R.  3 SONGS.  T,CL,BCL,VN,VA,PF                             ACA
PODEST, L.  TESKNICE.  V,FL,VA,VC,PF                                 CHF
PODESVA, J.  DOTAZNIK SRDCE (1965)                                  CHF
    V,BAR,FL,TPT,PERC,GUIT,PF,VN,VA, VC
POLGAR, T.  ANNABEL LEE (1974).  V,FL,HP                             CAN
POLIN, C.  NO-RAI.  S,FL,DB                                          SS
POLLOCK, R.  CHAMBER SETTING (1972).  BAR,OB,CL,BSN,VN,VA,VC         B-B
POLLOCK, R.  DESCENT, THE (1976).  S,FL,PF                           B-B
POLLOCK, R.  SONG (1967).  S,FL,CL                                   B-B
POLLOCK, R.  TUMBLING HAIR (1975).  A,AFL,BCL,PF                     B-B
PORENA, B.  4 KANONISCHE LIEDER (1958).  S,CL                        ESZ
POULENC, F.  RHAPSODIE NEGRE.  V,FL,OB,2VN,VA,VC,PF                  CHE
POUSSEUR, H.  ECHOES II DE VOTRE FAUST.  MS,FL,VC,PF                 UE
POWELL, M.  2 PRAYER SETTINGS.  T,OB,VN,VA,VC                        GS
POWELL, R.  OF THE FATHER'S LOVE BEGOTTEN.  SATB,2FL,ORG             CON
PRIETO, C.  ODA XIV (1967).  MS,AFL,EHN,BSN,PF,VA,2VC,LUTE           EDA
PURCELL, H.-TIPPETT.  BID THE VIRTUES.  S,OB,PF                      S&C
PURCELL, H.-BERGMANN.  HARK, HOW THE SONGSTERS                       S&C
    2S,2FL,PF,VC AD LIB
PURCELL, H.-FLOTHUIS.  ONE CHARMING NIGHT.  A,2FL,BC                 S&C
PURCELL, H.-TIPPETT.  STRIKE THE VIOL.  A,2FL,PF,VC AD LIB           S&C
PURCELL, H.-BERGMANN.  WHY SHOULD MEN QUARREL                        S&C
    S,2FL,PF,VC AD LIB
RAABE, F.-SACHS.  WAHRHAFFTIGE BESCHREIBUNG                          MRL
    S,A,T,B,FL,VN,VC,PF
RAICHL, M.  3 LIEDER (1963).  BAR,FL,CL,GUIT,DB,PF,PERC              CHF
RAMEAU, J.  5 ARIAS.  S(T),FL,BC                                     MR
RANDALL, J.  IMPROVISATION ON A POEM.  S,CL,ASAX,TPT,PF,GUIT         ACA
RANDS, B.  BALLAD I.  MS,FL,TRB,DB,PF,PERC                           UE
RAPHAEL, G.  PALMSTROM-SONATE, OP 69.  T,CL,VN,PF,PERC               BRH
RASMUSSEN, K.  DIESER AUGENBLICK.  3S,FL,PERC                        WH
RAVEL, M.  CHANSONS MADECASSES.  V,FL,VC,PF                          DUR
RAVEL, M.  FLUTE ENCHANTEE, LA.  V,FL,PF                             DUR
RAWSTHORNE, A.  TANKAS OF THE 4 SEASONS.  T,OB,CL,BSN,VN,VC          OX
RAXACH, E.  FRAGMENTO II (1966).  S,FL/PIC,2PERC                     SD
RAXACH, E.  PARAPHRASE                                              PET
    A,AFL/FL,CL/BCL,BSN,HN,TPT,HP,VN,VA,VC,2PERC
RAZZI, F.  IMPROVVISAZIONE III (1967).  2S,B,FL,DB,HPCD,PERC         ESZ
```

```
READ, T.  NAMING THE CHANGES.  S,FL,OB,VC,PF,2PERC              PET
REALE, P.  PANGE LINGUA.  BAR,2OB,CL,VC,2HN                     ACA
REALE, P.  3 SONGS FROM THE CHINESE.  MS,OB/EHN,XYL,TIMP        ACA
REALE, P.  TRAVELLER, THE.  T,FL,PF                             ACA
REDEL, M.  EPILOG AUF WORTE VON ANDREAS GRYPHIUS (1971)         B&B
    BAR,FL/AFL, GUIT
REDEL, M.  SUSS VERENDET DIE ENTZUCKTE FLOTE                    B&B
    S,FL,CL,BSN,2VN,VA,VC, HP,PERC
REGT, H. DE.  CANZONI E SCHERZI, OP 30 (1973).  S,FL,HP         SD
REGT, H. DE.  MEDEA.  S,OB,HPCD                                 SD
REGT, H. DE.  MUSICA, OP 14 (1972).  NAR,FL,PERC                SD
REGT, H. DE.  MUSICA, OP 19/2 (1972).  NAR,FL,PERC              SD
REGTEREN ALTENA, L. VAN.  POEME DISCONTINU (PIERRE BOURGUE)     SD
    S,FL,VN, VC,PF
REIF, P.  DUO FOR 3.  V,CL,VC                                   AB
REIF, P.  ENCOUNTER.  S,CL                                      SS
REIF, P.  KALEIDOSCOPE (1966).  V,FL,OB,CL,BSN,HN               SS
REIMANN, A.  3 SPANISCHE LIEDER (1958).  V,FL,HP,VC             B&B
REULAND, J.  MAGNIFICAT (1971).  V,FL,PF                        SD
REVEYRON, J.  CHANT DES NOCES, LE.  S,FL,HPCD,PERC              AB
REYNOLDS, R.  AGAIN.  2S,2FL,2TRB,2DB,2PERC,TAPE                PET
RICCIO, G.-ADRIO.  JUBILENT OMNES.  S(T),FL,VN,BSN,BC           B&N
RIDOUT, A.  EMPEROR & THE BIRD OF PARADISE, THE.  NAR,FL        CA
RIEGGER, W.  MUSIC, OP 23.  V,FL(OB)                            B-B
RILEY, D.  CANTATA I.  MS,TSAX,VC,PF,VIB                        PET
RILEY, D.  CANTATA II (1966).  SATB,FL,PF,HP                    CAN
RILEY, D.  5 SONGS ON JAPANESE HAIKU.  S,CL,VN,VC               PET
RINGGER, R.  4 LIEDER AUF JAPANISCHE LYRIK (1959)              EMO
    S,CL,HN,VN,VA,DB, HP
RODRIGO, J.  2 POEMAS.  V,FL                                    UME
ROETSCHER, K.  6 LIEDER.  S,4FL                                 B&B
ROHLIG, H.  BEHOLD, A BRANCH IS GROWING.  SATB,2FL,ORG          CON
ROHLIG, H.  O HOLY JESUS.  SATB,FL,ORG                          CON
ROLDAN, A.  DANZA NEGRA.  V,2CL,2VA,PERC                        PI
RONNEFELD, P.  2 LIEDER ZUR PAUKE (1955).  A,FL,TIMP            EMO
RONNEFELD, P.  4 WIEGENLIEDER (1955).  S,FL                     EMO
RONTGEN, J.  2 LIEDER.  S,FL,VA                                 ALS
RONTGEN, J.  O, 'T RUISCHEN VAN HET RANKE RIET.  MS,CL,PF       SD
RONTGEN, J.  3 REDELOZE DUETTEN (1954).  S,A,FL,CL,PF           SD
ROOSEVELT, J.  3 SONGS FROM POE.  S,CL,PF                       ACA
ROOSEVELT, J.  4 SONGS.  S,CL                                   ACA
ROREM, N.  ARIEL.  S,CL,PF                                      BH
ROSEN, J.  SERENADE.  S,ASAX                                    ACA
ROSENFELD, G.  5 LIEDER.  S,FL,OB,CL,BSN,HN,VN,VA,VC,DB         B&N
ROUSE, C.  APHRODITE CANTOS.  MS,CL,VA,VC,PF,PERC               ACA
ROUSE, C.  GACELA DEL AMOR IMPREVISTO                           ACA
    2S,OB D'AMORE,VA,PF,2PERC
ROUSE, C.  INSANI.  NAR,OB                                      ACA
ROUSE, C.  KISS, THE.  BAR,BCL,PF,HP,CEL,PERC                   ACA
ROUSE, C.  NOX AERIS TEMPORIS.  S,OB,3VN,VC,PERC,2PF            ACA
ROUSSEL, A.  2 POEMES DE RONSARD.  V,FL                         DUR
ROVICS, H.  ECHO.  V,FL,PF                                      ACA
ROVICS, H.  HAUNTED OBJECTS                                     ACA
    S,NAR,OB,EHN,BSN,HECKLEPHONE,TAPE
ROWLAND, D.  FRANCISCAN ROUNDS (1973).  S,FL,CL,VN,VC,PF,PERC   SD
ROWLAND, D.  ROUNDELAY (1979).  S,FL,CL,VN,VA,VC,PF,PERC        SD
RUDZINSKI, Z.  TUTTI E SOLO.  S,FL,HN,PF                        PWM
RUYNEMAN, D.  ANCIENT GREEK SONGS (1954).  B,FL,OB,VC,HP        SD
RUYNEMAN, D.  REFLEXIONS (1959).  S,FL,VA,GUIT,PERC,XYL,VIB     SD
RUYNEMAN, D.  SOUS LE PONT MIRABEAU (1936)                      SD
    S,A,FL,2VN,VA,VC,HP
RYCHLIK, J.  SUDBOHMISCHE LIEDER & LIEDCHEN (1948)             ART
    2V,CL,BCL,VN
```

```
SACKMAN, N.    PAIR OF WINGS, A.    3S,FL,VA,TRB,HP,2PERC              SCH
SAINT SAENS, C.    FLUTE INVISIBLE, UNE.    V,FL,PF                    DUR
SALBERT, D.    SPIELPLANE.    S,FL,OB,CL,HN,BSN,TAPE                    MV
SALOMON, K.    ELEGIE & TANZ.    S,2FL                                 IMP
SAMUEL, G.    RELATIVITY OF ICARUS, THE                                BE
    V,FL,OB,CL,VN,VA,VC,PF,PERC
SANCHEZ, B.    YOUPPI-YA.    V,FL,GUIT                                 ECH
SAPP, G.    SHIMO.    S,FL,PF                                          SS
SARGON, S.    PATTERNS IN BLUE.    V,CL,PF                             BH
SARY, L.    QUARTETTO.    S,FL,VN,HPCD                                 EMB
SAUGUET, H.    3 CHANTS DE CONTEMPLATION.    A,B,FL,OB,HN,BSN          ALE
SAXTON, R.    PROMENADE D'AUTOMNE, LA (1972)                           CHE
    S,FL,CL,VN,VA,VC,PF,PERC
SAXTON, R.    WHAT DOES THE SONG HOPE FOR? (1974)                      CHE
    S,FL,OB,CL,VN,VA,VC ,PF,TAPE
SCARLATTI, A.    CANTATA.    S,FL,PF                                   WZ
SCHAFER, R.    ARCANA (1972)                                          CAN
    V,FL/PIC,CL/ASAX,TPT,TRB,VN,VC,DB,HP,PF/ ELEC ORG,PERC
SCHAFER, R.    ENCHANTRESS (1971, REV 1972).    S,FL,8VC              CAN
SCHAFER, R.    MINNELIEDER (1956).    S,FL,OB,CL,BSN,IIN              BER
SCHAFER, R.    REQUIEMS FOR THE PARTY-GIRL (1966)                     BER
    MS,FL,CL,IIN,PF,HP,V N,VA,VC,PERC
SCHAFER, R.    5 STUDIES ON TEXTS BY PRUDENTIUS (1962).    S,4FL      BER
SCHALK, C.    IN ADAM WE HAVE ALL BEEN ONE.    SATB,2OB,ORG           CON
SCHAT, P.    ENTELECHIE II (1961)                                     SD
    MS,FL,CL,TPT,VN,VA,VC,HP,PF,PERC
SCHAT, P.    IMPROVISATIES UIT HET LABYRINT                           SD
    A,T,B,BCL,PERC,PF,DB
SCHEEL, J.    DORMI JESU, OP 59.    V,OB,PF                           HUG
SCHEINPFLUG, P.    WORPSWEDE, OP  5.    V,EHN,VN,PF                    M&M
SCHICKELE, P.    ON THIS PLAIN OF MIST (1961).    S,A,CL,MAR          CAN
SCHMID, R.    10 MADCHENLIEDER.    S,OB,PF                            LDO
SCHMIDT, W.    2 POEMS BY WILLIAM PILLIN.    NAR,OB                    WI
SCHMIT, C.    PSAUTIER (1946).    V,CL,OB/EHN,BSN,PF                   CBD
SCHMITT, F.    4 MONOCANTES.    V,FL,VN,VA,VC,HP                       DUR
SCHOECK, O.    GASELEN, OP 38.    BAR,FL,OB,BCL,TPT,PF,PERC           BRH
SCHOECK, O.    WANDERSPRUCHE, OP 42.    T(S),CL,HN,PF,PERC            BRH
SCHOENBERG, A.    NACHTWANDLER.    S,PIC,TPT,PF                        UE
SCHOENBERG, A.    PIERROT LUNAIRE, OP 21                              UE
    V,FL/PIC,CL/BCL,VN/VA,VC,PF
SCHOENBERG, A.-MAEGAARD.    SERENADE, OP 24                           WH
    BAR,CL,BCL,VN,VA,VC,GUIT,MANDOLIN
SCHOENBERG, A.-LEIBOWITZ.    3 SONGS, OP 48 (1933)                    B-B
    V,FL,OB,CL,BCL,BSN, HN,TPT,TRB,HP,PF
SCHOUWMAN, H.    3 GEDICHTEN, OP 32 (1943).    S,FL,OB,CL,HN,BSN      SD
SCHOUWMAN, H.    LOOFT GOD DEN HEER.    V,OB,PF                        SD
SCHOUWMAN, H.    NU LAET ONS ALLEN GODE LOVEN (1936).    V,FL,PF      SD
SCHOUWMAN, H.    OASEN (1954).    A,OB,PF                             SD
SCHRAMM, H.    SONG OF TAYUMANAVAR.    S,FL                           TP
SCHREIBER, J.    NOCI (1943).    S,FL,PF                              CHF
SCHRODER, H.    INCUNDUM MIHI PROPONIS AMOREM.    MS,BCL              ROB
SCHUBERT, F.    AVE MARIA.    V,FL,PF                                 GS
SCHUBERT, F.    HIRT AUF DEM FELSEN, DER, OP129.    S,CL,PF          BRH
SCHUBERT, F.    HIRT AUF DEM FELSEN, DER, OP129.    S(T),CL,PF       MRL
SCHUBERT, F.    HIRT AUF DEM FELSEN, DER, OP129.    S,CL,PF          S&B
SCHUBERT, F.    HIRT DEM FELSEN,DER.    S,CL,PF                       INT
SCHUBERT, F.-LANCELOT.    PATRE SUR LA MONTAGNE, LE.    S,CL,PF       BIL
SCHUBERT, F.-FLOTHUIS.    ROMANCE (DIE VERSCHWORENEN).    S,CL,PF     B&V
SCHUBERT, F.    ROMANZE (DIE VERSCHWORENEN).    S,CL,PF               OX
SCHUBERT, F.-STANDCHEN.    SERENADE.    V,FL,PF                       GS
SCHUBERT, F.-DEIS.    SHEPHERD ON THE ROCK, THE.    S,FL,PF           GS
SCHUBERT, F.    SHEPHERD ON THE ROCK, THE, OP129.    V,CL,PF         EDK
```

```
SCHUBERT, F.  TOTUS IN CORDE LANQUEO.  S,CL,PF                        LDO
SCHUBERT, F.  TOTUS IN CORDE LANQUEU, OP 46.  V,CL,PF                 M&M
SCHUBERT, M.  EVOCAZIONI (1975)                                      DEU
   S,CL,BSN,HN,VN,VA,VC,DB,HP,2PERC
SCHULLER, G.  POEMS OF TIME & ETERNITY (1972)                        MAR
   S,A,T,B,FL/PIC,CL,BSN ,HN,VN,VA,VC,PF
SCHULLER, G.  6 RENAISSANCE LYRICS.  T,FL,OB,VN,VA,VC,DB,PF          AMP
SCHUMAN, W.  IN SWEET MUSIC.  V,FL,VA,PF                              TP
SCHUSTER, G.  2 & RECITATIVE (1965) DIALOGUES.  V,FL(OB),PF          ISR
SCHUTZ, H.  FATHER ABRAHAM, HAVE MERCY ON ME                         CON
   SSATB,2VN,2FL,VC
SCHWAEN, K.  SPANISCHE LIEBESLIEDER.  S,FL,CL,BSN,HN,PF              B&N
SCHWANTNER, J.  SHADOWS II, CONSORTIUM IV                            ACA
   BAR,FL,CL,VN,VA,VC,BCL,GU IT,MANDOLINE,TAPE
SCLATER, J.  ERA-TIC BEHAVIOR.  MS,ASAX(CL)                          MTS
SCLATER, J.  KINDERSCENEN.  A,FL                                     MTS
SCLATER, J.  3 SONGS OF CHILDHOOD.  A,CL                             MTS
SCLATER, J.  4 SONGS ON TEXTS OF EMILY DICKINSON.  S,CL              MTS
SEARLE, H.  OWL & THE PUSSYCAT, THE.  NAR,FL,VC,GUIT                  OX
SEARLE, H.  2 PRACTICAL CATS.  NAR,FL,VC,GUIT                         OX
SEHLBACH, E.  KLEINE WEIHNACHTSKANTATE, EINE.  S(T),FL,OB,VC          MV
SEIBER, M.  3 MORGENSTERNLIEDER.  V,CL                                UE
SEMEGEN, D.  LIEDER AUF DER FLUCHT.  S,FL,CL,HN,VN,VC,PF,2PERC       ACA
SEREBRIER, J.  EROTICA.  V,FL,OB,CL,BSN,HN                            PI
SETER, M.  AUTUMN (STAV) (1970).  MS,CL,HP(PF)                       ISR
SETER, M.  KAMMERMUSIK '70.  MS,CL,HP                                ISR
SEYFRIT, M.  WINTER'S WARMTH.  B,CL,BSN,VN,VA,VC,HP                  ACA
SHERIFF, N.  ASHREI (1961).  A,FL,2HP,PERC                           ISR
SHIFRIN, S.  SATIRES OF CIRCUMSTANCE.  S,FL/PIC,CL,VN,VC,DB,PF       PET
SHORT, M.  REFLECTIONS.  MS,FL,CL,BSN,HN,2VN,VA,VC,HP                ROP
SIGTENHORST-MEYER, B.  LIEDEREN VAN DE NIJL, OP 44.  V,OB(FL)        ALS
SILSBEE, A.  SCROLL.  S,FL/AFL,TPT,VN,DB,PF,PERC                     ACA
SILVERMAN, F.  IN SHADOW.  S,CL,GUIT                                  SS
SIMEONOV, B.  MELO DRAMATA (1965).  S,A,CL(FL),BSN,TPT,TIMP          CAN
SIMON, H.  7 LIEDER ZU FAUST.  BAR,OB/EHN,CL,VA,VC                   MRL
SIMON, H.  PANS FLUCHT.  S(T),FL,OB/EHN,CL,BSN,HN                    MRL
SIMON, H.  5 PLATTDEUTSCHE LIEDER.  MS,OB,CL,PF                      MRL
SIMON, H.  VOM KINDERPARADIES.  MS(BAR),CL,VC                        MRL
SIMS, E.  CELEBRATION OF DEAD LADIES (1976)                          ACA
   V,AFL,BASSET HN,VA,VC,2 PERC
SIMS, E.  ELEGIE- NACH RILKE.  S,FL,CL,VN,VA,VC                      ACA
SIMS, E.  IN MEMORIAM ALICE HAWTHORNE.  T,BAR,NAR,4CL,HN,2MAR        ACA
SLOWINSKI, W.  MAKOWSKI FAIRY TALES (1961).  A,FL,OB,CL              AP
SMART, G.  BRITTLE MAN (1976).  S,FL/AFL,CL/BCL,VN,VC,PF             AMC
SMART, G.  SUNDOG EVENSONG (1976).  S,FL,PF,2 RADIOS                 AMC
SMIT, L.  4 MOTETS.  V,2FL,VN                                         BR
SMOLANOFF, M.  FROM THE ORIENT.  S,FL,HP,TAPE                         SS
SOMERS, H.  KUYAS (1967).  S,FL,PERC                                 BER
SOMERS, H.  ZEN, YEATS & EMILY DICKINSON (1975)                     CAN
   2NAR,FL/BFL,PF,TAPE
SOUKUP, V.  EROTISCHE LIEDER (1965).  A,FL,PF                        CHF
SOURIS, A.  AUTRE VOIX, L' (1947).  S,FL,CL,VA,VC,PF                 CBD
SOURIS, A.  COMPTINES POUR ENFANTS SINISTRES (1948)                 ESZ
   S,MS,CL,VN,PF
SPIES, C.  SHIRIM LE HATHUNATHAM (1975).  S,FL,CL,VN,VC,PF          AMC
SPOHR, L.-LEINERT.  6 DEUTSCHE LIEDER, OP103.  S,CL,PF              B&N
SPOHR, L.  6 GERMAN LIEDER, OP103.  V,CL,PF                          EDK
SPOHR, L.  6 GERMAN SONGS, OP103.  V,CL,PF                           INT
SPOHR, L.  6 GERMAN SONGS, OP103.  S,CL,PF                            MR
STAEMPFLI, E.  GEDANKEN UBER DER ZEIT (1972)                         B&B
   S,FL,OB,HP,PF,PERC
STAEMPFLI, E.  TAGEBUCH AUS ISRAEL.  A,CL,VN,VC                      IMP
```

```
STARER, R.    2 SACRED SONGS.  V,FL,OB,VN,VA,VC,HPCD                    PI
STEARNS, P.   3 LOVE SONGS.  S,CL,BCL,TPT,TRB,VN,VA,VC,HP               ACA
STEARNS, P.   5 LYRICS FROM "THE PROPHET".  S,FL,VA                     ACA
STEARNS, P.   3 SACRED SONGS.  S,OB,HN,VC                               ACA
STEDRON, M.   SIC ET NON, KANTATA.  T,B,PIC,OB,TRB,TU                   CHF
STEFFAN, W.   GERTRUD-KOLMAR-TRILOGIE, OP 35                            B&B
   S,PIC/FL/AFL,CL,PF,PERC
STEFFANI, A.-WASNER.  COME, MY DEAR ONE.  S,FL,OB,VC,HPCD               GS
STEFFANI, A.-WASNER.  O HOW OFTEN.  V,2FL,VC,HPCD                       GS
STEFFENS, W.  NEUE GLEICHNISSE, OP  3B.  S,FL,CL,VA                     BRH
STEFFENS, W.  OBOENLIEDER, OP  9.  V,OB                                 BRH
STEINKE, G.   SKETCHES (12TH).  B,CL                                    SS
STERNBERG, E. DISTANT FLUTE, THE (1959).  A,FL                          ISR
STEVEN, D.    IMAGES.  4BAR,ELEC FL,ELEC PF,ELEC DB                     CAN
STEVENS, H.   2 SHAKESPEARE SONGS.  MS,FL,CL                            ACA
STOCK, D.     SCAT (1971).  S,FL,BCL,VN,VC                              MAR
STOUT, A.     ALLEGORY, AN: PRIDE, OP 73/3.  S,CL,VC,PF,PERC            ACA
STOUT, A.     CANTICUM CANTICORUM, OP 66                                PET
   S,SOLO VA,FL,OB,CL,BSN,HN
STOUT, A.     COMMENTARY ON T'UNG JEN, OP 14.  S(T),OB,PF,DR            ACA
STOUT, A.     LANDSCAPE, OP 36.  MS,FL,EHN,HP,TAM-TAM                   ACA
STOUT, A.     2 SONGS OF ARIEL.  S,OB,BCL,VN,VC,CEL,HP,2PERC            ACA
STRAESSER, J. RAMASASIRI (1968).  MS,FL,PF,3PERC                       SD
STRAESSER, J. 7 SONGS ON EGYPTIAN TEXTS (1979).  S,CL,VN,PF            SD
STRATEGIER, H.  5 MINNELIEDEREN (1952).  MS(BAR),FL,2VN,VA,VC          SD
STRATEGIER, H.  PARTITA ARGENTEA (1957).  V,FL,OB,VN,VC,PF             SD
STRAVINSKY, I.  BERCEUSE DU CHAT.  A,3CL                                WII
STRAVINSKY, I.  ELEGIE FOR J.F.K..  MS(BAR),3CL                         BH
STRAVINSKY, I.  PASTORALE.  S,OB,EHN,CL,BSN                             SCH
STRAVINSKY, I.  3 SONGS FROM WILLIAM SHAKESPEARE                        BH
   MS(BAR),FL,CL,VA
STRAVINSKY, I.  4 SONGS.  V,FL,HP,GUIT                                  CHE
STRAVINSKY, K.  PRIBAOUTKI.  V,FL,OB,CL,BSN,VN,VA                       CHE
STUHEC, I.    2 FATAL SONGS.  S,FL,HP                                   EDD
STURZENEGGER, R.  TRICINIUM.  MS,FL,VN                                  S-V
SUCHON, E.    LIEDER AUS DEN BERGEN.  S,FL,VN,VA,GUIT                   SHF
SUSA, C.      SERENADE #5.  2T,OB,VC,PERC                               ECS
SUTER, R.     HEILIGE LEIER SPRICH, SEI MEINE STIMME.  S,FL,GUIT        HEI
SUTER, R.     MUSIKALISCHES TAGEBUCH #1 (1960)                         EMO
   A,OB,BSN,VN,VA,VC,DB
SUTER, R.     MUSIKALISCHES TAGEBUCH #2 (1968)                         EMO
   BAR,FL,CL,BCL,HN,VN,VA, VC
SUTERMEISTER, H.  4 LIEDER.  BAR,FL,OB,VN,BSN,HPCD                      SCH
SYDEMAN, W.   JABBERWOCKY.  S(T),FL,VC                                  ECS
SYMONDS, N.   ...DEEP GROUND, LONG WATERS... (1968).  V,FL,PF           CAN
SZALONEK, W.  SUITE FROM KURPIE (1955)                                  AP
   A,FL,OB,CL,BSN,HN,VN,VA,VC,P F
SZEKELY, E.   MAQAMAT.  S,CL,TPT,HPCD,2VN,VA,VC                         EMB
TAIRA, Y.     SONOMORPHIE II.  S,OB,VC,HP,PERC                          ERR
TAMBA, A.     ENNEA.  S,FL,CL,PF,2VN,VA,VC,DB                           ERR
TANENBAUM, E. MIRAGE & INCANTATIONS.  V,CL,VN,VC,PF,TAPE                ACA
TANENBAUM, E. PETER QUINCE AT THE CLAVIER                               ACA
   S,FL/PIC,CL,GUIT,VA,TRB
TARANU, C.    LIT DE PROCUSTE, LE (1968-70).  BAR,CL,VA,PF             EDS
TAUB, B.      O SWEET SPONTANEOUS EARTH.  S,FL                          ACA
TAUBERT, K.   HAUSSPRUCH.  V,FL,PF,GUIT AD LIB                          R&E
TAUSINGER, J. CMARANICE PO NEBI (1968).  S,FL,BCL,VIB,PERC,PF          ES
TAVENER, J.   CANCIONES ESPAGNOLES.  2T,2FL,ORG,HP,PERC                 CHE
TAYLOR, C.    QUATTRO LIRICHE.  V,ASAX,PF                               ACA
TAYLOR, C.    2 SONGS, OP  5.  S(T),CL,PF                               ACA
TELEMANN, G.-FOCK.  EW'GE QUELLE, MILDER STROM.  V,FL,BC                B&N
TELEMANN, G.-FOCK.  IHR VOLKER, HORT.  V,FL,BC                          B&N
```

```
TELEMANN, G.   JEDER LAUFT, EIN.  S,OB,BC                         B&N
TELEMANN, G.-ERMELER.   KLEINE KANTATE VON WALD UND AU            B&N
   S(T),FL,BC
TELEMANN, G.-MENKE.   SUSSE HOFFNUNG, WENN ICH FRAGE              B&N
   T,2BSN,2VN,VA,VC ,BC
TELEMANN, G.-BERGMANN.   TEMPT ME THEN (LOCKET NUR)               S&C
   S,FL,PF,VC AD LIB
TELEMANN, G.-ERMELER.   TOD UND MODER DRINGT HEREIN               WZ
   A,FL,PF,VC AD LIB
TERPSTRA, K.   SERENDIPITY (1976/77).  S,OB,CL,BSN,VN,VA,VC,DB    SD
TERZAKIS, D.   ETHOS GAMMA II (1977).  B,FL,PF                    HG
TERZAKIS, D.   NOMOI.  V,CL,VC,2PERC,SANTOURI                     B&N
TERZAKIS, D.   NOTTURNI NACH GEDICHTEN DER SAPPHO                 B&N
   2S,A,2T,B,CL,VN,PE RC,TAPE
THOMSON, V.   4 SONGS TO THE POEMS OF THOMAS CAMPION              SN
   MS,CL,VA,HP
TIENSUU, J.   LYRIC TRIO, OP 15.  V,FL,PF                         FIN
TIPEI, S.   TRANSLATION.  V,CL,PF                                 SS
TIRCUIT, H.   CANTATA #3.  S,FL,VC,PF                             AMP
TOGNI, C.   6 NOTTURNI (1965).  A,CL,VN,2PF                       ESZ
TRABADELO, A. DE.   MON VILLAGE.  V,OB,PF                         E&C
TREMBLAY, G.   ORALLELUIANTS (1975).  S,FL,BCL,HN,3DB,2PERC       CAN
TRIMBLE, L.   4 FRAGMENTS FROM THE CANTERBURY TALES               PET
   S,FL,CL,HPCD(PF)
TRIMBLE, L.   PETIT CONCERT.  V,OB,VN,HPCD                        PET
TROCHU, P.   ORANGE.  V,FL,PF,2PERC                               CAN
TROJAHN, M.   ...STILLER GEFAHRT DER NACHT (1978)                 B&N
   S,FL,VC,CEL,PERC
TROJAHN, M.   HOMAGE AU TEMPS PERDU.  S,FL,CL,VC,CEL/PF           HSM
TROJAHN, M.   RISSE DES HIMMELS.  S,FL,GUIT                       HSM
TROW, K.   MATIERE (1964).  V,FL,BCL,BSN,VA,VC                    SD
TUCAPSKY, A.   HLE, JAK NADHERNE.  BAR,CL,PF,PERC                 CHF
TUCAPSKY, A.   OD STMIVANI DO USVITU.  T,FL,BCL,PF                CHF
TUCAPSKY, A.   ON JE VSE.  BAR,CL,PF,PERC                         CHF
TUREK, R.   MUSINGS (1975).  T,FL,CL,BCL,BSN,2VN,VA,VC,PERC       AMC
TURNER, R.   ECLOGUE (1958).  S,OB(FL,CL),HPCD(PF)               CAN
TUROK, P.   3 SONGS.  S,FL                                        -SS
UDOW, M.   8 AMERICAN INDIAN CHILDREN'S POEMS.  S,OB/EHN,BSN,PF   ACA
UDOW, M.   ELECTRIC SILENCE                                       ACA
   B,FL/PIC,BCL,BSN,VN,VC,TRB,PF,2PERC
UNG, C.   MOHORI.  MS,FL,OB,VC,HP,PF,2PERC,GUIT                   PET
UNG, C.   TALL WIND:  S,FL,OB,VC,GUIT                             PET
VAJDA, J.   2 TESTS.  MS,FL,CL,BSN                                EMB
VALEK, J.   SHAKESPEARE-VARIATIONEN                               CHF
   V,FL,OB,CL,BSN,HN,VN,VA,VC,DB
VAN DIJK, R.   IMMOBILE EDEN (1972).  S,FL,PF                     CAN
VAN NOSTRAND, B.   EARTH MANUAL, A DAWN CEREMONY (1976)           AMC
   S,FL/PIC,CL/ BCL,VN,VC,PF,PERC
VAN NOSTRAND, B.   LUNAR POSSESSION MANUAL- 1973                  ACA
   S,FL/PIC,CL,VN,VC,D B,PF,PERC
VANDOR, I.   CANZONE DI ADDIO (1967).  V,FL,VA,PERC,MANDOLINE     ESZ
VAUGHAN WILLIAMS, R.   3 VOCALISES (1958).  S,CL                  OX
VERRALL, J.   ROSE OF THE WORLD, THE.  S,FL,PF                    ACA
VEYVODA, G.   THROUGH THE LOOKING GLASS                           SS
   MS,FL,OB,CL,HN,BSN,TAPE
VILLA ROJO, J.   APUNTES PARA UNA REALIZACION ABIERTA (1975)      EEC
   S,CL,PE RC,PF
VILLA ROJO, J.   JUEGOS GRAFICO-MUSICALIES-IV- PLANOS I (1972)    EDA
   S,CL, TRB,DB
VILLA-LOBOS, H.   POEMA DA CRIANCA E SUA MAMA (1923)              EES
   V,FL,CL,VC
VISSER, P.   7 PAUL VAN OSTAYEN SONGS (1977).  BAR,OB,PF          SD
```

VLAD, R. IMMER WIEDER. S,EHN,CL,BSN,VA,VC,VIB,HP,PF,MAR   UE
VLIJMEN, J. VAN. MYTHOS (1963). MS,FL,OB,CL,HN,BSN,2VN,VA,VC   SD
VOGEL, W. DAL QUADERNO DI FRANCINE SETTENNE (1952). S,FL,PF   ESZ
VRIES ROBBE, W. DE. POEMS (1973). V,FL,VIB   SD
VRIES ROBBE, W. DE. RONDEAUX. NAR,FL,VIB   SD
WALACINSKI, A. LYRIC BEFORE FALLING ASLEEP, A (1963)   AP
   S,FL,2PF
WALTON, W. FACADE ENTERTAINMENT   OX
   NAR,FL/PIC,CL/BCL,ASAX,TPT,VC,PERC
WARLOCK, P. CURLEW, THE. T,FL,EHN,2VN,VA,VC   S&B
WASHBURN, R. SCHERZO FOR SPRING (1960). SSA,FL,CL,PF   OX
WEBER, B. CONCERT ARIA AFTER SOLOMON, OP 29   ACA
   S,FL,OB,CL,BSN,HN,PF,V N,VC
WEBER, B. SYMPHONY ON POEMS OF W. BLAKE, OP 33 (1951)   B-B
   BAR,VC SOLO, FL,OB,2CL,BSN,HN,TRB,CEL,PERC
WEBER, C.M. VON-LIEBLING. INVITATION TO THE DANCE. S,FL,PF   GS
WEBERN, A. 5 CANONS, OP 16. S,CL,BCL   UE
WEBERN, A.-RILKE. 2 LIEDER, OP 8   UE
   V,CL,HN,TPT,CEL,HP,VN,VA,VC
WEBERN, A.-TRAKL. 6 LIEDER, OP 14. S,CL,BCL,VN,VC   UE
WEBERN, A. 3 LIEDER, OP 18. V,E FL CL,GUIT   UE
WEBERN, A. 5 RELIGIOUS SONGS, OP 15. S,FL,CL,TPT,VN(VA),HP   UE
WEBERN, A. 3 VOLKSTEXTE, OP 17. V,CL,BCL,VN,VA   UE
WEIGL, V. ALONG THE MOVING DARKNESS. V,FL,PF   ACA
WEIGL, V. BIRDS IN SPRINGTIME. V,FL,PF   ACA
WEIGL, V. BRIEF ENCOUNTERS. MS,EHN,HN   ACA
WEIGL, V. CARDINAL IN MARCH. V,FL,PF   ACA
WEIGL, V. CHALLENGE. MS(BAR),FL,PF   ACA
WEIGL, V. CHRISTCHILD'S LULLABY. MS,FL(OB),PF   ACA
WEIGL, V. CITY BIRDS. MS,FL(CL),PF   ACA
WEIGL, V. I SAW 2 BIRDS. MS(BAR),CL(FL),BCL(VC)   ACA
WEIGL, V. LYRICAL SUITE. MS,FL(CL),VC,PF   ACA
WEIGL, V. NATURE MOODS. V,CL(FL),VN   ACA
WEIGL, V. PLAYTHINGS OF THE WIND. BAR,MS,CL,PF   ACA
WEIGL, V. SEA MOVES ALWAYS, THE. V,FL,PF   ACA
WEIGL, V. SONGS FROM "NATIVE ISLAND". V,OB,CL,PF   ACA
WEIGL, V. SONGS OF CONCERN. MS,BAR,FL,PF   ACA
WEIGL, V. SOON. V,FL,PF   ACA
WEIGL, V. THISTLE, YARROW, CLOVER. V,FL,CL,BSN   ACA
WEIGL, V. WHEN THE VISION DIES. V,FL(CL),PF   ACA
WEIGL, V. WHO HAS SEEN THE WIND?. V,FL,PF   ACA
WEILL, K. GRAND LUSTUCRU, LE   UE
   MS,FL,OB,2CL,BSN,2TPT,VN,VA,VC,DB,PER C
WEILL, K.-BERIO. SURABAYA JOHNNY   UE
   MS,FL,CL,VN,VA,VC,DB,TPT,GUIT,PERC
WEINZWEIG, J. TRIALOGUE (1971). S,FL,PF   CAN
WEISGALL, H. FANCIES & INVENTIONS. BAR,FL,CL,VA,VC,PF   TP
WEISGARBER, E. OF LOVE & TIME (1971). S,FL,OB,VN,VA,VC,HPCD   CAN
WELLESZ, E. LEADEN ECHO, THE & THE GOLDEN ECHO. V,CL,VC,PF   S&C
WELMAN, S. MELOSPECTACULUM (1975). NAR,OB,TPT,5PERC   SD
WERNERT, W. PSALM #116. S,FL,VIB   GBV
WHITE, D. VESPERS. NAR,FL,VC(BSN),PF,2PERC   SO
WHITTENBERG, C. 2 DYLAN THOMAS SONGS. S,FL,PF   ACA
WHITTENBERG, C. EVEN THOUGH THE WORLD KEEPS CHANGING   ACA
   BAR,FL,VA,VIB
WILDBERGER, J. NOTTE, LA. MS,BCL,DB,HP,PERC,TAPE   HG
WILDGANS, F. AN DEN KNABEN ELIS. S,CL,VN,VC   LDO
WILDGANS, F. MISSA MINIMA. S,CL,VN,VC   LDO
WILLEY, J. DEATH OF MOZART, THE (1975)   AMC
   S,NAR,FL/PIC,OB/EHN,VC,PERC,TAPE
WILLIAMS, J. AWAIT THE WIND. S,FL,PF   ACA
WILLIAMSON, M. PIETA. S,OB,BSN,PF   JOW

```
WINSOR, P.   FLY, THE.   BAR,FL,BCL,VN,VC                              ACA
WINSOR, P.   SICK ROSE, THE.   S,FL,BCL,VN,VC                          ACA
WOLPE, S.   QUINTET WITH VOICE.   BAR,CL,HN,VC,HP,PF                    M&M
WOOD, H.   SONGS, OP 2 (1959/63).   A,CL,VA,VC                         CHE
WOYTOWICZ, B.   CRADLE SONG (1931).   S,FL,CL,BSN,HP                   AP
WOYTOWICZ, B.   LAMENTO (1960).   S,CL,PF                              AP
WRIGHT, M.   MOZARTIAN CONSTRAINT (1974).   S,FL,VN,DB,GUIT            AMP
WRIGHT, M.   SONNET AT TRIFLING INTERVALS (1976).   S,FL,CL           B-B
WUENSCH, G.   6 SONGS (1970).   V,FL,ACC                               CAN
WUORINEN, C.   MADRIGALE SPIRITUALE (1960)                            ACA
    T,BAR,2OB,2VN,VC,PF
WUORINEN, C.   MESSAGE TO DENMARK HILL.   BAR,FL,VC,PF                 PET
WYNER, Y.   LORD, LET ME KNOW MY END.   S,3FL                         AMP
WYNER, Y.   MAN COMES FROM DUST.   S,3FL                              AMP
XENAKIS, I.   AKANTHOS (1977).   S,FL,CL,2VN,VA,VC,DB,PF              EDS
YTTREHUS, R.   6 HAIKU.   V,FL,VC,HP                                  ACA
ZAGWIJN, H.   DE FLUITSPELER (1946).   S,FL,OB,CL,HN,BSN,PF           SD
ZAGWIJN, H.   HET HOOGLIED VAN SALOMO.   NAR,FL,VA,HP                 SD
ZAGWIJN, H.   HYMNE AN DIE NACHT.   NAR,FL,VN,PF,HARMONIUM            SD
ZAGWIJN, H.   KERTMIS BIJ DE VOLKEN (1947)                           SD
    MS,BAR,FL,OB,CL,HN,BSN,2VN,VA,VC,PF
ZAGWIJN, H.   MORGENZANG (1937).   S,FL,VN,VA,VC,HP                   SD
ZAGWIJN, H.   DIE STILLE STADT (1915).   MS,FL,VN,VA,VC,HP            SD
ZAGWIJN, H.   SUITE NEGRE (1947).   MS(BAR),FL,OB,CL,HN,BSN,PF        SD
ZAGWIJN, H.   VON DER DEMUT (1936).   S,FL,VN,VA,VC,HP                SD
ZELJENKA, I.   GALGENLIEDER.   S,FL,BCL,2VN,VA,VC,PF                  SHF
ZENDER, H.   3 RONDELS NACH MALLARME (1961).   A,FL,VA               B&B
ZENDER, H.   SIRENES CHANTENT QUAND LA RAISON S'ENDORT, LES          B&B
    S,FL,CL, VC,PF,VIB
ZIANI, M.   A TE RIEDO O CARO LIDO.   S,FL,BC                         EFM
ZIPP, F.   AUF EINER GOLDNEN FLOTE, OP 27.   BAR,FL,PF(VN,VA,VC)      WMS
ZUCKERMAN, M.   TWILIGHT SONGS (1970).   S,FL                        B-B
```

INDEX OF COMPOSERS/ARRANGERS

INDEX OF COMPOSERS/ARRANGERS

315

7 REGNUM DEI. MEDITATION
TRILOGIA SACRA #2: REGNU
AITKEN, H.
  CANTATA #1
  CANTATA #2
  CANTATA #3
  CANTATA #4
  PARTITA
  QUARTET
  QUINTET
  SERENADE
  8 STUDIES
AITKEN, R.
  KEBYAR (1971)
  KEBYAR (1971)
  SHADOWS (PART II) "LALIT
  SHADOWS (PART II) "LALIT
ALABIEFF, A.
  NIGHTINGALE, THE
  RUSSIAN NIGHTINGALE, THE
ALAIN, J.
  MESSE MODALE EN SEPTUOR
ALBAM, M.
  ESCAPADE
ALBENIZ, I.
  2 PIECES FROM ESPANA
  3 PIECES
  SEVILLA
ALBERT, K.
  QUINTETTE
ALBERT, R.
  IMAGENES DEL SOLITARIO.
ALBERT, S.
  TO WAKE THE DEAD (1977)
ALBERT, T.
  SOUND FRAMES
ALBICASTRO, H.
  SONATA, OP 1/3 IN B MI
ALBINONI, T.
  CONCERTO A 5, OP 9/ 3
  CONCERTO A 5, OP 9/ 6
  CONCERTO A 5, OP 9/ 9
  CONCERTO A 5, OP 9/12
  CONCERTO IN C MA
  CONCERTO IN C MA, OP 7
  CONCERTO IN C MA, OP 7
  CONCERTO IN F MA, OP 9
  SONATA IN A MI
ALBISI, A.
  MINIATURE SUITE #1
  MINIATURE SUITE #2
  MINIATURE SUITE #2
ALBRECHTSBERGER, J.
  PARTITA
ALBRIGHT, W.
  CAROMS
  DANSE MACABRE
  DOO-DAH
  MARGINAL WORLDS
ALCALAY, L.
  GLIEDERUNGEN (1970)
  3 SERENADES (1973)

3 STATISCHE GEBILDE
  TRIO (1971)
ALDEN, J.
  VARIATIONS ON "WALTZING
ALDRICH
  LOVE & FLOWERS
ALEMANN, E.
  3 MICROPOEMS
ALESSANDRO, R.D,
  SONATINE, OP 77
ALETTER, W.
  RENDEZVOUS
  RENDEZVOUS
  RENDEZVOUS
ALEXANDER, J.
  BRACE OF DUETS, A
  3 INVENTIONS
  3 PIECES FOR 8
ALEXANDROVA, N.
  SUITE
ALFVEN, H.
  BOURREE
ALIPRANDI, P.
  PAYSAGES
ALLEGRA, S.
  SONATA IN UN TEMPO
ALLEN, M.
  PROGRESSIVE SUITE
ALLENDE¬BLIN, J.
  SILENCES INTERROMPUS
ALLERS, H.
  ELEGIE UND CAPRICCIO
  SUITE
ALLGEN, C.
  ADAGIO OCH FUGA
  FUGA
ALMEIDA, L.
  PUKA SHELLS
  PUKA SHELLS
ALMEIDA, L. & M. ALLTON
  SEA & SAND
  SEA & SAND
ALMEIDA, L. & S. MANNE
  CANON PER QUAD
  CANON PER QUAD
ALMENRAEDER, K.
  VARIATIONS ON AN ANCIENT
ALMENRAEDER, W.
  2 DUOS, OP 8
ALPAERTS, F.
  MUSIQUE DU SOIR
  SERENADE
ALSINA, C.
  AUFTRAG (1967)
  FUNKTIONEN, OP 14 (1965)
  LETTER, A
  RENDEZ-VOUS, OP 24
  UNITY, OP 31 (1973)
ALTMANN, E.
  KLEINE TANZSUITE
  KLEINE TANZSUITE
  SUITE IM ALTEN STIL, OP

TANZ-SUITE
ALWYN, W.
  NAIADES (FANTASY SONATA)
AMANI
  ORIENTALE
AMBROSI, D. D'
  INTRODUZIONE E ALLEGRO
AMBROSIUS, H.
  3 PRELUDES & FUGUES
  SONATA
AMELLER, A.
  A LA FRANCAISE
AMES, W.
  AMONG THE GODS
  COMPOSITION
  DUO
  EMANATION
  HENRY IV. INCIDENTAL MUS
  MOVEMENT
  2 MOVEMENTS
  PREAMBLE
  QUARTET
  QUARTET
  QUINTET
  SEPTET
  SEXTET
  2 SKETCHES
  TRIO
  WALTZ IN 6 PARTS
  WOODWIND QUINTET
AMRAM, D.
  DISCUSSIONS
  HERACLES
  INCIDENTAL MUSIC TO "AFT
  QUINTET
  3 SONGS FOR AMERICA
  SUMMERNIGHT'S DREAM
  TRIO
AMY, G.
  ...D'UN DESASTRE OBSCUR
  ALPHA-BETH
  INVENTION I & II
  INVENTIONS I & II
  JEUX
  JEUX
  JEUX
AMZALLAG, A.
  MUSIK (1970)
ANCHARES
  VERSETS
ANDERBERG, C.
  HEXAFONI
  HOSTENS HOKAR
ANDERS, E.
  FLOTENLIEDER, OP109
ANDERSEN, J.
  QUINTET (1939)
  SCHERZINO
ANDERSEN, K.
  TRIO, OP 5
ANDERSON, L.
  PENNY WHISTLE SONG

SUITE OF CAROLS
ANDERSON, R.
  PRELUDE & RONDO
ANDERSON, T.
  5 BAGATELLES
  BEYOND SILENCE
  INTERVALS: SET II
  SET III
  SET IV
  SET V
  TRANSITIONS
  VARIATIONS ON A THEME BY
ANDERSON, T., JR.
  5 ETUDES & A FANCY
ANDRAUD, A.
  DUOS CONCERTANTS, SERIES
  DUOS CONCERTANTS, SERIES
  DUOS CONCERTANTS, SERIES
  3 LITTLE PIECES
  18 TRIOS
  22 WOODWIND QUINTETS
ANDRE, J.
  ORIGINAL TRIO, OP 27
  TRIO, OP 29
ANDRE, P.
  CONCERTINO
  ROMANCE D'AUTOMNE
ANDREAE, V.
  QUARTET, OP 43
ANDREWS, J.
  ILLUSIONS
ANDRIESSEN, H.
  CANZONE (1965)
  CONCERT SPIRITUEL (1967)
  DIVERTIMENTO A 5
  PADOVANA DI DON CHISIOTT
  PASTORALE (1942)
  QUINTET (1951)
  3 ROMANTISCHE LIEDEREN
  SERENADE
  THEMA MET VARIATIES
  LA VIERGE A MIDI (1966)
ANDRIESSEN, J.
  ANTIFONA E FUSIONE (1966
  ARS ANTIQUA MUSICAE
  ARS ANTIQUA MUSICAE
  AULOS (1959)
  CONCERTINO (1962)
  EPITAPH VOOR VAN TULDER
  HOMMAGE A MILHAUD (1948)
  HOMMAGE A MILHAUD
  INCONTRO DI CESARE E CLE
  OCTUOR (1948)
  PETIT CONCERT CHAMPETRE
  POLDERPASTICHES (1978)
  QUARTETTO BUFFO (1974)
  RESPIRATION-SUITE (1962)
  SCIARADA SPAGNULOA (1962
  SINFONIA DELL'ARTE (1972
  SONATA DA CAMERA (1959)
  SUITE DE NOEL (1944)
  TO WET A WIDOW'S EYE

TRIO (1957)
TRIO (1965)
TRIO #1 (1955)
TRIO #2 (1955)
4 TUCHOLSKY LIEDEREN
ANDRIESSEN, L.
AANLOOP EN SPRONGEN
ON JIMMY YANCEY (1973)
DE VOLHARDING (1972)
ANDRIEU, J.
FIFRES, LES
ANGERER, P.
CHANSON GAILLARDE
COGITATIO
CONCERTO
KONZERTANTES QUARTETT
MUSICA ARTICOLATA
OBLECTATIO VESPERTINA
QUINTA TOLEN
QUINTET
SERENATA (1951)
ANGULO, M.
SIGLAS
SIGLAS
ANHALT, I.
CHANSONS D'AURORE (1955)
ANONYMOUS
GREENSLEEVES TO A GROUND
MENUET EN AIR
TUBA GALLICALLIS
ANTONI, T.
2 EASY FANFARES
3 ENCORES
ANTONINI, A.
20TH CENTURY DOLL
ANTONIOU, T.
CONCERTINO, OP 21 (1963)
DIALOGUE, OP 19 (1963)
DO QUINTET, THE
EPILOG NACH HOMERS ODYSS
EVENTS III (1969)
EVENTS III (1969)
QUARTETTO GIOCOSO, OP 26
SYNTHESIS (1971)
TRIO, OP 14 (1961)
ANTUNES, J.
FLAUTATUALF
INTERVERTIGE (1974)
ANZAGHI, D.
REMOTA (1977)
APOSTEL, H.
BAGATELLES, OP 20
FISCHERHAUS-SERENADE, OP
KLEINES KAMMERKONZERT
5 LIEDER, OP 22
QUARTET, OP 14
STUDIE(1958),OP 29
APOTHELOZ, J.
PIPEAUX D'ARGENT, LES
APPLEBAUM
QUARTET
APPLEBAUM, E.

MONTAGES
APPLEBAUM, S.
DESCRIPTIVE DUETS, 2 VOL
SWINGING DUETS
ARBAN, J.
VARIATIONS ON NORMA
ARBATSKY, Y.
FROM A TO Z
SINFONIA SACRA UTICANA
ARCHDUKE RUDOLPH
TRIO
ARCHER, V.
DIVERTIMENTO (1949)
DIVERTIMENTO #2 (1957)
SONATA
2 SONGS (1958)
SUITE (1947)
ARDEVOL, J.
MUSICA DE CAMERA
SONATA #1
SONATA #2
SONATA #4
ARDITI, L.
BACIO, IL (THE KISS)
BACIO, IL (THE KISS)
IL BACIO (THE KISS)
AREND, J.
BOISMORTIER SUITE
SUITE ANTIQUE
ARENSKY, A.
6 CHILDREN'S SCENES
CUCKOO, THE
ARGENTO, D.
6 ELIZABETHAN SONGS
TO BE SUNG UPON THE WATE
ARMA, P.
CELUI QUI DORT ET DORT
DIVERTIMENTO #10
DIVERTIMENTO #2
3 MOUVEMENTS
3 RESONANCES
3 RESONANCES
3 TRANSPARENCES
3 TRANSPARENCES
3 TRANSPARENCES
7 TRANSPARENCES
7 TRANSPARENCES
7 TRANSPARENCIES
ARMBRUSTER, R.
TANKA
ZITATE
ARMENIAN, R.
PROGRESSIONS I (1972)
ARNE, T.
2 DANCES
MORNING, THE
SUITE OF DANCES
UNDER THE GREENWOOD TREE
WHEN DAISIES PIED
WOOD NYMPH, A
ARNELL, R.
CASSATION, OP 45

318

BABER, J.
  TRIO
BABUSEK, F.
  NONETO
BACEWICZ, G.
  QUINTET (1933)
  TRIO (1935)
  TRIO (1965)
  TRIO (1965)
BACH
  CANON (SONATA IN F MI)
  2 PIECES
BACH, C.
  SPRING'S AWAKENING
BACH, C.P.E.
  ALLEGRO
  CANTABILE
  CONCERTO #1 IN B FL MA
  DUET IN C MA, WQ 142
  DUET IN G MA
  DUET
  DUET
  2 DUETS
  2 DUETS
  DUO IN E MI WQ 140
  2 DUOS
  10 EASY DUETS(WQ.81,82,1
  12 KLEINE STUCKE, WQ 82
  12 KLEINE STUCKE
  10 KLEINE TRIOS, WQ 82,
  6 LITTLE MARCHES
  12 LITTLE PIECES, W 81
  12 LITTLE PIECES
  6 MARCHES
  2 MENUETS & 1 POLONAISE
  PASTORALE IN A MI
  6 PIECES
  QUARTET #1 IN A MI, WQ 9
  QUARTET #2 IN D MA, WQ 9
  QUARTET #3 IN G MA, WQ 9
  RONDO
  SONATA IN D MA
  SONATA IN G MI
  SONATA
  6 SONATAS
  6 SONATAS
  6 SONATES
  SONATINE IN C MA
  TRIO #1 IN D MA
  TRIO #1 IN D MA
  TRIO #2 IN A MI
  TRIO #2 IN A MI
  TRIO #3 IN G MA
  TRIO #3 IN G MA
  TRIO IN B FL MA
  TRIO IN B MI
  TRIO IN E FL MA
  TRIO IN E MA
  TRIO IN E MA, WQ162
  TRIO IN F MA
  TRIO SONATA IN B FL MA,
  TRIO SONATA IN B MI, WQ1

  TRIO SONATA IN D MA
  TRIO SONATA IN G MA, WQ1
  TRIO SONATE II
  TRIOSONATA IN G MA
  TRIOSONATE IN A MA
  TRIOSONATE IN A MI, WQ14
  TRIOSONATE IN C MA, WQ14
  TRIOSONATE IN D MA, WQ15
  TRIOSONATE IN D MI
BACH, J.C.
  ALLEGRETTO PIACEVOLE
  ALLEGRO (SINFONIA #2)
  ALLEGRO BRILLANTE
  BLASER-SINFONIEN, 2 VOLS
  DIVERTISSEMENT
  DIVERTISSEMENT
  3 MARCHES
  QUARTET IN A MA
  QUARTET IN B FL MA
  QUARTET IN C MA
  QUARTET IN C MA
  QUARTET IN C MA, OP 8/1
  QUARTET IN C MA,
  QUARTET IN D MA
  QUARTET IN D MA, OP 20/2
  QUARTET IN F MA, OP 8/4
  QUARTET IN G MA
  QUARTET, OP 8/2
  QUARTET, OP 8/5
  QUARTET, OP 8/6
  QUARTET, OP 17/6
  2 QUARTETS, OP 19/1,3
  6 QUARTETS
  3 QUARTETTES, OP 8/1,3,
  QUINTET #3
  QUINTET IN A MA, OP 11/5
  QUINTET IN C MA, OP 11/1
  QUINTET IN D MA
  QUINTET IN F MA
  QUINTET IN F MA, OP 11/3
  QUINTET IN G MA, OP 11/2
  QUINTET, OP 11/1 IN C MA
  QUINTET, OP 11/2 IN G MA
  QUINTET, OP 11/3 IN F MA
  QUINTET, OP 11/4 IN E FL
  QUINTET, OP 11/5 IN A MA
  QUINTET, OP 11/6 IN D MA
  4 QUINTETS, 2 VOLS
  SEPTETT
  SEXTET IN C MA
  SINFONIA IN B FLAT MA
  SINFONIA, #1
  SONATA IN A MA
  SONATA IN C MA
  SONATA IN F MA
  3 SONATAS IN D,G, AND C
  6 SONATAS, OP 2/1-6: PU
  3 SONATAS
  SYMPHONY #2
  TRIO #2 IN C MA
  TRIO IN B FL MA
  TRIO IN C MA

TRIO IN C MA
TRIO IN G MA
TRIO SONATA IN B FL MA
TRIO
BACH, J.C.F.
  QUARTET #2
  SEPTET IN C MA
  SONATA IN D MA
  SONATE IN D MA
BACH, J.S.
  ACH GOTT UND HERR, WIE G
  ACH LIEBEN CHRISTEN
  ADAGIO & AFFETUOSO
  ADAGIO
  AIR (SUITE #3 IN D MA)
  AIR (SUITE #3)
  AIR
  ALLEGRETTO
  ALLEGRO
  ANDANTE (TRIO SONATA)
  ANDANTE AND FUGHETTA
  ARIA
  AVE MARIA
  AWAKE,AWAKE,A VOICE IS C
  BACH CHORALES
  15 BACH CHORALES
  3 BACH CHORALES
  BACH FOR THE CLARINET.PA
  BACH FOR THE CLARINET, P
  BACH FOR THE CLARINET, P
  BACH FOR THE CLARINET, P
  2 BACH FUGUES
  BACH INVENTIONS
  2 BACH PRELUDES
  4 BACH PRELUDES
  BADINERIE (SUITE #2)
  BADINERIE (SUITE #2)
  BIST DU BEI MIR
  BIST DU BEI MIR
  BOUREE (OVERTURE #3)
  BOURREE (3RD CELLO SONAT
  BOURREE
  BOURREE
  CANON #4
  CANON #4
  CANON PERPETUUS
  CANONIC TRIO
  CANONICAL FUGUE
  3 CANONS & ROUNDS
  10 CANONS, BWV1080
  CELEBRATED AIR (SUITE #3
  CELEBRE ARIA
  CHORALE & PRELUDE ON ACH
  CHORALE PRELUDE
  CHORALES, 2 VOLS
  2 CHORALS
  CLARINET DUOS
  CLASSICAL QUINTET
  COMPLETE ARIAS & SINFONI
  COMPLETE ARIAS & SINFONI
  COMPLETE ARIAS & SINFONI
  COMPLETE ARIAS, VOLS #1-

CONCERTO #3 IN D MI
CONCERTO IN C MI
CONCERTO IN C MI, BWV106
CONCERTO IN C MI, S1060
CONCERTO IN D MI
CONCERTO, BWV1057
DUET (CANTATA #78)
DUO CONCERTO
DUO CONCERTO
ENSURIENTES (MAGNIFICAT)
EXCERPTS (SONATA IN C MA
EXCERPTS (SONATA IN C MA
EXCERPTS (SONATA IN C MA
FANTASIA & FUGUE IN C MI
FUGA #9
FUGA CANONICA
FUGA CANONICA
FUGA II
FUGA IX
FUGA XVI
FUGA XXIII
FUGHETTA
FUGUE #16 IN G MI
FUGUE #4
FUGUE #4
FUGUE #7
FUGUE #7
FUGUE III
FUGUE IN C MI
FUGUE IN C MI
FUGUE IN E FL MA
FUGUE IN E MI
FUGUE IN G MI
FUGUE IN G MI
FUGUE ON A THEME OF CORE
FUGUE V
FUGUE VII
FUGUE XIV
FUGUE XXI
FUGUE XXII
GAVOTTE (FRENCH SUITE #5
GAVOTTE (FRENCH SUITE #5
GAVOTTE IN G MI
GAVOTTE
GAVOTTE
2 GAVOTTES
2 GAVOTTES
GOLDBERG VARIATIONEN
I CALL UPON THY NAME O J
3 INVENTION #8
INVENTIONEN
3 INVENTIONS A DEUX VOIX
15 INVENTIONS
15 INVENTIONS
15 INVENTIONS
15 INVENTIONS
2-PART INVENTIONS
2-PART INVENTIONS
3 INVENTIONS
JESU PRAISE (CANTATA #15
JESU, JOY OF MAN'S DESIR
JESU, JOY OF MAN'S DESIR

JESUS NIMMT DIE SUNDER A
JIG FUGUE, THE
KANONISCHES TRIO, BWV104
KORAALBEWERKING (CANTATA
KUNST DER FUGE (CONTRAPU
LITTLE BACH SUITE #1
LITTLE BACH SUITE #2
LITTLE FUGUE IN G MI
LITTLE FUGUE IN G MI
LOURE
LOURE
MEDITATION (AVE MARIA)
MEDITATION (AVE MARIA)
MEDITATION AVE MARIA
MEINE SEUFZER, MEINE TRA
MENUETTO & POLACCA(BRAND
MINUET
MINUETS
MUSIKALISCHES OPFER, BWV
MY HEART EVER FAITHFUL
NUN KOMM, DER HEIDEN HEI
ORGAN WORKS
PASTORALE
4 PIECES
PRAELUDIUM IX
PRAELUDIUM XXII
PRELUDE (PARTITA #3)
PRELUDE & FUGUE #2
PRELUDE & FUGUE IN D MA
PRELUDE & FUGUE IN D MI
PRELUDE & FUGUE IN E MI
PRELUDE & FUGUE IN E MI
PRELUDE & FUGUE IN G MA
PRELUDE & FUGUE IN G MI
PRELUDE & FUGUE IN G MI
PRELUDE & FUGUE IN G MI
PRELUDE & FUGUE IN G MI
PRELUDE & FUGUE XXI
PRELUDE & FUGUE XXII
PRELUDE & FUGUE
PRELUDE #12
PRELUDE #22
PRELUDE #4
PRELUDE #4
PRELUDE #8
PRELUDE AND FUGUE IN F M
PRELUDE IN C MI
PRELUDE IN D MA
PRELUDE IN F MA
PRELUDE TO CANTATA #106
PRELUDE XXII, VOL #1
2 PRELUDES & FUGUES
2 PRELUDES
QUARTET IN E FL MA, OP
SACRED HEAD
SARABANDE (FRENCH SUITE
SARABANDE (FRENCH SUITE
SARABANDE & BADINERIE
SARABANDE & DOUBLE
SARABANDE & GAVOTTE
SARABANDE
SARABANDE

SARABANDE
3 SARABANDES
21 SELECTED PIECES
SEUFZER, TRANEN, KUMMER,
SEXTET IN E-FLAT
SHEEP MAY SAFELY GRAZE
SHEEP MAY SAFELY GRAZE
SHEEP MAY SAFELY
SICILIANO & MINUET
SICILIANO
SICILIANO, GIGUE & ARIA
SINFONIA (CANTATA #209)
SINFONIA (CHRISTMAS ORAT
SINFONIA #9
SINFONIA IN A MI
SONATA #1, BWV 1033
SONATA #3 IN E MA, BWV 1
SONATA #4 IN C MA (S 103
SONATA A 3
SONATA IN C MA (BWV1027,
SONATA IN C MA
SONATA IN C MI
SONATA IN G MA
SONATA IN G MA, BWV1038
SONATA IN G MA, BWV1039
SONATA IN G MI, BWV1030B
SONATA IN G
SONATA
SONATE #4
SONATE A TRE IN G MI
SONATE EN TRIO
SONATE IN G MA, BWV1039
2 SONATEN IN C MA & D MA
STONE ABOVE ALL OTHERS T
SUITE
TERZETTO (CANTATA #38)
TERZETTO (CANTATA #38)
4 TRANSCRIPTIONS
TRIO (THE MUSICAL OFFERI
TRIO #8, BWV1079
TRIO ALBUM
TRIO ALBUM
TRIO IN G MA
TRIO IN G MA, BWV1039
TRIO SONATA (MUSICAL OFF
TRIO SONATA & CANON PERP
TRIO SONATA #2 IN G MA
TRIO SONATA IN B MI
TRIO SONATA
TRIO SONATAS #3 IN G MA
3 TRIO SONATAS
6 TRIO SONATAS
TRIOSONATE IN G MA, BWM1
TRIOSONATE IN G MI
TWO PART INVENTIONS(12,
TWO PART INVENTIONS(3, 1
TWO PART INVENTIONS(4, 1
15 TWO-PART INVENTIONS
UNSCHULD, KLEINOD REINER
VERGNUGTE PLEISSEN-STADT
WAS GOTT THUT, DAS IST W
WENN WIR IN HOCHSTEN NOT

YET JESUS WILL THE RIGHT
15 3-PART INVENTIONS
BACH, J.S./MOZART
 ADAGIO E FUGA
BACH, JAN
 4 TWO-BIT CONTRAPTIONS
BACH, W.F.
 CANON (SONATA IN E MI)
 CANON (SONATA IN F MI)
 6 DUETS, 2 VOLS.
 6 DUETS,2VOL
 DUO #1
 DUO SONATA
 DUO SONATA
 DUO SONATA
 DUO SONATA
 DUO SONATA
 DUO SONATA
 SICILIANO
 SONATA # 4IN E MI
 SONATA #1 IN G MA
 SONATA IN B FL MA
 SONATA IN E-FLAT MA
 SONATA IN F MA
 SONATA
 3 SONATAS
 2 SONATAS IN E MI, F MI
 2 SONATAS
 SONATE IN D MA
 TRIO (ALLEGRO) IN A MI
 TRIO #1 IN D MA
 TRIO #2 IN D MA
 TRIO #3 IN A MI
 TRIO IN A MI
 TRIO IN B FL MA
 TRIO IN D MA, #1
 TRIO IN D MA, #2
 TRIO IN G MA
BACH, W.F.E.
 SEXTET IN E FL MA
 TRIO IN G MA
BACK, S.
 FAVOLA (1962)
 FAVOLA
 FAVOLA
 FAVOLA
 5 PRELUDIER (1966)
 SENTIRE
BACKES, L.
 BALLADE
BACKOFEN, J.
 GRAND DUO
 GRAND DUO, OP 37
BACON, E.
 COCK FIGHT, THE
 COCK FIGHT, THE
 OLD AIRS FROM MANY COUNT
BADEN, C.
 TRIO
BADINGS, H.
 CAPRICCIO
 CAVATINA (1952)

FUGA (1938)
3 GEESTELIJKE LIEDEREN
3 LIEDEREN UIT "LENTEMAA
OCTET (1952)
3 OLD DUTCH SONGS (1967)
QUINTET #2 (1929)
QUINTET #4 (1948)
SEXTET (1952)
SUITE #2
TRIO #10 (1977)
TRIO #2 (1943)
TRIO #4A (1946)
TRIO #5 (1947)
TRIO #9 (1962)
BADINSKI, N.
 MOSKAUER BLASERQUINTETT
 OCTET (DIE RUINEN UNTER
BAEKERS, S.
 QUARTETTO (1977)
 QUINTET (1975)
BAER, W.
 5 SATZE
BAERVOETS, R.
 MUSICA NOTTURNA (1969)
 QUATUOR (1974)
BAEYENS, A.
 CONCERTINO
 PIRANESI
 QUINTETTE (1950)
BAGATINI
 ODE TO HIAWATHA
BAGIN, P.
 AKVARELY
BAGINSKI, Z.
 VOYAGE TO THE OTHER SIDE
BAGLEY
 THISTLEDOWN
 THISTLEDOWN,
BAHK, J.
 ECH
BAILEY, M.
 2 STRUCTURES
BAINBRIDGE, S.
 PEOPLE OF THE DAWN
 QUINTET
 SPIROGYRA
 WIND QUARTET
BAINES, F.
 COMIC VARIATIONS
 DIVERTIMENTO
BAIRD, T.
 CHANSONS DES TROUVERES
 DIVERTIMENTO (1956)
BAKER, D.
 FANTASY, SERENADE & FUGU
BAKER, M.
 5 EPIGRAMS (1965)
 INTERLUDE & DIVERTIMENTO
 LETTER, THE (1974)
 MUSIC FOR 6 PLAYERS
 QUINTET
BAKSA, R.

324

326

OUD-HOLLANDSCHE MELODIE
VERRASSING (1928)
BEEKUM, J. VAN
  EASY DUETS
  INSTRUMENTAL DUETS, 2 VO
  MINI TRIOS
  PREMIERE
  2 SONATINAS
  TRIPHONIA
BEERMAN, B.
  COLORS
  COLORS
  CONSORT & SONG
  ENSEMBLE I
  FRAME
  MASS
  MIXTURES
  POINTS
  POLYGRAPH #1
  POLYGRAPH #3
  POLYGRAPH #5
  POLYGRAPH VI
  POLYGRAPH VI
  REFLECTIONS
BEETHOVEN
  ALLEGRO MOLTO QUASI PRES
  DUO #1
  DUO #2
BEETHOVEN, J.
  6 EASY DUETS
BEETHOVEN, L.
  ADAGIO CANTABILE (SONATA
BEETHOVEN, L. VAN
  ADAGIO & ALLEGRO
  ADAGIO CANTABILE (OP 87)
  ADAGIO CANTABILE (SONATA
  ADAGIO FOR A FLUTE CLOCK
  ADAGIO IN F MA (1799)
  ADAGIO
  ALLEGRETTO (TRIO, OP 2)
  ALLEGRO (OP 87)
  ALLEGRO (SYMPHONY #6)
  ALLEGRO & MINUET
  ALLEGRO & MINUET
  ALLEGRO & MINUET
  ALLEGRO & MINUET
  ALLEGRO & MINUET
  ALLEGRO AND MINUET
  ALLEGRO AND MINUET, WOO
  ALLEGRO CON BRIO (OP 18/
  ALLEGRO FOR A FLUTE CLOC
  BAGATELLE IN F MI
  BAGATELLE, OP 33/2
  2 BEETHOVEN SONATAS
  CI DAREM LA MANO, LA
  CLARINET DUETS
  CONTRA DANCE
  COUNTRY DANCE #1
  DEUTSCHER TANZ
  DIVERTIMENTO IN G MA
  3 DUETS
  DUO #1 IN C MA

DUO #2 IN F MA
DUO #2
DUO #3 IN B FL MA
DUO #3
DUO #3
DUOS
3 DUOS
3 DUOS
EXCERPTS FROM RONDO (SON
FIDELIO
FUGUE
GAVOTTE IN F MA
GRAND TRIO IN C MA, OP 8
GRAND TRIO, OP 87
HAPPY & SAD
6 KONTRATANZE
LARGHETTO (SYMPHONY #2)
MARCHE DES GRENADIERS
MARSCH IN B FL MA
MARSCH IN C MA
MENUET (SYMPHONY #1)
MENUET DE PRINTEMPS
MENUET IN G MA
MENUET
MENUET
MENUET
MENUET
MENUETT & FINALE, OP 87
MENUETTO (OP 10/3)
MENUETTO (OP 18/5)
MENUETTO & FINALE (OP 87
MENUETTO
MINUET (SEPTET, OP 20)
MINUET (SONATA, OP 22)
MINUET & MARCH
MINUET & MARCH
MINUET IN G MA
MINUET IN G MA
MINUET IN G MA
MINUET IN G MA
MINUET IN G MA
MINUET IN G MA, #2
MINUET
MINUET
MOONLIGHT SONATA (ADAGIO
MOONLIGHT SONATA (ADAGIO
MOONLIGHT SONATA (ADAGIO
OCTET IN E FL MA, OP103
OCTET, OP103
OKTETT IN E FL MA, OP103
PETIT TRIO
5 PIECES FOR MECHANICAL
PRELUDE & FUGUE
PRESTO (OP 87)
QUINTET IN E FL MA, OP 1
QUINTET
QUINTET, OP 16
QUINTET, OP 71 IN E FL M
RONDINO IN E-FLAT
RONDINO IN E FL MA
RONDINO IN E FL MA
RONDINO

CLARINET CAROUSEL
CLARINET RHAPSODY
PRELUDE & SCHERZO
RHAPSODETTE
SAX SOLILOQUY
SAXOPHONE SYMPHONETTE
WAY OF THE WASP
BENNETT, R.
COMMEDIA I
COMMEDIA II
CRAZY JANE (1968/69)
CROSSTALK
JAZZ PASTORAL (1969)
KONZERT FUR GITARRE
KONZERT FUR GITARRE
QUARTET
SOLILOQUY (1966)
BENNETT, R.R.
QUINTET (1967/68)
RONDO CAPRICCIOSO
TRIO (1965)
BENNETT, RICHARD
CONVERSATIONS
BENNETT, ROBERT RUSSELL
SUITE
BENNETT, W.
HYPERBOLEX
BENSON, W.
MARCHE
BENT, R.
SWISS BOY
SWISS BOY
SWISS BOY,
SWISS BOY,
BENTLEY, A.
SIXTEENTH CENTURY QUARTE
TRIOS OF THE 16TH CENTUR
BENTON, D.
LOVE SONG
QUARTET
SERIAL STRAINS
2 SHAKESPEARE SONGS
SHORT SERIAL SUITE
STATELY DANCES
BENTZON, J.
INTERMEZZO
MICROPHONY, OP 44 (1939)
RACCONTO #1, OP 25
RACCONTO #3, OP 31
RACCONTO #4, OP 45
RACCONTO #5, OP 46
SONATINE, OP 7
VARIAZIONI INTERROTTI
BENTZON, N.
CHAMBER CONCERTO, OP 52
CHAMBER CONCERTO, OP 52
CONCERTO, OP176
MOSAIQUE MUSICALE, OP 54
QUARTETTO TERTIO, OP385
SEXTET, OP278
SINFONIA CONCERTANTE, OP
SONATA, OP257

BENVENUTI, A.
CANTUS GEMELLUS (1961)
MORCEAU (EN FORME DE...)
STUDI (1960-61)
3 STUDIES
BERBIGUIER, B.
THEME & VARIATIONS
BERBIGUIER, T.
7 DUETS,OP 28
6 DUETS,OP 59
3 DUOS CONCERTANTES
3 DUOS,OP 4
3 DUOS,OP 22
3 DUOS,OP 46/1
6 EASY DUETS
6 EASY DUETS
6 EASY DUETS
18 EXERCICES OU ETUDES
3 GRANDS DUOS BRILLANS,O
3 GRANDS DUOS BRILLANS,O
3 GRANDS DUOS BRILLANS,O
3 GRANDS TRIOS, OP 40/1-
TRIO FOR FLUTES, OP 51/1
TRIO FOR FLUTES, OP 51/2
TRIO FOR FLUTES, OP 51/3
BEREAU, J.
SEXTUOR
BEREZOWSKY, N.
DUO
SUITE #2
BERG, A.
ADAGIO (CHAMBER CONCERTO
BERG, G.
POUR CLARINETTE ET VIOLO
BERGE, S.
YANG-GUAN (1967)
BERGEIJK, G. VAN
SONATE
BERGENFELD
CHROMA-TRIX
TWO MOODS
BERGER
3 DUETS
BERGER, A.
CANZON OCTAVI MODI
CHAMBER MUSIC
CHAMBER MUSIC
PARTITA
3 POEMS OF YEATS
QUARTET IN C MA
SEPTET
BERGER, J.
DIVERTIMENTO
6 SHORT PIECES
5 SONGS
BERGER, W.
TRIO IN G MI, OP 94
BERGMAN, E.
CONCERTINO DA CAMERA, OP
DIALOGUE
BERGMANN, W.
MUSIK FUR BLASERQUINTETT

PASTORALE
BERGSMA, W.
  CHANGES FOR 7
  CONCERTO
BERGT, A.
  TRIO
BERGT, C.
  DUET #1 IN C MA
  DUET #2 IN F MA
  DUET #3 IN B FL MA
BERIO, L.
  AGNUS (1971)
  CHAMBER MUSIC (1953)
  CHEMINS II ON SEQUENZA V
  CHEMINS II ON SEQUENZA V
  DIFFERENCES (1958-59)
  EL MAR LA MAR (1951)
  FOLKSONGS (1964)
  MELODRAMA (1969)
  O KING
  OPUS NUMBER ZOO
BERKELEY, L.
  CONCERTINO, OP 49
  OBOE QUARTET (1967)
  QUINTET (1975)
  SEXTET
BERKES, K.
  CLARINET DUOS, 3 VOLS
BERKOWITZ
  10 DUETS
BERKOWITZ, L.
  QUINTET (1966)
BERKOWITZ, S.
  SUITE FOR WINDS
BERLIN, D.
  FLUCTUATIONS
  INTERACTIONS
  3 MIXTURES
  OCTET
  QUINTET
BERLINSKI, H.
  BACH TRIO ALBUM
  CANONS & ROUNDS
  CANONS & ROUNDS
  CANONS & ROUNDS
  CANONS & ROUNDS
BERLIOZ, H.
  JEUNES ISMAELITES, DES
  TRIO (THE CHILDHOOD OF C
  TRIO DES JEUNES ISMAELIT
  TRIO OF THE YOUNG ISHMAE
  TRIO OF THE YOUNG ISHMAE
  TRIO OF THE YOUNG ISHMAE
  TRIO
  TRIO
  TRIO
  TRIO, OP 25
BERNAOLA, C.
  ARGIA EZTA IKUSTEN
  ASI
  SUPERFICIE #3
BERNARD, E.

DIVERTISSEMENT, OP 36
BERNARD, J.
  DIALOGUE D'ANCHES
BERNARDS, B.
  10 INSTRUKTIVE DUOS
BERNAUD, A.
  QUATUOR
BERNET, D.
  CAPRICES
BERNHARD, C.
  FURCHTET EUCH NICHT
BERNIER, R.
  SERINETTE
  SONATE A DEUX (1939)
  SUITE POUR LE PLAISIR DE
  TRIO (1942)
BERR, F.
  20 PETITS DUOS
BERRY, W.
  2 CANONS
  DIVERTIMENTO
BERTALI, A.
  SONATA I IN D MI
  SONATA II IN D MI
  SONATA III IN A MI
BERTHELEMY, N.
  RONDO POUR RIRE
BERTHOLD
  QUINTETTINO
BERTHOMIEU, M.
  ARCADIE
  CHATS
  5 NUANCES
  RONDO (SUITE BREVE)
BERTONI, F.
  CANZONA
BERTOUILLE, G.
  CONCERTINO (1977)
  PRELUDE & FUGUE (1955)
  PRELUDE & FUGUE (1957)
  PRELUDE ET FUGUE (1955)
  PRELUDE ET FUGUE (1959)
  QUARTET #4 (1948)
  QUINTET (1969)
BERWALD, F.
  KLAVIERQUARTETT, OP 1
  QUARTET IN E FL MA
  STOR SEPTETT
BESOZZI, A.
  SONATA A TRE IN F MA, OP
BESOZZI, C.
  PARTHIA IN D MA
  SONATA #13
  SONATA #20
  SONATA IN C MA
  SONATA
  6 TRIOS
BETJEMAN, P.
  SLOW BURN (1976)
BETTINELLI, B.
  OTTETTO (1975)
  TERRA, LA

330

BETTS, L.
  MUSIC FOR THEATRE (1950)
  PRELUDE FOR SPRING
  PRELUDE, PASTORAL & DANC
BEUGNIOT, J.
  PIECES
BEVAN, C.
  PARIS 1890'S. 3 ESQUISSE
BEVERSDORF, T.
  DIVERTIMENTO DA CAMARA
BEVIN
  BROWNING
BEYER, F.
  CONCERTINO A TRE (1974)
  CONCERTO (1966; 1969)
  CONCERTO (1968)
  QUINTET (1972)
BEYER, J.
  DUET
  MOVEMENT
  PARTITA #1
  PARTITA #2
  PARTITA IN C MA
  4 PIECES
  SUITE #3
  SUITE
BEZANSON, P.
  5 MINIATURES
  PETITE SUITE
  SEXTET
  TRIO
  WOODWIND QUINTET, HOMAGE
BIALAS, G.
  GESANG VON DEN TIEREN
  3 GESANGE NACH GEDICHTEN
  KANONISCHE ETUDEN
  MENSCH, EIN UND EINE FLI
  MOMENTS MUSICAUX III
  PARTITA (1969)
  PASTORALE UND RONDO (NON
  ROMANZA E DANZA. OKTETT
  TRIO (1946)
BIALOSKY, M.
  3 SONGS
  SUITE
  VARIATIONS ON AN ELIZABE
BIBALO, A.
  AUTUNNALE
  SONATINA 2A, ASTRALE
BIBER, C.
  SONATA
  SONATA
BIELER, H.
  QUICK FINGERS
BIENENMANN, F.
  14 DUETS
BIERSACK, A.
  DIVERTIMENTO
BIGGS, J.
  3 CANZONI
  INVENTION
  PASTORALE

SCHERZO
STUDIES IN TEXTURE
WIND COLLAGE
WOODWIND TRIO
BIGOT, P.
  3 SHORT PIECES
BIJL, T. VAN DER
  CONCERT IN F MA (1954)
BIJVANCK, H.
  2 LIEDREN (1951)
BILUCAGLIA, C.
  LIED (1974)
BINET, J.
  3 DIALOGUES (1958)
BINKERD, G.
  DUO
  TRIO
BIRTWISTLE, H.
  CANTATA (1969)
  ENTR'ACTES & SAPPHO FRAG
  3 LESSONS IN A FRAME
  MEDUSA (1969/70)
  MEDUSA (1969/70)
  MONODY FOR CORPUS CHRIST
  NENIA ON THE DEATH OF OR
  PROLOGUE (1970)
  REFRAINS & CHORUSES
  RING A DUMB CARILLON
  TRAGOEDIA
  TRAGOEDIA
  VERSES FOR ENSEMBLES
  WORLD IS DISCOVERED, THE
  WORLD IS DISCOVERED, THE
BISCARDI, C.
  TENZONE
BISCHOF, R.
  QUARTET, OP 5
  THEMA UND 7 VARIATIONEN,
BISCOGLI
  CONCERTO IN D MA
BISHOFF, R.
  DUO, OP 3
BISHOP, H.
  LO! HERE THE GENTLE LARK
BISHOP, SIR H.
  LO! HERE THE GENTLE LARK
BISSELL, K.
  FOLK-SONG SUITE, A (1960
  OVERHEARD ON A SALTMARSH
  SERENADE FOR 5 WINDS
  SUITE
BITSCH, M.
  DIVERTISSEMENT
  SONATINE
BIZET, G.
  ADAGIETTO (L'ARLESIENNE)
  ADAGIETTO (L'ARLESIENNE)
  ADAGIETTO DE L'ARLESIENN
  ADAGIETTO
  ADAGIETTO
  ADAGIETTO
  ADAGIETTO

331

ADAGIETTO
ALLEGRO & VIVACE (SYMPHO
ANDANTE & MINUET (L'ARLE
ANDANTE & MINUET
ARAGONAISE
ARAGONAISE
ARAGONAISE
CARILLON (L'ARLESIENNE)
CARILLON
CARILLON
CARILLON
CARILLON
ENTR'ACTE (CARMEN)
ENTR'ACTE
ENTR'ACTE
HABANERA (CARMEN)
INTERMEZZO (SUITE L'ARLE
LITTLE DUET IN C MI (187
MINUET
MINUET #2
MINUET #2
MINUET
MINUET
MINUETTO (L'ARLESIENNE S
5 PIECES FROM "CARMEN"
3 PIECES
3 PIECES
3 PIECES
PRELUDE (SCENE BOHEMIENN
QUARTET DE L'ARLESIENNE
QUINTET (CARMEN)
QUINTET (CARMEN)
SERENADE ESPAGNOLE
SERENADE ESPAGNOLE
SERENADE ESPAGNOLE
SERENADE ESPAGNOLE
SUITE (CARMEN)
BJELIK, M.
  AUTOGRAMM
  KONTUREN
  MOBILE
  OKTETT
BJELINSKI, B.
  SCHERZI DI NOTTE
BJERRE, J.
  MOSAIQUE MUSICALE (1936)
  MOSAIQUE MUSICALE #3
  SERENADE
BJORKLUND, S.
  PASTORAL (1970)
BJORKMAN, R.
  LITEN MUSIK (1972)
  MINIATYR (1974)
BLACHER, B.
  DIVERTIMENTO (1951)
  JAZZ-KOLORATUREN (1929)
  5 NEGRO SPIRITUALS (1962
  OCTET (1965)
  3 PSALMEN (1943)
  QUINTET (1973/74)
  TRIGA EINER CHROMATISCHE
BLACKWOOD, E.

CONCERTINO, OP 5
BLAHA, I.
  JARNI HRY (1964)
BLAKE, E.
  CHARLESTON RAG (1917)
BLAKE, H.
  FANTASY ALLEGRO
  TRIO
BLAKE, N.
  TRIO, OP 18
BLAND, E.
  TRIO
BLANK, A.
  AMERICAN MEDLEY
  2 BAGATELLES (1962)
  4 BAGATELLES
  BEING
  BICINIUM II
  BICINIUM
  COALITIONS II
  COALITIONS
  COMPOSITION FOR 11 PLAYE
  DON'T LET THAT HORSE EAT
  4 DREAM POEMS
  ESTHER'S MONOLOGUE
  2 HOLY SONNETS BY JOHN D
  4 MINIATURES
  3 ONE-NOTERS
  PAGANINI CAPRICE #24
  PENNYCANDYSTORE BEYOND T
  POEM
  4 POEMS BY EMILY DICKINS
  QUINTET
  3 RELATED PIECES
  2 SIMPLE CANONS
  VARIATIONS
  13 WAYS OF LOOKING AT A
BLANQUER PONSODA, A.
  DIVERTIMENTO GIOCOSO
BLATNY, J.
  SUITE
BLATNY, P.
  DREITEILIGER SATZ (1958)
  3 SATZE (1962)
BLAVET, M
  6 SONATAS, 2 VOLS.
  6 SONATAS
BLAVET, M.
  2 DUETS, OP 1/5 & 6
  2 DUETS, OP 1/5,6
  15 DUETTE
  FRENCH DUETS
  8 PIECES
  SONATA IN G MA, OP 1/4
  6 SONATAS, OP 1, VOL 1
  6 SONATEN, OP 1/1-3
BLAZEK, V.
  PSALM 134-100-93-133, OP
BLAZEK, Z.
  DIVERTIMENTI (1946)
BLEGER, A.
  SOUVENIR DE VALENCE

332

BLEZARD, W.
  3 DIVERSIONS
  4 SUITE PIECE
BLEZZARD, W.
  PAIR OF PIECES, A
BLICKHAN, T.
  QUINTET
  SPEAK SOFTLY
  VARIATIONS/PERMUTATIONS
BLIN, L.
  GRUPETTINO
  GRUPETTINO
BLINOV, Y.
  RUSSIAN SCHERZO
BLISS, A.
  CONVERSATIONS
  MADAM NOY
  2 NURSERY RHYMES
  QUINTET
BLOCH, A.
  SALMO GIOIOSO (1970)
BLOCH, E.
  CONCERTINO
  CONCERTINO
  PRELUDE & PROCESSIONAL
BLOCH, W.
  SERENADE (1966)
BLOCK, H.
  OCTET
BLOCK, R.
  BASS CLEF GALANT
  HOMAGE TO D. S.
  SOUND THE BRIGHT FLUTES
BLOCK, S.
  CHEMICAL WEDDING
  PUTTIN' IT TOGETHER
BLOMDAHL, K.
  DANS-SVIT #2
  DANS-SVIT NR 1
  TRIO (1938)
  TRIO
BLUM, R.
  MUSIK
BLUME, J.
  MUSIK
BLUME, O.
  12, DUETS
  12 MELODIOUS DUETS
BLUMENFELD, H.
  EXPANSIONS
BLUMER, T.
  QUINTET, OP 52
  SERENADE & THEME & VARIA
  SEXTET, OP 45
  SEXTET, OP 92
  TANZ-SUITE, OP 53
  TRIO, OP 55
BLUNT, M.
  3 CONTRASTS
BOATWRIGHT, H.
  QUARTET
  SERENADE

BOBESCU, C.
  PARAFRAZA PE MOTIVUL "HO
BOCCHERINI, L.
  MENUET
  MENUET
  MENUET
  MENUET
  MENUET,
  MINUETTO
  QUARTET
  QUINTET IN D MA, OP 21/1
  QUINTET IN E FL MA, OP 2
  QUINTETS, OP 45/1-3
  3 QUINTETS, OP 45/4-6
  QUINTETTO IN C MA
  QUINTETTO, OP 21/6
  SEXTET IN E FL MA, OP 42
  SONATA
  TERZETTO
BOCHSA
  ANDANTE & MINUETTO
BOCK, I. & A. JANETSKY
  10 PIECES
BOCKEMUEHL, E.
  CORTEGE
BODER, G.
  TRIO, OP 1
BODIN, L.
  PRIMARY STRUCTURES
BODINUS, S.
  CONCERTO #3 IN E MI
  SONATA IN E MA
  SONATA IN E MI
  SONATE
  TRIOSONATE #1
BOEDDECKER, P.
  SONATA SOPRA "LA MONICA"
BOEDIJN. G.
  BADINAGE IN EEN KNOLLENL
BOEDIJN, G.
  FOLKLORISCHE SUITE, OP 8
  KWINTET CONCERTANTE, OP1
BOEHM, F.
  12 PETITS DUOS, OP 5
BOEHM, T.
  3 DUETS
  PRESTO
  PRESTO
  PRESTO
BOEHM, Y.
  DIVERTIMENTO (1957)
BOEHMER, K.
  ZEITLAUFTE (1962)
BOEHNLEIN, F.
  ETHEREAT
  IDEALOGIES
  MEDITATIONS
BOELLMANN, L.
  MENUET GOTHIQUE
BOER, J. DE
  ELEMENTS (1978-79)
BOER, J. DEN

334

6, CONCERTI
6, CONCERTI
BOLCOM, W.
  DUETS FOR QUINTET
  SESSION I
  SESSION III
  SESSION IV
  SESSION IV
  WHISPER MOON
BOLLING, C.
  SUITE
BOLZONI, G.
  MINUETTO
  MINUETTO
BON, M.
  KRISTAL TEGEN SPIEGEL
BON, W.
  JADIS ET NAGUERE (1970)
  PASSACAGLIA IN BLUE
  3 POEMES DE VERLAINE
  QUINTET #1, OP 13
  QUINTET #2, OP 26 (1969)
  SANS PAROLES (1970)
  SILENCE (1978)
  SUNPHONEION I, OP 22
BOND, V.
  CAN(N)ONS
  CORNOGRAPHY
  RECITATIVE
BONDON, J.
  SOLEIL MULTICOLORE, LE
  SWING #1
BONNARD, A.
  BIS, OP 42
  SONATINE BREVE
BONNEAU, P.
  DIVERTISSEMENT
  3 NOELS ANCIENS
BONNER
  OVER THE HILLS
  OVER THE HILLS
BONNER, E.
  OVER THE HILLS
BONONCINI, G.
  7 SUITES, 2 VOLS.
BONSEL, A.
  ANTHRISCUS SYLVESTRIS
  KWINTET #1 (1949)
  MUSICA
  OCTET (1975)
BONVALET
  CLAIRIERE, LA- LA PINEDE
  SOUVENIR-CANZONE
BOOGAARD, B. VAN DEN
  KOSMOI (1974-75)
BOOGAARD, V. VAN
  SYNTHETIC POEME
BOOM, J.V.D.
  6 PIECES
BOONE, C.
  COOL GLOW OF RADIATION,
  LINEA MERIDIANA

QUARTET
  STARFISH (1966)
BOOREN, J.
  SPECTRA (1967)
BOOREN, J. VAN DEN
  AKIROB
  BIRDS (1975)
  COLLECTION OF PIECES
  FUR ELISE, AFTER L. VAN
  SONATA (1962)
  SPIEL I (1969)
  TRIO, OP 2 (1960)
BOOREN, J. VANDEN
  ESTREMI (1967)
BOOREN, JO VAN DEN
  EQUILIBRIO
BOREL, R.
  FUGATO IN F MA
BORGHI, L.
  5 CLARINET DUOS
  DIVERTIMENTO
BORGULYA, A.
  4 DUETTI
  TRIO
  TRIO
BORISSOV, L.
  WELTRAUMSZENEN (1958)
BORKOVEC, P.
  NONETTO (1940)
  WOODWIND QUINTET (1932)
BORNEFELD, H.
  CHORALSONATE "AUF MEINEN
BORNSCHEIN, F.
  FRENCH CLOCK, THE
BORODIN, A.
  INTRODUCTION & ALLEGRO V
  INTRODUCTION EN ALLEGRO
  NOCTURNE (QUARTET #4)
  SOLICITUDE
  SOLICITUDE
  SOLICITUDE
  SOLICITUDE
BORRIS, S.
  BLASER-OKTETT, OP 55
  DUETTINO, OP116/2
  DUO, OP116/1 (1964)
  KLEINE SUITE, OP 31/3
  OBOE QUARTET, OP 17/1
  OKTETT, OP 99/4
  PARTITA, OP 92/1
  RHAPSODIE, OP103
  SONATINA PER TRE, OP 45/
  SUITE, OP 92/2
  TRIO, OP 90
  TRIO, OP116/1B (1965)
  VILLANELLEN, OP 97
  WOODWIND QUINTET, OP 25/
BORSCHEL, E.
  BLASER-FAVORITEN
BORSTLAP, D.
  FANFARE II (1965)
  OVER DE VERANDERING

335

BORTOLOTTI, M.
  CONTRE VOCALIZZO (1965)
  PARENTESIS (1968)
  STUDI (1960)
  STUDIO PER CUMMINGS #2
BORTZ, D.
  KAMMARMUSIK (1964)
BOSKE, J.
  LEAVE SOMETHING UNEXPLAI
BOSKE, J. TEN
  SANGITA (1979)
BOSMANS, A.
  DIABELLIANA
BOSSLER, K.
  SONATINE
BOTH, H.
  TANZ- UND JAZZ- DUETTE
BOTTENBERG, W.
  3 AMERINDIAN SONGS (1961
  DIVERTIMENTO(1968)
  FA SO LA TI DO RE (1972)
  MY FUNNY LITTLE CLOCK
  OCTET (1972)
  QUARTET (1960)
  SONATA (1960)
  THOSE PASSIONS...WHICH Y
  TRIO (1961-63)
  TRIO (1963-64)
  VARIABLES (1969)
BOTTJE, W.
  CELESTIAL MOTIONS
  CONCERTINO
  DANCES, SOLEMN & JOYOUS
  DANCES: SOLEMN & JOYOUS
  DESIGNS
  DIVERSIONS (1961)
  3 ETUDES
  FLUCTUATUATIONS (1965)
  IN A WORD
  MODALITIES #2 (1970)
  MODALITIES
  MUSIC FOR A JOYOUS OCCAS
  MUSIC FOR A JOYOUS OCCAS
  4 PASTORALES OF SEASON A
  QUARTET #1 (1963)
  QUINTET
  QUINTET
  QUINTET
  REFLECTIONS
  REFLECTIONS
  SERENADE
  SYMBIOSIS
  THREESOME FOR FOUR
  THREESOME FOR 4 (1949)
  TRIO SONATE (1958)
  TRIO SONATE
BOTYAROV, E.
  3 PIECES
BOUCARD, M.
  QUARTETT-SINFONIA
  SUITE CHAMPETRE
  TRIADE

BOUCOURECHLIEV, A.
  GRODEK
BOUFFIL, J.
  GRAND TRIO, OP 8
  TRIO, OP 8/1
  TRIOS
  3 TRIOS, OP 7, PUB SEPA
  3 TRIOS, OP 7
  3 TRIOS, OP 8
BOUFIL, J.
  GRAND DUO, OP 2/1
BOULEZ, P.
  MARTEAU SANS MAITRE, LE
BOURGAULT¬DUCOUDRAY
  ABERGAVENNY
BOURGEOIS, E.
  AIR DE BALLET
BOURGUIGNON, F.
  2, PIECES
  SUITE EN TRIO, OP 80
BOURGUIGNON, F. DE
  QUINTET, OP100 (1952)
BOURLAND, R.
  7 POLLOCK PAINTINGS
BOURNE
  BOURNE TRIO ALBUM
  BOURNE TRIO ALBUM
BOUSCH, F.
  AU-DELA DU REVE (1977)
  COMME CHANTE LA SOURCE
BOUSQUET, N.
  FAVORITE FLUTE DUETS(TWO
  GOLDEN ROBIN POLKA
  GOLDEN ROBIN POLKA
  GOLDEN ROBIN POLKA
BOUSTEAD, A.
  3 MADRIGALE
BOUTRY, R.
  DIVERTISSEMENT
  2 PIECES EN SEXTUOR
  PRELUDE, PASTORAL & TARA
  TOCCATA, SARABAND & JIG
BOUVARD, J.
  4 DANSES
  3 IMAGES
  21 MINI DUETTE
  3 PIECES BREVES EN TRIO
  12 PIECES BREVES
BOVE, J.
  ANDANTE & ALLEGRO
BOWLES, P.
  MUSIC FOR A FARCE
BOWLES, R.
  SUITE
BOYAMYAN, A.
  MINIATURES
BOYCE, W.
  ALLEGRO (SYMPHONY #3)
  ANDANTE DOLCE
  MARCATO
  OVERTURE FOR HIS MAJESTY
  VIVACE

336

BOYD, A.
  METAMORPHOSES OF THE FEM
BOYKAN, M.
  CONCERTO (1973)
BOZAY, A.
  IMPROVISATIONS, OP 27
  MUHLE, DIE, OP 23
  QUINTET (1962), OP 8
  SERIE, OP 19
  SLIPS OF PAPER, OP 5
  SOROZAT
BOZIC, D.
  AUDIOGEM V
  COLLAGE SONORE
  CONCERTO GROSSO IN F MA
  GLASBENA SLIKANICA
  SONATA IN COOL #3
BOZZA, E.
  ANDANTE & SCHERZO
  BERCEUSE ET SERENADE
  CONTRASTES I
  CONTRASTES II
  CONTRASTES III
  DIVERTISSEMENTS
  DUETTINO
  2 ESQUISSES
  2 IMPRESSIONS
  JOUR D'ETE A LA MONTAGNE
  LUCIOLES
  3 MOUVEMENTS
  4 MOUVEMENTS
  NUAGES
  OCTANPHONIE
  PENTAPHONIE
  3 PIECES POUR UNE MUSIQU
  3 PIECES
  POLYDIAPHONIE
  SCHERZO, OP 48
  SERENADE EN TRIO
  SERENADE
  SONATINA
  SONATINE
  SONATINE
  SUITE BREVE EN TRIO
  VARIATIONS SUR UN THEME
BOZZA,E.
  3 PIECES
BRAAL, A. DE
  GIOCOSO (1972)
  PASTORALE EN SCHERZO
  TRIO (GIOCOSO)
  TRIO (1976)
BRADAC, J.
  BOHEMIAN SUITE
BRADLEY, W.
  DEEP QUARRY, THE
  HONEYSUCKLE & CLOVER
BRAEIN, E.
  GLADE MUSIKANTER, DE- SE
BRAGA, G.
  ANGEL'S SERENADE
  ANGEL'S SERENADE

ANGELS SERENADE
SERENATA
SERENATA, LA
BRAHE, M.
  BLESS THIS HOUSE
BRAHMS, J.
  ALLEGRETTO GRAZIOSO
  BERCEUSE
  CAPRICCIO
  CELEBRE VALSE
  CHORALE PRELUDE # 8
  CHROALE PRELUDE #11
  3 EASY QUARTETS
  FAMOUS WALTZ, OP 39/15
  FAMOUS WALTZ, OP 39/15
  FAMOUS WALTZ, OP 39/15
  HERZLICH TUT MICH VERLAN
  HUNGARIAN DANCE #5
  HUNGARIAN DANCE #5
  LILAC HILLSIDES
  O GOTT DU FROMMER GOTT,
  QUINTET IN B MI
  QUINTET IN B MI, OP115
  QUINTET
  QUINTET, OP115
  TRIO IN A MI, OP114
  TRIO, OP114
  WALTZ
BRAHMSTEDT
  FRIVOLITIES (CONCERT POL
  SOUVENIR OF VENICE
BRAHMSTEDT, N.
  FRIVOLITIES
BRANA, H.
  CINCO ENTRADAS
  ESTRIBILLO
  FILIGRANA
  LUNES AZUL
  METAMORPHOSIS
  TEMA
BRANDENBURG
  ASH GROVE, THE
  ASH GROVE, THE
BRANDON, S.
  CHACONNE & VARIATIONS
  CONCERT OVERTURE
  FABRICATION (1976)
  FROM GOULIES & GHOSTIES
  PIECE FOR 5 (1976)
  RONDO (1971)
  SONATINA (1971)
  2 SONGS OF EAST OREGON
  TRIO DA CAMERA
  2 VISIONS (1970)
BRANT, H.
  ANGELS & DEVILS
  CONCERTO
  ICE AGE (1954)
  PREVAILING WINDS
BRASHER, J.
  DIADELPHOS
BRAUN, G.

FRAGMENTE (1974)
PORTRAIT #1 (1969)
SONATINE
BRAUN, P.
ESSAY (1960-69)
BRAUN, R.
AIR FROM ERIN, AN
ANGEVIN CAROL
BASSOON BUG
DIVERTIMENTO
SONGS FROM YE OLDE ENGLA
SUITE
BRAUN, Y.
4 EASY PIECES (1974)
BRAUNLICH, H.
QUARTET
QUINTET
BRAUTIGAM, H.
FROHLICHE MUSIK
KLEINE JAGDMUSIK, OP 11
TANZERISCHE SPIELMUSIK
BRAVNICAR, M.
4 PIECES
TRIO QUASI FANTASIA
BRAZINSKAS, A.
QUINTET
BRECK, E.
CHRISTMAS JOYS
BREDOW, E.
5 APHORISMEN
QUINTETTINO
SERENADE OF FRANCONIA
BREHM, A.
COLLOQUY & CHORALE
DIALOGUES
DIVERTIMENTO
BREIT & WARD
BOY WHO WANTED A TUBA,
BRENET
MELANCOLIE
BRENET, T.
FLANERIE
BRENTA, G.
SOLDAT FANFARON, LE
BREPSANT, E.
15 DUETS, 3 VOLS
BRERO, C.
TRIO (1935)
BRESGEN, C.
4 CAPRICCIOS
4 GESANGE (1965)
KAMMERKONZERT, OP 6
5 MINIATUREN
QUARTET "UMREM, UMREM"
SALZBURGER DIVERTIMENTO
BRETTINGHAM SMITH, J.
GYRE FOR A WIND QUINTET,
O RISE, OP 6 (1973)
SONGS FOR A FOOL, OP 4
TWO TIMES PAST, OP 18
WIND IN THE REEDS, OP 12
BREUER, H.

IN MEMORIAM HANS ARP
BREUER, P.
SERENADE
BREVAL, J.
SYMPHONIE CONCERTANTE IN
BRICCETTI, T.
PARTITA, OP 9 (1956)
BRICCIALDI, G.
DUO CONCERTANT #2, OP100
DUO CONCERTANT, OP100/2
16 FLUTE DUETS "DIALOGUE
BRICKMAN, J.
SUITE
BRIDGE, F.
DIVERTIMENTI
BRIGHT, H.
3 SHORT DANCES
BRINGS, A.
BURLETTE
DIVERTIMENTO
SUITE
SUITE
BRITAIN, R.
DANCE GROTESQUE
4 SARABANDES
BRITTEN, B.
GEMINI VARIATIONS
GEMINI VARIATIONS, OP 73
PHANTASY QUARTET
BRIXEL, E.
COMMEDIA DELL'ARTE
BRIXI, F.
INTERMEZZO
BROD, H.
QUINTET, OP 2/1
QUINTET, OP 2/2
SONATA #1
6 SONATAS
BRODER, T.
6 RUBAIYYAT OF KHAYYAM
BROECKX, J.
PETITE SUITE
BROGUE, R.
QUODLIBET
SONATINA
TRIO
TRIO
BRONS, C.
BALLETTO (1961)
CONCERTINO (1977)
MUTAZIONE (1964)
SERENATA II (1965)
SERENATA III (1974)
BROOKE, A.
THREE MUSKETEERS
BROOKS, K.
CLASSICAL ALBUM
10 TRIOS FOR DEVEL PING
BROOKS, R.
LAST NIGHT I WAS THE WIN
QUINTET
TRIO

BROPHY, W.
  HAPPY BIRTHDAY TO YOU
BROQUA, A.
  3 CANTOS URUGUAYOS
BROSH, T.
  DIALOGUE
  MISTERIOSO
  MUSIC
  MUSIC
BROTONS, S.
  ENFASIS
  SAX-QUINTET-VENT
  SUITE A TRES
BROTT, A.
  3 ACTS FOR FOUR SINNERS
  MINI-MINUS (1968)
  SAXI-FONI-SATIES (1972)
  SEPT FOR SEVEN (1954)
  3 ON A SPREE (1963)
BROWN
  PARMI LES PRES
BROWN, A.
  ADDITIONS
  QUARTET #1
  QUARTET #2
  SOUNDSCAPES #1
  SOUNDSCAPES 3
  SURFACE TEXTURES
BROWN, C.
  DIVERTIMENTO
  QUINTET
  TRIO
BROWN, E.
  HODOGRAPH I (1959)
  NOVARA
  PENTATHIS
  SYNTAGM III (1970)
  SYNTAGM III (1970)
  TIMES FIVE (1963)
  TIMES FIVE (1963)
BROWN, J.
  CHALUMEAU CANONS
  CHALUMEAU CANONS
  FRAGMENTS
  QUARTET
  TRIO
BROWN, N.
  CHANT AND JUBILEE
  GLASER SET
  PASTORALE
  4 PIECES
  QUINTET
  SET OF THREE POEMS
BROWN, R.
  DIVERTIMENTO
  FUGUE
  FUGUES
  3 FUGUES
  MUSIC
  PARTITA "WICKED POLLY"
  PASSACAGLIA WITH FUGUES
  PHOENIX AVATARA

  QUINTET
  SHENANDOAH
  SONATA
  SYMPHONY FOR CLARINETS
  TRIO
BROWN, T.
  FRECKLES & FLOWERS
  FRECKLES & FLOWERS
  FRECKLES & FLOWERS
  PERPETUAL COMMOTION
BROZAK, D.
  KOROZE (1977)
  REINE DE JOIE (1978)
BRUBECK, H.
  6 PIECES
BRUCH, M.
  CONCERTO, OP 88
  8 PIECES, OP 83
  8 STUCKE, OP 83
BRUGK, H.
  DIVERTIMENTO, OP 29
  LEUCHTENDE NACHT, OP 18
  QUARTET, OP 32
  SERENADE, OP 22
  ZUM VORTRAG
BRUN, G.
  PASSACAILLE
BRUN, H.
  GESTURES FOR 11
  TRIO
BRUNETTI, G.
  QUINTET #4
BRUNIAU, A.
  TOI ET MOI (FANTAISIE-DU
  TOI ET MOI
BRUNO, C.
  3 SONETTI DI RUSTICO DI
BRUNS, V.
  BLASERQUINTETT, OP 16
  TRIO, OP 49
BRUNSWICK, M.
  SEPTET IN 7 MOVEMENTS
BRUSSELMANS, M.
  PRELUDE & FUGUE
BRUYNEL, T.
  DIALOGUE #1 (1976)
  INTRA I (1971)
  LOOKING EARS (1972)
  MECANIQUE (1967)
  SIGNS (1969)
  SOFT SONG (1974)
BRUZDOWICZ, J.
  ESQUISSES (1969)
  SKETCHES FROM THE HARBOU
BUBAK, J.
  NONETTO, OP 17
BUBALO, R.
  SOUNDPOSTS
BUCHANAN, G.
  SWEETS
BUCHT, G.
  QUINTETTO AMICHEVOLE

339

BUCHTEL, F.
  AZURE SKIES
  BLUE TAIL FLY
  BONITA
  COMRADES
  DANCING NYMPHS
  ELF IN DANCE
  ENCHANTED FOREST
  ENCHANTMENT
  FAIR ARE THE MEADOWA
  2 IMPS
  MARIANINA
  MERRY HEARTS
  MEXICAN CLAPPING SONG
  PIPERS 3
  ROVING MINSTRELS
  ROVING MINSTRELS
  SKYLARKS
  SKYLARKS
  SOFT SHOE DANCE
  TIRITOMBA
  TIRITOMBA
  TWO IMPS
  TWO PALS
  TWO PALS
  WALTZ "ALPHENS"
  WALTZ "SIBYL"
  WOOD NYMPHS
  WOODLAND WHISPERS
BUCHTGER, F.
  CONCERTINO II
BUCHWALD, R.
  TRIO (1967/73)
BUCK, O.
  JAN & MAJ (1968)
  SIGNES (1967)
  SUMMER TRIO (1968)
BUCKMANN, R.
  5 KLEINE STUCKE
  8 ZWEISTIMMIGE SATZE
BUCQUET, P.
  SUITE #1
  SUITE #1
  SUITE #1
  SUITE #1
  SUITE #2
  SUITE #2
  SUITE #2
  SUITE #2
  SUITE IN G MI
BUCZYNSKI, W.
  DIVERTIMENTO, OP 15
  2 FRENCH LOVE POEMS
  HOW SOME THINGS LOOK
  MILOSC (LOVE) (1967)
  2 PIECES (1975)
  QUARTET/74 (1974)
  SEXTET/74 (1974)
  SUITE, OP 13 (1955)
  TALES OF NANABOZHO, THE
  TRIO/67
  TRIO/74 (1974)

  TWO & A HALF SQUARES IN
BUDD, H.
  BISMILLAHI 'RRAHMANI 'RR
  BISMILLAHI 'RRAHMANI 'RR
  III FOR DOUBLE ENSEMBLE
BUECHE, G.
  FUGUE
  FUGUE
BUEL, C.
  4 3-PART CANONS (1978)
BUGGY, B.
  TRIO
BUHE, K.
  EUROPAISCHE VOLKS-UND TA
  EUROPAISCHE VOLKS-UND TA
  VOLKS-UND TANZWEISEN AUS
BUICLIU, N.
  QUINTET
BUJARSKI, Z.
  CHAMBER PIECE (1963)
BULL
  4 ELIZABETHAN PIECES
BULL, E.
  AD USUM AMICORUM
  3 BUCOLIQUES
BULL, J.
  FANTASIA
  PRELUDIO E CANZONE
BULLERIAN, H.
  SEXTET, OP 38
BULLING, B.
  SUITE, OP 30
BUMCKE, G.
  38 DUOS (OP 43)
BUNGE, S.
  DUO (1966)
  SPEELDOOS, DE (1971)
BUOT
  CHANSON DES NIDS, LA
BURGE, D.
  AEOLIAN MUSIC
BURGHARDT, H.
  PARTITA BREVIS II
BURGHAUSER, J.
  POSSIBILITA
BURGON, G.
  CANTATA ON MEDIAEVAL LAT
  GLORIA (1973)
BURGSTAHLER, E.
  DUETS FOR CLARINETS
  LET'S PLAY QUARTETS
  13 SAXOPHONE QUARTETS
BURIAN, E.
  QUINTET (1933)
BURKHARD, W.
  CANZONA, OP 76A (1947)
  LYRISCHE MUSIK, OP 88
  SERENADE (1953)
  SERENADE, OP 71/3 (1944)
BURKHART, F.
  3 ADVENTLIEDER
  VON GUTER ART

340

BURT, G.
  EXIT MUSIC
BURTON
  ALLEGRETTO
BUSCH, A.
  HAUSMUSIK, OP 26/1
  HAUSMUSIK, OP 26/2
  HAUSMUSIK, OP 26/3
BUSCH, C.
  CONTENTMENT
  EVENING PROMENADE
  FROLIC
  IN PLAYFUL MOOD
  JOYFULNESS
  OZARK REVERIE, AN
  QUIETUDE
  SOLITUDE
BUSCHMANN, R.
  EINFACH FUR DREI
  MINIATURES FUR ZWILLINGE
BUSH, G.
  QUINTET
  TRIO
BUSONI, F.
  BERCEUSE ELEGIAQUE
BUSSER, H.
  NOCTURNE
BUTTERFIELD, N.
  WHEN YOU & I WERE YOUNG
BUTTERWORTH, A.
  3 DIALOGUES
BUTTERWORTH, N.
  3 DIALOGUES
  3 DIALOGUES
  3 DIALOGUES
  3 MOZART MOVEMENTS
  THEME & VARIATIONS
  THREE TIMES THREE
  TUDOR SUITE
BUTTING, M.
  FESTSCHRIFT FOR BACH, OP
  HAUSMUSIK, OP119
  HAUSMUSIK, OP119
  4 SATZE
  SPIEL, EIN, OP 30
BUTTS, C.
  DESERT DANCES
  MODERATO & ALLEGRO
  MODERATO & SCHERZO
  QUARTET
  SONG
  TRIO
  TRIO
BUXTEHUDE, D.
  FUGUE
  SONATA IN F MA
  SONATA IN G MA
BYRD, W.
  PAVANA
BYRNE, A.
  INTRODUCTION, BLUES & FI
  INTRODUCTION, BLUES & FI

  INTRODUCTION, BLUES & FI
CABLE, H.
  WIND SONG
CABUS, P.
  CLARINET QUARTET
  HOUTBLAZERSKWARTET
  QUARTET
  QUINTET
  RAPSODIE
  SONATE
  SONATE
  TREDECIM
CACAVAS, J.
  BARCAROLLE
  CLARINETS 3
  FLUTES 3
  IMPRESSIONS
  2 MINIATURES
  30 PLUS-CLARINET TRIOS
  30 PLUS-FLUTE TRIOS
  ROMANTICA
  SHIMMERING FLUTES
  WINDETTE
CADOW, P.
  ELEGIE UND RONDO
  KLEINE SUITE
  PASTORALE IM ALTEN STIL
  VARIATIONS UBER EIN NORW
  VARIATIONS UBER EINE SCH
CAGAN, S.
  DIVERTISSEMENT- SUITE FO
CAGE, J.
  16 DANCES (1951)
  MUSIC FOR WIND INSTRUMEN
  3 PIECES(1935)
  6 SHORT INVENTIONS
CAHUZAC, L.
  SONATE CLASSIQUE #1
  SONATE CLASSIQUE #2 (AFT
CAILLIET, L.
  CAPRICE SENTIMENTAL
  CARNAVAL
  CARNAVAL
  CLARINET POEM
  CONCERTINO
  DIVERTISSEMENT
  FANTAISIE
  FANTASY & FUGUE ON O'SUS
  QUARTET ALBUM
  QUARTET FOR SAXOPHONES
  YOUTHFUL ADVENTURE
CAIX D,HERVELOIS, L. DE
  MARCHE DU CZAR, LA
CALABRESE, T.
  BRASIL
CALABRO, L.
  DIVERTIMENTO
  5 DUOS
CALAFATO, S.
  GUERRA A LA GUERRA POR L
CALATAYUD, B.
  DIVERTIMENTOS

CALDARA, A.
  DAS DO-RE-MI. 28 KANONS
  GRAVE
  QUELL' USIGNUOLO
CALIFANO, A.
  SONATA A TRE IN G MA
  SONATA A TRE IN G MA
CALL, L. DE
  NOTTURNO, OP 85
  NOTTURNO, OP 89
  NOTTURNO, OP 93
  SERENADE, OP 75
  TRIO, OP 31
  TRIO, OP134
  TRIO, OP134
  VARIAZIONI
CALLHOFF, H.
  BLASERQUINTETT (1967-69)
  BLASERQUINTETT (1972)
  5 EPISODES (1970/71)
  MOVIMENTI (1973)
CALMEL
  CLAIR MATIN-PASTORALE
  PETITE MARCHE-CHANSON D'
CALMEL, R.
  QUATUOR
CAMARA, J.
  SUITE
CAMBERT, R.
  OVERTURE, AN
CAMBINI, G.
  DUO, OP 11/4 (E MI)
  DUO, OP 11/5 (A MA)
  DUO, OP 11/6 (G MA)
  QUINTET #1
  QUINTET #2 IN D MI
  QUINTET #3
  6 QUINTETTI, OP 8, 9
  TRIO #5 IN F MA; TRIO #6
  TRIO IN F MA
  TRIO, OP 3/6
  TRIO, OP 45/6
  3 TRIOS, OP 26/1-3
  2 TRIOS, OP 45
CAMERON, R.
  KYRIE (MANTRA)
CAMMAROTA
  INTRODUCTION, CHROMATIC
CAMMAROTA, P.
  ARIOSO & FUGUE
CAMPAGNOLI, B.
  DUET IN D MA
CAMPBELL
  RAGGED DIVERSION #2
CAMPO, F.
  CONCERTINO, OP 32
  5 PIECES, OP 18
  PRELUDES, OP 51
  TRES CUBITO
  VIAGGI, OP 56
CAMPOLIETI, L.
  TRIO IN D MI

CAMPRA, A.
  MENUET VIF & GIGUE
CANINO, B.
  CADENZE (1962)
  CADENZE (1962)
  CANTATA #2
  FORTIS
  IMPROMPTU #1 (1969)
CANNABICH, C.
  6 DUETS, 2 VOLS
  QUARTET IN B FL MA
  QUARTET IN G MA
CANO, F.
  DIFERENCIAS AGOGICAS
  MUSICA A SEIS (1976)
  PAJARO DE COBRE, EL
CANTELOUBE, J.
  RUSTIQUES
CAPDEVIELLE, P.
  AMOURS DE PIERRE DE RONS
  CHANT D'ALPHESIBEE, LE
  SONATINA PASTORALE
CAPLET, A.
  ECOUTE, MON COEUR!
  VIENS! UNE FLUTE INVISIB
CARAVAN, R.
  CANZONA
  LAMENT FOR AN UNKNOWN IN
  3 MODAL DANCES
CARCASIO
  SONATA
CARDEW, P.
  WHIRLWIND POLKA
CARDON, J.
  3 DUO CONCERTANS
CARDY, P.
  GOLDEN DAYS, SILVER NIGH
CAREY
  FLUTE DUET ALBUM
CARION, F.
  BAGATELLES, OP 19
  FANTAISIE CONCERTANTE
  LIED
  PETITE PIECE
CARLE
  ENCHANTMENT
CARLE¬WHEELER
  ENCHANTMENT,
CARLES, M.
  5 ETUDES CONCERTANTES
  PRELUDE & DANCE
CARLS
  CELEBRATION
CARLSTEDT, J.
  DIVERTIMENTO, OP 17
  KVINTETT, OP 19 (1962)
  PENTASTOMOS, OP 27 (1972
  SINFONIETTA (1959)
CARLUCCIO, F.
  MON MANDARIN (1973-74)
CARMAN
  PETIT RONDO

CARMEL, D.
  FRACTIONS
  TERZETTINO
CARMICHAEL, H.
  STAR DUST
  STAR DUST
CAROL-KLAUSE, G.
  WAKE, NIGHTINGALE, AWAKE
CAROLO
  SONATA #1 IN B FL MA
CAROSO, F.
  BALLETTO
CARRENO, I.
  QUINTETO
CARRIERE, G.
  AIR MEDIEVAL
CARRILLO, J.
  PRELUDIO A COLON
CARROLL, B.
  ARGUMENT
  VELOCITY
CARTAN, J.
  SONATINE
CARTER, A.
  SIX PIECES (1980)
CARTER, E.
  CANON IN MEMORIAM IGOR S
  CANONIC SUITE
  8 ETUDES & A FANTASY
  SONATA (1952)
  WOODWIND QUINTET (1948)
CARULLI, B.
  TRIO IN C MA, OP 1
CARULLI, F.
  CONCERTO
  FANTASIA, OP337
  NOCTURNE, OP190
  NOTTURNO IN A MI
  NOTTURNO IN C MA
  SERENADE, OP109/1
  SERENADE, OP109/6
  5 SERENADES
  TRE GRAN TRIO
  3 TRIOS, OP 9
CASADESUS, R.
  SEXTUOR, OP 58
CASAGRANDE, A.
  FRASI
CASANOVA, A.
  DIVERTIMENTO
  DUE CANZONI, OP 49
  DUE CANZONI, OP 49
  SERENATA
  SERENATA
CASELLA, A.
  SERENATA
  SINFONIA (1932), OP 54
CASSEDAY, A.
  QUARTET IN G MI
CASTALDI, P.
  CLAUSOLA (1961/68)
CASTEEL & MC CATHREN

LONDONDERRY AIR
CASTELLO
  QUARTA SONATA A DUE
CASTELLO, D.
  SONATAS NOS. 3 & 4
  SONATAS 3 & 4
CASTELNUOVO-TEDESCO, M.
  DIVERTIMENTO
  ECLOGHE
  SONATINA, OP205 (1965)
CASTERA, R. DE
  CONCERT
CASTEREDE, J.
  FLUTES EN VACANCES
  MUSIC FOR THE OBOE FAMIL
  QUINTET
CASTET, F.
  4 PIECES (FITZWILLIAM VI
CASTIGLIONI, N.
  TROPI
CASTIL-BLAZE, F.
  SEXTET #1 IN E FL MA
CASTLE, A.
  FLUTOCYCLE
  SUMMER SKETCHES
CASTRO, C. DE
  PAN (1974)
  PENTE (1970)
  TUCUMBALAM (1973)
  10 + 1 (1975)
CATURLA, A.
  BEMBE
CAURROY, E.D.
  DOUBLE CANON
CAUSSINUS, V.
  6 CONCERT DUOS, OP 14
CAVALLINI, E.
  3 GRAND ARTISTIC DUETS
  2 GRAND DUETS
CAVALLY, R.
  FLUTE FAMILY SKETCH
  8 MADRIGALS
CAZDEN, N.
  3 CONSTRUCTIONS, OP 38
  10 CONVERSATIONS, OP 34
  6 DEFINITIONS
  FORMATION #4 (6 DISCUSSI
  INSISTENCE, OP 40/2
  ROUND DANCE #6, OP 40
  TRIO #2, OP 40
  WALTZ, OP 40/1
CECCONI, M.
  AUBADE- DANSE
  JEUX
  SILENCES
CEELY, R.
  MODULES
  MUSIC FOR 10 INSTRUMENTS
  RITUALS
  SPECULATION
CELLIER, A.
  IMAGES MEDIEVALES

343

344

CANON
CANON
FUGUE IN G MA
2 FUGUES
MARCIA IN F MA
CHEVREUILLE, R.
DIVERTISSEMENT, OP 21
MUSIQUE DE SALON, OP 49
MUSIQUE LILLIPUTIENNE, O
SERENADE, OP 65 (1956)
TRIO, OP 90 (1968)
CHEYETTE & ROBERTS
FOUR-TONE FOLIO, 3 VOL
CHEYETTE, I.
VIENNESE LULLABY
CHIARAMELLO, G.
CONCERTO DA CAMERA (1962
CHIEREGHIN, S.
4 TEMPI
CHIHARA, P.
BRANCHES
CEREMONY I
CEREMONY II ("INCANTATIO
WILLOW, WILLOW
CHILDS, B.
BARNARD II
CHANGES
DAY SEQUENCE, THE: 2
DUO
7 EPIGRAMS (1955)
HORN & OBOE MUSIC
INTERBALANCES I
INTERBALANCES V
JACK'S NEW BAG
LOCATION OF MUSIC,THE
MUSIC FOR...
MUSIC
MUSIC; THAT IT MIGHT BE.
3 PLAYERS I
QUARTET
TAKE 5
WIND QUINTET #1 (1962)
WIND QUINTET #2
WIND QUINTET #3
WIND QUINTET #4
WIND QUINTET #5
WIND QUINTET
CHINI, A.
3 CRIS POUR 4 (1974)
CHON
DOUBLE TOOTIN' FLUTES
CHOPIN, F.
CHOPIN FAVORITES
MINUTE WALTZ
NOCTURNE, OP POSTH.
NOCTURNE, OP 15/3
POLONAISE MILITAIRE
PRELUDE IN B FLAT MA
PRELUDE IN E MI
PRELUDE
PRELUDE, OP 28/14
PRELUDES, OP 28/7, 20

PRELUDES, OP 28/7,20
CHOU WEN¬CHUNG
YU KO
CHOU, WEN¬CHUNG
3 FOLK SONGS
2 MINIATURES FROM T'ANG
2 MINIATURES FROM T'ANG
SUITE
YUN
CHOWMAN, H.
EEN GOED LYEDEKEN (1953)
CHRISTENSEN, J.
COMEDY FOR SAXOPHONES
FIVE FOR THE FUN OF IT
HEY RIDE!
HOLIDAY ON ICE
ROMANCE IN B FL MA
SONGS OF AMERICA
CHRISTIANSEN, A.
TRIO
CHRISTIANSEN, C.
TOY BOX, THE
CHRISTLIEB, D.
3 PIECES
3 PIECES
4 PIECES
CHRISTOPHE
GRAND DUO
CHRISTOV, D.
CONCERTO
CONCERTO
QUARTET (1973)
CHUGUNOV, Y.
12 STUDIES
CIGLIC, Z.
ABSURDI
CILENSEK, J.
SONATA
SONATE (1950)
CIMA¬GREBE
SONATA #3 IN A MA
3 SONATAS (1610)
CIMA, G.
SONATA A TRE
CIMAROSA, D.
CONCERTANTE
CONCERTO IN G MA
CONCERTO IN G MA
GLORIA PATRI
QUARTET #1 IN D MA
QUARTET #2 IN F MA
QUARTET #3 IN A MI
QUONIAM TU SOLUS SANCTUS
CIORTEA, T.
DIN "ISPRAVILE LUI PACAL
CIPCI, K.
MINIATURE
CIRRI, G.
ARIOSO
CIRRI, M.
ARIOSO
CIUCIURA, L.

MUSICA (1976)
CLAFLIN, A.
  PASTORAL- THE ORIOLE
CLAPP, P.
  PRELUDE, VARIATION & FUGUE
CLARK
  SEICENTO
CLARKE, H.
  CONCATENATA; QUODLIBET
  GAME THAT 2 CAN PLAY, A
  LIFE IN GHANA
  LORD IS MY SHEPHERD, THE
  MERCY, PITY, PEACE, & LO
  QUALITY OF MERCY, THE
  RONDEAU REDOUBLE
  SARABAND FOR THE GOLDEN
  SONG TO A YOUNG PIANIST
  WOMAN OF VIRTUE, A
CLARKE, J.
  AIR
CLARKE, M.
  SOLO SUITE
CLARKE, R.
  HAPPENINGS
  SCHERZANDO
CLASSENS, H.
  DANZA SCHERZETTINO
CLEBER
  RICKSHAW RIDE
CLEEMPUT, W. VAN
  5 BAGATELLEN
CLEMENTI
  TRIO
CLEMENTI, A.
  CONCERTINO IN FORMA DI V
  CONCERTO (1970)
  INTERMEZZO
  3 PICCOLI PEZZI (1955)
  SILBEN (1966)
  TRIPLUM (1960)
CLEMENTI, M.
  CANON
  CANON
  NONETTO IN E FL MA
  SONATINA, OP 36/3
  TRIO IN D MA, OP 22/1
CLERAMBAULT, L.
  ORPHEUS
CLERGUE, J.
  MELODIE- EN BALANCELLE
  PRIMAVERA-VOLUTE
CLERISSE, R.
  CACHE-CACHE
  CARAVAN
  CHANSON DU ROUET
  INTRODUCTION & SCHERZO
  POLKA VALAISANE
  RECUEIL DE QUATUORS CLAS
  SERENADE MELANCOLIQUE
  VIELLE CHANSON
CLIQUET
  CHANT D'ESPERANCE
CLODOMIR, P.

12 DUOS
12 DUOS
12 DUOS
12 DUOS
CLOSTRE, A.
  CONCERTO
COCKELL, R.
  SUITE
COCKSHOTT, G.
  VARIATIONS ON A PASSEPIE
COHEN, E.
  MADRIGAL (1967)
COHEN, S.
  ALABAMA SKETCHES
  DIVERTIMENTO
  FOREST LULLABY (SUITE)
  HAUNTED HOUSE
  MADRIGAL
  MADRIGALE
  MARCH-MILITAIRE (SUITE)
  MARCH-MINIATURE
  MINUET-FANTASY (SUITE)
COKER, W.
  CONCERTINO
  QUINTET IN 3 MOVEMENTS
COLACO OSORIO
  SUITE (1940)
  WIJZANG, (1937)
COLACO OSORIO¬SWAAB, R.
  KWARTET #1 (1952)
  SUITE (1948)
  TRIO #4 (1956)
COLBY
  THREE BLIND MICE
COLE, B.
  CAESURA
  FENESTRAE SANCTAE
  PANTOMIMES
  SPRAY OF DEAD ARROWS
COLE, H.
  SERENADE
COLERIDGE¬TAYLOR, S.
  QUINTET
COLF, D.
  3 PIECES
COLGRASS, M.
  LIGHT SPIRIT
  LIGHT SPIRIT
  WOODWIND QUINTET
COLIN, G.
  QUATUOR
COMES, L.
  DIVERTISMENT (1970)
CONCONE, G.
  5 DUETS
CONE, E.
  STANZAS
CONKLIN
  HANDY ANDY
CONLEY, L.
  CHRISTMAS CAROL, A
  DIALOGUE
  DIVERSION #1

346

349

A LINEAR CEREMONY
NOETICAL ROUNDS
PASTEL DESIGNS
PASTEL DESIGNS
PHASES
SERENADE
SONATINA
SPRING SONNET
TRIO #3, OP 59
TRIPLE SONATA
CUOMO, J.
FOR ZEBULON PIKE & HENRY
CURRAN, A.
HOME-MADE
CURTIS-SMITH, C.
ENSEMBLES/SOLOS (1977)
ENSEMBLES/SOLOS (1977)
ENSEMBLES/SOLOS (1977)
CUSTER, A.
FOUND OBJECTS #6
2 MOVEMENTS
PASTORALE & HORNPIPE
PERMUTATIONS
CYTRON, W.
DANCES FOR TWO TREBLES
CZERNY, C.
SERENADE IN E FL MA
CZYZEWSKI, H.
QUINTET
D'AUVERGNE, B.
PLAINS OF PEACE
D'HARCOURT & BENNETT
PERUVIAN INCA MELODIES
D'HOIR, J.
VARIATIES OP "EEN KIND I
DA-OZ, R.
10 MINIATUREN
DADAK, J.
PARTITA (1967)
DAESON, D.
ENTROPY
DAHL, I.
ALLEGRO & ARIOSO (1942)
CONCERTO A TRE
5 DUETS (1970)
DUETTINO CONCERTANTE
SERENADE (1960)
SERENADE
VARIATIONS ON A SWEDISH
DAHM, P.
CONCERT ALBUM
CONCERT ALBUM
PARADE OF THE SCOUTS
PARIS SOIR
DAKIN, C.
PRELUDE & DANCE (1956)
DALLAPICCOLA, L.
6 CARMINA ALCAEI (1943)
DIVERTIMENTO IN QUATTRO
GOETHE LIEDER (1953)
SICUT UMBRA
DALLIN, L.

AUBADE IN BLUE
AUTUMN VIGNETTE
FOUNTAINS AT DAWN
DALLINGER, F.
CONCERTINO
QUINTET
SONATINE
SUITE #1
DAMASE, J.
DOUBLE CONCERTO
NOCTURNE
QUARTET
QUINTET
RITOURNELLES
SONATE FOR CONCERT
SONATE
TRIO
TRIO
17 VARIATIONS, OP 22
DAME, E.
CONTES DE GRAND-MERE
DANCLA, C.
TUNEFUL TRIO
DANDELOT, G.
QUINTETTE
DANDRIEU, J.
FIFRES, LES
TOURBILLONS, LES
TOURBILLONS, LES
DANFELT, D.
DIVERTIMENTO
DANIELS, M.
3 OBSERVATIONS, OP 41
DANKS, H.
SILVER THREADS AMONG THE
DANSBY, E.
DANDY DUO
DANDY DUO
DANDY DUO
DANZI, F.
ALLEGRETTO (OP 56/2)
BLASERQUINTETT IN F MA,
BLASERQUINTETT IN G MA,
3 DUETS, OP 64
GYPSY DANCE
QUARTET IN B FL MA, OP 4
QUARTET IN B FL MA, OP 4
QUARTET IN D MA, OP 56/1
QUARTET IN D MI, OP 56/2
QUARTET, OP 40/1
3 QUARTETS, OP 40
QUINTET IN B FL MA, OP 5
QUINTET IN B FL MA, OP 5
QUINTET IN D MI, OP 41
QUINTET IN D MI, OP 68/3
QUINTET IN E MI, OP 67/2
QUINTET IN F MA, OP 56/3
QUINTET IN G MI, OP 56/2
QUINTET, OP 41
QUINTET, OP 53/1 IN F MA
QUINTET, OP 54/2 IN D MA
QUINTET, OP 67/2, IN E M

350

QUINTET, OP 67/3, IN E F
QUINTET, OP 68/1, IN A M
QUINTET, OP 68/2
SEXTET IN E FL MA
SINFONIA CONCERTANTE IN
TRIO #1, OP 71
TRIO #2, OP 71
TRIO IN D MA, OP 71/3
TRIO IN E MI, OP 71/2
TRIO, OP 24
TRIO, OP 71/1
TRIO, OP 71/2 IN E MI
TRIO, OP 71/3 IN D MA
2 TRIOS, OP 71/7, 2
2 TRIOS, OP 71
DAO NGUYEN THIEN
 TUYEN LUA (1968)
 TUYEN LUA (1968)
DAQUIN, L.
 COUCOU, LE
DARMSTADT, H.
 TRIO (1973)
DARNLEY, C.
 8 EASY PIECES
DASHOW, J.
 MAXIMUS, TO HIMSELF
DAUBE, J.
 TRIO IN D MI
DAUS, A.
 SONGS OF RACHEL
DAUTREMER, M.
 DUO-CONCERTINO
DAVENPORT, L.
 3 DUETS
 3 DUETS
 3 DUETS
DAVID, F.
 CHARMANT OISEAU
 THOU BRILLIANT BIRD
DAVID, G.
 QUINTET #1 (1949)
 QUINTET #3 (1964)
 QUINTET #4
 ROSE IS FLAMING, THE
 SERENADE
DAVID, J.
 FROHLICH WIR NUN ALL FAN
 KUME, KUMGESELLE MIN, OP
 SONATE, OP 26A (1940)
 SONATE, OP 32/1
 SONATE, OP 32/4
 TRIO, OP 30
 TRIO, OP 73
 VARIATIONEN, OP 32/2
DAVID, T.
 BLASERQUINTETT (1966)
 FLUTE QUARTET, OP 11
 KONZERT (1961)
 QUINTET
 SONATINE (1958)
 TRIO, OP 1/1
 TRIO, OP 8

DAVIDOVSKY, M.
 INFLEXIONS
 JUNCTURES
 NONETO
 SYNCHRONISMS #1
 SYNCHRONISMS #2 (1964)
DAVIDSON, J.
 TWO INVENTION
 ROW #1
DAVIES, P.
 ALL SONS OF ADAM
 ALL SONS OF ADAM
 ALMA REDEMPTORIS MATER
 ANTECHRIST
 AVE MARIS STELLA
 AVE MARIS STELLA
 BLIND FIDDLER, THE
 CANON IN MEMORY OF IGOR
 ERAM QUASI AGNUS
 ERAM QUASI AGNUS
 FIDDLERS AT THE WEDDING
 FROM STONE TO THORN
 FROM STONE TO THORN
 HYMN TO SAINT MAGNUS
 MISS DONNITHORNE'S MAGGO
 POINTS & DANCES FROM TAV
 POINTS & DANCES FROM TAV
 PSALM 124
 PSALM 124
 RENAISSANCE SCOTTISH DAN
 RENAISSANCE SCOTTISH DAN
 RICERCAR & DOUBLES
 SI QUIS DILIGIT ME
 8 SONGS FOR A MAD KING
 STEDMAN CATERS
 TENEBRAE SUPER GESUALDO
 VESALII ICONES
DAVIS
 OLD KING COLE VARIATIONS
DAVIS, D.
 PREFACE & FUGUE
 TRIO
DAVIS, S.
 3 POEMS OF WILLIAM BLAKE
 THOUGH MEN CALL US FREE
 WILDFLOWER SUITE
DAVIS, V.
 SPINNING WHEEL, THE
DAVIS, W.
 QUINTET
DAVISON, J.
 CANZONA & CHORALE (1965)
 CANZONA & CHORALE (1965)
 SUITE (1954)
DAWE, M.
 SEASONS, THE
DE BERADINIS, J.
 INTERLUDE
 4 MINIATURES
 3 MOMENTS
 SONG CYCLE
DE BUERIS, J.

GAVOTTE CAPRICE
DE COURSEY, R.
  WIND ENCORES
DE ELIAS
  4 UBERLIEFERTE MEXIKANIS
DE FILIPPI, A.
  AXIOMS
  HORNPIPE FOR A GAY DOLPH
  IN A NOSTALGIC MOOD
  MARCH OF THE LITTLE TUMB
DE JESU, J.
  AVE VERUM CORPUS
  MENUETTO
DE JONG, C.
  HIST WIST
DE JONG, M.
  SUITE, OP127
DE LAMATER, E.
  ADESTE FIDELIS
  ADESTE FIDELIS
DE LASSUS, O.
  DOMINE CONVERTERE
  SOYONS JOYEUS
DE LULLI
  CHOPSTICKS
  CHOPSTICKS
DE MEYER, C.
  MELODIE
DE ROYE, E.
  TRIO
DE SCHRIJVER, K.
  SUITE A 3
DE VILLE, P.
  SWISS BOY, THE
  SWISS BOY, THE
DE YOUNG, L.
  CHAMBER MUSIC
  HOMAGE TO DIXIELAND
  TEXTURE
DEAK, C.
  DUO SUITE
  KVINTETT (1965)
  UNGERSKA DANSER (1977)
DEARNLEY, C.
  MORE EASY PIECES
DEASON, D.
  POLARITY
  QUARTET
DEBRAS, L.
  ROTATIONEN (1967)
DEBUSSY, C.
  ANDANTINO & VIF
  ARABESQUE #1
  ARABESQUE #2
  1ST ARABESQUE
  ARABESQUES #1 & #2
  BALLET (PETITE SUITE)
  BILITIS
  CLAIR DE LUNE
  CLAIR DE LUNE
  CORTEGE (PETITE SUITE)
  DANSE

DEBUSSY SUITE #2
DEBUSSY SUITE #3
DEBUSSY SUITE, A
EN BATEAU (PETITE SUITE)
GIRL WITH THE FLAXEN HAI
IL PLEURE DANS MON COEUR
IL PLEURE DANS MON COEUR
LITTLE NEGRO, THE
LITTLE NEGRO, THE
LITTLE SHEPHERD, THE/GOL
MANDOLINE
MANDOLINE
MANDOLINE
MAZURKA
MINUET (PETITE SUITE)
NOCTURNE
NUAGES
PETIT NEGRE, LE
REVERIE
SARABANDE
SONATE
DEBUSSY, C,
  CHANSONS DE BILITIS, LES
DECADT, J.
  TRIO
DECSENYI, J.
  COLLOIDES
DEDRICK, A.
  WALTZ FOR FOUR
DEDRICK, C.
  SENSITIVITY
  SENSITIVITY
DEDRICK, R.
  GENTLE WINDS
  IMPRESSIONISM (THE MODER
  MY BABY'S SMILE
  MYSTICISM (THE MODERN AR
  PURISM & SURREALISM (THE
  REALISM (THE MODERN ART
  SAXSAFARI
DEEMER, C.
  TEN LITTLE INDIANS
  TEPEE
DEFOSSEZ, R.
  DUO
  TRIO (1946)
DEGEN, H.
  SONATA
DEJESU, J.
  LARGO APPASSIONATA
  PRELUDE TO "TRAVIATA"
  TO A WILD ROSE
DEKKER, D.
  LITTLE JOHN'S MORNING AF
  ZERO DYNAMIQUE (1972)
DEL BORGO, E.
  DODECAPHONIC ESSAY
DEL TREDICI, D.
  NIGHT CONJURE-VERSE
DELA, M.
  DIVERTIMENTO (1972)
  PETITE SUITE MARITIME

POLONAISE #1
SPANISH WALTZ
SPANISH WALTZ,
SUMMERTIME
SUMMERTIME,
DEXTER, H.
AU CLAIR DE LA LUNE
AU CLAIR DE LA LUNE
AU CLAIR DE LA LUNE
COUNTRY DIALOGUES
COUNTRY DIALOGUES
COUNTRY DIALOGUES
DI CAPUA, E.
O SOLE MIO (MY SUNSHINE)
O SOLE MIO (MY SUNSHINE)
O SOLE MIO (MY SUNSHINE)
DI DOMENICA, R.
QUARTET
QUARTET
QUINTET
SEXTET
SONATA AFTER ESSAYS (197
DI LASSO, O.
ECHO SONG
MATONA, LOVELY MAIDEN
DIABELLI/SCHUBERT
TANZE
DIABELLI, A.
DUO IN A MA
DUO IN D
3 PIECES
POTPOURRI FROM BEETHOVEN
SERENADE, OP 99
TRIO
DIAMOND, A.
TRIO
DIAMOND, D.
MAD MAID'S SONG, THE
PARTITA
QUINTET (1957)
QUINTET
QUINTET
DIAS, J.
MEU BEM
DIEMENTE, E.
DIARY (PART II- 1972)
DIMENSIONS #3
FOR LADY DAY
MIRRORS #5
3 PIECES
QUARTET (1966)
QUARTET (1967)
TRIO (1969)
VARIATIONS
DIEMER, E.
MOVEMENT
MUSIC FOR WOODWIND QUART
DIEPENBROCK, A.
COME RAGGIO DI SOL (1917
WENN ICH IHN NUR HABE (1
DIEPPO
VIRTUOSO STUDIES

DIERCKS, J.
WIND QUINTET (1955)
DIETERICH, M.
CHANSON JOYEUSE
CHANSON TRISTE
DIETHELM, C.
DUET, OP124
SEPTET, OP110
SERENATA NOTTURNA, OP119
DIETTER, C.
SONATA VI
10 STUCKE
DIJK, J. VAN
CANZON ALL CAPRICCIO (19
CHORALES
DIVERTIMENTO (1941)
DUO (1952)
HET MASKER VAN DEN ROODE
6 LIEDEREN (1952)
5 LIEDEREN (1954)
PASTORALE (1938)
SEPTET (1950)
SUITE (1956)
DILLON, B.
FLAUTISSIMO
DILLON, H.
NIGHTSHADE
DILLON, R.
ALLEGRETTO FESTOSO
JUNANBE
4 QUARTETS
SONG
DIMOV, B.
COMPOSITION III (1968)
INCANTATIONES I (1963)
INCANTATIONES II (1967)
RAUMSPIEL (1969/70)
DINERSTEIN, N.
SERENADE (1963)
DIONISI, R.
2 CANTI SACRI
DIVERTIMENTO
2 PEZZI
PICCOLE COMPOSIZIONI
DISPA, R.
ODE TO THE CHILD (1976)
DITTERS, K.
3 PARTIEN (FMA,AMA,DMA)
DITTERSDORF, C.
CASSATION IN D MA
DITTERSDORF, K.
DIVERTIMENTO
NOTTURNO
DITTERSDORF, K. VON
ANDANTE (QUARTET IN B FL
DITTRICH, P.
ACTION-REACTION (1976)
CONCERT AVEC PLUSIEURS I
KAMMERMUSIK III
QUA-SIE (1971)
DJAMBAZIAN, A.
QUINTET #2, OP 13

DJEMIL
  PETITE SUITE MEDIEVALE
DOBIAS, V.
  O RODNE ZEMI (1952)
  QUINTETTO PASTORALE
  WOODWIND QUINTET (1934)
DOBOS, K.
  INNERE BEWEGUNGEN
DOBROWOLSKI, A.
  KRABOGAPA (1969)
  MUSICA
  8 STUDIES
  TRIO (1956)
DOBRY
  ALLEGRO GIOCOSO
DOBRZYNSKI, I.
  DUET
  DUO IN E FL MA
  DUO
DODGE, C.
  FOLIA (1964)
  SOLOS & COMBINATIONS (19
DODGSON, S.
  CADILLY (REYNOLDS)
  DUO
  OLD CIGARETTE LIGHTER, T
  SUITE
  TRIO
  3 WINGET SONGS
DOFLEIN
  BICINIEN.20 FANTASIES
DOHL, F.
  EPITAPH "TICH YUANG TUC"
  FRAGMENT "SYBILLE" (1963
  7 HAIKU (1963)
  KLANGFIGUREN (1962)
  OKTETT (VARIANTI) (1961)
  SOTTO VOCE (1973)
  SZENE UBER EINEN KLEINEN
  TOCCATA (1962-63)
DOHNANYI, E.
  SEXTET IN C MA, OP 37
DOLIN, S.
  SONATA #2 (1973)
DOMAZLICKY, F.
  BLASERQUINTETT I (1956)
  3 DUETS, OP 3 (1953)
  KAMMERMUSIK (1966)
  POLNI KVITI (1962)
  TRIO (1953)
  WOODWIND QUINTET #2
DOMENICO, O. DI
  QUINTETTO
DONAHUE, R.
  5 CANONIC DUETS
  TRIO
DONATELLI, V.
  DUET #1
  DUET #2
DONATO, A.
  DRAG & RUN
  PASTORALE & DANCE

3 PIECES
QUINTET
DONATONI, F.
  ASH (1976)
  ETWAS RUHIGER IM AUSDRUC
  FOR GRILLY (1960)
  LIED (1972)
  LIED (1972)
  LUMEN (1975)
  MOVIMENTO (1959)
  QUARTO ESTRATTO
  QUARTO ESTRATTO
  QUARTO ESTRATTO
  TERZO ESTRATTO (1975)
DONDEYNE
  POUR SE DISTRAIRE
  POUR SE DIVERTIR
DONDEYNE, D.
  SUITE D'AIRS POPULAIRES
DONIZETTI, G.
  FURTIVA LAGRIMA, UNA
  LUCIA DI LAMMERMOOR
  MAD SCENE (LUCIA DI LAMM
  MAD SCENE, THE (LUCIA DI
  SEXTET (LUCIA DI LAMMERM
  SEXTET (LUCIA)
  SEXTET (LUCIA)
  SEXTET (LUCIA)
  SEXTETTE (LUCIA DI LAMME
  SEXTETTE (LUCIA DI LAMME
  SINFONIA FOR WINDS
  SINFONIA
  SONATA
  SONATE
  TRIO IN F MA
DONOVAN, R.
  FANTASIA
  MUSIC FOR 6
  QUARTET
  RICERCARE
  SERENADE
  SOUNDINGS
DONT, J.
  LARGHETTO & SCHERZO
DOPPELBAUER, J.
  BLASERQUINTETT (1970)
  DIVERTIMENTO (LEOBNER TR
  DIVERTIMENTO (1967)
  3 GESANGE (1949)
  7 LITTLE DUETS
  MINIATURES
  QUARTET
  TRIO (1962)
  TRIO (1965)
  TRIO (1967)
  TRIO #1 (1963)
  TRIO I
DOPPLER, F.
  ANDANTE & RONDO
  ANDANTE & RONDO, OP 25
  BIRD OF THE FOREST, THE
  CONCERTO IN D MI

DUETTINO HONGROIS, OP 36
HUNGARIAN PHANTASY, OP 3
NOCTURNE, OP 19
SOUVENIR DU RIGI, IDYLLE
SOUVENIR DU RIGI, IDYLLE
VALSE DI BRAVURA
VALSE DI BRAVURA, OP 33
DOPPLER, F. & K.
  RIGOLETTO-FANTAISIE, OP
  SOUVENIR DE PRAGUE, OP 2
DORADO
  2 FRIENDS
DORAN, M.
  ANDANTE & ALLEGRO
  QUARTET
  SONATINA
  SONATINA
  SUITE
  TRIO
DORFF, D.
  FANTASY, SCHERZO & NOCTU
DORMOLEN, J.
  OUT-OF-DATE APPARATUS
DORN, K.
  PAVAN
  SI DORMIERO
  TART ARA
DORNEL, L.
  SUITE IN D MI
DOTZAUER, J.
  QUARTET, OP 36
DOUGLAS, R.
  DANCE CARICATURES (1939)
DOWLAND, J.
  MY LORD CHAMBERLAIN: HIS
DOWNEY, J.
  AGORT
DRAGAN, R.
  AUS DER JUGEND
DRAPER, P.
  GUITAR/FLUTE DUETS
DRDLA, R.
  SOUVENIR
DREIFUS, G.
  SEASONS, THE
DREJSL, R.
  BLASERQUINTETT (1948)
DRESDEN, S.
  KLEIN TRIO (1912)
  KLEIN TRIO, (1921)
  KLEINE SUITE IN C MA
  SONATA
  SUITE #3 (1920)
  SUITE NAAR RAMEAU (1916)
  4 VOCALISES (1935)
DRESSEL, E.
  CONCERTO
  TRIO MINIATURE
DRESSLER, R.
  3 DUOS, OP 46/1-3, IN C
  MINIATUREN (1966)
DREYFUS, G.

TRIO, OP 1
DRIESSLER, J.
  APHORISMEN, OP 7A
  SERENATA A TRE, OP 34/2
DRIGO, R.
  SERENADE
  VALSE BLUETTE
DRING, M.
  TRIO
DROGOZ, P.
  TRIPTYQUE
DROUET, J.
  3 TRIOS, OP 33
DROUET, L.
  2 AIRS
  GRANDS DUOS BRILLANS & F
  GRANDS DUOS BRILLANS & F
  GRANDS DUOS BRILLANS & F
DRUCKMAN, J.
  ANIMUS #3
  DELIZIE CONTENTE CHE L'A
  DIVERTIMENTO (1950)
  INCENTERS
  LAUDE (1952)
DRUSCHETZKY, G.
  PARTITA # 9 IN F MA
  PARTITA #10 IN F MA
  PARTITA #13 IN B FL MA
  PARTITA #21 IN G MA
  PARTITA IN E FL MA
  PARTITAS I-VI
  QUARTET IN E FL MA
  QUARTET IN F MA
  QUARTET IN G MI
  SESTETTO
DU CAURROY
  DOUBLE CANON
DUARTE, J.
  SONATINE, OP 15
DUBANOWICZ, W.
  MUSICAL PICTURES
DUBENSKY, A.
  PRELUDE & FUGUE
DUBOIS
  CHANSON LOINTAINE. SCHER
  OUVERTURE, SERENADE AMIC
  SARABANDE POUR UNE TORTU
DUBOIS, F.
  QUINTET
DUBOIS, P.
  BERCEUSE ET RONDO CAPRIC
  6 CAPRICES
  6 CAPRICES
  CIRCUS PARADE
  DOUBLE CONCERTINO
  18 DUOS PROGRESSIFS
  FANTASIA
  HUIT-UN
  LOU GASCARELET
  5 MOUVEMENTS BREFS
  PETITE SUITE
  QUARTET

DUETTI
STRAVAGANZA (1966)
EARL OF KELLY
TRIO SONATA
EATON, J.
LION, THE, & ANDROCLES
EBEN, P.
BLASERQUINTETT (1965)
MUSIC
ORDO MODALIS (1964)
EBENHOH, H.
4 SCENES FOR 10, OP 21/1
EBERHARD, D.
PARAPHRASES
PARODY (1972)
EBERL, A.
GRAND TRIO IN E FL MA, O
SEXTET
ECK, E.
QUARTET ALBUM
VALSETTE
ECKERBERG, S.
DUO
TRIO CONCERTANTE (1966)
ECKERT, M.
SEA-CHANGES
WISPS
ECKHARDT¬GRAMATTE, S.
DUO CONCERTANTE (1956)
NONET (1966)
TRIO (1967)
WIND QUARTET (1946)
WOODWIND QUINTET
ECKLEBE, A.
BLASERTRIO (1975)
EDER DE LASTRA, E.
WIND QUINTET
EDER, H.
DUO
LITZLBERG-SERENADE, OP 6
MUSICA SEMPLICE, OP 23/1
OTTETTO BREVE, OP 33
QUARTET (1955)
QUINTET, OP 25
SEPTET, OP 55
SEPTUAGESIMA INSTRUMENTA
WAECHTER-DIVERTIMENTO (1
EDLER, R.
REFLEXIONS (1963)
VARIANTEN (1962)
EDMONDSON, J.
LITTLE SUITE
LITTLE SUITE
EDWARDS, G.
BITS
CAPTIVE, THE
EXCHANGE-MISERE (1974)
KREUZ UND QUER (1971)
UROBOROS
UROBOROS
UROBOROS
EDWARDS, R.

SHADOW D-ZONE (1977)
EGGE, K.
QUINTET, OP 13
EGK, W.
DIVERTISSEMENT
POLONAISE, ADAGIO & FINA
5 STUCKE
EHLBACH, E.
3 ALTE DEUTSCHE LIEBESLI
EHLE, R.
ALGORHYTHMS
ESTRANGEON
5 PIECES FOR INSTRUMENTS
5 PIECES FOR INSTRUMENTS
EHRENBERG, C.
QUARTET, OP 40
EHRLICH, A.
TESTIMONY(1962)
WRITING OF HEZEKIAH, THE
EICHENWALD, P.
ASPEKTE (1958)
ASPEKTE
EICHNER, E.
CONCERTO
EINEM, G. VON
QUINTET, OP 46
EINFELDT, D.
SIZILIANISCHE IMPRESSION
STATIONEN (1973)
EISENHAUER, W.
LEARN TO PLAY DUETS
LEARN TO PLAY DUETS
EISLER, H.
14 ARTEN DEN REGEN ZU BE
CANTATA IN EXILE, OP 62
CANTATA ON THE DEATH OF
KRIEGSKANTATA, OP 65
NONETT #1
NONETT 2 (1939)
OHNE KAPITALISTEN GEHT E
OUVERTURE ZU EINEM LUSTS
PALMSTROM, OP 5
ROMAN CANTATA, THE, OP 6
SEPTET #2 (1947)
SONATENSATZ, OP 49
SUITE FOR SEPTET #1, OP
EISMA, W
.CHEVAL MORT, LE (1976)
EISMA, W.
AFFAIRS #3
BECAUSE IT IS (1968)
DIAPHONIA (1962)
10 FLUTES & TAPE (1973)
GIBET, LE (1971)
IF... (1970)
PRAU LAS CAGLIAS (1977)
SONATA (1959)
WORLD WITHIN WORLD
EISMAN, W.
FONTAMARA (1966)
EK, G.
OKTETT (1970)

EKLUND, H.
  SMALL SERENADE
  SMAPRAT (1965)
  4 TEMPERAMENTI (1965)
  ZODINAI (1966)
EKLUND, HANS
  IMPROVISATA (1958)
  SOMMARPARAFRAS (1968)
EL¬DABH, H.
  LOOK AT LIGHTNING, A
  TAHMEELA
  THULATHIYA
  THUMANIYA
ELER, A.
  QUARTET IN D MI, OP 11/2
  QUARTET IN F MA, OP 11/1
  QUARTET IN F MA, OP 11/3
  QUARTET, OP 6/1
  TRIO, OP 9/1
ELGAR, E.
  LOVE'S GREETING
  LOVE'S GREETING
  LOVE'S GREETING
  SALUT D'AMOUR
  SALUT D'AMOUR
  SALUT D'AMOUR
  SALUT D'AMOUR
  SALUT D'AMOUR, OP 12
  SALUT D'AMOUR, OP 12
ELIASSON, A.
  PICKNICK (1972)
ELIEZER, B.
  KLEINE SUITE (1952)
ELKAN, H.
  CLASSICAL ALBUM
  DUET ALBUM
  ENSEMBLE TRIO ALBUM
  ENSEMBLE TRIO ALBUM
  ENSEMBLE TRIO ALBUM
ELKUS, J.
  5 SKETCHES
  TRIPTYCH
ELLIOT, W.
  6 FRENCH SONGS OF THE 15
  POEM
ELLIOTT, W.
  SENECIO HERREIANUS (1975
ELLIS, D.
  GOLDEN APPLES OF THE SUN
  TIME TRIP
ELLIS, M.
  DREAM FANTASY, A
  DREAM FANTASY, A
ELLIS, R.
  DIXIELAND DUET
ELLMENREICH, A.
  SPINNING SONG
ELTON, A.
  SHORT SONATA
ELY, R.
  ACCURACY IN RYTHM
EMMANUEL, M.

  3 ODELETTES ANACREONTIQU
  SONATA
EMMER, H.
  CAMERA EYE (1978-79)
  CAMERA EYE (1978-79)
EMMERT, A.
  TRIO IN E MA
EMMETT, D.
  DIXIE'S LAND
ENCINAR, J.
  HOMENAJE A J. CORTAZAR
  MUSICA PER A UN AMIC
  OP 15 (1977)
  SAMADHI (1972)
  TUKUNA
END, J.
  6 MINIATURES
  2 MODERN SAXOPHONE QUART
ENDO, R.
  DESSEIN IMPROVISATION
  WANDERING FLAMES (1971)
ENDRESEN, R.
  CLARINET QUARTET #1
  PEPPERINO
  PRAIRIE WARBLERS
  PRAIRIE WARBLERS
  PROMENADE
  PROMENADE
  TWO FLYERS, THE
  WOODWIND MOODS
  WOODWIND REVELS
  2 FLIERS, THE
ENESCO, G.
  DIXTUOR
ENGEL, J.
  SUITE I
ENGELMANN, H.
  PERMUTAZIONI (1959), OP
ENRIQUEZ, M.
  TZICURI (1977)
EPSTEIN, A.
  CANONS & POSTLUDE
  4 DIALOGUES
  QUINTET
ERB, D.
  CONVERSATION (1963)
  HEXAGON (1963)
  MIRAGE
ERBACH
  6 DUOS
ERBACH, C.
  CANZONA
ERBACH, F.
  DIVERTISSEMENT MELODIEUX
  3 DIVERTISSEMENTS MELODI
ERBSE, H.
  12 APHORISMEN
  NONETT, OP 28
  QUARTET, OP 20
  3 STUDIEN, OP30
ERDLEN, H.
  KLEINE VARIATIONEN, OP 2

360

ERDMANN, D.
  DIVERTIMENTO
  IMPROVISATION (1967)
  MINIATUREN (1972)
  NOTTURNO
  VARIATIONS
ERDMANN, G.
  RAUMKOMPOSITION
ERDMANN, H.
  RAUMKOMPOSITION
  TRIO II
  TRIO III
ERDMANN, V.
  4 BAGATELLEN (1972)
  MOBILE
ERICKSON, E.
  AMERICAN DANCE
  COUNTRY GARDENS
  COUNTRY GARDENS
  FESTIVE MOOD
  FESTIVE MOOD
  NOVELETTE
  SCHERZO, OP 33
  SONGS SAILORS SING
  SUNSHINE & SHADOWS
ERICKSON, F.
  CARNIVAL OF VENICE
  RONDINO
  SCHERZINO
ERICKSON, M.
  PETITE SUITE
ERICSSON, J.
  QUINTET
ERIKSON, A.
  MUSIC (1974)
ERIKSSON, G.
  FLOJTDUETTER
ERIKSSON, N.
  QUARTETTO
  RONDINO ALLA MARCIA
ERIXON, P.
  DIVERTIMENTO, OP 11
  DUO, OP 9(1964)
  ELEGIA OCH ALLEGRO, OP
  LENTO OCH ALLEGRO, OP 3
  PHANTASY, OP 13 (1964)
  RONDO, OP 2 (1963)
ERLANGER, G.
  SEXTET, OP 41
ERNST, D.
  SHAPES
  SUMMERTIME
EROD, I.
  CAPRICCIO (1976/77)
  RICERCARE ED ARIA
ERRANTE, B.
  SCHIZZO MODERNO
  TERZETTO IN G MI
  3 TRIO ETUDES
ERVIN, K.
  5 LITTLE PIECES
  TRACKS

ESCHER
  GROSSES DUO, OP120
  7 KLEINE DUOS, OP122
ESCHER, P.
  DIVERTISSEMENT, TRIO
  NAGA-UTA, OP 48 (1949)
ESCHER, R.
  QUINTET (1967)
  SINFONIA (1976)
  SONATA, OP 8 (1944)
  TOMBEAU DE RAVEL, LE
  TRIO D'ANCHES (1946), OP
ESCOBAR, A.
  MOVEMENTOS (1970)
ESCUDIE, L.
  ANDANTE
ESSEX, K.
  WIND QUINTET (1941)
ESTES, A.
  CLARISTHENICS
ESTRADE-GUERRA D', O.
  SONATINE PASTORALE
ETLER, A.
  CONCERTO
  DUO
  FRAGMENTS
  3 PIECES
  QUARTET
  QUINTET #1 (1955)
  QUINTET #2 (1957)
  SEXTET (1959)
  SONATA
  SUITE (1960)
EVANS
  5 VARIATIONS ON AN OLDE
EVANS, R.
  DUET SUITE (1965)
  PRELUDE & FUGUE
EVANS, S.
  EACH TOLLING SUN
EVERETT, T.
  3 COMMENT
  DUOS
EVETT, R.
  BILLY IN THE DARBIES
EWERS, J.
  TRIO, OP 2
EXAUDET, J.
  COUR DE LA MARQUISE, LA
  COUR DE LA MARQUISE, LA
  COUR DE LA MARQUISE, LA
EXCOFFIER
  FANTASIA-GRACIOSO
EYCHENNE, M.
  CANTILENE & DANSE
EYMANN
  PRELUDE & FUGUE
EYNDEN, F. VAN DEN
  MYCROPHONY (1971)
EYSER, E.
  BAROQUE (LE SAXOPHONE BI
  OTTOLETTO (1975)

POLYMORPHY 1 (1968)
QUINTET (1968)
QUINTETT 70 (1970)
SERENATA (1973)
SERENATA II (1976)
SERENATA SPAGNOLA (1959)
TRIOLETTO (1973)
TRIPIKO II (1974)
TRIS (1976)
FABER, J.
6 MELODIES IN ANCIENT ST
SUITE, "PARTIES SUR LES
FABRE, C.
REVERIE #2
REVERIE #2
REVERIE #2
REVERIE #2
REVERIE #2
REVERIE
REVERIE
REVERIE
REVERIE
FACKLER, H.
INTRODUCTION & RONDO GIO
FAHRES, M.
IMITATION, VERSION 211/S
MINIMAL (1977)
MINIMAL (1977)
FAITH, R.
QUINTET
SOLITARY REAPER, THE
FALLA, M. DE
CONCERTO (1926)
PSYCHE
FARAGO, M.
4 DUETS, OP 27
4 DUETS, OP 27
FARBER, O.
QUARTET, OP 15
FARBERMAN, H.
PROGRESSIONS
QUINTESSENCE
TRIO
FARHART, H.
DIVERTIMENTO
FARINAS, C.
IN RERUM NATURA
IN RERUM NATURA
TIENTO I
TIENTO I
FARKAS, F.
ANTICHE DANSE UNGHERESI
ANTICHE DANZE UNGHERESI
DIVERTISSEMENT (1967)
NOTTURNO
SERENADE (1951)
SERENADE (1965)
3 TANZPARAPHRASEN
TIBICINIUM
FARNABY, R.
NOBODYES GIGGE
NOBODYES GIGGE

FARRAND, N.
DUO
FARRENC, J.
ANDANTE
ANDANTE
ANDANTE
FASCH, J.
CONCERTO IN C MA
CONCERTO IN E MI
CONCERTO IN G MA
CONCERTO
DOUBLE CONCERTO IN D MI
SONATA A 3 IN E MI
SONATA A 4
SONATA IN D MA
SONATA IN D MI
SONATA IN F MA
SONATA IN G MA
SONATE IN B FL MA
SONATE IN D MA
TRIO SONATA IN D MA
TRIO SONATA IN G MA
FAUCONIER, C.
SEXTUOR FACILE
FAURE, G.
EN PRIERE
EN PRIERE
NOCTURNE
PAVANE
PAVANE, OP 50
PAVANE, OP 50
PAVANE, OP 50
SICILIENNE
FAURE, J.
PALMS, THE
RAMEAUX, LES (THE PALMS)
FAVRE, G.
GOUACHES
METOPE
PNYX
FELCIANO, R.
CONTRACTIONS (MOBILE FOR
CRASIS
CRASIS
CRASIS
LAMENTATIONS FOR JANI CH
NOOSPHERE #1
SOUNDSPACE FOR MOZART
SPECTRA
FELD, J.
CAPRICCIO (1964)
2 DANCES
DUO (1964)
FANTAISIE CONCERTANTE
5 INVENTIONS
KAMMERSUITE (1961)
PETIT DIVERTISSEMENT
QUINTET #1 (1949)
QUINTET #2 (1968)
TRIO (1963)
FELDERHOF, J.
RONDO (1960)

SHORT STORY
SUITE (1974)
THEMA MET VARIATIES (194
TRIO (1968)
FELDMAN, H.
WIND QUINTET #1
FELDMAN, J.
WOODWIND QUINTET (1966)
FELDMAN, M.
3 CLARINETS, CELLO & PIA
DURATIONS #1 (1960)
I MET HEINE ON THE RUE F
11 INSTRUMENTS (1953)
INSTRUMENTS I
IXION
JOURNEY TO THE END OF TH
MADAME PRESS DIED LAST W
NUMBERS (1964)
2 PIECES (1961)
PROJECTION II (1951)
PROJECTION 5 (1951)
RABBI AKIBA (1963)
STRAITS OF MAGELLAN, THE
STRAITS OF MAGELLAN, THE
VERTICAL THOUGHTS III (1
VIOLA IN MY LIFE I, THE
VIOLA IN MY LIFE II, THE
FELDSHER, H.
2 FUGUES
FELIX, V.
QUINTET
SONATA DA REQUIEM
FELLAGARA, V.
SERENATA
FELLEGARA, V.
EPITAPHE (1964)
OTETTO (1953)
SERENATA (1960)
FENIGSTEIN, V.
6 FOLKSONGS
ICARES
7 MINIATURE
FENNELLY, B.
EVANESCENCES
2 MOVEMENTS
SONGS WITH IMPROVISATION
WIND QUINTET (1967)
FENNER, B.
QUINTET
STUDY
SUITE
FERGUSON, H.
OCTET
FERLING, W.
DUO CONCERTANTE #1, OP 1
FERNANDEZ, O.
2 INVENCOES SERESTEIRAS
3 INVENTIONS-SERENADES
FERNEYHOUGH
SONATINA
SONATINA
FERNSTROM, J.

KVINTETT, OP 59 (1943)
LITEN SERENAD, OP 73
FERRARI, D.
PASTORALE
FERRARI, G.
MUSICA A 5
FERRARI, L.
FLASHES
INTERRUPTEUR (1967)
FERRITTO, J.
CONCERTINO, OP 15
DIFFUSIONE (1964)
DIFFUSIONE
4 MADRIGALI
OGGI, OP 9
QUARTETTO, OP 13
FERRO, P.
SUITE AGRESTE
FERROUD, P.
TRIO IN E MA
FESCH, W. DE
ANDANTE & MENUET
CONCERTO IN B FL MA, OP
CONCERTO IN G MA, OP 10/
8 DUETS (OP 11)
3 LEICHTE SONATEN
SONATA IN D MA, OP 7/2
SONATA IN E MI, OP 7/8
SONATA IN G MI, OP 7/4
SONATAS, OP 9
6 SONATAS, OP 9
3 SONATAS, OP 12/1/3
SONATE A 3
SONATE, OP 12/1-3
3 SONATEN, OP 7/2,4,8
TRIOSONATEN, OP 12/1-3
FETHERSTON
IN THE FOREST
FETHERSTON, E.
VALSE STACCATO (RUDENSTE
FIALA, G.
MUSIQUE DE CHAMBRE (1948
SAXOPHONE QUARTET #1 (19
SAXOPHONE QUARTET #2 (19
SONATA BREVE (1972)
FIALA, J.
DUO CONCERT
DUO CONCERTANTA IN F MA
DUO CONCERTANTE # 1 IN F
2 QUARTETS
QUINTETS (EFLMA,BFLMA,EF
3 QUINTETS
FIBICH, Z.
IDYLISCHE SUITE
QUINTET, OP 42
FICHER, J.
QUARTET
FIELDS, F.
CHANT RITUAL #1
FILAS, T.
'ROUND & 'ROUND SHE GOES
CHASE, THE

CLARINET ECHOES
DOUBLE OR NOTHING
INTERVAL DUETS
FILIPPI, A. DE
CORYDON SUITE
7 MODES
SERENADE
FILTZ, A.
SONATA, OP 2/3 IN G MA
SONATA, OP 2/4 IN D MA
FINCH, R.
QUINTET
FINDLAY, F.
FROM SWEDEN
FINE, A.
DANCE PIECE #2
FINE, I.
PARTITA
ROMANZA
FINE, V.
DIVERTIMENTO
GREAT WALL OF CHINA, THE
FINGER, B.
ADAGIO (SONATA IN F MA)
FINGER, G
2 SONATAS
FINGER, G.
LEICHTE DUETTE
SONATA A 5 IN B FL
SONATA IN B FL MA
SONATA IN C MA
SONATA IN C MA
SONATA IN C MA, OP 5/10
SONATA IN C MA, OP 5/13
SONATA IN C
SONATA IN G MA, OP 2/6
SONATA
2 SONATAS, # 3 IN G MI &
SUITE #1
SUITE #2
FINK, S.
IMPRESSION #1
SERENADE IN PERCUSSIONE
TRIO OSTINATO
FINKBEINER, R.
QUARTET (1966)
FINKE, F.
QUINTET
SUITE #5 (1955)
FINNEY, R.
3 ACTS FOR 3 PLAYERS
DIVERTISSEMENT
FINNISSY, M.
AFAR (1966/67)
LOST LANDS (1977)
PIANO CONCERTO #2 (1975/
FIORILLO, F.
SINFONIA CONCERTANTE IN
SINFONIA CONCERTANTE IN
TRIO, OP 29/1
FIRAT, E.
UYGAR CIGLIKLARLA

FISCHER
BANQUET MUSIC
FISCHER, A.
TIME PRISMS
FISCHER, I.
DIVERTIMENTO IN D MA
FISCHER, J
7 .DOPISU SONATORUM
FISCHER, J.
7 BRIEFE (1971)
7 DIVERTIMENTI
QUINTET
FISCHER, J.C.
3 DIVERTIMENTI
FISCHER, J.C.F.
SUITEN
FISHER, S.
INVOLUTION
MUSIC FOR 9 INSTRUMENTS
FISHMANN, M.
6 STUDIES IN SONORITIES
FITELBERG, J.
CAPRICCIO
FLAGELLO, N.
BURLESCA
FLANAGAN, W.
GOOD-BYE, MY FANCY
WEEPING PLEIADES, THE
FLEGIER, A.
CONCERT SUITE
QUATUOR
FLEMING, R.
A 2 PIECE SUITE (1959)
DIVERTIMENTO (1970)
INDIAN LEGEND (1967)
MARITIME SUITE (1962)
2-PIECE SUITE, A (1958)
FLEURY, L.
OEUVRES ORIGINALES DES X
FLORENZO, L.
SUD-AMERICA
FLOSMAN, O.
4 DON QUIJOT-SERENADEN
NONETTO II (SUITE)
QUINTET #2
ROMANZA E SCHERZO
SONATA (1970)
FLOTHIUS, M.
EEN AMSTERDAMSCH LIED
CONCERTINO (1967)
4 MINIATURES RUMANTSCHAS
NEGRO LAMENT (1953)
NOCTURNE, OP 22 (1941)
FLOTHUIS, M.
CANZONE, OP 76/4 (1978)
DIVERTIMENTO, OP 46
LIEDEREN (1943; REV.
LOVE & STRIFE, OP 34
NOCTURNE, OP 11 (1941)
QUINTET, OP 13 (1942)
SONATA, OP 76/2 (1975)
FLOTOW, F.

AH! SO FAIR (MARTHA)
AH! SO FAIR (MARTHA)
FOCKING, H.
  SONΛTΛ, OP 1/2
FODI, J.
  CALIGO (1972; REV 1973)
  FOUR FOR FOUR, OP 20 (19
  PARTIMENTO
  POLYPHONY, OP 15 (1967)
  SIGNALS, OP 22 (1969)
  TRIO
  VARIATIONS II, OP 42 (19
  VARIATIONS, OP 37 (1972)
FODOR, A.
  WERKE DEUTSCHER KOMPONIS
FOERSTER, J.
  NONET, OP147
  NONETT, OP147 (1931)
  WOODWIND QUINTET, OP 95
FOLPRECHT, Z.
  CONCERTINO, OP 21 (1940)
  KLEINE SUITE IN ALTEM ST
  WIND QUINTET, OP 17 (193
FONTAINE, F.
  CONCERTINO DE DINANT
FONTANA, G.
  SONATA # 9
  SONATA #10
  SONATA #12
FONTYN, J.
  COLLOQUE
  FILIGRANE
  7 LITTLE PIECES (1956)
  5 MOSAICS
  MUSICA A QUATRO
FORBES & FRANK, A.
  2 CLARINETS, 2 VOLS
FORBES, S.
  DEATH'S DOMINION
  PARTIA
FORD, C.
  ALLIANCES FOR WINDS (197
  THORYBOPOIOUMENOI (1972)
FORD, T.
  SUITE
FORET, F.
  SUITE EN TRIO
FORSBERG, R.
  VARIATIONER OVER ETT EGE
FORSTER
  CONCERTO IN E MI
FORSTER, E.
  QUINTET
FORSTER, K.
  SONATA A 7
FORSYTH, M.
  INTIMACIES
  MELANCHOLY CLOWN, THE (1
  MELANCHOLY CLOWN, THE (1
  QUARTET 61 (1961)
FORTNER, J.
  FLOW CHART I - APRES JON

SPRING
FORTNER, W.
  5 BAGATELLEN (1960)
  9 INVENTIONEN UND EIN AN
  NEW-DELHI-MUSIK
  SERENADE (1945)
FOSS, L.
  CAVE OF THE WINDS, THE (
  ECHOI FOR 4 VIRTUOSI (19
FOSTER
  TIOGA WALTZ
FOSTER, S.
  COME WHERE MY LOVE LIES
  COME WHERE MY LOVE LIES
  VILLAGE FESTIVAL, A
  VILLAGE FESTIVAL, A
  VILLAGE FESTIVAL, A
  VILLAGE FESTIVAL, A
  VILLAGE FESTIVAL, A
  VILLAGE FESTIVAL, A
FOTE, R.
  AMIGOS
  TUTTI FLUTI
  TUTTI FLUTI
FOTEK, J.
  TRIMORPHIE (1966)
FOUGSTEDT, N.
  DIVERTIMENTO
FOURCHOTTE
  MARCHE
  PIECE BREVE
FOX
  PAVANNE
FOX, F.
  BEC 3
  BEC-4
  TIME EXCURSIONS (1976)
  VARIABLES 6
FRACKENPOHL, A.
  CHORALE AND CANON
  DIVERTIMENTO
  FANFARE, AIR & FINALE
  FLUTE RAG
  FLUTE WALTZ
  FLUTES 4
  FLUTES 4
  FRENCH SUITE
  PRELUDE & ALLEGRO
  RAGTIME SUITE
  SUITE
  TOCCATA
FRAENKEL, W.
  5 LIEDER NACH GEDICHTEN
FRAGALE, F.
  SPRIGHTLY FLIGHT
FRANCAIX, J.
  7 DANSES D'APRES "LES MA
  DIVERTISSEMENT
  GAY PARIS, LE
  HEURE DU BERGER, L'
  HEURE DU BERGER, L'
  KLEINES QUARTETT

MUSIQUE DE COUR
5 PICCOLI DUETTI
9 PIECES CARACTERISTIQUE
QUARTET
QUARTET
QUINTET
QUINTET
QUINTETTE
FRANCIS, A.
CONTEXTURE IN PARALAX I
CONTEXTURE IN PARALAX II
FRANCK
AUX PETITS ENFANTS
FRANCK, C.
ALLEGRETTO
SCHERZO (STRING QUARTET
TO LITTLE CHILDREN
FRANCK, M.
TRIO D'ANCHES, #2
FRANCL, J.
QUINTETTO
TRIO
FRANCO, J.
CANTICLE (1958)
DIPTYCH
DIVERTIMENTO
2 DUETS
7 EPIGRAMS
LORD COMETH, THE!
PILGRIM'S PROGRESS, THE
SONATINA
SONG OF LIFE, THE
SONGS OF THE SPIRIT
TRIO
TRITTICO CAPRICCIOSO
6 VARIATIONS
FRANGKISER, C.
AUTUMN SKIES
DANCING NYMPHS
EN ESCAPADES
FUGUEREST
INVENTRIOLE
LAVIOLETTES, LES
MELODIE PETITE
SNOWFLAKES
THREE BLIND MICE
FRANK
MINKA, MINKA
3 SHORT DUOS
FRANK M.
CLASSICAL IMPROVISATION
FRANK, A.
DIVERTIMENTO
DUO
SONATA DA CAMERA
SUITE
FRANK, A. & W. FORBES
30 EASY CLASSICAL DUETS
FRANK, M.
CANON & FUGUE
CONVERSATION PIECE
20 DUETS

20 EASY WOODWIND DUETS
3 GROOVY FLUTES
INTRODUCTION & SCHERZO
PRELUDE & FUGUETTE
WIND TRIO #2
3 DANCING FLUTES, THE
3 GROOVY FLUTES, THE
FRANKEL, B.
BAGATELLES (5 PEZZI NOTT
PEZZI PIANISSIMI, OP 41
QUINTET
TRIO, OP 10
FRANKEN, W.
DIVERTIMENTO (1948)
SERENADE (1958)
FRANKS, W.
HAIKU (1969)
FRANZEN, O.
H-MUSIK (1975-76)
SPEL (1969)
FREED, I.
DIVERTIMENTO
QUINTET
FREEDMAN, H.
EXPLAINER, THE
LOVE & AGE (1975)
PAN (1972)
QUARTET (1973)
QUINTET (1962)
TIKKI TIKKI TEMBO (1971)
TOCCATA (1968)
TSOLUM SUMMER
VARIATIONS (1965)
2 VOCALISES (1954)
FREISTADT, M.
WOODWIND QUARTET
WOODWIND QUINTET #1
WOODWIND QUINTET #2
WOODWIND TRIO, OP 38
FRENSEL¬WEGENER, E.
SEXTET (1927)
FRESCOBALDI
2 CANZONAS
FRESCOBALDI, G.
CANZONA
5 CANZONI PER SONAR
FUGUE IN C MI
FUGUE IN G MI
FUGUE
GAGLIARDA
GAGLIARDA
GALLIARD & COURANTE
GALLIARD & COURANTE
RICERCAR #10; CANZON #5
RICERCARE
FREUDENTHAL, O.
12 VERANDERUNGEN
FREUND, D.
PAS DE DEUX
FREUNDLICH, R.
5 LITTLE MELODIES
4 OLD DANCES

FREYER, J.
  DIVERTIMENTO
FRIBEC, K.
  DANZA DI GIOJA
  PANTA RHEI
FRICKER, P.
  3 ARGUMENTS, OP 59 (1969
  5 KANONS
  OCTET, OP 30
  TRIO, OP 35 (SERENADE #2
FRICKER, P.R.
  QUINTET, OP 5 (1947)
FRID, G.
  CHEMINS DIVERS, OP 75
  DUBBELTRIO, OP 73 (1967)
  FRUHLINGSFEIER (1952)
  KLEINE SUITE (1975)
  12 METAMORPHOSEN, OP 54
  12, METAMORPHOSES
  NOCTURNES, OP 24 (1925)
  3 POEMS (1976)
  SERENADE, OP 4 (1928)
  SEXTET
  SONS ROUMAINS, OP 87
  SONS ROUMAINS, OP 87
FRIEDLANDER, E.
  RHAPSODY FOR BASSOON
FRIEDRICHSEN, J.
  GRANDFATHER'S DUET BOOK
FRIEDRICHSEN, J.M.
  GRANDFATHER'S DUET BOOK
FRITCHIE, W.
  COMO PARK SUITE
  2 PIECES
FRITSCH, J.
  BESTANDTEILE DES VORUBER
  HOCHTONER (1974)
  HOCHTONER (1974)
  IM DUNKEL DEM WERDENDEN
  MODULATION 11
  SEPTEMBER 70, GRAND QUAT
FRITTER, J.
  8 RONDELS
FRITZ, G.
  SONATA IN D MA, OP 4/5
FROBERGER, J.
  CAPRICCIO
  CAPRICCIO
FROCK, G.
  VARIATIONS
FROHLICH, T.
  WALZER
FROIDEBISE, P.
  AMERCOEUR
FROMM¬MICHAELS, I.
  MUSICA LARGA
FROMM, H.
  CHAG HA-MATSOT
FROMMEL, G.
  BLASER-SUITE, OP 18
FROSCHAUER, H.
  SEXTET

FRUHLING, C.
  TRIO IN A MI, OP 40
FRUMERIE, G. DE
  SUITE, OP 71
FUCHS, F.
  MUSIC, OP 94
  SERENADE
FUCHS, F., JR.
  LITTLE SUITE
FUCHS, G.
  DUO, OP 5
FUCHS, J.
  SINFONIA
FUCHS, R.
  QUINTET, OP102
FUERSTENAU, A.
  3 CONCERTANTE DUOS
  6 DUETS, OP137, 2 VOLS.
  6 DUETS,OP137,2 VOLS
  3 DUOS
  GRANDS DUOS CONCERTANT,
  48 LITTLE FLUTE DUETS
  TRIO, OP118
FUERSTENAU, C.
  6 DUETS
  3 DUOS,OP 2
  12 STUCKE, OP 16
FUERSTENAU, K.
  12 ORIGINALKOMPOSITIONEN
  STUCKE, OP 37
FUERSTNER, C.
  BERCEUSE
FULEIHAN, A.
  ACROBATICS (HUMORISTIC P
  EXIT (HUMORISTIC PRELUDE
  IN A BARNYARD (HUMORISTI
  OVERTURE (HUMORISTIC PRE
  SERENADE FOR JUDY, A (HU
FULKERSON, J.
  CO-ORDINATIVE SYSTEMS #3
  PATTERNS #1(1971)
FURER, A.
  BLASERQUINTETT, OP 21
FURRER¬MUNCH, F.
  DIALOG (1970)
  SOLENOID II (1972)
  SOLENOID II (1972)
FURST, P.
  APROPOS BLASERQUINTETT,
  BEAT THE BEAT
  BLASERQUARTETT, OP 40
  KONZERTANTE MUSIK, OP 25
  PETITIONEN, OP 51
  QUINTET #3, OP 29
FURSTENAU, A.
  RONDO BRILLANT, OP102
  RONDO BRILLANT
  3 TRIOS (PUB SEPARATELY)
  UNION, L', OP115
FURSTENAU, K.
  12 STUCKE, OP 38
  SUITE, OP 34

SUITE, OP 35
FUSSAN, W.
  DIE CHINESISCHE FLOTE
FUSSEL, K.
  MIORITA
FUSSELL, C.
  DANCE SUITE (1963)
  3 INVENTIONS (1959)
FUSSL, K.
  DIALOGUE IN PRAISE OF TH
FUTTERER, C.
  QUARTET
  QUINTET IN B FL MA
FUX, J.
  LARGO #1
  LARGO #2
  NURNBERGER PARTITA
  NURNBERGER PARTITA
  SINFONIA
  SINFONIA
  SONATA A TRE IN D MI
  SONATA A 3 IN D MI
GAAL, J.
  BLASERQUINTETT
  QUINTET #2
  SEXTETT
GABAYE, P.
  QUINTET (1959)
  SONATINA
GABELLES, G.
  2 PIECES
  3 PIECES
GABER, J.
  VOCE II
GABLER, W.
  QUINTET FOR YOUNG PLAYER
GABRIELI, A.
  RICERCARE #2
  SONATA PIAN' E FORTE
  SONATA PIAN'E FORTE
GABRIELI, D.
  CANON
GABRIELI, G.
  CANZON SEPTIMI TONI
  CANZONA # 7 (1597)
  CANZONA #2 (1597)
  CANZONA NONI TONI A 12
  CANZONA PER SONARE #2
  CANZONA PER SONARE #2
  CANZONE #10
  CANZONI A 6
  SONATA #13 (1615)
GABRIELSKI, W.
  GRAND DUO CONCERTAN #1,
  GRAND DUO CONCERTAN, D M
  GRAND QUARTET
GABRIELSKY, J.
  GRAND TRIO, OP 31
GABRIELSKY, W.
  GRAND QUARTET, OP 53/1
  GRAND QUARTET, OP 53/2
  GRAND QUARTET, OP 53/3

GABUCCI, A.
  50 DUETTI
GABURO, K.
  LINE STUDIES
  TWO
GADE, N.
  MERRY-GO-ROUND
  NOVELETTE, OP 19
  ROMANCE, OP 19
GAGLIANO, G.
  DITTICO #1 (ARIA E TOCCA
GAGNON, A.
  OIES SAUVAGES, LES
  SEPTUOR
GAGRIELSKI, W.
  GRAND DUO CONCERTAN IN A
GAL, H.
  CONCERTINO, OP 82
  DIVERTIMENTO, OP 22
  DIVERTIMENTO, OP 90/1
  FANTASIEN, OP 5
  HUYTON-SUITE, OP 92
  QUINTET, OP107
  SERENADE, OP 93
  TRIO SERENADE, OP 88
  TRIO, OP 94
  TRIO, OP 97
GALLAHER, C.
  4 PIECES
  QUARTET #2, OP 31
GALLON, N.
  SONATA
GALUPPI, B.
  CONCERTO IN E MI
  CONCERTO IN E MI
  GIGA
  TOCCATA
  TOCCATA
  TOCCATA
  TOCCATA
  TRIOSONATE IN G MA
GAMBARO, G.
  3 DUOS, OP 10
  QUARTET #1 IN F MA
  QUARTET #1 IN F
  QUARTET #2 IN D MI
  QUARTET #3 IN G MA
  QUARTET #3 IN G
GAN, N.
  SUITE (CHILDREN'S PICTUR
GANDINI, G.
  MUSICA NOCTURNA
GANICK, P.
  OCTET
GANNE, L.
  EXTASE
  EXTASE
GANTVOORT¬HILLER
  CLASSIC QUARTET #2
GANZ, R.
  WOODY SCHERZO
GARANT, S.

ANERCA (1961; REV 1963)
GARBARINO, G.
  DIALOGHI. 20 DUETTI
GARBER, H.
  VOCE II
GARCIA, M.
  CANCIONES POPULARES DE E
GARDONYI, Z.
  DIVERTIMENTI UBER TANZWE
  DIVERTIMENTO
  3 RONDOS
GARIBOLDI, G.
  DUOS GRADUES,OP145
  6 EASY DUETS
  6 MELODIC DUETS, OP145 I
GARIGLIO, R.
  FANTASIE & FUGUE
GARLICK, A.
  DUO
  PIECE
  QUARTET
  SUITE PER SALOTTO
  2 TRIO MANUSCRIPTS
  2 TRIOS
GARNIER, F.
  ANFANGER-DUETTE (METHODE
GARNIER, FL
  DUO CONCERTANT, OP 4/4
GARRIDO¬LECCA, C.
  DIVERTIMENTO
GARSCIA, J.
  MINIATURES
  THEME WITH VARIATIONS, O
  TRIFLES, OP 42
GARTLEY, G.
  FANTASIA ON A BRITISH TE
GARUN, C.
  TRIO
GASLINI, G.
  MAGNIFICAT
GASSMANN, F.
  3 DIVERTIMENTI
  3 DIVERTIMENTI
  DIVERTIMENTO IN G MA
  QUARTET IN B FL MA
  QUARTET IN B FL MA
  TRIO SONATA IN A MA
  TRIO SONATA IN B FL MA
  TRIO SONATA IN C MA
  TRIO SONATA IN D MA
  TRIO SONATA IN E FL MA
  TRIO SONATA IN G MA
GASTYNE, G. DE
  SUITE RHETAISE, OP 26
GASTYNE, S. DE
  ABACUS IN TRIO, OP 60 (1
  2 CHANSONS FRANCAISES
  IL BACIO, OP 45
  LA CORBUSIERE (1968)
  PARTITA (1956)
  QUARTET, OP 53
  SUMI-E, OP 74,A

TRIO, OP 65 (1970)
GATES, E.
  ODD METER DUETS
  SEASONAL SKETCHES
GATTERMEYER, H.
  DIVERTIMENTO, OP114
  QUARTET, OP 81/2
  TRIO, OP 62/2
GATTI, D.
  30 PROGRESSIVE DUETS
GATTI, G.
  COMPOSIZIONI PER 2 FLAUT
  15 DUETS BY CONTEMPORARY
GATTI, L.
  QUARTET IN F MA
GAUBERT, P.
  DIVERTISSEMENT GREC
  DIVERTISSEMENT GREC
  PIECE ROMANTIQUE
  SOIR PAIEN
  TARENTELLE
GAVEAUX, P.
  ARIA (LE TROMPEUR TROMPE
GAY, E.
  16 DUOS CLASSIQUES
  18 GRANDS MORCEAUX CLASS
  15 MINATURES, 2 VOLS
  15 MINIATURES, 2 VOLS
  10 PETITES PIECES CLASSI
  10 PETITES PIECES CLASSI
  10 PETITES PIECES CLASSI
  20 PETITS DUOS
GAYFER, J.
  QUINTET CONCERTANTE (197
  SUITE (1947)
  WHO ARE YOU, LITTLE I? (
GEARHART, L.
  BASS CLEF SESSIONS
  CLARINET SESSIONS
  CLARINET SESSIONS
  CLARINET SESSIONS
  DUET SESSIONS
  FLUTE SESSIONS
  FLUTE SESSIONS
  FLUTE SESSIONS
GEBAUER, A.
  5 MINIATUREN
GEBAUER, E.
  DUO #5
  3 TRIOS
GEBAUER, F.
  3 AUSGEWAHLTE DUOS, OP 4
  BLASERQUINTETT, #2, IN E
  BLASERQUINTETT, #3, IN C
  DUET #2
  DUET #2
  DUETTO #2
  DUO CONCERTANTE, OP 16/3
  6 DUOS CONCERTANTS, OP
  6 DUOS, OP 2
  QUARTET #1
  QUARTET

3 QUARTETS
QUINTET IN E FL MA
TRIO #1 IN F
TRIO #2 IN C MI
TRIO #3 IN F MA
TRIO, OP 33/3
GEBAUER, M.
  POLONAISE
GEE H.
  SAX DUETS
GEE, H.
  BRANSLE
  FUGUE IN BAROQUE STYLE
  FUGUE IN BAROQUE STYLE
  4 SAXOPHONE QUARTETS
  12 SAXOPHONE TRIOS
GEFORS, H.
  INVENTION, OP 5 (1972)
GEHLHAAR, R.
  HELIX (1967)
GEHOT, J.
  24 MILITARY PIECES
GEISSLER, F.
  FRUHLINGSQUINTETT
  HEITERE SUITE
  LIEDER NACH TEXTEN VON J
  NONETT
  ODE AN EINE NACHTIGALL
GELBRUN, A.
  CONCERTO FANTASIA (1963)
GELLI, V.
  2 DIVERTIMENTI
GELLMAN, S.
  MYTHOS II (1968)
  SONATE (1975)
  SONATE (1975)
GEMINIANI, &.
  SONATA IN E MI
GENDELEV, D.
  QUARTET ON RUSSIAN THEME
GENIN, P.
  CARNIVAL OF VENICE, THE
  GRAND DUO CONCERTANT
  GRAND DUO CONCERTANT, OP
  GRAND DUO CONCERTANT, OP
  GRAND DUO CONCERTANT, OP
  GRAND DUO CONCERTANT,OP
GENTILUCCI, A.
  CILE (1973)
  DIAGRAMMA (1970)
  DIARIO II (1971)
  FANTASIA #2 (1968)
GENZMER, H.
  BLASER-QUINTETT (1956-57
  DIVERTISSEMENT
  NONETT (CAPRICCIO)
  SEPTET
  SEXTET
  SONATA IN F SH MI
  SONATA
  SONATA
  TRIO

GEORGE, G.
  QUARTET (1972)
  SONATA
GEORGE, T.
  6 CANONIC SONATAS
  DUET (PATADAH)
GERAEDTS, J.
  DIVERTIMENTO #1 (1943)
  DIVERTIMENTO #2 (1946)
  4 INVENTIES(1943)
  3 INVENTIES
  KLEINE WATERMUZIEK
  MOTO PERPETUO (1968)
  6 STUDIES IN TOONGESLACH
GERBER, R.
  SUITE (1948)
GERBER, S.
  TRAUMWERK
  WOODWIND QUARTET
GERBIGUIER, T.
  6 DUETS,OP 59
GERHARD, F.
  TRIO
GERHARD, R.
  CONCERT FOR 8
  CONCERT FOR 8
  7 HAIKU
  HYMNODY
  LEO
  LIBRA
  LIBRA
  NONET
  QUINTET (1928)
GERHARDT, C.
  SEXTET IN G MA
GERMAN, E.
  PASTORALE DANCE
GERSCHEFSKI, E.
  "AMERICA" VARIATIONS FOR
  AMERICA VARIATIONS FOR W
  AMERICA VARIATIONS FOR W
  AMERICA VARIATIONS, OP 4
  PRELUDE, OP 6/5
  PRELUDE, OP 6/5
  TRIO ("AMERICA" VARIATIO
GERSHWIN, G.
  LIZA
  PROMENADE
GERSTEL, O.
  PETITE MUSIQUE DE NUIT
GERSTER, O.
  DIE AMSEL
  HEITERE MUSIK
GERVAISE, C.
  4 DANCES
  4 DANCES
GESENSWAY, L.
  8 MINIATURES
GESSNER, J.
  ADAGIO & ALLEGRO
GESUALDO, D.
  OCCHI DEL MIO COR VITA

SONATA IN G MA
GESZLER, G.
 TRIO (1963)
GETHEN, F.
 SCHERZO
GEUSS¬BIRKNER
 8 DUETS
GHEDINI, G.
 CONCERTO A CINQUE
 MUSICHE PER 3 STRUMENTI
GHENT, E.
 2 DUOS
 QUARTET
 TRIALITY I & II
GHEZZO, D.
 CANTOS NUEVOS
 KANONES
 MUSIC
 PONTICA 2
GHISI, F.
 MUSICHE CONCERTATE
GHYS, J.
 AMARYLLIS & COUNTRY GARD
 AMARYLLIS & COUNTRY GARD
 AMARYLLIS
GIAMPIERI, A.
 26 PEZZI DI CELEBRI AUTO
GIANELLA, L.
 NOCTURNE IN G MA
 NOCTURNE IN G MA, OP 28/
 QUARTET
GIBBONS, O.
 2 CORANTOS   -
 FANTASIA FOR 3
 FANTASIA FOR 3
 FANTASIA FOR 3
 FANTASIA FOR 3
 6 FANTASIAS,2 VOLS.
 FANTAZIA
 SILVER SWAN, THE
 SILVER SWAN, THE
GIBBS, A.
 HARLEQUINADE
 HARLEQUINADE
 HARLEQUINADE
GIBBS, C.
 HARLEQUINADE
GIBSON, D.
 LIGATURES
GIBSON, J.
 MELODY IV (1975)
 MELODY, PARTS B, I-III
GIDEON, M.
 CONDEMNED PLAYGROUND, TH
 DIVERTIMENTO
 FANTASY ON IRISH FOLK-MO
 HOUND OF HEAVEN, THE
 NOCTURNES
 QUESTIONS ON NATURE
 RHYMES FROM THE HILL
GIEFER, W.
 CANTI (1970)

CHORALE (1973)
DISKONTINUUM (1974)
EINES SCHATTENS TRAUM
PRO-KONTRA (1970)
GIESBERT, F.
 DUOS OF ENGLISH MASTERS
GIESEKING, W.
 QUINTET
GILBERT
 PERCUSSINET
GILBERT, A.
 BRIGHTON PIECE
 INTROIT, GRADUAL & 2 CHO
 9 OR 10 OSANNAS, OP 10
GILBERT, P.
 INTERRUPTED SUITE
GILET
 PROMENADE
 QUARTET-VALSE
GILET, R.
 10 QUATUORS FACILES
GILLAM, R.
 CONVERSATION #1
 DUET #1
 PRELUDE IN B FL MA
 SONATA #1
 THEME IN C MA
GILLIS, D.
 BR'ER RABBIT DREAMS
 FIVE PIECE COMBO
 FROLIC IN B-BOP MA
 MR. TORTOISE WINS THE RA
 SERMONETTE (SOUTHERN STY
 THEY'RE OFF
GILMORE, B.
 DUO (1969)
GILSE, J. VAN
 NONET (1916)
 TRIO
GILSON, P.
 TRIO
GILTAY, B.
 ELEGIE (1969)
 4 MINIATURES (1972)
 POLYCHROMY II
 QUINTETTO (1956)
 SONATA A TRE (1953)
GINASTERA, A.
 DUO
 IMPRESSIONS OF PUNA
GIORDANI, G.
 18TH CENTURY AIR, AN
 18TH CENTURY AIR, AN
 18TH CENTURY AIR, AN
GIORDANI, T.
 EIGHTEENTH CENTURY AIR,
 QUARTET IN G MA
 QUARTET, OP 2/5
 QUARTET, OP 25/3
 TRIO IN G MA
 6 TRIOS, OP 12, 2 VOLS
 18TH CENTURY AIR, AN

SONATE, OP 13
GOETHALS, L.
  FANTASIA EN HUMORESKE
GOEYVAERTS, K.
  GOATHEMALA
  PIECE POUR 3 (1960)
GOLABEK, J.
  PARTITA
GOLDBERG, T.
  QUARTET (1962)
  QUINTET, OP 7 (1952)
  SAMOGONSKI-TRIO, OP 8
GOLDMAN, R.
  CHAMBER MUSIC SUITE
  SONATINA
GOLDMANN, F.
  SO UND SO (1972)
  ZUSAMMENSTELLUNG (1976)
GOLDMANN, M.
  HEVEL II
GOLEMINOV, M.
  QUINTET #2 (1947)
GOLESTAN, S.
  PETITE SUITE BUCOLIQUE
GOLZ, W.
  FOR FLUTE & MUTED STRING
COMEZ, A.
  IL GUARANY
GONZALEZ¬ZULETA, F.
  QUINTETO 1960
GOODE, D.
  SYMPHONIA, WOODWIND QUIN
GOODENOUGH, F.
  WOODWIND QUINTET
  WOODWIND TRIO
GOODMAN
  2 STUDIES
GOODMAN, A.
  KLEINE SUITE
GOODMAN, J.
  5 BAGATELLES
  JADIS (IN DAYS OF YORE)
  MUSIC
  TRIO
  WOODWIND QUINTET (1954)
GOORHUIS, R.
  5 MINIATURES (1977)
  NADER TOT U (NEAR YOU)
GOOSSEN, J.
  QUARTET
GOOSSENS, E.
  FANTASY
  5 IMPRESSIONS OF A HOLID
  PASTORAL & HARLEQUINADE
  4 SKETCHES, 2 VOLS
GORDON
  ENGLISH DANCE SUITE
GORDON, L.
  3 MOVEMENTS
GORDON, P.
  CALLING ALL CLARINETS
  CAPRICCIO

ELKAN-VOGEL WOODWIND ENS
GORECKI, H.
  CONCERTO (1957), OP 11
  CONCERTO (1957), OP 11
  MUSIQUETTE #4, LA, OP 28
GORLI, S.
  SERENATA SECONDA
GORNER, H.
  CONCERTINO, OP 31
  DUO, OP 37
  KAMMERKONZERT, OP 29
  TRIO, OP 24
GORNSTON, D. & H. HUFFNAGLE
  STANDARD CLARINET DUETS
GOSSEC, F.
  ANDANTINO
  CHASSE DE CHANTILLY, LA
  GAVOTTE
  GAVOTTE
  OVERTURE
  OVERTURE
  TAMBOURIN
GOSSEC, J.
  TAMBOURIN
GOTKOWSKY, I.
  EOLIENNE
GOTTLIEB, J.
  TWILIGHT CRANE
GOTTSCHALK, A.
  PHASES
  SESSION, THE
GOULD
  AWAY IN A MANGER; O LITT
  IT CAME UPON THE MIDNIGH
GOULD, E.
  DISCIPLINES
GOULD, M.
  DUO
GOUNOD, C.
  AVE MARIA
  AVE MARIA
  BARCAROLLA
  D'UN COEUR QUI T'AIME
  FLOWER SONG (FAUST)
  FLOWER SONG (FAUST)
  FLOWER SONG (FAUST)
  PETITE SYMPHONIE
  TELL ME, BEAUTIFUL MAIDE
GOW, D.
  QUARTET, OP 28
GRAAP, L.
  DIVERTIMENTO (1964)
GRABNER, H.
  KLEINE SERENADE, OP 47/1
  MUSIC (1956)
  TRIO (1951)
GRABOCZ, M.
  ALTE UNGARISCHE TANZE DE
GRABS, M.
  QUINTET (1965)
GRAF ZU ERBACH, F.
  DIVERTISSEMENT MELODIEUX

GRAF, F.
  TRIO IN D MA
GRAHN, U.
  CHANSON (1969)
  DIALOG (1969)
  FOR 2 ENGLISH HORNS (196
  LITEN SERENADE (1965)
  OPUS III (1964)
  PACE
  SOUNDSCAPE I (1973)
  TENSTA EMOTIONS (1971)
  THIS REMINDS ME OF... (1
  TRIO
GRAINER
  DISCUSSIONS
GRAINGER, P.
  LISBON
  MY ROBIN IS TO THE GREEN
  WALKING TUNE
GRAMATGES, H.
  PRELUDE & INVENTION
GRANADOS, E.
  ORIENTAL, OP 5
GRANDERT, J.
  AIAKURA (1966)
  KAMMARMUSIK (1961)
  KAMMARMUSIK (1961)
  NONETT (1964)
  OKTETT (1966)
  POUR PHILIPPE (1970)
  QUINTET (1975)
  86 T
GRANDIS, R. DE
  CANTI SULLE PAUSE (1961)
  INSTRUMENTALMUSIK ("IL C
  INSTRUMENTALMUSIK ("IL C
GRANT, J.
  DUO #1
GRANT, P.
  PRELUDE & CANONIC PIECE
GRANT, W.
  SOLILOQUY & JUBILATION,
  VARIED OBSTINACY
GRAUN, C.
  SONATE IN E FL MA
  TRIO
  TRIOSONATE IN F MA
  TRIOSONATE IN F MA
GRAUN, J.
  CONCERTO IN E MI
  CONCERTO IN F MA
  SONATA IN G
  TRIO IN F MA
  TRIO SONATA IN F MA
GRAUN, K.
  TRIO #1 IN D MA
  TRIO #1 IN G MA
  TRIO #2 IN E MI
  TRIOSONATE IN D MA
GRAUPNER, C.
  CANON IN F MA
  CONCERTO #35

CONCERTO IN E MI
CONCERTO
SONATA IN C MA
SUITE #1
SUITE #2
SUITE IN F MA
TRIOSONATE IN B FL MA
GRAVES, M.
  WATERCOURSE
GRAZIOLI
  MINUETTO (SONATA IN G MA
GREAVES, T.
  BEETHOVEN'S 5TH BOSSA NO
  DANCE TRIOS
  FLUTE TRIOS
GREEN, D.
  4 CONVERSATIONS (1959)
GREEN, G.
  QUINTET
GREEN, H.
  3 CAVATINAS
GREEN, R.
  HOLIDAY FOR FOUR-CHAMBER
  3 PIECES FOR A CONCERT
  3 PIECES FOR A CONCERT
GREENBERG, L.
  QUARTET (1964)
  SEXTET (1963)
GREENWOOD & ROSENBLUM
  ROSEWOOD BOOK, THE
GRENSER, K.
  GRAND DUO
GRETRY, A.
  3 DANSES VILLAGOISES
  ENTR'ACTE
  RECITATIV ET AIR
  TAMBOURINE
GRIEG, E.
  ALBUM LEAF
  ALBUM LEAF, OP 12/7
  AN DER WIEGE
  ANITRA'S DANCE
  ASE'S DEATH (PEER GYNT S
  BUTTERFLIES
  ELEGIE
  ELF DANCE
  ELFIN DANCE
  EROTIKON, OP 43/4
  GNOMES' PARADE, OP 54
  GRANDMOTHER'S MINUET
  HOLBERG SUITE
  I LOVE YOU
  LAST SPRING
  LAST SPRING, THE
  3 LITTLE PIECES
  LYRIC PIECE #2
  MARCH OF THE DWARFS
  MORNING MOOD (OP 46/1)
  NORWEGIAN DANCE
  NORWEGIAN DANCE, OP 47/2
  7 NORWEGIAN MINIATURES
  RIGAUDON

RIGAUDON, OP 40/5
SARABANDE, OP 40/2
TO SPRING
TO SPRING
TO SPRING
WATCHMAN'S SONG, OP 12/3
WATCHMAN'S SONG, OP 12/3
WATCHMAN'S SONG, OP 12/3
WEDDING DAY AT TROLDHAUG
GRIEND, K. VAN DE
  TRIO (1929)
GRIESBACH, K.
  MUSIK
GRIEVE
  SHERLOCK HOLMES SUITE
GRIFFIS, E.
  SUITE FOR TRIO
GRIFFITHS, J.
  CONVERSATION PIECE
  2 OPPORTUNITIES
GRILLO, G.
  CANZONA #1
  CANZONE #2
GRIM, C.
  SALUTE TO QUANTZ
GRIMM, C.
  ALLA SARABANDA
  DIVERTIMENTO
  5 ETUDES
GRIMS
  POLYFON POLKA-POLONAISE
GRIPPE, R.
  ELECTRA GLIDE
  SITUATION #1 (1976)
CRISONI, R.
  QUARTET
GROFE, F.
  TABLE D'HOTE
GRONEMAN, A.
  SONATA, OP 2/2
GROOMS
  FAMOUS SCOTCH AIRS, VAR.
  HOME FAVORITES, VAR.
  NEAPOLITAN FAVORITES, VA
  OCEAN ECHOES, VAR.
  PLANTATION ECHOES, VAR.
  TWO GUITARS (RUSSIAN SON
GROOMS, C.
  DARK EYES (RUSSIAN SONG)
  DARK EYES (RUSSIAN SONG)
  TWO GUITARS (RUSSIAN SON
  TWO GUITARS (RUSSIAN SON
GROOT, C. DE
  SERENADE (1949)
GROOT, H. DE
  BURLA RITMICA
  SOUVENIR SUD AMERICAN
  SUITE
  VARIATIESUITE (1944)
  VARIATIONS ON "AUPRES DE
  VARIATIONS
GROSS, R.

CHO-SEN VARIATIONS
GROSSI, P.
  COMPOSITION #3 (1958)
  COMPOSIZIONE #3 (1959)
GROSSKOPF, E.
  CONCERTO: FLECKTREUE RAF
  DIALECTICS (1969)
  NEXUS (1968)
  NEXUS (1968)
  SONATA #3 (1967)
GRUBER, H.
  BOSSA NOVA, OP 21 IN E M
  BOSSA NOVA, OP 21E
GRUDZINSKI, C.
  PRELUDE & FUGUE
GRUNAUER, I.
  BESICHTIGUNG, VERSTEIGER
  BLASERQUARTETT
  FAMA E FOME
  MADRASHE
GRUNDMAN, C.
  BAGATELLE
  CAPRICE
  FLUTATION
  FLUTATION
  WALTZ & INTERLUDE
  WALTZ & INTERLUDE
GRUNENWALD, J.
  FANTASIE ARABESQUE
GUACCERO, D.
  ...ITER SEGNATO, UN
  STUDIO PER UN QUARTETTO
GUBBY, R.
  SUITE
GUBITOSI, E.
  COLLOQUI
  FLAUTO NOTTURNO, IL
GUDMUNDSEN¬HOLMGREEN, P.
  2 IMPROVISATIONS
  TERRACE
GUENTHER, F.
  MASTERWORKS FOR 2 FLUTES
GUENTHER, R.
  CANZONE AMABILE
  FOLK DANCE
  PETIT RONDEAU, LE
  RONDO
  RUSTIC SCHERZO
  TRIO ALBUM FOR FLUTES
GUENTZEL, G.
  SCHERZO
  TARANTELLA
GUEZEC, J.
  CONCERT EN 3 PARTIES
GUIGNARD
  32 SHORT DUETS
GUIGNON, J.
  SONATAS, OP 2
GUILLEMAIN, G.
  TAMBOURIN
GUILLEMAIN, L.
  CONVERSATION GALANTE ET

QUARTET IN A MA, OP 12/4
QUARTET IN B MI, OP 12/2
QUARTET IN C MA, OP 12/6
SONATE #3
GUILLEMANT, B.
6 SONATAS, OP 3
GUILLOU, J.
COLLOQUES #1
COLLOQUES #3
GUILMANT, A.
CANTILENE PASTORALE
CANZONETTA
GUINFOAN, J.
TRIPTICO (1965)
GUINJOAN, J.
ACTA EST FABULA (1975)
FRAGMENT (1970)
IMPROVISACION I (1973)
GUION, D.
HARMONICA PLAYER, THE
GULKE
ALTNIEDERLANDISCHE TRAUE
GUREWICH, J.
17 CLASSIC DUETS
GURKOV, V.
3 IRONIES
GURLITT, C.
LITTLE SUITE
GURSCHING, A.
ANAKREONTIKA
QUARTET (1962)
GURSHING, A.
TRIO
GUSSAGO
PORCELLAGA, LA (SONATA)
GUYONNET, J.
POLYPHONIE #3
GWILT, D.
SUITE
GWINNER, V.
6 NIEDERDEUTSCHE VOLKSTA
GYRING, E.
10 CANONS FOR 2 & 3 WOOD
10 CANONS FOR 2 & 3 WOOD
CAPRICCIO
CHORALE
DUO
DUO #2
FUGUE # 1
FUGUE # 2
FUGUE # 3
FUGUE # 4
FUGUE # 5
FUGUE # 6
FUGUE # 7
FUGUE # 9
FUGUE #10
FUGUE #11
FUGUE #12
FUGUE #13
FUGUE #14
FUGUE #15

FUGUE #16
QUINTET
TRIO
GYROWETZ, A.
DIVERTISSEMENT IN A MA
DRITTE NACHTMUSIK, OP 26
QUARTET IN G MI, OP 19/2
HA, J.
SONATA
TRIO
HAAGER, M.
MUSIC FOR 3 INSTRUMENTS,
HAAN, S. DE
DIVERTIMENTO
MARCH- WALTZ- QUASI ADAG
HAAN, ST. DE
TRIO
HAAS, P.
QUINTET, OP 10 (1929)
HABA, A.
ERSTES NONETT (1931), OP
NONETT 3, OP 82 (1953)
QUARTET, OP 74 (1951)
HABA, K.
SEPTET (1929)
HABASH, J.
ADAGIO & RONDO
HABER, L.
6 MINIATURES
PARADE, BLUES & ALLEGRO
HABERLING, A.
KLEINES TRIO
NEW CHAMBER MUSIC
3 TANZE
HABICHT, G.
QUARTETTINO (1969)
HACQUART, C.
3 SONATEN (HARMONIA PARN
HADDAD, D.
BLUES AU VENT
ENCORE "1812"
HADDRILL, P.
RECITATION
HADSHIEV, P.
3 STUCKE (1942)
HAGERUP¬BULL, E.
AD USUM AMICORUM
HAHN, R.
ROMANESQUE
HAHNEL, H.
QUINTET
HAIDMAYER, K.
QUINTET #3
SYMBIOSE II
HAIEFF, A.
3 BAGATELLES
3 BAGATELLES
DANCE SUITE
DANCE SUITE
DANCE SUITE
SERENADE
HAIK¬VENTOURA, S.

BEAU DIMANCHE, UN
HAINES, E.
  CONCERTINO
HAJDU, M.
  CLARINET DUETS (1951)
  TRIO
HALACZINSKY, R.
  EPITAPH
  VARODIE (1972)
HALEN, W.
  MEDITATION
HALETZKI, P.
  FATHER & SON
HALFFTER, C.
  ANTIPHONISMOI
  ODA (1969)
HALIER, R.
  COLOURED VEIL (1976)
HALL, C.
  PETITE SUITE
HALL, J.
  DIVERTIMENTO #3
  QUARTET
HALL, P.
  QUINTET (1944)
HALL, R.
  2 DIVERSIONS
HALLAUER, D.
  KLEINE SUITE
  3 LEICHTE STÜCKE
HALLER, H.
  OCTET, OP 51 (1976)
HALLNAS, H.
  CANTATA
  3 DIALOGER (1971)
  HOSTBALLADER (1976)
  KVINTETT
  SPEL FOR TVA
HALLORAN, D.
  5 MINIATURES
  TRIO
HALTENBERGER
  DIVERTIMENTO
HAMBRAEUS, B.
  DIPTYCHON (TABU-MANU), O
  GACELAS Y CASIDAS DE FED
  GIUCO DEL CAMBIO
  INTRODUZIONE-SEQUENZE-CO
  INTRODUZIONE-SEQUENZE-CO
  JEU DE 5
  KAMMARMUSIK
  MIKROGRAM
  MIKROGRAM
  SPECTROGRAMM, OP 34
HAMERIK, E.
  QUINTET (1942)
HAMILTON, I.
  SERENATA
HAMMERSCHMIDT, A.
  O BELOVED SHEPHERDS
HAND, F.
  4 EXCURSIONS

HANDEL
  2 FLUTE DUETS
HANDEL, F.
  KAMMERTRIO #1 IN B FL MA
HANDEL, G.
  ADAGIO & ALLEGRO (CONCER
  ADAGIO & ALLEGRO
  AIR (WATER MUSIC)
  ALEXANDER IN SERVEUS OVE
  ALLEGRO (SONATA #2)
  ALLEGRO (SONATA #2)
  ALLEGRO (SONATA #2)
  ALLEGRO (SONATA #2)
  ALLEGRO
  ALLEGRO(SONATA #2)
  2 ALLEGROS
  ANDANTE
  ANDANTE-LARGHETTO
  ARIA (ALMIRA)
  ARIA (BERENICE)
  2 ARIAS
  ARIOSO
  BAROQUE DUET #3
  BAROQUE TUNE
  BOUREE
  BOURREE (ROYAL FIREWORKS
  BOURREE (ROYAL FIREWORKS
  BOURREE (SONATA #3)
  BOURREE (WATER MUSIC)
  BOURREE
  BOURREE
  BOURREE, AIR EN GAVOTTE
  CARA SPOSA (RINALDO)
  CHACONNE
  CHAMBER TRIO # 8 IN G MI
  CHAMBER TRIO #1 IN B FL
  CHAMBER TRIO #13 IN G MI
  CHAMBER TRIO #14 IN G MI
  CHAMBER TRIO #19 IN G MA
  CHAMBER TRIO #2 IN D MI
  CHAMBER TRIO #24 IN F MA
  CONCERTO #1 IN D MI
  CONCERTO IN F MI
  CONCERTO
  DUO
  EINLEITUNGEN ZU 3 ANTHEM
  EXCERPTS (SONATA IN C MI
  EXCERPTS (SONATA IN C MI
  EXCERPTS (SONATA IN C MI
  EXULTATION
  FARAMONDO OVERTURE
  FIREWORK MUSIC I
  FIREWORK MUSIC II
  FIREWORKS SUITE
  FRAGMENT DU 5TH CONCERTO
  FUGUE (CELLO SONATA #2)
  2 GESANGE AUS DEN "DEUTS
  HALLELUJAH CHORUS
  HORNPIPE
  HOW BEAUTIFUL ARE THE FE
  HOW BEAUTIFUL ARE THE FE
  HOW BEAUTIFUL ARE THE FE

377

HUSH YE PRETTY WARBLING
KAMMERTRIO #2 IN D MI
KAMMERTRIO #24 IN F MA
KAMMERTRIO #4 IN F MA
KAMMERTRIO #6 IN D MA
KAMMERTRIO #7 IN C MI
KORAALBEWERKING (ST. JOH
LARGHETTO
LARGO (XERXES)
LARGO (XERXES)
LARGO & GIGUE
LARGO
LARGO
LIEBLICHE WALDER (ALMIRA
LITTLE FUGUE
6 LITTLE FUGUES
LITTLE HANDEL SUITE
MARCHES
MENUET (BERENICE)
MENUET
MINUET
3 MOVEMENTS
NACHTIGALLENARIE
NELL DOLCE DELL'OBLIO
OUVERTURE (SUITE)
OVERTURE IN C MA
OVERTURE IN PARNASSO IN
OVERTURE TO "JULIUS CAES
PASTORAL SYMPHONY (MESSI
PASTORAL SYMPHONY
PASTORALE
PETITE FUGUE
8 PSALMOUVERTUREN, 2 VOL
QUARTETTINO
RIGAUDON, BOURREE & MARC
RINALDO'S ARIA
SARABANDA
SARABANDA
SARABANDE & AIR
SARABANDE & ALLEGRO (CON
SARABANDE & BOURREE
SARABANDE ET MENUET
SARABANDE
SARABANDE
SINFONIA (MESSIAH)
SINFONIA (MESSIAH)
SINFONIA (SOLOMON)
SINFONIA
SONATA #1 IN B FL MA
SONATA #1
SONATA #2 IN G MI
SONATA IN A MI, OP 1/4
SONATA IN C MA
SONATA IN C MI
SONATA IN C MI, OP 2/1
SONATA IN D MA
SONATA IN D MA
SONATA IN D MA
SONATA IN D MA
SONATA IN D MI
SONATA IN D MI
SONATA IN E FL MA

SONATA IN E MI
SONATA IN E MI
SONATA IN E MI
SONATA IN F MA
SONATA IN F MA
SONATA IN G MI
SONATA IN G MI, OP 2/2
SONATA
SONATA
6 SONATAS
8 STUCKE
SUSSE STILLE
SWEET FORGETTING
THEME & VARIATIONS (CHAC
TRIO & MENUET
TRIO & MENUET
TRIO & MENUET
TRIO #2 IN D MI
TRIO SONATA IN B FL MA
TRIO SONATA IN F MA, OP
TRIO SONATA IN G MI
4 TRIO SONATAS
TRIO SONATE IN B FL MA
TRIO
TRIO: THEME & VARIATIONS
TRIOSONATE IN E MI
TRIOSONATE
TRIOSONATEN, OP 5
TRIUMPH OF TIME & TRUTH
UM DIE FLAMME
HANMER, R.
  CUCKOO QUARTET
  SUITE FOR 7
HANNA, J.
  TRIO
HANNAY, R.
  CABARET VOLTAIRE
  FANTOME
  PIED PIPER
HANNIKEN, J.
  BLUES & SCHERZO
  4 INVENTIONS
HANSCHKE, H.
  VARIATIONS ON A CHILDREN
HANSEL, A.
  CONCERTINO, OP 80
HANSEN, T.
  COLLAGE
  CONTRASTS
  TOCCATA
HANSON, S.
  PLAY POWER #1 (1976)
HANUS, J.
  SHORT STORY, OP 29/5
  SUITA DOMESTICA, OP 57
HARBISON, J.
  KURZE, DIE
  4 PRELUDES
  SERENADE
HARCOURT, D'
  RHAPSODIE PERUVIENNE
HARDISTY, D.

378

THE HARFLEUR SONG
QUARTET
SATIRICAL SUITE
HASELBACH, J.
  OUT-SIDE (1976)
  TONUNGEN (1976)
HASHAGEN, K.
  COLLOQUIUM
  SEPTALIE (1966)
HASQUENOPH, P.
  DIVERTISSEMENT
  SONATA ESPRESSA
  SONATE A 4
HASSE, J.
  CANZONE
  CANZONE
  CHAMBER MUSIC
  CONCERTO IN A MA
  CONCERTO IN D MA
  CONCERTO IN G MA
  CONCERTO
  13 DUETTE
  20 KLEINE DUETTE
  KONZERT IN B MI
  SONATA A 3 IN D MA, OP
  SONATA IN C MA
  TRIO SONATA IN D MA
  TRIO SONATA IN F MA
  TRIO SONATA IN G MA
  TRIO-SONATE IN E MI
  TRIO-SONATE IN G MA
  TRIOSONATE IN C MA
HASSE, J.A.
  SINFONIA A 5 IN G MA
HASSELMANN, V.
  KLEINE GAVOTTE
  MENUETT
HASSLER, H.
  2 SHORT PIECES
HATRIK, J.
  DENNIK TANE SAVICOVEJ
HATTORI, K.
  DIALOGUE
HAUBENSTOCK
  INTERPOLATIONS
HAUBENSTOCK¬RAMATI, R.
  BLESSINGS (SEGENSSPRUCHE
  MULTIPLE #5 (1970)
  MULTIPLE II (1970)
  MULTIPLE III (1970)
HAUBENSTOCK¬RAMATI, RC
  CREDENTIALS, OR "THINK,
HAUBIEL, C.
  FOR LOUIS XVI
  IN PRAISE OF DANCE
  IN THE DORIAN MODE
  IN THE FRENCH MANNER
  IN THE LYDIAN MODE
  IN THE PHRYGIAN MODE
  MASKS
  NOSTALGIA
  PARTITA

PASTORAL TRIO
PASTORAL
5 PIECES
WILL O' THE WISP
HAUBIEL, J.
  IN THE FRENCH MANNER
HAUER, J.
  DANCE SUITE #1, OP 70
  DANCE SUITE #2, OP 71
  ZWOLFTONSPIEL (1951)
  ZWOLFTONSPIEL (1957)
  ZWOLFTONSPIEL (1957)
HAUFRECHT, H.
  CAPRICE
  DIALOGUES
  FANTASY FOR 4 ON HAITIAN
  FROM THE GROUND UP
  FROM THE HILLS
  LET'S PLAY MACCABEES
  OVERTURE FOR A NEW YEAR
  WOODLAND SERENADE, A
HAUG, H.
  CAPRICCIO (1963)
HAUGHTON, P.
  10 CLARINET TRIOS
  12 CLARINET TRIOS
HAUGLAND, A.
  LITTLE SUITE
HAUPTMANN
  TRIO
HAUPTMANN, M.
  TRIO
HAUSDORFER
  SUITE
HAUSER, M.
  SONG WITHOUT WORDS
HAUTA¬AHO, T.
  SEPTETTO
  SONATINA
  TRIO #1
  TRIO
HAUTVAST
  MEISTER PERLEN
HAVLICEK, L.
  2 CANARIES
HAWES, J.
  PIECES OF 8
HAWKINS
  QUINTET
HAWKINS, J.
  8 MOVEMENTS (1966)
HAWO¢TH, F.
  GLORY & THE DREAM, THE
HAWORTH, F.
  GLENROSE SUITE (1960)
  KERNWOOD SUITE (1972)
  TRIO
HAYDN, F.
  ADAGIO (PIANO SONATA)
  ADAGIO (QUARTET #29)
  ADAGIO (SYMPHONY # 99)
  ADAGIO

ALLEGRETTO (SYMPHONY #11
ALLEGRO (OCTET)
ALLEGRO CON BRIO (STRING
ALLEGRO DECISO
ALLEGRO GIOCOSO
ALLEGRO
ALLEGRO
ALLEGRO, A (OP 74/3)
ANDANTE (OP 33/6)
ANDANTE (SURPRISE SYMPHO
CAPRICCIETTO
CAPRICCIO
CAPRICCIO
CASSATIO IN G MA, HOB II
CASSATION IN F MA
CASSATION
CHORAL ST. ANTHONY
4 CLOCK PIECES
CONCERTO #1 IN C MA, HOB
CONCERTO #2 IN G MA, HOB
CONCERTO #3 IN G MA, HOB
CONCERTO #4 IN F MA, HOB
CONCERTO #5 IN F MA, HOB
CONCERTO IN D MA
DIVERTIMENTI IN A MA & G
DIVERTIMENTO #1
DIVERTIMENTO #1
DIVERTIMENTO #1, HOB II:
DIVERTIMENTO #16
DIVERTIMENTO #2, HOB II:
DIVERTIMENTO #3, HOB II:
DIVERTIMENTO #4, HOB. II
DIVERTIMENTO #5 IN D MA,
DIVERTIMENTO #6, HOB II:
DIVERTIMENTO #7 IN G MA
DIVERTIMENTO #8 IN D MA
DIVERTIMENTO IN B FL MA
DIVERTIMENTO IN C MA
DIVERTIMENTO IN C MA, "M
DIVERTIMENTO IN C MA, HO
DIVERTIMENTO IN C MA, HO
DIVERTIMENTO IN D MA
DIVERTIMENTO IN D MA
DIVERTIMENTO IN E FL MA
DIVERTIMENTO IN E FL MA
DIVERTIMENTO IN F MA
DIVERTIMENTO IN F MA
DIVERTIMENTO IN F MA, HO
DIVERTIMENTO TRIO
DIVERTIMENTO
DIVERTIMENTO
DIVERTIMENTO
DIVERTIMENTO
DIVERTIMENTO, OP100
DIVERTISSEMENT
6 DUETS, 2 VOLS
6 DUOS CONCERTANTS
6 DUOS, 2 VOLS
ECHO
EMPEROR VARIATIONS, OP 7
FELD-PARTHIE IN C MA
FELD-PARTHIE IN F MA

FELDPARTIE
FINALE (FAREWELL SYMPHON
FINALE (QUARTET, OP 9/3
FINALE (SONATA IN C MA)
FLUTE CLOCK SONATAS
FLUTE CLOCK SONATAS
FLUTE CLOCK SONATAS
GAVOTTE
6 GERMAN DANCES
7 GERMAN DANCES
GIPSY RONDO
HUSBAND & WIFE OR THE BI
KATHARINEN-TANZE #4,6,8,
KLAVIERTRIO #30 IN D MA
KLAVIERTRIO #31 IN G MA
LARGO (OP 76/5)
LARGO (QUARTET, OP 76/5)
LONDON TRIO
4 LONDON TRIOS, HOB IV,1
4 LONDON TRIOS
5 LYRE CONCERTI
MARCHE REGIMENTO DE MARS
7 MARCHES
MARSCHE
MENUET & ALLEGRO
MENUET
MENUETTO (SYMPHONY #45)
MENUETTO & PRESTO (OP 1
MENUETTO & SCHERZANDO
MENUETTO & TRIO (SYMPHON
MENUETTO & TRIO (SYMPHON
MENUETTO & TRIO (SYMPHON
MENUETTO AL ROVESCIO (SO
MINUET IN D MA
MINUETTO (DIVERTIMENTO #
MINUETTO (SYMPHONY #2)
MOVEMENT #2 (SYMPHONY #1
MOVEMENT #3 (SYMPHONY #
MOVEMENT #3 (SYMPHONY #1
MOVEMENT #3 (SYMPHONY #1
MOVEMENT #3 (SYMPHONY #1
MUSICAL CLOCK PIECES
MUSIK IN F MA
12 NOCTURNOS IN D MA, HO
NOTTURNO #1 IN CMA, HOB
OCTET IN F MA
OCTET
OP 55, #3, IN B FL MA
OXEN MINUET
OXEN MINUET
OXEN MINUET
OXEN MINUET
OXFORD SYMPHONY
PARTHIA IN F MA
2 PIECES FOR CLOCKWORK O
2 PIECES FOR CLOCKWORK O
7 PIECES FOR THE MUSICAL
POCO ADAGIO CANTABILE (O
PRESTO SCHERZANDO (OP 20
PRESTO
QUARTET (MAN & WIFE)
QUARTET #18, OP 3/5

QUARTET IN C MA
QUARTET IN C MA, OP 75/3
QUARTET IN D MA
QUARTET IN D MA, OP 5/1
QUARTET IN G MA, OP 5/2
QUARTET IN G MA, OP 5/4
QUARTET, HOB II:B4
QUARTET, OP 2/6
6 QUARTETS, 2 VOLS
QUARTETTE, OP 5/4
QUINTET #1
QUINTET #4
QUINTET
QUINTET
RONDO (DIVERTIMENTO #1)
RONDO (DIVERTIMENTO #1)
RONDO (OP 33/3)
RONDO SCHERZANDO
SCHERZANDO #1 IN F MA
SCHERZANDO #2 IN C MA
SCHERZANDO #3 IN D MA
SCHERZANDO #4 IN G MA
SCHERZANDO #5 IN E MA
SCHERZANDO #6 IN A MA
SCHERZANDO
SERENADE
12 SHORT PIECES
SINFONIE CONCERTANTE
SINFONIE CONCERTANTE, OP
SONATA IN D MA
SONATAS #5 & 6
3 SONATAS
3 SONATAS
SURPRISE! SURPRISE!
SYMPHONY CONCERTANTE, OP
THEME & VARIATIONS (EMPE
TRIO #28 IN D MA, HOB XV
TRIO #29 IN F MA
TRIO #29 IN F MA
TRIO #29 IN G MA, HOB XV
TRIO #30 IN F MA, HOB XV
TRIO #31 IN G MA
TRIO IN D MA
TRIO IN G
TRIO, OP 2/4
3 TRIOS IN F MA, D MA, G
TRIOS, H XV:15-17
TRIOS, OP 11/4-6
3 TRIOS, OP 11/4-6
6 TRIOS, OP100, 2 VOLS
3 TRIOS
3 TRIOS
WITCHES' CANON, THE
WITCHES' CANON, THE
WITCHES' CANON, THE
ZINGARESE #1, #6, #8
HAYDN, J.
  QUARTET, OP 50/5
HAYDN, M.
  DIVERTIMENTO A 5 IN G MA
  DIVERTIMENTO IN B FL MA
  DIVERTIMENTO IN C MA

DIVERTIMENTO IN D MA
DIVERTIMENTO IN D MA
DIVERTIMENTO IN G MA
DIVERTIMENTO IN G MA
4 MINUETS
QUARTET IN C MA
QUARTET IN F MA
QUINTETTO
SONATA IN G MA
HAYDN, F.
  DUET #3, IN F MA
HAYS, D.
  SCHEVENINGEN BEACH
HAZZARD, P.
  DUET
  MUSIC IN COUNTERPOINT
  QUARTET #2
  SONATA #2
  SUITE
  SUITE
  VOYAGE
HEAD, M.
  BIRD-SONG
  PIPER
  TRIO
  WORLD IS MAD, THE
HEALEY, D.
  LAUDES, OP 26 (1967)
  LAUDES, OP 26 (1967)
  5 MINIATURE, OP200
  MOVEMENTS
HECHTEL, H.
  TRIAL (1973)
HEDGES, A.
  RONDO CONCERTANTE, OP 21
HEDWALL L.
  SONATIN (1964-75)
HEDWALL, L.
  DUO (1952)
  5 EPIGRAMS (1959)
  KVINTETT (1965)
  LITEN DUO (1975)
  METAMORFOSI
  PARTITA (1961)
  TRIO (1945)
  TRIO (1962)
  VARIATIONER OCH FUGA
HEER, H. DE
  SONATINA #3 (1975)
  SONATINE (1967)
  SONATINE #2
  TRIO (1975)
HEIDEN, B.
  INTRADA
  4 MOVEMENTS (1976)
  SERENADE (1955)
  SINFONIA (1949)
  WOODWIND QUINTET (1965)
HEIDER, W.
  KUNST-STOFF
  MUSIK IM DISKANT
  PASSATEMPO

PICASSO-MUSIK
SONATINA
SONATINA
HEILBUT, P.
  MUSIZIERBUCH
HEILLER, A.
  SEXTET
HEIM, N.
  ELEGY
  FESTIVAL SUITE
  PRELUDIUM & CANZONA
  SUITE
HEINEMAN, J.
  VIEWS
HEINICHEN, H.
  NISI DOMINUS AEDIFICAVER
HEINICHEN, J.
  CONCERTO IN G MA
  CONCERTO IN G MA
  SONATA A TRE IN C MI
  SONATA A 3 IN C MI
  SONATA A 3
  SONATA IN G MA
  SONATE IN C MI
  TRIO SONATA IN C MI
  TRIO SONATA
  TRIO-SONATE IN F MA
  TRIOSONATE IN C MI
  WEIHNACHTS-PASTORALE
HEINICK, D.
  RITUAL
HEININE, P.
  SUITE
HEININEN, P.
  MUSIQUE D'ETE (1963)
  QUINTETTO (1961)
HEINIO, M.
  QUATTROFONIA, OP 29
  QUINTET, OP 12
  SUITE, OP 16/1
  TRIO
  TRIO
HEINSCH, W.
  QUINTET (1977)
HEISS, H.
  GALGENLIEDER NACH GEDICH
  KONZERTMUSIK I & II
  LIEDER
  MUSIKALISCHES GASTGESCHE
  ZUM NEUEN JAHR (1954)
HEISS, J.
  CAPRICCIO (1976)
  FLUTE CONCERTO (1977)
  4 MOVEMENTS
  QUARTET (1971)
  SONGS OF NATURE (1975)
HEKSTER, W.
  CREDENCES OF SUMMER
  DIALOGUES
  DIVERSITIES
  ECHOES OF SUMMER (1975)
  EPICYCLE I & II (1975)

EPICYCLE I & II (1975)
FRESCO (1970)
3 HAIKU SONGS (1977)
INCENTER (1970)
5 MOMENTS OF DAY (1977-7
MONOLOGUES & CONVERSATIO
PENTAGRAM
PULSATIONS (1967)
REED MUSIC (1970)
REFLECTIONS (1964)
RELIEF #III (1968)
RELIEF #1 (1968)
RELIEF #4
RELIEF #5
SNOW MAN, THE (1969)
SONG OF PEACE, A (1979)
STATEMENT (1974)
TROPOS N1974-75)
WINDSONG #3 (1977)
WINDSONG II (1970)
HELBERGER, H.
  MUSIC (1978)
HELFRITZ, H.
  TANZSUITE
HELLERMAN, W.
  LONG ISLAND SOUND
HELLERMANN, W.
  COLUMBUS CIRLE
  ONE INTO ANOTHER
  POEM
HELM, E.
  QUARTET
  QUARTET
  WOODWIND QUINTET
HELMSCHROTT, R.
  INVENTION (1967)
HELPS, R.
  QUINTET (1975)
HEMBERG, E.
  TIO VARIATIONER (1960)
HEMEL, O. VAN
  ABOUT COMMEDIA DELL'ARTE
  CLARINET QUINTET (1958)
  SEXTET (1962)
  TRIO (1959)
  WIND QUINTET (1972)
HEMON, S.
  CONCERTO (1970)
HEMPEL, C.
  MINERALI. 8 STUCKE
HEMPEL, R.
  MOVIMENTO (1966)
HEMPEL, C.
  10 DUETTE
HENDERSON
  CAPRICCIO (1966)
  CLASSIC DUETS
HENDERSON¬STOUTAMIRE
  QUARTETS FOR ALL
HENKEMANS, H.
  PRIMAVERA (1944)
  QUINTET #2 (1962)

383

MELODIC STUDIES
QUARTET
HEUSSENSTAMM, G.
  AMBAGES, OP 29
  CALLICHOREO, OP 23
  CANONOGRAPH I
  DOUBLE SOLO
  7 ETUDES, OP 17
  INSTABILITIES, OP 21
  MINI-VARIATIONS, OP 25
  MUSIC FOR 3, OP 33
  POIKILOS, OP 32
  SAXOCLONE (1971)
  SET FOR DOUBLE REEDS
  8 SHORT DUETS
  TETRALOGUE, OP 36
  TEXTURE VARIATIONS
  TRIO, OP 3 (1959)
HEWITT, H.
  9 PRELUDES
  SAXERCISES
HEYER, F.
  QUARTET IN F MA
HIBBARD, W.
  BASS TROMBONE, BASS CLAR
  GESTURES
  GESTURES
  4 PIECES
  SENSUOUS EXTRACTIONS
  TRIO
HIDALGO, J.
  CAURGA (1957)
  JA-U-LA (1964)
HIDAS, F.
  QUINTET #2
HIER, E.
  SUITE FOR CHAMBER ENSEMB
HILDEMANN, W.
  SERENATA
HILFIGER, J.
  MIRAGE
HILL
  DANCE CHROMATIQUE
HILL, E.
  SEXTET, OP 39
HILL, J.
  ENTOURAGE
  SERENADE
HILLER, L.
  DIVERTIMENTO
HILLERT, R.
  AND YOU, O BETHLEHEM
HILLIARD, J.
  SAXONATA
HILSE, B.
  SUITE, OP 6
HINDEMITH, P.
  ABENDKONZERT #2
  ABENDKONZERT #4
  CONCERTO (1949)
  CONCERTPIECE
  DIE SERENADEN, OP 35

2 DUETS
JUNGE MAGD, DIE, OP 23/2
KANONISCHE SONATINE, OP
KLEINE KAMMERMUSIK, OP 2
OCTET (1957/58)
QUARTET (1938)
QUINTET, OP 30
SEPTET (1948)
3 STUCKE (1925)
TRIO, OP 47
HINDEMTH, P.
  STUCKE (1942)
HIRNER, T.
  WIND QUINTET (1960)
HIRSCH
  KAMMERMUSIK
HIRSCH, H.
  QUINTETTO SERENO
HLAVAC, M.
  LYRICKE PRELUDIUM A CAPR
  WOODWIND QUINTET (1970)
HLOBIL, E.
  ARIA E RONDO
  EVOCATION
  KAMMERMUSIK, OP 67 (1965
  NONETTO, OP 27 (1946/47)
  OCTET (1956)
  QUARTET (1964)
  TRIO
  WIND QUINTET, OP 20
HLOUSCHEK, T.
  QUARTET
HOBSON, B.
  QUINTET (1970)
  TRIO (1966)
HOBSON, M.
  TRIO
HOCH, F.
  C'E KARL E KARL (1972)
  OGGETTO DISINCANTATO, L'
  TRASPARENZA PER NUOVI EL
HOCH, P.
  LIEDER FREMDER LANDER
HOCHEL, S.
  QUINTET
HOCKNER, W.
  DAS FLOTENQUARTETT
HODDINOTT, A.
  DIVERTIMENTI FOR 8 INSTR
  DIVERTIMENTO
  ITALIAN SUITE
  NOCTURNES & CADENZAS
  RITORNELLI, OP 85
  SEXTET
  VARIATIONS
HODEIR, A.
  AMBIQUITE I
  AMBIQUITE I
  FLAUTANDO
HODGE, T.
  3 SKETCHES
HODGSON

385

FANFARES
FANFARES
FANFARES
FLUTE ALBUM, 2 VOLS
HODKINSON, S.
 ARC (1969)
 DRAWINGS, SET #6
 INTERPLAY (1967)
HOESSLIN, F. VON
 QUINTET IN C SH MI
HOFFDING, F.
 CHAMBER MUSIC (1927)
 DIALOGUES
 QUINTET, OP 35
HOFFER, P.
 BLASERQUINTETT (1947)
 KLEINE SUITE (1944)
 SERENADE "INNSBRUCK, ICH
 THEMA MIT VARIATIONEN
 TRIOSONATE
HOFFMAN, A.
 DUO
HOFFMANN, R.
 DECADANSE
HOFFMEISTER, F.
 CONCERTO IN E FL MA
 3 DUETS, OP 30
 3 DUETS, OP 31
 DUO IN F MA
 3 DUOS, OP 38
 QUARTET IN C MI, OP 16/2
 QUARTET IN G MA
 2 QUARTETS
 SERENADE IN E FL MA
 SERENATA IN F MA, OP 9
 TERZETTO
 TRIO IN D MA
HOFMANN, L.
 DIVERTIMENTO IN C MA
HOFMANN, W.
 BLASERQUINTETT IN D MA
 5 INVENTIONS
 SERENADE
HOHENSEE, W.
 3 APHORISMEN
 QUINTET IN D MA
 SERENATA 3
HOLBORNE, A.
 SUITE FOR BRASS
HOLEWA, H.
 CON 4 FLAUTI (1975)
 CONCERTINO (1960)
 CONCERTINO (1960)
 KVINTETT (1962)
 LAMENTI (1976)
HOLLER, K.
 CLARINET QUINTET, OP 46
 DIVERTIMENTO, OP 11
 SERENADE, OP 42A
HOLLFELDER, W.
 SERENADE
HOLLIGER, H.

CARDIOPHONIE
H (1968)
MOBILE (1962)
TRIO
HOLLOWAY, R.
 CONCERTINO #3
 DIVERTIMENTO (1972)
 3 POEMS
 RIVERS OF HELL, OP 34, T
HOLM, M.
 BECAUSE I AM LONELY, OP
 PHILEMON & BAUCIS, OP 16
 SONATA, OP 25
 ST. ANNALAND, OP 24
 TRANSITIONS II
HOLM, P.
 2 PIECES
 TO SVENSKE VISER
 VIDEVIDEVIT
 VILDGAESSENE
HOLMBOE, V.
 CHAMBER CONCERTO #2, OP
 QUARTETTO MEDICO
 QUARTETTO, OP 90 (1972)
HOLMES
 SYMPHONY ENSEMBLE SERIES
HOLMES, G.
 AULD LANG SYNE
 AULD LANG SYNE
 AULD LANG SYNE
 CASTILLIA (BOLERO)
 SPIRITUAL FANTASIA
 SYMPHONY ENSEMBLE SERIES
HOLMES, G.& LONG
 SYMPHONY ENSEMBLE SERIES
HOLOUBEK, L.
 TRIO, OP 21
HOLST, G.
 FUGAL CONCERTO, A
 TERZETTO (1925)
HOLSTEIN, J.
 DUETTISTES, LES
HOLT, S. TEN
 DIFFERENTIES (1969)
HOLZBAUER, I.
 DIVERTIMENTO
 QUINTET IN G MA
HOMBERG, J.
 MENSAGEM
HOMILIUS, G.
 KLEINES TRIO IN G MA
HOMS, J.
 MUSICA PARA 11
 OCTET DE VENT (1968)
 TRIO (1954)
HONEGGER, A.
 CANON SUR BASSO OBSTINEE
 CHANSONS- SIRENES, POIRE
 CHORAL A 3 VOIX (3 CONTR
 CONCERTO DA CAMERA (1948
 PETITE SUITE
 PRELUDE (3 CONTREPOINTS,

DIRECTIONS (1970)
M.P. 5 (1967)
TRIO (1958)
HRUBY, F.
FOR THE BIRDS
HRUSKA, J.
WOODWIND QUINTET (1949)
HRUSOVSKY, I.
COMBINAZIONI SONORICHE
HUBBELL, F.
CANON BALL
HUBEAU, J.
SONATINE HUMORESQUE
HUBER, K.
ASCENSUS (1969)
ASKESE
AUF DIE RUHIGE NACHT-ZEI
CONCERTO PER LA CAMERATA
ENGELS ANREDUNG AN DIE S
6 MINIATUREN
OISEAUX D'ARGENT
OISEAUX D'ARGENT
PSALM OF CHRIST (1967)
SABETH (1966/67)
3 SATZE IN 2 TEILEN
HUBER, N.
CHRONOGRAMM (1966)
HUBICKI
4 SCOTTISH & IRISH AIRS
HUBNER, W.
BRUMMKREISEL & ANDERE KO
BRUMMKREISEL, DER
CAPRICCIOSO
FACETTEN II
HUDADOFF, I.
24 CLARINET QUARTETS
24 FLUTE TRIOS
24 SAXOPHONE QUARTETS
HUE, G.
SOIR PAIEN
HUFFNAGLE
BLACK VELVET
CHOPIN BALLADE
HUFFNAGLE, H.
RHYTHM DUETS
RHYTHM DUETS
STREAMLINED DUETS, 2 VOL
HUFSCHMIDT, W.
3 ALTTESTAMENTLICHE SPRU
HUGGLER, J.
BITTERE NUESSE
FOR COLORATURA, CLARINET
MUSIC FOR 13 INSTRUMENTS
MUSIC, OP 63
QUARTET, OP 27
QUARTET, OP 47
HUGHES, K.
CHANCE #2
SECOND CHANCE
HUGHES, L.
ALLEGRO SCHERZOSO, OP 92
HUGON, G.

PRELUDE A 4 EGLOGUES DE
HUGUES, L.
ALLEGRO SCHERZOSO
LA SCUOLA DEL FLAUTO,OP
HUINJOAN, J.
VARIORUM (1975)
HULA, Z.
4 MARCHEN--STIMMUNGEN, N
HUMEL, G.
TRIO (1964)
HUMMEL
2 ALLEGRETTOS
HUMMEL, B.
5 BAGATELLEN
LUDI A 3
MOMENTS MUSICAUX
QUINTET
HUMMEL, H.
CLARINET POLKA
CLARINET POLKA
HUMMEL, J.
ALLEGRETTO
GAVOTTE
HUMMEL, J.F.
TRIO IN B FL MA
HUMMEL, J.N.
MILITARY SEPTET, OP114
OCTET-PARTITA IN E FL MA
QUARTET IN E FL MA
QUARTET
SEPTET, OP 74
SEPTETT MILITAIRE, OP114
TRIO IN A MA, OP 78
TRIO, OP 78
HUMPERDINCK, E.
CHILDREN'S PRAYER
HANSEL & GRETEL MELODIES
HUMPHREYS, D.
CHILDREN'S SUITE
HUNDZIAK, A.
LYRICS (1963)
HUNT, R.
MOTO PERPETUO
4 SONGS
HUNTER, E.
DANCE HUMORESQUE, OP 1/
HUPFER, K.
MUSIK FUR TRIAL & ERROR
HURNIK, I.
DIE VIER JAHRESZEITEN
ESERCIZI (1963)
ROZMARNA HUDBA
SONATA DA CAMERA (1953)
TRIO
HURRELL, C.
GALWAY PIPERS
GALWAY PIPERS
GIRL FRIENDS, THE
HUSA, K.
EVOCATIONS DE SLOVAQUIE
2 PRELUDES
SERENADE

HUSE, P.
  OBJECTS (1962)
  RECURRENCES (1966)
HUTCHESON, J.
  PASSING,PASSING
  RONDO BRILLANTE
HUTCHISON, W.
  CHRYSALIS
  SUITE
HUTH, G.
  MUSIK DER NACHTE AN DER
HUYBRECHTS, A.
  QUINTETTE (1936)
  SONATINE (1934)
  SUITE (1929)
  TRIO (1926)
HYAMS, A.
  7 MICRO-ORGANISMS
  PRELUDE, BLUES AND FUGUE
  QUINTET
HYDE
  FISHERMAN, THE & HIS WIF
HYE-KNUDSEN, J.
  2 CHAMBER DUETS
  QUARTET
IASILLI, G.
  GOLDIE
IBARRONDO, F.
  LUEGO EL SILENCIO
IBERT, J.
  ARIA
  ARIA
  CAPRICCIO
  ENTR'ACTE
  ENTR'ACTE
  3 HISTOIRES
  2 INTERLUDES
  2 INTERLUDES
  2 MOUVEMENTS
  3 PIECES BREVES
  5 PIECES EN TRIO
IKONOMOV, B.
  SUITE (1951)
  TRIO #2 (1968)
ILIEV, I.
  QUINTET #2, OP 62 (1968)
  QUINTET #6, OP101 (1974)
  TRIO #3, OP 69 (1968)
ILJINSKY, A.
  BERCEUSE
  BERCEUSE
  BERCEUSE
IM, K.
  SUITE
IMBRIE, A.
  DANDELION WINE
  SERENADE
  SERENADE
  TO A TRAVELLER
INDY, V. D'
  CHANSON ET DANSES, OP 50
  SARABANDE & MINUET, OP 2

SUITE EN PARTIES
SUITE EN RE
SUITE IN OLDEN STYLE, OP
TRIO, OP 29
IOANNIDIS, Y.
  ACTINIA (1969)
IPPOLITOV-IVANOV, M.
  2 KIRGHIZ SONGS
IPPOLITOV, I.
  PROCESSION OF THE SARDAR
IRELAND, J.
  SEXTET
ISAAC, H.
  BENEDICTUS
ISAAC, M.
  SACRED MUSIC
ISHII, M.
  LA-SEN (SPIRALE, 1969)
  LA-SEN (SPIRALE, 1969)
  LA-SEN (SPIRALE, 1969)
  NUCLEUS (1973)
ISTVAN, M.
  CHAMBER MUSIC FOR BEGINN
IVES, C.
  ADAGIO SOSTENUTO
  ADAGIO SOSTENUTO
  ALL THE WAY AROUND & BAC
  ALLEGRETTO SOMBREOSO
  CALCIUM LIGHT NIGHT
  HOLIDAY QUICKSTEP
  LARGO
  REMEMBRANCE
  SCHERZO (OVER THE PAVEME
  SEER, THE
IVEY, J.
  ANDROCLES & THE LION
JABLONSKI, H.
  3 MINIATURES
  SUITE
JACCHINI, C.
  TRIO SONATA, OP 5/3, IN
JACHINO, C.
  TRIO
JACKSON, D.
  MIKROKOSMOS "M"- DANCE S
  THEME & VARIATIONS
JACKSON, J.
  9 MINIATURES
JACOB, G.
  DIVERTIMENTO IN E FL MA
  4 FANCIES
  INTRODUCTION & RONDO
  3 INVENTIONS
  3 LITTLE PIECES
  MINIATURE SUITE
  MORE OLD WINE IN NEW BOT
  4 OLD TUNES
  OLD WINE IN NEW BOTTLES
  2 PIECES
  QUARTET
  QUARTET
  QUINTET # 2

391

LYRIC WALTZ SUITE
SEPTET
SERENADE
JONES, J.
  SONATE A 3
JONES, K.
  3 IMPROMPTUS
  QUINTET (1968)
  SONATA DA CAMERA (1957)
  SONATA DA CHIESA (1967)
JONES, S.
  SUITE MODERNE
JONES, W.
  QUINTET
JONG, M. DE
  APHORISTISCH TRIPTIEK, O
  QUINTET #3, OP157 (1971)
  TRIO, OP126 (1961)
JONGBLOED, D.
  ROMANCE
JONGEN, J.
  CONCERT FOR 5, OP 71
  CONCERTO, OP124
  DANCE LENTE
  ELEGY
  2 PARAPHRASES ON WALLOON
  2 PIECES (PREAMBULE ET D
  2 PIECES EN TRIO, OP 80
  QUATUOR, OP122 (1942)
  RHAPSODIE, OP 70 (1922)
  TRIO
JONGEN, L.
  DIVERTISSEMENT (1937)
  QUINTUOR (1958)
JOOSEN, B.
  20 EENVOUDIGE KLASSIEKE
  SPIRITUAL QUARTET I
  WELSH DANCES
JOPLIN, S.
  EASY WINNERS, THE
  ENTERTAINER, THE
  ENTERTAINER, THE
  ENTERTAINER, THE
  ENTERTAINER, THE
  2 JOPLIN RAGS
  4 RAGS
  RAGTIME DANCE
  SWIPESY CAKEWALK
JORDAN, J.
  LITTLE RED MONKEY
JORNS, H.
  7 FORMS, OP 15
JOSEPHS, W.
  CONCERTO A DODICI, OP 21
  5 FICTITIOUS FOLKSONGS
  OCTET, OP 43
  TRIO, OP 50
JOSQUIN DES PRES
  VIVE LE ROY
JOSTEN, W.
  CANZONA SERIA
  CONCERTANTE MUSIC

JOUBERT, J.
  OCTET, OP 33
  SONATA A 5, OP 43
JULIAN, J.
  WAVE
  WAVE
JUNGK, K.
  CHACONNE
JUON, P.
  ARABESKEN, OP 73 (1940)
  DIVERTIMENTO, OP 34
  DIVERTIMENTO, OP 51
  OCTET, OP 27A
  TRIO-MINIATUREN
JURDZINSKI, K.
  DIVERTIMENTO (1956)
JURISALU, H.
  QUINTET #2
JUST, J.
  6 DUETTINOS, OP 3
JYRKIAINEN, R.
  CONTRADICTIONS
KABALEVSKY, D.
  ALLEGRO (SONATINA #1)
  CHILDRENS SUITE, OP 27
  DANCE (OP 27)
  PARADE
KABALEWSKI, W.
  5 PIECES
KABELAC, M.
  SEXTETT, OP 8 (1940)
KADERAVEK, M.
  INTRODUCTION & ALLEGRO
KADOSA, P.
  QUINTET, OP 49A (1954)
  VOLKSLIEDERKANTATE, OP 3
KAGEL, M.
  MARE NOSTRUM
KAHMANN, C.
  DANCES
KAHN, E.
  ACTUS TRAGICUS
  7 CHANSONS POPULAIRES DE
  PETITE SUITE BRETONNE
KAHN, R.
  SERENADE, OP 73
KAHOWEZ, G.
  BARDO-PULS
  SOMMERPOESIE-WINTERPOESI
  STRUCTURES
KAI, S.
  TRIGA EINER CHROMATISCHE
KAISER, D.
  RITOURNELLE
KALABIS, V.
  DIVERTIMENTO (1952)
  KLASICKY NONET (1956)
  KLEINE KAMMERMUSIK, OP 2
KALACH, J.
  KAMMERMUSIK
KALINNIKOV, V.
  CHANSON TRISTE

CHANSON TRISTE
KALLIWODA, J.
  CONCERTINO
KALLSTENIUS, E.
  DIVERTIMENTO, OP 29
  KLARINETTKVINTETT
  LYRISK SVIT, OP 55
  PICCOLO TRIO SERIALE, OP
  PICCOLO TRIO SERIALE, OP
  TRIO DIVERTENTE, OP 38
  TRIO SVAGANTE, OP 51
KALMAN, E.
  COIN SOUS LES TOITS, UN.
KALMAR, L.
  TRIANGOLI
  TRIO (1968)
  TRIO (1968)
KAM, D.
  GO
KAMMEL, A.
  SERENATA IN G MA
KAMMELL, A.
  NOTTURNO #2
KANETSCHEIDER, A.
  SERENADE NACH DEUTSCHEN
KANITZ, E.
  NOTTURNO
KANTOR, J.
  SERENADE
  WOODWIND QUINTET #1
KANTUSER, B.
  2 IMAGES
KAPLAN, D.
  COUNTRY STORY, A
  GOTHAM COLLECTION OF DUE
  GOTHAM COLLECTION OF OBO
  GOTHAM COLLECTION
  GOTHAM COLLECTION
  GOTHAM COLLECTION
KAPLAN, L.
  2-PART INVENTION
KAPR, J.
  BARVY TICHA (FARBEN DER
  CONCERTINO
  DIALOGE
  DREAMBOOK, THE
  5 TESTIMONIES
  UBUNGEN FUR GYDLI
KARAS, RUDOLF
  SUITE (1967)
KARDOS, D.
  CONCERTO, OP 47
KARDOS, I.
  DUO
  GROTESQUE
  NOTTURNO
KAREL, L.
  ELEGY & DANSE
KAREL, R.
  NONETTO (1945)
KARG-ELERT, S.
  NOW THANK WE ALL OUR GOD

TRIO IN D MI
TRIO IN D MI, OP 49/1
TRIO, OP 49/1
KARJALAINEN, A.
  SEXTET
KARKOFF, M.
  5 AFORISMER
  DIVERTIMENTO, OP 29
  DUO, OP 3 (1951)
  2 IMPRESSIONER, OP 36
  KLEINE SUITE
  KLEINE SUITE
  KVINTETT, OP 24 (1956-57
  LITEN MUSIK, OP 74 (1965
  MINIATYRSVIT #1, OP 34A
  MINIATYRSVIT #2, OP 34B
  QUARTETTO PICCOLO, OP 53
  SERENATA PICCOLA, OP 34C
  SERENATA, OP 61A
  TIO AFORISMER, OP104
  TRIO PICCOLO, OP 55
KARKOSCHKA, E.
  ANTINOMIE (1968)
  AUS DREIEN (1969)
  IM DREIECK
  IM DREIECK
  PSYLEX (1968)
KARLINS, M.
  BIRTHDAY MUSIC #2
  BLUES
  CELEBRATION
  MUSIC
  QUARTET
  QUARTET #2
  QUINTET
  SONG FOR SOPRANO
  3 SONGS FROM 16TH & 17TH
  VARIATIONS (1963)
  WOODWIND QUINTET 1970
KARP
  NINETEENTH CENTURY MASTE
KASANDSHIEV, V.
  KLEINE SUITE (1956)
  QUINTET (1971)
  VARIATIONS FOR 7 INSTRUM
KASBERGEN, M.
  CHACONNE
  3 EPISODES
KASEMETS, U.
  CANCIONES (1955-56)
  QUINTET, OP 48 (1957)
KASILAG, L.
  TOCCATA
KASZYCKI, J.
  CHAMBER MINIATURES
KAT, J.
  CONVULSIONS (1979)
KATZ, E.
  3 CANONIC DANCES
  TOY CONCERTO
KAUDER, H.
  QUARTET (1948)

SONATA (1958)
SONG
TRIO (1951)
TRIO (1957)
TRIO #1 (1929)
TRIO #1 (1936)
TRIO #2 (1946)
TRIO #2 (1960)
VARIATIONS ON A DANCE
KAUFFMAN, G.
 CHORALE PRELUDE
KAUFFMANN, G.
 6 CHORALES
KAUFFMANN, L.
 QUINTET
KAUFMANN, A.
 CONCERTINO #2, OP 86
 DROSSER TRIO, OP101
 4 PIECES, OP 77
 4 PIECES, OP 77
 QUARTET, OP 17
KAUFMANN, W.
 PARTITA
KAY, N.
 MINIATURE QUARTET
KAY, U.
 AULOS
 SUITE
KAYN, R.
 INERZIALI
KAZACSAY, T.
 2 DUETTE, OP113 (1956)
KEANE, D.
 CARPOPHAGOUS CANON #4
 CARPOPHAGOUS CANON #4
KEE, C.
 12 ORIGINAL TRIOS
 12 ORIGINAL TRIOS
KEETBAAS, D.
 QUINTET (1961)
KEETMAN, G.
 STUCKE
KEFALIDI, I.
 SEXTET
KEISER, R.
 SONATA A TRE
 TRIOSONATE #2 IN G MA
 TRIOSONATE #3 IN D MA
KEITH, G.
 INTERLUDE
 SCHERZO & CONTINUO
KELDORFER, R.
 MUSIK (1968)
 QUARTET
 RICORDO DI FAETIS
 TRIO
KELEMEN, M.
 ENTRANCES
 ETUDES CONTRAPUNTIQUES
 MUSIC FOR HEISSENBUTTEL
 RADIANT
 RADIANT

KELKEL, M.
 DIVERTIMENTO, OP 3
KELLAM, I.
 CASSATION
KELLER, G.
 QUINTET IN D MI
 SONATA IN C
 SONATA IN G MA
 TRIO SONATA IN B FL MA
KELLER, H.
 5 PIECES
 PUZZLE (1973)
 QUINTET
 REDUKTION
 REFRAINS
 REFRAINS
KELLNER, D.
 GAVOTTE ANCIENNE
KELLY, B.
 NEW ORLEANS SUITE
 QUINTET
KELLY, R.
 PASSACAGLIA & FUGUE
 QUINTET
 SONATA
KELTERBORN, R.
 7 BAGATELLEN
 CONSORT-MUSIC (1975)
 DER TRAUM MEINES LEBENS
 5 FANTASIEN
 INCONTRI BREVI (1967)
 KAMMERMUSIK (1957)
 KAMMERMUSIK (1974)
 LYRISCHE KAMMERMUSIK
 MEDITATIONEN
 4 MINIATUREN
 MONODIE #1 (1976)
 MUSIK
 OKTETT (1969)
 SESTINA (1957)
 VARIANTI
KEMPE, H.
 TRIO SENZA PRETESE
KEMPFF, W.
 QUARTET, OP 15
KEMPIS, N.
 SYMPHONIA AI, OP 3/XVIII
KEMPIS, N. A
 SYMPHONIA A 3 IN D
KENDALL, R.
 6 CLARINET DUETS
KENDELL, I.
 VARIATIONS ON A LONDON S
KENINS, T.
 CONCERTINO A CINQUE
 FANTASY-VARIATIONS
 PRELUDE & SCHERZO (1949)
 SEPTUOR (1949)
 SERENADE (1973)
KENNAWAY, L.
 DOWNSTREAM
 TANDEM

KENNEDY
  STAR OF HOPE (REVERIE)
  STAR OF THE EAST
  STAR OF THE EAST
  STAR OF THE EAST
KENNEDY, H.
  STAR OF HOPE (REVERIE)
  STAR OF HOPE (REVERIE)
KERKHOF, F.
  TRIO
KERN, F.
  4 STUCKE, OP 25
KERN, J.
  WALTZ IN SWING TIME
KERN, M.
  CANTICUM EZECHIAE
KERR, H.
  3 DUOS
  NOTATIONS ON A SENSITIZE
  TRIO
KERSTERS, W.
  BERCEUSE EN HUMORESQUE,
  KLEINE SUITE
  QUARTET, OP 55 (1971)
  QUINTET
  SEPTET, OP 37 (1966)
  VARIATIONS OP THEMA VAN
  VARIATIONS, OP 49 (1969)
KESNAR, M.
  CAPRICCIO
  PETIT RIEN, UN
  PETIT RIEN, UN
KESSNER, D.
  6 APHORISMS
KESZTLER-KOVACS
  BAROQUE MUSIC FOR WOODWI
KETELBEY, A.
  SANCTUARY OF THE HEART
KETTERING, E.
  15 CAROLS
KETTING, O.
  MARCH (1979)
  QUINTET "A SET OF PIECES
  THEMA EN VARIATIES
KETTING, P.
  FANTASIA (1969)
  PARTITA(1936)
  SONATA (1936)
  TRIO (1929)
KEULEN, G. VAN
  SOUVENIR NOSTALGIUQE
KEULER, J.
  PICCOLA PARTITA
KEURIS, T.
  CONCERTINO (1976-77)
  MUSIC (1973)
  MUSICA CONCERTANTE
  QUARTET
KEYES
  BASSOONERIES
KHACHATURIAN, A.
  ARMENIAN SONG

TRIO
KHACHATURYAN, A.
  TRIO (1932)
  TRIO
KIBBE, M.
  3 CANONS
  QUINTET #1
  SONATA
  SONATINA
  TRIO
  TRIO
  VARIATIONS ON A THEME OF
KIEFER, W.
  ELENA POLKA
  ELENA POLKA
KIESEWETTER, P.
  SZENEN (1968)
  LE TOMBEAU DE LULLY, OP
KIETZER, R.
  4 DUETS IN SYMPHONIC STY
  DUETTE, OP 94, 3 VOLS
KIEVMAN, C.
  SIROCCO (1975)
KILAR, W.
  TRAINING 68 (1968)
KILLMAYER, W.
  BLASONS (1968)
  3 DANCES
  KINDERTAGE
  KINDERTAGE
  PETIT SAVOYARD, LE
  WOODS SO WILDE, THE
  WOODS SO WILDE, THE
KIM, E.
  DEAD CALM
KIM, Y.
  3 MOVEMENTS
  QUINTET
KIMBELL, M.
  5 DIALOGUES
KING, H.
  A FLEUR D'EAU (1964)
  CONCERTINO AVIUM (1965)
  ETRE POETE (1954)
  3 FABELEN (1942)
  KWINTET (1949)
KING, K.
  NIGHT IN JUNE
  NIGHT IN JUNE
  NIGHT IN JUNE, A
KINGMA, P.
  SERENATA GEMINI
  SEXTET (1973)
KINGMAN
  4 MINIATURES
KINGMAN, D.
  QUINTET
KIRCHNER, V.
  NACHTMUSIK (1971)
KIRCK, G.
  RESULTANTS
KIRNBERGER, J.

GAVOTTE
GAVOTTE
KISIELEWSKI, S.
  SUITE
KJELLBERG, J.
  KVINTETT
KLAMI, U.
  RAGTIME
KLAUSS, N.
  CAPE KENNEDY SKETCHES
  CLARINETICS
  CLOWNS, THE
  DOLCE (WITH A BEAT)
  FUGUE IN C MA
  INVENTION
  SONG FOR TWILIGHT
KLEBE, G.
  AL ROVESCIO, OP 67
  AL ROVESCIO, OP 67
  7 BAGATELLEN, OP 35
  7 BAGATELLEN, OP 35
  GRATULATIONS-TANGO, OP 4
  RECITATIVO, ARIA E DUETT
  TENNEN NO BI, OP 62
KLEIMAN, S.
  FESTIVITY
KLEIN, L.
  QUINTET (1952)
  TRIO SONATA
KLEIN, R.
  3 CHORALES FOR ADVENT, C
  FANTASIE
  FANTASIE
  FESTTAGSMUSIKEN. CHORALE
  SERENADE
KLEINKNECHT, J.
  SONATA IN C MI
  SONATA IN C MI
  SONATA IN G MA
  SONATA IN G
KLEINKNECHT, W.
  3 SONATAS
KLEINSINGER, G.
  DESIGN FOR WOODWINDS
KLEPPER, W.
  SONATA
KLERK, A. DE
  MISSA MATER SANCTAE LAET
  5 NOELS FRANCAIS (1963)
  SARABANDE EN SICILIENNE
KLERK, J. DE
  KLEINE PARTITA
  KLEINE PARTITA
KLICKMANN, F.
  SWEET HAWAIIAN MOONLIGHT
  TRAIL TO LONG AGO
KLING, H.
  OLIFANT EN MUG ·
  TWO LITTLE BULFINCHES PO
  TWO LITTLE BULFINCHES PO
KLINGSOR, T.
  SERENADE

KLOSE, H.
  3 CONCERT DUETS
  6 DUETS
KLOTZMAN, A.
  FUN
KLUGHARDT, A.
  QUINTET, OP 79
  SCHILFLIEDER, OP 28
KLUSAK, J.
  CONCERTINO (1955)
  CONTRAPPUNTO FIORITO
  5 INVENTION "SCHACHSPIEL
  SONATA (1963/65)
  VI. INVENTION (1969)
KNAB, A.
  LINDEGGER LANDLER
  SERENADE
  SERENADE
KNAPE, W.
  2 SUITES
KNELLWOLF, J.
  DUETS, 4 VOLS
KNEZEK, V.
  12 PARTITEN
KNIGHT
  QUARTET
KNIGHT, M.
  SELFISH GIANT SUITE
KNIGHT, V.
  10 TRIOS
KNIGHTON, M.
  LITTLE MINUET
  QUARTET #1
KNUSSEN, O.
  OCEAN DE TERRE, OP 10
  PANTOMINE
  PUZZLE MUSIC
  PUZZLE MUSIC
  PUZZLE MUSIC
  QUARTET, OP 15 (1977)
  ROSARY SONGS, OP 9
  TRUMPETS (1975)
KNUSSEN,O.
  OPHELIA DANCES I,OP 13A
KOCH, &.
  3 DANCE EPISODES
KOCH, E.
  MINIATYRER (1970)
KOCH, E. VON
  CANTO E DANZA (1975)
  CONCERTO PICCOLO
  DIALOGUE (1975)
KOCH, F.
  ANACLETS
  SCHERZO FOR 5 WINDS
KOCHAN, G.
  DIVERTIMENTO, OP 12
KOCSAR, M.
  DIVERTIMENTO (1956)
  QUINTET #1
  UNGARESCA
  VARIAZIONI (1968)

KODALY, Z.
  ZONGORA MUSZIKA #2
KOECHLIN, C.
  EPITAPHE DE JEAN HARLOW,
    IDYLLE
  4 LITTLE PIECES, OP173
  SEPTUOR
  SONATE,OP 75
  SONATINE MODALE, OP155
  SUITE EN QUATUOR
  TRIO D'ANCHES
  TRIO
KOEHLER, E.
  40 PROGRESSIVE DUETS, OP
  PROGRESSIVE DUETS,OP 55,
  40 PROGRESSIVE DUETS,OP
  6 SONATINAS, OP 96,AND 3
  6 SONATINES, 3 DUOS CONC
  VALSE DES FLEURS
KOEHLER, H.
  3 QUARTETS, OP149
KOEHLER, M.
  14 PROGRESSIVE DUETS
KOELLREUTER, H.
  CONSTRUCTIO AD SYNESIN
  CONSTRUCTIO AD SYNESIN
KOELLREUTTER, H.
  8 HAIKAI DES PEDRO XISTO
KOEPKE, P.
  AUBADE
  AUTUMN IDYLL
  BADINAGE
  DANSE CAPRIOLE
  EVENSONG
  FOX FIRE
  HARLEQUINADE
  SHIVAREE
KOERPPEN, A.
  DUO
  SERENADE (1952)
  SERENADE IN F MA (1952)
  VAGANTENBALLADE, DIE
KOETSIER, J.
  AMSTERDAM (1948)
  6 BAGATELLEN, OP 16/2
  DIVERTIMENTO #2, OP 35/1
  DIVERTIMENTO, OP 16/1
  INTRODUCTION ET FOLATRER
  NONETT (1967)
  OCTET (1968)
  3 PEZZI
  QUINTET (1968)
  QUINTET, OP 3 (1932; RE
  QUINTET, OP 43 (1955)
  RONDO SERENO (1976)
  SEPTETT, OP 4 (1932)
  TRIO
  TRIO, OP 13/1 (1936)
  TRIO, OP 13/2 (1937)
  TRIO, OP 81 (1978)
KOGOJ, M.
  EPISODES

KOHLER, E.
  AU VOL D'OISEAU, OP 98
  DIE WELLE, OP 83
  GRAND QUARTET, OP 92
  GRAND QUARTETTE, OP 92
  SCHERZO (QUARTET, OP 92)
KOHN, K.
  CAPRICCIOS
  CONCERT MUSIC
  DIVERTIMENTO
  IMPROMPTUS
  INTRODUCTIONS & PARODIES
  LITTLE SUITE
  PROPHET BIRD, THE: CONCE
  PROPHET BIRD, THE: CONCE
  SERENADE
  SOUVENIRS #2
KOHOUT, J.
  6 MINIATUREN
  MINIATURES
  VARIATIONEN AUF EIN TSCH
KOHOUTEK, C.
  SUITE (1959)
KOHS, E.
  NIGHT WATCH (1944)
  WOODWIND QUINTET
KOKAI, R.
  QUARTETTINO
KOKKONEN, J.
  WOODWIND QUINTET (1972/7
KOLASINSKI, J.
  LITTLE SUITE
KOLB, B.
  HOMAGE TO K. JARRETT & G
  3 PLACE SETTINGS
  REBUTTAL
  SOUNDINGS (1972)
  SOUNDINGS (1972)
  TROBAR CLUS
  TROBAR CLUS
  VERNISSAGE
  VERSETS
KOLBERG, K.
  A WIND QUINTET
KOLINSKI, M.
  CONCERTINO (1974)
  6 FRENCH FOLKSONGS
  LYRIC SEXTET (1929)
KOLMAN, P.
  DUE CASTI, OP 2
  SONATA CANONICA
KOLZ, E.
  GALANTE MENUETTE
  KLEINE VARIATIONEN
KOMADINA, V.
  MICROSONATES
KOMMA, K.
  ESTAMPIE
  MAGNIFICAT 1965
KOMOROUS, R.
  UNTITLED 4
  UNTITLED 5

YORK
YORK
KOMTER, J.
  ANDANTE IN D MA
  CHANSON D'AUTOMNE (1954)
  DIVERTIMENTO IN G MA
  TRIO-SONATINE (REV 1973)
KONARSKI, J.
  MUSIC (1962)
KONDOROSSY, L.
  LITTLE SUITE
  SERENADE
KONIETZNY, H.
  ISOMETRISCH-ISORHYTHMISC
  KLEINE KAMMERMUSIK #2
  PAS DE DEUX(1968)
KONIG, H.
  DUO
  5 KLEINE SATZE
  KLEINE SUITE
KONOWALSKI, B.
  MINI-RONDO
KONT, P.
  BALLADE
  CONCERTO LIRICO, OP 61/2
  DUO
  QUINTET IN MEMORIAM FR.
  SEPTET, OP 61/3
  SERENATA A TRE, OP 61/1
  SUITE EN PASSANT
  TRAURIGEN JAGER (1958)
  TRIO
KOPELENT, M.
  CANTO INTIMO (1964)
  FEW MINUTES WITH AN OBOI
  FEW MINUTES WITH AN OBOI
  FEW MINUTES WITH AN OBOI
  MUSIK FUR FUNF
  TRISTE E CONSOLANTE
KOPP, F.
  CONVERSATIONS
  3 MOVEMENTS
  OCTOBER '55
  PASSACAGLIA IN THE OLDEN
KOPPEL, H.
  DIVERTIMENTO PASTORALE,
KOPSCH, J.
  TRIO
KORDA, V.
  DIVERTIMENTO
  QUARTETTINO
KORINEK, M.
  KONCERTNA FANTAZIA
  TRIO, A (1962)
KORINGER, F.
  APHORISMEN
  SONATA PROFANA
KORN, P.
  ALOYSIA SERENADE, OP 19
  QUINTET FOR WINDS, OP 40
KORNAUTH, E.
  CLARINET QUINTET, OP 33

KAMMERMUSIK, OP 31
KORTE, K.
  DIABLERIE
  DIALOGUE!
  FACETS, 1970
  MATRIX 7
  MATRIX
  QUINTET (1959)
  REMEMBRANCES
  RONDINO
  SYMMETRICS
KOSA, G.
  TRIO
KOSCHAT, T.
  MELODIE CELESTE
KOSCHINSKY, F.
  VARIATIONS UBER DAS MANT
KOSKEY, G.
  FUGUE
KOSMA, J.
  DIVERTISSEMENT
KOSTECK, G.
  REFRAINS & CANONS (1965)
KOTONSKI, W.
  MUSICAL GAMES
  POUR QUATRE
  QUINTET (1964)
  SELECTION I
  TRIO (1960)
KOTSCHAU, J.
  BLASERQUINTETT, OP 14
  DIVERTIMENTO IN B FL MA
  DIVERTIMENTO
KOUGUELL, A.
  MELODIE & DANSE HEBRAIQU
  3 PIECES
  SUITE FOR WOODWINDS
KOUMANS, R.
  TRIO, OP 30
KOUNADIS
  CHOREIA I
KOUNADIS, A.
  "WER OHREN HAT ZU HOREN,
  2 GEDICHTE DES KONSTANTI
  3 NOCTURNES NACH SAPPHO
  4 PEZZI
  4 PEZZI
KOUTZEN, B.
  MUSIC
KOVACH, A.
  TRIO #1, MUSIQUE D'AUTOM
KOVAR, V.
  SONATA
  WO DIE VOGLEIN LEBEN
KOVATS, B.
  SONATINA (1948)
KOWALSKI, J.
  DIVERTIMENTO
  GRIMACES
  5 INVENTIONS
  MINIATURY
KOX, H.

CYCLOPHONY VIII
SEXTET (1957)
SEXTET #3 (1959)
SEXTET #4 (1960)
KOZHEVNIKOV, B.
2 PIECES (SONG-MARCH)
KRAEHENBUEHL, D.
VARIATIONS
KRAFT, K.
MUSIK UNTERM FENSTER, OP
KRAFT, L.
LINE DRAWINGS
LITTLE SUITE
PARTITA #3
PARTITA 4 (1975)
SEXTET
SHORT SUITE
TRIOS & INTERLUDES
KRAFT, W.
HEINZELMANNCHEN-BALLADE
KRAKAMP, E.
CONCERT SUITE,OP139
KRAMAR¬KROMMER, F.
OCTET, OP 79
KRAMER, M.
LAWD
KRASKO, J.
SIT DOWN SUN
KRATOCHVIL, J.
SUITE
TRIO (1958)
TRIOS TSCHECHISCHER KLAS
TRIOS TSCHECHISCHER KLAS
KRATOCHWIL, H.
PARTITA RITMICA, OP 92
SUITE, OP101
KRATZSCHMAR, W.
ANAKREONTISCHE PHANTASIE
KRAUS, J.
QUINTET IN D MA (1783)
SONATA IN D MA
WIENER FLOTENQUINTETT IN
KRAUSE¬GRAUMNITZ
CADENZA QUINTET #1
KRAUSE¬GRAUMNITZ, H.
BLASERQUINTETT #1
KRAUSS
ALLEGRO
KRAUZE, Y.
MUSICIANS, THE & THE DRU
KRAUZE, Z.
3 MALAY PANTUNS (1961)
POLYCHROMY (1968)
WIR BESITZEN KEINERLEI F
KRCEK, J.
CONCERTO E GIOCO (1969)
KREBS
CONTEMPLATION
KREBS, J.
SUITE IN D MA
TRIO IN D MA
TRIO IN D MA

TRIO IN D MI
TRIO IN E MI
TRIO SONATA IN B MI
TRIO-SONATE IN B MI
TRIOSONATE IN B MI
TRIOSONATE IN G MA
KREIN, M.
TRIO
VALSE CAPRICE
KREISLER, F.
LIEBESFREUD
LIEBESFREUD
RONDINO ON A THEME OF BE
RONDINO ON A THEME OF BE
SCHON ROSMARIN
SCHON ROSMARIN
KREITH, K.
DUETTE
KREJCI, I.
BLASERTRIO (1935)
DECHOVY KVINTET (1964)
TRIO (1936)
KREJCI, M.
DIVERTIMENTO (1925)
MOMENTKY
SERENATA
SEXTET
KREK, U.
EPISODI CONCERTANTI
KRENEK, E.
ALPBACH-QUINTETT
AULOKITHARA (1971/72)
AULOKITHARA (1971/72)
PENTAGRAM (1952/57)
SESTINA (1957)
3, SHORT PIECES
SINFONISCHE MUSIK, OP 11
SONATINA, OP 92/2B
THEY KNEW WHAT THEY WANT
TRIO
KRESKY, J.
MUSIC AT NIGHT (1976)
KRETSCHMAR, W.
MUSIC IN C MA
KREUTZER, C.
DUETTO IN C MA
DUO IN C MA
GRAND SEPTUOR, OP 62
QUARTET IN E FL MA
QUATUOR IN E FL MA
QUINTET
SEPTET, OP 62
TRIO
TRIO, OP 23/2
KREUTZER, J.
QUARTET
TRIO IN D MA, OP 9/3
TRIO, OP 16
KREUTZER, K.
DUO IN C MA
TRIO, OP 43
KREUTZER, R.

TRIO
KRIEGER, J.
  PARTIE IN F MA
  SING, OH MY SPIRIT
KRIEGER, S.
  JOHANN KRIEGER SUITE
KRIENS, C.
  RONDO DES LUTINS
KROEGER, K.
  TOCCATA
KROEPSCH, F.
  5 DUETS
  5 DUOS
KROL, B.
  CAPRICCIO DA CAMERA, OP
  HARFEN-SEPTETT, OP 7
  KONZERTANTE MUSIK, OP 6
  LINZER HARMONIEMUSIK, OP
  QUARTET, OP 9
KROLL, G.
  INVOCAZIONI
  MAGNIFICAT (1958)
KROMMER¬KRAMAR, F.
  CONCERTO IN F MA
  QUARTET
  2 QUARTETS
KROMMER, F.
  CONCERTANTE
  CONCERTO IN E FL MA, OP
  OCTET-PARTITA, OP 57
  OCTET-PARTITA, OP 67
  OCTET-PARTITA, OP 69
  PARTITA IN C MI
  13 PIECES, OP 47
  QUARTET #2
  QUARTET IN B FL MA, OP 4
  QUARTET IN B FL MA, OP 8
  QUARTET IN C
  QUARTET IN D MA, OP 82
  QUARTET IN E FL MA, OP 6
  QUARTET IN F
  QUINTET IN B FL MA, OP 9
  13 STUCKE, OP 47
  VARIATIONS ON A THEME BY
  VARIATIONS ON A THEME OF
KROPFREITER, A.
  ALTDORFER-PASSION
  QUINTET (1968)
  TANZ-BALLADE
KROPFREITER, A.F.
  IN MEMORIAM (1963)
KRTICKA
  DUETTE AUS TSCHECHISCHEN
KRTICKA, S.
  ALBUM DER KOMPOSITIONEN
KRULL, D.
  KVARTETT
  QUARTET (1957)
KRUMPHOLTZ, J.
  SONATA IN F MA
KRUTZFELD, W.
  RELATIONEN, OP 34 (1961)

KRUYF, T. DE
  EINST DEM GRAU (1964)
  MOSAICO, OP 24 (1969)
  QUARTETTO
  SERENATA, OP 21 (1968)
KUBIK, G.
  5 BIRTHDAY PIECES
  DIVERTIMENTO #1 (1959)
  LITTLE SUITE
KUBIN, R.
  HUMORESKEN
  NONETTO
KUBIZEK, A.
  KAMMERQUINTETT, OP 15
  KLEINE TANZ-SUITE
  4 PIECES
  QUARTETTO DA CAMERA, OP
  SINFONIA DA CAMERA, OP 2
  SONATA, OP 24B
  TRIO, OP 26A
  VERGNUGLICHE MINIATUREN,
KUCERA, V.
  DIPTYCHON (1966)
  DRAMATA (1961)
  PANTA RHEI (1963)
  SCENARIO, ZYKLUS (1969)
KUEFFNER, J.
  DUET #3
  24 EASY DUETS
KUEGERL, H.
  QUINTET
KUFFNER, J.
  DRITTES POTPOURRI, OP103
  27 DUETS
  DUO CONCERTANS, OP 84/1,
  NOTTURNO, OP110
  50 PROGRESSIVE DUETS
  SERENADE
  SERENADE, OP 21
  2 SERENADES, OP 20, 49
  TRIO, OP 34
KUHLAU
  DIVERTISSEMENT IN G MA,
KUHLAU, F.
  ALLEGRETTO GRAZIOSO (SON
  ALLEGRO (OP 20/2)
  3 BRILLIANT DUETS, OP 13
  3 BRILLIANT DUETS, OP 80
  3 BRILLIANT DUETS, OP102
  3 BRILLIANT DUETS,OP 80
  CONCERT DUETS, OP 10
  DUET, OP 80/1
  3 DUETS, OP 10
  3 DUETS, OP 81
  3 DUETS,OP 80
  3 DUOS BRILLANTS, OP 81
  3 DUOS BRILLANTS, OP110/
  3 DUOS BRILLANTS,OP 13 B
  3 DUOS BRILLANTS,OP 81
  3 DUOS BRILLANTS,OP102
  3 DUOS CONCERTANTES, OP
  3 DUOS CONCERTANTS, OP 8

400

DUOS CONCERTANTS,OP 10
3 DUOS CONCERTANTS,OP 10
3 DUOS, OP 10
3 DUOS, OP 57 BIS (PUB S
3 DUOS, OP 57 BIS
3 DUOS,OP 80
3 DUOS,OP 81
3 GRAND DUETS CONCERTANT
3 GRAND DUETS,OP 39
3 GRAND DUOS, OP 39
3 GRAND DUOS,OP 39
GRAND QUARTET, OP103
GRAND QUARTET, OP103
GRAND TRIO, OP 86, VOL I
GRAND TRIO, OP 86, VOL I
GRAND TRIO, OP 86, VOL I
GRAND TRIO, OP 90
3 GRANDS DUOS CONCERTANT
3 GRANDS DUOS, OP 39 (PU
3 GRANDS DUOS, OP 39
3 GRANDS TRIOS, OP 86,
QUARTET IN E MA, OP103
QUARTET, OP103
QUATUOR IN E MA, OP103
QUINTET, OP 51/1 (1823)
QUINTET, OP 51/3
SONATINA (OP 20/1)
TRIO, OP 86/1
TRIO, OP119
TRIO, OP119
3 TRIOS, OP 13
KUHMSTEDT, P.
MIKRONETTEN
QUINTET
KUHN, M.
SERENATA NOTTURNA
KUHNAU, J.
GIGUE
GIGUE
KUHNEL, E.
QUINTET (SUITE), OP 29
KUKUCK, F.
KAMMERMUSIK
KUMMER, F.
TRIO #6, OP 56
KUMMER, G.
CONCERT TRIO, OP 24
2 DUETS, OP 46
3 DUETS, OP132
3 DUETS,OP132
2 DUOS CONCERTANTS, OP 4
DUOS CONCERTANTS,OP   9
3 DUOS FACILES,OP 74
NOCTURNE
3 PETITS DUOS,OP 20
SONATINA,OP 36/3
TRIO #6, OP 59
TRIO BRILLANT IN D MA, O
TRIO BRILLANT, OP 58
TRIO IN A MA, OP 59
TRIO IN C MA, OP 53
TRIO IN G MA, OP 24

TRIO, OP 24
TRIO, OP 24
TRIO, OP 30
TRIO, OP 53
TRIO, OP 58
TRIO, OP 59
24 TRIOS, OP 11 & 13
KUMMER, K.
2 DUETS, OP 46
TRIO IN F MA
KUNAD, R.
COMMEDIA "DIE EHE" (1969
MELODIE, DIE ICH VERLORE
MUSIK FUR BLASER (1965)
KUNERT, K.
DIVERTIMENTO #2, OP 18
OCTET, OP 19
QUINTET #4
QUINTET, OP 14
SONATA IN G MA, OP 15
SONATA, OP 15A
SONATA, OP 20
TRIO IN C MI
TRIO IN C MI, OP 7
TRIO IN D MA, OP 5
TRIO, OP 5
ZWEITES BLASERQUINTETT,
KUNST, J.
NO TIME XXI:4 (1974)
KUNZ, A.
EMANATION #2 (1964)
FUN FOR TWO (1964)
FUN FOR TWO (1964)
FUN FOR 2 (1964)
FUN FOR 3 (1964)
LOVE, DEATH & FULLMOONNI
QUINTET (1964)
SONG OF THE CLARINET, TH
KUPFERMAN, M.
AVAILABLE FORMS (1966)
4 CHARADES
CONCEPTUAL WHEEL, THE
4 CONSTELLATIONS
4 DOUBLE FEATURES
DUO DIVERTIMENTO
GARDEN OF MY FATHER'S HO
INFINITIES 13
SHORT SHRIFT
THREE FOR TWO
KUPKA, K.
3 CANZONAS
GESANG, LIED
KUPKOVIC, L.
PRAPARIERTER TEXT 2
PRAPARIERTER TEXT 2
TREFFPUNKT
KURI-ALDANA, M.
CANDELARIA
CANTARES
KURKA, R.
7 MORAVIAN FOLK-SONGS
KURTAG, G.

QUINTET (1959)
QUINTET, OP 2
KURTZ, E.
  CONVERSATIONS
KURTZ, J.
  2 STUDIES
KURTZ, S.
  3 IMPRESSIONS
  SUITE
KURZ, W.
  VARIATIONENSUITE (1953)
KURZBACH, P.
  BLASERSEXTETT
  TRIO
KUSZING
  KLARINETTENMUSIK FUR ANF
KUTSCH, B.
  JUNGE FLOTIST, DER
  JUNGE FLOTIST, DER
KUUSISTO, I.
  CASSAZIONE (1961)
  DUO (1957)
KUUSISTO, T.
  CHRISTMAS SONATINE, OP 1
KVANDAL, J.
  3 HYMN TUNES
  QUINTET, OP 34
KWIATKOWSKI, R.
  BALTIC SONNETS
LA CAPRIA, V.
  NOTTURNINO
LA FORGE, F.
  MENUET VARIE
LA MOTTE, D. DE
  GESAMMELTE WERKE
LA ROSA, M.
  THE ANCIENT OF ANCIENTS
  COMING IN GLORY
LA VIOLETTE, W.
  DUET ALBUM
LABITZKY, A.
  HERD GIRL'S DREAM, THE
LABITZKY, T.
  DREAM OF THE SHEPHERDESS
  HERD GIRL'S DREAM, THE
  HERD GIRL'S DREAM, THE
LABOR, J.
  QUINTET, OP 11
LABURDA, J.
  KASACE #1
LACERDA, O.
  VARIATIONS & FUGUE
LACHENMANN, H.
  INTROVERSION II (1964)
  INTROVERSION II (1964)
  TEMA (1968)
  TRIO FLUIDO (1966)
LACHNER, F.
  OCTET, OP156
LACHOWSKA, S.
  TRIPTYCH (1964)
LACK, T.

IDILIO
LACOMBE, P.
  SERENADE
  SERENADE, OP 47
LACOME, P.
  PASSEPIED
  PASSEPIED,
LACOUR, G.
  DIVERTISSEMENT
  QUATUOR
  SUITE EN DUO
  SUITE EN DUO
  SUITE EN DUO
LADERMAN, E.
  CELESTIAL BODIES
  DOUBLE HELIX
  FROM THE PSALMS
  NONETTE
  OCTET IN 1 MOVEMENT
  SINGLE VOICE
  THEME, VARIATIONS, & FIN
LADMIRAULT, P.
  CHORAL ET VARIATIONS
  CHORAL ET VARIATIONS
LAGRENZE, G.
  LA BUSCHA
LAJOVIC, A.
  DIALOGUE
LAJTHA, L.
  4 HOMAGES
  MARIONNETTES
  QUINTET #2, OP 46
  TRIO #1, OP 22
  TRIO #2, OP 47
LAKE, M.
  ANDANTINO
  ANNIE LAURIE
  ANNIE LAURIE
  ANNIE LAURIE
  CLEVELAND MARCH
  IRON MOUNTAIN
  LONG, LONG AGO
  LOUISIANA
LAKEY, C.
  SAXET #4-5
LAKNER, Y.
  SEXTET (1951)
LALLIET, T.
  TERZETTO
LAMB, J.
  6 BAREFOOT DANCES
  MADRIGAL
LAMB, P.
  PASTORAL
LAMBERT, J.
  FOR A WHILE
LAMPE, G.
  PERMUTAZIONI
LAMPERSBERG, G.
  CONCERTINO
  QUARTETT
  SINFONIE

402

TWILIGHT CAROL POLKA, OP
LAYTON, B.
  DIVERTIMENTO, OP 6
LAYZER, A.
  WOODWIND QUINTET
LAZAROF, H.
  ASYMPTOTES
  CADENCE #5 (1972)
  CONCERTAZIONI
  CONCERTAZIONI
  CONCERTAZIONI
  CONCERTINO DA CAMERA
  ESPACES
  OKTETT
  TEMPI CONCERTATI
  TEMPI CONCERTATI
  TEMPI CONCERTATI
  TEMPI CONCERTATI
LAZARUS, H.
  3 CONCERT DUETS
  24 EASY & PROGRESSIVE DU
  20 EASY PROGRESSIVE DUET
  GRAND ARTISTIC DUETS
  3 GRAND ARTISTIC DUETS
  3 GRAND CONCERT DUETS
LE CLAIR, J.
  SONATE #8 IN D MA
LE FANU, N.
  OBOE QUARTET
  SAME DAY DAWNS, THE
LE FLEMING, C.
  HOMAGE TO BEATRIX POTTER
LE JEUNE, C.
  REVECY VENIR DU PRINTANS
LE MARE, E.
  ANDANTINO
LE SIEGE, A.
  DIALOGUE
  PHIDIAN
LEAHY, M.
  AGITATION
  4 SHORT SKETCHES
LEBEIRRE, O.
  STYRIENNE
LEBIC, L.
  KONS (A)
  KONS (B)
  KONS (B)
  KONS IN A MI
LECHNER, K.
  CANTICA I (1965)
  CANTICA II (1971)
  REQUIEM
LECLAIR, J.
  CONCERTO IN C MA
  MINUET & HUNTING SCENE
  RECREATION DE MUSIQUE #2
  SARABANDE & TAMBOURIN
  SONATA IN C MA
  SONATA IN D MA
  SONATA IN F MA
  SONATA

SONATA, OP 9/2
SONATE A 3
TRIO SONATA IN D MA, OP
LECLERC, M.
  3 BLUETTES
LECLERCQ, E.
  INTRODUCTION & SCHERZAND
  PRELUDE & MOUVEMENT PERP
LECUONA, E.
  LA COMPARSA
LEDERER, J.
  QUINTET, OP 45
  ROKOKO-SUITE, OP 43
LEDUC, J.
  QUINTETT A VENT
  3, STUKJES
  SUITE EN QUATUOR
LEE, E.
  COMPOSITION FOR 8 INSTRU
  COMPOSITION
LEE, N.
  QUINTET
  VARIATIONS
LEES, B.
  3 DUOS (1969)
  2 MINIATURES
LEEUW, T. DE
  ANTIPHONIE (1960)
  MOUNTAINS (1977)
  RIME (1974)
  SCHELP (1964)
  5 SCHETSEN (1952)
  DE TOVERFLUIT (1954)
  TRIO (1952)
LEEUWEN, A. VAN
  4 MINIATURES
  4 MINIATURES
  SONATINA IN THE OLD STYL
  TURKEY IN THE STRAW
LEFEBVRE, C.
  CANON (SUITE, OP 57)
  INTERMEZZO (SUITE #2)
  PRELUDE FOR QUINTET
  PRELUDE
  SUITE, OP 57
LEFEVRE, C.
  BALLADE
LEFEVRE, J.
  TRIO IN B FL MA
LEFEVRE, X.
  6 DUOS
  6 PETITS DUOS FACILES
  3 QUARTETS
LEGE, G.
  TRIO
  UBI CARITAS (1967)
LEGLEY, V.
  5 MINIATURES, OP 54
  QUATUOR, OP 14 (1943)
  QUINTETTE, OP 58 (1961)
  SERENADE, OP 44/3 (1957)
  TRIO, OP 11 (1942)

TRIO, OP 55 (1959)
LEGRAND, M.
  PORCELAINE DE SAXE
LEGRENZI, G.
  BONACOSSA
  FINI, LA
  SECCA SOARDA, LA
LEGRON, L.
  PETITE SUITE
LEHMANN, D.
  WOODWIND QUINTET
LEHMANN, H.
  BRINGEN UM ZU KOMMEN
  EPISODEN (1963/64)
  FACES (1972)
  GEGEN-(BEI-)SPIELE
  REGIONS III
  SPIELE
  TANTRIS (1976/77)
  TRACTUS (1971)
LEIBOWITZ, R.
  CAPRICCIO, OP 41 (1956)
  CHAMBER CONCERTO, OP 10
  CHAMBER SYMPHONY, OP 16
  CHANSON DADA, OP 76B
  MOTIFS, OP 74 (1967)
  PETITE SUITE, OP 90
  3 POEMS OF GEORGES LIMBO
  QUINTET, OP 11 (1944)
  SERENADE, OP 38 (1955)
  SONATINA, OP 69 (1966)
  SONNET, OP 77 (1967)
  SUITE, OP 81
  VARIATIONS
LEICHTLING, A.
  CANTICLE #1, OP 51
  NACHTMUSIK
  NACHTMUSIK, OP 36
  2 PROVERBS
  QUARTET #2, OP 25
  QUINTET #2, OP 24
  QUINTET #3
  QUINTET, OP 33
  RUBAIYAT FRAGMENTS, OP 5
  TRIAL & DEATH OF SOCRATE
LEIGH, W.
  TRIO
LEITERMEYER, F.
  DIVERTIMENTO, OP 38
  DIVERTIMENTO, OP 53
  TIENTO (FANTASIE), OP 62
LEJET, E.
  MUSIQUE
LELEU, J.
  SUITE SYMPHONIQUE
LEMAIRE
  MINI-TRIO
LEMARE, E.
  ANDANTINO
  ANDANTINO
  ANDANTINO
  ANDANTINO

ANDANTINO
ANDANTINO
CATHEDRAL MEDITATION
CATHEDRAL MEDITATION
CATHEDRAL MEDITATION
LEMELAND, A.
  CAPRICCIO, OP 43
  DIVERTISSEMENT, OP 45
  EPILOGUE NOCTURNE, OP 22
  ETAT D'HORIZON, 2: L'ETE
  MOUVEMENT CONCERTANT
  MUSIQUE NOCTURNE, OP 18
  NOCTURNE
  NOCTURNE, OP 10
  PASTORALE
  5 PORTRAITS, OP 49
LENDVAI, E.
  KAMMERSUITE, OP 32
LENDVAY, K.
  4 DUETTI
LENNON/MC CARTNEY
  YESTERDAY; MAXWELL'S HAM
LENOT, J.
  CLAMEURS
  COMME AU LOIN (1977)
  JULIAN TRIO
  SOLACIUM
LEONARD
  SARABANDE & WALTZ
LEONARD, B.
  CANZONETTA & SCHERZO
  DRINK TO ME ONLY WITH TH
  IDYL
  IDYL
  MOON WALK
  NIGHTFALL
  OLD FRENCH SONG, AN
  PALM DESERT NOCTURNE
  ROMANZA
  SENTIMENTAL NOCTURNE
  SUMMER ROMANCE
  TRIO CON BRIO
LEONCAVALLO, R.
  ARIOSO (PAGLIACCI)
LEONI, C.
  CONCLAVE & FUGUE PATROL
  SOUTHERN WALTZ
LERDAHL, F.
  EROS (1975)
LERICH, R.
  TRIO IN C MA
LESSARD, J.
  CONCERTO FOR WIND INSTRU
  MUSIC FOR THE WEDDING
  OCTET
  PARTITA
  TRIO
LESSEL, F.
  QUARTET
LESTER
  CRIMSON BLUSHES
LESTER, L.

405

CLARINET TWOSOME
CRIMSON BLUSHES
FUN FOR 4 CLARINETS
3 PIECES
LESUR, D.
  4 LIEDER
  SEXTUOR
  SUITE MEDIEVALE
  SUITE
LETELLIER, L.
  RECUEIL DE DUOS ET TRIOS
LETELLIER, R.
  NOUVEAUX DUOS & TRIOS
  14 NOUVEAUX DUOS & TRIOS
  14 NOUVEAUX DUOS & TRIOS
  14 NOUVEAUX DUOS ET TRIO
  PIECE RECREATIVE
  PIECE RECREATIVE
  RECUEIL DE DUOS & TRIOS
  RECUEIL DE DUOS ET TRIOS
  RECUEIL DE DUOS ET TRIOS
LETNAN, J.
  STYRI SKICE(1963)
LEUKAUF, R.
  ALTSPANISCHE SUITE
  BLASERQUINTETT, OP 25
  QUINTET, OP 32A
LEVI, P.
  5 PROGRESSIONS
  TRUTH, THE
LEVI, W.
  DANCE OF THE REEDS
  FLUTE FLIRTATION
  FOUR FOR FUN
  SAXOPHONE CANTABILE
  WALKING LIGHTLY
LEVIN, G.
  LOVE'S BLOOM
LEVINAS, M.
  STRETTES TOURNANTES- MIG
  VOIX DANS UN VAISSEAU D'
LEVINE, B.
  DUET
  INTRODUCTION & ALLEGRO
  QUINTET
LEVINE, J.
  HARPSICHORD QUARTET
LEVITT, R.
  WOODMEN OF THE WORLD
LEVY, F.
  ADAGIO AND SCHERZO
  DUO
  QUINTET
  SERENADE
  SEXTET
  SUITE
  TRIO
LEWIN, F.
  DUNLAP'S CREEK
LEWIN, G.
  CARIBBEAN SKETCHES
  3 LATIN AMERICAN IMPRESS

TWO OF A KIND
LEWIS
  BEGINNING DUETS
LEWIS, J.
  MILANESE STORY, THE
  MILANESE STORY, THE
LEWIS, P.
  DUET
  MANESTAR
  MANESTAR
  SEPTET
  SEPTET
  SESTINA
LEWIS, R.
  MUSIC FOR 12 PLAYERS
  MUSIC FOR 12 PLAYERS
  OSSERVAZIONI I
  TRIO (1966)
LEWKOVITCH, B.
  CANTATA SACRA
  3 ORATIONES
LEYBACH, I.
  NOCTURNE #5 IN G MA
  NOCTURNE #5 IN G MA
LEYE, L.
  SUITE
LIADOV, A.
  MOSQUITO DANCE
  MUSICAL SNUFF BOX
  MUSICAL SNUFF BOX
  8 RUSSIAN FOLKSONGS
LIADOW, A.
  MUSIC BOX, THE
  MUSICAL SNUFF BOX
  8 RUSSIAN FOLK DANCES, O
  SARABANDE & FINALE
LIANI, D.
  CJANTIS
LIBAEK, S.
  6 MOODS
LICHT, D.
  3 PIECES
LICKL, J.
  QUINTETTO CONCERTANTE IN
  TRIO IN E FL MA
  3 TRIOS
LIDDLE, S.
  HOW LOVELY ARE THY DWELL
LIDHOLM, I.
  CONCERTINO
  INVENTION (1954)
LIDL, V.
  ABENDS AM WASSER
  CANTUS VARIABILIS (1967)
  DIVERTIMENTO (1951)
  PAMPELISKY (1966)
LIEBERSON, P.
  ACCORDANCE (1975-76)
  ACCORDANCE
  CONCERTO FOR VIOLONCELLO
  CONCERTO FOR VIOLONCELLO
  CONCERTO FOR VIOLONCELLO

CONCERTO FOR 4 GROUPS OF
LIEDBECK, S.
  FANTASI
  IMPROMPTU
  SUITE (1945)
LIER, B. VAN
  3 OUD-PERZISCHE KWATRIJN
LIGETI, G.
  6 BAGATELLES
  FRAGMENT
  10 STUCKE
LIJNSCHOTEN, V.
  4 CANONS
LILDL, V.
  3 MILOSTNE PTSNE (1970)
LILGE, H.
  VARIATIONEN UND FUGE UBE
LILIEN, I.
  SONATINE APOLLINIQUE
  VOYAGE AU PRINTEMPS
LIMMERT, E.
  GRIECHISCHE ESSAYS
  SERENADE (1962)
  SUITE EN MINIATURE
LINCKE, P.
  GLOWWORM, THE
  THE GLOWWORM
LINDA, B.
  MUSICA PER SYLVANUM
LINDBOM, A.
  KVARTETT (1948)
LINDE, B.
  DANS (1952)
  DIVERTIMENTO, OP 25
  QUATUOR EN MINIATURE, OP
  VINJETTSVIT (1959)
LINDE, H.
  CAPRICCIO (1963)
  TRIO (1960)
  TRIO
LINDEMAN, B.
  CONCERT MASTERS ON THE H
LINDGREN, O.
  SVIT IN G MI, OP 1
LINDGREN, P.
  ODYPASSE (1976)
LINDLEY, R.
  TRIO
LINICKE, J.
  CONCERTO IN G MA
  OVERTURE IN C MA
  2 SUITEN
  2 SUITES
LINIKE, J.
  SONATA "MORATORIUM" A 5
LINKE
  TANZE AUS 5 JAHRHUNDERTE
LINKE, N.
  BENN-EPITAPH
  BLASERQUINTETT IN EINEM
  CHESAGE (PUZZLE #3)
  COLORATURA

PERCUZZLE PUZZLE (PUZZLE
PROFIT TOUT CLAIR (1967)
LINN, R.
  CONCERTINO
  DUO
  FANFARES
  5 PIECES
  PRELUDE & DANCE
  QUARTET
  QUINTET
LIPATTI, D.
  AUBADE
LIPKIN, M.
  SUITE (1961)
LIPSCOMB, H.
  DESIGN
LIPTAK, D.
  ENCOUNTER II
  FEUILLET D'ALBUM
LISCHKA, R.
  KONTAKTE
LIST
  OLD & NEW DUETS, 2 VOLS
LISZT, F.
  3 CONCERT PIECES
  LIEBESTRAUM
  LIEBESTRAUM;
  LOVE DREAMS (LIEBESTRAUM
  LOVE DREAMS (LIEBESTRAUM
  LOVE DREAMS (LIEBESTRAUM
  PASTORALE (LES PRELUDES)
  WEIHNACHTSLIED
LITTLE, L.
  GREAT DUETS, 2 VOLS
LLOYD
  PUZZLE CANON
LOCATELLI, P.
  2 DUETS,OP 4/4&5
  SONATA IN D MA,OP 1/6
  SONATA IN E MI
  SONATA IN G MA
  SONATA
  SONATA, E
  6 SONATAS,OP 4,VOL.1(1-
  SONATE A TRE
  SONATE IN E MI
  TRIO #2 IN B FL MA
  TRIO IN G MA, OP 3/1
  TRIO SONATA IN D MI, OP
  TRIO SONATA IN G MA, OP
  TRIO-SONATE IN C MA, OP
  TRIO-SONATE IN E MA, OP
  TRIOSONATE, OP 5/1, IN
LOCKE, M.
  MUSIC FOR HIS MAJESTY'S
  MUSIC FOR HIS MAJESTY'S
  3 WORKS
LOCKWOOD, N.
  CLARINET QUINTET
  FUN PIECES
  THREE
LOEBNER, R.

WINDVOGEL UBER OKLAHOMA
LOEFFLER, C.
  2 RHAPSODIES
LOEFFLER, E.
  HEITERE TANZSUITE
  SPIELMUSIK
LOEILLET, J.
  CONCERTO IN D MA
  COURANTE
  6 DUETS, OP 5, 2 VOLS
  6 DUETS,OP 5,2 VOLS
  3 DUETS
  3 DUETS
  QUINTET IN B MI
  SONATA A 3
  SONATA IN A MI, OP 1/1
  SONATA IN D MI
  SONATA IN E MI
  SONATA IN E MI, OP 1 #6
  SONATA IN F MI, OP 1 #1
  SONATA IN F MI, OP 2/5
  SONATA IN G MA, OP 1 #2
  SONATA IN G MA, OP 1/3
  SONATA IN G MI
  SONATA IN G MI, OP 1 #3
  SONATA, OP 5/1
  SONATA, OP 5/2
  SONATA, OP 5/4
  2 SONATAS, OP 5/1, 4
  6 SONATAS, 2 VOLS
  SONATE EN TRIO IN B MI,
  SONATE EN TRIO IN G MI
  SONATE EN TRIO, OP 2/8
  SONATE IN E MI(NO.942)
  SONATE IN G MI(NO.943)
  SONATE, OP 5/1
  SONATE, OP 5/2
  SONATE, OP 5/3
  SONATE, OP 5/4
  SUITE IN E MI
  TRIO SONATA, OP 1/1
  TRIO-SONATE IN F MA, OP
  TRIOSONATE IN F MA, OP
  TRIOSONATE IN G MA, OP
  TRIOSONATE, OP 1/1 IN F
  TRIOSONATE, OP 1/3 IN G
  TRIOSONATE, OP 1/5 IN C
  TRIOSONATEN, OP 2/2 IN
  TRIOSONATEN, OP 2/4 IN
  TRIOSONATEN, OP 2/6 IN
LOEILLET, J.B.
  COURANTE
  COURANTE
  SONATA A 3, #17
  SONATA IN C MI
  SONATA IN D MI
  TRIO SONATA IN D MA, OP
  TRIO SONATA IN D MA, OP
  TRIO SONATA IN E MI, OP
  TRIO SONATA IN E MI, OP
  TRIO SONATA IN F MA, OP
  TRIO SONATA IN G MA, OP

TRIO SONATA IN G MA, OP
TRIOSONATE IN G MA, OP
LOEVENDIE, T.
  3 PEZZI (1968)
  3 STUKKEN (1964)
  6 TURKISH FOLKPOEMS
LOGAN, R.
  ANDANTE
LOHSE, D.
  QUINTET
LOLOV, V.
  SUITE, OP 10 (1947)
LOMBARDI, L.
  GESPRACH UBER BAUME
  TUI-GESANGE (1977)
LOMBARDO, R.
  EROGENOUS ZONES, OR NEGL
  FROSTED WINDOW
  IN MEMORIAM MICHELE LOMB
  2 LYRIC POEMS (1962)
  YES!
LONDON, E.
  QUINTET
  TRIO
LONG, N.
  IN THE AQUARIUM
LONGO, A.
  SCENETTA PASTORALE
LONGTIN, M.
  IMMORTELS D'AGAPIA, LES
  2 RUBANS NOIRS III
  THRENE POUR RACHEL ET DI
  THRENE POUR RACHEL ET DI
LONGUE, A.
  MELODIE
LONQUICH, H.
  MISSA (1971)
  MUSIK IN DIE STILLE
LORA, A.
  6, DANCES
  2 SKETCHES (1960)
LORD, D.
  SEPTET
LORENTZEN, B.
  DANISH WIND
  SYNCRETISM
LORENZINI, D.
  TRE LIRICHE HAN (1970)
LORENZO, L. DE
  CAPRICCIO, OP 82/3
  I QUATTRO VIRTUOSI, OP 8
  I SEGUACI DE PAN, OP 32
  I TRE VIRTUOSI, OP 31
  SINFONIETTA, OP 75
  SUITE MODERNA,OP 83
  TRIO ECCENTRICO, OP 76
  TRIO ROMANTICO, OP 78
LORRAIN, D.
  ANGELUS (1971), L'
LOTHAR, M.
  8 HAIKU, OP 85
  MITSCHULDIGEN, DIE, OP 7

OBOEN-LIEDER, OP 47
SPITZWEG-IMPRESSIONEN, O
LOTTERER, G.
  38 SELECTED SONGS
LOTTI, A.
  ARIETTA
  ARIETTA
  ARIETTA
  SONATA IN G MA
  SONATA
  SONATE
  TRIO IN A MA
  VERE LANGUORUS
  VERE LANGUORUS
LOTZ, H.
  9 FLUTE DUETS
LOUCHEUR
  DIVERTISSEMENT
LOUCHEUR, R.
  CONCERTINO
  DIALOGUES
  EN FAMILLE
  EN FAMILLE
  4 PIECES EN QUINTETTE
  PORTRAITS
LOUEL, J.
  QUINTETTE (1958)
  SUITE (1967)
  SUITE (1967)
LOUMEY
  SHADOWS ON THE WATER
LOUP & FRANCOIS
  QUATUOR IN G MI
LOURIE, A.
  PASTORALE DE LA VOLGA
LOUVIER
  9 CARRES, AVEC 10 DIAPOS
  5 PORTRAITS & 1 IMAGE
LOVE, R.
  QUARTET #2
LOVEC, V.
  PARTITA
LOVREGLIO, D.
  DUO CONCERTANTE
LOVREGLIO, E.
  ANDANTE
LOWE, T.
  SUITE OF DANCES
LOWMAN, K.
  LOS ANGELES SKETCHES
  LOS ANGELES SKETCHES
LOWRY, R.
  FARCE AND FANTASY
LU, Y.
  CONCERT PIECE I
  QUARTET
LUBIN, E.
  SCHERZO #1
LUCAS, L.
  AUBADE
LUCAS, T.
  METAMUSIC

LUCK, H.
  KLEINE VORTRAGSSTUCKE
LUCK, R.
  VERANDERUNGEN...OBERPFAL
LUCKE, G.
  KLEINER DIALOG (1966)
LUCKY, S.
  WOODWIND QUINTET (1946)
LUDEWIG, W.
  APOKALYPTISCHE VISION
  MOSAIK (1973/74)
  REFLEXIONEN (1975)
LUDWIG, J.
  STENOGRAMME
LUEDEKE, R.
  15 INVENTIONS
  5 PIECES
LUENING, O.
  BASS WITH THE DELICATE A
  3 DUETS
  LYRIC SCENE
  SONORITY CANON
  SUITE FOR DIVERSE HIGH &
  SUITE
  TRIO #2
  TRIO
LUFT, H.
  24 ETUDES IN DUET FORM
LUFT, J.
  24 ETUDES IN DUET FORM
  12 ETUDES, OP 11
LUIGINI, A.
  BALLET EGYPTIAN
  SERENADE ROMANTIQUE
LUKAS, Z.
  WOODWIND QUINTET WITH TR
LULLY, J.
  AIRS DE TABLE
  CARROUSEL DU ROY, LE, 1E
  CARROUSEL DU ROY, LE, 2E
  CHACONNE
  COURANT
  FRENCH DANCES
  FRENCH DANCES
  GAVOTTE
  20 STUCKE
  5 WORKS
LUMSDAINE, D.
  ANNOTATIONS OF AUSCHWITZ
  EASTER FRESCO (1966, REV
LUNDBORG, E.
  BUTTE CHORD
  BUTTE CHORD
  COMBONE
  COMBONE
  SOUNDSOUP
  TRIO
LUNDE, I.
  3 BAGATELLES
  ELEGI, OP 5
  L'ECOLE, OP 11, A
  NUANCES, OP 55

SERENADE
LUNDE, I. JR.
  PETITE SUITE, UNE
LUNDEN-WELDEN, G.
  4 SMABITAR (1976)
LUNDEN, L.
  AFTONSTUND
  QUADRILLE
  QUEEN CHRISTINA'S SONG
  RONDINO
  SVART LEK (1957)
  3 SWEDISH TUNES
  VARIATIONER ON "BYSSAN L
  WHEATEAR, THE
LUNDKVIST, P.
  EN LITEN MORGONMUSIK
  KVINTETT
LUNDQUIST, T.
  INTUIZIONE/VARANING
  4 RONDEAUX (1969)
  TEAMWORK (1967)
LUNETTA, S.
  FREE MUSIC
  QUARTET 1965
LURIE
  CLASSICS FOR CLARINETS
  CLASSICS FOR CLARINETS
LUTI, V.
  MIXED QUINTET
LUTOSLAWSKI, W.
  DANCE PRELUDES VERSION
  INVITATION AU VOYAGE, L'
  KUKULCAN (1969/72)
  STRAW CHAIN, A (1951)
  TRIO (1944-45)
LUTYENS, E.
  CONCERTANTE, OP 22
  MUSIC FOR WIND
  6 TEMPI
  TRIO, OP 52
  WIND QUINTET
LUYKENAAR, C.
  DUO (1974)
LYBBERT, D.
  LEOPARDO CANTI
  OCTAGON
  SONORITIES
  TRIO FOR WINDS
  VARIANTS
LYNCH, T.
  ANDROMEDA
LYONS, G.
  PASTORALE
MA'AYANI, A.
  IMPROVISATION VARIEE
MAASZ, G.
  CONCERTINO
  DIVERTIMENTO
  DUO IN C MA
  DUO IN G MA
  FINCKENSCHLAG
  HAMBURGISCHE TAFELMUSIK

5 INVENTIONS
SUITE
MAC DOWELL, E.
  DESERTED FARM, A
  IDYL, OP 28/2
  INTERMEZZO
  TO A WILD ROSE
  2 TONE POEMS
  WOODLAND SKETCHES
  2 WOODLAND SKETCHES
MAC KINNON, R.
  SUITE
MAC PERRIN
  CAREFREE
  FOOLIN' AROUND
  JOLLY CAPERS
  SOMETHIN'
MACBETH, A.
  INTERMEZZO "FORGET ME NO
  INTERMEZZO "FORGET ME NO
  INTERMEZZO/"FORGET ME NO
MACCHI, E.
  COMPOSIZIONE 3 (1960)
MACE, T.
  PRELUDE
MACERO, T.
  CANZONA #1
  CANZONA #1
  ELECTRIQUE
  ONE-THREE QUARTERS
MACHA, O.
  MALY TRIPTYCH
MACHAUT, G.
  DOUBLE HOQUET
  KYRIE
MACHAUT, G. DE
  HOQUETUS DAVID
MACHI, T.
  3 VIRTUOSO STUDIES
MACIEJEWSKI, S.
  STUBBORN CLARINET, THE
MACONCHY, E.
  CONVERSATIONS
  QUARTET
  QUINTET
  REFLECTIONS
MACUDZINSKI, R.
  MEDITATION & DANCE, OP 4
MADDEN, J.
  QUINTET # 3
MADERNA, B.
  DIALODIA
  MUSICA SU DUE DIMENSIONI
  SERENATA #2 (1957)
  SERENATA #2 (1957)
  SERENATA #2
  SERENATA #2
  SERENATA PER UN SATELLIT
  SERENATA PER UN SATELLIT
  SERENATA PER UN SATELLIT
MAEGAARD, J.
  TRIO (1950)

MAES, J.
  4 CONTRASTES (1965)
  MINIATURE TRIC
  SONATINE (1934)
  TRIO
MAESSEN, A.
  CASSATION (1958)
  TRIO (1956)
MAGANINI, Q.
  AIR & DOUBLE
  ARS CONTRAPUNCTUS
  BEGINNER'S LUCK
  BEGINNER'S LUCK
  BEGINNERS' LUCK
  BEGINNERS' LUCK
  BOA CONSTRICTOR & THE BO
  BOA CONSTRICTOR, THE, &
  BOA-CONSTRICTOR AND THE
  CANONICO ESPRESSIVO
  CANONICO E. PRESSIVO
  CANONICO E. PRESSIVO
  CANONICO ESPRESSIVO
  CONCERT ALBUM
  CONCERT ALBUM
  CONCERT ALBUM
  COUPERIN SUITE
  COUPERIN SUITE
  COUPERIN SUITE
  HAVANA
  2 HUMMING BIRDS
  IN THE BEGINNING
  IN THE BEGINNING
  IN THE BEGINNING
  IN THE BEGINNING
  ISTANBOUL
  3 LITTLE KITTENS
  3 LITTLE KITTENS
  3 LITTLE KITTENS
  3 LITTLE KITTENS
  3 LYRICS
  MILADY'S FAN
  MOONLIGHT ON THE PAINTED
  MOONLIGHT ON THE PAINTED
  PARIS SOIR
  PARIS SOIR
  PATROL OF THE WOODEN IND
  PETITE SUITE CLASSIQUE
  PETITE SUITE CLASSIQUE
  PETITE SUITE CLASSIQUE
  PETITE SUITE CLASSIQUE
  PETITE SUITE CLASSIQUE
  REVERIE
  REVERIE
  REVERIE
  RUBIA, LA
  SHENANDOAH
  SHEPHERDS IN ARCADIA
  SIMPLE AVEU
  TRIO ALBUM
  TRIO ALBUM
  TRIPLE PLAY
  TRIPLE PLAY

  TRIPLE PLAY
  TRIPLE PLAY
  TROUBADORS
  TROUBADOURS
  TROUBADOURS
  TWINS
  VIENNA WALTZ
MAGDIC, J.
  APEIRON
  APEIRON
MAGI, E.
  DIALOGUES
  OSTINATO
MAGNANI, A.
  6 DUETTI CONCERTANT
  REVERIE
  SONATA
MAGNARD, A.
  QUINTET
MAHAUT, A.
  6 SONATE DA CAMERA,2 VOL.
MAHLER, G.
  IN PRAISE OF LOFTY INTEL
MAI, P.
  COMMEDIA "DIE EHE"
MAIGUASHCA, M.
  OELDORF 8 (1974)
  UBUNGEN (1972)
MAILLOT, J.
  12 DUOS PROGRESSIFS, 3 V
  TRIO
MAINARDI, E.
  TRIO (1967)
MAJO, E.
  SUITE PER 4
  TRIO
MAKLAKIEWICZ, J.
  VIERGES AUX CREPUSCULES,
MAKLAKIEWICZ, T.
  BIBLICAL TRIPTYCH
  QUINTET
MAKOVECKY, J.
  DUO CONCERTANT #1
MAKSYMIUK, J.
  DECET
  IMPROMPTU #2 (1969)
  TRIO
MALEC, I.
  MINIATURES POUR LEWIS CA
  MINIATURES POUR LEWIS CA
MALIGE, F.
  7 DUOS
  7 DUOS
  QUINTET #2
  6 ZWEISTIMMIGE INVENTION
MALIPIERO, G.
  DIALOGUE IV
  EPODI E GAMBI
  RICERCARI
  RITROVARI
  SERENATA MATTUTINA
  SONATA A CINQUE

SONATA A CINQUE
SONATA A QUATTRO (1954)
4 VECCHIE CANZONI (1940)
MALIPIERO, R.
IN TIME OF DAFFODILS
MOSAICO (1961)
MUSICA DA CAMERA (1959)
SEI POESIE DI DYLAN THOM
WINTERQUINTET (1976)
MALOVEC, J.
PRELUDIUM A BURLESKA
MAMANGAKIS, N.
KASSANDRA (1963)
KONSTRUKTIONEN (1958)
MUSIK FUR VIER PROTAGONI
PARASTASIS
MAMLOK, U.
8 EASY DUETS
FESTIVE SOUNDS
FOR 7
HAIKU SETTINGS
QUINTET
SEXTET
SINTRA
SONATINA
5 SONGS FROM "STRAY BIRD
MANASSEN, A.
DEATH, AND (1974)
MEI (1974)
MANCINELLI, D.
2 SONATEN
MANCINI, F.
SONATA #4 IN A MI
MANCINI, H.
FLUTERS' BALL
MANEN, C.
QUINTET
MANGS, R.
6 BAGATELLEN
MANICKE, D.
QUARTET IN D MI
SEXTET
MANIET, R.
CONCERT D'ANCHES
CUBA, SUITE-QUARTETT
HABANERA
HABANERA
QUINTETTE A VENT #1
TRIO D'ANCHES I
TRIO D'ANCHES II
MANN, I.
3 BAGATELLES, OP 3
MANN, L.
MUSIC, OP 26 (1973)
PARTITA, OP 28 (1972)
3 SONGS TO POEMS OF SHAK
4 STUDIES IN THE BLUES I
TOCCATA ALLA BAROCCO, OP
TRIO, OP 6 (1952)
WIND QUINTET, OP 19
MANNEKE, D.
WALKING IN FOGPATCHES

MANNINO, F.
EPITAFFIO PER GLI AMICI
FEUILLES D'AUTOMNE, LES
LITTLE MUSIC FOR 3 FRIEN
MINI QUINTETT
SONS ENCHANTES
MANSON, E.
FUGUE
MANZIARLY, M. DE
TRIO
MANZO, S.
2 TEMPI
MANZONI, A.
PRELUDIO- GRAVE DI WARIN
MANZONI, G.
MUSICA NOTTURNA (1966)
PARAFRASI CON FINALE
MAR¬CHAIM, J.
TRIO
MARAIS, M.
FOLIES D'ESPAGNE, LES
SUITE #5 DI BRANI IN TRI
MARCELLI, N.
MUSIC BOX MINUET
MARCELLO
TOCCATA IN C MI
MARCKHL, E.
SONATE
MARCLAND, P.
METRES
MARCO, I.
KITICA
MARCO, T.
ALBOR (1970)
CAR EN EFFET (1971)
HOQUETUS (1973)
HOQUETUS (1973)
HOQUETUS (1973)
KUKULCAN
NUBA (1973)
ROSA-ROSAE (1969)
TEA-PARTY (1969)
ULTRAMARINA (1975)
MARCONI, L.
COLLAGE PER UN DUO
COLLAGE PER UN DUO
INTRODUZIONE E FUGA
MARECHAL, H.
AIR DU GUET
MAREZ OYENS, T. DE
INTER-TIMES (1977)
MOSAIC (1979)
OCTET
RYOANJI TEMPLE
2 SKETCHES
SUITE DU PETIT PRINCE
SWATCHES TRIO
MARGOLA, F.
LONGOBARDA, LA
PARTITA
SONATA #4
SONATINA A SEI

412

MARIASSY & VIGH
  CHAMBER MUSIC II
MARIATTI, F.
  OUVERTURE BREVE
  3 PEZZI
MARIE, G.
  BERCEUSE
  BERCEUSE
  BERCEUSE
  CINQUANTAINE, LA
  CINQUANTINE, LA
  DANS LA CALME NUIT
  DIALOGUE TENDRE
  EN SE JOUANT
  FEUILLES AU VENT
  GOLDEN WEDDING
MARIETAN, P.
  RECIT SUIVE DE LEGENDE
MARKEVITCH, I.
  SERENADE
MARKOVIC, Z.
  NOCTURNO & SCHERZO
MAROS, M.
  DESCORT
  DISCUSSION (1969)
  IZE
  MONONOME (1971)
  QUINTET #1 (1961-62)
MAROS, R.
  CONSORT (1970)
  MUSICA DA CAMERA
  MUSICA DA CAMERA
  MUSICA LEGGIERA (1956)
  SERENATA (1951)
MARSAL, E.
  NANINE
  NANINE
MARSHALL, J.
  GOLDRUSH SUITE
MARSHALL, N.
  SUITE
MARTEAU, J.
  TERZETTO, OP 32
MARTELLI, H.
  CONCERTO
  5 IMAGES, OP110
  TRIO
  TRIO, OP 45
  TRIO, OP 77
MARTIN
  HOMMAGE A BARTOK
MARTIN & PIZZUTO
  MUSIC OF THE RENAISSANCE
MARTIN, D.
  RONDO FOR WOODWINDS
  5 SKETCHES (1961)
MARTIN, F.
  PIECE BREVE (1957)
  4 SONNETS
  3 WEIHNACHTSLIEDER
MARTIN, V.
  CHAMBER SYMPHONY

MARTINI, G.
  BOURREE
  CONCERTO IN G MA
  GAVOTTE
MARTINI, J.
  GAVOTTE
  PLAISIR D'AMOUR
  PLAISIR D'AMOUR
  PLAISIR D'AMOUR
  PLAISIR D'AMOUR
  PLAISIR D'AMOUR
  PLAISIR D'AMOUR
MARTINI, P.
  PLAISIR D'AMOUR
  PLAISIR D'AMOUR
MARTINO, D.
  7 CANONI ENIGMATICI
  CONCERTO
  5 FRAMMENTI
  NOTTURNO
  QUARTET
  RISOLUZIONI
  TRIO
  TRIPLE CONCERTO (1977)
MARTINON, J.
  DOMENON
  SONATINE #4
MARTINU, B.
  DIVERTIMENTO
  MADRIGAL-SONATE (1936)
  4 MADRIGALE (1937)
  MAZURKA-NOCTURNE (1949)
  MUSIQUE DE CHAMBRE #1
  NONETTO (1959)
  NONETTO- FRAGMENT (1927)
  PASTORALS (1951)
  PROMENADES (1940)
  QUARTET (1924)
  QUARTET (1947)
  REVUE DE CUISINE, LA
  REVUE DE CUISINE, LA
  RONDI (1930)
  SERENADE #1 (1932)
  SERENADE #4 (DIVERTIMENT
  SERENADE
  SERENATA III (1932)
  SEXTET (1929)
  TRIO (1944)
MARTIRANO, S.
  O,O,O,O, THAT SHAKESPEHE
  OCTET (1963)
MARTTINEN, T.
  ALFA (1962)
  DIVERTIMENTO, OP127
  ILMATAR, ILMAN IMPI
  ILMATAR, ILMAN IMPI
  NONET
MARX, K.
  CHRISTUS GEBOREN WAR, DA
  DIE UNENDLICHE WOGE, OP
  DIVERTIMENTO, OP 21A
  KAMMERMUSIK, OP 56

413

TRIO
MATUSZCZAK, B.
  CHAMBER DRAMA, A
  MUSICA DA CAMERA (1967)
MATYS, J.
  INVENCE (1969)
  KINDERBALLETTE (1959)
  MUSIC FOR WOODWIND QUINT
  QUIPS
  3 SATZE (1969)
MATZ, R.
  5 MOVEMENTS
MAURICE, P.
  SUITE
MAURICE, R.
  AURORE
MAURY
  CHANGES
MAURY, L.
  COCK OF THE WALK
MAVES, D.
  DUET
  OKTECHOS
MAW, N.
  CHAMBER MUSIC
MAXWELL
  IDYLS OF FOUR GOBLINS
  TRIO
  WATER OF TYNE, THE
MAXWELL, C.
  TRIO
MAVER, W.
  CELEBRATION
  MESSAGES
MAYEUR, L.
  QUARTET #1
MAYR, A.
  LITTLE SUITE
MAYR, G.
  12 BAGATELLES
MAYR, S.
  BAGATELLE A TRE
MAYUZUMI, T.
  METAMUSICA
  SPHENOGRAMMES
MAZAS, J.
  DUETS
  DUO
  PETIT DUOS #S 1, 2, 3, 5
  RONDO
MAZELLIER, J.
  10 FUGUES
  10 FUGUES
MC AFEE, D.
  QUARTET
MC BRIDE
  MELODY BY CHOPIN
  MELODY BY GRIEG
MC BRIDE, R.
  COMFORTABLE FLIGHT
  CUATRO MILPAS
  FANFARE FOR YOUNG PEOPLE

FUGUE
GO-GO
HOME ON THE RANGE
INTERWOVEN
JAM SESSION
MEXICAN DANCE
2 MEXICAN FOLK SONGS
NON-SLIP SOFT SOAP
NONSENSE SYLLABLES
PAJARILLO BARRENQUENO
QUINTET
ROCK 'EM COWBOY
RUDIMENTS OF RUGCUTTING
SERENADE TO COUNTRY MUSI
SHUT UP, MOCKINGBIRD
TELEVISION SPECIAL
VARIATIONS ON VARIOUS PO
VOCALISE
WATCH YOUR DRIVIN' BABY-
5 WINDS BLOWING
MC CABE, J.
  BAGATELLES
  CONCERTO
  MOVEMENTS, OP 29
  QUARTET (1968)
  SONATA (1969)
MC CALL, H.
  ANNIE LAURIE
  INSTRUMENTAL HYMN FAVORI
  2 SPIRITUALS
  2 TUNES FROM MOTHER GOOS
  VALSE ELISE
MC CARTY, F.
  5 SITUATIONS
MC CATHREN, D.
  CLARINETTE VALSANTE
  ELECTRONIC BRAIN
  INTRODUCTION, ROUND & FU
  SCHERZINO
MC CAUGHEY, W.
  ENCHANTED ISLE
  ENCHANTED ISLE
MC CAULEY, W.
  KALEIDOSCOPE QUEBECOIS
  5 MINIATURES (1972)
  5 MINIATURES
MC CLELLAN, R.
  GEESE OVER THE WATER
  MAZE
  3 MODES
  OCCURRENCES
  PARAMETERS
MC CULLOH, B.
  LAMENT
  LAMENT
MC DANIEL, W.
  WOODWIND QUINTET #1
MC INTYRE, P.
  FANTASY ON AN ESKIMO SON
  OUT OF THE CRADLE ENDLES
MC KAY
  INSTRUMENTAL DUO SUITE

2 SCHUMANN SELECTIONS
MC KAY, D.
BAGATELLES FOR GEN WASHI
COLONIAL BAND MUSIC
MC KAY, F.
AMERICAN SKETCH
3 AMIGOS
ANITA
AT THE PUPPET SHOW
AT THE PUPPET SHOW
BAINBRIDGE ISLAND SKETCH
BLUE TAPESTRY
BLUE TAPESTRY
3 CADETS
CARMELA
CHIQUITA
CHROMATIC CAPRICE
CLARINET QUARTETS
DANCER, THE
HALLOWE'EN TIME
HALLOWE'EN TIME
HALLOWE'EN TIME
3 JESTERS
LYRIC POEM
MUSETTE
MUSETTE
ON THE BOULEVARD
PASTORAL
2 PROMENADES
SICILIANO
SONG & DANCE
SUMMER ETCHING
TRAIL TO SUNNY POINT
TRAIL TO SUNNY POINT
WITH GAY SPIRIT
WOODS IN APRIL
MC KAY, G.
AMERICAN PANORAMA
AMERICAN PANORAMA
CHORALE, AUBADE & NOEL
CHRISTMAS MORNING SUITE
EPISODES
FIESTA MEJICANA
FIESTA MEJICANA
JOYFUL DANCE
LYRIC POEM
3 NAUTICAL CHARACTERS
3 NAUTICAL CHARACTERS
ON A PASTORALE THEME
5 PIECES
3 SEA SKETCHES
4 SEASONS
SONATINA GIOCOSA
SUITE MATINALE
SUITE PASTORALE
MC KINLEY, W.
PAINTINGS #2 (1974-75)
MC KUSICK, H.
ATONAL DUETS
MC LEAN, H.
RONDO
MC LIN, E.

FOR FOUR B FL CLARINETS
MC LUCKIE, I.
12 BELOW B
MC NICOL, R.
3 DANCES
QUARTET
MC PEEK, B.
CRAZY JANE (1957)
WOODWIND QUINTET (1961)
MC PHEE, C.
CONCERTO
MEACHAM
AMERICAN PATROL
MEALE, R.
INCREDIBLE FLORIDAS
LAS ALBORADAS
PLATEAU
QUINTET (1969)
MECHAM, K.
TRIO
MECHEM, K.
DIVERTIMENTO, OP 12
MEDEK, T.
QUINTET #1
MEDERACKE, K.
BOHMISCHE SUITE, OP 43
MEEK, K.
SUITE
MEESTER, L. DE
DIVERTIMENTO (1946)
SPIELEREI (1969)
MEFANO, P.
MADRIGAL (1972)
PERIPLES (1978)
MEIER, D.
EPI
KUKLOS (1974)
KUKLOS
MEIJERING, C.
UTAH (1978)
MEIJERLING, C.
UGLY HOWLING MONKEY
MEIMA, H.
2 CHANSONS (1976)
MELARTIN, E.
SONATA (1920)
TRIO
MELBY, J.
ZONNORITIES
MELILLO, P.
CLARINET TRIO
DUO
MELLERS, W.
TRIO
MELLNAS, A.
CEREMUS (1973)
DIVERTIMENTO
PER CASO (1963)
SONATA A TRE
VAXLINGAR
MELNIK
CLARINET HOLIDAY

416

MENDELSSOHN
 ON WINGS OF SONG
MENDELSSOHN, F.
 ALLEGRO VIVACE
 ANDANTE CON MOTO
 CANZONETTA
 CAPRICCIO #2
 CONCERT PIECE #1 IN F MI
 CONCERT PIECE #1
 CONCERT PIECE IN F MI, O
 CONCERTPIECE #1 IN F MI,
 CONCERTPIECE #1 IN F MI,
 CONCERTPIECE #2 IN D MA,
 CONCERTPIECE #2 IN D MI,
 DUO CONCERTANT, OP114
 EQUALE #3
 EVENING SONG
 EVENING SONG
 FIGURATE HYMN
 FOLK SONG
 ICH WOLLT' MEINE LIEB' E
 ICH WOLLT' MEINE LIEBE E
 ICH WOLLT'MEINE LIEB ERG
 INTERMEZZO (MIDSUMMER NI
 INTERMEZZO (MIDSUMMER NI
 JOYOUS SONG, A
 KONZERTSTUCK #1, OP113
 KONZERTSTUCK #2, OP114
 KONZERTSTUCK, OP113
 KONZERTSTUCK, OP114
 KONZERTSTUCKE #1, OP113
 KONZERTSTUCKE #2 IN D MI
 2 KONZERTSTUCKE, OP113-1
 LIFT THINE EYES & CAST T
 LIFT THINE EYES & CAST T
 MAIGLOCKCHEN UND DIE BLU
 MAIGLOCKCHEN UND DIE BLU
 MENUET EN TRIO
 MORNING SONG
 NOCTURNE
 NOCTURNO (MID-SUMMER NIG
 NOCTURNO (MID-SUMMER NIG
 NOCTURNO
 NOCTURNO
 NOCTURNO
 NOTTURNO
 O WIE SELIG IST DAS KIND
 O WIE SELIG IST DAS KIND
 ON WINGS OF SONG
 ON WINGS OF SONG
 ON WINGS OF SONG
 ON WINGS OF SONG
 RETROSPECTION
 RONDO CAPRICCIOSO
 RONDO CAPRICCIOSO
 SALTARELLO (SYMPHONY #4)
 SCHERZETTO, OP102/3
 SCHERZO, OP110
 SCHERZO, OP110
 SHEPHERD'S COMPLAINT, TH
 SONG OF THE HEATHER
 SONG WITHOUT WORDS #48

 SONG WITHOUT WORDS #48
 SONG WITHOUT WORDS #48
 SONG WITHOUT WORDS, OP 6
 SPINNING SONG
 SPINNING SONG
 SPRING SONG
 SPRING SONG
 SPRING SONG
 TARANTELLA, OP102/3
 TARANTELLE
 VARIATION SERIEUSES, OP
 WAR MARCH OF THE PRIESTS
MENGAL, J.
 3 WOODWIND QUARTETS
MENGELBERG, K.
 BALLADE
 TRIO (1940)
MENGELBERG, M.
 DRESSOIR (1977)
 HELLO WINDY BOYS
 OMRENT EEN COMPONISTEN-A
MENICHETTI, F.
 BOUQUET ORIENTAL (1934)
MERCADANTE, S.
 3 SERENADES
MERCIER
 DUO CURIEUX
MERCURE, P.
 TETRACHROMIE (1963)
 TETRACHROMIE (1963)
MERIKANTO, A.
 CONCERTO
 NONETTO
MERILAINEN, U.
 IMPRESSION (1965)
MERKELT
 11 CELEBRATED MARCHES
MERRIMAN, L.
 DUET CLASSICS, BK #1
MERSSON, B.
 KLEINE SUITE, OP 10
 MUSIK, OP 20
 SUITE, OP 17
MESRITZ
 3 LIEDEREN (1945)
 RIWAJAK KAMPONG (1946)
MESSIAEN, O.
 QUATUOR POUR LA FIN DU T
MESTRAL, P.
 ALLIAGES
MESTRES-QUADRENY, J.
 DIVERTIMENTO "LA RICARDA
 INVENCIONS MOVLIS I (196
METRAL, P.
 ALLEGRETTO (DISPARATES)
 DIAPARATES IMPRESSIONS S
 PETITE SUITE
 RAPSODIE (1965)
 VARIANTI
 VARIATIONS
METZLER, F.
 ES IST EIN ROS ENTSPRUNG

417

```
    TRIO PASTORALE (1959)              6 MINIATURES, OP 31/1
MEULEMANS, A.                           OKTOPUS, OP 29/5
  ANDANTE ET SCHERZO                    SERENATA PICCOLA
  AUBADE (1934)                     MICHAELIS, A.
  QUATUOR (1953)                       3 SONATEN
  QUATUOR (1962)                    MICHAELSON, C.
  QUINTET #1 (1931)                    GAME
  QUINTET #2 (1932)                    PALAEMON
  QUINTET #3 (1958)                 MICHALEK, S.
  RAPSODIE (1961)                      DIVERTIMENTO (1964)
  SERENATA (1961)                   MICHALSKY, D.
  SONATE (1948)                        DIVERTIMENTO
  TRIO (1933)                          FANFARE AFTER 17TH CENTU
  TRIO #2 (1960)                       SONATINA
MEYER                                  THREE TIMES FOUR
  DIVERTISSEMENT                       TRIO CONCERTINO
  VARIATIONS SUR UN THEME           MICHEELSEN, H.
MEYER-TORMIN, W.                        SINGET DEM HERRN
  KLEINES QUINTETT (1951)          MICHEL
MEYER, E.                               TRIO #1
  CLARINET QUINTET                  MICHEL, P.
  KLEINE EROFFNUNGSMUSIK               HOMMAGE A RABELAIS
MEYER, J.                           MICHEL, W.
  VARIATIONS ON A THEME OF             BLASMUSIK (1972)
MEYER, K.                               DEKLAMATION
  5 CHAMBER PIECES, OP 18             MULTIPLIKATIONSSPIEL
  HOMMAGE A NADIA BOULANGE            STANDPUNKTE (1974)
  INTERLUDIO STATICO, OP 1         MIEG, P
MEYER, L.                               MORCEAU ELEGANT
  REFLECTIONS                      MIEG, P.
MEYERBEER, G.                           DUO (1977)
  CORONATION MARCH (THE PR             MUSIK (1954)
  CORONATION MARCH (THE PR             PIECES POUR 1, 2 & 3 FLU
  CORONATION MARCH (THE PR             PIECES POUR 1, 2 ET 3 FL
  CORONATION MARCH (THE PR             QUINTUOR (1969)
  CORONATION MARCH (THE PR         MIELENZ, H.
  CORONATION MARCH (THE PR             SCHERZO
  CORONATION MARCH (THE PR             SCHERZO
  CORONATION MARCH                 MIEREANU, C.
  HIRTENLIED (RELLSTAB)                MUSIQUE ELEMENTAIRE DE C
  HIRTENLIED                           PLANETARIUM I (1975)
  ROBERT LE DIABLE                     SEGUNDAFEIRA (1974)
MEYEROVICH, M.                          SOURCE DE JUIN (1972)
  TRIO                                 SOURCE DE JUIN (1972)
MEYERS, E.                              SURSUM CORDA I (1967)
  SUITE                            MIGNION, R.
MEZO, I.                                PETIT ENFANT
  QUINTET                          MIGOT, G.
MIASKOVSKY, N.                          CONCERT
  FUGUE IN A CLASSIC STYLE             LIVRE DES DANCERIES, LE
MICA, J.A.                              PASTORALE
  QUARTET IN C MA                      3 PASTORALES
MICHAEL                                 6 PETITS PRELUDES, 2 VOL
  NEPENTHES RAJAH (1970)               6 PETITS PRELUDES,2 VOLS
MICHAEL, D.                             PREMIER LIVRE DE DIVERTI
  PARTHIA II                           PREMIER LIVRE DE DIVERTI
MICHAEL, E.                             QUARTET
  PETITE SUITE ANTIQUE                 QUINTETTE
  3 RITUELS                            SONATE
  SONATINE (1962)                      SUITE EN 3 MOUVEMENTS
MICHAEL, F.                             THRENE
  GINKO(1968),OP 23/1                  TRIO
```

418

TRIO
MIHALOVICI, M.
  SONATA, OP 35
  TRIO, OP 71
MIHALY, A.
  3 APOCRYPHA (1962)
MIHELCIC, P.
  TEAM
MIHELCIC, S.
  3 PIECES
MIKODA, B.
  NONETTO, OP 30 (1948)
  SONATA (1934)
  TRIO, OP 7
  WOODWIND QUINTET, OP 28
MILHAUD, D.
  ACTUALITES
  ASPEN SERENADE
  CHEMINEE DU ROI RENE, LA
  CONCERTINO D'AUTOMNE
  CONCERTINO D'ETE
  CONCERTO
  DIVERTISSEMENT IN 3 PART
  MACHINES AGRICOLES
  MUSIQUE POUR GRAZ
  PASTORALE
  PASTORALE
  PETITE SYMPHONIE #5 (DIX
  PRINTEMPS, LE
  QUINTET
  REVES DE JACOB, LES
  SCARAMOUCHE
  SERENADE
  2 SKETCHES
  SONATE
  STANFORD SERENADE
  STANFORD SERENADE
  SUITE D'APRES CORRETTE
  SUITE
  VI. SINFONIE
MILLER, E.
  MISTS & WATERS
  PIECE FOR CLARINET & TAP
  3 PIECES
MILLER, J.
  SETTIGNANO (1968)
MILLER, K.
  ODE TO SPRING
MILLER, L.
  SONATINA (1962)
MILLER, M.
  IN-TALK (1975)
  INTERACTION, A DIVERTIME
  TRIO FANTASY
  TRIO
MILLER, R.
  3 AMERICAN DANCES, OP 25
  LIVELY MOOD
  MARTIAL SPIRIT
  PRELUDE & SCHERZO, OP 20
  QUARTET #2
MILLNAS, A.

PER CASO
MILLOCKER, K.
  HERINNERINGEN
MILLS, C.
  CHAMBER CONCERTO
  PAUL BUNYAN JUMP
  PIECE
  SERENADE, OP 68
  SONATA FANTASIA
  SUITE FOR 2 FLUTES SOLI
MILLS, D.
  MARCH, MADRIGAL & SCHERZ
MILNE, J.
  SCHERZETTO
MILNER, A.
  QUARTET
MIMAROGLU, I.
  CONJECTUS 2
  MUSIC
  PIECE FUTILE
  TRIO (1961)
MINGUS, C.
  REVELATIONS (1957)
  REVELATIONS (1957)
  REVELATIONS (1957)
MINOR
  FUN DUETS
MIRANDOLLE, L.
  3 DUOS
MIRK, V.
  NONET
MIROGLIO, F.
  ESPACES IV
  ESPACES V
  FLUCTUANCES (1961)
  MAGIES (1960)
  MASQUES
  PHASES
  PHASES
  RESEAUX
  RESEAUX
MIROGLIO, R.
  REFRACTIONS
MIROUZE, M.
  PIECE EN SEPTUOR
MISSAL, J.
  RONDO CAPRICE
MISTAK, A.
  QUARTET
MITREA¬CELARIANU, M.
  SETH (1969)
  SIGNAUX (SUR L'OCEAN U)
MIYAKE, H.
  MUSIK
MIZELLE, J.
  GREEN & RED
  STRAIGHT AHEAD
  STRAIGHT AHEAD
MOCKL, F.
  IPHIGENIE IN DELPHI
MOERAN, E.
  FANTASY QUARTET

419

MOESCHINGER, A.
  5 CAPRICCI (1960)
  CAPRICCI E DANZE
  IMAGES
MOEVS, R.
  DUO
MOFFITT
  WHAM DOODLE
MOFFITT, D.
  FRISKY
  IN THE SPOTLIGHT
MOGILL, L.
  12 DUETS
MOJSISOVICS, R. VON
  SERENADE, OP 70
MOLINO, F.
  NOCTURNE #2, OP 38
  TRIO, OP 45
MOLINO, G.
  NOCTURNO, OP 37
MOLIQUE, B.
  CONCERTANTE
MOLLERS, C.
  SERENADE
  SERENADE
MOLLICONE, H.
  TRIO
MOLLOY, A.
  KERRY DANCE
MOLLOY, J.
  KERRY DANCE
  KERRY DANCE,
  LOVE'S OLD SWEET SONG
MOLS, R.
  EXCURSION
  20 MODERN DUETS
MOLTER, J.
  3 CONCERTI
  CONCERTINO A 4 IN A MI
  CONCERTO A 4, #S 1,2,3;
  CONCERTO IN A MA
  SINFONIA CONCERTANTE #1
  SINFONIA CONCERTANTE #2
  SONATA A QUATRO IN F MA
MOMMER, H.
  HEILIGEN DREI KONIGE, DI
MONACO, R.
  3 MINIATURES
  5 SHORT PIECES
MONDONVILLE, J.
  SONATA IN G MA
MONGER
  ENSEMBLE ALBUM #1
MONKEMEYER, H.
  TRICINIEN DES 17. JAHRHU
MONNIKENDAM, M.
  SUITE IN C MA (1960)
MONOD, J.
  CHAMBER ARIA (1952)
MONONEN, S.
  TRIO
MONSIGNY, P.

  ARIETTE (LE MAITRE EN DR
MONTANARI, N.
  5 INVENZIONI
MONTECLAIR, M. DE
  6 CONCERTI, 2 VOLS
  CONCERTO #1 IN D MA
  CONCERTO #2 IN E MI
  CONCERTO #3 IN G MA
  CONCERTO #3
  6 CONCERTOS, 2 VOLS
MONTEVERDI, C.
  ARIA CON SINFONIA
  5 INSTRUMENTAL-CANZONETT
  OH, LET ME DIE
  SINFONIA
MONTI, V.
  CSARDAS
  CSARDAS
MOOR, E.
  SUITE, OP103
MOORE, C.
  MUSEUM PIECE
  QUINTET (1964)
MOORE, D.
  BALLAD OF WILLIAM SYCAMO
  QUINTET
  QUINTET
  SONGS
MOORE, T.
  POEM
  RHONDALLET
MOORER, P.
  AUTUMN'S EVEN (1977-78)
MOORTEL, A. VAN DE
  TRIO #1
MOORTEL, L. VAN DE
  DIVERTIMENTO I
  DIVERTIMENTO III
MORAN, R.
  4 VISIONS
MORATIN
  QUINTETTE
MORAWETZ, O.
  TRIO (1960)
MOREL
  NORWEGIAN CRADLE SONG
MORIGI, A.
  DUO
MORITZ, C.
  HEITERE SUITE, OP 12
MORITZ, E.
  DIVERTIMENTO
  DIVERTIMENTO, OP150
  QUARTET
  QUINTET, OP 41
  QUINTET, OP169
MORLEY, T.
  ALMAN
  CONTRASTS
MOROSCO, V.
  6 CONTEMPORARY ETUDES IN
MOROSS, J.

SONATINA
SONATINA
MORRICONE, E.
  IMMOBILE (1978)
  MOLTO LONTANO, DA
MORRIS
  MORNING SCENES
MORRISON, J.
  JULIA STREET
MORSCH, J.
  12 CLARINET QUARTETS
  3 INTERLUDES
MORTARI, V.
  CANZONE
  3 DANZE ANTICHE
  2 LAUDE
  POESIE RUMENE
MORTENSEN, F.
  3 PIECES, OP 22/3
  QUINTET, OP 4
  SUITE, OP 36
MORTENSEN, O.
  QUATUOR CONCERTANT
  QUINTET
MORTHENSON, J.
  INTIMI
  SOLI
MORTON, D.
  TEARS
MORYL, R.
  ATLANTIS
  ATLANTIS
  CHAMBERS #2
  IMPROVISATIONS
  LIED, DAS
  SUMMER'S MUSIC
  SUNDAY MORNING
  SUNDAY MORNING
MOSCHELES, I.
  FANTASY, VARIATIONS, & F
MOSER, C.
  VARIAZIONI DIATONIQUE
MOSER, F.
  TRIO, OP 38
MOSKOWSKI, M.
  SERENADE, OP 15/1
  SPANISH DANCE
MOSS, L.
  AUDITIONS
  EVOCATION AND SONG
  EXCHANGES (1968)
  NIGHTSCAPE, A THEATERPIE
  PATTERNS
  REMEMBRANCES
  TOOT-SWEET
  UNSEEN LEAVES (1975)
  WINDOWS
MOSS, P.
  TRIO
MOST, A.
  MINIATURE SUITE (1966)
MOSZKOWSKI, M.

MARCH OF THE DWARFS,
  SPANISH DANCE, OP 12/1
MOSZUMANSKA NAZAR, K.
  INTERPRETATIONS
MOSZUMANSKA-NAZAR, K.
  5 DUETS
MOSZUMANSKA, K.
  RENDITION
MOTTE, D. DE LA
  CONCERTO (1973)
  NIEMANDSROSE, DIE
  SEPTET (1965)
MOULAERT, P.
  PASSEPIED EN RONDO
MOULAERT, R.
  ANDANTE, FUGUE ET FINAL
  ANDANTE, FUGUE ET FINAL
  ANDANTE, FUGUE ET FINAL
  CONCERT (1950)
MOUQUET, J.
  DANSE GREQUE
  DIVERTISSEMENT GREC
  SUITE
MOURANT, W.
  BURLETTA
  ELEGY
  EVENING SONG
  HALLOWE'EN DANCE
  QUARTET
  SCHERZO
MOURET, J.
  12 AIRS A CHANTER ET A D
  6 SONATAS, 2 VOLS.
MOUSSORGSKY, M.
  BALLET OF THE CHICKENS
MOYLAN, W.
  DUET
MOYSE, L.
  ALBUM OF FLUTE DUETS
  4 DANCES
  30 EASY DUETS
  LITTLE PIECES
  4 PIECES
  QUINTET
  40 SHORT DUETS FOR BEGIN
  SUITE, C
MOYSE, M.
  ALBUM OF 30 CLASSICAL DU
MOYZES, A.
  SONATINA, OP 75
  WIND QUINTET, OP 17
MOZART
  COSI FAN TUTTE
  5 PIECES
  3 TRIOS
MOZART, F.
  2 POLONAISEN, OP 2
MOZART, L.
  DIVERTIMENTO IN G MA
  16 DUETS
  4 SHORT PIECES
  4 SHORT PIECES

421

4 SHORT PIECES
MOZART, TRIEBENSEE/VOXMAN
  CLEMENZA DI TITO, LA
MOZART, W.
  ABDUCTION FROM THE SERAG
  ADAGIO (CLARINET CONCERT
  ADAGIO (CLARINET CONCERT
  ADAGIO (K356)
  ADAGIO (QUINTET IN G MI)
  ADAGIO (SERENADE #11, K3
  ADAGIO (SERENADE, K375)
  ADAGIO (SONATINA #5)
  ADAGIO & ALLEGRO, K594
  ADAGIO & ALLEGRO, K594
  ADAGIO & MINUET
  ADAGIO & RONDO IN C MI,
  ADAGIO & RONDO, K617
  ADAGIO AND RONDO, K617
  ADAGIO FOR GLASHARMONIKA
  ADAGIO IN B FL MA
  ADAGIO IN B FL MA, K411
  ADAGIO IN B FL MA, K411
  ADAGIO IN B FL MA, K411
  ADAGIO IN C MA, K580A
  ADAGIO, KV580A
  ADAGIO, K411
  ADAGIO, K411
  ADAGIO, K411
  ADAGIO, K516
  ADAGIO, K580A
  ADAGIO, K580A
  ADAGIO, K580A
  2 ADAGIOS
  ALLEGRO (DIVERTIMENTO #3
  ALLEGRO (K464)
  ALLEGRO (K581)
  ALLEGRO (PIANO SONATA IN
  ALLEGRO (QUARTET, K157)
  ALLEGRO (SONATA, K402)
  ALLEGRO & ALLEGRETTO (DI
  ALLEGRO & MENUETTO
  ALLEGRO CONCERTANTE
  ALLEGRO IN B FL MA
  ALLEGRO MAESTOSO (K417)
  ALLEGRO VIVACE, K387
  ALLELUIA
  ALLELUIA
  ALLELUIA
  ANDANTE (DIVERTIMENTO #1
  ANDANTE (FUR EINE ORGELW
  ANDANTE & MENUETTO
  ANDANTE & RONDO (K417)
  ANDANTE CANTABILE (K330)
  ANDANTE FUR EINE ORGELWA
  ANDANTE GRAZIOSO
  ANDANTE IN F MA (KV616)
  ANDANTE IN F MA FUR EINE
  ANDANTE IN F MA, K616
  ANDANTE IN RONDO FORM IN
  ANDANTE IN RONDO FORM IN
  ANDANTE
  ANDANTE, K616

ARIA (LA CLEMENZA DI TIT
AVE VERUM CORPUS
AVE VERUM CORPUS
AVE VERUM
BEI MANNERN (MAGIC FLUTE
BERCEUSE
CADENZA TO CONCERTO, K29
CADENZAS FOR THE CONCERT
CADENZAS TO CONCERTO, K2
3 CADENZAS TO CONCERTO,
CANON,
CASSAZIONE
CLARINET DUET #4
CLARINET QUINTET
CLARINET QUINTET, K581
CONCERTO IN C MA, K299
CONCERTO, K299
CONTRADANCE IN RONDO FOR
CONTREDANSE & MINUET
4 DEUTSCHE TANZE
DIVERTIMENTI #4, #5, IN
DIVERTIMENTI
DIVERTIMENTI
5 DIVERTIMENTI, K229
2, DIVERTIMENTI
DIVERTIMENTO (KV240 & KV
DIVERTIMENTO (K251)
DIVERTIMENTO # 8 IN F MA
DIVERTIMENTO # 9 IN B FL
DIVERTIMENTO # 9 IN B FL
DIVERTIMENTO #1
DIVERTIMENTO #1, K229
DIVERTIMENTO #12 IN E FL
DIVERTIMENTO #12 IN E FL
DIVERTIMENTO #12, K252
DIVERTIMENTO #12, K252
DIVERTIMENTO #13 IN F MA
DIVERTIMENTO #13 IN F MA
DIVERTIMENTO #13, K253
DIVERTIMENTO #14 IN B FL
DIVERTIMENTO #14 IN B FL
DIVERTIMENTO #14, KV270
DIVERTIMENTO #14, K270
DIVERTIMENTO #14, K270
DIVERTIMENTO #16 IN E FL
DIVERTIMENTO #16 IN E FL
DIVERTIMENTO #16, K289
DIVERTIMENTO #2
DIVERTIMENTO #2, K229
DIVERTIMENTO #2, K439B
DIVERTIMENTO #3 IN B FL
DIVERTIMENTO #3 IN E FL
DIVERTIMENTO #3, K229
DIVERTIMENTO #3, K439B
DIVERTIMENTO #4 IN B FL
DIVERTIMENTO #4, K439B
DIVERTIMENTO #5 IN C MA,
DIVERTIMENTO #5
DIVERTIMENTO #6 IN B FL
DIVERTIMENTO #6 IN C MA,
DIVERTIMENTO #6
DIVERTIMENTO #6

DIVERTIMENTO #6, K229
DIVERTIMENTO #8 IN F MA,
DIVERTIMENTO IN B FL MA,
DIVERTIMENTO IN B FL MA,
DIVERTIMENTO IN D MA, 16
DIVERTIMENTO IN E FL MA,
DIVERTIMENTO IN E FL MA,
DIVERTIMENTO IN E FL MA,
DIVERTIMENTO IN E FL MA,
DIVERTIMENTO
DIVERTIMENTO
DIVERTIMENTO
DIVERTIMENTO, KV229/1
DIVERTIMENTO, K213
DIVERTIMENTO, K240
DIVERTIMENTOS #4 & #5, K
5 DIVERTISSEMENTS, K439
DON GIOVANNI HARMONIEMUS
DON GIOVANNI
DRITTER SATZ (SONATA IN
DUE PUPILLE, K439
DUET #2
DUET #3
DUET, OP 75/1
3 DUETS (K. 367-369)
17 DUETS (MAGIC FLUTE)
12 DUETS, K487
DUETS, OP 70/ 7, 8
DUETS, OP 70/ 9, 10
DUETS, OP 70/11, 12
6 DUETS, OP 70, 2 VOLS
6 DUETS, OP 77, 2 VOLS
6 DUETS, 2 VOLS.
6 DUETS, 2 VOLS
DUETS,OP 74/1 IN D MA
DUETS,OP 74/2 IN E MI
DUETS,OP 74/3 IN D MA
6 DUETS,OP 75,2 VOLS
12 DUETS
12 DUETS
6 DUETTE, K.V.156(1-3)
6 DUETTE,K.V. 157(4-6)
DUO
DUO, K487
12 DUOS
3 DUOS
12 EASY DUETS, K487
ECCO QUEL FIERO ISTANTE,
ECCO QUEL FIERO ISTANTE,
EINE KLEINE NACHTMUSIK
EINE KLEINE NACHTMUSIK
EINE KLEINE NACHTMUSIK
EINE KLEINE NACHTMUSIK
EINE KLEINE NACHTMUSIK
ENTFUHRUNG AUS DEM SERAI
EXCERPT (PIANO SONATA #1
EXCERPT (SONATA #4)
EXCERPT FROM PIANO SONAT
EXCERPT FROM PIANO SONAT
FAITHFUL HEART ENRAPTURE
FANTASIE FUR EINE ORGELW
FANTASIE IN F MI, K594

FANTASIE IN F MI, K608
FANTASY IN F MI, K594
FANTASY IN F MI, K608
FANTASY IN F MI, K608
FLOTENUHRSTUCK, ANDANTE
FUGA, K546
GALIMATHIAS MUSICUM
IDOMENEE, MARCHE
IMPRESARIO OVERTURE
KANONISCHES ADAGIO, KV41
KEGEL-DIVERTIMENTO
KEGELDUETTE, K. 487
4 KLEINE STUCKE
3 KONTRATANZE, K462
KONZERT IN C MA, K299
KONZERTANTES QUARTETT IN
KONZERTANTES QUARTETTE,
K458 (HUNT QUARTET)
K478 IN G MI
LARGHETTO & MENUETTO
LUCI CARE, LUCI BELLE, K
LULLABY
MAGIC FLUTE, THE
MAGIC FLUTE, THE
MARRIAGE OF FIGARO OVERT
MARRIAGE OF FIGARO, THE
MARRIAGE OF FIGARO, THE
MENUET (DON JUAN)
MENUET FAVORITE
8 MENUETS, K315A
MENUETT
MENUETTO (DIVERTIMENTO #
MENUETTO (DIVERTIMENTO #
MENUETTO (DON GIOVANNI)
MENUETTO (EINE KLEINE NA
MENUETTO (QUINTET IN G M
MENUETTO (SERENADE #1)
MENUETTO & TRIO, K516
MENUETTO
MI LAGNERO TACENDO, K437
MI LAGNERO TACENDO, K437
MINUET (SYMPHONY IN E FL
MINUET (SYMPHONY IN E FL
MINUET & TRIO (SYMPHONY
MINUET & TRIO (SYMPHONY
MINUET & TRIO (SYMPHONY
MINUET & TRIO
MINUET #6, K355
MINUET
MINUETTO (K282)
4 MIRROR CANONS
MOLTO ALLEGRO (K387)
4 MOVEMENT (LES PETIT RI
MOVEMENT #1 (EINE KLEINE
11 MOZART DUETS
MOZART HORN QUINTET
OBOE QUARTET, KV370
OBOE QUARTET, K370
OCTET, K196E
OVERTURE TO COSI FAN TUT
PARTO! MA TU BEN MIO!
PARTO!

PARTO,PARTO
PETITE MUSIQUE DE NUIT
PHANTASIE F EINE ORGELWA
PIANO SONATA #4, EXCERPT
PIECES
PIU NON SI TROVANO, K549
PRESTO (SINFONIA CONCERT
QUARTET (K298)
QUARTET IN A MA
QUARTET IN A MA, K298
QUARTET IN C MA
QUARTET IN D MA
QUARTET IN D MA, K285
QUARTET IN F MA, K 370
QUARTET IN F MA, K370
QUARTET IN G MA, K285A
QUARTET, K370
3, QUARTET
QUARTETS K465, K387, K57
QUARTETS, KV285,285A,285
3 QUARTETS, K285,298,370
3 QUARTETS
4 QUARTETS
QUINTET #6
QUINTET IN A MA, KV581
QUINTET IN A MA, K581
QUINTET IN C MI, KV406
QUINTET IN D MI (K422)
QUINTET IN E FL MA, KV45
QUINTET IN E FL MA, K452
QUINTET IN F MA, KV370
QUINTET
QUINTET, K406
QUINTET, K452
QUINTET, K581
QUINTET, K581; DIVERTIME
QUINTET, K593
ROMANZE
ROMANZE, MENUETTO & TRIO
RONDO (PIANO SONATA #1)
RONDO (PIANO SONATA #1)
RONDO (SERENADE IN B FL
RONDO (SERENADE IN B FL
RONDO (8TH VIOLIN SONATA
RONDO ALLA TURCA
RONDO
RONDO
RONDO
SCENE & DANCE (MARRIAGE
SE LONTAN, BEN MIO, TU S
SELECTIONS FROM COSI FAN
SERENADE #1, KV439B
SERENADE #10 IN B FL MA,
SERENADE #10, K361
SERENADE #10, K361
SERENADE #11 IN E FL MA,
SERENADE #11, K375
SERENADE #12 IN C MI, K3
SERENADE #12, K388
SERENADE #2, KV439B
SERENADE #3, KV439B
SERENADE IN B FL MA

SERENADE IN B FL MA, KV1
SERENADE IN B FLAT MA
SERENADE IN C MI, K388
SERENADE IN E FL MA, K37
SERENADE IN E FL MA, K37
SERENADE, K182
SERENADE, K375
SERENADES #4, #5, KV439B
SEXTET
SEXTET, K608
4 SHORT PIECES
SINFONIA CONCERTANTE IN
SINFONIA CONCERTANTE IN
SINFONIA CONCERTANTE, K2
SINFONIETTA
SONATA IN B FL MA
SONATA IN B FL MA
SONATA IN B FL MA, K292
SONATA IN B FL MA, K358
SONATA
SONATA, K292
3 SONATAS
3 SONATAS
SONATE #1
SONATE IN B FL MA, K292
SONATE
SONATINE
SONATINE
SONATINE
SPRING RONDO, A (K320)
12 STUCKE (DON GIOVANNI)
5 STUCKE
SUITE #2 IN G MA
SUITE #2 IN G MA
THEME (CONCERTO #21)
2 THEMES & VARIATIONS, K
TRIO #4, KV498
TRIO #7 (K498)
TRIO #7, K498
TRIO IN E FL MA, K498
TRIO
TRIO
TRIO
TRIO
TRIO, K498
TRIO, K498
VARIATIONS ON A THEME BY
12 VARIATIONS, K265
6 VIENNESE SONATINAS
VIVAT BACCHUS, BACCHUS L
WIENER SERENADEN, K439B
MUCZYNSKI, R.
  6 DUOS, OP 34
  FANTASY TRIO, OP 26
  FRAGMENTS
  MOVEMENTS, OP 16
MUELLER, F.
  EASY DUETS
  5 PIECES
  SUITE FOR FOUR
  3 TRANSCRIPTIONS
MUELLER, I.

6 EASY DUETS, OP 41
6 EASY DUOS, OP 41
MUELLER, P.
  35 DUETS
  QUINTET #1 IN E FL MA
  QUINTET #2 IN E FL MA
  QUINTET #3 IN A MA
MUFFAT, G.
  COURANTE
MUL, J.
  GALANT KWARTET (1952)
  KWINTET (1957)
MULDER, E.
  FUGA #3 (1940)
  FUGA #4 (1940)
  FUGA #7 (1940)
  QUARTET (1946)
  SEXTET (1946)
  TRIO IN CONTRAPUNTISCHE
MULDER, H.
  KWINTET, OP119 (1961)
  3 LIEDEREN (1959)
  QUINTET, OP141 (1966)
  TRIO, OP 17 (1960)
MULLER
  CONCERTANTE
  SYMPHONIE CONCERTANTE IN
MULLER¬MEDEK, W.
  KLEINE STUCKE ALTER MEIS
  LEINEWEBER, DIE
  WOODWIND QUINTET #1
MULLER¬SIEMENS, D.
  SANGLOTS LONGS, LES
MULLER, I.
  QUATUOR #2
MULLER, J.
  COMPTINES
MULLER, L.
  TANZERISCHE IMPRESSIONEN
  12 VERANDERUNGEN
MULLER, S.
  KAMMERMUSIK IN A MA, OP
MULLINS, H.
  DUETS
MULOT, A.
  SUITE DANS LE STYLE ANCI
MUNTZIG, A.
  KVARTETT
  SOMMARMUSIK
MUNZING, A.
  TRIO (1966)
MURPHY
  NOTTURNO
MURPHY, L.
  CADENZAS & RECITATIVOS
  PRELUDE & CANON
  RONDINO
  SUITE
MURRAY, L.
  CLARINET CAPRIOLE
MUSGRAVE, T.
  CHAMBER CONCERTO #1

CHAMBER CONCERTO #2
CHAMBER CONCERTO #3
CHAMBER CONCERTO
IMPROMPTU #2
IMPROMPTU
PRIMAVERA
SERENADE
SONATA
TRIO
MUSSORGSKY, M.
  BALLET OF THE CHICKS IN
  BALLET OF THE CHICKS IN
  BALLET OF THE CHICKS IN
  MUSHROOMS
  MUSHROOMS
  MUSHROOMS
MUTTER, G.
  DIVERTIMENTO
MYERS, G.
  MINI-SONG CYCLE, A
MYERS, R.
  DIVERTMENTS
  FANTASY DUOS
  3 INVENTIONS
  QUARTET
  SEXTET
  TRIO
MYSLIVECEK, J.
  3 OCTETS
  SONATA IN B FL MA
  SONATA, OP 1/3
  TRIO IN B FL MA, OP 1/4
  TRIO IN B FL MA, OP 1/4
  TRIO
  TRIO, OP 1/4
NABERT
  METABOLE #1 & #2
NAGAN, Z.
  ISRAELI MINIATURES
  SERENADE FOR LISA
NAGEL
  SUITE IN D MI
  TRIO IN G MA
NAGEL, R.
  DIVERTIMENTO
NANCARROW, C.
  SARABANDE & SCHERZO
NAPOLI, C.
  MOMENTI
NARDINI, P.
  SHEPHERD'S PIPES
  SHEPHERD'S PIPES
  SHEPHERD'S PIPES
  SHEPHERD'S PIPES
  SHEPHERD'S PIPES
  TRIO IN C MA
NASH, R.
  IMPRESSIONS
NATANSON, T.
  3 PICTURES (1960)
  6 PIECES
  TOCCATA

NATRA, S.
  MUSIC (1964)
NAUDOT, J.
  BABIOLES, OP 10, 2 VOLS
  BABIOLES,OP 10,2 VOLS
  CONCERTO IN G MA, OP 17
  SONATA
  6 SONATAS, OP 5
  6 SONATAS,2 VOLS
  6 SONATAS
NAUMANN, J.
  DUETT IN B FL MA
  DUO
  DUO
  PETIT DUO
  QUARTET IN E FL MA, OP
NAUMANN, S.
  CADENZE (1964)
  DUO (1948)
  RISPOSTE I (1956)
  RUOLI, OP 1 (1959)
NAVARRO, J.
  INTEMPERANCES 1962
NAYLOR, B.
  DEJECTION (1973)
  NYMPH COMPLAINING FOR
NAZARIAN, A.
  DIVERTIMENTO
NECKE, H.
  MILL OF SANS SOUCI
NEDBAL, M.
  KLEINES TRIO
NEIKRUG, M.
  CONCERTINO (1976)
NELHYBEL, V.
  AURIEL VARIATIONS
  CASTLE MUSIC
  CHORALE & DANZA
  COUNTERPOINT #1
  4 DUETS
  EPISODES
  IMPROMPTUS FOR 6 WOODWIN
  IMPROMPTUS
  ORATIO II
  3 PIECES
  QUINTET #3
  RICERCARE
  RUSTIC DANCES
  SHORT STORIES
  SUITE #1
  TAKE TIME
  9 TRIOS FOR CLARINET
  WOODWIND QUINTET #2
NELSON, B.
  ADVANCED DUETS, 3 VOLS
NELSON, L.
  FLUTE THING
  MUSIC
NEMIROFF, I.
  PERSPECTIVES
  4 TREBLE SUITE
  VARIATIONS TO A THEME

  VARIATIONS TO A THEME
NERO, P.
  MONSOON
NESSLER, R.
  MOTIONEN (1964)
  POISSONS MAGIQUES (1968)
NESTICO, S.
  CHRISTMAS: THE JOY & SPI
  STUDY IN CONTRASTS, A
  STUDY IN CONTRASTS, A
  STUDY IN CONTRASTS, A
NEUBAUER, F.
  4 PIECES
  TRIO IN C MA, OP 3/3
  TRIO IN D MA
NEUBERT, G.
  MUSIK (1968/69)
NEUKOMM, S. VON
  QUINTET, OP 8
  SEPTET
NEUMANN, F.
  5 STUCKE
NEUMANN, H.
  GRAND TRIO, OP 14
NEVIN, E.
  GONDOLIERI
  NARCISSUS
  NARCISSUS
NEVIN, M.
  INVENTIONS
NEWMAN
  RONDO BRILLANTE
NICHIFOR, S.
  3 NOUVELLES IMPRESSIONS
  3 NOUVELLES IMPRESSIONS
NICULESCU, S.
  TRIPLUI (1971)
  TRIPLUM II (1974)
NIEHAUS, L.
  DANCING TOY SOLDIERS
  FUGUE
  FUSION
  HALLOWEEN FANTASY
  JAZZ CONCEPTION
  MARCHE MAESTOSO
  MELODIQUE CANTABILE
  MOSAICS
  ROMANTIC SKETCH
  STORM, THE
  SUMMER NOCTURNE
  SYMPHONETTE
  THEME & VARIATIONS
  TICK TOCK CLOCK
NIEHAUS, M.
  IT HAPPENS (1972)
NIELSEN, C.
  FAITH & HOPE
  FOG IS LIFTING, THE
  HUMORESQUE BAGATELLES, O
  QUINTET, OP 43
  SERENATA INVANO
NIELSEN, S.

426

PERSPECTIVES (1970)
OLAN, D.
  COMPOSITION (1976)
  GATHERING (1972)
  MUSIC (1966)
  SATZ
  STARTING WINTER
  4 STUDIES
OLAVIDE, G. DE
  COMPOSICION (1963)
OLDFIEDL, A.
  TRIO
OLDFIELD, A.
  SOLOS FOR WOODWIND QUINT
OLIVADOTI, J.
  AIR & TARANTELLA
  DANCE IN OLDEN STYLE
  DIVERTIMENTO
OLIVE, J.
  MAR-RI-IA-A (1975)
  STUDY #3
OLIVEIRA, J.
  ITERACOES
OLIVER
  TROPICAL SERENADE
OLIVER, A.
  GRUPOS DE CAMARA (1975)
  INTERPOLACIONES (1970)
  OMICRON 73 (1973)
  VERSOS A CUATRO (1976)
OLIVER, H.
  QUINTET
  SAMSARA: A TRIO (1974)
OLIVER, R.
  AMERICAN FOLK SONG
  LORD RANDALL
  LORD RANDALL
OLIVEROS, P.
  AEOLIAN PARTITIONS
  TRIO (1963)
  VARIATIONS FOR SEXTET
OLKUSNIK, J.
  CHAMBER MUSIC
OLLER, J.
  DUO (1936)
OLSEN, P.
  PROLANA, OP 33 (1955)
OLSEN, S.
  INVENTION
  NOCTURNE, OP 57/2
  QUINTET, OP 35
  SUITE, OP 10
OLSSON, S.
  QUINTET (1975)
OLTHUIS, K.
  ALMANACH AUX IMAGES
ONSLOW, G.
  GRAND SEXTUOR, OP 77 BIS
  NONETTO, OP 77
  QUINTET IN F MA, OP 81/3
  QUINTET
  SEXTUOR, OP 77

OPITZ, E.
  SONATINE
ORBAN, M.
  SONATINE
ORFF, C.
  KLEINES KONZERT NACH LAU
ORGAD, B.
  LANDSCAPES (NOFIM)
  LEAVE OUT MY NAME (1947)
  OUT OF THE DUST (1956)
ORLAND, H.
  FUGA
  FUGHETTA
  LOVE & PITY
  PERPETUUM MOBILE
OROMSZEGI
  FAGOTTDUOS
ORREGO¬SALAS, J.
  DIVERTIMENTO
  GARDEN SONGS, OP 47
  SEXTET
  SONATA A QUATTRO
ORTHEL, L.
  OTTO ABBOZZI
  4 SONGS, OP 64 (1972)
ORTOLANI, O.
  MORE (THEME FROM MONDO C
OSIECK, H.
  DIVERTIMENTO (1950)
  SONATINE (1961)
  TRIO (1975)
  VARIATIES OVER VIER WEVE
OSTENDORF, J.
  BLASERQUINTETT
OSTERC, S.
  BLASERQUINTETT (1932)
  SONATINE (1929)
  SUITE
  WOODWIND TRIO
ØSTERLING, E.
  BEGUINE FOR FLUTES
  SAMBA FOR FLUTES
OSTLING
  DUETS, 2 VOLS
OSTLING¬WEBER
  DUETS, 2 VOLS
OSTLING, A.
  ALOUETTE CLARINETTE
  POP GOES THE WOODWINDS
  QUAR-TETE-A-TETE
  YANKEE DOODLE DANDIES
OSTRANDER
  DUET ALBUM
  SUITE FOR 3
OSTRANDER, A.
  BAROQUE SUITE
  DUET ALBUM
  DUET ALBUM
  DUET ALBUM;
  DUET ALBUM,
  FIRST PALS
OSTRANSKY, L.

428

TRIO (SEMPLICIA)
PAISIBLE, J.
  6 DUETS, OP 1, 2 VOLS
  6 DUETS, OP 1, 2 VOLS
  SONATA, OP 1/1 (D MI)
  SONATA, OP 1/2 (F MA)
  SONATA, OP 1/4 (G MI)
  SONATA, OP 1/5 (C MA)
  SONATAS #1-5 (PUB SEPARA
PAISIELLO, G.
  ARIA (IL BARBIERE DI SIV
  6 DIVERTIMENTI
  DIVERTISSEMENT
  QUARTET IN G MA
  RIEN NE PEUT CALMER MA P
  SERENATA IN C MA
PAISNER, B.
  SWING DUETS
  SWING DUETS
PALA
  QUARTET IN C MI
PALA, J.
  BONJOUR
  3 MINIATUREN
  3 MINIATUREN
  3 MINIATURES
  PRELUDE & SCHERZO
PALESTRINA, G.
  ADORAMUS TE
  ALLELUIA & CHORAL
  ALMA REDEMPTORIS
  QUITE THEME, A
PALKOVSKY, O.
  CONCERTINO (1966)
  KAMMERMUSIK (1964)
  3 STUCKE (1965)
  3 STUDIEN (1967)
  WOODWIND QUINTET #2
PALLASZ, E.
  FRAGMENTS TO SAPPHO'S TE
  PAINTED TOWER
PALMER, R.
  QUINTET
PANNI, M.
  4 MELODIE (1964)
PANNIER, O.
  TRIO #2 IN E FL MA, OP 4
PAPINEAU¬COUTURE, J.
  CHANSON DE RAHIT (1972)
  EGLOGUES (1942)
  FANTAISIE (1963)
  NOCTURNES (1969; REV 197
  NOCTURNES (1969; REV 197
  SEXTUOR (1967)
  SUITE (1947)
  TRIO IN 4 MOUVEMENTS
PAPORISZ, Y.
  ARROGANCES (1969)
  PICCOLI DUETTI
PAPP, L.
  IMPRESSIONI
PAQUE, J.

DUO DE LA NORMA, #1
DUO DE LA NORMA, #2
DUO DE LA NORMA, #7
PARADIES, P.
  GRAZIOSO
  GRAZIOSO
PARCHMAN, G.
  SEXTET (1966)
  SONATA
PARERA, A.
  EL CAPEO
PARFREY, R.
  TRIO
PARIK, I.
  EPITAF #2
  HUDBA PRE TROCH
  2 LIEDER
  MUSIC FOR 3
PARK, S.
  PASTORALE
  PASTORALE
PARODI, R.
  CONCERTO
  CONCERTO
PARR
  BACH-HANDEL ALBUM
PARRIS, H.
  WOODWIND MINIATURES
PARRIS, R.
  BOOK OF IMAGINARY BEINGS
  DIRGE FOR THE NEW SUNRIS
  DREAMS
  DUO
  GOLDEN NET, THE
  4 PIECES
  QUINTET
  RITE OF PASSAGE (1978)
  RITE OF PASSAGE (1978)
  RITE OF PASSAGE (1978)
  SONATINA FOR WINDS
  ST. WINEFRED'S WELL
PARRY, C.
  NONET IN B FL MA, OP 70
PARSCH, A.
  ESERCIZII (1970)
  POETICA #4 (1970)
  TRANSPOSIZIONI I
PARTOS, O.
  5 ISRAELI SONGS (1960)
  MAQAMAT
  NEBULAE (1966)
PASATIERI, T.
  FAR FROM LOVE
PASCAL, C.
  OCTUOR
  QUATUOR
PASQUINI, B.
  SONATA II
  SONATA
PASQUOTTI, C.
  LUTETIA
PASSANI, E.

QUINTET (1954)
PASSMORE, J.
  ADAGIO & ALLEGRO, OP 2
PATACHICH, I.
  BALKAN
  DUETTINO
  PETITE SUITE
  3 QUADRI
  QUARTET
  4 STUCKE
PATTERSON, P.
  COMEDY
  DIVERSIONS (1976)
  FLOATING MUSIC
  INTERSECTIONS
  QUINTET (1967)
  WIND TRIO
PATZIG, G.
  MILITARMARSCHE DES 18. J
  MILITARMARSCHE DES 18. J
  MILITARMARSCHE DES 18, J
PAUBON, P.
  COLLOQUE A 3
  QUATUOR
  SUITE
PAUER, E.
  QUINTET, OP 44
PAUER, J.
  BLASERQUINTETT (1960)
  MUSICA DA CONCERTO
PAUK, A.
  CUMULUM
  MAGARU
  WHEREVER THERE IS DISTAN
PAUL, B.
  SERENADE
PAULSON, G.
  DIVERTIMENTO, OP113
  DUBBEL RORBLADSGLADJE, O
  DUO, OP 84 (1955)
  LITEN SERENAD, OP 22
PAULUS
  WIND SUITE
PAUMGARTNER, B.
  DIVERTIMENTO
PAYNE, A.
  PARAPHRASES & CADENZAS
  SONATAS & RICERCARS
  WORLD'S WINTER, THE
PAYNE, F.
  2 CONTRASTS
  MINIATURES
  PAVANE AND OSTINATO
  QUARTET
  TOCCATA
PAZ, J.
  CONCRECION
PEACOCK, K.
  SONGS OF THE CEDAR
PEARSON, W.
  HUNT, THE
  3 PASTORAL FUGUES

PASTORELLA
PECK, R.
  AUTOMOBILE
  SIX PAK
PEDERSEN, P.
  CHORALE PRELUDE #2
  COME AWAY (1959)
  OLD SONG (1973), AN
  RICERCARE (1958)
  SERIAL COMPOSITION
  WIND QUINTET (1959)
  WOODWIND TRIO #1 (1956)
  WOODWIND TRIO #2 (1957)
PEDLEY, D.
  3 ENGLISH TUNES
  5 FOLK TUNES
PEETERS, F.
  TRIO, OP 80
PEHKONEN, E.
  CONCERTO
PEHRSON, J.
  ENTELECHIES
PELEMANS, W.
  AD MUSICAM
  BLAZERSKWARTET
  CONCERTINO #3
  KLEIN DUO
  KWARTET
  ONDER DE APPELBOMEN
  QUARTET #2
  QUINTET #1
  QUINTET #2
  SAXOPHONE QUARTET
  SONATE I
  SONATE II
  SONATE
  TRIO #2
  TRIO #3
  TRIO
  TRIO
PELLEGRINI, E.
  SONATINA
PELZ, W.
  BALLAD
  CANDLELIGHT WALTZ
  FIRESIDE REVERIES
  GRADUATION WALTZ
  MINUET PETITE
  THREE OF A KIND
PENDERECKI, K.
  CAPRICCIO
PENN, W.
  NIGHT MUSIC
  TRIO
PENNISI, F.
  CHORALIS CUM FIGURIS (19
  FOSSILE (1966)
  QUINTETTO IN 4 PARTI (19
  TRIO (1968)
PENTLAND, B.
  CANZONA (1961)
  OCTET FOR WINDS (1948)

PEPIN, C.
  SEQUENCES (1972)
PEPUSCH, J.
  CONCERTO, OP 8/1
  CONCERTO, OP 8/2
  CONCERTO, OP 8/3
  CONCERTO, OP 8/4
  CONCERTO, OP 8/5
  CONCERTO, OP 8/6
  CORYDON
  SONATA A TRE IN F MA
  SONATA DA CAMERA IN G MI
  SONATA DA CAMERA IN G MI
  SONATA IN C MA
  SONATA IN D MI
  SONATA IN F MA
  SONATA IN G MA
  SONATA
  TRIO SONATA IN B FL MA
  TRIO SONATA IN E MI
  TRIO SONATA IN G MA
  TRIO SONATA IN G MI
  TRIO SONATA IN G MI
  6 TRIO SONATAS, 2 VOLS
  TRIO-SONATE IN B FL MA
  TRIO-SONATE IN D MI
  TRIOSONATE IN D MA
  TRIOSONATE IN F MA
  TRIOSONATE IN F MA
  TRIOSONATE IN G MA
  6 TRIOSONATEN, 2 VOL
PERCEVAL, J.
  SERENATA
PERFECT, A.
  TWO LITTLE CHUMS
  TWO LITTLE CHUMS
  TWO LITTLE CHUMS;
PERGAMENT, M.
  ADAGIO (1973)
  FANTASIA (1973)
  INTERMEZZO (1973)
  LITEN SVIT (1970)
  PEZZO (1972)
  SCHERZO (1973)
PERGOLESI, G.
  CONCERTO IN D MA
  SICILIAN AIR
  SICILIAN AIR
  SICILIAN AIR
  SICILIAN AIR
  SICILIANO
PERIER, A.
  STUDY-CAPRICES IN THE FO
PERKOWSKI, P.
  SAPPHO'S SONGS
PERLE, G.
  QUINTET #1
  QUINTET #2, OP 4 (1960)
  QUINTET #3 (1967)
PERRAULT, M.
  QUATUOR (1953)
  SEXTUOR (1955)

PERRY, G.
  PETITE TOOT SUITE
PERRY, J.
  PASTORAL
PERSICHETTI, V.
  KING LEAR, OP 35
  PASTORAL, OP 21 (1943)
  SERENADE #1
  SERENADE #10
  SERENADE #13
PERSSON, B.
  FYRHANDIG INVENTION
  OM SOMMAREN SKONA II
  OM SOMMAREN SKONA II
PERT, M.
  AKHENATEN, OP 15
  ALPHA CENTAURI, OP 10
  ALPHA CENTAURI, OP 10
  ANCIENT PATTERN, OP 34
  ANCIENT PATTERN, OP 34
  CERNUNNOS, OP 24
  EARTH DANCES, OP 31
  EARTH DANCES, OP 31
  EOASTRION, OP 30
  OMEGA CENTAURI, OP 11
  OMEGA CENTAURI, OP 11
  5 SONGS FROM THE JAPANES
PERUTI, C.
  AUTUMN MUSIC
  CONFLUENCE
  ENDGAME
  HALLOWEEN MUSIC
  LEFTOVERS
  4 MOVEMENTS
  3 SUNDAY PIECES
PESCETTI, G.
  PRESTO
PESSARD, E.
  ANDALOUSE
  AUBADE, OP 6
PESTALOZZA, H.
  CIRIBIRIBIN
PETERSEN, T.
  MINIATURE SUITE
PETERSMA, W.
  SAXOPHONE QUARTET
  WIND QUINTET (1976)
PETERSON, W.
  ENCOUNTERS (1976)
  METAMORPHOSES
  PHANTASMAGORIA
PETKOV, D.
  3 POLYPHONE STUCKE
PETRASSI, G.
  DIALOGO ANGELICO (1948)
  DUE LIRICHE DI SAFFO
  PROPOS D'ALAIN
  SERENATA (1958)
  SONATA DA CAMERA (1948)
  TRE PER SETTE (1966)
PETRESCU, D.
  MUSIQUE (1969)

MUSIQUE (1969)
PETRIC, I.
  CAPRICCIO
  7 COMPOSITIONS
  CONCERT IMPROVISATIONS
  CROQUIS SONORES
  CROQUIS SONORES
  DIVERTIMENTO FOR SLAVKO
  DIVERTIMENTO FOR SLAVKO
  3 ESQUISSES
  GAME FOR THREE-GAME FOR
  GAME FOR 3-GAME FOR 4
  GEMINICONCERTINO
  INLAID-WORK
  MOSAICS
  MOSAICS
  NUANCES EN COULEUR
  PETIT CONCERTO DE CHAMBR
  5 PIECES
  WOODWIND QUINTET #1
  WOODWIND QUINTET #2
  WOODWIND QUINTET #3
PETROVICS, E.
  WIND QUINTET (1964)
PETRUSHKA, S.
  V'SAMACHTA BEHAGECHA
PETTERSSON, A.
  FUGA IN E MA
PETYREK, F.
  ARABISCHE SUITE
  ARABISCHE SUITE
  DIVERTIMENTO
  GUTE NACHT, O WELT
PETZ, J.
  SYMPHONIA
PETZOLD, J.
  CHRISTMAS STORY, THE
PEYROT, F.
  TRIO, OP 7
PEYTON, M.
  SONGS FROM SHAKESPEARE
PEZ, J.
  MENTRE FRA MILLE FIORI
  TRIO SONATA IN C MA
PEZEL, J.
  BICINIA 75
  18 PIECES
  3 PIECES
  6 SONATINAS (NOS.1,2,3,7
PEZZATI, R.
  CORRESPONDANCES (1972)
PFEIFFER, G.
  MUSETTE
  MUSETTE, OP 47/1
  SONATA
  SONATA
PFISTER, H.
  BALLADE
  MOBILI A TRE
  OTTOBEUREN QUINTET
  PREAMBOLO, ARIA E BALLO
PHILIDOR, F.

ARIA (LE MARECHAL FERRAN
ARIA (SANCHO PANCA)
PHILIDOR, P.
  SUITE
PHILIPP, F.
  SERENADE, OP 23
PHILIPPOT, M.
  OCTUOR (1974)
PHILLIPOT, M.
  TRIO INACHEVE
PHILLIPS, B.
  HUNTINGDON TWOS & THREES
  MUSIC FOR THIS TIME OF Y
PHILLIPS, D.
  LULLABIC DIGRESSIONS
PHILLIPS, G.
  PASTORALE
  SUITE
PHILLIPS, I.
  6 SHORT ARRANGEMENTS
  6 SHORT ARRANGEMENTS
PHILLIPS, P.
  LITTLE PRELUDE & BLUES
PICHA, F.
  WOODWIND QUINTET, OP 31
PICHAUREAU, C.
  RAFFLESIA
PICHL, V.
  2 DIVERTIMENTI
PICKER, T.
  SEPTET
  SEXTET #2 "HALLE'S RAVIN
PIECHOWSKA, A.
  IMAGINAIRE (1976)
  SONGS OF BILITIS
PIER, G.
  3 ETUDEN
PIERCE, A.
  JOB 22:28
  MY LADY HUNDSON'S PAVANE
PIERCE, E.
  ROMANCE
PIERNE, G.
  CHANSON D'AUTREFOIS
  CHANSON DE LA GRAND'MAMA
  GUARDIAN ANGEL & SONG OF
  INTRODUCTION & VARIATION
  MARCH OF THE LITTLE TIN
  MARCH OF THE LITTLE TIN
  MARCH OF THE LITTLE TIN
  MARCH OF THE LITTLE TIN
  PASTORALE VARIEE, OP 30
  PASTORALE, OP 14/1
  PRELUDIO & FUGHETTA, OP
  PRELUDIO & FUGHETTA, OP
  PRELUDIO ET FUGHETTA, OP
  SONATA DA CAMERA, OP 48
  VARIATIONS AU CLAIR DE L
  VARIATIONS LIBRE ET FINA
  VEILLEE DE L'ANGE GARDIE
  VOYAGE AU PAYS DU TENDRE
PIERNE, P.

BUCOLIQUE VARIEE
3 CONVERSATIONS
SUITE PITTORESQUE
PIERSOL, F.
  SCHERZO
PIETRAGRUA, G.
  2 CANZONE, OP1
PIETRZAK, B.
  TRIO (1964)
PIETSCH, E.
  MINIATURE SUITE
PIJPER, W.
  QUINTET (1929)
  SEPTET (1920)
  SEXTET (1923)
  TRIO (1927)
PIKET, F.
  LEGEND & JOLLITY
  REFLECTION & CAPRICE
  TRIO
PILLEVESTRE, J.
  ANCHES REBELLES, LES
  IDYLLE BRETONNE
  MOUVEMENT PERPETUEL, LE
PILLIN, B.
  3 PIECES FOR DOUBLE-REED
  SCHERZO
  SERENADE
  SUITE
PILLNEY, K.
  IN DULCI JUBILO
PILLOIS, J.
  5 HAI-KAI
PILSS, K.
  OCTET IN C MI
  SERENADE
  SONATINA (1942)
PINCHARD, M.
  INTERLUDES POUR L'ODYSSE
  TOMBEAU DE MARIN MARAIS
PINKHAM, D.
  ECLOGUE
  FOR EVENING DRAWS ON
  HE SCATTERS THE SNOW
  2 MOTETS
  PRELUDE
PINOS¬SIMANDEL, A.
  GENESIS (1970)
  GENISIS (1970)
  KONFLIKTE (1964)
PINOS, A.
  KARIKATUREN
PIRANI, O.
  IMPRESSIONE GROTESCA
  MOMENTO DINAMICO, STUDIO
  REVERIE
PISK, P.
  DUO, OP106
  ELEGY & SCHERZINO, OP 70
  ENVOY, OP104
  LITTLE WOODWIND MUSIC, A
  MEADOW SAFFRONS

SUITE
SUITE, OP 80
WOODWIND QUINTET, OP 96
PISTON, W.
  DIVERTIMENTO
  3 PIECES (1926)
  QUINTET (1956)
  QUINTET
PITFIELD, T.
  DUETTO
  TRIO
  VARIEGATIONS
PLA, J.
  6 SONATAS
  6 SONATAS
PLACHETA, H.
  DIVERTIMENTO, OP 8
  QUARTET, OP 10
PLAETNER, J.
  NOCTURNE (1963)
PLAIN, G.
  SCENARIO
PLANQUETTE, R.
  CLOCHES DE CORNEVILLE
PLATTI, G.
  SONATA
  TRIO IN G MA
  TRIO SONATA IN G MA
PLATZ, R.
  FOR ROLF
PLESKOW, R.
  3 BAGATELLES (1967)
  BAGATELLES (1975)
  DUE BICINIA
  FOR 5 PLAYERS & BARITONE
  MOTET & MADRIGAL (1973)
  MOVEMENT (1962)
  MOVEMENT FOR 9 PLAYERS
  3 MOVEMENTS
  ON 2 ANCIENT TEXTS
  ON 3 OLD ENGLISH RHYMES
  3 SONGS
  TRIO (1977)
PLEYEL, I.
  ANDANTE & RONDO; OP 48/1
  ANDANTE & RONDO, OP 48/1
  ANDANTE & RONDO, OP 48/1
  DUETS #1 & 2
  6 DUETS, OP 8
  6 DUETS, OP 8
  12 DUETS, 4 VOLS
  6 DUETTE
  DUO IN D MI
  DUO IN F MA
  3 DUOS CONCERTANTS, OP 6
  DUOS, OP 14/1-3
  3 DUOS
  GRAND TRIO, OP 29
  6 LITTLE DUETS
  QUARTET IN B FL MA, OP 2
  QUARTET IN C MA, OP 20/3
  QUARTET IN E FL MA

434

QUARTET IN G MA, OP 20/1
QUARTET, OP 17/2
3 QUARTETS, OP 41
QUINTET IN C MA
QUINTET IN E FL MA, OP 1
RONDO IN B-FLAT
RONDO
RONDO
2 RONDOS
SEXTET IN E FL MA
SINFONIA CONCERTANTE
SONATA IN C MA, OP 16/2
SONATA IN E MI, OP 16/5
SONATA IN G MA, OP 16/1
SYMPHONIE CONCERTANTE #5
TRIO #1 IN G MA, OP 73
TRIO #2 IN C MA
TRIO IN B FL MA, OP 20/1
TRIO IN C MA
TRIO IN E FL MA
TRIO IN E FL MA, OP 20/2
TRIO, OP 20/1
6 TRIOS (OP 8)
PLUISTER, S.
  DIVERTIMENTO (1937)
PLUMBY
  PICTURE OF A HUNT
PODEST, L.
  TESKNICE
PODESVA, J.
  DOTAZNIK SRDCE (1965)
POELMAN, R.
  MUSIC (1974)
POESSINGER, F.
  TRIO IN F MA
  TRIO, OP 28
POGLIETTI, A.
  SONATA A TRE IN C MA
POLDINI, E.
  DANCING DOLL, THE
  GENERAL BOOM-BOOM
  POUPEE VALSANTE (DANCING
POLDOWSKI, D.
  SUITE MINIATURE
POLGAR, T.
  ANNABEL LEE (1974)
  SONATINA (1971)
POLIN, C.
  DEATH OF PROCRIS, THE
  KLWRK DIURNAL, A
  MAKIMONO I
  NO-RAI
  O, ADERYN PUR
  SONATA #2
  SONATA
  SYNAULIA II
  TELEMANICON
  TELEMANICON
  TOWER SONATA
POLK, M.
  3 SHORT DIALOGUES
POLLET

2 WOODWIND QUINTETS
POLLOCK, R.
  CHAMBER SETTING (1972)
  DESCENT, THE (1976)
  QUINTET (1975)
  REVOLUTION (1976)
  REVOLUTION (1976)
  SONG (1967)
  STUDY (1970)
  TRIO #2 (1969)
  TUMBLING HAIR (1975)
POLOLANIK, Z.
  MUSICA CONCISA (1963)
  MUSICA SPINGENTA III
  SCHERZO CONTRARIO
PONCE, M.
  ESTRELLITA
  ESTRELLITA
  ESTRELLITA
PONCHIELLI, A.
  DANCE OF THE HOURS
  QUARTETTO
PONJEE, T.
  QUATUOR D'ANCHES (1979)
PONSE, L.
  EUTERPE, OP 37 (1964)
  KWINTET, OP 25 (1956)
  KWINTET, OP 32 (1961)
  2 PIECES (1943)
  SEXTET, OP 27 (1958)
  TRIO (1941)
POOT, M.
  BALLADE
  CONCERTINO (1962)
  CONCERTINO (1963)
  CONCERTINO
  DIVERTIMENTO
  LEGEND (1967)
  LEGENDE (1967)
  MOSAIQUE
  MUSIQUE (1964)
  OCTUOR (1948)
  PETITE MARCHE DE FETE
  SCHERZO (1941)
  TERZETTO
POPOVICI, D.
  QUINTETTE (1967)
POPP, W.
  EASY DUETS
  MELODIC SUITE, OP281
PORADOWSKI, S.
  CONCERTO
PORCELIJN, D.
  AMOEBE FOR X FLUTES
  CONTINUATIONS (1968)
  PULVERIZATIONS
  SHADES (1975)
  12 NOVEMBER 1819 (1976)
PORENA, B.
  4 KANONISCHE LIEDER
  NEUMI (1963)
PORRET, J.

5TH DUO CONCERTANT
6TH DUO CONCERTANT
PREMRU, R.
  CONCERTINO (1954)
PRESSER, W.
  BAROQUE SUITE
  7 BASSOON DUETS
  CHORAL FANTASY
  5 DUETS
  5 DUETS
  7 DUETS
  7 DUETS
  7 DUETS
  JOREPI
  MINUET, SARABANDE & GAVO
  NOCTURNE
  PASSACAGLIA
  QUINTET
  3 ROUNDS
  SERENADE
  SONG & MARCH
  SONG & WORKOUT
  SUITE (1961)
  TRIO
  TRIO
  TRIO
  WALTZ & SCHERZO
  3 WHITE SPIRITUALS
PREVOST, A.
  MOBILES (1959)
  TRIPTYQUE (1962)
PRIETO, C.
  ARAMBOL (1976)
  IMPROVISACION (1966)
  JUEGO DE LA MUSICA, EL
  ODA XIV (1967)
  SOLO A SOLO (1968)
PRIETOK C.
  REFLEJOS (1973)
PRIN, Y.
  MOBILE I
  MOBILE I
PRINZ, A.
  QUINTET
PROCACCINI, T.
  CLOWN MUSIC
PROCUREUR, J.
  ROSE DE NOEL
PROKOFIEV, S.
  FLEETING MOMENTS, OP 22
  HUMOROUS SCHERZO
  HUMOROUS SCHERZO, OP 12
  HUMOROUS SCHERZO, OP. 12
  OVERTURE ON HEBREW THEME
  OVERTURE ON HEBREW THEME
  OVERTURE ON JEWISH THEME
  QUINTET IN G MI, OP 39
  QUINTET
  QUINTET, OP 39
  ROMANCE & TROIKA
  VISIONS FUGITIVES
PROSPERI, C.

4 INVENZIONI (1952/53)
PROVINCIALI, E.
  DANSE VILLAGEOISE
PROWO, P.
  CONCERTO A 5, #1 IN F MA
  CONCERTO A 6 IN C MA
  CONCERTO IN D MI
  CONCERTO IN D
  SONATA A 3, #5
  SONATA A 3, #6
  SONATA
  TRIO SONATA IN C MI
PRUNTY, W.
  TRIO ALLEGRO
PRZYBYLSKI, B.
  PERMUTARE
PUCCINI, G.
  MUSETTA'S WALTZ (LA BOHE
  MUSETTA'S WALTZ SONG
  MUSETTA'S WALTZ SONG
  ONE FINE DAY (MADAMA BUT
  ONE FINE DAY (MADAMA BUT
  THEY CALL ME MIMI (LA BO
  VISSI D'ARTE (TOSCA)
  VISSI D'ARTE
  VISSI D'ARTE, VISSI D'AM
  VISSI D'ARTE, VISSI D'AM
PUHAKKA, J.
  DUO, OP 14/1
  EPITAPHE I, OP 11
PURCELL
  INTRADA AND AIR
PURCELL, D.
  TRIO-SONATE IN D MI
PURCELL, H.
  BID THE VIRTUES
  CHACONNE
  CHACONNE
  CHACONNE
  CHACONNE
  DIOCLESIAN
  FANTASIA #1
  FANTASIA #3
  GAVOTTE
  HARK, HOW THE SONGSTERS
  KING JAMES II SUITE
  ONE CHARMING NIGHT
  PRELUDE
  STRIKE THE VIOL
  SUITE
  2 SYMPHONIES
  3 SYMPHONIES
  TRIOSTUCKE
  WHY SHOULD MEN QUARREL
PURDIE, H.
  CANON APERTUS
PUSZTAI, T.
  CANTICLES (1971)
  EPISODES (1975)
  QUINTET (1974)
PUTSCHE', T.
  THEME AND VARIATIONS

```
THEME SONG & VARIATIONS            TRIOSONATE IN G MA
WIND QUINTET (1964)                TRIOSONATE IN G MA
PUTSCHE',T.                      QUENSEL, A.
  3 STUDIES                         ENTR'ACTE, OP 12
PYLE, F.                         QUENTIN, J.
  SONATA FOR 3                      SONATA IN E MI
PYLKKANEN, T.                    QUERAT, M.
  DIVERTIMENTO                      LIED-CANONICA
QUANTZ                           QUINET, M.
  TRIO SONATA IN E MI               BALLADE (1962)
QUANTZ, J.                          CONCERTINO (1960)
  CONCERTO #1 IN G MI               CONCERTO GROSSO (1964)
  DUETS, OP  2/1-2                  PETITE SUITE (1959)
  6 DUETS, OP  2, 2 VOLS.           8 PETITES PIECES (1946)
  6 DUETS, OP  2, 2 VOLS            POCHADES
  3 DUETS, OP  2                    POLYPHONIES (1971)
  6 DUETS, OP  2                    QUATUOR (1964)
  6 DUETS, OP  5, 2 VOLS            QUINTET (1949)
  GAVOTTE (DER RUHMESTEMPE          SONATE EN TRIO (1977)
  SONATA A 3                        TRIO (1967)
  SONATA ANDANTE                 QUINTANAR, H.
  SONATA IN A MI, OP  2/2           ILLAPSO
  SONATA IN D MA (K 46) &        RAABE, F.
  SONATA IN D MA                    WAHRHAFFTIGE BESCHREIBUN
  SONATA IN D MA                 RAASTED, N.
  SONATA IN D MI                    SERENADE, OP 40
  SONATA IN F MA, OP  3/6        RABAUD, H.
  SONATA IN G MA                    ANDANTE & SCHERZO
  SONATA                         RABE, F.
  6 SONATAS, OP 2                   IMPROMPTU 1962
  6 SONATAS, OP 2                   IMPROMPTU
  SONATE EN TRIO                 RABL, W.
  SONATE IN D MA                    QUARTET, OP  1
  SUITE IN D MA                  RACEK, F.
  TRIO IN A MI                      EINE KLEINE HAUSMUSIK
  TRIO IN D MA                   RACHMANINOFF, S.
  TRIO IN F MA                      POLKA ITALIENNE
  TRIO SONATA IN C MA               POLKA ITALIENNE
  TRIO SONATA IN C MA               PRELUDE, OP  3/2
  TRIO SONATA IN C MI (K33          VOCALISE
  TRIO SONATA IN C MI               VOCALISE
  TRIO SONATA IN C MI               VOCALISE
  TRIO SONATA IN D MA               VOCALISE
  TRIO SONATA IN D MA               VOCALISE
  TRIO SONATA IN D MA            RACUSEN, D.
  TRIO SONATA IN D MA               CANONIC ETUDES
  TRIO SONATA IN E MI (K28       RADULESCU, M.
  TRIO SONATA IN E MI               BLASERQUINTETT
  TRIO SONATA IN G MA (K 4       RAE, A.
  TRIO SONATA IN G MA               AUTUMN COLORS (1969)
  TRIO SONATA IN G MI               FUN & GAMES (1968)
  TRIO-SONATE IN C MI               IMPRESSIONS (1971)
  TRIOSONATE #33 IN E MI            IMPROVIZATIONS
  TRIOSONATE IN A MI                MAIDEN OF DECEPTION PASS
  TRIOSONATE IN B MI                RAINBOW SKETCHES (1976)
  TRIOSONATE IN C MA                SLEEP WHISPERING (1971)
  TRIOSONATE IN D MA             RAFF, J.
  TRIOSONATE IN E MI                CAVATINA
  TRIOSONATE IN E MI                SINFONIETTA, OP188
  TRIOSONATE IN F MI             RAGWITZ, E.
  TRIOSONATE IN G MA                MUSIC, OP 32
  TRIOSONATE IN G MA             RAICHL, M.
```

3 LIEDER (1963)
RAINER, G.
  MINIATUREN FUR ZWILLINGE
RAINIER, P.
  6 PIECES
  QUANTA
RAITIO, P.
  QUINTET
RAJTER, L.
  WIND QUINTET (1946)
RAKUJAS, B.
  PASTORAL TRIO
  SUMOM DRAGANOM
RALSTON, A.
  3 ENGLISH FOLK TUNES
  NOCTURNE SENTIMENTALE
RAMEAU
  SUITE IN G MI
RAMEAU, J
  BALLET MUSIC (ASGANTE &
RAMEAU, J.
  5 ARIAS
  5 CONCERTI
  GAVOTTE EN RONDEAU
  GAVOTTE WITH 6 DOUBLES
  GAVOTTE
  HEN, THE
  HEN, THE
  HEN, THE
  L'AGACANTE & L'INDISCRET
  LE TAMBOURIN
  MENUET (SUITE #1)
  MENUETT & PASSEPIED (CAS
  PIECES DE CLAVECIN EN CO
  PIECES DE CLAVECIN, KONZ
  PIECES DE CLAVECIN, KONZ
  2 PIECES
  RIGAUDON
  RIGODON DE DARDANUS
  RIGODON DE DARDANUS
  RIGODON DE DARDANUS
  RIGODON DE DARDANUS
  RIGODON DE DARDANUS
  SYMPHONIES & DANCES
  TAMBOURIN
RAMOVS, P.
  ANSWERS
  APEL
  ENNEAPHONIA
  ENNEAPHONIA
  FLUCTUATIONS
  IMPULSIONS (1967)
  3 LITTLE PASTORALS
  OSCILLATION
  OSCILLATIONS
  PIANISSIMO
  PORTRAIT
  PORTRAIT
  SIGNALS
  THEME DONNE
  WOODWIND QUINTET
RAMSEY, G.

MIRROR & BAGATELLE
RAMSOE, W.
  QUARTET #5, MOVEMENT #1
RANDALL, J.
  IMPROVISATION ON A POEM
RANDOLPH, D.
  PRELUDE & VARIATIONS
  PRELUDE & VARIATIONS
RANDS, B.
  ACTIONS FOR 6 (1962/63)
  ACTIONS FOR 6 (1962/63)
  BALLAD I
  FORMANTS II- LABYRINTHE
  SCHERZI
  TABLEAU
RANGER, A.
  COUNTRY GARDENS
  WREATH OF HOLLY, A
  WREATH OF HOLLY, A
  WREATH OF HOLLY, A
RANKI, G.
  PENTAEROPHONIA (1958)
RANSOM, D.
  PAVANNE
  PRELUDE & SAMBA
RAPF, K.
  6 PIECES (1963)
RAPHAEL, G.
  DIVERTIMENTO, OP 74
  KAMMERMUSIK, OP 47/6, DU
  KANONISCHE SUITE, OP 47/
  PALMSTROM-SONATE, OP 69
  QUARTET, OP 61 (1945)
  QUINTET, OP 4
  SONATINE, OP 65/1
  SONATINE, OP 65/2 (1948)
  SONATINE, OP 65/4
  TRIO (1940) IN B MA, OP
  TRIO-SUITE, OP 44
  TRIO, OP 70 (1950)
RAPHLING, S.
  CONCERT SUITE
  CONCERT SUITE
  DUOGRAMS
  DUOGRAMS
  SONATINA
  SONATINA
  SONATINA
  SQUARE DANCE
  SQUARE DANCE
  SQUARE DANCE
  SQUARE DANCE
  SQUARE DANCE
  SUITE IN MODERN STYLE
  SUITE IN MODERN STYLE
  VARIATIONS
  VARIATIONS
RASCHER, S.
  COLLECTION
RASCHER, S. & L. PATRICK
  5 CENTURIES FOR SAX QUAR
  MASTERPIECES FOR SAX QUA

RASMUSSEN, K.
  DIESER AUGENBLICK
RATHAUS, K.
  ALLEGRO CONCERTANTE
  ALLEGRO CONCERTANTE
  COUNTRY SERENADE
RATHBURN, E.
  CONVERSATION (1956)
  2 INTERPLAYS (1972)
  MINIATURE (1949)
  PARADE (1949)
  PASTORELLA (1949)
  WALTZ FOR WINDS (1949; R
  WALTZ FOR WINDS #2
RATIU, A.
  CONCERTO PER LA "MUSICA
RATTENBACH, A.
  SERENATA
RAUSCH, C.
  PARA GERARDO (PHONOS #2)
  TRIO, OP 3
RAUTAVAARA, E.
  OCTET, OP 21
  QUARTET (1965)
  WIND OCTET (1964)
RAUTAVVARA, E.
  SONATA
RAVEL, M.
  CHANSONS MADECASSES
  FLUTE ENCHANTEE, LA
  INTRODUCTION & ALLEGRO
  MA MERE L'OYE
  PAVANE POUR UNE INFANTE
  PAVANE POUR UNE INFANTE
  PAVANE POUR UNE INFANTE
  PAVANE
  PAVANE
  PIECE EN FORME DE HABANE
  PIECE EN FORME DE HABANE
  TOMBEAU DE COUPERIN
RAVIN, I.
  SONATINA FOR WOODWINDS
RAWSTHORNE, A.
  CONCERTO FOR 10 INSTRUME
  QUARTET
  QUINTET
  QUINTET
  SONATINA
  SUITE
  TANKAS OF THE 4 SEASONS
RAXACH, E.
  CHIMAERA (1974)
  ESTROFAS (1962)
  FRAGMENTO II (1966)
  IMAGINARY LANDSCAPE
  PARAPHRASE
  SCATTERTIME (1917)
RAYKI, G.
  BURLESKE
RAYMOND, L.
  DIVERTISSEMENT
RAZZI, F.

IMPROVVISAZIONE III (196
INVENZIONE A 3 (1964)
4 INVENZIONI (1961)
MUSICA (1968)
REA, J.
  ANAPHORA (1970)
  FANTAISIES &/ET ALLUSION
  JEUX DE SCENE
  RECEPTION & OFFERING MUS
  SESTINA (1968)
READ, G.
  NINE BY SIX
  SCHERZINO, OP 24 (1935)
  SONORIC FANTASIA (1968)
  SONORIC FANTASIA (1968)
READ, T.
  NAMING THE CHANGES
  5 SKETCHES
READY, E.
  PETITE CLASSIQUE
REALE, P.
  PANGE LINGUA
  3 SONGS FROM THE CHINESE
  TRAVELLER, THE
REASER, R.
  LIBERARE SONARE
REBER, H.
  BERCEUSE
REBIKOV, V.
  MUSICAL SNUFFBOX
RECHBERGER, H.
  SONATINE
  WAYS
  YLISTYSLAULU HOYRYVETURI
RECK, D.
  NUMBER 1 FOR 12 PERFORME
  NUMBER 1 FOR 12 PERFORME
  NUMBER 2
  NUMBER 2
REDDING, J.
  QUINTET
REDEL, M.
  DISPERSION (1972)
  EPILOG AUF WORTE VON AND
  INTERPLAY (1975)
  MOBILE (1976)
  RELIEFS (1970)
  RELIEFS (1970)
  SUSS VERENDET DIE ENTZUC
REED, A.
  DOUBLE WIND QUINTET
  SYMPHONIC DANCE
REED, H.
  SYMPHONIC DANCE
REGAMEY, K.
  QUINTET (1944)
REGER, M.
  CANON IN D MI
  FUGUE, OP 56/2
  QUINTET, OP146
  SERENADE #1, OP 77A
  SERENADE #2, OP141A

440

SERENADE, OP 77A
REGNER, H.
  DIVERTIMENTO
  EINE KLEINE WALDMUSIK
  HEITERES IDYLL
  MUSIKALISCHE BILDER
  SERENADE
  SPIEL
  SPIELHEFT II
  SPIELHEFT 1
  8 SPIELSTUCKE
REGT, H.
  MUSICA (1971)
  POEME, OP 63 (1979)
REGT, H. DE
  CANZONI E SCHERZI, OP 30
  CIRCE, OP 44 (1975)
  MEDEA
  METAMORPHOSES, OP 39
  MUSIC, OP 32 (1973-74)
  MUSIC, OP 33 (1974)
  MUSICA OP 12, (1972)
  MUSICA PER 4 SASSOFONI
  MUSICA
  MUSICA, OP 3 (1969)
  MUSICA, OP 4 (1970)
  MUSICA, OP 4 (1970)
  MUSICA, OP 5 (1970)
  MUSICA, OP 11
  MUSICA, OP 11
  MUSICA, OP 13 (1971)
  MUSICA, OP 14 (1972)
  MUSICA, OP 15 (1972)
  MUSICA, OP 17
  MUSICA, OP 18
  MUSICA, OP 18
  MUSICA, OP 19/2 (1972)
  MUSICA, OP 20 (1972)
  MUSICA, OP 21 (1972)
  MUSICA, OP 22 (1972-73)
  MUSICA, OP 25 (1973)
  MUSICA, OP 26 (1973)
  MUSICA, OP 27 (1973)
  MUSICA, OP 28 (1973)
  MUSICA, OP 29 (1973)
  MUSICA, OP 31 (1973)
  MUSICA, OP 36 (1974)
  MUSICA, OP 47 (1975)
  PASTORALE, OP 43
  PROTEUS, OP 38 (1974)
  SILENUS EN BACCHANTEN, O
REGTEREN ALTENA, L. VAN
  DIVERTIMENTO
  POEME DISCONTINU (PIERRE
REICHA, A.
  ANDANTE & MENUETTO ALLEG
  2 ANDANTES & ADAGIO
  2 ANDANTES & ADAGIO
  INTRODUCTION & ALLEGRO
  MINUET (QUARTET, OP 12)
  OCTET, OP 96
  QUARTET, OP 19

3, QUARTETS
QUINTET IN B FL MA
QUINTET IN B FL MA, OP 8
QUINTET IN C MI, OP 91/6
QUINTET IN D MI, OP 88/4
QUINTET IN D MI, OP 91/4
QUINTET IN E FL MA, OP 8
QUINTET IN E MI, OP 88/1
QUINTET IN F MA
QUINTET IN F MA, OP107
QUINTET IN G MI, OP 91/4
QUINTET
QUINTET, OP 88/2
QUINTET, OP 88/6
QUINTET, OP 91/1 IN C MA
QUINTET, OP 91/2 IN A MI
QUINTET, OP 91/3 IN D MA
QUINTET, OP 91/5 IN A MA
QUINTET, OP 99/2
QUINTET, OP100/4 IN E MI
3 QUINTETS, OP 88/3, OP
QUINTETTO, OP107
3 ROMANCES, OP 21
3 ROMANCES
3 ROMANZEN, OP 21
SINFONICA, OP 12
SINFONICO QUARTETTE
SINFONICO, OP 12
TRIO IN G MA
TRIO, OP 26
TRIOS, OP 92, 2 VOLS
18 VARIATIONS & A FANTAS
VARIATIONS, OP 20
REICHARDT, J.
  6 PIECES
REICHBERGER, H.
  MAYENZEIT OHNE NEIDT
REID, A.
  SKETCHES OF YOUTH
REIF, P.
  DUO FOR 3
  ENCOUNTER
  INTERPOLATIONS
  KALEIDOSCOPE (1966)
  QUINTET
  QUINTET
  SEXTET
  TRIO (1971)
  TRIO
  WIND SPECTRUM (1966)
REIMANN, A.
  CANZONI E RICERCARI
  3 SPANISCHE LIEDER
REINECKE, C.
  OCTET, OP216
  TRIO IN A MA, OP264
  TRIO IN A MI, OP188
  TRIO IN B FL MA, OP264
  TRIO, OP264
REINER, H.
  EICHENENDORFF-OCTET
REINER, K.

2 COMPOSIZIONI (1962)
DODICI SUITA (1963)
KLEINE SUITE (1960)
MUSIC (1966)
SENTENCE
TERZETTI (1971)
TRIO (1964)
VOLNE LISTY (1969)
ZEICHNUNGEN (1970)
REINHARDT, B.
  4 SCHERZI
REINHOLD, O.
  BLASERQUINTETT (1962)
  KONZERTANTE MUSIC
REITER, A.
  MUSIK
REIZENSTEIN, F.
  DUO, OP 38
  THEME, VARIATIONS & FUGU
  TRIO IN A MA, OP 25
  TRIO, OP 39
RENOSTO
  MIXAGE
RENOSTO, P.
  AR-LOTH
RENZI, A.
  5 BAGATELLE
REUCHSEL, A.
  SEXTUOR
REULAND, J.
  CONCERTINO (1959)
  MAGNIFICAT (1971)
  PARTITA (1967)
REUTER
  9 PIECES FOR 3 WIND INST
REUTER, F.
  SPIELMUSIK IN F MA, OP 3
REVEYRON, J.
  CHANT DES NOCES, LE
REVUELTAS, S.
  LITTLE SERIOUS PIECE #1
  LITTLE SERIOUS PIECE #2
  OCHO POR RADIO
  3 SONNETS
  TOCCATA (WITHOUT A FUGUE
REX, H.
  SHENANDOAH
REYNOLDS, R.
  ACQUAINTANCES
  AGAIN
  4 ETUDES
  GATHERING
  PROMISES OF DARKNESS, TH
  QUICK ARE THE MOUTHS OF
  TRACES
  WEDGE
REYNOLDS, V
  WOODWIND QUINTET
REYNOLDS, V.
  CONCERTARE III
  CONCERTARE V
REZNICEK, P.

MUSICA DA CONCERTO
RHEINBERGER, J.
  INTRODUCTION & PASSACAGL
  NONET, OP139
RHENE-BATON
  AUBADE, OP 53
RHODES, P.
  ENSEMBLE ETUDES
  MUSEUM PIECES
  QUARTET
RHYS, S.
  6 INVENTIONS
RIBARI, A.
  CHAMBER MUSIC (1970)
  5 MINIATUREN
RICARD, C.
  BADINERIE
RICCHI, M.
  FAMOUS SONATAS, 2 VOLS.
RICCIO, G.
  JUBILENT OMNES
RICE, T.
  CARLSON'S KIT
  FANTASY
  SONATINA
RICHARDS, J.
  TRIAD
RICHARDSON, A.
  SONATINA
RICHTER, C.
  DUETS FOR CLARINETS, 2 V
  KLARINETTEN-DUOS
RICHTER, F.
  DIVERTIMENTO, OP 91
  SONATA DA CAMERA
  SONATA IN G MA
  TRIO IN G MA
RICHTER, N.
  SERENADE (1934)
  SERENADE (1945)
  TRIO (1935)
RICKER
  ORIENTAL DANCE
RICKER, R.
  10 DUETS FOR THE 20TH CE
RIDKY, J.
  QUINTET (1926)
RIDOUT, A.
  CONCERTANTE
  EMPEROR & THE BIRD OF PA
  PIGS, A PRESENT FOR GORD
RIDOUT, G.
  INTRODUCTION & ALLEGRO
RIEDT, F.
  DUETT IN F MA
RIEGGER, W.
  BLASERQUINTETT, OP 51
  3 CANONS, OP 9 (1930)
  3 CANONS, OP 9/2
  CONCERTO, OP 53
  DIVERTISSEMENT
  DUO, OP 35, #1

BALLADE
ROGERS, J.
  ROTATIONAL ARRAYS
ROHINSKY, A.
  CLARINET CHORALES
ROHLIG, H.
  BEHOLD, A BRANCH IS GROW
  O HOLY JESUS
ROHOZINSKY, L.
  SUITE BREVE
ROHWER, J.
  QUARTET
  2 QUARTETTSATZE
  TRIO
ROJO, J.
  MUSICA SOBRE UNOS MODULO
  PLANIFICACIONES
  UNOS RESULTADOS
ROLAND
  RONDELS DE PERONNELLE D'
ROLAND-MANUEL, A.
  SUITE DANS LE GOUT ESPAG
ROLDAN, A.
  DANZA NEGRA
  RITMICA #1
ROLLA, A.
  CONCERTINO
  VIRTUOSO STUDY
ROLLIN, R.
  SUITE
ROMAN, J.
  SONATA A TRE
  12 SONATAS
ROMBERG, A.
  QUINTET, OP 57
ROMBERG, H.
  TRIO (INTERMEZZI CONCERT
ROMITI
  SUITE
RONNEFELD, P.
  2 LIEDER ZUR PAUKE
  4 WIEGENLIEDER (1955)
RONSHEIM, J.
  FRAGMENT (1964)
RONTGEN, J.
  LAMENTO (1956)
  2 LIEDER
  O, 'T RUISCHEN VAN HET R
  3 REDELOZE DUETTEN
  TRIO, OP 86
ROOS, R. DE
  INCIDENZE (1967)
  INCONTRI
  4 PEZZI (1971)
  QUATTRO PER DUE
  SEXTUOR (1935)
ROOSEVELT, J.
  SERENADE
  3 SONGS FROM POE
  4 SONGS
ROPARTZ, G.
  LAMENTO

ROPARTZ, J.
  ENTRATA A SCHERZETTO
  2 PIECES
  PRELUDE, MARINE ET CHANS
ROREM, N.
  ARIEL
  BOOK OF HOURS
  LOVERS
  ROMEO & JULIET
  11 STUDIES FOR 11 PLAYER
  11 STUDIES FOR 11 PLAYER
  TRIO
RORICH, C.
  BURLESKE, OP 64
  QUINTET, OP 58
ROSAS, J.
  OVER THE WAVES
  OVER THE WAVES
ROSEMAN, R.
  SUITE OF RENAISSANCE PIE
ROSEN, J.
  PETITE SUITE
  QUINTET (1974)
  QUINTET
  SERENADE
  SONATA
ROSENBERG, H.
  KVINTETT (1959)
  SERENAD, OP 82
  TRIO (1927)
  TRIO
ROSENFELD, G.
  5 LIEDER
ROSENGREN, F.
  QUINTET (1949)
ROSENTHAL, C.
  CLARINET DUOS
  CLARINET QUARTETTES
  CLARINET TRIOS (18TH CEN
  CLARINET TRIOS FROM CORE
  CLARINET TRIOS-RUSSIAN
  15 EASY DUETS
ROSENTHAL, L.
  COMMEDIA
ROSETTI, A.
  PARTHIA IN B FL MA
  PARTHIA IN F MA
  PARTITA IN F MA
  PARTITA IN F MA
ROSETTI, F.
  NOTTURNO IN D MA
  PARTHIA #3 IN D MA
  PARTHIA IN B FL MA
  PARTHIA IN D MA
  PARTIA IN B FL MA
  PARTITA IN B FL MA
  QUINTET IN E FL MA
ROSLAVETZ, N.
  NOCTURNE
ROSS, W.
  DIVERTIMENTO
  TOWARD THE EMPYREAN

444

ROSSEAU, N.
  PENTAPHONIUM, OP164
  QUINTET, OP 54 (1955)
  RAPSODIE, OP 81 (1958)
  TRIO, OP 60 (1956)
ROSSI
  ANDANTINO IN A FL MA
ROSSI, M.
  ANDANTINO & ALLEGRO
ROSSI, S.
  3 SINFONIAS
ROSSINI, G.
  ANDANTE E VARIAZIONI
  ITALIAN IN ALGIERS
  POWER ETERNAL (STABAT MA
  QUARTET #1
  QUARTET #2 IN A MA
  QUARTET #3 IN B FL MA
  QUARTET #4 IN D MA
  QUARTETTE, 2 VOLS
  SERENADE FOR SMALL ENSEM
  SERENATA PER PICCOLO COM
  12 WALTZES
ROSSLER¬ROSETTI, F.
  PARTITA
ROSSUM, F.
  PYROGRAVURES, OP 19 BIS
ROTA, N.
  PETITE OFFRANDE MUSICALE
  QUINTET
  QUINTET
  SONATA
ROTH, M.
  BASSOON DUETS
ROUGERON
  3 PIECES EN TRIO
ROUSE, C.
  APHRODITE CANTOS
  GACELA DEL AMOR IMPREVIS
  INSANI
  KISS, THE
  NOX AERIS TEMPORIS
  PHOENIX, THE
  SUBJECTIVES IX
ROUSSAKIS, N.
  CONCERTINO
  MARCH, SONG & DANCE
  MARCH, SONG & DANCE
  6 SHORT PIECES
ROUSSEAU, J.
  AIRS POUR JOUES A LA PRO
ROUSSEAU, N.
  3 JOUETS, OP 53 (1955)
ROUSSEL, A.
  DIVERTISSEMENT, OP 6
  DUO
  2 POEMES DE RONSARD
  SERENADE, OP 30
  TRIO, OP 40
ROVICS, H.
  CYBERNETIC STUDY #2
  ECHO

EVENTS II
HAUNTED OBJECTS
SERENADE
TRANSACTIONS
ROWE, P.
  FUN FOR FLUTES
ROWLAND, D.
  FRANCISCAN ROUNDS (1973)
  MONOLOGUES (1977)
  ROUNDELAY (1979)
  TETRAD (1970)
  TETRAD 1970)
  TROPISMS (1979)
ROWLEY, A.
  NOCTURNE
ROXBURGH, E.
  ECLISSI
ROY, K.
  DUO
  STERLINGMAN SUITE
ROYER
  ZAIDE, LA
ROZMANN, A.
  5 PEZZI (1963/75)
RUBBRA, E.
  SUITE: THE BUDDHA
RUBIN, M.
  SERENADE
RUBINSTEIN, A.
  MELODIE
RUDHYAR, D.
  3 MELODIES
RUDINGER, G.
  DIVERTIMENTO IN G MI, OP
RUDOLF, ARCHDUKE
  TRIO IN E FL MA
RUDZINSKI, W.
  CANZONETTA (1940)
  NONET (1947)
  PRELUDES (1967)
  PRELUDES (1967)
  QUINTET (1954)
RUDZINSKI, Z.
  TRIO
  TUTTI E SOLO
RUEFF, J.
  CONCERT EN QUATUOR
  3 PIECES
RUELLE, F.
  AUTOUR DU CHATEAU
  PRELUDE
  ROMANCE
  ROMANCE
RUF, H.
  2 DUOS ALTER ENGLISCHER
  2 DUOS ALTER ENGLISCHER
RUGGIERI
  ALLEGRO
RUGGIERO, G.
  3 PIECES
RUITER, W. & J. BANK
  QUINTET (1976)

445

RUITER, W. DE
  OFF & ON (1976)
  QUARTET (1978)
  QUARTET
  QUINTET II (1978)
  2 QUARTETS TOGETHER
RUSCH, H.
  CHACONNE
RUSHBY¬SMITH, J.
  QUARTET
RUSSEL¬SMITH, G.
  ALICE & THE MAD HATTER
RUSSELL, A.
  BRIGHT RITUAL
  TRIO IN E FL MA
RUSSELL, R.
  ABSTRACT #1
  DUO
  WOODWIND QUINTET
RUT, J.
  KINDERSERENADE
RUYNEMAN, D.
  AMATERASU (1953)
  ANCIENT GREEK SONGS
  DIVERTIMENTO (1927)
  DIVERTIMENTO (1927/1974)
  HIEROGLYPHS (1918)
  HIEROGLYPHS (1918)
  HIEROGLYPHS
  NIGHTENGALE QUINTET
  REFLEXIONS (1959)
  REFLEXIONS #2
  REFLEXIONS #3 (1960-61)
  REFLEXIONS #4 (1961)
  SOUS LE PONT MIRABEAU
RYAN, P.
  3 COUPERIN MOVEMENTS
  HAYDN MOVEMENT, A (SONAT
RYBAR, J.
  TRIO (1968)
RYCHLIK, J.
  AFRICKY CYKLUS (1961)
  QUINTET
  RELAZIONI (1963)
  SERENADE (ERINNERUNGEN)
  SUDBOHMISCHE LIEDER & LI
RYDMAN, K.
  KHOROS #1 (1964)
  KHOROS #1 (1964)
  7 MINIATURES
RYGER, A.
  TRIO (1957)
RYKER, R.
  4 ELIZABETHAN PIECES, OP
RYTERBAND, R.
  DIALOG
RYTTERKVIST, H.
  TRE SATIRER
RZEWSKI, F.
  SONG & DANCE
SABATINI, G.
  PUPPET WALTZ

  QUARTET
SABATINI, W.
  MUSIC FOR KORRI
SABON
  CLOCHES BLEUES, LES
  HELVETIE
SACCHINI, A.
  ANDANTINO GRAZIOSO (RENA
SACHSSE, H.
  BLASERSUITE, OP 32
SACKMAN, N.
  PAIR OF WINGS, A
SADLER, H.
  QUARTETTINO
SAEYS, E.
  LENTO & ALLEGRO
  SUITE
SAGNIER
  PETITE SUITE ARMORICAINE
SAGVIK, S.
  GUENILLES DES JONGLEURS,
  14 KORTA BAGATELLDUETTER
  8 MEDITATIONER, OP 61
  QUIN-TAT, OP 62 (1976)
  SEPTET, OP 37 (1974-76)
  SUITE DANSANT, OP 32
  3 TRIOS, OP 68 (1976)
SAIKKOLA, L.
  TRIO
SAINT SAENS, C.
  FLUTE INVISIBLE, UNE
SAINT¬MARCOUX, M.
  GENESIS (1975)
SAINT¬SAENS, C.
  CAPRICE ON DANISH & RUSS
  CAPRICE SUR DES AIRS DAN
  CYGNE, LE (THE SWAN)
  FEUILLET D'ALBUM, OP 81
  MARCHE HEROIQUE
  MY HEART AT THY SWEET VO
  MY HEART AT THY SWEET VO
  MY HEART AT THY SWEET VO
  MY HEART AT THY SWEET VO
  REVERIE DU SOIR
  ROMANCE IN F MA
  SERENADE
  SERENADE
  SERENADE
  SWAN, THE
  SWAN, THE
  SWAN, THE
  SWAN, THE
  SWAN, THE
  SWAN, THE
  TARANTELLA, OP 6
  TARANTELLE, OP 6
  TARENTELLE, OP 6
SALBERT, D.
  KAMMERMUSIK
  MUSIK FUR 3
  SPIELPLANE
SALIERI, A.

446

ARMONIA PER UN TEMPLO DE
DANSE (TARARE)
DANSE (TARARE)
DANSE (TARARE)
DANSE (TARARE)
DANSE (TARARE)
DANSE (TARARE)
KONZERT IN C MA
PICCOLA SERENATA IN B FL
SERENATA IN B FL MA
SERENATA IN E FL MA "PIC
TRIPLE CONCERTO IN D MA
SALIERI, G.
  ADAGIO CON VARIAZIONI
SALLINEN, A.
  SERENADE (1963)
  4 PER QUATTRO
SALMENHAARA, E.
  QUARTET
SALOMON, K.
  ELEGIE & TANZ
  ELEGIE & TANZ
  ELEGIE UND TANZ
SALONEN, S.
  QUINTET, OP 25
SAMBIN, V.
  DUO DE LA SOMNAMBULE
SAMMARTINI, G.
  CONCERTO
  NOTTURNO A QUATRO
  SONATA IN D MA
  SONATA IN G
  SONATA, OP 1/6
  6 SONATAS, OP 6, 2 VOLS
  6 SONATAS, OP 4
  12 SONATAS, 3 VOLS
SAMONOV
  SUITE
SAMONOV, A.
  GREEK RHAPSODY
SAMTER, A.
  SKETCH
SAMUEL¬ROUSSEAU
  BERGERS ET MAGES
SAMUEL, G.
  COLD WHEN THE DRUM SOUND
  RELATIVITY OF ICARUS, TH
SAMYN, N.
  5 TRIOS (PUB SEPARATELY)
  5 TRIOS, PUB SEPARATELY
SANCHEZ, B.
  YOUPPI-YA
SANDELEWSKI, W.
  TRIO
SANDERS, R.
  IMP, THE
SANDNER, P.
  QUINTET #2
SANDRE, G.
  SOUS LA FEUILLEE
SANNER, L.
  SEXTETT

SANTA CRUZ, D.
  QUINTET
SANTIAGO, R. DE
  CONCORDANCIAS I (1976)
  TERSURA MUSICAL SI BECUA
SANTORSOLA, G.
  QUARTET #2
SAPP, G.
  SHIMO
SARAI, T.
  QUARTET (1961-62)
SARDA, A.
  ISORRITME
SARGENT
  NIP & TUC
  NIP & TUC,
SARGON, S.
  PATTERNS IN BLUE
SARKOZY, I.
  SALMO E GIOCO
SARLIT, H.
  20 ETUDES DE DECHIFFRAGE
SARO, H.
  STUDIES IN CANON FORM
  STUDIES IN CANON FORM
  STUDIES IN CANON FORM
SARRI, D.
  SONATA IN A MI
SARY, L.
  IMAGE
  INCANTO
  QUARTETTO
  SONANTI #2
SATIE, E.
  GYMNOPEDIE #1
  GYMNOPEDIES #3
  3 GYMNOPEDIES
  MESSE DES PAUVRES
  MESSE DES PAUVRES
  SPORTS & DIVERTISSEMENTS
SATZENHOFER, J.
  24 DUETS
SAUCIER, G.
  2 PIECES
SAUGUET, H.
  BARCAROLLE
  3 CHANTS DE CONTEMPLATIO
  6 PIECES FACILE
  PRES DU BAL
  TRIO
SAUPE
  AIR VARIE
SAUTER
  QUARTET #1
SAVAGE
  MOMENTO GIOJOSO
  MOMENTO GIOJOSO
SAVELIEV, B.
  SUITE
SAVINA, C.
  MUSICA PER SUONARE INSIE
SAVNIK, V.

FUGHETTA
INVENTIONS
SAXTON, R.
ECHOES OF THE GLASS BEAD
PROMENADE D'AUTOMNE, LA
REFLECTIONS OF NARZISS &
WHAT DOES THE SONG HOPE
SAYGUN, A.
SEZISLER (INTUITIONS)
TRIO, OP 56
SCARLATTI
ARIA & MINUET
DUETS
PASTORALE
5 SCARLATTI SONATAS
SCARLATTIANA
SONATA #1
SONATA #2
SONATA #3
SONATA #44
SONATA #79
SONATA ALLEGRISSIMO
SONATA IN C MA
SONATA VIII IN F MA
SCARLATTI, A.
ARIA & MINUET
CANTATA
PRELUDE & FUGUE
QUARTET IN F MA
QUARTET IN F MA
QUARTETTINO
SONATA IN A MA
SCARLATTI, D.
CATS FUGUE
DUETS FROM PIANO SUITES
NEAPOLITAN SUITE
NEAPOLITAN SUITE
PASTORALE
SONATA IN D MI
SONATA
5 SONATAS
6 SONATAS
SUITE IN F MA
SCARMOLIN, A.
BARCAROLLE & PETITE HUMO
BARCAROLLE & PETITE HUMO
BY THE SLEEPING NILE
DANSE GROTESQUE
DUET TIME
FOUR OF A KIND
GHOSTLY TALE, A
PETITE SUITE
3 PIECES
SCHERZO
3 SWINGSTERS
WILL O' THE WISP
SCARMOLIN, L.
FOUR OF A KIND
MERRYMAKERS
QUINTET
SUITE
SCHADE, W.

20 EASY & PROGRESSIVE DU
SCHADEWITZ, C.
SERENADE, OP 49
SCHAEFER, A.
TROUBADOURS
SCHAEFERS, A.
QUINTET
SCHAEFFER, D.
ANCIENT FUGUE
CHRISTMAS DUETS
CHRISTMAS DUETS
CHRISTMAS DUETS
CHRISTMAS DUETS
CLARINET CHOIR, THE
CLARINET TRIO ALBUM
CLARINETS TWO
CONTRASTS
CONVERSATIONS
DUETS ARE FUN
DUETS ARE FUN
DUETS ARE FUN
DUETS ARE FUN
DUETS ARE FUN
ENCORE (12 TRIOS)
ENCORE
FIFTEENTH CENTURY MADRIG
FLUTES TWO
GRANT US PEACE
PROGRAM DUETS
QUIET THEME, A
21 RHYTHMIC DUETS
21 RHYTHMIC DUETS
21 RHYTHMIC DUETS
21 RHYTHMIC DUETS
21 RHYTHMIC DUETS
SELECT TRIOS
12 TRIOS
12 TRIOS
10 WOODWIND TRIOS
10 WOODWIND TRIOS
SCHAFER, G.
QUINTET
SCHAFER, R.
ARCANA (1972)
CONCERTO FOR HARPSICHORD
DIVISIONS FOR BAROQUE TR
ENCHANTRESS (1971, REV 1
MINNELIEDER (1956)
REQUIEMS FOR THE PARTY-G
5 STUDIES ON TEXTS BY PR
SCHAFFER, B.
PERMUTATIONEN
PERMUTATIONEN
QUARTET SG (1967)
TRIO (1966)
SCHAFFNER, N.
2 WOODWIND QUARTETS
SCHAFFRATH, C.
DUET IN F MI
SCHALK, C.
IN ADAM WE HAVE ALL BEEN
RICERCARE ON AN OLD ENGL

CONCERTINO
DUO WITH CADENZAS
FINALE (QUARTET #4)
3 LITURGICAL PRELUDES
2 POEMS BY WILLIAM PILLI
PRELUDE & FUGUE
PRELUDE & RONDO
SEPTIGRAMS (1956)
SONATA BREVE
SONATINA
SUITE
TURKISH LADY, THE
VENDOR'S CALL
SCHMIT, C.
BURLESQUES (1964-65)
PSAUTIER (1946)
TRIO (1945)
SCHMITT
ALTE BLASERSATZE
SCHMITT, F.
A TOUR D'ANCHES, OP 97
CHANTS ALIZES, OP125
LIED ET SCHERZO, OP 54
4 MONOCANTES
POUR PRESQUE TOUS LES TE
QUATUOR, OP102
QUATUOR, OP106
SONATINE EN TRIO, OP 85
SUITE EN ROCAILLE, OP 84
TELEMANN MINUETS
SCHMITT, J.
CONCERTO IN G MA, OP 15
TRIO IN G MA
SCHMITT, M.
4 STUCKE
SCHMUTZ, A.
ALLEGRO CAPRICCIOSO
INTRODUCTION, RECITATIVE
PRELUDE & FINALE
PRELUDIAL FANTASIA
SCHERZO POETIQUE
SCHERZOSO
SCHNABEL, A.
DUODECIMET
DUODECIMET
SCHNEBEL, D.
ANSCHLAGE- AUSSCHLAGE
SCHNEIDER
ALTHOLLANDISCHE TANZ-SUI
SCHNEIDER & HETSCHKO
DUETTE FUR ANFANGER
SCHNEIDER, G.
3 DUETS
DUETTE FUR TIEFE INSTRUM
3 DUOS CONCERTANT, OP 78
HARMONIE-MUSIK IN F MA
SCHNEIDER, O.
SUITE, OP 20
SCHNEIDER, U.
KREUZE (1964/67)
SCHNEIDER, W.
ALLERLEI ALTE MARSCHWEIS

30 DUETTE
ERSTES KLARINETTENSPIEL
HEITERES DIVERTIMENTO
HOHENHEIMER TANZE
KLASSISCHE SPIELSTUCKE
KLEINES QUARTETT
PARTITA
QUINTET
SONATA
SONATA
SONATINE
2 SONATINES
SUITE CAPRICIEUSE
TRIOSPIEL NACH ALTEN MEI
TRIOSPIEL NACH ALTEN MEI
VARIATIONEN UBER EIN SOM
SCHNITTKE, A.
DIALOG
HYMNUS III
SERENADE
SCHOECK, O.
GASELEN, OP 38
WANDERSPRUCHE, OP 42
SCHOEMAKER, M.
SUITE CHAMPETRE (1940)
VOLIERE (1961)
SCHOENBERG, A.
KAMMERSYMPHONIE, OP 9
NACHTWANDLER
PIERROT LUNAIRE, OP 21
QUINTET, OP 26
SERENADE, OP 24
3 SONGS, OP 48 (1933)
SUITE, OP 29
SCHOLLUM, R.
MOSAIK, OP 75
OCTET, OP 63
5 STUCKE, OP 82
TRIO, OP 45
TRIO, OP 45
TRIO, OP 71
SCHOLTES
SWISS BOY
WE THREE
SCHONBACH, D.
CANZONA DA SONAR IV
SCHONBERG, A.
SERENADE, OP 24
SCHONBERG, S.
DIALOGUES (1960)
DUO (1959)
LITET STYCKE, OP 8/3
5 PIECES
SCHONFELDER
MICH HAT GROB UMBEGEN
SCHONHERR, M.
IM DUETT
SCHOONENBEEK, K.
ARAGARA (1974)
COMBINATIONS (1973)
SEANCE A 3 (1973)
SUITE (1979)

SET #2 (1967)
SCHULHOFF, E.
  CONCERTINO
SCHULLER, G.
  ABSTRACTION
  ABSTRACTION
  ATONAL STUDY IN JAZZ (19
  AUTOMATION (1962)
  AUTOMATION (1962)
  COUNTRY DANCE MUSIC
  COUNTRY DANCE MUSIC
  CURTAIN RAISER (1960)
  DENSITIES I
  DOUBLE QUINTET
  DUO SONATA
  2 MOVEMENTS (1952)
  MUSIC FROM YESTERDAY IN
  PERPETUUM MOBILE (1948)
  POEMS OF TIME & ETERNITY
  PROGRESSION IN TEMPO
  6 RENAISSANCE LYRICS
  SONATA (1941)
  SUITE
  TEAR DROP (1967)
  TEAR DROP (1967)
  TRIO (1948)
  TWELVE BY ELEVEN
  TWELVE BY ELEVEN
  VARIANTS ON A THEME OF J
  VARIANTS ON A THEME OF J
  WOODWIND QUINTET (1958)
SCHULTZE, J.
  OUVERTURE I IN F MA
  OUVERTURE II IN B MA
  OUVERTURE III IN A MI
  SONATA
  SUITE
SCHUMACHER, S.
  SYMMETRIES
SCHUMAN, W.
  IN SWEET MUSIC
  QUARTETTINO
  QUARTETTINO
  QUARTETTINO
SCHUMANN, G.
  AUDIOGRAMME
  MINIATUR-TRIO
SCHUMANN, R.
  ALLEGRETTO (SONATA #1)
  ALLEGRETTO (SONATA #1, O
  CANCION DE CUNA
  ETUDE
  ETUDE, OP 56/5
  ETUDE, OP 56/6
  FAIRY TALES, OP132
  FAIRY TALES, OP132
  FUGA
  FUGUE, OP 60/1
  KNIGHT, THE
  LENTELIED
  MARCHENERZAHLUNGEN, OP13
  MELODY, OP 68/1

7 MINIATURES
OPUS 68, #30
2 PIECES (ALBUM FOR THE
3 PIECES (ALBUM FOR THE
5 PIECES
7 PIECES
REVERIE
4 SHORT PIECES
SKETCH, OP 58/4
SOLDIER'S MARCH, OP 68/2
SOLDIER'S MARCH, OP 68/2
SONG & MARCH
SPRING SONG
SUITE
TRAUMEREI
TRAUMEREI
TRAUMEREI
VOICE OF LOVE
SCHURINK, B.
  QUARTET (1975)
SCHURTZ, F.
  DIVERTIMENTO
  KLEINE MUSIK
SCHUSTER, G.
  3 ARABESKEN
  2 DIALOGUES
  INTERMEZZI
SCHUTZ, H.
  FATHER ABRAHAM, HAVE MER
SCHUYT, N.
  ALLA NOTTURNA
  ALLA NOTTURNA
  QUATUOR DE BALLET (1962)
  SONATA A TRE (1954)
SCHWADRON, A.
  2 CONTRAPUNTAL DUOS
  DUO,
  PROGRESSIVE ENSEMBLE STU
  PROGRESSIVE ENSEMBLE STU
  PROGRESSIVE ENSEMBLE STU
  PROGRESSIVE ENSEMBLE STU
  SHORT SUITE
  TRIO
  WALTZ
SCHWAEN, K.
  MAHRISCHES HOLZBLASERQUI
  SPANISCHE LIEBESLIEDER
SCHWANTNER, J.
  CANTICLE OF THE EVENING
  CONSORTIUM II
  CONSORTIUM
  DIAPHONIA INTERVALLUM
  ELIXIR
  ENTROPY
  SHADOWS II, CONSORTIUM I
SCHWARTZ
  VIENNA BAROQUE
SCHWARTZ, E.
  CONCERT PIECE
  DIALOGUE #2
  DIVERTIMENTO
  ECHO MUSIC I

452

QUARTETTO
TERZETTO
SENAILLE, J.
  RONDO SERIOSO
SENSTIUS, K.
  SERENADE, OP 36 (1952)
SEREBRIER, J.
  EROTICA
  LITTLE SUITE
  MINUETTO
  QUARTET
  SUITE CANINA
  6 FOR TELEVISION
SERINI, G.
  ARIA & GIUGE
SERMILA, J.
  COLOURS & CONTRASTS
  CRISIS
  PERCEPTION (1973)
  3 PEZZI PICCOLI
SEROCKI, K.
  KRASNOLUDKI (DIE ZWERGE)
  SWINGING MUSIC (1970)
SERRADELL
  GOLONDRINA, LA
SESTAK, Z.
  DIVERTIMENTO
  SONATA (1967)
SETER, M.
  AUTUMN (STAV) (1970)
  DIPTYQUE (1955)
  EPIGRAMS (MITCHTAMIM)
  KAMMERMUSIK '70
SEVERN, A.
  SCHERZO BRILLIANTE
SEYFRIT, M.
  CONTINUUM, VACUUM, RESID
  IN SEARCH OF
  LATENT IMAGES
  PORTAL
  WINTER'S WARMTH
SGRIZZI, L.
  ELEGIA E SCHERZO
SHAKARIAN, R.
  ABSTRACTS (CHAMBER BALLE
SHANKS, E.
  SONATA OF MOODS & HUMORS
SHAPERO, H.
  3 PIECES
SHAUGHNESSY, R.
  DUO
SHEINKMAN
  DIVERTIMENTO
SHEPPARD, J.
  BITTER ICE
  SEXTET
SHERARD
  ADAGIO & ALLEGRO
SHERIFF, N.
  ASHREI (1961)
SHERMAN, N.
  REUNION, THE (1971)

TRADITIONS (1948)
SHERMAN, R.
  QUINTET
SHEWAN, D.
  WIND OCTET
SHIELD, W.
  QUARTET IN F MA, OP 3/2
  SPORTSMAN'S RHAPSODY, TH
SHIFRIN, L.
  SERENADE
SHIFRIN, S.
  IN EIUS MEMORIAM
  SATIRES OF CIRCUMSTANCE
SHIMOYAMA, H.
  STRUCTURE (1961)
SHINOHARA, M.
  CONSONANCE (1967)
  CONSONANCE (1967)
SHORT, D.
  CONFIGURATIONS
SHORT, J.
  FLIRTY FLUTES
SHORT, M.
  REFLECTIONS
SHOSTAKOVICH, D.
  DUET (KING LEAR)
  POLKA (GOLDEN AGE)
SHOSTAKOVITCH, D.
  PRELUDES
  PRELUDES
  4 WALTZES
SHRUDE, M.
  QUARTET
SIBELIUS, J.
  ANDANTE FESTIVO
  ANDANTE FESTIVO
  CANZONETTA, OP 62A
  PASTORALE (PELLEAS & MEL
  VALSE TRISTE (KUOLEMA)
  VALSE TRISTE (KUOLEMA)
  VALSE TRISTE (KUOLEMA)
  VALSE TRISTE (KUOLEMA)
  VALSE TRISTE (KUOLEMA)
  VALSE TRISTE
SICHLER, J.
  TRIO D'ANCHES
SIEBERT, F.
  SCHERZETTO
SIEBERT, W.
  FLUTE BY FLUTE
SIEGEL, A.
  COUNTRY CHURCHYARD
SIEGL, O.
  QUINTET (1972)
  QUINTET-SERENADE
  SONATA
  TRIFOLIUM, OP145
  TRIO
SIEGRIST, B.
  TRUCS ET SI-FLAT
SIEKMANN, F.
  DESCRIPTIVE PIECE

RELATIONS
SIXTA, J.
  KVINTETO
  NONETO
  OCTET
SJOBLOM, H.
  LITEN SVIT I SPELMANSTON
  MUSIKANTISK SVIT (1976)
SKALKOTTAS, N.
  OCTET
  QUARTET
SKINNER, I.
  CAPRICIETTA
SKLENICKA, K.
  QUARTET (1967)
SKOGLUND, E.
  LITEN FUGA (1954/1975)
SKOLD, Y.
  KVARTETT
  SERENAD, OP 25
  SONATIN
SKOLNIK, W.
  3 CANONIC TUNES
  3 CANONIC TUNES
  3 CANONIC TUNES
  3 CANONIC TUNES
  4 IMPROVISATIONS
  PASTORALE
SKORNICKA, J.
  QUARTET ALBUM
SKORZENY, F.
  EINE NACHTMUSIK (1963)
  TRIO (1957)
SKVOR, F.
  DUET IN A MI
  NONET II. "PRAZSKY" (196
  NONETTO IN B MI (1955)
  VALSE MELANCOLIQUE
SLACK
  TOO MANY CLARINETS
SLAVICKY, K.
  INTERMEZZI MATTUTINI
  TRIALOG (1966)
  TRIO (1937)
SLAVICKY, M.
  LYRICAL MUSIC
SLECHTA, T.
  FATHER OF WATERS
  FATHER OF WATERS
  FATHER OF WATERS
SLIMACEK, M.
  QUINTET (1970)
SLONIMSKI, S.
  DIALOGE
SLONIMSKY, N.
  EXOTIC SUITE
  EXOTIC SUITE
SLOWINSKI, W.
  MAKOWSKI FAIRY TALES (19
  QUINTET (1958)
SMALLEY, R.
  MISSA PARODIA II (1967)

SMART, G.
  BRITTLE MAN (1976)
  SUNDOG EVENSONG (1976)
SMETANA, B.
  POLKA (BARTERED BRIDE)
  POLKA (BARTERED BRIDE)
SMETSKY, J. DE
  MARCH OF THE SPANISH SOL
SMIM, P.
  DUET ALBUM
  PARIS SOIR
SMIT, A.
  TRIO
SMIT, L.
  4 MOTETS
  QUINTET (1928)
  SEXTUOR (1933)
  SUITE (1938)
  TRIO (1938)
  TRIO
SMITH
  DRINK TO ME ONLY WITH TH
  OLD BLACK JOE,
SMITH & HOLMES
  THROUGH SHADOWED VALES
SMITH, C.
  AMONG THE SYCAMORES
  BELIEVE ME IF ALL
  BELIEVE ME IF ALL
  CALL OF THE SEA
  CARIBBEAN, THE
  CARIBBEAN, THE
  DE DIE IN DIEM
  DRINK TO ME ONLY WITH TH
  DRINK TO ME ONLY WITH TH
  FROM DAY TO DAY
  HELEN
  HELEN
  HELEN
  IMOGENE
  ITALIANA
  LIFE'S LIGHTER HOURS
  MILADY'S PLEASURE
  MY SONG OF SONGS
  OLD BLACK JOE
  OLD BLACK JOE
  ON PLEASURE BENT
  ON PLEASURE BENT
  ON PLEASURE BENT
  RAINBOW HUES
  SMITHSONIAN
  SPIRIT OF JOY; THE
  SPIRIT OF JOY, THE
  SPIRIT OF JOY, THE
  TRUMPETER, THE
SMITH, C. & HOLMES, G.
  ITALIANA
  MASSA'S IN THE COLD COLD
  SILVER THREADS AMONG THE
  THROUGH SHADOWED VALES
  WAYFARER, THE
SMITH, G.

456

MOOD MUSIC I (1973)
SMITH, H.
  INTRODUCTION, CADENZAS &
  VARIATIONS FOR 6 PLAYERS
SMITH, J.
  QUINTET
  TWO TIMES PAST
SMITH, L.
  2 DUETS
  INTRODUCTION & DIVERTIME
  PELDIMXY #1
  QUINTET
  SUITE FOR TRIO
  TRIO FOR WOODWINDS
  WIND QUINTET
SMITH, R.
  DUO
  INTRADA
SMITH, S.
  FACES
  FINE OLD TRADITION, A
SMITH, T.
  SUITE
SMITH, W.
  CLARINET DUO
  ELEGY FOR ERIC
  JAZZ SET
  4 PIECES
  5 PIECES
  QUARTET
  SUITE
SMOLANOFF, M.
  FROM THE ORIENT
  SONATA DA CAMERA
SMUTNY, J.
  3 SATZE (1969)
  3 STUCKE (1969)
SNAVELY, J.
  MOTIF & VARIATIONS
  WOODWIND SERENADE
SNOSKO¬BOROVSKY, A.
  SCHERZO, OP 13
SNYDER, R.
  QUINTET
SOBAJE, M.
  ANGELS WE HAVE HEARD ON
  GREENSLEEVES
SOBECK, J.
  ALLEGRETTO GIOJOSO (OP 1
  ALLEGRO MOSSO (OP 14)
  ANDANTE SOSTENUTO (OP 11
  DUET, OP 8
  LARGHETTO
  TARANTELLA
SOCOR, M.
  3 SALVIRI
SODERHOLM, V.
  PRELUDIUM OCH FUGA (1970
SODERLUNDH, L.
  IDEA I & II
SODOMKA, K.
  MUSICA

SOEGIJO, P.
  TO CATCH A FLY (1969)
SOKOLOFF, N.
  QUINTET
SOKORSKI, J.
  LITTLE QUINTET (1963)
SOLER, J.
  QUETZALCOATL (1966)
  SONATINA (1964)
SOLLBERGER, H.
  CHAMBER VARIATIONS
  COMPOSITIONS
  DIVERTIMENTO
  GRAND QUARTET (IN MEMORI
  2 PIECES
  RIDING THE WIND I
  SOLOS FOR VIOLIN & 5 INS
  SOLOS
  TWO OBOES TROPING
SOLO, C.
  GRAND SONATA, A, OP 31
SOLOMON
  QUATRO GIOCOSO
SOLOMON, E.
  2 ESCAPADES
SOMER, A.
  CONCERTINO
SOMERS, H.
  KUYAS (1967)
  THEME FOR VARIATIONS
  TRIO (1950)
  ZEN, YEATS & EMILY DICKI
SOMIS, G.
  ADAGIO & ALLEGRO
SOMMERFELDT, O.
  4 NORWEGIAN RELIGIOUS FO
SONNINEN, A.
  DIVERTIMENTO (1970)
SONSTEVOLD, K.
  SELECTED (1975)
  WINDSTOCK (1976)
SONTAG
  EVENING SERENADE, AN
SONTAG, H.
  EVENING SERENADE, AN
  QUARTET ON OLD TUNES
SOPRONI, J.
  MUSICA DA CAMERA #2 (CAP
SORCE, R.
  THEME & VARIATIONS
SORENSON, T.
  LITEN MUSIK (1971/72)
  MUSIC ON "VENI REDEMPTOR
  SERENATA PER TRE (1966)
  TRIO #1, OP 19
  TRIO #2, OP 33 (1959)
SORGE, E.
  KOMM, DER VOLKER HEILAND
SORRENTINO, C.
  BENEATH THE COVERED BRID
SOUFFRIAU, A.
  SONATE

457

STALLAERT, A.
  BESTIARE
  EPITAPHES ET BAGATELLAS
  QUINTET
STALVEY, D.
  POINTS, LINES, CIRCLES
  POINTS, LINES, CIRCLES
  POINTS, LINES, CIRCLES
STAM, H.
  SONATE (1959)
  TROPIC
STAMITZ
  ANDANTE
  ANDANTE
STAMITZ, A.
  CONCERTO IN G MA
STAMITZ, C.
  ANDANTINO
  CONCERTO IN B FL MA
  3 DUETS, OP 27
  QUARTET #6
  QUARTET IN A MA, OP 4/6
  QUARTET IN C MA
  QUARTET IN D MA, OP 8/1
  QUARTET IN E FL MA
  QUARTET IN E FL MA, OP
  QUARTET IN E FL MA, OP
  QUARTET IN E FL MA, OP 1
  QUARTET IN E FL MA, OP 8
  QUARTET IN F MA
  QUARTET IN F MA, OP 8/3
  QUARTET, OP 8/2
  QUARTET, OP 19/2
  2 QUARTETS, OP 19/5, 6
  2 QUARTETS,
  2 QUARTETS
  TRIO #1, OP 14
  TRIO IN G MA
  TRIO IN G MA, OP 14/1
  TRIOSONATE IN F MA, OP 1
  TRIOSONATE, OP 14/5
STAMITZ, J.
  CONCERTO IN C MA
STAMITZ, K.
  CONCERTO #4
  DOUBLE CONCERTO IN B FL
  6 DUETS, OP 27, 2 VOLS.
  6 DUETS, OP 27, 2 VOLS
  3 DUETS, OP 27
  QUARTET IN D MA, OP 8/1
  QUARTET, OP 8/4
  QUINTET
  QUINTETS, OP 11/1, 2
  12 SERENADES
  SONATA #1 IN G MA
  TRIO IN G MI, OP 14/4
STANDFORD, P.
  SUITE FRANCAISE
STANLEY, J.
  8 SOLOS, OP 1
  6 SOLOS, OP 4
  TRIO MOVEMENT

STANNARD, D.
  MINIATURE SUITE CANADIEN
STARER, R.
  CADENZA
  CADENZA
  CONCERTO A TRE
  LIGHT & SHADOW
  2 SACRED SONGS
  SERENADE
  TRIO
  WOODWIND QUARTET
STARK, R.
  ANDANTE & MARCIA (SERENA
  4 DUETS
  SONATA #1 IN E FL MA
STARY, K.
  SUITE
STEARNS, P.
  CHAMBER SET #2
  DUO
  3 LOVE SONGS
  5 LYRICS FROM "THE PROPH
  MAY 27TH, 1956
  NOCTURNE
  OCTET
  QUINTET
  3 SACRED SONGS
  SEPTET
  SEXTET
  5 SHORT PIECES
  3 SHORT STUDIES
  SUMMER NOCTURNE
  TRIO VARIATIONS
  TRIO
STECKL, K.
  MUSIK, OP 82A
STEDRON, M.
  MUSICA FICTA (1969)
  SIC ET NON, KANTATA
  VIA CRUCIS (STAZIONI DI
STEEN
  NOCTURNE IN E FL MA
STEFANSSON, F.
  DUO
STEFFAN, W.
  GERTRUD-KOLMAR-TRILOGIE,
STEFFANI, A.
  COME, MY DEAR ONE
  O HOW OFTEN
STEFFEN, W.
  MUSIC, OP 44
  TRIO, OP 2
  TRIO, OP 37
  TRIPLUM 72, OP 39
STEFFENS, W.
  NEUE GLEICHNISSE, OP 3B
  OBOENLIEDER, OP 9
STEFFES, G.
  HOLIDAYS
STEIN, H.
  SOUR SUITE
STEIN, L.

459

QUINTET,
QUINTETTE
SEXTET
SUITE (1962)
SUITE
TRIO
TRIO
STEINBERG, P.
  EBONATA
STEINBRENNER, W.
  BICINIUM
STEINER, G.
  SUITE (1958)
STEINER, H.
  ICH HATT' EINEN KAMERADE
STEINKE, G.
  4 DESULTORY EPISODES (19
  MUSIC FOR OBOE, CONTRABA
  MUSIC FOR 3
  MUSIC FOR 3
  SKETCHES (12TH)
  TRICINIUM (1972)
STEKL, K.
  KLEINE DUO-MUSIK
  MUSIC, OP126
  MUSICA SEMISERIA, OP 92
STERANS, P.
  NOCTURNE, DANCE & AUBADE
STERN
  QUARTET
STERN, A.
  VARIATIONS ON "ES WOLLT
STERN, R.
  LITTLE BIT OF MUSIC, A
STERNBERG
  VARIATIONS ON GERMAN FOL
  VARIATIONS ON GERMAN FOL
STERNBERG, E.
  DISTANT FLUTE, THE (1959
STERNFELD, R.
  RETURN TO ISRAEL
  THOUGHTS OF C & C
STEVEN, D.
  IMAGES
STEVENS, H.
  6 CANONS
  5 DUOS
  2 PIECES
  QUINTET
  SEPTET
  2 SHAKESPEARE SONGS
  TRIO
STEWART, D.
  CONCERT DUET, OP 8
  FLUTISTE BONNE ANNIVERSA
STEWART, F.
  TOCCATA SONORA
STEWART, L.
  6 SHORT PIECES
STEWART, R.
  2 MOVEMENTS
  5 MOVEMENTS

NONET
3 PIECES
2 RICERCARE
TRIO #4
TRIO #5
5 VISIONS
STIBILJ, M.
  MONDO
STICH-PUNTO, J.
  SONATA
STIEBER, H.
  SPIELMUSIK #1
  SPIELMUSIK #2
STIEBLER, E.
  CONTINUO (1974)
  EXTENSION II (1972)
  STADIEN (1964)
  STUDIE (1958)
STILL, R.
  CLARINET QUINTET
  CLARINET TRIO
STILL, W.
  MINIATURES BASED ON AMER
STINE, R.
  HEAVEN TREE, THE
STINGL, A.
  5 STUCKE, OP 34
STOCK, D.
  ICICLES
  QUINTET, OP 12
  SCAT (1971)
  SERENADE FOR 5 INSTRUMEN
  TRIPLE PLAY (1970)
STOCKHAUSEN, K.
  ADIEU
  KONTRA-PUNKTE #1 (1952/5
  KREUZSPIEL (1951)
  ZEITMASSE (1955/56)
STOCKMEIER, W.
  REAKTIONEN
  3 STUCKE
STOJANOV, P.
  QUARTET #3 (1973)
STOJANOVIC, J.
  SUMMER QUARTET, A VISIT
STOKER
  MUSIC FOR 3 OBOES
STOKER, R.
  4 DIALOGUES
  LITTLE SUITE
  LITTLE SUITE
  4 MINIATURES
  QUINTET
  ROUNDS & CANONS
  ROUNDS & CANONS
  ROUNDS & CANONS
STOLZEL, G.
  ADAGIO
  ALLEGRO
  DOPPELKONZERT IN F MA
  SONATA I IN D MA
  SONATA IN F MA

SONATA IN G MA
SONATA
SONATA
SONATE IN G MA
TRIO SONATA IN E MI
TRIOSONATE IN F MI
TRIOSONATE IN G MA
STONE, D.
  MINSTREL'S GALLERY, THE
  RENAISSANCE, LA
STONE, G.
  JOYFUL FOUR
STORP, S.
  KAMMERMUSIK
STOUFFER
  TICK-TACK-TOE
STOUFFER, D.
  TOCCATA
STOUFFER, P.
  ALBUM OF 10 BAROQUE COMP
  ALBUM OF 10 BAROQUE COMP
  ALBUM OF 10 BAROQUE COMP
  ALBUM OF 10 BAROQUE COMP
  CONCERTINO FOR 2
  DUET ALBUM
  DUET ALBUM
  SIX FOR TWO
  SIX FOR TWO
  SIX FOR TWO
  SIX FOR TWO
STOUT, A.
  ALLEGORY, AN: PRIDE, OP
  3 CANONS, OP 61A
  CANTICUM CANTICORUM, OP
  CAPRICCIO (1967)
  CAPRICCIO (1967)
  COMMENTARY ON T'UNG JEN,
  LANDSCAPE, OP 36
  RECITATIVE, CAPRICCIO, &
  RECITATIVE, CAPRICCIO, &
  2 SONGS OF ARIEL
  SUITE, OP 73/1
  TOCCATA
STOUTAMIRE
  DUETS FOR ALL
STOUTAMIRE, A. & K. HENDERSON
  TRIOS FOR ALL
STOVER, F.
  ECOLOGUE
  3 TRIFLES
STRADELLA, A.
  SINFONIA A 3
  SONATA IN G MA
STRAESSER, E.
  CLARINET QUINTET, OP 34
STRAESSER, J.
  ALLIAGES #2 (1964)
  EMERGENCY CASE (1970; RE
  ENCOUNTERS (1973; REV 19
  INTERSECTIONS IV (1972)
  INTERSECTIONS V (A SAXOP
  INTERSECTIONS V-1 (1977)

MUZIEK (1962)
RAMASASIRI (1968)
7 SONGS ON EGYPTIAN TEXT
STRANBERG, N.
  VERSES FOR 5
STRANG, G.
  CONCERTO FOR CELLO
  CONCERTO GROSSO
  LOST & WANDERING
  5 PIECES
  VARIATIONS
STRANGE, A.
  HAIRBREATH RING SCREAMER
STRASSER, J.
  ALLIAGES #2 (1964)
STRATEGIER, H.
  5 MINNELIEDEREN (1952)
  PARTITA ARGENTEA (1957)
  QUARTET (1968)
  SEXTET (1951)
  SONATA DA CAMERA (1978)
  3 STUKKEN (1937)
STRAUCH
  WEIHNACHTLICHE KAMMERMUS
STRAUSS, E.
  MIT CHIC, OP221
  WO MAN LACHT UND LEBT, OP
STRAUSS, J.
  DIPLOMATEN-POLKA, OP448
  LOB DER FRAUEN, OP315
  LUST'GER RAT, OP350
  TALES FROM THE VIENNA WO
  TALES FROM THE VIENNA WO
  TAUBEN VON SAN MARCO, DI
  TELEGRAMME, OP318
  TRITSCH-TRATSCH POLKA
  WILHELMINEN-WALZER, OP 3
STRAUSS, J. JR.
  EISELE U. BEISELE SPRUNG
  FRISCH DURCHS LEBEN, OP
  SCHERZ-POLKA, OP 72
STRAUSS, J. SR.
  ANNEN-POLKA, OP137
  JUGENDFEUER-GALOPP, OP 9
  SEUFZER-GALOPP, OP 9
STRAUSS, JOS.
  DITHYRAMBE, OP236
  EINGESENDET, OP240
  MARIENKLANGE, OP214
  SCHLARAFFEN-POLKA, OP179
STRAUSS, O.
  WALTZ DREAM, A
  WALTZ DREAM, A
STRAUSS, R.
  ALLERSEELEN, OP 10/8
  DUET CONCERTINO
  SERENADE IN E FL MA, OP
  SERENADE, OP 7
  SUITE IN B FL MA, OP 4
  SUITE
  TILL EULENSPIEGEL EINMAL
  ZUEIGNUNG

461

462

CATENA II (1962)
CATENA II (1962)
CATENA III (1976)
SURDIN
  A LA BASSOON
SURDIN, M.
  PIECE (1969)
SURINACH, C.
  3 BERBER SONGS
  HOLLYWOOD CARNIVAL (1954
  RITMO JONDO
  TIENTOS
  TIENTOS
SURTEL, M.
  TRIO, OP 10 (1978-79)
SUSA, C.
  SERENADE #5
SUSSMAYER, F.
  QUINTET
SUSSMAYR, F.
  GUITAR QUINTET IN C MA
SUTER, R.
  DIVERTIMENTO (1955)
  DUETTI
  ESTAMPIDA
  4 ETUDES (1962)
  HEILIGE LEIER SPRICH, SE
  IMPROVISATION
  INVENTIONS 1956
  JEUX A 4 (1976)
  MUSIC (1975)
  MUSIKALISCHES TAGEBUCH
  MUSIKALISCHES TAGEBUCH
  SERENATA
  SONATINA (1966)
SUTERMEISTER, H.
  4 LIEDER
  MODESTE MIGNON NACH EINE
  SERENADE #2
  SERENADE
SUTHERLAND, M.
  QUARTET
SUTHOFF¬GROSS, R.
  FETZEN
SVARA, D.
  QUINTET, OP 92
  WOODWIND TRIO
SVENSSON, SVEN
  SEXTET
SWACK, I.
  ALLEGRO
  4 BURLESQUES
  WOODWIND QUINTET
SWEELINCK
  2 CONTRAPUNTAL DUOS
SWEELINCK, J.
  ANGELUS AD PASTORES AIT
  VARIATIONS ON A FOLKSONG
SWICKARD, R.
  4 DUETS
SWIDER, J.
  LYRICAL MINIATURES

SWIFT, R.
  FOLK SONG SUITE
SYDEMAN, W.
  DIVERTIMENTO (1957)
  DUO (1959)
  DUO
  DUO
  DUO
  FANTASY & 2 EPILOGUES
  HAUS MUSIC
  JABBERWOCKY
  MUSIC
  MUSIC
  MUSIC
  PIECE
  QUARTET (1955)
  QUARTET (1962)
  QUARTET (1963)
  QUARTET
  QUINTET #1
  QUINTET #2
  QUINTET
  QUINTET
  2 SHORT PIECES & FINALE
  STUDY (1956)
  TEXTURE STUDIES (1966)
  TRIO (1957)
  TRIO (1961)
  TRIO (1963)
  TRIO (1968)
  TRIO MONTAGNANA (1972)
  TRIO
  TRIO
  VARIATIONS
SYLVAN, S.
  QUINTET, OP 5 (1949)
SYMONDS, N.
  ...DEEP GROUND, LONG WAT
  IIND PERSPECTIVE (1967)
  IIND PERSPECTIVE (1967)
SYVERUD, S.
  DEPARTURES
SZABELSKI, B.
  APHORISMS "9" (1962)
SZABO, F.
  SERENADE
SZALONEK, W.
  AARHUS MUSIC
  IMPROVISATIONS SONORISTI
  PROPORZIONI II
  SUITE FROM KURPIE (1955)
SZALOWSKI, A.
  DUO
  WIND QUINTET
SZALOWSKY, A.
  TRIO
SZATHMARY, Z.
  ALPHA (1968)
  MONOLOG (1971)
SZCZENIOWSKI, B.
  TRIO #2 (1960)
SZEKELY, E.

DIVERTIMENTO (1958)
MAQAMAT
QUINTET #1
QUINTET #3
SESTETTO
SZEKELY, E. & T. SZESZLER
OBOE DUOS FOR BEGINNERS
SZELENYI, I.
SUITE
TRIO
SZELIGOWSKI, T.
QUINTET (1950)
SZERVANSKY, E.
QUINTET #1 (1953)
QUINTET #2 (1957)
SUITE (1956)
TRIO
SZERVANSZKY, E.
TRIO (1951)
SZONYI, E.
5 ALTE TANZE
TAEGGIO, G.
PORTA, LA
TAFFANEL, P.
QUINTET
TAILLEFERRE, G.
IMAGE
TAIRA, Y.
EVEIL
PENTALPHA
SONOMORPHIE II
STRATUS
TAJCEVIC, M.
7 BALKAN DANCES
TAKACS, J.
EINE KLEINE TAFELMUSIK,
HOMAGE TO PAN, OP 87/1
OCTET, OP 96
SERENADE NACH ALTGRAZER
TAKAHASHI, Y.
BRIDGES II
CHROMAMORPHE I
FOR YOU I SING THIS SONG
NIKITE
OPERATION EULER
OPERATION EULER
TAKEMITSU, T.
BRYCE (1976)
BRYCE (1976)
EUCALYPTS II
MASQUE-CONTINU/INCIDENTA
MASQUE-INCIDENTAL # 2
RING (1962)
VALERIA (1965)
WATERWAY (1978)
WATERWAY (1978)
WAVES (1976)
TAKEMITSY, T.
QUATRAIN II (1976)
TAL, J.
QUINTET (1966)
TALMA, L.

SUMMER SOUNDS
TALMELLI, A.
BACCANALE
TAMANO, Y.
REACTION RELATIVISTE (19
TAMAS, J.
QUARTET IN B FL MA
TAMBA, A.
ENNEA
TAMIAMI, C.
4 EARLY AMERICAN SPIRITU
TANENBAUM, E.
CHAMBER PIECE #1
CONSORT
CONSORT
JAZZ SET
JAZZ SET
MIRAGE & INCANTATIONS
MUSIC FOR 3 CHAMBER GROU
NOVE
PETER QUINCE AT THE CLAV
REMEMBRANCE
REMEMBRANCE
REMEMBRANCE
SONATINA
TRANSFORMATIONS
TRIO
WOODWIND QUINTET #2
WORDS OR BLUES FOR US
WORDS OR BLUES FOR US
TANEYEV, A.
ANDANTE
TANG, J.
A LITTLE SUITE
TANSMAN, A.
DANCE OF THE SORCERESS
4 IMPRESSIONS
MUSIQUE A 6
SUITE
TAPKOFF, D.
GRENOUILLE PRESOMPTUEUSE
TAPKOV, D.
QUARTET (1973)
TARABA, B.
3 MEDITATIONS (1922)
TARANOV, G.
QUINTET
TARANU, C.
DIALOGUES (1966)
LIT DE PROCUSTE, LE (196
TARDOS, B.
DIVERTIMENTO
QUARTETTINO
TARENSKEEN, B.
MACHTELT SUITE (1978)
TARLOW, K.
MUSIC FOR WIND QUINTET
MUSIC
TARP, S.
SERENADE (1930)
TARTINI, G.
ARIOSO IN E MI

DUO, OP108
KAMMERKONZERT IN D MA, O
MARCH FOR 3 TRUMPETS
QUARTET, OP 60
QUINTET
TRIO (1960)
TRIO
TRIO, OP 59
TCHEREPNIN, I.
CADENZAS IN TRANSITION
SOMBRES LUMIERES
TCHEREPNIN, N.
DIVERTIMENTO
SONATINE, OP 61
TCHEREPNINE, I.
WHEELWINDS
TCHEREPNINE, N.
6 PIECES
TEAL, L.
10 SAXOPHONE QUARTETS
TELCS, A.
KVINTETT
TELEMANN
TRIOSONATE D MA
TELEMANN, G.
CACCIA, LA
CACCIA, LA
6 CANONIC SONATAS
9 CANONS MELODIEUX
CHASSE, LA
CONCERT IN C MA
CONCERTO #2
CONCERTO #2
CONCERTO A 4
CONCERTO A 6
CONCERTO A 7
CONCERTO DI CAMERA
CONCERTO FOR FOUR CLARIN
CONCERTO IN A MA
CONCERTO IN A MA
CONCERTO IN A MI
CONCERTO IN A MI
CONCERTO IN A MI
CONCERTO IN A MI
CONCERTO IN B FL MA
CONCERTO IN B FL MA
CONCERTO IN B FL MA
CONCERTO IN B MI
CONCERTO IN D MA
CONCERTO IN D MA
CONCERTO IN D MA
CONCERTO IN D MI
CONCERTO IN E MA
CONCERTO IN E MI
CONCERTO IN E MI
CONCERTO IN F MA
CONCERTO IN G MA
CONCERTO IN G MA
CONCERTO IN G
CONCERTO PRIMO IN G MA
CONCERTO SECONDO IN D MA
CONCERTO

CONCERTO
3 DANCES IN A MI
DRESDEN DUETS IN E MI, A
DRESDEN DUETS IN G MA, A
DUET IN D MA
DUET IN G MA
DUET IN G
6 DUETS
6 DUETS
EW'GE QUELLE, MILDER STR
EXCERPTS (SONATA IN G MA
EXCERPTS (SONATA IN G MA
EXCERPTS (SONATA IN G MA
EXCERPTS (SONATA IN G MI
EXCERPTS (SONATA IN G MI
EXCERPTS (SONATA IN G MI
EXCERPTS (SUITE IN A MI)
EXCERPTS (SUITE IN A MI)
EXCERPTS (SUITE IN A MI)
IHR VOLKER, HORT
JEDER LAUFT, EIN
6 KANONSONATEN
KLEINE KANTATE VON WALD
KLEINE TRIO-SATZE
KLEINE TRIO-SATZE
LARGO & PRESTO (SUITE IN
MARBURG DUETS IN B FL MA
MARBURG DUETS IN F MI, B
MENUET & POLONAISE (SUIT
6 MINUETS (7 FOIS 7 & 1)
6 MINUETS (7 FOIS 7 & 1)
6 MINUETS.(7 FOIS 7 & 1)
6 MINUETS;(7 FOIS 7 & 1)
6 MINUETS,(7 FOIS 7 & 1)
6 MINUETS
60 MINUETS
OUVERTURE A 7 IN C MA
OUVERTUREN-SUITE
2 OUVERTURENSUITEN
OVERTURE BAROQUE (SUITE
OVERTURE-SUITE IN D MA
PARTITA #2 IN G MA
PARTITA #5 IN E MI
PARTITA IN E MI
POLONAISE & PASSEPIEDS
QUARTET IN B MI
QUARTET IN D MA
QUARTET IN D MI (TAFELMU
QUARTET IN D MI
QUARTET IN D MI
QUARTET IN D MI
QUARTET IN D MI
QUARTET IN E MI
QUARTET IN F MA
QUARTET IN G MA (TAFELMU
QUARTET IN G MA
QUARTET IN G MI
QUARTET IN G
QUATUOR
SONATA (QUARTET) IN G MA
SONATA #1
SONATA #2

SONATA #4
SONATA IN A MA
SONATA IN A MI
SONATA IN A MI
SONATA IN A MI
SONATA IN A MI
SONATA IN A MI
SONATA IN A
SONATA IN B FL MA
SONATA IN C MA
SONATA IN C MI
SONATA IN C MI
SONATA IN C MI
SONATA IN D MI
SONATA IN E FL MA
SONATA IN E MI
SONATA IN E MI, OP 2/5
SONATA IN F MA
SONATA IN F MA
SONATA IN F MA
SONATA IN F MA
SONATA IN G MA
SONATA IN G MA
SONATA IN G MI
SONATA IN G MI
SONATA IN G MI
SONATA PRIMA IN A MA
SONATA
SONATA
SONATA
SONATAS IN CANON FORM, O
6 SONATAS IN CANON, OP
6 SONATAS IN CANON
6 SONATAS, OP 2 (DRESDE
SONATAS, OP 2, 2 VOLS
SONATAS, OP 5, 2 VOLS
6 SONATAS, SERIES #2 (MA
6 SONATAS, 2 VOLS.
6 SONATAS, 2 VOLS
6 SONATAS
SONATE EN TRIO IN E MI
SONATE EN TRIO IN E MI
SONATE EN TRIO
SONATE IN D MI
SONATINA IN E MI
SUITE #2 IN B FL MA
SUITE #3 IN B MI
SUITE #4 IN E MA
SUITE #5 IN A MI
SUITE #6 IN D MI
SUITE IN A MI
SUITE IN B FL MA
SUITE IN B MI
SUITE IN B MI
SUITE IN D MI
SUITE IN E MA
SUITE IN E MI
SUITE IN E MI
SUITE IN G MA
SUITE
SUSSE HOFFNUNG, WENN ICH
TEMPT ME THEN (LOCKET NU

TOD UND MODER DRINGT HER
3 TRIETTI E III SCHERZI
TRIO (TAFELMUSIK II, #4)
TRIO #1 IN B FL MA
TRIO #2 IN A MI
TRIO #3 IN G MA
TRIO IN C MI
TRIO IN C MI
TRIO IN D MI
TRIO IN E MI
TRIO IN F MA
TRIO IN G MI
TRIO SONATA IN A MA
TRIO SONATA IN A MI (ESS
TRIO SONATA IN A MI
TRIO SONATA IN A MI
TRIO SONATA IN C MA
TRIO SONATA IN C MA
TRIO SONATA IN C MI (ESS
TRIO SONATA IN C MI
TRIO SONATA IN C MI
TRIO SONATA IN E FL MA
TRIO SONATA IN E MI
TRIO SONATA IN F MA
TRIO SONATA IN F MA
TRIO SONATA IN F MA
TRIO SONATA IN G MA
TRIO SONATA IN G MI
TRIO SONATA IN G MI
TRIO-SONATE IN A MA (ESS
TRIOSONATE IN A MI
TRIOSONATE IN B FL MA
TRIOSONATE IN B FL MA
TRIOSONATE IN E MA
TRIOSONATE IN E MI
TRIOSONATE IN E MI
TRIOSONATE IN E MI
TRIOSONATE IN F MA
TRIOSONATE IN F
TRIOSONATE IN G MA
TELEMANN,G .
3 SCHERZI E 3 TRIETTI ME
TEMPLE¬SHAW, N.
AUDACITY
DUPLICITY
FELICITY
PERPLEXITY
TEMPLETON¬STRONG, G.
5 AQUARELLES
TEMPLETON, A.
PASSEPIED
PASSEPIED
TRIO IN D MI
TENAGLIA, A.
ARIA ANTICA
ARIA ANTICA
ARIA ANTICA
ARIA ANTICA
ARIA
ARIA
TEPPER
SUITE

TERMOS, P.
  SEMANTIC HEDONISM (1976)
TERPSTRA, K.
  PLURI-INTERPRETABLE
  SERENDIPITY (1976/77)
TERSCHAK, A.
  12 CHARACTERISTIC PIECES
  DUOS PROGRESSIFS, OP 70
TERVOORT, L.
  HOFMANNIANA
TERZAKIS, D.
  CHRONIKO
  ETHOS GAMMA II (1977)
  HOMMAGE A MORSE (1970)
  ICHOCHRONOS II (1972/73)
  NOMOI
  NOTTURNI NACH GEDICHTEN
TESSIER, R.
  "A"
  "A"
  TRIEDRE
TEUBER, F.
  INTRODUCTION PIECE
THARICHEN, W.
  DUO, OP 47
  OCTET, OP 40
THEILE, J.
  SONATA A 4
THEOBALD, J.
  PLANE-5
THEVET
  EXERCICES RYTHMIQUES
  100 EXERCICES RYTHMIQUES
  100 EXERCICES RYTHMIQUES
  100 EXERCICES RYTHMIQUES
  100 EXERCICES RYTHMIQUES
  100 EXERCICES RYTHMIQUES
  EXERCISES RYTHMIQUES
  100 EXERCISES RYTHMIQUES
THIELE, S.
  PROPORTIONEN (1971)
  SERENADE (1969)
THILMAN, J.
  APHORISMEN
  CLARINET QUINTET, OP 73
  DAS KLEINE REQUIEM, OP 2
  EPIGRAMME
  4 GESPRACHE
  OSTINATI
  OSTINATI
  QUINTET, OP 44A
  SEXTET, OP 74
  TRIO PICCOLO, OP 90
THILMANN
  ASPEKTE
THIRIET, A.
  3 OUVERTURES MINIATURES
THIRIET, M.
  LAIS ET VIRELAIS
  SUITE EN TRIO
THOMAS
  ROMANCE

THOMAS, A.
  FEAR NO MORE THE HEAT O'
  GAVOTTE (MIGNON)
THOMAS, C.
  ILLUMINATIONS (1976)
THOMAS, D.
  VOICES
THOMAS, R.
  4 DUETS FOR YOUNG MUSICI
THOME, F.
  PIZZICATO
  PIZZICATO,
  SIMPLE AVEU (CONFESSION)
  SIMPLE AVEU
  SIMPLE AVEU
THOMPSON
  OLD REFRAIN, THE
  7 PIECES FROM A MUSIC BO
  SWING LOW, SWEET CHARIOT
THOMPSON, R.
  SUITE
THOMPSON, T.
  CAPTAIN MORGAN'S MARCH &
  6 TRADITIONAL TUNES, 2 V
THOMSEN
  SERENATA (1964)
THOMSEN¬MUCHOVA, G.
  NONETT
THOMSON
  ONDINE
  ONDINE
THOMSON, V.
  BARCAROLLE
  5 PORTRAITS
  SERENADE
  SONATA DA CHIESA
  4 SONGS TO THE POEMS OF
THORARINSSON, L.
  KADENSAR
THORNTON, R.
  DIVERSION PROJECT
THORPE, R.
  6 SHORT CLASSICS
THUILLE, L.
  GAVOTTE (SEXTET, OP 6)
  SEXTET IN B FL MA, OP 6
THURNER, E.
  TRIO, OP 56
THYBO, L.
  QUARTET "NON SI LEVAVA A
TICCIATI, N.
  VOI, CHE SAPETE
TIENSUU, J.
  CONCERTO DA CAMERA
  LYRIC TRIO, OP 15
TIESSEN, H.
  KLEINE SUITE, OP 51
  SEPTET IN G MA, OP 20
TIKKA, K.
  3 FANTASIESTUCKE
TILLENIUS, L.
  INTERLUDIUM IN E MI

TILLIS, F.
  QUINTET (1962)
  3 PLUS 1
  3 PLUS 1
TILLMETZ, R.
  12 EXERCISES IN MODERN R
  12 EXERCISES ON MODERN R
TIPEI, S.
  TRANSLATION
TIPPETT, M.
  "CROWN OF THE YEAR": #8-
  PRELUDE- SPRING
  PRELUDE-AUTUMN
  PRELUDE-SUMMER
TIRCUIT, H.
  CANTATA #3
TISNE
  CARACTERES
TISNE, A.
  ALIAGES
  DISPARATES
  STRATES COLOREES
TITL/BUCHTEL
  SERENADE
TITL, A.
  SERENADE
  SERENADE
  SERENADE
  SERENADE
TOCCHI, G.
  ARLECCHINO
TOCH, E.
  CANZONETTA, CAPRICE, NIG
  CAVALCADE
  QUARTET
  ROUNDELAY
  SONATINETTA, OP 84
TOEBOSCH, L.
  MAYETMAR, OP 99 (1968)
  SARABANDE EN ALLEGRO, OP
  THEMA MET VARIATIES, OP
TOESCHI, C.
  6 DUETS, OP 11, 2 VOLS
  6 DUETS, OP 11,2 VOLS.
TOGNI, C.
  AUBADE (1965)
  AUBADE
  6 NOTTURNI (1965)
  5 PEZZI (1975/76)
TOKUNAGA, H.
  QUARTET IN 12 FRAGMENTS
TOLL, R.
  2 DUETS IN CANONIC TREAT
  6 LITTLE GEMS FROM THE M
  6 LITTLE GEMS FROM THE M
  PALS
TOMAN, J.
  WOODWIND QUINTET (1967)
TOMASI, H.
  CONCERT CHAMPETRE
  CROQUIS
  5 DANSES PROFANES ET SAC

  3 DIVERTISSEMENTS
  INCA PASTORAL
  JEUX DE GEISHAS
  JEUX DE GEISHAS
  3 PASTORALES
  PRINTEMPS
  QUINTETTE
  RECUERDOS DE LAS BALEAUS
  RECUERDOS DE LAS BALEAUS
  TOMBEAU DE MIREILLE, LE
  VARIATIONS SUR UN THEME
TON
  NIEM
TON¬THAT TIET
  INCARNATIONS STRUCTURALE
  TU DAI CA'NH
TON¬THAT¬TIET
  TUONG-NIEM
TOPLIFF, R.
  REFLECTIONS
TORRENGA, B.
  TRIO (1978)
TOSELLI, E.
  SERENADE
TOSELLI, G.
  SERENADE
TOSTI, F.
  GOOD-BYE
TOUMA, H.
  ORIENTAL RHAPSODIE
TOURNIER, M.
  SUITE
TOVEY, D.
  TRIO IN D MI, OP 14
  TRIO, OP 8
TOWER, J.
  BLACK TOPAZ
  BREAKFAST RHYTHMS I & II
  BRIMSET
  PRELUDE FOR 5 PLAYERS
TOWNSEND, D.
  BALLET SUITE
  EIGHT BY EIGHT, OP 3/1
TRABADELO, A. DE
  MON VILLAGE
TRAFFORD, E.
  DESCENT TO PERIHELION
  WYNDE
TREDE, Y.
  CHANT DES OISEAUX, LE
  QUINTETT IN EINEM SATZ
TREMBLAY, G.
  CHAMPS II (SOUFFLES) (19
  CHAMPS II (SOUFFLES) (19
  CHAMPS III (VERS) (1969)
  ORALLELUIANTS (1975)
  5 PIECES (1966)
  SERENADE
  SEXTET
  SOLSTICES (1971)
  WIND QUINTET
TREMBLOT DE LA CROIX

469

DIVERTIMENTO
10 INVENTIONS
TREXLER, G.
  SPITZWEG-SUITE (1956)
TRIEBENSEE, J.
  MENUETTO CON VARIAZIONI
  TRIO IN B FL MA
  TRIO IN B FL MA
  VARIATIONS ON A THEME OF
TRIMBLE, L.
  CONCERTO
  4 FRAGMENTS FROM THE CAN
  PANELS I
  PANELS I
  PETIT CONCERT
TRINKAUS, G.
  LAMENT
  LAMENT
  LAMENT
  16 ORIGINAL & TRANSCRIBE
  WORLD'S BEST-KNOWN PIECE
TROCHU, P.
  ORANGE
TROJAHN, M.
  ...STILLER GEFAHRT DER N
  COULEURS DE LA PLUIE, LE
  HOMAGE AU TEMPS PERDU
  KAMMERKONZERT
  RISSE DES HIMMELS
TROJAN, V.
  QUINTET, OP 8 (1937)
TROJE¬MILLER, N.
  CHINESE CHECKERS
TROMBLY, P
  IN EGALE
TROMBLY, P.
  CANTILENA
  CHAMBER CONCERTO
  CHAMBER CONCERTO
  IN MEMORIAM: I. STRAVINS
  KINETICS #3
  TRIO DA CAMERA (1975)
  TRIO IN 3 MOVEMENTS
  WINDMILLS OF PARIS, THE
TROW, K.
  MATIERE (1964)
TROWBRIDGE, L.
  PENSIVELY
TRUHLAR, J.
  QUARTET, OP 14 (1963)
  SONATINA SEMPLICE, OP 18
TSOUYOPOULOS, G.
  MUSIK
TSUJII, E.
  NAPTHA
TUCAPSKY, A.
  HLE, JAK NADHERNE
  OD STMIVANI DO USVITU
  ON JE VSE
TUFILLI, W.
  CHARM
  ROSE BLUSH

TULL, F.
  CYCLORAMA I
  5 INVENTIONS
  SCHERZINO
  SUITE
TULOU, J.
  6 DUET ETUDES
  3 DUETS, OP104
  6 DUETS
  3 DUOS, OP 14
  24 DUOS, 9 VOLS
  3 EASY DUETS, OP102
  3 EASY DUETS, OP103
  3 EASY DUETS, OP104
  3 EASY DUETS, OP193
  3 GRAND DUOS, OP 72
  TRIO, OP 65
TURCHI, G.
  TRIO (1945)
TURECHEK, E.
  D'VERTISSEMENT IN F MI
TUREK, R.
  MUSINGS (1975)
TURINI, G.
  FANFARE & PROCESSIONAL
TURK, D.
  CUCKOO
  CUCKOO
  CUCKOO
  CUCKOO
TURNER, R.
  DIVERSITIES (1967)
  ECLOGUE (1958)
  LAMENT (1951)
  SERENADE (1960)
  VARIATIONS & TOCCATA (19
TUROK, P.
  DUO CONCERTANTE, OP 27A
  PICTURE #99, OP 34/2
  SARABANDE
  3 SONGS
  TRIO, OP 38
  WIND QUINTET, OP 17
TUSTIN, W.
  ALLEGRO CON SPIRITO
  CHEERFUL ELEGY
  30 DUETS
  IMPROVISATION
  PASTORALE MODERNE
  TARANTELLA
  WALTZING WOODWINDS
TUTHILL, B.
  DIVERTIMENTO
  DUO, OP 18/2 (1940)
  FUGUE, OP 10/4
  INTERMEZZO
  NOCTURNE
  QUARTET
  SAILOR'S HORNPIPE, OP 14
  SCHERZO
  SONATINE IN CANON
  TRIO

VARIATIONS ON "WHEN JOHN
TUULSE, T.
  MENUETT (1976)
TWINN, S.
  OLD ENGLISH SONGS
  12 OLD ENGLISH SONGS
  6 OLD ENGLISH SONGS
  12 OLD WELSH SONGS
TYLNAK, I.
  DIVERTIMENTO (1961)
  WOODWIND QUINTET #2 (196
UBER, D.
  ANDANTE & DANZA (OP109)
  10 CONCERT DUETS
  INTERDIFFUSIONS & SCHERZ
  MASQUES (OP 68)
  PARADE, OP 68
  3 SKETCHES
UDOW, M.
  8 AMERICAN INDIAN CHILDR
  BULLRUSHES
  ELECTRIC SILENCE
  PATTERNS
UGGEN, E.
  PLAYWELL TRIO & QUARTET
  PLAYWELL TRIO & QUARTET
  PLAYWELL TRIO & QUARTET
  PLAYWELL TRIO & QUARTET
UHL, A.
  DIVERTIMENTO
  EINE VERGNUGLICHE MUSIK
  KLEINES KONZERT
ULLMAN, B.
  KVARTETT (1956)
  RACCONTO II
ULRICH, H.
  ENSEMBLE MUSIC FOR 5 INS
ULRICH, J.
  5 DUETS (1966)
  5 DUETS (1966)
  5 DUETS (1966)
  5 DUETS (1966)
  5 DUETS
  IN COOL AUGUST
ULTAN, L.
  EXPLORATIONS
  MEDITATION
  SEXTET
UNDERWOOD, T.
  SUITE
UNG, C.
  MOHORI
  TALL WIND
UNGVARY, T.
  AKONEL #2 (1976)
URAY, E.
  HOMMAGE A JOHANN STRAUSS
  MUSIK FUR BLASERQUINTETT
  SCHLADMINGER TANZE
URBANEC, B.
  QUINTET
URBANNER, E.

8 APHORISMEN
  ETUDE FUR BLASER (1965)
  IMPROVISATION III (1969)
  LYRICA
  LYRICA
  SEXTET (1973)
URQUHART, D.
  EXCHANGES
  PUNCTUS
VACCHI, F.
  SUITE
VACHEY, H.
  4 INSTANTANES
  MENUET
  QUINTETTEA VENT
VACKAR, D.
  QUARTET (1948)
VAILLANT, R.
  DE-CI, DE-LA
VAJDA, J.
  2 TESTS
VALCARCEL, E.
  MONTAJE 59 PARA LUDWIG
VALDAMBRINI, F.
  19 MOVEMENTS
  QUARTINE (1971)
VALEK, J.
  SHAKESPEARE-VARIATIONEN
  SYMPHONIE #6
VALEN
  SERENADE, OP 42 (1947)
VALENTINE, R.
  4 DUETS, OP 6/1-4
  3 SONATAS, OP 14
  4 SONATAS
  6 SONATAS
  TRIO SONATA IN A MI
  TRIO SONATA IN C MA
  TRIO SONATA IN D MI
  3 TRIO SONATAS
VALK, A.
  CIRCLES
VALLEE, G.
  MENUET & RIGODON
VALLIER, J.
  ANDANTINO-SCHERZANDO
  SUITE
  TRIO D'ANCHES
VAN BOER
  PASTORALE
VAN BOOM, J.
  6 PIECES
VAN DEN BROECK, L.
  SLANGENBEZWEERDER, DE
VAN DER VELDEN, R.
  SEXTET
VAN DIJK, R.
  IMMOBILE EDEN (1972)
VAN HULSE, C.
  QUINTET, OP 3
VAN LYN SCHOOTEN, H.
  4 CANONS

471

VAN NOSTRAND, B.
  EARTH MANUAL, A DAWN CER
  FANTASY MANUAL FOR URBAN
  LUNAR POSSESSION MANUAL-
  VENTILLATION MANUAL
VAN ROSSUM, F.
  PYROGRAVURES, OP 19
VAN SLYCK, N.
  12 FOR 3 (1973)
VAN VACTOR, D.
  CANONS ON VARIOUS INTERV
  DUETTINO (1974)
  MUSIC FOR WOODWINDS, 2 V
  QUINTET (1932)
  5 SONGS (1974)
  SUITE (1934)
  SUITE (1959)
VANDOR, I.
  CANZONE DI ADDIO (1967)
  SERENATA (1964)
  WINDS 845 (1969)
VANHAL, J.
  6 DUETS, VOLS. 1 AND 2
VANHALL, J.
  TRIO IN E FL MA, OP 20/5
VARCARCEL, E.
  CHECAN I
VARESE, E.
  HYPERPRISM
  INTEGRALES
  OCTANDRE
VASQUEZ DIAS, A.
  RAIZ (1977)
VASZY, V.
  QUINTET
VAUBOURGOIN, M.
  12 CANONS
VAUCLAIN, C.
  SUITE FOR YOUTH
VAUGHAN WILLIAMS, R.
  3 PRELUDES (HOUSEHOLD MU
  3 VOCALISES (1958)
VAUGHAN, R.
  QUATTRO BICINIE
VAZZANA, A.
  QUINTET
  TRIO
VECCHI, O.
  CRICKET, THE
  CRICKET, THE
VEERHOFF, C.
  BLASER-QUINTETT
  QUINTET #2 (1971)
VEIT, G.
  KASSATION
VELDEN, R. VAN DER
  CONCERT #1
  CONCERTO #2
  DIVERTIMENTO (1957)
  FANTAISIE (1967)
VELLEKOOP, G.
  LISTEN TO OUR RECORDERS

6 SUITES
VELLERE, L.
  BAGATELLES
  PRELUDE
  QUARTETTO
  QUATUOR
VELLONES, P.
  AU JARDIN DES BETES SAUV
  CAVALIERS ANDALOUS, LES
  DAUPHINS, LES
  PRELUDE & RONDO FRANCAIS
  RAPSODIE, OP 92
  TRIO, OP 94
  VALSE CHROMATIQUE
VENT, J.
  PARTHIA #17
VERACINI, A.
  SONATA DA CAMERA, OP 3/
VERACINI, F.
  LARGO (OP 2/6)
  SONATE TERZA
VERDI, G.
  CELESTE AIDA (AIDA)
  CELESTE AIDA
  DONNA E MOBILE, LA
  MISERERE, IL TROVATORE
  QUARTET (RIGOLETTO)
  QUARTET (RIGOLETTO)
  QUARTET (RIGOLETTO)
  QUARTET
VEREECKEN, B.
  16 ARTISTIC DUETS
VEREMANS, M.
  TRIO #1 (1953)
VERESS, S.
  SONATINA (1931)
VERETTI, A.
  DIVERTIMENTO
VERHAAR, A.
  DIVERTIMENTO, OP 12
  TRIO-SONATE, OP 7
  TRIO, OP 18 (1940)
  TRIO, OP 38 (1949)
VERHEY, T.
  QUINTET, OP 20
VERIKIVSKY, M.
  QUARTET
VERN, A.
  NOCTURNE EN HARMONIE
VERRALL, J.
  DIVERTIMENTO
  INTRODUCTION & RONDINO
  INTRODUCTION, VARIATIONS
  NONETTE
  PASTORAL ELEGY
  ROSE OF THE WORLD, THE
  SERENADE (1944)
  SERENADE #2
  SERENADE
  SUITE
VERRALL, P.
  CAMEOS FOR CLARINET

472

CONCERTO IN G MI, P404
CONCERTO
CONCERTO, OP 46/1
CONCERTO, OP 47/2, IN C
CONCERTO, P 85 (F. VII/3
CONCERTO, P402
CORRENTE
CORRENTE
GAVOTTA
GIGA
GIGA
GIGA
GIGA
GIGA
GIGA
GIGA
GIGA
GIGA
GIGA
GLORIA
GLORIA
PASTORALE (OP 13/4)
PASTORALE IN A MA, OP 13
PASTORALE, OP 13/4
PRELUDIO
SARABANDA
SONATA A DUE IN A MI
SONATA DA CAMERA
SONATA DA CAMERA
SONATA DA CAMERA
SONATA IN A MI, F. XV/1
SONATA IN C
SONATA IN D MA
SONATA IN G MI
TRIO IN A MI
TRIO IN D MI
TRIOSONATA IN G MI
TRIOSONATE IN D MA
VIVALDI, A.DISHINGER
  GLORIA
VIVIER, C.
  POUR VIOLON ET CLARINETT
VLACH¬VRUTICKY, J.
  CASSAZIONE (1966)
VLAD, R.
  IMMER WIEDER
  SERENATA (1959)
VLIEGER, H. DE
  MOBILE (1977)
VLIET, H.
  PRELUDIO E FUGA (1973)
  SCHERZO (1969)
VLIET, H. VAN DER
  CONCERTINO (1968)
VLIJMEN, J.
  QUINTETTO (1960)
VLIJMEN, J. VAN
  MYTHOS (1963)
  QUINTET #2 (1972)
VODAK, J.
  OCTET
VOGEL, E.

OCTET (1970)
VOGEL, J.
  DUO IV IN D MI
  QUARTET, OP 5/1
VOGEL, R.
  DIVERTIMENTO
  SUITE IN G MA
  TEMPORAL LANDSCAPE
VOGEL, W.
  "INSPIRE PAR JEAN ARP"
  DAL QUADERNO DI FRANCINE
  HORFORMEN (1974)
  TERZETT
  TICINELLA (1941)
  12 VARIETUDES
VOGLER, E.
  KLEINE STADT, DIE (1962)
VOGLER, G.
  QUARTET IN B FL MA
VOGT
  BOAT SONG
  DREAM WALTZ
  REMEMBRANCE
  SAX-O-MOAN
  SAXOMOLA
  SAXONADE
VOGT, G.
  ADAGIO RELIGIOSO
  ADAGIO RELIGIOSO
  ADAGIO RELIGIOSO
VOIRIN
  2 PETITES PIECES (NOCTIL
VOLBACH, F.
  QUINTET, OP 24
VOMACKA, B.
  NONETT (1957)
VON KREISLER, A.
  ANDANTE & ALLEGRO
  LITTLE TRIO
  PASTELS
  PASTORALE (MUSIC FOR WOO
  2 PORTRAITS
  TRIO SONATA
VOORN, J.
  DIVERTIMENTO (5 CONSTELL
  QUINTET (PRELUDE & FUGUE
  SUCEVITA CHORALS (1974)
  TRIO (1975)
  TRIO "NAKUPENDA"
VOORTMAN, R.
  HEXAPHONIE (1976)
VORLOVA, S.
  SERENATA DESTA, OP 58
VOSS, F.
  CAPRICCIOSO (1965)
  NOTTURNO (1958)
  SERENADE (1959)
VOSTRAK, Z.
  AFEKTY (1963)
VOXMAN, H.
  CHAMBER MUSIC FOR FLUTES
  CHAMBER MUSIC FOR 3 CLAR

476

DIVERTIMENTO
SCHERZO FOR WINDS
3 SHORT PIECES
WAXMAN, D.
TRIO
WEAIT, C.
2 CANADIAN FOLKSONGS (19
4 MARCHES FROM THE AMERI
SUITE OF EARLY AMERICAN
WEAVER
7 DIALOGUES
WEBER
DUETS, 2 VOLS
WEBER & OSTLING
DUETS, 2 VOLS
WEBER, A.
EPODES
QUINTETTE
SONATINA
TRIO D'ANCHES
WEBER, B.
AUBADE
BALLET, OP 26, THE POOL
CHAMBER FANTASIE, OP 51
CONCERT ARIA AFTER SOLOM
CONCERTINO, OP 11B
CONCERTINO, OP 45 (1956)
CONCERTO, OP 32
CONSORT OF WINDS, OP 66
NOCTURNO, OP 55
PRELUDE & NOCTURNE
SERENADE, OP 39
SYMPHONY ON POEMS OF W.
WEBER, C. VON
GRAND DUO CONCERTANTE, O
HUNTERS' CHORUS
MARCH
MARCIA IN C MA
QUINTET IN B FL MA
WEBER, C.M. VON
ADAGIO (CONCERTO #1)
ADAGIO & RONDO
FREISCHUTZ SELECTION, DE
FREISCHUTZ, DER
GRAND QUINTET, OP 34
INTRODUKTION, THEMA UND
INVITATION TO THE DANCE
MENUET & TRIO
MENUETT (DONNA DIANA)
MENUETT UND TRIO
MINUET (QUINTET, OP 34)
OBERON OVERTURE
QUINTET IN B FL MA, OP 3
QUINTET, OP 34
TRIO IN G MI, OP 63
TRIO, OP 63
WEBER, E. VON
TRIO
WEBER, L.
QUINTET
WEBERN, A.
5 CANONS, OP 16

CONCERTO, OP 24
2 LIEDER, OP 8
6 LIEDER, OP 14
3 LIEDER, OP 18
5 RELIGIOUS SONGS, OP 15
3 VOLKSTEXTE, OP 17
WECKERLIN, J.
PASTORALE
WECKMAN, M.
NOW DANCE & SING
WECKMANN, M.
SONATA A 4
WEEGENHUISE, J.
3 PEZZI (1954)
TRIO D'ANCHES (1973)
WEELINK, K.
MOVEMENT IN A CLASSICAL
WEELKES
GAY TUNE, A
WEHNER, W.
20 MODERN DUETS
WEIGEL, E.
QUINTET
SHORT, SLOW & FAST
WEIGL
AIR VARIE
AIR VARIE,
WEIGL, K.
4 BAGATELLES
WEIGL, V.
ALONG THE MOVING DARKNES
BIRDS IN SPRINGTIME
BRIEF ENCOUNTERS
BRIEF ENCOUNTERS
CARDINAL IN MARCH
CHALLENGE
CHERRY TREE, THE- VERSIO
CHRISTCHILD'S LULLABY
CITY BIRDS
I SAW 2 BIRDS
LYRICAL SUITE
MOOD SKETCHES
NATURE MOODS
NEW ENGLAND SUITE
PLAYTHINGS OF THE WIND
SEA MOVES ALWAYS, THE
SONGS FROM "NATIVE ISLAN
SONGS OF CONCERN
SOON
THISTLE, YARROW, CLOVER
TRIALOGUE
WHEN THE VISION DIES
WHO HAS SEEN THE WIND?
WEIJERS, J.
CONCERTINO
WEILL, K.
GRAND LUSTUCRU, LE
SURABAYA JOHNNY
WEINER, I.
DUO
WEINER, K.
3 PIECES, OP 20

477

WESTERING, P.
  SONATINE (1966)
WESTON, P.
  ALBUM OF DUETS, 3 VOLS
  ARBEAU SUITE
  8 CLARINET TRIOS
  CLASSICAL ALBUM
  CLASSICAL ALBUM
WESTRUP, J.
  DIVERTIMENTO
WETTSTEIN, P.
  TONUNGEN. NONETT (1976)
WHEAR, P.
  QUINTET (1956)
  TRIO VARIATIONS
WHEELER
  MEDITATION
WHETTAM, G.
  OBOE QUARTET
WHITE, C.
  PETITE SUITE,
  SUITE SPIRITUAL
WHITE, D.
  CONCERTINO
  6 MINIATURES
  SUITE
  THREE FOR FIVE
  VESPERS
WHITE, T.
  QUARTET
WHITLOCK, P.
  FOLK TUNE
WHITNEY
  MOSQUITOES' DANCE, THE
WHITNEY, M.
  ADAGIO & FUGUE
  MOSQUITOES' PARADE
  ROULADE
WHITTENBERG, C.
  A DUE, OP 49
  COMPOSITION
  2 DYLAN THOMAS SONGS
  EVEN THOUGH THE WORLD KE
  FANTASY
  3 FORMS WITH VARIATIONS
  GAMES OF 5
  IAMBI IN TWO PARTS
  SEXTET
  STRUCTURES WITH CHORALE
  STUDY
  TRIO DIVERTIMENTO
  VARIATIONS FOR 9
WIDDOES, L.
  FROM A TIME OF SNOW (197
WIDMER, E.
  COCO 1961 (DIVERTIMENTO
  ECLOSAO
WIDOR, C.
  SERENADE
  SERENADE, OP 10
WIEDEMANN, L.
  DUETS, VOLS. 2 & 3 OF CL

30 EASY & MELODIOUS DUET
30 EASY DUETS, 2 VOLS
WIENANDT, E.
  3 EASY CANONS
  11 FLUTE DUETS
  MINUET & GAVOTTE
WIESLANDER, I.
  MISSOLOGI: LITEN SVIT
WIGGLESWORTH, F.
  DUO
  DUO
  SERENADE
  TRIO
WIGY, F.
  2 ESQUISSES
WIJDEVELD, W.
  QUINTET (1934)
  TRIO, OP 64 (1958)
WILBRANDT, J.
  QUARTET
WILDBERGER, J.
  DOUBLE REFRAIN (1972)
  DOUBLE REFRAIN (1972)
  NOTTE, LA
  QUARTET (1967)
  QUARTETTO (1952)
  RENCONTRES
  TRIO (1952)
WILDER A.
  7 DUETS
WILDER, A.
  AIR
  CHILDREN'S SUITE
  DEBUTANTE'S DIARY, A
  DUETS
  7 EASY DUETS
  MOOSACAGLIA
  MOVEMENT FOR FLUTE ENSEM
  MOVEMENT
  QUARTET
  QUINTET # 1
  QUINTET # 3
  QUINTET # 4
  QUINTET # 5
  QUINTET # 6
  QUINTET # 7
  QUINTET # 8
  QUINTET # 9 (SUITE)
  QUINTET #10
  QUINTET #12
  QUINTET #13
  SEXTET
  SHE'LL BE 7 IN MAY
  SUCH A TENDER NIGHT
  SUITE #1
  SUITE #2
  SUITE FOR BAROQUE QUARTE
  SUITE
  SUITE
  SUITE
  SUITE
  SUITE

480

ATREES (1960)
CHARISMA (1971)
EPEI (1976)
PHLEGRA (1975)
ST/10-1,080262
ST/10-1,080262
YANNAY, Y.
MUTATIS MUTANDIS
PRE FIX-FIX-SUFFIX
YASHIRO, A.
SONATA
YATES
AIR
YAVELOW, C.
DIMENSION - L
EXPLANATION OF 1 MECHANI
INTERCOSMOS
PHI-LINGS
SERMON
YEVSEYEV, S.
BURLESQUE, OP 70
YODER, P.
BACH SUITE
DRY BONES
DRY BONES
DRY BONES
JERICHO
RELAX!
YOFFE, S.
AFFETUOSO
YORK, W.
NEO GOTHICS
YOSHIOKA, E.
ALLEGRO
ARIA (ARIA & ALLEGRO)
YOST, M.
DUO #4 IN A MI
DUO II IN F MA
6 DUOS, OP 5/1-3
6 FAVORITE DUETS, OP 12
TRIO IN F MA
YOUNG
KING JAMES' PLEASURE
17TH-CENTURY SUITE
YOUNG, D.
KROYER VARIATIONS
NORTHERN LEGEND
YOUNG, W.
19 TANZSATZE
YRADIER, C.
PALOMA, LA
YRADIER, S.
DOVE, THE (LA PALOMA)
PALOMA, LA
YTTREHUS, R.
6 HAIKU
MUSIC FOR WINDS, PERCUSS
YUASA, J.
INTER-POSI-PLAY-TION II
INTER-POSI-PLAY-TION II
INTER-POSI-PLAY-TION
INTERPENETRATION

YUN, I.
DOPPELKONZERT (1977)
IMAGES (1968)
MUSIK (1959)
OCTET (1977)
PIECE CONCERTANTE (1976)
RONDELL (1975)
TRIO (1972/73)
ZACHAU, F.
CHORALE
ZACHERT, W.
6 SUITEN IM ALTEN STIL
ZACHOW, F.
KAMMERTRIO IN F MA
TRIO
ZAFRED, M.
QUINTET
ZAGWIJN, H.
ENTRATA E FUGA (1950)
DE FLUITSPELER (1946)
HET HOOGLIED VAN SALOMO
HYMNE AN DIE NACHT
INTRODUZIONE EN SCHERZET
KERTMIS BIJ DE VOLKEN (1
MORGENZANG (1937)
NOCTURNE (1918)
NOCTURNE
PASTORALE (1937)
PASTORALE & SCHERZO
PASTORALE & SCHERZO
PASTORALE E SCHERZO (195
QUINTET (1954)
QUINTETTO (1948)
SCHERZO (1946)
SONATA (1950)
DIE STILLE STADT (1915)
SUITE (1912)
SUITE (1951)
SUITE NEGRE (1947)
TRIO (1944)
TRIO (1952)
TRIO #2 (1949)
VON DER DEMUT (1936)
ZAHRADNIK, Z.
STELE
WOODWIND QUINTET
ZAJAC, E.
5 MINIATURES
ZAMARA, A.
CAPRICCIETTO
ZAMECNIK, J.
ALLEGRO GIUBILOSO
GONDOLIERA, LA
ZANABONI, G.
PICCOLA SUITE
ZANDER, H.
5 BAGATELLES
QUINTET
ZANETTOVICH, D.
AIRS DE LA RENAISSANCE E
5 BERCEUSES POPULAIRES
NOCTURNE ET PANTOMIME

BALUN, VOLKSTANZ AUS IST
ZOELLER, C.
  AUF DER ALM PASTORALE
ZONN, P.
  CANZONNI, OVERO SONATE C
  CANZONNI, OVERO SONATE C
  COMPOSITIONS FOR QUARTET
  CONCERT PIECE
  DANCE SET
  DIVERTIMENTO #2
  DIVERTIMENTO #2
  LIBERATA III
  MICRODITTIES
  MOVEMENT
  2 MOVEMENTS
  ONE SLOW TURN OF THE WOR
  PERIPHRASIS
  SONORUM #3
  SONORUM I
  TURNAROUND
  TURNAROUND
  VOYAGE OF COLUMBUS, THE
ZOUHAR, Z.
  151- MUSIC FOR WOODWIND
ZUCKERMAN, M.
  REUNION
  TWILIGHT SONGS (1970)
ZUCKERT, L.
  DOS IMPROVISACIONES (196
  LITTLE PRINCE IN MONTREA
ZULAWSKI, W.
  ARIA CON VARIAZIONI (195
ZUR, M.
  CONCERTINO
  DISCUSSIONS
ZWEDBERG, T.
  CARE OF (1976)

ENSEMBLE CODES

ENSEMBLE CODES

2 Flutes-200
2 Flutes (Collections)-201
2 Oboes-202
2 Oboes (Collections)-203
2 Clarinets-204
2 Clarinets (Collections)-205
2 Bassoons (Collections)-207
2 Saxophones-208
2 Saxophones (Collections)-209
2 Parts: Woodwinds-210
2 Parts: Woodwinds (Collections)-222
2 Parts: Woodwind-Brass (Incl. Horn)-231
2 Parts: Woodwind-String-233
2 Parts Including Harp-238
2 Parts Including Guitar-239
2 Parts Including Percussion-240
2 Parts Including Tape-243
3 Flutes-300
3 Flutes (Collections)-301
3 Oboes-302
3 Clarinets-304
3 Clarinets (Collections)-305
3 Bassoons-306
3 Saxophones-308
3 Saxophones (Collections)-309
3 Parts: Woodwinds-310
3 Parts: 2 Flutes-Keyboard-311
3 Parts: 2 Oboes-Keyboard-312
3 Parts: 2 Clarinets-Keyboard-313
3 Parts: 2 Bassoons-Keyboard-314
3 Parts: 2 Saxophones-Keyboard-315
3 Parts: Woodwinds (Collections)-322
3 Parts: Woodwind-Keyboard-327
3 Parts: Woodwind-Keyboard (Collections)-329
3 Parts: Woodwind-Brass (Incl. Horn)-331
3 Parts: Woodwind-String-333
3 Parts: Woodwind-Brass-String-334
3 Parts: Woodwind-Brass-Keyboard-335
3 Parts: Woodwind-String-Keyboard-336
3 Parts Including Harp-338
3 Parts Including Guitar-339
3 Parts Including Percussion-340
3 Parts Including Recorder-342
3 Parts Including Tape-343
4 Flutes-400
4 Oboes-402
4 Clarinets-404
4 Clarinets (Collections)-405
4 Bassoons-406
4 Saxophones-408
4 Saxophones (Collections)-409
4 Parts: Woodwinds-410

487

4 Parts: 3 Flutes-Keyboard-416
4 Parts: 3 Clarinets-Keyboard-418
4 Parts: 3 Saxophones-Keyboard-420
4 Parts: Woodwind-Keyboard-427
4 Parts: Woodwind-Brass (Incl. Horn)-431
4 Parts: Woodwind-String-433
4 Parts: Woodwind-Brass-String-434
4 Parts: Woodwind-Brass-Keyboard-435
4 Parts: Woodwind-String-Keyboard-436
4 Parts: Woodwind-Brass-String-Keyboard-437
4 Parts Including Harp-438
4 Parts Including Guitar-439
4 Parts Including Percussion-440
4 Parts Including Recorder-442
4 Parts Including Tape-443
5 Flutes-500
5 Oboes-502
5 Clarinets-504
5 Saxophones-508
5 Parts: Woodwinds (Fl,Ob,Cl,Hn,Bsn)-523
5 Parts: Woodwind Quintet (Collections)-524
5 Parts: Woodwinds (w/o Fl,Ob,Cl,Hn,Bsn)-525
5 Parts: Woodwind-Keyboard (Incl. Horn)-528
5 Parts: Woodwind-Brass-532
5 Parts: Woodwind-String-533
5 Parts: Woodwind-Brass-String-534
5 Parts: Woodwind-Brass-Keyboard-535
5 Parts: Woodwind-String-Keyboard-536
5 Parts: Woodwind-Brass-String-Keyboard-537
5 Parts Including Harp-538
5 Parts Including Guitar-539
5 Parts Including Percussion-540
5 Parts Including Recorder-542
5 Parts Including Tape-543
6 Clarinets-604
6 Saxophones-608
6 Parts: Woodwinds Including Horn-621
6 Parts: Woodwind Quintet-Keyboard-626
6 Parts: Woodwind-Keyboard-627
6 Parts: Woodwind-Keyboard (Incl. Horn)-628
6 Parts: Woodwind-Brass-632
6 Parts: Woodwind-Strings-633
6 Parts: Woodwind-Brass-String-634
6 Parts: Woodwind-Brass-Keyboard-635
6 Parts: Woodwind-String-Keyboard-636
6 Parts: Woodwind-Brass-String-Keyboard-637
6 Parts Including Harp-638
6 Parts Including Guitar-639
6 Parts Including Percussion-640
6 Parts Including Recorder-642
6 Parts Including Tape-643
7 Parts: Woodwinds Including Horn-721
7 Parts: Woodwind-Keyboard-727

7 Parts: Woodwind-Brass-732
7 Parts: Woodwind-String-733
7 Parts: Woodwind-Brass-String-734
7 Parts: Woodwind-Brass-Keyboard-735
7 Parts: Woodwind-String-Keyboard-736
7 Parts: Woodwind-Brass-String-Keyboard-737
7 Parts Including Harp-738
7 Parts Including Guitar-739
7 Parts Including Percussion-740
7 Parts Including Tape-743
8 Parts: Woodwinds Including Horn-821
8 Parts: Woodwind-Keyboard (Incl. Horn)-828
8 Parts: Woodwind-Brass-832
8 Parts: Woodwind-String-833
8 Parts: Woodwind-Brass-String-834
8 Parts: Woodwind-Brass-Keyboard-835
8 Parts: Woodwind-String-Keyboard-836
8 Parts: Woodwind-Brass-String-Keyboard-837
8 Parts Including Harp-838
8 Parts Including Guitar-839
8 Parts Including Percussion-840
8 Parts Including Recorder-842
8 Parts Including Tape-843
9 Parts: Woodwinds Including Horn-921
9 Parts Including Harp-938
9 Parts Including Guitar-939
9 Parts Including Percussion-940
9 Parts w/o Harp, Guitar, or Percussion-941
10 Parts: Woodwinds Including Horn-1021
10 Parts Including Harp-1038
10 Parts Including Guitar-1039
10 Parts Including Percussion-1040
10 Parts w/o Harp, Guitar, or Percussion-1041
11 Parts: Woodwinds Including Horn-1121
11 Parts Including Harp-1138
11 Parts Including Guitar-1139
11 Parts Including Percussion-1140
11 Parts w/o Harp, Guitar, or Percussion-1141
12 Parts: Woodwinds Including Horn-1221
12 Parts Including Harp-1238
12 Parts Including Guitar-1239
12 Parts Including Percussion-1240
12 Parts w/o Harp, Guitar, or Percussion-1241
13 Parts: Woodwinds Including Horn-1321
13 Parts Including Harp-1338
13 Parts Including Guitar-1339
13 Parts Including Percussion-1340
13 Parts w/o Harp, Guitar, or Percussion-1341
Flute Choir-1400
Clarinet Choir-1401
Woodwind Choir-1402
Flexible Instrumentation-1404
Voice With Instruments-1410

489

KEY TO PUBLISHERS

KEY TO PUBLISHERS

A&S   Ahn & Simrock, Taunusstrasse 66, 6200 Wiesbaden, West Germany
AB   Alexander Broude, Inc., 225 West 57th Street, New York, New York
ABE   Anton J. Benjamin, Werderstrasse 44, Hamburg 13, West Germany (AMP)
ABS   Anton Böhm & Sohn, Lange Gasse 26, 89 Augsburg 2, West Germany
ACA   American Composers Alliance, 170 West 74th Street, New York, New York
ACC   Accura Music, Box 887, Athens, Ohio
AEP   Aeolus, 60 Park Terrace West, New York, New York
AL   Alfred Publishing Co., Inc., 15335 Morrison Street, Sherman Oaks, California
ALB   Albersen & Company, Groot Hertoginnelaan 182, The Hague, Holland
ALE   Alphonse Leduc, 175 Rue Saint-Honoré, Paris, France
ALL   Allans Music (Australia) Pty., Ltd., 276 Collins Street, Melbourne, Australia
ALS   Alsbach & Doyer, Flevolaan 41, Naarden, Holland
AM   Atlantic Music (See Philharmusica PB)
AMC   American Music Center, Inc., 2109 Broadway, Suite 15-79, New York, New York
AME   American Music Edition, 439 Lafayette Street, New York, New York
AMP   Associated Music Publishers, Inc., 866 Third Avenue, New York, New York
AP   Ars Polona, Krakowskie Przedmieście 7, Warsaw, Poland
APH   Amphion Editions Musicales, 9 Rue d'Artois, Paris 8e, France (BE)
ARM   Artisan Music Press (See Philharmusica PB)
ARP   Arsis Press, 1719 Bay Street, S.E., Washington, D.C.
ART   Artia, Ve Smečkách 30, Prague 1, Czechoslovakia (BH)
ASH   Ashley Dealers Service, Inc., 263 Veterans Blvd., Carlstadt, New Jersey
AU   Autograph Editions (See Philharmusica PB)
AUG   Augsburg Publishing House, 426 S. Fifth Street, Minneapolis, Minnesota

B&B   Bote & Bock, Hardenbergstrasse 9a, 1 Berlin 12, West Germany (AMP)
B&N   Bärenreiter & Neuwerk, Heinrich-Schütz-Allee 35, D3500 Kassel-Wilhelmshöhe, West Germany
B&V   Broekmans & Van Poppel, Van Baerlestraat 92-94, Amsterdam, Holland
B-B   Boelke-Bomart Publications, Hillsdale, New York
BA   C.L. Barnhouse Co., Oskaloosa, Iowa
BAR   Barry E.C.I., Talcahuano 860 bajo B, Buenos Aires, Argentina (BH)
BD   Byron-Douglas Publications,25 Deshon Drive, Melville, New York
BE   Belwin-Mills Publishing Corp., 25 Deshon Drive, Melville, New York
BEL   M.P. Belaieff, Kennedyallee 101, 6 Frankfurt a/Main 70, West Germany (PET)
BER   Berandol Music Limited, 11 St. Joseph Street, Toronto, Canada
BF   Brodt Music Co., P.O. Box 9345, Charlotte, North Carolina
BH   Boosey & Hawkes, Lawson Blvd., P.O. Box 130, Oceanside, New York
BHL   Breitkopf & Härtel, Ltd., 8 Horse and Dolphin Yard WIV 7LG, London, England
BIL   Billaudot Editions Musicales, 14 Rue de l'Echiquier, Paris 10c, France (TP)
BNA   Bach N' All, 4109 23rd Ave. South, Minneapolis, Minnesota
BO   Bourne Co. (See G. Schirmer GS)
BOS   Bosworth & Co., Ltd., 14/18, Heddon Street, London, W1, England (BE)
BOW   Bowdoin College Music Press, Brunswick, Maine
BR   Broude Brothers, Ltd., 170 Varick Street, New York, New York
BRH   Breitkopf & Härtel, Walkmühlstrasse 52, D 6200 Wiesbaden 1, West Germany (AMP)
BRM   Brazilliance Music Publishing, Inc., 4104 Witzel Drive, Sherman Oaks, California
BRU   Aldo Bruzzichelli (See Margun Music MAR)
BT   Boston Music Company, 116 Boylston St., Boston, Massachusetts
B3   Big 3, 230 Clay Avenue, Lyndhurst, New Jersey

CA   Chappell & Co., Inc., 50 New Bond Street, London WIA 1DR, England (HL)
CAM   Camara Music Publishers, 23 La Fond Lane, Orinda, Canada
CAN   Canadian Music Centre, 1263 Bay Street, Toronto M 5R2C1, Ontario, Canada
CAR   Carisch S.P.A. 20124 - Via General Fara, 39, Milan, Italy
CBD   Centre Belge de Documentation Musicale, Rue de l'Hôpital, 31, B-1000, Brussels, Belgium (HE)
CC   Chas. Colin, 315 West 53rd Street, New York, New York
CEN   Century Music Publishing Co., Inc. (See Ashley Dealers Service ASH)
CF   Carl Fischer, Inc., 62 Cooper Square, New York, New York
CFV   Chr. Friedrich Vieweg, Limonenstr. 10, 1 Berlin 45, West Germany (PET)
CGM   Carl Gehrmans Musikförlag, Apelbergsgatan 58, Box 505, 101 26, Stockholm 1, Sweden (BH)

CHE J. & W. Chester Ltd., Eagle Court, London, EC1, England (M-B)
CHF Ceský Hudební Fond, Ustredni archív, Pǎrízská 13, Prague 1, Czechoslovakia
CHM Le Chant du Monde, 32 Rue Beaujon, Paris 8e, France
CHP Chappel, 4 Rue d'Argenson, Paris 8e, France
CL   Clarmar, 2588 Riverside Drive, Green Bay, Wisconsin
CM   Camera Music, 112 South Street, Boston, Massachusetts
CO   Cole Publishing Co., 919 N. Michigan, Suite 1602, Chicago, Illinois
COA Composers' Autograph Publications, Box 671, Hamilton, Ohio
COF Composers' Facsimile Edition, 170 West 74th Street, New York, New York
COM Consortium Musical, 24 Blvd. Poissonnière, Paris 9e, France
CON Concordia Publishing House, 3558 South Jefferson Avenue, St. Louis, Missouri
COR Cor Publishing Co., 67 Bell Place, Massapequa, New York
CP   Christlieb Products, 3311 Scadlock Lane. Sherman Oaks. California
CPE Composers Performing Edition, 330 University Avenue, Davis, California
CPR Consort Press, Box 4012, Champaign, Illinois (See Mark Foster MF)
CPS Contemporary Publications, 562 Eastvale Drive, Ottawa, Ontario, Canada
CRA J.B. Cramer, 99 St. Martin's Lane, London WC2, England
CRE Crescendo Music Sales, Box 395, Naperville, Illinois
CST Consort Trios, Box 424, Cathedral Station, New York, New York
CU   Claude Benny Press, 1401 State Street, Emporia, Kansas
DAN Dantalian, Inc., 11 Pembroke Street, Newton, Massachusetts
DEU VEB Deutscher Verlag, Postfach 147, 701 Leipzig, East Germany (AB)
DEW De Wolfe, 80-82 Wardour Street, London W1, England
DG   David Gornston (See Sam Fox SF)
DMH Deiro Music Headquarters, 133 7th Avenue South, New York, New York
DOR Dorn Productions, 1492 Highland Avenue, No. 4, Needham, Massachusetts
DSS DSS Editions, Misarska 12-14, Belgrade, Yugoslavia
DUR Editions Durand & Cie, 4 Place de la Madeleine, 75008 Paris 8e, France (TP)

E&C Enoch & Cie., 27 Boulevard des Italiens, Paris 2e, France (AMP)
EAM European American Music, Inc., 11 West End Road, Totowa, New Jersey
EBE Edizioni Musicali Berben, via Redipuglia 65, 60100 Ancona, Italy (TP)
EBL Editions Boileau, Post Box 6026, Barcelona 22, Spain
EBM Eble Music, Post Box 2570, Iowa City, Iowa
EBR Editions Musicales Brogneaux, 73 Avenue Paul Janson, Brussels, Belgium (HE)
ECH Editions Choudens, 38 Rue Jean Mermoz, Paris 8e, France (PET)
ECK E.C. Kerby, Ltd., 198 Davenport Road, Toronto 5, Ontario, Canada
ECM Editions A. Cranz Musikverlag, Adelheidstrasse 68, 62 Wiesbaden, West Germany (HE)
ECS E.C. Schirmer Music Co., 112 South Street, Boston, Massachusetts
EDA Editorial Alpuerto, S.A., Agustín de Bethencourt, 19, Madrid, Spain
EDB Edizioni Bongiovanni, Via Rizzoli, 28/E, Bologna, Italy (BE)
EDC Editions Costallat, 60 Rue de la Chaussée-d'Antin, Paris 9e, France (See Billaudot BIL-TP)
EDD Edicije Društva slovenskih skladateljev, Trg francoske revolucije 6, 61000 Ljubljana, Yugoslavia
EDF Edition Fazer, Postbox 260, 00101 Helsinki 10, Finland
EDH Edition Heuwekemeyer, Weteringstraat 19, Amsterdam 1002, Holland (HE), (PET)
EDI Edizioni Curci, Galleria del Corso, 4 Milan, Italy
EDK Edwin F. Kalmus, Opa Locka, Florida
EDL Editions de L'Oiseau-Lyre, Les Remparts, Monaco
EDM Editions Musicus-New York, Inc., Box 1341, Stamford, Connecticut
EDR Editions Robert Martin, 106, Grande-rue de la Coupée, 71, Charnay-Lès-Mâcon, France
EDS Editions Salabert, 22 Rue Chauchat, Paris 9e, France (GS)
EDT Edition Tonos, Ahastrasse 7-9, 6100 Darmstadt, West Germany
EEC Editorial de musica española contemporanea, Alcalá 70, Madrid 9, Spain
EES Editions Max Eschig, 48 Rue de Rome, Paris 8e, France (AMP)
EFM E.F.M. Technisonor, 14 Rue Magellan, Paris 8e, France
EHE Edition Helbling, 8604 Volketswil, Zürich, Switzerland
EHR Ehrling Musik, Box 5268 AB, Stockholm, Sweden
EJ   E.J. Erickson Publications, 606 N. 4th Street, St. Peter, Minnesota
EK   Edition Kneusslin, Amselstrasse 43, Basel 24, Switzerland
EM   Edward B. Marks Music Corporation, 1790 Broadway, New York, New York (BE)
EMB Editio Musica Budapest, Pf. 322, Budapest 5, Hungary (BH)
EMC Eastlane Music Corp., 623 Latona Avenue, Trenton, New Jersey
EME Editions Metropolis, van Ertbornstraat 5, Antwerp, Belgium (HE)
EMF Eriks Musikhandel & Forlag AB, Karlavagen 40, Stockholm, Sweden
EMI EMI Music Publishing, Ltd., 20 Manchester Square, London WI, England
EMO Edition Modern, Elisabethstrasse 38, D8000 Munich, West Germany

494

EMP   Edition Maurice et Pierre Foetisch, 6 Rue de Bourg, Lausanne, Switzerland
EMT   Editions Musicales Transatlantiques, 14 Avenue Hoche, Paris 75008, France (TP)
EMU   Editura Muzicala, Compozitorilor Din R.S.R., Bucharest, Rumania
EP   Ensemble Publications, Inc., Box 98, Bidwell Station, Buffalo, New York
EQM   Etoile Music, Inc., Shell Lake, Wisconsin
ER   Edition Reimers AB, Fack 30, S-161 15 Bromma, Stockholm, Sweden
ERM   Emil Ruh Musikverlag, Zürichstrasse 33, Ch-8134 Adliswil, Zürich, Switzerland
ERR   Editions Rideau Rouge, 24 Rue de Longchamp, Paris 75116, France (TP)
ES   Editio Supraphon, Palackého 1, Prague 1, Czechoslovakia
ESA   Edizioni De Santis, Via Cassia 13, Rome, Italy
ESU   Edition Suecia, Stockholm, Sweden
ESZ   Edizioni Suvini Zerboni, Via Quintiliano 40, 20138 Milan, Italy (BH)
ETB   Musikverlag Elisabeth Thomi-Berg, Am Klopferspitz 12, Box 322, 8000 Munich 60, West Germany
ETH   Ethos Publications, Box 2043, Oswego, New York
ETP   Edu-Tainment (See A. Broude AB)
EUL   Eulenburg GmbH., Grütstrasse 28, 8134 Adliswil-Zürich, Switzerland (EAM)
EV   Elkan-Vogel Co., Inc., c/o Theodore Presser, Presser Place, Bryn Mawr, Pennsylvania
EXM   Experimental Music, 208 Ladbroke Grove, London W 10, England

FAM   Fana Music, Box 393, Amherst, Maine
FB   Faber Music Ltd., 3 Queen Square, London WC1 N3AU, England (GS)
FEE   Feedback-Studio-Verlag, Cologne, West Germany (B&N)
FEM   Fentone Music (See Breitkopf & Härtel, London BHL) (AB)
FER   Fereol Publications, 14381 Aden Road, Nokesville, Virginia
FH   Frederick Harris Music, Box 670, Oakville, Ontario, Canada
FIN   Finnish Music Information Centre, Runeberginkatu 15 A, 00100, Helsinki 10, Finland
FO   Charles Foley, Inc., (See Carl Fischer CF)
FOR   Robert Forberg-P. Jurgenson, Mirbachstrasse 9, 53 Bonn-Bad Godesberg, West Germany
FRH   Friedrich Hofmeister-Verlag, Ubierstrasse 20, 6238 Hofheim am Taunus, West Germany and Karlstrasse 10, 701 Leipzig, East Germany (AB)
FS   Fritz Schultz, Am Märzengraben 6, 7800 Freiburg-Tiengen, West Germany
FZ   H.T. FitzSimons, 357 W. Erie Street, Chicago, Illinois

GA   Galaxy Music Corporation, 131 West 85th Street, New York, New York (ECS)
GAL   Galliard, Ltd., 82 High Road, London N29PW, England
GBV   Gustav Bosse Verlag, Postfach 417, 84 Regensburg 2, West Germany
GD   Edition Delrieu, 45 Palais Bellecour 1314 Rue Trachel, Nice, France (GA)
GEN   General Music Publishing Co. (See Boston Music Co. BT)
GHE   G. Henle Verlag, Forstenrieder Allee 122, D-8000 Munich 71, West Germany
GP   Gamut Publications, Cambridge Music Shop, All Saints' Passage, Cambridge, CB 23 LT, England
GS   G. Schirmer, Inc., 866 Third Avenue, New York, New York
GZ   G. Zanibon, Piazza Dei Signori 24/26, 35100 Padua, Italy

H-V   Hänssler-Verlag, Neuhausen-Stuttgart, West Germany
HA   T.B. Harms Co., c/o Cimino Publications, 1646 New Highway, Farmingdale, New York
HAM   Hamelle & Cie, 24 Boulevard Malesherbes, Paris 8e, France (See Alphonse Leduc ALE)
HAT   Harris Teller, Inc., 7400 S. Mason Street, Chicago, Illinois
HE   Henri Elkan Music Publisher, 1316 Walnut Street, Philadelphia, Pennsylvania
HEI   Heinrichshofen Verlag, Liebigstrasse 4, Wilhelmshaven, West Germany (PET)
HEN   Edition Henn, 8, Rue de Hesse, Ch-1211 Genève 11, Switzerland
HEU   Heugel & Cie, 56 à 62, Galerie Montpensier, Paris 2, France (TP)
HG   Hans Gerig Musikverlag (See Breitkopf & Härtel BRH) (AMP)
HI   Hinrichsen Edition, Ltd., 10 Baches Street, London, England (PET)
HIM   Highland Music Co., Ryder Plaza 14751 Carmenita Road, Norwalk, California
HL   Hal Leonard Publishing, Inc., 8112 W. Bluemound Road, Milwaukee, Wisconsin
HLE   Henry Lemoine & Cie, 17 Rue Pigalle, Paris 9e, France (TP)
HLY   Harold Lyche & Co., Postboks 2171, Oslo, Norway
HMO   Hermann Moeck Verlag, Postfach 143, D 3100 Celle, West Germany
HMP   Hargail Music Press, 51 East 12th Street, New York, New York
HN   Charles Hansen Publishing, 1860 West Avenue, Miami Beach, Florida
HOH   Hohner Verlag, 7218 Trossingen, Würtemberg, West Germany
HSM   Hans Sikorski Musikverlag, Johnsallee 23, 2 Hamburg 13, West Germany (GS)
HU   Harmonia-Uitgave, Roeltjesweg 23-Postbus 126, Hilversum, Holland (PET)
HUG   Hug & Co., Musikverlag, CH-8022 Zürich, Switzerland
HY   Hyperion Press, Inc., 45 Riverside Avenue, Westport, Connecticut

IMP   Israeli Music Publications, Ltd., P.O. Box 6011, Tel-Aviv, Israel (AB)

INT   International Music Company, 545 Fifth Avenue, New York, New York
ISR   Israel Music Institute, P.O. Box 11253, Tel-Aviv, Israel (BH)

JB   Joseph Boonin, Inc., (See European American Music EAM)
JE   June Emerson-Wind Music, Ampleforth York, England
JER   Jerona Music Corp., 81 Trinity Place, Hackensack, New Jersey
JOB   Jobert & Cie, 44 Rue du Colisée, Paris 8e, France (TP)
JOW   Josef Weinberger Musikverlag, Oederweg 26, Frankfurt, West Germany

KAW   KaWe, Brederodestraat 90, Amsterdam 13, Holland
KIS   Kistner & Siegel & Co., Postfach 101, Cologne, West Germany
KJ   Neil A. Kjos Music Co., 4382 Jutland Drive, San Diego, California
KN   Kendor Music, Inc., Main & Grove Streets, Delevan, New York
KPM   Keith Prowse Music Publishing Co., Ltd., 21 Denmark Street, London WC2H 8NE, England

LDO   Ludwig Doblinger Verlag, Dorotheergasse 10, Vienna, Austria (AMP)
LEN   Alfred Lengnick & Co., Purley Oaks Studios, 421a Brighton Road, South Croydon, Surrey, England (FH)
LEU   F.E.C. Leuckart Verlag, Nibelungenstr. 48, Munich 19, West Germany (AMP)
LIT   H. Litolff's Verlag, Forsthausstrasse 101, Frankfurt, West Germany (PET)
LK   Ludwig Krenn, Reindorfgasse 42, Vienna 15, Austria
LMP   Littlehall Music Publishers, 3315 Dellwood Drive, Parma, Ohio
LN   Lang Music Publications, P.O. Box 11021, Indianapolis, Indiana
LU   Ludwig Music Publishing Co., 557-67 East 140th Street, Cleveland, Ohio
LYA   Lyric Arts Publications, P.O. Box 975, Harrisonburg, Virginia

M-B   Magnamusic-Baton, Inc., 10370 Page Industrial Parkway, St. Louis, Missouri
M&M   McGinnis & Marx, 201 West 86th Street, New York, New York
MAN   Manuscript Publications, 120 Maple Street, Wrightsville, Pennsylvania
MAR   Margun Music, Inc., 167 Dudley Road, Newton Centre, Massachusetts
MAU   J. Maurer, Avenue du Verseau 7 Watermanlaan, Brussels 15, Belgium
MB   Maurice Baron Co., P.O. Box 149, Oyster Bay, Long Island, New York
MC   MCA Music (See Belwin BE)
MCK   McKinley Publishers, Inc., 797 8th Avenue, New York, New York
MEN   Mentor Music, Inc., Broadview Drive, Brookfield, Connecticut
MEP   Media Press, Inc., 153 Latches Lane, Media, Pennsylvania (TP)
MF   Mark Foster Music Co., P.O. Box 4012, Champaign, Illinois
MFP   Music for Percussion, 170 N.E. 33rd Street, Fort Lauderdale, Florida
MIT   Mitteldeutscher Verlag, Robert-Blum-Strasse 37, Halle/Saale, East Germany
MJ   MJQ Music, Inc., 200 West 57th Street, New York, New York
MKE   Mezhdunarodnaya Kniga Editions (USSR), (GS)
MOL   Molenaar's Muziekcentrale nv, Auideinde 18, Wormerveer, Holland (HE)
MR   Musica Rara, Le Traversier, Chemin de la Buire, 84170 Monteux, France
MRL   Musikverlag Robert Lienau, Lankwitzer Strasse 9, 1 Berlin 45, West Germany (PET)
MS   Music Sales Corporation, Bellvale, Chester, New York
MT   Musiikin Tiedotuskeskus, Runeberginkatu 15 A, 00100 Helsinki 10, Finland
MTS   Mt. Salus Music, 709 E. Leake Street, Clinton, Mississippi
MUC   Musica da Camera, Box 3935, Westlake Village, California
MV   Möseler Verlag, D3340 Wolfenbüttel, West Germany
NM   Norsk Musikforlag A/S, Karl Johans Gata 39, P.O. Box 1499 Vika, Oslo, Norway
NO   Novello & Co., Ltd., Borough Green, Sevenoaks, Kent, England (TP)
NOM   Nova Music, 4 Normanhurst Road, Streatham Hill, London SW2 3T-A, England (GA)
NOR   Nordiska Musikforlaget, Drottninggatan 37, 101 30 Stockholm 1, Sweden (AMP)
NV   Nagels Verlag, Heinrich Schütz Allee 31, Kassel, West Germany (AMP)
NVM   New Valley Music Press, Sage Hall, Smith College, Northampton, Massachusetts

OHN   Otto Heinrich Noetzel, Liebigstrasse 4, Wilhelmshaven, West Germany (PET)
OJE   Raymond A. Ojeda, 98 Briar Road, Kentfield, California
ONG   Ongaku No Tomo Sha Corp., Kagurazaka 6-30, Shinjuku-ku, Tokyo, Japan (TP)
OP   Opus Music Pub., Inc., 1880 Holste Road, Northbrook, Illinois
OR   Orion Music Press, P.O. Box 145 University Station, Berrien Springs, Michigan
OV   Orlando Verlag, Lugano, Switzerland
OX   Oxford University Press, Inc., 1600 Pollitt Drive, Fairlawn, New Jersey and 44 Conduit Street, London W1 RODE, England

PAN   Panton, Ricni 12, 11839 Prague, Czechoslovakia (BH)
PAT   Paterson's Publications, Ltd., 38-40 Wigmore Street, London W1 HOEX, England (CF)

PB   Philharmusica Corporation, Box 180, West Nyack, New York
PEL   Pelikan Musikverlag, Hadlaubstrasse 63, 8044 Zürich, Switzerland (PET)
PET   C.F. Peters Corporation, 373 Park Avenue South, New York, New York
PG   Pagani & Bro., Inc. (ASH)
PGM   Philipp Grosch Musikverlag, 8000 Munich 8, West Germany
PI   Peer International (See Southern Music Publishing Co. SN)
PM   Pro Musica Verlag, Karl-Liebknecht-Strasse 12, 701 Leipzig 1, East Germany
PMP   Providence Music Press, P.O. Box 2362, East Side Station, Providence, Rhode Island
PO   Pro Art Publications, Inc. (See Belwin BE)
PWM   Polski Wydawnictwo Muzyczne, Krakowśkie Przedmieście 7, 00-068 Warsaw, Poland
         (See Ars Polona AP)

R&E   Ries & Erler, Charlottenbrunner Strasse 42, Berlin 33 (Grunewald),
         West Germany
RBM   Richard Birnbach Musikverlag, Dürerstrasse 28, 1000 Berlin 45, West Germany (PET)
RC   G. Ricordi & Co., Via Salomone 77, Milan, Italy (GS)
RD   Roger Dean Publishing Co., 345 W. Jackson, Macomb, Illinois
REU   Reuter & Reuter, Stockholm, Sweden
RH   Rochester Music Publishers, Inc. (ACC)
ROB   Edition Corona Rolf Budde, Hohenzollern Damm 54A, D-1000 Berlin 33, West Germany
         (See Möseler Verlag MV)
RON   Rongwen Music, Inc. (BR)
ROP   Roberton Publications, The Windmill, Wendover, Aylesbury, Bucks, England
RR   Roger Rhodes Music, Ltd., Box 855, Dept. N. Radio City Station, New York, New York
RS   Richard Schauer, 67 Belsize Lane, Hampstead, London NW3 5AX, England
RU   Rubank, Inc., Box A, Norland Branch, Miami, Florida

S&   Schmitt Music Centers (See Belwin BE)
S&B   Stainer & Bell, Ltd., 82 High Road, East Finchley, London N2 9PW, England (GA)
S&C   Schott & Co., Ltd., 48 Great Marlborough Street, London W 1, England (EAM)
S-V   Sirius-Verlag, Wiclefstrasse 67, Berlin 21, West Germany
SB   Summy-Birchard Co., Box CN 27, Princeton, New Jersey
SCF   Schott, Freres, 30 Rue Saint-Jean, Brussels 1, Belgium
SCH   B. Schotts' Söhne, Weihergarten 1-9, D-6500 Mainz, West Germany (EAM)
SD   Stichting Donemus, Jacob Obrechtstraat 51, Amsterdam, Holland (PET)
SEM   S.E.M.I., 5 Rue Lincoln, 75008 Paris, France
SER   Serenus (GEN)
SF   Sam Fox Music Sales Corporation, 170 N.E. 33rd Street, Ft. Lauderdale, Florida
SH   Shawnee Press, Inc., Delaware Water Gap, Pennsylvania
SHB   Shapiro, Bernstein & Co., Inc., 170 N.E. 33rd Street, Ft. Lauderdale, Florida
SHF   Slovenský Hudobný Fond, Gorkého 19, Bratislava, Czechoslovakia
SID   Sidem Editions, 8 Rue de Hesse, Geneva, Switzerland
SIM   N. Simrock, Werderstrasse 44, Hamburg 13, West Germany (AMP)
SLP   Swing Lane Publications, Box 128, Beverly, New Jersey
SMI   Smith Publications, 2617 Gwynndale Avenue, Baltimore, Maryland
SMO   Shall-u-mo Publications, P.O. Box 2824, Rochester, New York
SN   Southern Music Publishing Co., Inc., 1740 Broadway, New York, New York
SO   Southern Music Co., 1100 Broadway, Box 329, San Antonio, Texas
SP   Studio Publications, 224 South Lebanon, Lebanon, Indiana
SPD   The Society for Publishing Danish Music, Graabrodretorv 7, 1154 Copenhagen,
         Denmark (PET)
SPR   Spratt Music Publishers, 170 N.E. 33rd Street, Ft. Lauderdale, Florida
SS   Seesaw Music Corporation, 2067 Broadway, New York, New York
STI   STIMS Informationscentral för Svensk Musik, Birger Jarlsgatan 6B, S-102 42
         Stockholm 5, Sweden
STM   Standard Music Publishing, Inc., P.O. Box 1043 Whitman Square, Turnersville,
         New Jersey
STR   Strombeck Music Publications, P.O. Box 484, Deerfield, Illinois
T&J   Tischer & Jagenberg (See Leuckart LEU) (AMP)
T-M   Tierolff-Muziekcentrale, Markt 90/92, Roosendaal, Netherlands (HE)
THP   Thames Publishing (See J.B. Cramer CRA)
TM   Tempo Music Publications, Inc., P.O. Box 392, Chicago, Illinois
TON   P.J. Tonger Musikverlag, Bergstrasse 10, 5038 Rodenkirchen/Rhein, West Germany
TP   Theodore Presser Co., Bryn Mawr, Pennsylvania
TRI   Tritone Press (See Theodore Presser TP)

UE   Universal Editions, Karlsplatz 6, Vienna 1, Austria (EAM)

UME   Union Musical Española, Carrera de San Jeronimo 26, y Arenal, 18 Madrid 14, Spain (AMP)
UMP   United Music Publishers Ltd., 1 Montague Street, Russell Square, London WC 1, England (TP)
UNI   University Music Press, P.O. Box 1267, Ann Arbor, Michigan

VA   Viola d'Amore Society, 14 Chestnut Way, Godalming, Surrey, England
VNM   Verlag Neue Musik (See Bärenreiter & Neuwerk B&N)
VO   Volkwein Bros., Inc., 117 Sandusky Street, Pittsburgh, Pennsylvania

WAT   Waterloo Music Co., Ltd., 3 Regina Street N., Waterloo, Ontario, Canada (AMP)
WB   Warner Bros. Publications, 265 Secaucus Road, Secaucus, New Jersey
WH   Wilhelm Hansen Musik-Forlag, Gothersgade 9-11, 1123 Copenhagen, Denmark (M-B)
WI   Western International Music, Inc., 2859 Holt Avenue, Los Angeles, California
WIL   Willis Music, 7380 Industrial Road, Florence, Kentucky
WJ   Wingert-Jones Music, Inc., P.O. Box 1878, Kansas City, Missouri
WLP   World Library Publications, 5040 N. Ravenswood, Chicago, Illinois
WM   Wimbledon Music, Inc., 1888 Century Park East, Century City, California
WMI   Wind Music Inc., 153 Highland Parkway, Rochester, New York
WMS   Willy Müller-Süddeutscher Musikverlag, Marzgasse 5, Heidelberg, West Germany (PET)
WZ   Wilhelm Zimmermann Musikverlag, Zeppelinalle 21, 6000 Frankfurt, West Germany (GS)

YM   Ybarra Music, Box 665, Lemon Grove, California

Z-O   Zen-On Music Co., 25 Higashi Goken-cho, Shinjuku-ku, Tokyo, Japan
ZA   Zalo Publications, Box 913, Bloomington, Indiana